S0-ACZ-398

TEACHER'S EDITION

Volume 2 Chapters 7–12

PRENTICE HALL COURSE 3

MATHEMATICS

Randall I. Charles
Judith C. Branch-Boyd
Mark Illingworth
Darwin Mills
Andy Reeves

PEARSON
Prentice Hall

Needham, Massachusetts
Upper Saddle River, New Jersey

Teacher's Edition package (Volumes 1 and 2): ISBN 0-13-068557-7
Volume 1: ISBN 0-13-180763-3
Volume 2: ISBN 0-13-180764-1

8 9 10 07 06

Teacher's Edition Contents
Volume 2

Teacher Handbook

Student Edition With Teacher Notes

Authors

Series Author

Randall I. Charles, Ph.D., is Professor Emeritus in the Department of Mathematics and Computer Science at San Jose State University, San Jose, California. He began his career as a high school mathematics teacher, and he was a mathematics supervisor for five years. Dr. Charles has been a member of several NCTM committees and is the former Vice President of the National Council of Supervisors of Mathematics. Much of his writing and research has been in the area of problem solving. He has authored more than 75 mathematics textbooks for kindergarten through college.
Scott Foresman-Prentice Hall Mathematics Series Author
Kindergarten through Algebra 2

Program Authors

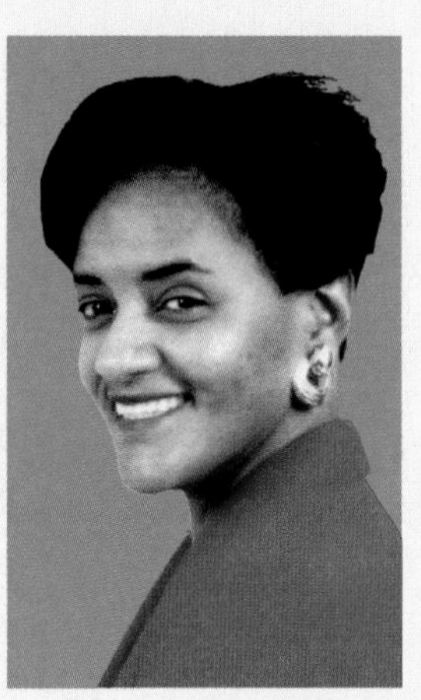

Judith C. Branch-Boyd, Ph.D., is the Area 24 Mathematics Coordinator for the Chicago Public School District. She works with high school teachers to provide quality instruction to students who are mandated to take Algebra, Geometry, and Advanced Algebra-Trigonometry. She also works with middle school and high school teachers to help students transition to Algebra 1. Dr. Branch-Boyd is active in several professional mathematics organizations at the state and national levels, including the National Council of Teachers of Mathematics. She believes,"All children can learn to love mathematics if it is taught with energy!"

ISBN 0-13-068555-0

2 3 4 5 6 7 8 9 10 07 06 05 04 03

Mark Illingworth has taught fifth-graders and enrichment programs for fifteen years. During this time, he received the Christa McAullife sabbatical to develop problem-solving materials and projects for middle-grades math students, and he was granted the Presidential Award for Excellence in Mathematics Teaching. In addition to serving as the district math task force coordinator for the last six years, he has written two of his own books and has contributed to both math and science textbooks at Prentice Hall. Mr. Illingworth has recently shifted from teaching fifth-graders to teaching math to high school students.

Darwin Mills is a mathematics lead teacher for the public schools in Newport News, Virginia and a mathematics adjunct professor at Thomas Nelson Community College in Hampton, Virginia. He has received various teaching awards, including teacher of the year for the 1999–2000 school year and an Excellence in Teaching Award from the College of Wooster, Ohio in 2002. He is a frequent presenter for staff development, especially in the area of graphing calculator usage in the classroom. He believes that all students can learn mathematics if given the proper instruction.

Andy Reeves, Ph.D., teaches at the University of South Florida in St. Petersburg. His career in education spans 30 years and includes seven years as a middle grades teacher. He subsequently served as Florida's K-12 mathematics supervisor and more recently he supervised the publication of the *Mathematics Teacher*, *Mathematics Teaching in the Middle School*, and *Teaching Children Mathematics* for NCTM. Prior to entering education, he worked as an engineer for Douglas Aircraft.

Contributing Author

Denisse R. Thompson, Ph.D., is Associate Professor of Mathematics Education at the University of South Florida. She has particular interests in the connections between literature and mathematics and in the teaching and learning of mathematics in the middle grades. Dr. Thompson contributed to the Reading Math lessons and features.

Reviewers

Course 1 Reviewers

Donna Anderson
Math Supervisor 7–12
West Hartford Public Schools
West Hartford, Connecticut

Nancy L. Borchers
West Clermont Local Schools
Cincinnati, Ohio

Kathleen Chandler
Walnut Creek Middle School
Erie, Pennsylvania

Jane E. Damaske
Lakeshore Public Schools
Stevensville, Michigan

Frank Greco
Parkway South Middle School
Manchester, Missouri

Rebecca L. Jones
Odyssey Middle School
Orlando, Florida

Marylee R. Liebowitz
H. C. Crittenden Middle School
Armonk, New York

Kathy Litz
K. O. Knudson Middle School
Las Vegas, Nevada

Don McGurrin
Wake County Public School System
Raleigh, North Carolina

Ron Mezzadri
K–12 Mathematics Supervisor
Fair Lawn School District
Fair Lawn, New Jersey

Sylvia O. Reeder-Tucker
Prince George's County Math Department
Upper Marlboro, Maryland

Julie A. White
Allison Traditional Magnet Middle School
Wichita, Kansas

Charles Yochim
Bronxville Middle School
Bronxville, New York

Course 2 Reviewers

Cami Craig
Prince William County Public Schools
Marsteller Middle School
Bristow, Virginia

Donald O. Cram
Lincoln Middle School
Rio Rancho, New Mexico

Pat A. Davidson
Jacksonville Junior High School
Jacksonville, Arkansas

Yvette Drew
DeKalb County School System
Open Campus High School
Atlanta, Georgia

Robert S. Fair
K–12 District Mathematics Coordinator
Cherry Creek School District
Greenwood Village, Colorado

Michael A. Landry
Glastonbury Public Schools
Glastonbury, Connecticut

Nancy Ochoa
Weeden Middle School
Florence, Alabama

Charlotte J. Phillips
Wichita USD 259
Wichita, Kansas

Mary Lynn Raith
Mathematics Curriculum Specialist
Pittsburgh Public Schools
Pittsburgh, Pennsylvania

Tammy Rush
Consultant, Middle School Mathematics
Hillsborough County Schools
Tampa, Florida

Judith R. Russ
Prince George's County Public Schools
Capitol Heights, Maryland

Tim Tate
Math/Science Supervisor
Lafayette Parish School System
Lafayette, Louisiana

Dondi J. Thompson
Alcott Middle School
Norman, Oklahoma

Candace Yamagata
Hyde Park Middle School
Las Vegas, Nevada

Course 3 Reviewers

Linda E. Addington
Andrew Lewis Middle School
Salem, Virginia

Jeanne Arnold
Mead Junior High School
Schaumburg, Illinois

Sheila S. Brookshire
A. C. Reynolds Middle School
Asheville, North Carolina

Jennifer Clark
Mayfield Middle School
Putnam City Public Schools
Oklahoma City, Oklahoma

Nicole Dial
Chase Middle School
Topeka, Kansas

Christine Ferrell
Lorin Andrews Middle School
Massillon, Ohio

Virginia G. Harrell
Education Consultant
Hillsborough County, Florida

Jonita P. Howard
Mathematics Curriculum Specialist
Lauderdale Lakes Middle School
Lauderdale Lakes, Florida

Patricia Lemons
Rio Rancho Middle School
Rio Rancho, New Mexico

Susan Noce
Robert Frost Junior High School
Schaumburg, Illinois

Carla A. Siler
South Bend Community School Corp.
South Bend, Indiana

Kathryn E. Smith-Lance
West Genesee Middle School
Camillus, New York

Kathleen D. Tuffy
South Middle School
Braintree, Massachusetts

Patricia R. Wilson
Central Middle School
Murfreesboro, Tennessee

Patricia Young
Northwood Middle School
Pulaski County Special School District
North Little Rock, Arkansas

Content Consultants

Courtney Lewis
Mathematics
Prentice Hall Senior National Consultant
Baltimore, Maryland

Deana Cerroni
Mathematics
Prentice Hall National Consultant
Las Vegas, Nevada

Kimberly Margel
Mathematics
Prentice Hall National Consultant
Scottsdale, Arizona

Sandra Mosteller
Mathematics
Prentice Hall National Consultant
Anderson, South Carolina

Rita Corbett
Mathematics
Prentice Hall Consultant
Elgin, Illinois

Cathy Davies
Mathematics
Prentice Hall Consultant
Laguna Niguel, California

Sally Marsh
Mathematics
Prentice Hall Consultant
Baltimore, Maryland

Addie Martin
Mathematics
Prentice Hall Consultant
Upper Marlboro, Maryland

Rose Primiani
Mathematics
Prentice Hall Consultant
Brick, New Jersey

Loretta Rector
Mathematics
Prentice Hall Consultant
Foresthill, California

Charlotte Samuels
Mathematics
Prentice Hall Consultant
Lafayette Hill, Pennsylvania

Margaret Thomas
Mathematics
Prentice Hall Consultant
Indianapolis, Indiana

Contents in Brief

Algebra

Integers and Algebraic Expressions

Student Support

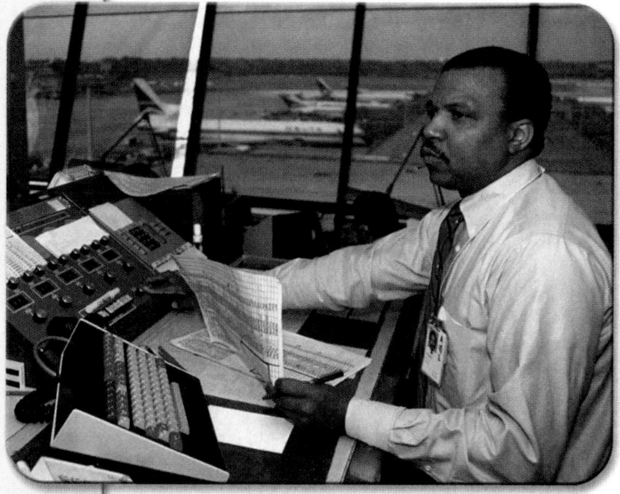

Chapter 2

Equations and Inequalities

Student Support

Instant Check System

Diagnosing Readiness, 60

Check Skills You'll Need, 61, 69, 73, 78, 85, 90, 97, 103

Check Understanding, 62, 63, 64, 69, 70, 74, 75, 76, 79, 80, 86, 91, 92, 98, 100, 103, 104

Checkpoint Quiz, 83, 102

Comprehensive Test Prep

Daily Test Prep, 66, 72, 77, 83, 88, 95, 102, 106

Test-Prep Tip, 80

Test-Taking Strategies, 107

Cumulative Test Prep, 111

Reading Math

Reading Math, 62, 90, 91, 92, 99

Understanding Word Problems, 89

Understanding Vocabulary, 108

Reading Comprehension, 95

Writing in Math

Daily Writing Practice, 65, 67, 71, 77, 82, 87, 93, 101, 105, 107, 110

Writing to Explain, 84

Real-World Problem Solving

Strategies: Draw a Diagram and Write an Equation, 85–88

Bicycles, 66

Math at Work, 72

Fundraising, 79

Kites, 85

. . . and more!

Chapter 3

Graphing in the Coordinate Plane

Algebra

Student Support

Instant Check System

Diagnosing Readiness, 116

Check Skills You'll Need, 117, 122, 128, 136, 142, 147, 152, 157, 163, 169

Check Understanding, 117, 118, 123, 124, 129, 130, 137, 138, 143, 147, 148, 152, 153, 158, 159, 164, 165, 170, 171

Checkpoint Quiz, 141, 156

Comprehensive Test Prep

Daily Test Prep, 121, 126, 133, 141, 145, 150, 155, 162, 168, 174

Test-Prep Tip, 129

Test-Taking Strategies, 175

Cumulative Test Prep, 179

Reading Math

Reading Math, 117, 118, 123, 130, 157

Understanding Word Problems, 146

Understanding Vocabulary, 176

Reading Comprehension, 133, 179

Writing in Math

Daily Writing Practice, 120, 125, 127, 132, 140, 144, 149, 155, 161, 166, 173, 178

Real-World Problem Solving

Strategies: Write an Equation and Make a Graph, 142–145
Woodworking, 120
Math at Work, 121
Landscaping, 137
Police Work, 145
. . . and more!

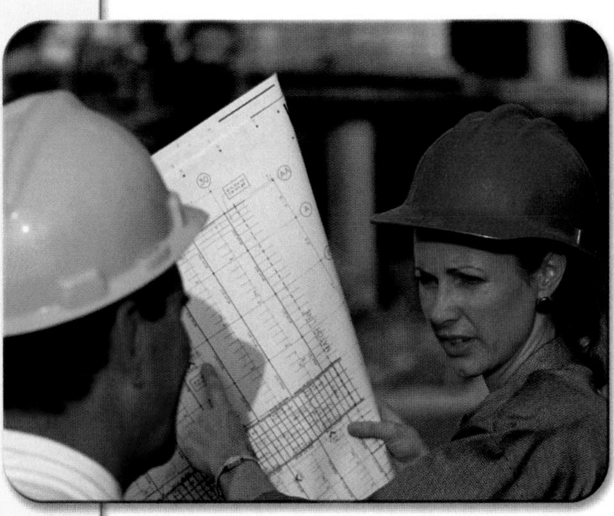

Table of Contents

Chapter 4

Real Numbers

Student Support

Instant Check System

Diagnosing Readiness, 184

Check Skills You'll Need, 185, 190, 196, 201, 205, 212, 217, 221, 226

Check Understanding, 185, 186, 187, 190, 191, 192, 196, 197, 198, 201, 202, 205, 206, 207, 212, 213, 218, 221, 222, 223, 227, 228

Checkpoint Quiz, 210, 231

Comprehensive Test Prep

Daily Test Prep, 189, 195, 200, 204, 210, 215, 220, 225, 230

Test-Prep Tip, 206

Test-Taking Strategies, 233

Cumulative Test Prep, 237

Reading Math

Reading Math, 190, 194, 212, 223

Learning Vocabulary, 211

Understanding Vocabulary, 234

Reading Comprehension, 215

Writing in Math

Daily Writing Practice, 188, 194, 199, 203, 209, 214, 219, 224, 230, 236

Real-World Problem Solving

Strategies: Try, Check, and Revise and Work Backward, 217–220

Practice Game, 189

Baseball, 191

Running, 219

Ferris Wheels, 224

. . . and more!

Chapter 5

Applications of Proportions

Student Support

Table of Contents

Chapter 6

Applications of Percent

Student Support

Instant Check System

Comprehensive Test Prep

Reading Math

Writing in Math

Real-World Problem Solving

Chapter 7

Exponents and Powers

Student Support

Instant Check System

Diagnosing Readiness, 364

Check Skills You'll Need, 365, 370, 376, 383, 388, 392

Check Understanding, 366, 367, 371, 372, 376, 377, 378, 379, 383, 384, 388, 389, 393

Checkpoint Quiz, 374, 387

Comprehensive Test Prep

Daily Test Prep, 369, 373, 381, 387, 391, 395

Test-Prep Tip, 371

Test-Taking Strategies, 397

Cumulative Test Prep, 401

Reading Math

Reading Math, 377, 380, 383

Understanding Word Problems, 382

Understanding Vocabulary, 398

Reading Comprehension, 369, 401

Writing in Math

Daily Writing Practice, 368, 380, 386, 390, 394, 400

Real-World Problem Solving

Strategy: Write an Equation, 388–391
Science, 366
Volcanoes, 386
Consumer Issues, 390
Math at Work, 395
. . . and more!

Table of Contents

Chapter 8

Geometry

Student Support

Instant Check System

Diagnosing Readiness, 406

Check Skills You'll Need, 407, 413, 420, 426, 430, 436, 441, 447, 454

Check Understanding, 408, 409, 414, 415, 421, 422, 427, 430, 431, 436, 437, 442, 443, 448, 449, 455, 456, 457

Checkpoint Quiz, 429, 459

Comprehensive Test Prep

Daily Test Prep, 412, 418, 425, 429, 433, 439, 446, 452, 458

Test-Prep Tip, 421

Test-Taking Strategies, 461

Cumulative Test Prep, 465

Reading Math

Reading Math, 422, 430, 431, 438, 447, 456

Connecting Ideas With Concept Maps, 434

Understanding Vocabulary, 462

Reading Comprehension, 418

Writing in Math

Daily Writing Practice, 411, 416, 424, 428, 433, 438, 445, 446, 450, 453, 458, 464

Writing to Compare, 453

Real-World Problem Solving

Strategies: Solve a Simpler Problem and Look for a Pattern, 426–429

City Planning, 408

Math at Work, 412

Human Pyramid, 426

Construction, 442

. . . and more!

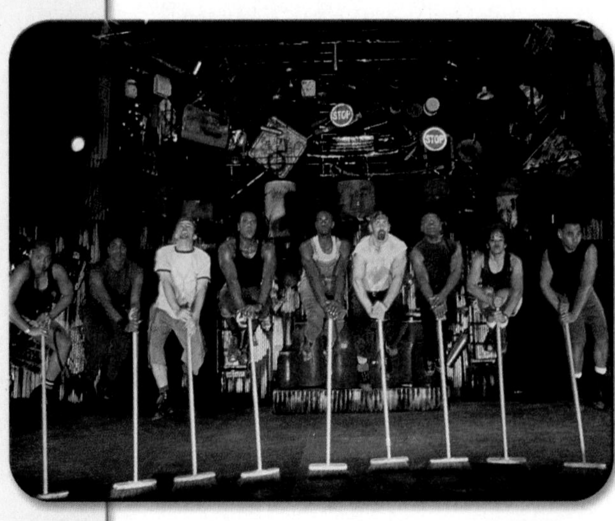

Chapter 9

Geometry and Measurement

Student Support

Instant Check System

Diagnosing Readiness, 470

Check Skills You'll Need, 471, 476, 481, 488, 494, 500, 506, 512, 517

Check Understanding, 472, 473, 477, 478, 488, 489, 490, 491, 494, 495, 496, 501, 502, 507, 508, 513, 517, 519

Checkpoint Quiz, 485, 515

Comprehensive Test Prep

Daily Test Prep, 475, 480, 485, 493, 499, 505, 510, 515, 521

Test-Prep Tip, 496

Test-Taking Strategies, 523

Cumulative Test Prep, 527

Reading Math

Reading Math, 471, 488, 502

Using the Correct Formula, 516

Understanding Vocabulary, 524

Reading Comprehension, 505, 527

Writing in Math

Daily Writing Practice, 474, 479, 484, 487, 492, 498, 504, 509, 514, 520, 526

Real-World Problem Solving

Strategies: Draw a Diagram and Make a Table, 512–515
Design, 474
Archaeology, 479
Math at Work, 493
Glassblowing, 508
. . . and more!

Table of Contents

Chapter 10

Using Graphs to Analyze Data

Student Support

Instant Check System

Diagnosing Readiness, 532

Check Skills You'll Need, 533, 540, 546, 552, 557, 563, 569, 576

Check Understanding, 533, 534, 535, 540, 541, 546, 547, 553, 558, 559, 563, 564, 569, 570, 577

Checkpoint Quiz, 551, 568

Comprehensive Test Prep

Daily Test Prep, 538, 544, 550, 556, 562, 567, 574, 579

Test-Prep Tip, 547

Test-Taking Strategies, 581

Cumulative Test Prep, 585

Reading Math

Reading Math, 535, 548, 558, 566

Reading Graphical Displays, 539

Understanding Vocabulary, 582

Reading Comprehension, 574

Writing in Math

Daily Writing Practice, 536, 543, 545, 550, 555, 561, 566, 573, 578, 584

Writing to Persuade, 580

Real-World Problem Solving

Strategies: Draw a Diagram and Use Logical Reasoning, 576–579
Marathon, 543
Practice Game, 544
Baseball, 561
Weather, 570
. . . and more!

Chapter 11

Probability

Student Support

Instant Check System

Diagnosing Readiness, 590

Check Skills You'll Need, 591, 595, 600, 606, 611, 616, 621

Check Understanding, 591, 592, 596, 597, 601, 607, 608, 612, 617, 621, 622, 623

Checkpoint Quiz, 604, 625

Comprehensive Test Prep

Daily Test Prep, 594, 599, 604, 610, 614, 619, 624

Test-Prep Tip, 592

Test-Taking Strategies, 627

Cumulative Test Prep, 631

Reading Math

Reading Math, 597, 601, 622

Understanding Vocabulary, 628

Reading Comprehension, 614, 631

Writing in Math

Daily Writing Practice, 593, 598, 603, 609, 613, 618, 624, 630

Real-World Problem Solving

Strategies: Simulate a Problem and Make an Organized List, 616–619

Science Fair, 597
Practice Game, 615
Recycling, 618
In-line Skating, 623
. . . and more!

Table of Contents

Chapter 12

Algebra

Algebraic Relationships

Student Support

✓ Instant Check System

Comprehensive Test Prep

Reading Math

Writing in Math

Real-World Problem Solving

End-of-Book Features

For a complete list, see Contents in Brief on page vi.

Pacing Options for Course 3

Pacing Guide

This chart is provided merely as a guide to help you customize your course. To accommodate flexible scheduling, most lessons are subdivided into objectives. Within the lessons of the Student Edition, these objectives are indicated in red by the symbol ▼. The Assignment Guide for each lesson indicates which exercises in the Student Edition correspond to each objective of the lesson.

Detailed Chapter Pacing Options precede each chapter and give you lesson-by-lesson pacing suggestions for that specific chapter.

CHAPTER	Traditional (45-minute class periods)	Block (90-minute class periods)
1	14 days	7 days
2	12 days	6 days
3	15 days	8 days
4	15 days	8 days
5	14 days	7 days
6	15 days	7 days
7	10 days	5 days
8	13 days	6 days
9	14 days	7 days
10	11 days	5 days
11	12 days	6 days
12	15 days	8 days
Total	160 days	80 days

Differentiated Scope of Course

B = Basic Course   C = Core Course   A = Advanced Course

	B	C	A
Chapter 1 Integers and Algebraic Expressions			
1-1: Algebraic Expressions and the Order of Operations	✓	✓	✓
1-2: Use a Problem-Solving Plan	✓	✓	✓
1-3: Integers and Absolute Value	✓	✓	✓
1-4: Adding and Subtracting Integers	✓	✓	✓
1-5: Multiplying and Dividing Integers	✓	✓	✓
1-6: Using Integers With Mean, Median, and Mode	✓	✓	✓
1-7: Powers and Exponents	✓	✓	✓
• Technology: Evaluating Expressions	✓	✓	✓
1-8: Properties of Numbers	✓	✓	✓
Chapter 2 Equations and Inequalities			
2-1: Solving One-Step Equations	✓	✓	✓
• Extension: Number Squares		✓	✓
• Investigation: Solving Equations Using Tiles	✓	✓	✓
2-2: Solving Two-Step Equations	✓	✓	✓
2-3: Simplifying Algebraic Expressions	✓	✓	✓
2-4: Solving Multi-Step Equations	✓	✓	✓
2-5: Draw a Diagram and Write an Equation	✓	✓	✓
2-6: Solving Inequalities by Adding or Subtracting	✓	✓	✓
• Extension: Compound Inequalities			✓
2-7: Solving Inequalities by Multiplying or Dividing	✓	✓	✓
2-8: Solving Two-Step Inequalities	✓	✓	✓
Chapter 3 Graphing in the Coordinate Plane			
3-1: Graphing Points	✓	✓	✓
3-2: Graphing Equations With Two Variables	✓	✓	✓
• Technology: Graphing Lines		✓	✓
3-3: Understanding Slope	✓	✓	✓
• Extension: Rate of Change		✓	✓
3-4: Using the *y*-Intercept	✓	✓	✓
3-5: Write an Equation and Make a Graph	✓	✓	✓
3-6: Using Graphs of Equations	✓	✓	✓
• Extension: Inequalities With Two Variables			✓
3-7: Solving Linear Systems by Graphing			✓
3-8: Translations	✓	✓	✓
3-9: Reflections and Symmetry	✓	✓	✓
3-10: Rotations	✓	✓	✓

	B	C	A
Chapter 4 Real Numbers			
4-1: Factors	✓	✓	✓
4-2: Equivalent Forms of Rational Numbers	✓	✓	✓
4-3: Comparing and Ordering Rational Numbers	✓	✓	✓
4-4: Adding and Subtracting Rational Numbers	✓	✓	✓
4-5: Multiplying and Dividing Rational Numbers	✓	✓	✓
4-6: Formulas	✓	✓	✓
• Technology: Using Formulas		✓	✓
4-7: Try, Check, and Revise and Work Backward	✓	✓	✓
4-8: Exploring Square Roots and Irrational Numbers	✓	✓	✓
4-9: The Pythagorean Theorem	✓	✓	✓
• Extension: Area and the Pythagorean Theorem			✓
Chapter 5 Applications of Proportions			
5-1: Ratios and Rates	✓	✓	✓
5-2: Choosing and Converting Units	✓	✓	✓
5-3: Write an Equation	✓	✓	✓
5-4: Solving Proportions	✓	✓	✓
5-5: Similar Figures and Proportions	✓	✓	✓
5-6: Similarity Transformations	✓	✓	✓
• Technology: Geometry Software and Dilations			✓
5-7: Scale Models and Maps	✓	✓	✓
5-8: Similarity and Indirect Measurement		✓	✓
5-9: The Sine and Cosine Ratios			✓
• Extension: The Tangent Ratio			✓
Chapter 6 Applications of Percent			
6-1: Fractions, Decimals, and Percents	✓	✓	✓
6-2: Estimating With Percents	✓	✓	✓
6-3: Percents and Proportions	✓	✓	✓
6-4: Percents and Equations	✓	✓	✓
6-5: Percent of Change	✓	✓	✓
6-6: Markup and Discount	✓	✓	✓
6-7: Write an Equation	✓	✓	✓
6-8: Simple and Compound Interest		✓	✓
• Extension: Compounding Interest Semiannually			✓
6-9: Probability			

	B	C	A
Chapter 7 Exponents and Powers			
7-1: Scientific Notation	✓	✓	✓
7-2: Exponents and Multiplication	✓	✓	✓
• Technology: Scientific Notation	✓	✓	✓
7-3: Exponents and Division	✓	✓	✓
7-4: Power Rules	✓	✓	✓
7-5: Write an Equation	✓	✓	✓
7-6: Number Systems			✓
• Extension: Bar Codes			✓
Chapter 8 Geometry			
8-1: Pairs of Angles	✓	✓	✓
8-2: Angles and Parallel Lines	✓	✓	✓
• Extension: Parallel and Perpendicular Lines			✓
8-3: Congruent Polygons	✓	✓	✓
8-4: Solve a Simpler Problem and Look for a Pattern	✓	✓	✓
8-5: Classifying Triangles and Quadrilaterals	✓	✓	✓
• Investigation: Sum of the Angles of a Polygon		✓	✓
8-6: Angles and Polygons	✓	✓	✓
• Extension: Tessellations		✓	✓
8-7: Areas of Polygons	✓	✓	✓
8-8: Circumferences and Areas of Circles	✓	✓	✓
8-9: Constructions		✓	✓
• Technology: Geometry Software and Constructions			✓
Chapter 9 Geometry and Measurement			
9-1: Solids	✓	✓	✓
9-2: Drawing Views of Solids	✓	✓	✓
9-3: Nets and Solids	✓	✓	✓
• Investigation: Precision and Greatest Possible Error		✓	✓
9-4: Surface Areas of Prisms and Cylinders	✓	✓	✓
9-5: Surface Areas of Pyramids and Cones	✓	✓	✓
9-6: Volumes of Prisms and Cylinders	✓	✓	✓
9-7: Volumes of Pyramids and Cones	✓	✓	✓
• Extension: Formulas for Spheres		✓	✓
9-8: Draw a Diagram and Make a Table	✓	✓	✓
9-9: Exploring Similar Solids			✓
• Extension: Significant Digits		✓	✓

	B	C	A
Chapter 10 Using Graphs to Analyze Data			
10-1: Displaying Frequency	✓	✓	✓
10-2: Reading Graphs Critically	✓	✓	✓
• Extension: Stacked and Sliding Bar Graphs			✓
10-3: Stem-and-Leaf Plots		✓	✓
10-4: Box-and Whisker Plots		✓	✓
10-5: Making Predictions From Scatter Plots	✓	✓	✓
10-6: Circle Graphs	✓	✓	✓
10-7: Choosing an Appropriate Graph			✓
• Technology: Graphing Data Using Spreadsheets		✓	✓
10-8: Draw a Diagram and Use Logical Reasoning	✓	✓	✓
Chapter 11 Probability			
11-1: Counting Outcomes	✓	✓	✓
11-2: Permutations	✓	✓	✓
11-3: Combinations		✓	✓
• Extension: Pascal's Triangle			✓
11-4: Theoretical and Experimental Probability	✓	✓	✓
11-5: Independent and Dependent Events		✓	✓
11-6: Simulate a Problem and Make an Organized List	✓	✓	✓
• Technology: Simulations With Random Numbers			✓
11-7: Conducting a Survey	✓	✓	✓
Chapter 12 Algebra: Algebraic Relationships			
12-1: Sequences	✓	✓	✓
• Technology: Exploring Sequences		✓	✓
12-2: Functions	✓	✓	✓
12-3: Graphing Linear Functions	✓	✓	✓
12-4: Writing Rules for Linear Functions	✓	✓	✓
12-5: Relating Graphs to Events		✓	✓
12-6: Quadratic and Other Nonlinear Functions	✓	✓	✓
12-7: Write an Equation			✓
12-8: Exploring Polynomials		✓	✓
12-9: Adding and Subtracting Polynomials			✓
12-10: Multiplying Polynomials			✓

Scope and Sequence for Prentice Hall Mathematics

This scope and sequence of content is organized around the major strands and specific objectives in the **National Assessment of Educational Progress (NAEP) 2005 Assessment Specifications.** These NAEP skills are an important benchmark for No Child Left Behind. Also included here are the process skills referenced in the **NCTM Principles and Standards for School Mathematics 2000.**

Since **Prentice Hall Mathematics** is a complete Grades 6–12 program, a detailed scope and sequence chart for the entire program—middle school through high school—is available at PHSchool.com/math. Also available is a Grades Pre-K–8 scope and sequence chart that shows the careful articulation between **Prentice Hall Mathematics Courses 1–3** and **Scott Foresman-Addison Wesley Mathematics Grades Pre-K–5**, which together provide a complete mathematics curriculum for Grades Pre-K–8.

Number Properties and Operations

Course	1	2	3
Number Sense			
• **Use place value to model numbers**			
— *whole numbers*	Maintain & Apply	Maintain & Apply	Maintain & Apply
— *decimals*	Develop	Develop	Maintain & Apply
• **Model rational numbers or numerical relationships**			
— *number line models*	Develop	Develop	Develop
— *other models*	Develop	Develop	Develop
• **Write or rename rational numbers**			
— *read and write decimals*	Develop	Develop	Maintain & Apply
— *read and write integers*	Develop	Maintain & Apply	Maintain & Apply
— *read and write rational numbers*	Develop	Maintain & Apply	Maintain & Apply
— *irrational numbers*		Introduce	Introduce/Develop
— *real numbers*			Introduce
• **Express multiple representations of rational numbers and translate between them**			
— *equivalent decimals*	Develop	Maintain & Apply	Maintain & Apply
— *equivalent fractions*	Develop	Maintain & Apply	Maintain & Apply
— *simplest form*	Develop	Maintain & Apply	Maintain & Apply
— *mixed numbers and improper fractions*	Develop	Maintain & Apply	Maintain & Apply
— *convert between fractions and decimals*	Develop	Develop	Maintain & Apply
• **Use scientific notation**			
— *scientific notation*	Introduce	Develop	Develop
• **Find or model absolute value**			
— *absolute value*	Introduce	Develop	Maintain & Apply
• **Compare and order rational numbers**			
— *whole numbers*	Maintain & Apply	Maintain & Apply	Maintain & Apply
— *decimals*	Develop	Maintain & Apply	Maintain & Apply
— *fractions*	Develop	Develop	Maintain & Apply
— *integers*	Introduce/Develop	Maintain & Apply	Maintain & Apply
— *rational numbers*		Introduce/Develop	Develop
— *irrationals numbers*			Introduce
Estimation			
• **Establish benchmarks**			
— *fractions*	Develop	Develop	Maintain & Apply
• **Make appropriate estimates**			
— *rounding*	Develop	Develop	Maintain & Apply
— *operations*	Develop	Develop	Maintain & Apply
— *clustering*	Develop	Develop	Maintain & Apply
— *compatible numbers*	Introduce/Develop	Develop	Maintain & Apply
— *front-end*	Introduce/Develop	Develop	Maintain & Apply
• **Determine reasonableness of results**			
— *determine reasonableness of answers*	Develop	Develop	Develop
• **Estimate square and cube roots**			
— *squares and square roots*	Introduce/Develop	Develop	Develop
Number Operations			
• **Perform computation with rational numbers**			
— *add, subtract, multiply, and divide whole numbers*	Maintain & Apply	Maintain & Apply	Maintain & Apply
— *add and subtract decimals*	Develop	Develop	Maintain & Apply
— *multiply and divide decimals*	Develop	Develop	Maintain & Apply
— *add and subtract fractions, like denominators*	Develop	Maintain & Apply	Maintain & Apply
— *add and subtract fractions, unlike denominators*	Develop	Develop	Maintain & Apply
— *add and subtract mixed numbers*	Develop	Develop	Maintain & Apply
— *multiply and divide fractions*	Develop	Develop	Maintain & Apply
— *multiply and divide mixed numbers*	Develop	Develop	Maintain & Apply
— *add and subtract integers*	Develop	Develop	Maintain & Apply

INTRODUCE *DEVELOP* *MAINTAIN & APPLY*

Course	1	2	3
— *multiply and divide integers*			
— *use mental math*			
— *choose a computation method*			
• **Describe the effect of operations**			
— *check for reasonableness*			
• **Interpret rational number operations**			
— *add and subtract*			
— *multiply and divide*			
• **Solve application problems**			
— *solve problems using rational numbers*			
Ratios and Proportional Reasoning			
• **Use ratios to describe problem situations**			
— *read and write*			
— *equal ratios*			
• **Use fractions to represent ratios and proportions**			
— *equivalent forms for ratios*			
• **Use proportional reasoning**			
— *solve proportions*			
— *estimate solutions to proportions*			
— *reasoning with proportions*			
— *unit rate*			
— *unit price*			
— *distance, rate, time problems*			
• **Solve problems involving percent**			
— *use percent models*			
— *write as ratio and decimal*			
— *greater than 100%*			
— *less than 1%*			
— *estimate*			
— *find using a proportion*			
— *find using an equation*			
— *find percent of a number*			
— *find percent one number is of another*			
— *find number when percent is known*			
— *percent change*			
Properties of Number and Operations			
• **Describe odd and even integers**			
— *integers*			

Course	1	2	3
• **Use factors, multiples, or prime factorization**			
— *factors*			
— *prime factorization*			
— *greatest common factor*			
— *multiples*			
— *least common multiple*			
• **Use prime and composite numbers**			
— *prime and composite numbers*			
• **Use divisibility or remainders**			
— *divisibility rules*			
• **Apply basic properties of operations**			
— *order of operations*			
— *positive exponents*			
— *negative exponents*			
• **Explain a mathematical concept or relationship**			
— *verbalize and define concepts*			

Measurement

Measuring Physical Attributes	1	2	3
• **Compare objects by attribute (length, area, volume, angle, weight, mass)**			
— *use customary units of length, area, volume, weight, capacity*			
— *use metric units of length, area, volume, weight, capacity*			
• **Estimate size by attribute**			
— *estimate length*			
— *estimate area of irregular figures*			
— *estimate volume*			
— *estimate time*			
• **Use appropriate measurement instruments**			
— *compasses*			
— *graph paper*			
— *protractors*			
— *rulers (metric and customary)*			
• **Solve measurement problems**			
— *area of squares and rectangles*			
— *area of parallelograms*			
— *area of triangles*			
— *area of trapezoids*			
— *area of circles*			

Course	1	2	3
— *area of composite figures*	Introduce/Develop	Develop	Maintain & Apply
— *surface area of prism*	Introduce/Develop	Develop	Maintain & Apply
— *surface area of cylinders*	Introduce	Develop	Maintain & Apply
— *volume of prisms*	Develop	Develop	Maintain & Apply
— *volume of cylinders*	Introduce	Develop	Maintain & Apply
— *volume of cones and pyramids*			Introduce/Develop
— *volume of spheres*			Introduce
— *dimension analysis*		Introduce	Develop
Systems of Measurement			
• **Select appropriate type of unit for a particular attribute**			
— *use length, area, or volume*	Develop	Develop	Develop
• **Use conversion to solve problems**			
— *convert within customary system*	Develop	Develop	Maintain & Apply
— *convert within metric system*	Develop	Develop	Maintain & Apply
— *convert units of time*	Develop	Maintain & Apply	Maintain & Apply
• **Estimate measurement from one system to another**			
— *use conversion factors*		Introduce/Develop	Develop
• **Determine appropriate size of measurement units**			
— *choose appropriate units*	Develop	Develop	Maintain & Apply
• **Determine accuracy of measurement**			
— *precision*		Introduce/Develop	Develop
— *significant digits*			Introduce
• **Solve problems using scale drawings**			
— *scale drawing*	Introduce/Develop	Develop	Develop

Geometry

Course	1	2	3
Dimension and Shape			
• **Describe/draw shortest length between points**			
— *line*	Develop	Develop	Maintain & Apply
— *line segment*	Develop	Develop	Maintain & Apply
— *points on a line*	Develop	Develop	Maintain & Apply
• **Identify geometric object by description of its properties**			
— *identify polygons*	Develop	Develop	Maintain & Apply
— *classify quadrilaterals*	Develop	Develop	Maintain & Apply
— *classify triangles*	Develop	Develop	Maintain & Apply
— *congruent angles*	Develop	Develop	Develop

Course	1	2	3
• **Identify geometric objects in plane and space by visual representation**			
— *spatial visualization*	Introduce/Develop	Develop	Develop
• **Draw figures from written description**			
— *polygons*	Develop	Develop	Develop
— *circles, semicircles*	Develop	Develop	Develop
— *similar triangles*	Introduce/Develop	Develop	Develop
• **Represent 3-dimensional figures in 2-dimensional space**			
— *use nets*	Develop	Develop	Develop
• **Demonstrate understanding of 2- and 3-dimension shapes in the real world**			
— *different viewpoints*	Develop	Develop	Maintain & Apply
— *spatial visualization*	Develop	Develop	Maintain & Apply
Transformation of Shapes and Preservation of Properties			
• **Identify lines of symmetry and classify types of symmetry**			
— *symmetry*	Develop	Develop	Develop
• **Recognize effect of transformations on 2-dimensional shapes**			
— *reflections across lines of symmetry*	Introduce	Develop	Develop
— *rotations*	Introduce	Develop	Develop
— *translations*	Introduce	Develop	Develop
— *enlargements*			Introduce/Develop
— *reductions*			Introduce/Develop
— *dilations*			Introduce/Develop
• **Predict results of combining, subdividing, and changing shapes**			
— *plane figures*	Introduce	Develop	Develop
• **Justify and apply relationships of congruence and similarity**			
— *congruence*	Introduce	Develop	Develop
— *congruent polygons*		Develop	Develop
— *similarity*	Introduce	Develop	Develop
— *similar polygons*	Introduce	Develop	Develop
• **Use relationships of proportionality and conservation of angle**			
— *congruent angles*	Introduce	Develop	Maintain & Apply
— *proportions in similar figures*	Introduce	Develop	Develop
Relationships Between Geometric Figures			
• **Use properties and relationships to solve problems**			
— *draw a diagram*	Develop	Develop	Develop
— *use a proportion*	Develop	Develop	Develop
— *congruent angles*	Introduce	Develop	Develop

INTRODUCE *DEVELOP* *MAINTAIN & APPLY*

Course	1	2	3
— *similar triangles*			
— *trigonometric ratios (sine, cosine, tangent)*			
• **Use geometric models to solve problems**			
— *make a model*			
• **Use Pythagorean theorem to solve problems**			
— *Pythagorean theorem*			
— *trigonometric ratios*			
• **Describe properties and relationships among polygonal plane figures**			
— *angles*			
— *congruence*			
— *similarity*			
— *ratio of sides and areas*			
— *ratio of sides and volume*			
• **Describe properties and relationships of parallel or intersecting lines**			
— *parallel lines*			
— *perpendicular lines*			
Position and Direction			
• **Describe relative positions of points and lines**			
— *coordinate geometry*			
• **Describe intersection of two or more figures in a plane**			
— *coordinate geometry*			
• **Represent figures in the coordinate plane**			
— *coordinate geometry*			
Mathematical Reasoning			
• **Make and test a conjecture about regular polygons**			
— *make and test conjectures*			

Data Analysis and Probability

Course	1	2	3
Data Representation			
• **Read and interpret data**			
— *analyze and interpret data*			
• **Represent data set graphically and then solve a problem**			
— *decide how to present data*			
— *tables and charts*			
— *frequency tables*			
— *line plots*			
— *histograms*			
— *bar graphs*			
— *double bar graphs*			
— *stacked bar graphs*			
— *sliding bar graphs*			
— *line graphs*			
— *multiple line graphs*			
— *circle graphs*			
— *scatter plots*			
— *stem-and-leaf plots*			
— *back-to-back stem-and-leaf plots*			
— *box-and-whisker plots*			
— *draw and compare different representations*			
• **Use estimation and computation to solve problems from data sets**			
— *interpolation and extrapolation*			
— *determine trends from data*			
• **Determine appropriateness and effectiveness of data representations**			
— *choose an appropriate graph or statistic*			
• **Compare and contrast different representations of same data**			
— *draw and compare different representations*			
Characteristics of Data Sets			
• **Calculate, use, interpret mean, median, mode, range**			
— *mean, median, mode*			
— *range*			
— *quartiles*			
— *analyze data*			
• **Identify outliers and determine their effect**			
— *outlier*			
• **Compare two or more data sets using appropriate statistical measures**			
— *identify misleading graphs and statistics*			
— *choose an appropriate graph or statistic*			
• **Select "best fit" line and use it to make predictions**			
— *trend lines*			
— *make predictions from graphs*			
Experiments and Samples			
• **Identify sources of bias in sampling**			
— *analyze bias in surveys*			

Course	1	2	3
• **Distinguish between random and non-random samples**			
— *analyze sampling techniques*		Develop	Develop
• **Evaluate design of an experiment**			
— *plan and analyze surveys*		Develop	Develop
Probability			
• **Analyze probability of independent events**			
— *theoretical probability*	Develop	Develop	Maintain & Apply
— *experimental probability*	Develop	Develop	Maintain & Apply
— *probability of complements*	Introduce/Develop	Develop	Develop
— *odds*	Introduce	Develop	Develop
• **Determine theoretical probability of simple and compound events**			
— *counting principle*	Introduce/Develop	Develop	Develop
• **Estimate probability of simple and compound events**			
— *estimate probability*	Introduce	Develop	Develop
— *simulations*	Introduce/Develop	Develop	Develop
• **Distinguish between experimental and theoretical probability**			
— *analyze probability*	Introduce/Develop	Develop	Maintain & Apply
• **Determine sample space for a given situation**			
— *tree diagrams/sample space*	Develop	Develop	Develop
• **Use sample space to determine probability of possible outcomes**			
— *simple probability*	Introduce/Develop	Develop	Develop
— *compound probability*	Introduce	Develop	Develop
• **Represent probability using fractions, decimals, percents**			
— *find and write probability*	Develop	Develop	Develop
— *permutations*	Introduce/Develop	Develop	Develop
— *combinations*		Introduce/Develop	Develop
• **Determine probability of dependent and independent events**			
— *independent events*	Introduce/Develop	Develop	Develop
— *dependent events*		Introduce/Develop	Develop
• **Interpret probability within a given context**			
— *conduct experiments and simulations*	Develop	Develop	Develop

Algebra

Course	1	2	3
Patterns, Relations, and Functions			
• **Use, describe, extend numerical and geometric patterns**			
— *numerical patterns*	Develop	Develop	Develop
— *geometric patterns*	Introduce/Develop	Develop	Develop
• **Generalize pattern in a number sequence, table or graph**			
— *look for and describe a pattern*	Develop	Develop	Develop
• **Analyze or create patterns, sequences, functions**			
— *write a rule*	Introduce/Develop	Develop	Develop
— *input-output tables*	Develop	Develop	Develop
— *sequences*	Introduce/Develop	Develop	Develop
— *Fibonacci sequence*	Introduce	Develop	Develop
• **Identify linear and nonlinear functions**			
— *functions*	Introduce	Develop	Develop
— *linear*	Introduce	Develop	Develop
— *quadratic*		Introduce	Introduce/Develop
— *other nonlinear*		Introduce	Develop
• **Interpret meaning of slope or intercepts in linear functions**			
— *using slope*		Introduce/Develop	Develop
— *graphing and using intercepts*			Introduce/Develop
Algebraic Representations			
• **Translate between different linear expressions**			
— *evaluate*	Develop	Develop	Develop
• **Analyze or interpret linear relationships**			
— *use linear relationships*	Introduce	Develop	Develop
• **Graph or interpret points represented by ordered pairs**			
— *ordered pairs*	Develop	Develop	Maintain & Apply
• **Solve problems in the coordinate system**			
— *graphing equations*	Introduce	Develop	Develop
— *graphing inequalities*		Introduce	Develop
• **Make conclusions and generalizations about linear relationships**			
— *make generalizations*	Introduce/Develop	Develop	Develop
• **Represent functional relationships**			
— *linear functions*	Introduce	Develop	Develop
— *quadratic functions*		Introduce	Introduce/Develop
Variables, Expressions, and Operations			
• **Write algebraic expressions, equations, inequalities**			
— *write from word phrases*	Develop	Develop	Maintain & Apply
— *write from word sentences*	Develop	Develop	Maintain & Apply
— *write inequalities*	Introduce/Develop	Develop	Develop
• **Perform basic operations on linear algebraic expressions**			
— *evaluate*	Develop	Develop	Develop
— *simplify*	Develop	Develop	Develop

INTRODUCE *DEVELOP* *MAINTAIN & APPLY*

Course	1	2	3
— *commutative property*	→	→	→
— *associative property*	→	→	→
— *distributive property*	→	→	→
Equations and Inequalities			
• **Solve linear equations or inequalities**			
— *solve one-step equations*	→	→	→
— *solve two-step equations*	→	→	→
— *solve systems of linear equations*			→
— *solve one-step inequalities*	→	→	→
— *solve two-step inequalities*			→
• **Understand the concept of equivalence**			
— *properties of equations*	→	→	→
— *properties of inequalities*	→	→	→
• **Solve problems using equations and inequalities with coefficients**			
— *write from word sentences*	→	→	→
— *solve equations with integer solutions*	→	→	→
— *solve inequalities*	→	→	→
• **Relate linear expressions and graphs of lines using slope, intercept**			
— *write and graph equations*		→	→
• **Use and evaluate common formulas**			
— *formulas*	→	→	→

Mathematical Processes

Course	1	2	3
Problem Solving			
• **Problem-solving skills**			
— *use a problem-solving plan*	→	→	→
— *too much or too little information*	→	→	→
— *check for reasonableness*	→	→	→
— *use a proportion*	→	→	→
— *use a calculator*	→	→	→
— *use a computer*	→	→	→
— *use estimation*	→	→	→
— *use formulas*	→	→	→
— *use graphs*	→	→	→
• **Problem-solving strategies**			
— *choosing a strategy*	→	→	→
— *draw a diagram*	→	→	→
— *look for a pattern*	→	→	→
— *make a graph*	→	→	→
— *make an organized list*	→	→	→
— *make a table*	→	→	→
— *simulate a problem*	→	→	→
— *solve a simpler problem*	→	→	→
— *try, check, and revise*	→	→	→
— *use logical reasoning*	→	→	→
— *use multiple strategies*	→	→	→
— *work backward*	→	→	→
— *write an equation*	→	→	→
Reasoning and Proof			
— *justify answers*	→	→	→
— *make and test conjectures*	→	→	→
— *make generalizations*	→	→	→
— *reason from graphs*	→	→	→
— *reason with proportions*	→	→	→
— *recognize patterns*	→	→	→
— *use logical reasoning*	→	→	→
— *evaluate mathematical arguments*	→	→	→
— *use or construct Venn diagrams*	→	→	→
Communication			
— *interpret mathematical ideas through discussing, writing, reading*	→	→	→
— *make convincing arguments using mathematical ideas*	→	→	→
— *relate mathematical language to everyday language*	→	→	→
— *analyze and evaluate mathematical thinking of others*	→	→	→
Connections			
— *use connections among mathematical ideas*	→	→	→
— *apply mathematics in contexts outside of mathematics*	→	→	→
— *use technology*	→	→	→
Representation			
— *use representations to develop mathematical ideas*	→	→	→
— *use tables, graphs, words, and symbols interchangeably*	→	→	→
— *solve problems using pictures/diagrams*	→	→	→
— *algebra tiles*	→	→	→
— *decimal models*	→	→	→
— *fraction models*	→	→	→
— *number line models*	→	→	→
— *two-color chips*	→	→	→

CHAPTER 7

Exponents and Powers

Chapter at a Glance

7-1 Scientific Notation
pp. 365–369

Objectives
1. Standard Form and Scientific Notation
2. Ordering Numbers in Scientific Notation

New Vocabulary
scientific notation

NCTM Standards
1, 2, 4, 6, 7, 8, 9, 10

Local Standards

7-2 Algebra — Exponents and Multiplication
pp. 370–374

Objectives
1. Multiplying Powers With the Same Base
2. Multiplying Numbers in Scientific Notation

NCTM Standards
1, 2, 6, 7, 8, 9, 10

Local Standards

✓ Checkpoint Quiz 1

7-3 Algebra — Exponents and Division
pp. 376–381

Objectives
1. Dividing Powers With the Same Base
2. Using Zero or Negative Exponents

NCTM Standards
1, 2, 4, 6, 7, 8, 9, 10

Local Standards

7-4 Algebra — Power Rules
pp. 383–387

Objectives
1. Raising a Power to a Power
2. Raising a Product to a Power

NCTM Standards
1, 2, 6, 7, 8, 9, 10

Local Standards

✓ Checkpoint Quiz 2

7-5 Problem Solving — Write an Equation
pp. 388–391

Objectives
1. Solving Problems by Writing Equations

NCTM Standards
1, 2, 4, 6, 7, 8, 9, 10

Local Standards

7-6 Number Systems
pp. 392–395

Objectives
1. Understanding the Base of a Number System

New Vocabulary
expanded form, binary

NCTM Standards
1, 6, 7, 8, 9, 10

Local Standards

Reaching All Students

Additional Instructional Options in Chapter 7

Reading and Math Literacy

Reading Math

Understanding Word Problems, pp. 382

Reading Math hints, pp. 377, 380, 383

Reading Comprehension, p. 369

Understanding Vocabulary, p. 398

Writing in Math

Daily Writing Practice, pp. 368, 374, 380, 386, 390, 394, 400

Above Level

Challenge exercises

pp. 368, 373, 380, 386, 391, 394

Extension

Bar Codes, p. 396

Hands-On and Technology

Investigations

Multiplying by Powers of Ten, p. 365

Exploring Exponents, p. 370

Modeling Number Systems, p. 392

Technology

Scientific Notation, p. 375

Activities and Projects

Real-World Snapshots

Applying Scientific Notation, pp. 402-403

Chapter Project

One Small Step, p. 699

Test Prep

Daily Test Prep

pp. 369, 373, 381, 387, 391, 395

Test-Taking Strategies

Answering True/False Questions, p. 397

Test Prep

Reading Comprehension, p. 401

Chapter Assessment

Checkpoint Quiz

pp. 374, 387

Chapter Review

pp. 398–399

Chapter Test

p. 400

Pacing Options

This chart suggests pacing only for the core lessons and their parts. It is provided as a possible guide. It will help you determine how much time you have in your schedule to cover the additional features and assessment, as described at the left.

Day	Traditional 45-minute class periods	Block 90-minute class periods
1	7-1 ▼1	7-1 ▼1 ▼2
2	7-1 ▼2	7-2 ▼1 ▼2
3	7-2 ▼1	7-3 ▼1 ▼2
4	7-2 ▼2	7-4 ▼1 ▼2
5	7-3 ▼1	7-5 ▼1 7-6 ▼1
6	7-3 ▼2	
7	7-4 ▼1	
8	7-4 ▼2	
9	7-5 ▼1	
10	7-6 ▼1	
11		
12		
13		
14		
15		

NCTM STANDARDS 2000

1 Number and Operations
2 Algebra
3 Geometry
4 Measurement
5 Data Analysis and Probability
6 Problem Solving
7 Reasoning and Proof
8 Communication
9 Connections
10 Representation

Math Background

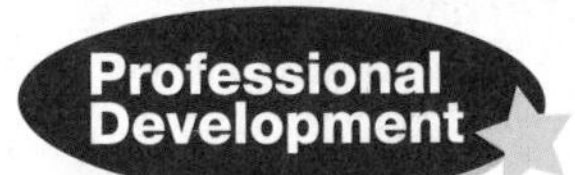

Skills Trace

BEFORE Chapter 7

Course 2 introduced powers and scientific notation.

DURING Chapter 7

Course 3 reviews and extends work with powers to include power rules for multiplication and division.

AFTER Chapter 7

Throughout this course students use exponents and large and small numbers.

Scientific Notation

Math Understandings

- Scientific notation is a brief way to write very large or very small numbers.
- You can often more easily compare large or small numbers when they are expressed in scientific notation.
- To multiply a number by 10^p, when $p > 0$, you move the decimal point in the number p places to the right to increase the size of the number.
- The number 10^p, written without an exponent, is 1 followed by p zeros.

A number is in **scientific notation** if the first factor is greater than or equal to 1 and less than 10 and the second factor is a power of 10. Examples below are provided for positive integer exponents.

Example:	Standard Form	Scientific Notation
	14.83	1.483×10^1
	148.3	1.483×10^2
	1,483.	1.483×10^3
	14,830	1.483×10^4
	148,300	1.483×10^5
	1,483,000	1.483×10^6

Exponents and Multiplication

Math Understandings

- Exponential notation with positive exponents is a mathematical shorthand for repeated multiplication.
- A positive exponent tells how many times the base is used as a factor.
- An exponent applies only to its base and not to the coefficient in front of the base, so -3^2 is $-(3 \cdot 3)$ or -9 but $(-3)^2$ is $(-3) \cdot (-3)$ or 9.
- To multiply two powers with the same base, you keep the common base and add the exponents to find the new exponent.

Multiplying Powers With the Same Base	
To multiply numbers or variables with the same base, add the exponents.	
Arithmetic	**Algebra**
$3^2 \cdot 3^7 = 3^{(2+7)} = 3^9$	$a^m \cdot a^n = a^{(m+n)}$

You can apply the rule for multiplying powers with the same base when you multiply numbers in scientific notation.

Example:
$$\begin{aligned}(7 \times 10^5)(8 \times 10^6) &= (7 \times 8) \times (10^5 \times 10^6)\\ &= 56 \times (10^5 \times 10^6)\\ &= 56 \times 10^{11}\\ &= 5.6 \times 10^1 \times 10^{11}\\ &= 5.6 \times 10^{12}\end{aligned}$$

Exponents and Division

Math Understandings

- An exponent that is a negative number indicates that you are to take a reciprocal.
- A zero exponent on an nonzero base means the power has a value of 1.
- To divide two powers with the same base, you keep the common base and subtract the exponent of the divisor from the exponent of the dividend to find the new exponent.

Just as you can multiply powers with the same base, you can divide powers with the same base. So, numbers expressed in scientific notation can be divided as well as multiplied

Dividing Powers With the Same Base	
To divide nonzero numbers or variables with the same nonzero base, subtract the exponents.	
Arithmetic	**Algebra**
$\frac{8^5}{8^3} = 8^{(5-3)} = 8^2$	$\frac{a^m}{a^n} = a^{(m-n)}$, where $a \neq 0$

Zero as an Exponent
For any nonzero number a, $a^0 = 1$ **Example:** $9^0 = 1$ because $1 = \frac{x^a}{x^a} = x^{a-a} = x^0$, $x \neq 0$.

Negative Exponents
For any nonzero number a and integer n, $a^{-n} = \frac{1}{a^n}$. **Example:** $8^{-5} = \frac{1}{8^5}$

Numbers in scientific notation can have negative exponents. Multiplying a number by 10^n, when n is negative, moves the decimal point n places to the left. To write a number that is less than 1 in scientific notation, determine the first factor by moving the decimal point. Then write the second factor as a negative power of ten.

Example:	**Standard Form**	**Scientific Notation**
	1.483	1.483×10^1
	0.1483	1.483×10^{-1}
	0.01483	1.483×10^{-2}

7-4 Power Rules

Math Understandings

- The word power means an expression such as 3^5, but you also use the same word to read 3^5 as "3 to the fifth power."
- You can raise a product to a power using repeated multiplication.

Raising a Power to a Power	
To raise a power to a power, multiply the exponents.	
Arithmetic	**Algebra**
$(2^5)^3 = 2^{(5 \cdot 3)} = 2^{15}$	$(a^m)^n = a^{(m \cdot n)}$ where m and n are integers.

Raising a Product to a Power	
To raise a product to a power, raise each factor to the power.	
Arithmetic	**Algebra**
$(3 \cdot 5)^2 = 3^2 \cdot 5^2$	$(ab)^m = a^m \cdot b^m$ where m is an integer.

7-5 Write an Equation

Math Understandings

- Many problems in mathematics can be solved by writing an equation.

You can use formulas and write equations to solve problems that involve numbers written in scientific notation.

7-6 Number Systems

Math Understandings

- The base-b number system uses b digits.
- You multiply a digit in the last place by b^0, in the next-to-last place by b^1, and in the next place to the left by b^2, and so on.

You can write base-10 and base-2 numbers in standard form or expanded form.

Example:	**Standard Form**	**Expanded Form**
base 10	287	$(2 \cdot 10^2) + (8 \cdot 10^1) + (7 \cdot 10^0)$
base 2	10010_2	$(1 \cdot 2^4) + (0 \cdot 2^3) + (0 \cdot 2^2) + (1 \cdot 2^1) + (0 \cdot 2^0)$

Additional Professional Development Opportunities

Chapter 7 Math Background notes:
pp. 366, 371, 377, 384, 389, 393

Additional resources available from SkyLight Professional Development:

On-site courses, workshops, summer institutes. Online courses and chat rooms. Videocassettes and books. Visit www.skylightedu.com.

Ongoing Assessment and Intervention

The *Prentice Hall Mathematics* program provides many options for assessment in the Student Edition, Teacher's Edition, and teaching resources. From these options you may choose instructional materials that are appropriate for your students and that support your district's curriculum requirements.

Daily Assessment

Instant Check System™ in Chapter 7

Allows students to check their own learning before, during, and after each lesson.

Diagnosing Readiness before the chapter (p. 364)

Check Skills You'll Need exercises in each lesson (pp. 365, 370, 376, 383, 388, 392)

Check Understanding questions with each Example (pp. 366, 367, 371, 372, 376, 377, 378, 379, 383, 384, 388, 389, 393)

Checkpoint Quiz (pp. 374, 387)

Formal Assessment

Assessment in the Student Text and in Additional Resources

Assess student progress throughout the Course 2 textbook and with blackline masters and CD-ROM.

Student Edition
- Chapter 7 Review, with Vocabulary, Skills, and Concepts Review, pp. 398–399
- Chapter 7 Test, p. 400

Assessment Resources
- Checkpoint Quizzes 1 & 2
- Chapter Test, forms A & B
- Chapter Alternative Assessment

Spanish versions available.

Computer Test Generator CD-ROM
- Instant Chapter Tests™—pre-made tests with items that vary every time you print.
- Online Testing allows you to give tests online and receive progress reports.
- Prepare students by making tests based on standardized test objectives.

Algebra Readiness Tests
- Includes Basic Skills Tests and Concept-Readiness Tests.
- Assess understanding of skills and concepts needed for success in algebra.

Intervention

Skills Intervention Kit

Online Intervention

Integrated within the iText, this online intervention system includes diagnostic tests and prescribed remediation, plus reports to track student mastery.

A *complete* system for the student who is struggling with course-level work

Eight intervention units cover core skills and allow you to:
- **Diagnose** students' gaps in basic skills
- **Prescribe** an individualized course of study
- **Monitor** student progress

Includes print workbooks, tutorial CD-ROM, teacher editions, progress folders, and more. *Available in Spanish.*

Standardized Test Preparation

The *Prentice Hall Mathematics* program integrates preparation for high-stakes standardized tests in every lesson of the Student Edition and continues this support in the Prentice Hall Assessment System.

Test Prep

In Student Text, Chapter 7

Teaches students strategies and gives them practice with all the test item formats they will encounter on high-stakes tests.

Test Prep exercises in each lesson (pp. 369, 373, 381, 387, 391, 395)

Test-Taking Strategies Answering True/False Questions, p. 397

Test Prep (p. 401: Reading Comprehension)

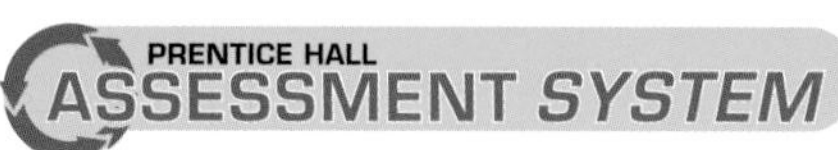

A three-step approach to preparing students for high stakes, national, and state exams.

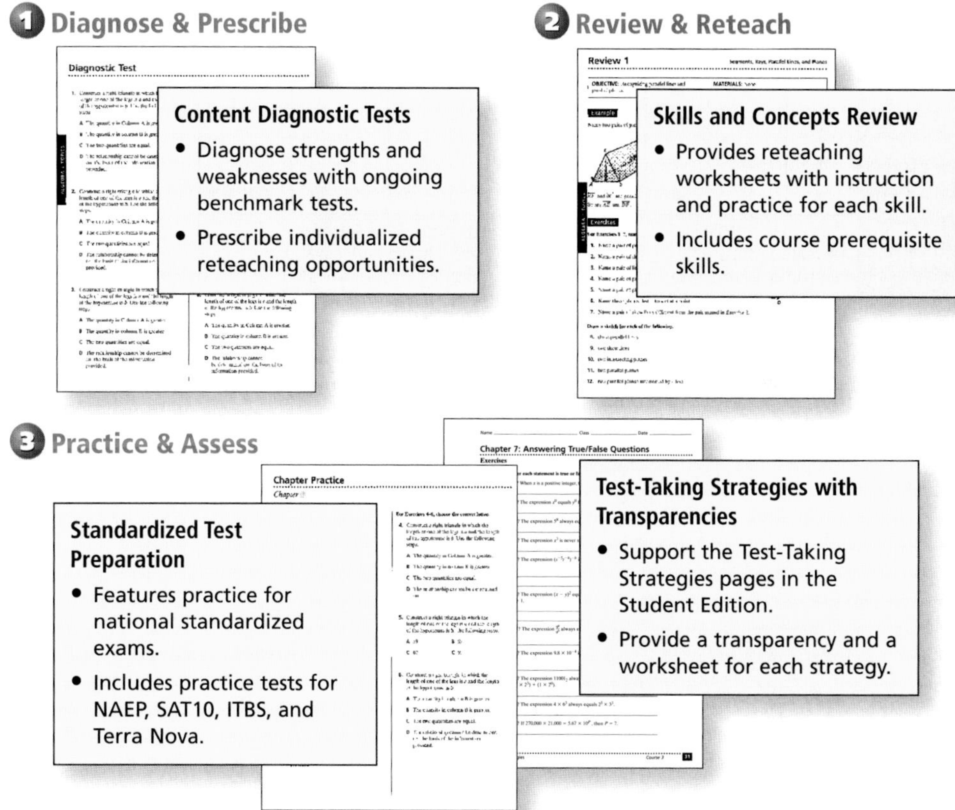

1 Diagnose & Prescribe
Diagnostic Test
Content Diagnostic Tests
• Diagnose strengths and weaknesses with ongoing benchmark tests.
• Prescribe individualized reteaching opportunities.
2 Review & Reteach
Review 1
Skills and Concepts Review
• Provides reteaching worksheets with instruction and practice for each skill.
• Includes course prerequisite skills.
3 Practice & Assess
Chapter Practice
Chapter 7: Answering True/False Questions
Standardized Test Preparation
• Features practice for national standardized exams.
• Includes practice tests for NAEP, SAT10, ITBS, and Terra Nova.
Test-Taking Strategies with Transparencies
• Support the Test-Taking Strategies pages in the Student Edition.
• Provide a transparency and a worksheet for each strategy.

Correlation to Standardized Tests

Lesson		NAEP	Terra Nova		ITBS	SAT10	Local Test
			CAT6	CTBS			
7-1	Scientific Notation	N1f	■			■	
7-2	Exponents and Multiplication	N5e			■	■	
7-3	Exponents and Division	N5e			■	■	
7-4	Power Rules	N5e			■	■	
7-5	Write an Equation	A3a			■		
7-6	Number Systems	N5f			■		

NAEP National Assessment of Educational Progress
CAT6/Terra Nova California Achievement Test, 6th Ed.
CTBS/Terra Nova Comprehensive Test of Basic Skills
ITBS Iowa Test of Basic Skills, Form M.
SAT10 Stanford Achievement Test, 10th Ed.

Program Resources

	Resources in Grab & Go™ Files				Resources for Reaching All Students				Spanish Resources			Presentation Assistant Plus! Transparencies					Presentation Assistant Plus!
	Practice	Reteach	Enrich	Checkpt Quiz	Reading & Math Literacy	Technology Activities	Hands-On Activities	Guided Problem Solving	Practice	Reading & Math Literacy	Checkpt Quiz	Skills Check	Problem of the Day	Additional Examples	Answers to Exercises	Lesson Quiz	Prentice Hall Presentation Pro CD-ROM
7-1	■	■	■		■		■	■	■	■		■	■	■	■	■	■
7-2	■	■	■	■	■			■	■	■	■	■	■	■	■	■	■
7-3	■	■	■					■	■			■	■	■	■	■	■
7-4	■	■	■	■	■	■		■	■	■	■	■	■	■	■	■	■
7-5	■	■	■					■	■			■	■	■	■	■	■
7-6	■	■	■					■	■			■	■	■	■	■	■
For the Chapter	Chapter Projects, Chapter Tests, Alternative Assessment, Cumulative Review, Cumulative Assessment				**On web site only:** Home Activities, Interdisciplinary Activities, Algebra Readiness Puzzles				Spanish Chapter Tests, Alternative Assessment, Cumulative Review, Cumulative Assessment			Classroom Aid Transparencies					

Also available for use with the chapter:

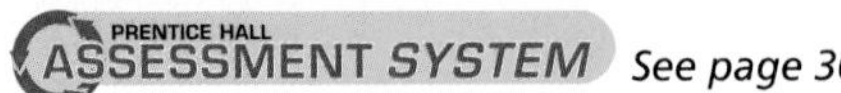

See page 362F.

- Practice Workbook
- Solution Key
- MathNotes folder

- For teacher support and access to student Web materials, use the Web Code abk-5500.
- For additional online and technology resources, *see below.*

Technology

Online and on CD-ROM

Complete Interactive Student Text online and on CD-ROM—with instant feedback assessment, tutorial help, dynamic activities, instructional and real-world videos, audio, and additional practice.

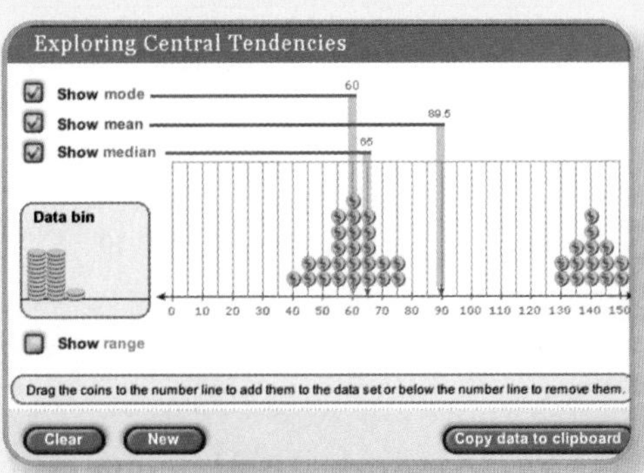

www.PHSchool.com For Students

Use Web codes for easy access to online activities, chapter projects, self-grading lesson quizzes, chapter tests, vocabulary quizzes, updated data sources, graphing calculator procedures, and more.

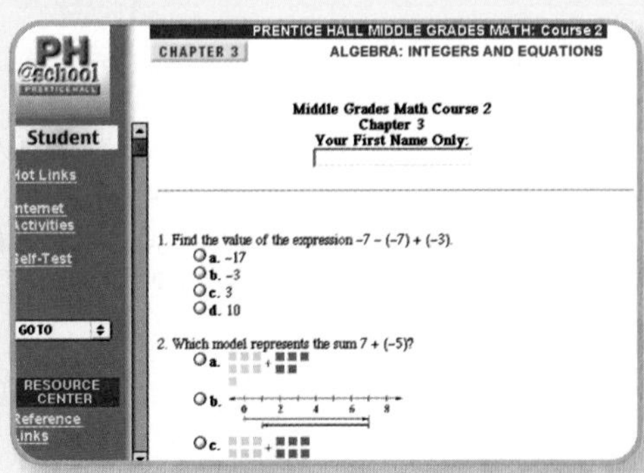

PH SuccessNet **For Teachers**

Online lesson planning with built-in state correlations, all the teaching resources, complete reference library, your own calendar and Teacher Web page, professional development, and more.

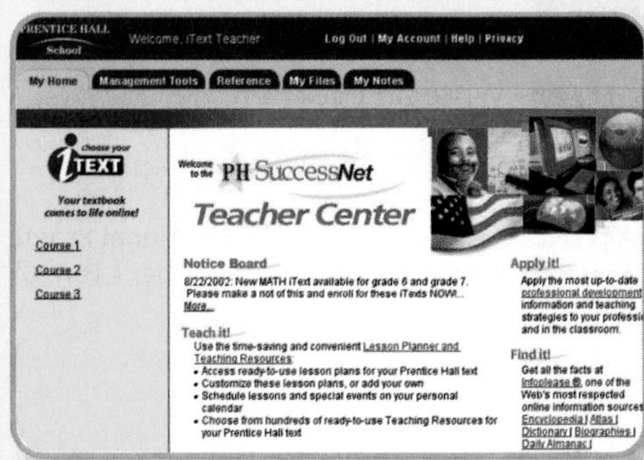

Presentation Assistant Plus!

The *Prentice Hall Presentation Assistant Plus!* provides you with the material you need to teach a lesson from beginning to end. Two easy-to-use formats—Transparencies and PowerPoint®—allow you to present a lesson the way you are most comfortable.

Transparencies

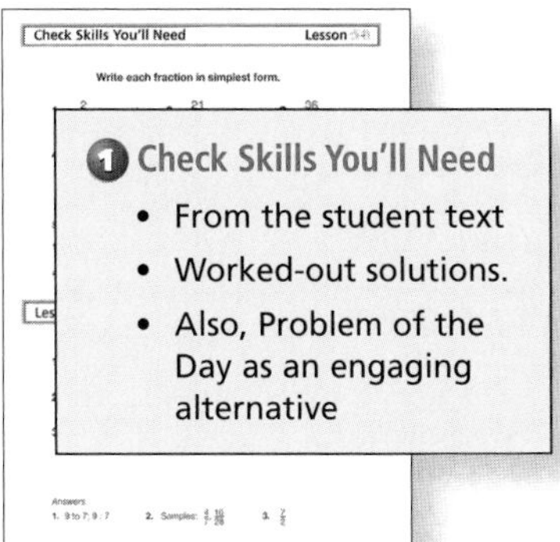

Check Skills You'll Need
Lesson
Write each fraction in simplest form.
1 Check Skills You'll Need
• From the student text
• Worked-out solutions.
• Also, Problem of the Day as an engaging alternative

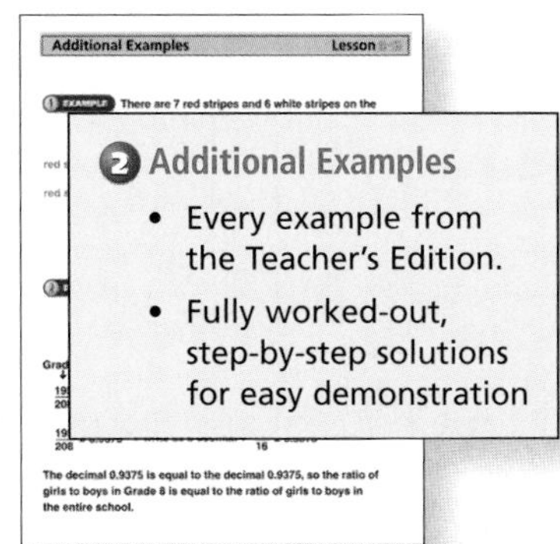

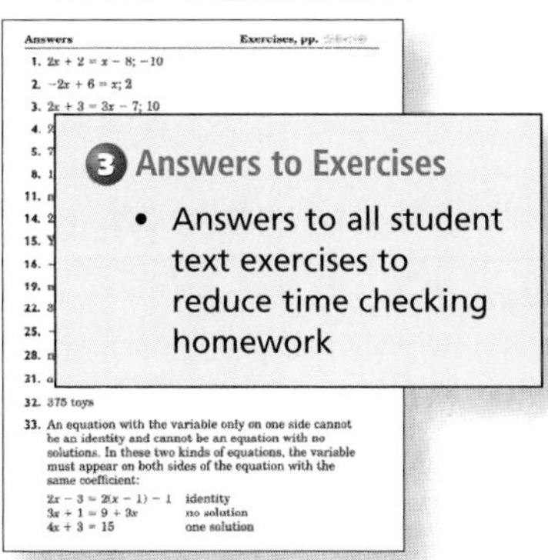

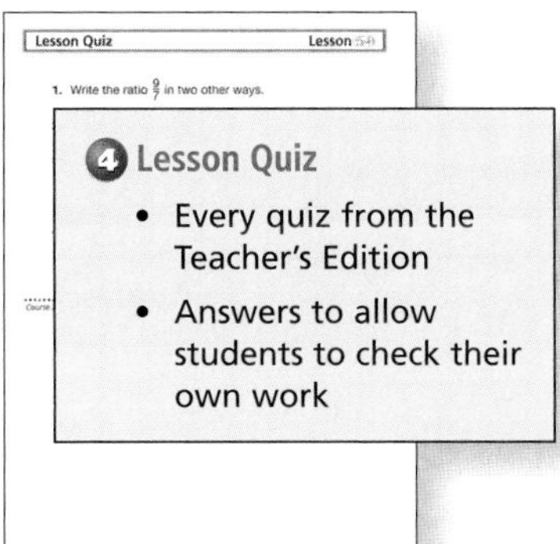

Lesson Quiz
Lesson
4 Lesson Quiz
• Every quiz from the Teacher's Edition
• Answers to allow students to check their own work

Throughout the Teacher's Edition, this symbol indicates material that is available in the Presentation Assistant Plus!

Prentice Hall Presentation Pro CD-ROM

- Includes all Transparencies.
- Conveniently organized by lesson so you can easily ❶ Introduce, ❷ Teach, ❸ Check Homework, and ❹ Assess each lesson.
- Animated examples allow step-by-step instruction at your own pace.
- Easy to edit so you can create custom presentations.

Teaching Chapter 7 Using Presentation Assistant Plus!

	❶ Introduce	❷ Teach	❸ Check Homework	❹ Assess
	Check Skills You'll Need	Additional Examples	Student Edition Answers	Lesson Quiz
7-1	p. 54	pp. 125–126	✔	p. 54
7-2	p. 55	pp. 127–128	✔	p. 55
7-3	p. 56	pp. 129–130	✔	p. 56
7-4	p. 57	p. 131	✔	p. 57
7-5	p. 58	pp. 132–133	✔	p. 58
7-6	p. 59	p. 134	✔	p. 59

Prentice Hall Presentation Pro

CD-ROM with dynamic PowerPoint® presentations for every lesson. Helps you introduce and develop concepts, check homework, and assess progress. Part of Presentation Assistant Plus! *(See above.)*

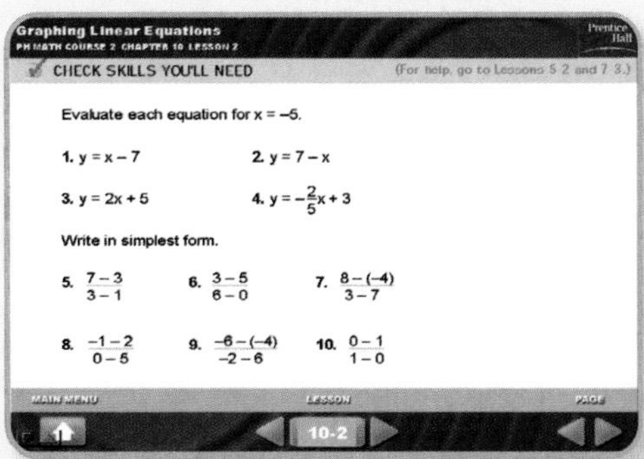

Computer Test Generator

CD-ROM to create practice sheets and tests for course objectives and standardized tests. Includes Instant Chapter Tests™, online testing, and student reports. Part of the PH Assessment System. *(See page 362F.)*

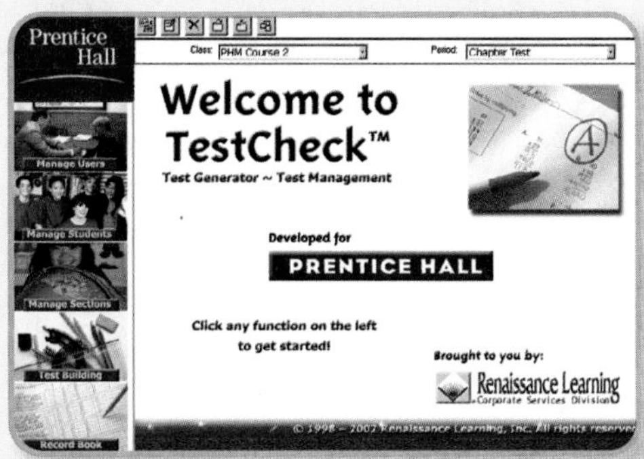

Resource Pro® with Planning Express®

CD-ROM with a lesson planning tool that allows you to import state and local objectives. Includes electronic versions of all the teaching resources.

Chapter Resources

Reading and Math Support

Reading and Math Literacy Masters

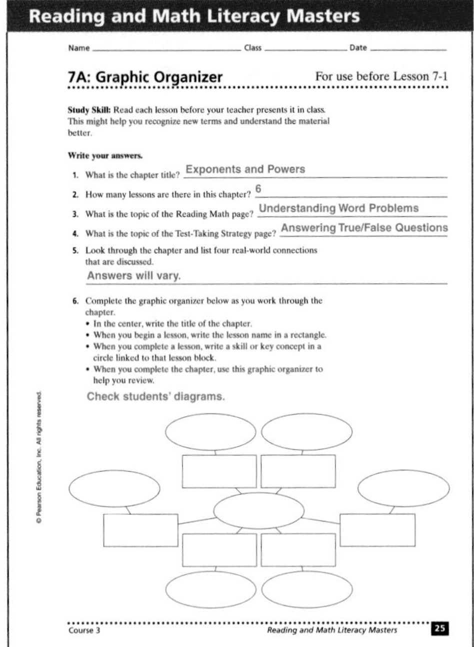

Name ________ Class ________ Date ________

7A: Graphic Organizer For use before Lesson 7-1

Study Skill: Read each lesson before your teacher presents it in class. This might help you recognize new terms and understand the material better.

Write your answers.

1. What is the chapter title? Exponents and Powers
2. How many lessons are there in this chapter? 6
3. What is the topic of the Reading Math page? Understanding Word Problems
4. What is the topic of the Test-Taking Strategy page? Answering True/False Questions
5. Look through the chapter and list four real-world connections that are discussed. Answers will vary.
6. Complete the graphic organizer below as you work through the chapter.
   - In the center, write the title of the chapter.
   - When you begin a lesson, write the lesson name in a rectangle.
   - When you complete a lesson, write a skill or key concept in a circle linked to that lesson block.
   - When you complete the chapter, use this graphic organizer to help you review.

   Check students' diagrams.

© Pearson Education, Inc. All rights reserved.

Course 3 Reading and Math Literacy Masters 25

Available in Spanish

Reading and Math Literacy Masters

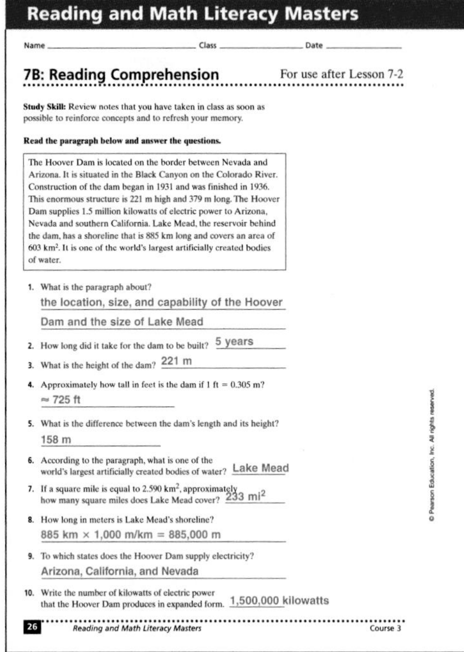

Name ________ Class ________ Date ________

7B: Reading Comprehension For use after Lesson 7-2

Study Skill: Review notes that you have taken in class as soon as possible to reinforce concepts and to refresh your memory.

Read the paragraph below and answer the questions.

The Hoover Dam is located on the border between Nevada and Arizona. It is situated in the Black Canyon on the Colorado River. Construction of the dam began in 1931 and was finished in 1936. This enormous structure is 221 m high and 379 m long. The Hoover Dam supplies 1.5 million kilowatts of electric power to Arizona, Nevada and southern California. Lake Mead, the reservoir behind the dam, has a shoreline that is 885 km long and covers an area of 603 km². It is one of the world's largest artificially created bodies of water.

1. What is the paragraph about? the location, size, and capability of the Hoover Dam and the size of Lake Mead
2. How long did it take for the dam to be built? 5 years
3. What is the height of the dam? 221 m
4. Approximately how tall in feet is the dam if 1 ft = 0.305 m? ≈ 725 ft
5. What is the difference between the dam's length and its height? 158 m
6. According to the paragraph, what is one of the world's largest artificially created bodies of water? Lake Mead
7. If a square mile is equal to 2.590 km², approximately how many square miles does Lake Mead cover? 233 mi²
8. How long in meters is Lake Mead's shoreline? 885 km × 1,000 m/km = 885,000 m
9. To which states does the Hoover Dam supply electricity? Arizona, California, and Nevada
10. Write the number of kilowatts of electric power that the Hoover Dam produces in expanded form. 1,500,000 kilowatts

© Pearson Education, Inc. All rights reserved.

26 Reading and Math Literacy Masters Course 3

Available in Spanish

Reading and Math Literacy Masters

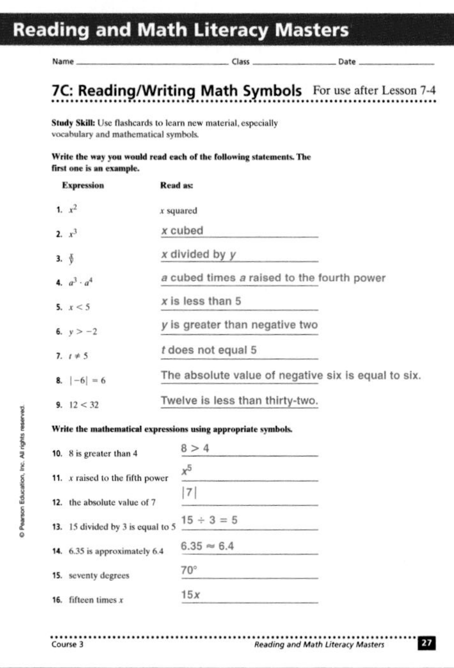

Name ________ Class ________ Date ________

7C: Reading/Writing Math Symbols For use after Lesson 7-4

Study Skill: Use flashcards to learn new material, especially vocabulary and mathematical symbols.

Write the way you would read each of the following statements. The first one is an example.

	Expression	Read as:
1.	x^2	x squared
2.	x^3	x cubed
3.	$\frac{x}{y}$	x divided by y
4.	$a^3 \cdot a^4$	a cubed times a raised to the fourth power
5.	$x < 5$	x is less than 5
6.	$y > -2$	y is greater than negative two
7.	$t \neq 5$	t does not equal 5
8.	$\lvert -6 \rvert = 6$	The absolute value of negative six is equal to six.
9.	$12 < 32$	Twelve is less than thirty-two.

Write the mathematical expressions using appropriate symbols.

10. 8 is greater than 4 $8 > 4$
11. x raised to the fifth power x^5
12. the absolute value of 7 $\lvert 7 \rvert$
13. 15 divided by 3 is equal to 5 $15 \div 3 = 5$
14. 6.35 is approximately 6.4 $6.35 \approx 6.4$
15. seventy degrees $70°$
16. fifteen times x $15x$

© Pearson Education, Inc. All rights reserved.

Course 3 Reading and Math Literacy Masters 27

Available in Spanish

Reading and Math Literacy Masters

Name ________ Class ________ Date ________

7D: Vocabulary For use with the Chapter Review

Study Skill: Ask questions in class if you are unclear on a topic.

Match the term in Column A with its definition in Column B.

Column A		Column B
1. solution	F	A. figures that have the same shape and size
2. principal	L	B. the value that occurs most often in a data set
3. median	I	C. transformation that turns a figure about a fixed point
4. sample space	N	D. the change in y divided by the change in x
5. cosine	K	E. a mathematical statement that contains an equal sign
6. sine	P	F. the value of a variable that makes an equation true
7. outlier	R	G. A ratio comparing quantities that are measured in different units
8. congruent	A	H. transformation that flips a figure over a line
9. rotation	C	I. the middle value in a data set that has been ordered from least to greatest value
10. tangent	J	J. the ratio of the opposite side to the adjacent side of a right triangle
11. mode	B	K. the ratio of the adjacent side to the hypotenuse of a right triangle
12. prime	Q	L. the original deposit into a bank account
13. slope	D	M. tells how many times the base is used as a factor
14. rate	G	N. a collection of all the possible outcomes in an experiment
15. exponent	M	O. the longest side of a right triangle
16. mean	S	P. the ratio of the opposite side to the hypotenuse of a right triangle
17. reflection	H	Q. a number with exactly two factors, one and itself
18. equation	E	R. a data item that is much greater or less than the other items in the data set
19. hypotenuse	O	S. the sum of the data values in a set divided by the number of values in the set

© Pearson Education, Inc. All rights reserved.

28 Reading and Math Literacy Masters Course 3

Available in Spanish

Problem Solving

Guided Problem Solving Masters

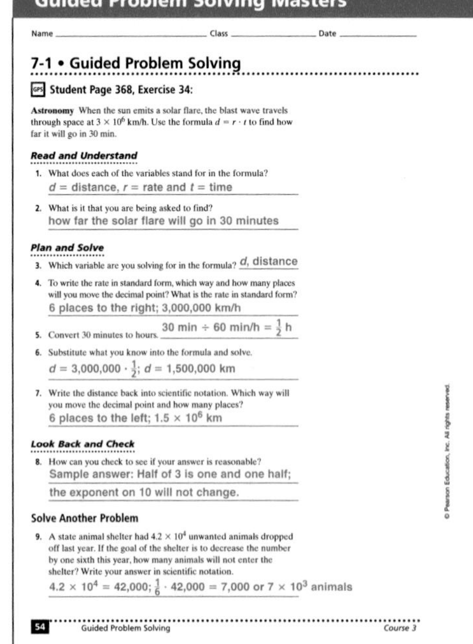

Name ________ Class ________ Date ________

7-1 • Guided Problem Solving

Student Page 368, Exercise 34:

Astronomy When the sun emits a solar flare, the blast wave travels through space at 3×10^6 km/h. Use the formula $d = r \cdot t$ to find how far it will go in 30 min.

Read and Understand

1. What does each of the variables stand for in the formula? d = distance, r = rate and t = time
2. What is it that you are being asked to find? how far the solar flare will go in 30 minutes

Plan and Solve

3. Which variable are you solving for in the formula? d, distance
4. To write the rate in standard form, which way and how many places will you move the decimal point? What is the rate in standard form? 6 places to the right; 3,000,000 km/h
5. Convert 30 minutes to hours. 30 min ÷ 60 min/h = $\frac{1}{2}$ h
6. Substitute what you know into the formula and solve. $d = 3{,}000{,}000 \cdot \frac{1}{2}$; $d = 1{,}500{,}000$ km
7. Write the distance back into scientific notation. Which way will you move the decimal point and how many places? 6 places to the left; 1.5×10^6 km

Look Back and Check

8. How can you check to see if your answer is reasonable? Sample answer: Half of 3 is one and one half; the exponent on 10 will not change.

Solve Another Problem

9. A state animal shelter had 4.2×10^4 unwanted animals dropped off last year. If the goal of the shelter is to decrease the number by one sixth this year, how many animals will not enter the shelter? Write your answer in scientific notation. $4.2 \times 10^4 = 42{,}000$; $\frac{1}{6} \cdot 42{,}000 = 7{,}000$ or 7×10^3 animals

© Pearson Education, Inc. All rights reserved.

54 Guided Problem Solving Course 3

Guided Problem Solving Masters

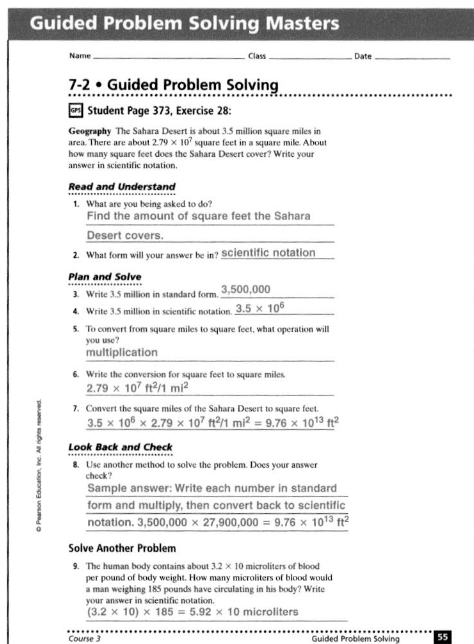

Name ________ Class ________ Date ________

7-2 • Guided Problem Solving

Student Page 373, Exercise 28:

Geography The Sahara Desert is about 3.5 million square miles in area. There are about 2.79×10^7 square feet in a square mile. About how many square feet does the Sahara Desert cover? Write your answer in scientific notation.

Read and Understand

1. What are you being asked to do? Find the amount of square feet the Sahara Desert covers.
2. What form will your answer be in? scientific notation

Plan and Solve

3. Write 3.5 million in standard form. 3,500,000
4. Write 3.5 million in scientific notation. 3.5×10^6
5. To convert from square miles to square feet, what operation will you use? multiplication
6. Write the conversion for square feet to square miles. 2.79×10^7 ft²/1 mi²
7. Convert the square miles of the Sahara Desert to square feet. $3.5 \times 10^6 \times 2.79 \times 10^7$ ft²/1 mi² $= 9.76 \times 10^{13}$ ft²

Look Back and Check

8. Use another method to solve the problem. Does your answer check? Sample answer: Write each number in standard form and multiply, then convert back to scientific notation. $3{,}500{,}000 \times 27{,}900{,}000 = 9.76 \times 10^{13}$ ft²

Solve Another Problem

9. The human body contains about 3.2×10 microliters of blood per pound of body weight. How many microliters of blood would a man weighing 185 pounds have circulating in his body? Write your answer in scientific notation. $(3.2 \times 10) \times 185 = 5.92 \times 10$ microliters

© Pearson Education, Inc. All rights reserved.

Course 3 Guided Problem Solving 55

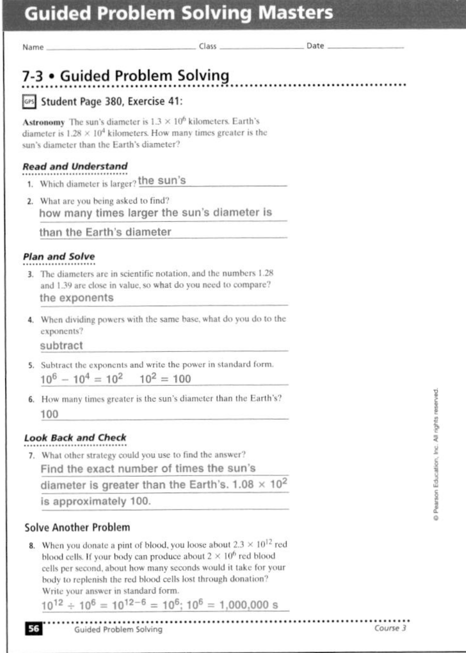

Guided Problem Solving Masters

Name ______________ Class ______________ Date ______________

7-3 • Guided Problem Solving

Student Page 380, Exercise 41:

Astronomy The sun's diameter is 1.3×10^6 kilometers. Earth's diameter is 1.28×10^4 kilometers. How many times greater is the sun's diameter than the Earth's diameter?

Read and Understand

1. Which diameter is larger? the sun's
2. What are you being asked to find? how many times larger the sun's diameter is than the Earth's diameter

Plan and Solve

3. The diameters are in scientific notation, and the numbers 1.28 and 1.39 are close in value, so what do you need to compare? the exponents
4. When dividing powers with the same base, what do you do to the exponents? subtract
5. Subtract the exponents and write the power in standard form. $10^6 - 10^4 = 10^2$ $10^2 = 100$
6. How many times greater is the sun's diameter than the Earth's? 100

Look Back and Check

7. What other strategy could you use to find the answer? Find the exact number of times the sun's diameter is greater than the Earth's. 1.08×10^2 is approximately 100.

Solve Another Problem

8. When you donate a pint of blood, you loose about 2.3×10^{12} red blood cells. If your body can produce about 2×10^6 red blood cells per second, about how many seconds would it take for your body to replenish the red blood cells lost through donation? Write your answer in standard form. $10^{12} \div 10^6 = 10^{12-6} = 10^6$; $10^6 = 1{,}000{,}000$ s

56 Guided Problem Solving Course 3

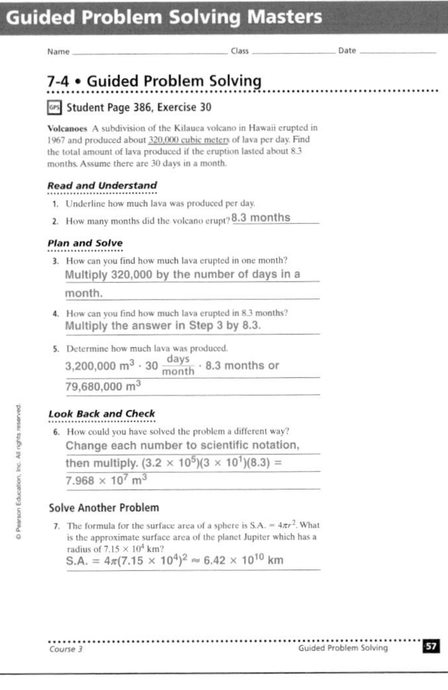

Guided Problem Solving Masters

Name ______________ Class ______________ Date ______________

7-4 • Guided Problem Solving

Student Page 386, Exercise 30

Volcanoes A subdivision of the Kilauea volcano in Hawaii erupted in 1967 and produced about 320,000 cubic meters of lava per day. Find the total amount of lava produced if the eruption lasted about 8.3 months. Assume there are 30 days in a month.

Read and Understand

1. Underline how much lava was produced per day.
2. How many months did the volcano erupt? 8.3 months

Plan and Solve

3. How can you find how much lava erupted in one month? Multiply 320,000 by the number of days in a month.
4. How can you find how much lava erupted in 8.3 months? Multiply the answer in Step 3 by 8.3.
5. Determine how much lava was produced. $3{,}200{,}000\ m^3 \cdot 30\ \frac{days}{month} \cdot 8.3$ months or $79{,}680{,}000\ m^3$

Look Back and Check

6. How could you have solved the problem a different way? Change each number to scientific notation, then multiply. $(3.2 \times 10^5)(3 \times 10^1)(8.3) = 7.968 \times 10^7\ m^3$

Solve Another Problem

7. The formula for the surface area of a sphere is $S.A. = 4\pi r^2$. What is the approximate surface area of the planet Jupiter which has a radius of 7.15×10^4 km? $S.A. = 4\pi(7.15 \times 10^4)^2 \approx 6.42 \times 10^{10}$ km

Course 3 Guided Problem Solving 57

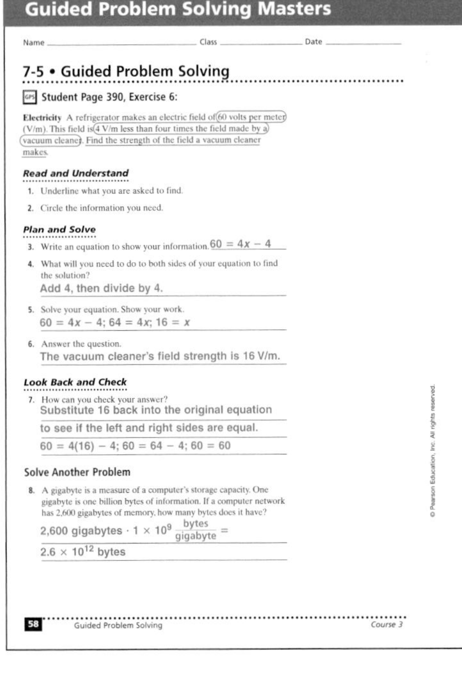

Guided Problem Solving Masters

Name ______________ Class ______________ Date ______________

7-5 • Guided Problem Solving

Student Page 390, Exercise 6:

Electricity A refrigerator makes an electric field of 60 volts per meter (V/m). This field is 4 V/m less than four times the field made by a vacuum cleaner. Find the strength of the field a vacuum cleaner makes.

Read and Understand

1. Underline what you are asked to find.
2. Circle the information you need.

Plan and Solve

3. Write an equation to show your information. $60 = 4x - 4$
4. What will you need to do to both sides of your equation to find the solution? Add 4, then divide by 4.
5. Solve your equation. Show your work. $60 = 4x - 4$; $64 = 4x$; $16 = x$
6. Answer the question. The vacuum cleaner's field strength is 16 V/m.

Look Back and Check

7. How can you check your answer? Substitute 16 back into the original equation to see if the left and right sides are equal. $60 = 4(16) - 4$; $60 = 64 - 4$; $60 = 60$

Solve Another Problem

8. A gigabyte is a measure of a computer's storage capacity. One gigabyte is one billion bytes of information. If a computer network has 2,600 gigabytes of memory, how many bytes does it have? $2{,}600 \text{ gigabytes} \cdot 1 \times 10^9 \frac{\text{bytes}}{\text{gigabyte}} = 2.6 \times 10^{12}$ bytes

58 Guided Problem Solving Course 3

Activities and Projects

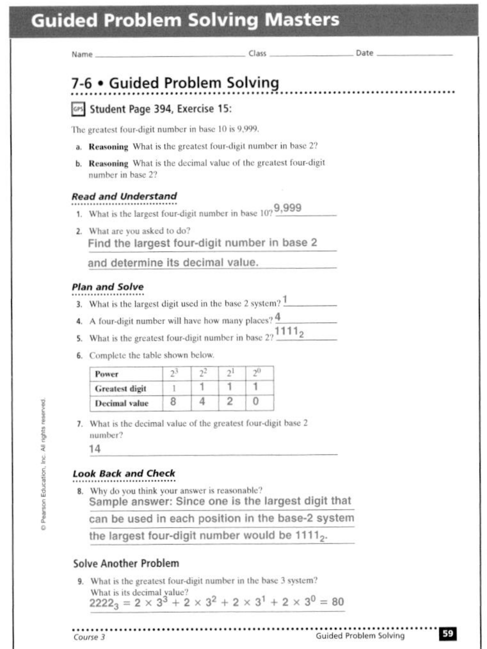

Guided Problem Solving Masters

Name ______________ Class ______________ Date ______________

7-6 • Guided Problem Solving

Student Page 394, Exercise 15:

The greatest four-digit number in base 10 is 9,999.

a. **Reasoning** What is the greatest four-digit number in base 2?

b. **Reasoning** What is the decimal value of the greatest four-digit number in base 2?

Read and Understand

1. What is the largest four-digit number in base 10? 9,999
2. What are you asked to do? Find the largest four-digit number in base 2 and determine its decimal value.

Plan and Solve

3. What is the largest digit used in the base 2 system? 1
4. A four-digit number will have how many places? 4
5. What is the greatest four-digit number in base 2? 1111_2
6. Complete the table shown below.

Power	2^3	2^2	2^1	2^0
Greatest digit	1	1	1	1
Decimal value	8	4	2	0

7. What is the decimal value of the greatest four-digit base 2 number? 14

Look Back and Check

8. Why do you think your answer is reasonable? Sample answer: Since one is the largest digit that can be used in each position in the base-2 system the largest four-digit number would be 1111_2.

Solve Another Problem

9. What is the greatest four-digit number in the base 3 system? What is its decimal value? $2222_3 = 2 \times 3^3 + 2 \times 3^2 + 2 \times 3^1 + 2 \times 3^0 = 80$

Course 3 Guided Problem Solving 59

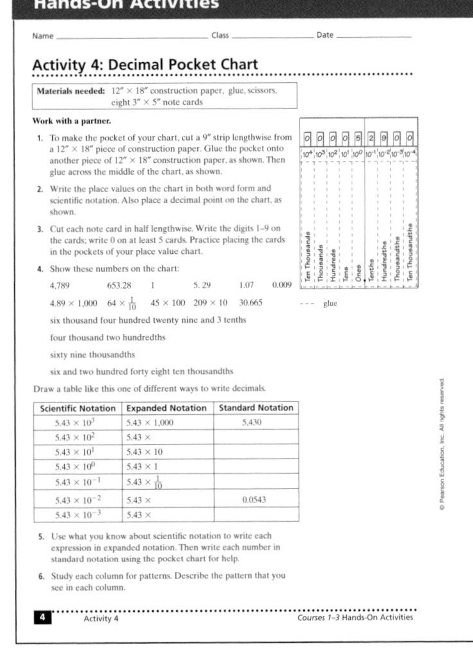

Hands-On Activities

Name ______________ Class ______________ Date ______________

Activity 4: Decimal Pocket Chart

Materials needed: 12″ × 18″ construction paper, glue, scissors, eight 3″ × 5″ note cards

Work with a partner.

1. To make the pocket of your chart, cut a 9″ strip lengthwise from a 12″ × 18″ piece of construction paper. Glue the pocket onto another piece of 12″ × 18″ construction paper, as shown. Then glue across the middle of the chart, as shown.
2. Write the place values on the chart in both word form and scientific notation. Also place a decimal point on the chart, as shown.
3. Cut each note card in half lengthwise. Write the digits 1–9 on the cards; write 0 on at least 5 cards. Practice placing the cards in the pockets of your place value chart.
4. Show these numbers on the chart:

4,789 653.28 1 5. 29 1.07 0.009

$4.89 \times 1{,}000$ $64 \times \frac{1}{10}$ 45×100 209×10 30.665

six thousand four hundred twenty nine and 3 tenths

four thousand two hundredths

sixty nine thousandths

six and two hundred forty eight ten thousandths

Draw a table like this one of different ways to write decimals.

Scientific Notation	Expanded Notation	Standard Notation
5.43×10^3	$5.43 \times 1{,}000$	5,430
5.43×10^2	$5.43 \times$	
5.43×10^1	5.43×10	
5.43×10^0	5.43×1	
5.43×10^{-1}	$5.43 \times \frac{1}{10}$	
5.43×10^{-2}	$5.43 \times$	0.0543
5.43×10^{-3}	$5.43 \times$	

5. Use what you know about scientific notation to write each expression in expanded notation. Then write each number in standard notation using the pocket chart for help.
6. Study each column for patterns. Describe the pattern that you see in each column.

4 Activity 4 *Courses 1–3* Hands-On Activities

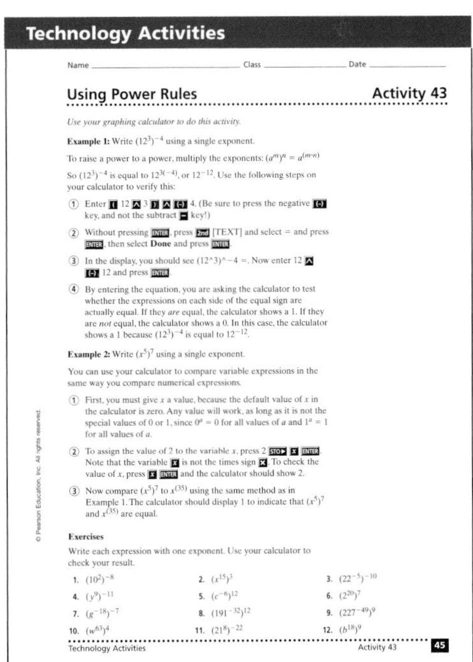

Technology Activities

Name ______________ Class ______________ Date ______________

Using Power Rules Activity 43

Use your graphing calculator to do this activity.

Example 1: Write $(12^3)^{-4}$ using a single exponent.

To raise a power to a power, multiply the exponents: $(a^m)^n = a^{(m \cdot n)}$

So $(12^3)^{-4}$ is equal to $12^{3(-4)}$, or 12^{-12}. Use the following steps on your calculator to verify this:

① Enter (12 ^ 3) ^ (-) 4. (Be sure to press the negative (-) key, and not the subtract − key!)

② Without pressing ENTER, press 2nd [TEXT] and select = and press ENTER, then select **Done** and press ENTER.

③ In the display, you should see (12^3)^−4 =. Now enter 12 ^ (-) 12 and press ENTER.

④ By entering the equation, you are asking the calculator to test whether the expressions on each side of the equal sign are actually equal. If they *are* equal, the calculator shows a 1. If they are *not* equal, the calculator shows a 0. In this case, the calculator shows a 1 because $(12^3)^{-4}$ is equal to 12^{-12}.

Example 2: Write $(x^5)^7$ using a single exponent.

You can use your calculator to compare variable expressions in the same way you compare numerical expressions.

① First, you must give x a value, because the default value of x in the calculator is zero. Any value will work, as long as it is not the special values of 0 or 1, since $0^a = 0$ for all values of a and $1^a = 1$ for all values of a.

② To assign the value of 2 to the variable x, press 2 STO▸ X ENTER. Note that the variable X is not the times sign ×. To check the value of x, press X ENTER and the calculator should show 2.

③ Now compare $(x^5)^7$ to $x^{(35)}$ using the same method as in Example 1. The calculator should display 1 to indicate that $(x^5)^7$ and $x^{(35)}$ are equal.

Exercises

Write each expression with one exponent. Use your calculator to check your result.

1. $(10^2)^{-8}$
2. $(x^{15})^3$
3. $(22^{-5})^{-10}$
4. $(y^9)^{-11}$
5. $(c^{-6})^{12}$
6. $(2^{20})^7$
7. $(g^{-18})^{-7}$
8. $(191^{-32})^{12}$
9. $(227^{-49})^9$
10. $(w^{63})^4$
11. $(21^8)^{-22}$
12. $(b^{18})^9$

Technology Activities Activity 43 45

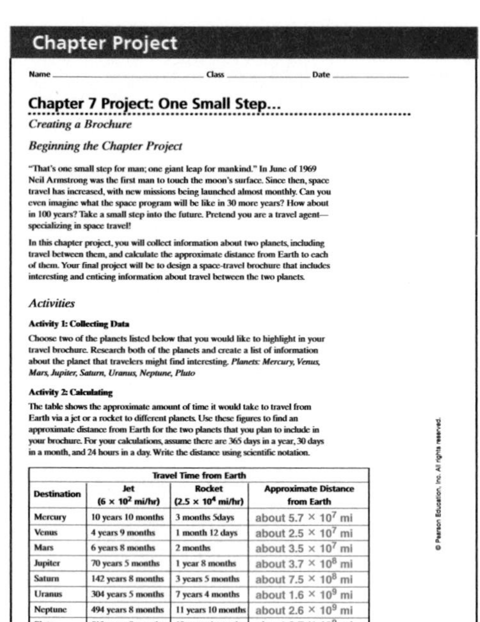

Chapter Project

Name ______________ Class ______________ Date ______________

Chapter 7 Project: One Small Step...

Creating a Brochure

Beginning the Chapter Project

"That's one small step for man; one giant leap for mankind." In June of 1969 Neil Armstrong was the first man to touch the moon's surface. Since then, space travel has increased, with new missions being launched almost monthly. Can you even imagine what the space program will be like in 30 more years? How about in 100 years? Take a small step into the future. Pretend you are a travel agent—specializing in space travel!

In this chapter project, you will collect information about two planets, including travel between them, and calculate the approximate distance from Earth to each of them. Your final project will be to design a space-travel brochure that includes interesting and enticing information about travel between the two planets.

Activities

Activity 1: Collecting Data

Choose two of the planets listed below that you would like to highlight in your travel brochure. Research both of the planets and create a list of information about the planet that travelers might find interesting. *Planets: Mercury, Venus, Mars, Jupiter, Saturn, Uranus, Neptune, Pluto*

Activity 2: Calculating

The table shows the approximate amount of time it would take to travel from Earth via a jet or a rocket to different planets. Use these figures to find an approximate distance from Earth for the two planets that you plan to include in your brochure. For your calculations, assume there are 365 days in a year, 30 days in a month, and 24 hours in a day. Write the distance using scientific notation.

Travel Time from Earth			
Destination	Jet (6×10^2 mi/hr)	Rocket (2.5×10^4 mi/hr)	Approximate Distance from Earth
Mercury	10 years 10 months	3 months 5days	about 5.7×10^7 mi
Venus	4 years 9 months	1 month 12 days	about 2.5×10^7 mi
Mars	6 years 8 months	2 months	about 3.5×10^7 mi
Jupiter	70 years 5 months	1 year 8 months	about 3.7×10^8 mi
Saturn	142 years 8 months	3 years 5 months	about 7.5×10^8 mi
Uranus	304 years 5 months	7 years 4 months	about 1.6×10^9 mi
Neptune	494 years 8 months	11 years 10 months	about 2.6×10^9 mi
Pluto	513 years 8 months	12 years 4 months	about 2.7×10^9 mi

20 Project Course 3 Chapter 7

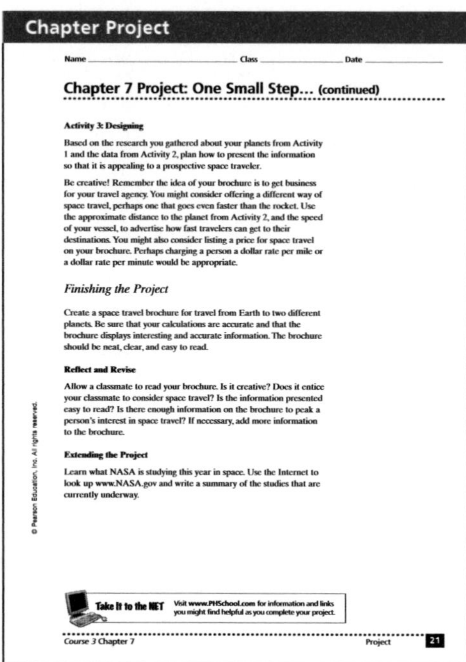

Chapter Project

Name ______________ Class ______________ Date ______________

Chapter 7 Project: One Small Step... (continued)

Activity 3: Designing

Based on the research you gathered about your planets from Activity 1 and the data from Activity 2, plan how to present the information so that it is appealing to a prospective space traveler.

Be creative! Remember the idea of your brochure is to get business for your travel agency. You might consider offering a different way of space travel, perhaps one that goes even faster than the rocket. Use the approximate distance to the planet from Activity 2, and the speed of your vessel, to advertise how fast travelers can get to their destinations. You might also consider listing a price for space travel on your brochure. Perhaps charging a person a dollar rate per mile or a dollar rate per minute would be appropriate.

Finishing the Project

Create a space travel brochure for travel from Earth to two different planets. Be sure that your calculations are accurate and that the brochure displays interesting and accurate information. The brochure should be neat, clear, and easy to read.

Reflect and Revise

Allow a classmate to read your brochure. Is it creative? Does it entice your classmate to consider space travel? Is the information presented easy to read? Is there enough information on the brochure to peak a person's interest in space travel? If necessary, add more information to the brochure.

Extending the Project

Learn what NASA is studying this year in space. Use the Internet to look up www.NASA.gov and write a summary of the studies that are currently underway.

Take It to the NET Visit www.PHSchool.com for information and links you might find helpful as you complete your project.

Course 3 Chapter 7 Project 21

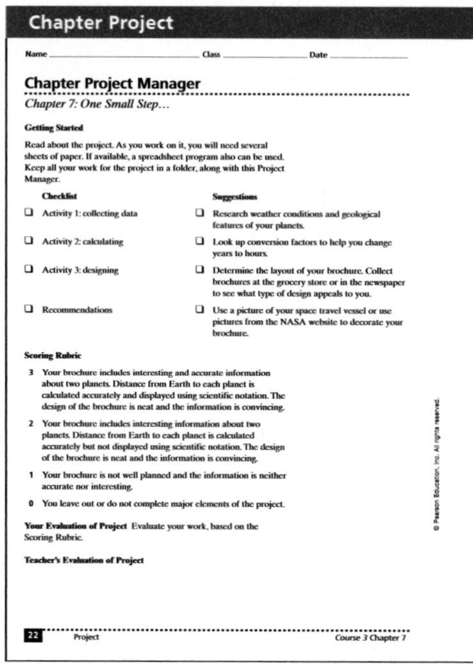

Chapter Project

Name ______________ Class ______________ Date ______________

Chapter Project Manager

Chapter 7: One Small Step...

Getting Started

Read about the project. As you work on it, you will need several sheets of paper. If available, a spreadsheet program also can be used. Keep all your work for the project in a folder, along with this Project Manager.

Checklist	Suggestions
❑ Activity 1: collecting data	❑ Research weather conditions and geological features of your planets.
❑ Activity 2: calculating	❑ Look up conversion factors to help you change years to hours.
❑ Activity 3: designing	❑ Determine the layout of your brochure. Collect brochures at the grocery store or in the newspaper to see what type of design appeals to you.
❑ Recommendations	❑ Use a picture of your space travel vessel or use pictures from the NASA website to decorate your brochure.

Scoring Rubric

3 Your brochure includes interesting and accurate information about two planets. Distance from Earth to each planet is calculated accurately and displayed using scientific notation. The design of the brochure is neat and the information is convincing.

2 Your brochure includes interesting information about two planets. Distance from Earth to each planet is calculated accurately but not displayed using scientific notation. The design of the brochure is neat and the information is convincing.

1 Your brochure is not well planned and the information is neither accurate nor interesting.

0 You leave out or do not complete major elements of the project.

Your Evaluation of Project Evaluate your work, based on the Scoring Rubric.

Teacher's Evaluation of Project

22 Project Course 3 Chapter 7

Transparencies

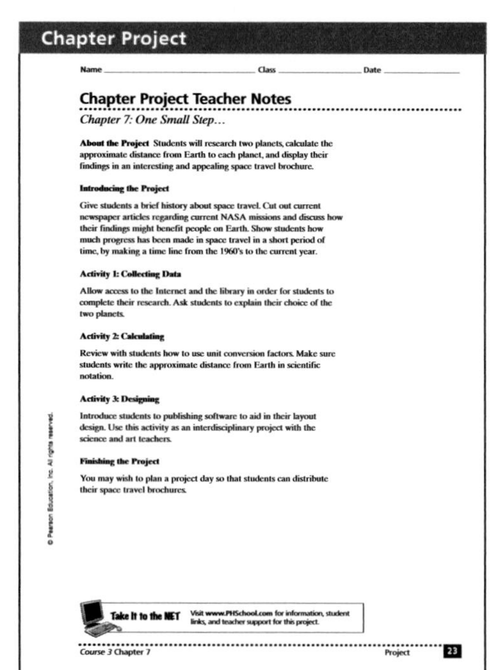

Chapter Project

Name ______________ Class ______________ Date ______________

Chapter Project Teacher Notes

Chapter 7: One Small Step...

About the Project Students will research two planets, calculate the approximate distance from Earth to each planet, and display their findings in an interesting and appealing space travel brochure.

Introducing the Project

Give students a brief history about space travel. Cut out current newspaper articles regarding current NASA missions and discuss how their findings might benefit people on Earth. Show students how much progress has been made in space travel in a short period of time, by making a time line from the 1960's to the current year.

Activity 1: Collecting Data

Allow access to the Internet and the library in order for students to complete their research. Ask students to explain their choice of the two planets.

Activity 2: Calculating

Review with students how to use unit conversion factors. Make sure students write the approximate distance from Earth in scientific notation.

Activity 3: Designing

Introduce students to publishing software to aid in their layout design. Use this activity as an interdisciplinary project with the science and art teachers.

Finishing the Project

You may wish to plan a project day so that students can distribute their space travel brochures.

Take It to the NET Visit www.PHSchool.com for information, student links, and teacher support for this project.

Course 3 Chapter 7 Project 23

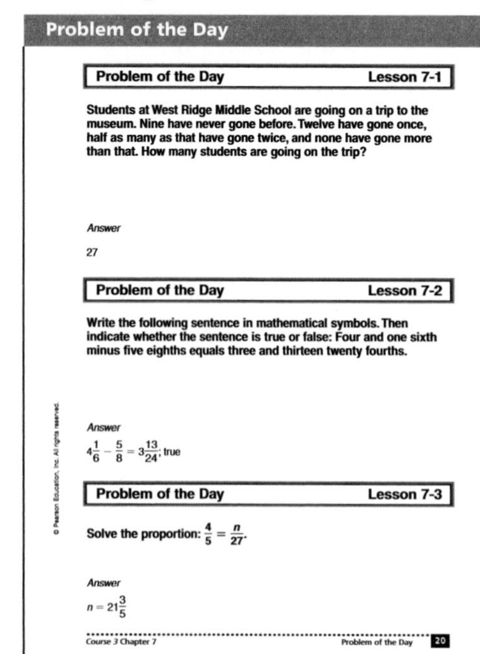

Problem of the Day

Problem of the Day — Lesson 7-1

Students at West Ridge Middle School are going on a trip to the museum. Nine have never gone before. Twelve have gone once, half as many as that have gone twice, and none have gone more than that. How many students are going on the trip?

Answer

27

Problem of the Day — Lesson 7-2

Write the following sentence in mathematical symbols. Then indicate whether the sentence is true or false: Four and one sixth minus five eighths equals three and thirteen twenty fourths.

Answer

$4\frac{1}{6} - \frac{5}{8} = 3\frac{13}{24}$; true

Problem of the Day — Lesson 7-3

Solve the proportion: $\frac{4}{5} = \frac{n}{27}$.

Answer

$n = 21\frac{3}{5}$

Course 3 Chapter 7 Problem of the Day 20

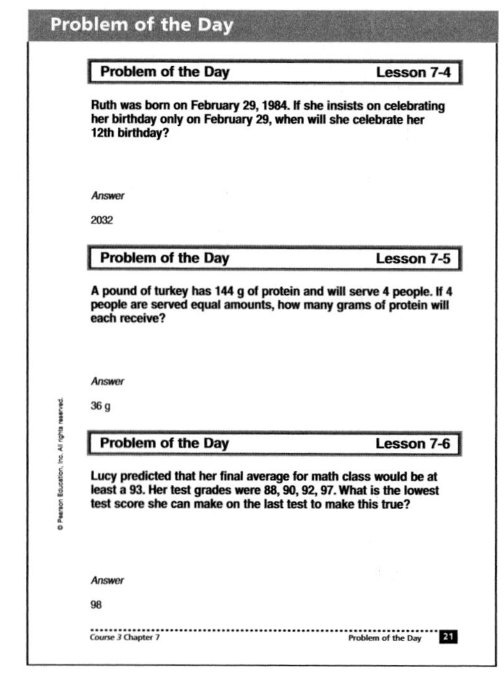

Problem of the Day

Problem of the Day — Lesson 7-4

Ruth was born on February 29, 1984. If she insists on celebrating her birthday only on February 29, when will she celebrate her 12th birthday?

Answer

2032

Problem of the Day — Lesson 7-5

A pound of turkey has 144 g of protein and will serve 4 people. If 4 people are served equal amounts, how many grams of protein will each receive?

Answer

36 g

Problem of the Day — Lesson 7-6

Lucy predicted that her final average for math class would be at least a 93. Her test grades were 88, 90, 92, 97. What is the lowest test score she can make on the last test to make this true?

Answer

98

Course 3 Chapter 7 Problem of the Day 21

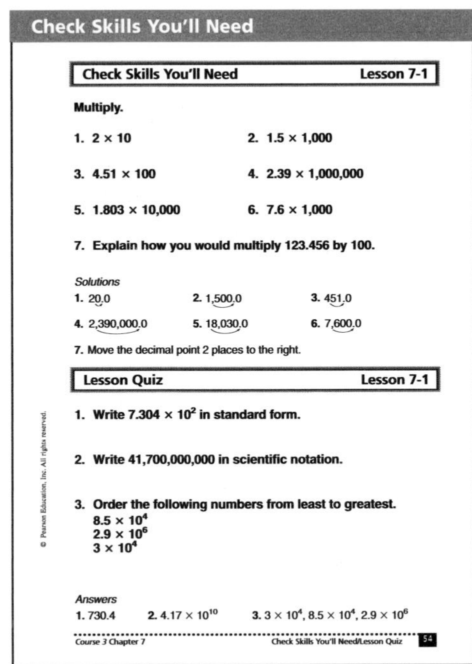
Check Skills You'll Need

Check Skills You'll Need	Lesson 7-1

Multiply.

1. 2×10
2. $1.5 \times 1{,}000$
3. 4.51×100
4. $2.39 \times 1{,}000{,}000$
5. $1.803 \times 10{,}000$
6. $7.6 \times 1{,}000$
7. Explain how you would multiply 123.456 by 100.

Solutions

1. 20.0 2. 1,500.0 3. 451.0
4. 2,390,000.0 5. 18,030.0 6. 7,600.0
7. Move the decimal point 2 places to the right.

Lesson Quiz	Lesson 7-1

1. Write 7.304×10^2 in standard form.
2. Write 41,700,000,000 in scientific notation.
3. Order the following numbers from least to greatest.
8.5×10^4
2.9×10^6
3×10^4

Answers

1. 730.4 2. 4.17×10^{10} 3. 3×10^4, 8.5×10^4, 2.9×10^6

Sample page; see p. H for complete list.

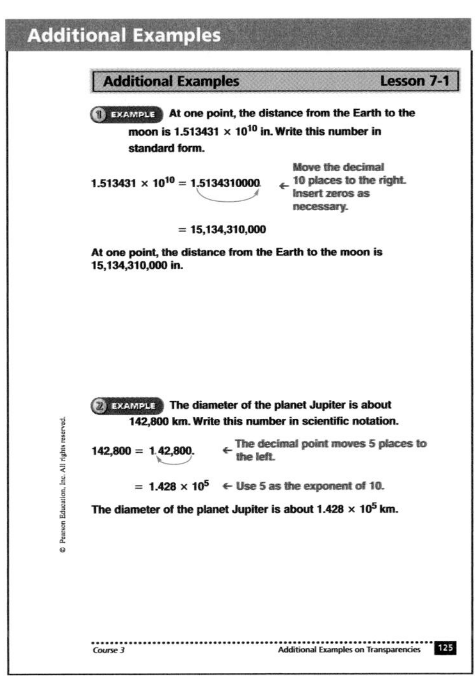
Additional Examples

Additional Examples	Lesson 7-1

1 EXAMPLE At one point, the distance from the Earth to the moon is 1.513431×10^{10} in. Write this number in standard form.

$1.513431 \times 10^{10} = 1.5134310000$ ← Move the decimal 10 places to the right. Insert zeros as necessary.

$= 15{,}134{,}310{,}000$

At one point, the distance from the Earth to the moon is 15,134,310,000 in.

2 EXAMPLE The diameter of the planet Jupiter is about 142,800 km. Write this number in scientific notation.

$142{,}800 = 1.42{,}800.$ ← The decimal point moves 5 places to the left.

$= 1.428 \times 10^5$ ← Use 5 as the exponent of 10.

The diameter of the planet Jupiter is about 1.428×10^5 km.

Sample page; see p. H for complete list.

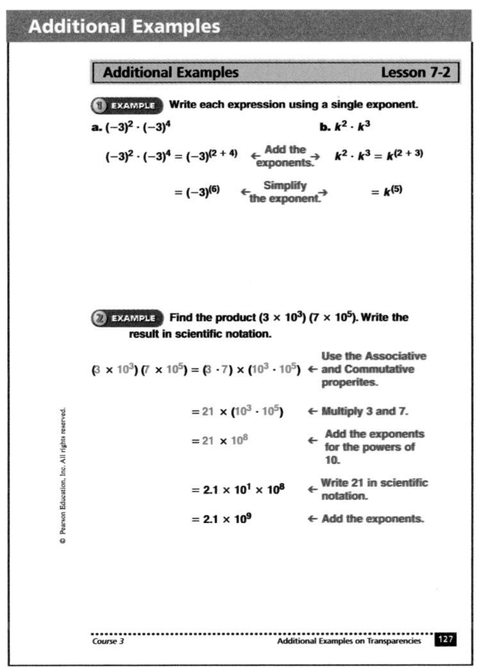
Additional Examples

Additional Examples	Lesson 7-2

1 EXAMPLE Write each expression using a single exponent.

a. $(-3)^2 \cdot (-3)^4$ b. $k^2 \cdot k^3$

$(-3)^2 \cdot (-3)^4 = (-3)^{(2+4)}$ ← Add the exponents. → $k^2 \cdot k^3 = k^{(2+3)}$

$= (-3)^{(6)}$ ← Simplify the exponent. → $= k^{(5)}$

2 EXAMPLE Find the product $(3 \times 10^3)(7 \times 10^5)$. Write the result in scientific notation.

$(3 \times 10^3)(7 \times 10^5) = (3 \cdot 7) \times (10^3 \cdot 10^5)$ ← Use the Associative and Commutative properites.

$= 21 \times (10^3 \cdot 10^5)$ ← Multiply 3 and 7.

$= 21 \times 10^8$ ← Add the exponents for the powers of 10.

$= 2.1 \times 10^1 \times 10^8$ ← Write 21 in scientific notation.

$= 2.1 \times 10^9$ ← Add the exponents.

Sample page; see p. H for complete list.

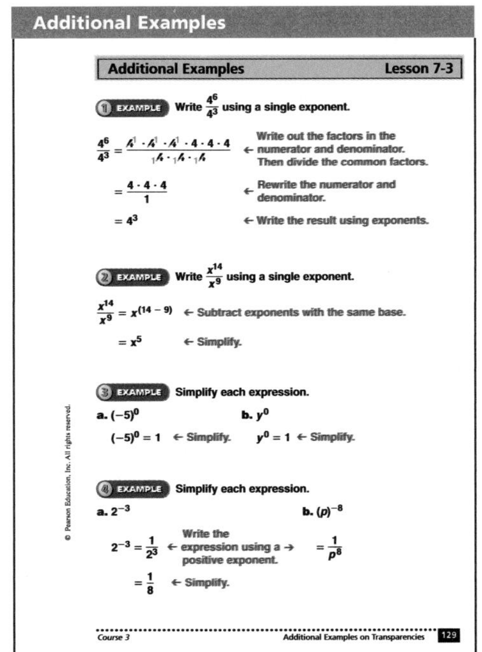
Additional Examples

Additional Examples	Lesson 7-3

1 EXAMPLE Write $\frac{4^6}{4^3}$ using a single exponent.

$\frac{4^6}{4^3} = \frac{4 \cdot 4 \cdot 4 \cdot 4 \cdot 4 \cdot 4}{4 \cdot 4 \cdot 4}$ ← Write out the factors in the numerator and denominator. Then divide the common factors.

$= \frac{4 \cdot 4 \cdot 4}{1}$ ← Rewrite the numerator and denominator.

$= 4^3$ ← Write the result using exponents.

2 EXAMPLE Write $\frac{x^{14}}{x^9}$ using a single exponent.

$\frac{x^{14}}{x^9} = x^{(14-9)}$ ← Subtract exponents with the same base.

$= x^5$ ← Simplify.

3 EXAMPLE Simplify each expression.

a. $(-5)^0$ b. y^0

$(-5)^0 = 1$ ← Simplify. $y^0 = 1$ ← Simplify.

4 EXAMPLE Simplify each expression.

a. 2^{-3} b. $(p)^{-8}$

$2^{-3} = \frac{1}{2^3}$ ← Write the expression using a positive exponent. → $= \frac{1}{p^8}$

$= \frac{1}{8}$ ← Simplify.

Sample page; see p. H for complete list.

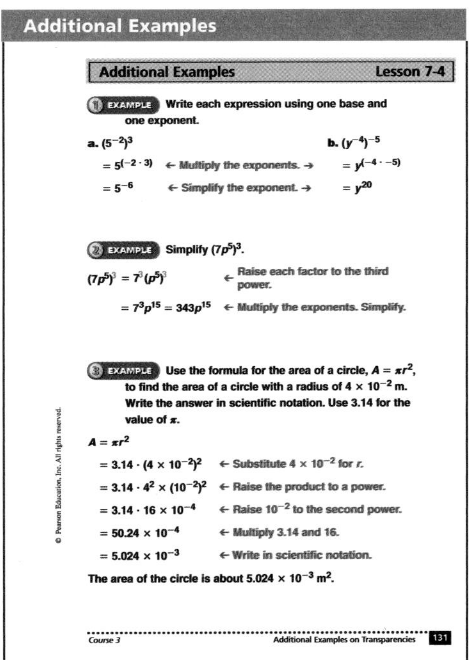
Additional Examples

Additional Examples	Lesson 7-4

1 EXAMPLE Write each expression using one base and one exponent.

a. $(5^{-2})^3$ b. $(y^{-4})^{-5}$

$= 5^{(-2 \cdot 3)}$ ← Multiply the exponents. → $= y^{(-4 \cdot -5)}$

$= 5^{-6}$ ← Simplify the exponent. → $= y^{20}$

2 EXAMPLE Simplify $(7p^5)^3$.

$(7p^5)^3 = 7^3(p^5)^3$ ← Raise each factor to the third power.

$= 7^3p^{15} = 343p^{15}$ ← Multiply the exponents. Simplify.

3 EXAMPLE Use the formula for the area of a circle, $A = \pi r^2$, to find the area of a circle with a radius of 4×10^{-2} m. Write the answer in scientific notation. Use 3.14 for the value of π.

$A = \pi r^2$

$= 3.14 \cdot (4 \times 10^{-2})^2$ ← Substitute 4×10^{-2} for r.

$= 3.14 \cdot 4^2 \times (10^{-2})^2$ ← Raise the product to a power.

$= 3.14 \cdot 16 \times 10^{-4}$ ← Raise 10^{-2} to the second power.

$= 50.24 \times 10^{-4}$ ← Multiply 3.14 and 16.

$= 5.024 \times 10^{-3}$ ← Write in scientific notation.

The area of the circle is about 5.024×10^{-3} m^2.

Sample page; see p. H for complete list.

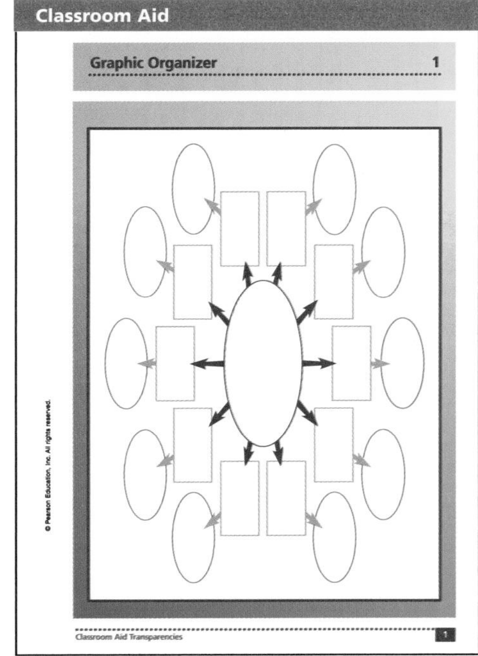
Classroom Aid

Graphic Organizer 1

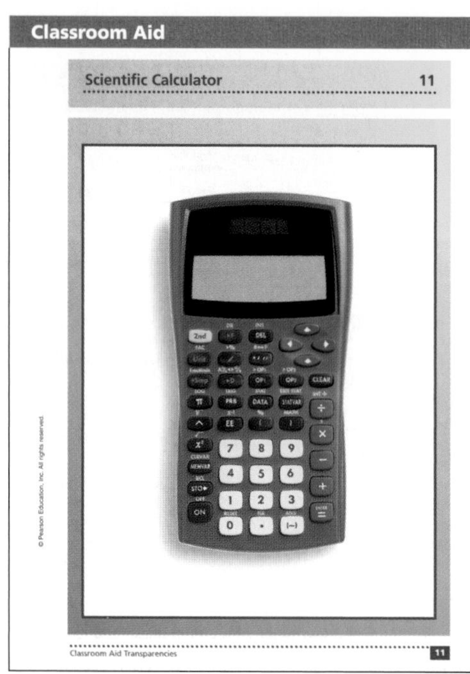

Classroom Aid
Scientific Calculator
11
Classroom Aid Transparencies
11

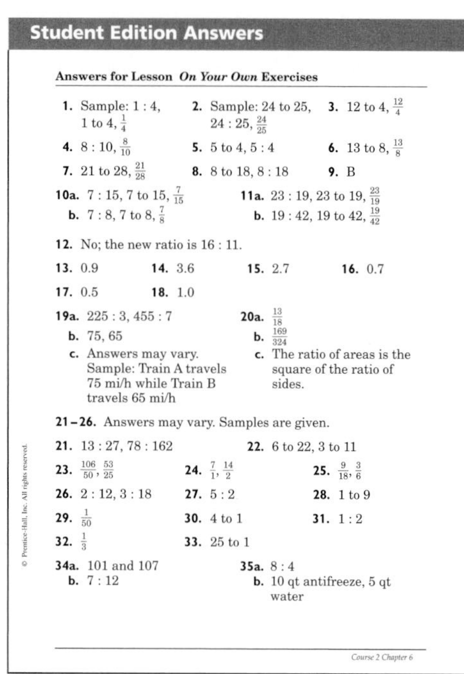

Student Edition Answers

Answers for Lesson *On Your Own* Exercises

1. Sample: 1 : 4, 1 to 4, $\frac{1}{4}$
2. Sample: 24 to 25, 24 : 25, $\frac{24}{25}$
3. 12 to 4, $\frac{12}{4}$
4. 8 : 10, $\frac{8}{10}$
5. 5 to 4, 5 : 4
6. 13 to 8, $\frac{13}{8}$
7. 21 to 28, $\frac{21}{28}$
8. 8 to 18, 8 : 18
9. B

10a. 7 : 15, 7 to 15, $\frac{7}{15}$
b. 7 : 8, 7 to 8, $\frac{7}{8}$

11a. 23 : 19, 23 to 19, $\frac{23}{19}$
b. 19 : 42, 19 to 42, $\frac{19}{42}$

12. No; the new ratio is 16 : 11.
13. 0.9
14. 3.6
15. 2.7
16. 0.7
17. 0.5
18. 1.0

19a. 225 : 3, 455 : 7
b. 75, 65
c. Answers may vary. Sample: Train A travels 75 mi/h while Train B travels 65 mi/h

20a. $\frac{13}{18}$
b. $\frac{169}{324}$
c. The ratio of areas is the square of the ratio of sides.

21–26. Answers may vary. Samples are given.

21. 13 : 27, 78 : 162
22. 6 to 22, 3 to 11
23. $\frac{106}{50}, \frac{53}{25}$
24. $\frac{7}{1}, \frac{14}{2}$
25. $\frac{9}{18}, \frac{3}{6}$
26. 2 : 12, 3 : 18
27. 5 : 2
28. 1 to 9
29. $\frac{1}{50}$
30. 4 to 1
31. 1 : 2
32. $\frac{1}{3}$
33. 25 to 1

34a. 101 and 107
b. 7 : 12

35a. 8 : 4
b. 10 qt antifreeze, 5 qt water

Course 2 Chapter 6

Sample page; see p. H for complete list.

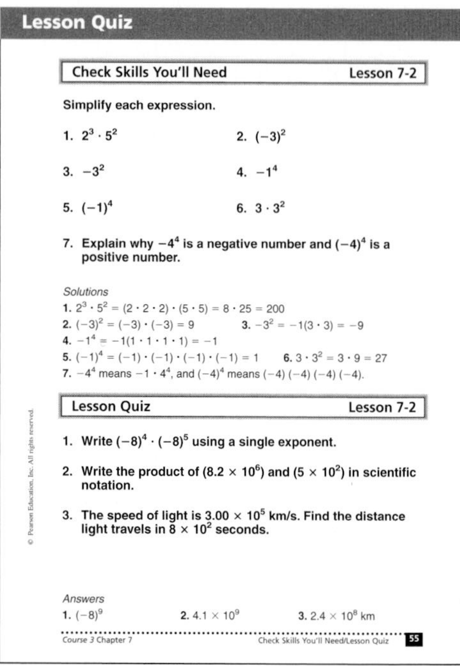

Lesson Quiz

Check Skills You'll Need — Lesson 7-2

Simplify each expression.

1. $2^3 \cdot 5^2$
2. $(-3)^2$
3. -3^2
4. -1^4
5. $(-1)^4$
6. $3 \cdot 3^2$
7. Explain why -4^4 is a negative number and $(-4)^4$ is a positive number.

Solutions
1. $2^3 \cdot 5^2 = (2 \cdot 2 \cdot 2) \cdot (5 \cdot 5) = 8 \cdot 25 = 200$
2. $(-3)^2 = (-3) \cdot (-3) = 9$
3. $-3^2 = -1(3 \cdot 3) = -9$
4. $-1^4 = -1(1 \cdot 1 \cdot 1 \cdot 1) = -1$
5. $(-1)^4 = (-1) \cdot (-1) \cdot (-1) \cdot (-1) = 1$
6. $3 \cdot 3^2 = 3 \cdot 9 = 27$
7. -4^4 means $-1 \cdot 4^4$, and $(-4)^4$ means $(-4)(-4)(-4)(-4)$.

Lesson Quiz — Lesson 7-2

1. Write $(-8)^4 \cdot (-8)^5$ using a single exponent.
2. Write the product of (8.2×10^6) and (5×10^2) in scientific notation.
3. The speed of light is 3.00×10^5 km/s. Find the distance light travels in 8×10^2 seconds.

Answers
1. $(-8)^9$
2. 4.1×10^9
3. 2.4×10^8 km

Course 3 Chapter 7 — Check Skills You'll Need/Lesson Quiz — 55

Sample page; see p. H for complete list.

Assessment

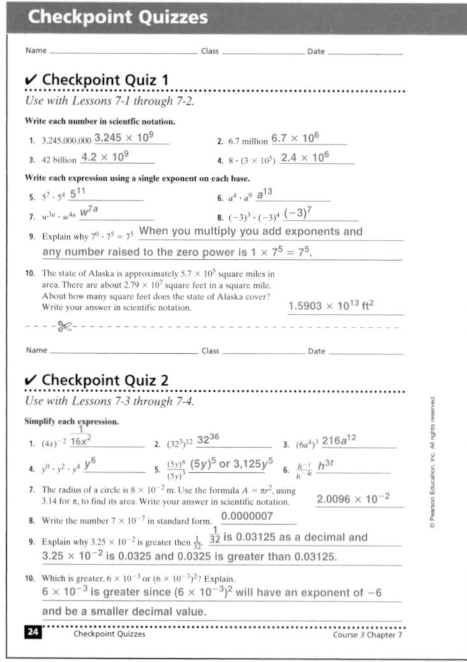

Checkpoint Quizzes

Name ______ Class ______ Date ______

✔ Checkpoint Quiz 1

Use with Lessons 7-1 through 7-2.

Write each number in scientific notation.

1. 3,245,000,000 3.245×10^9
2. 6.7 million 6.7×10^6
3. 42 billion 4.2×10^9
4. $8 \cdot (3 \times 10^5)$ 2.4×10^6

Write each expression using a single exponent on each base.

5. $5^7 \cdot 5^4$ 5^{11}
6. $a^4 \cdot a^9$ a^{13}
7. $w^{3a} \cdot w^{4a}$ w^{7a}
8. $(-3)^3 \cdot (-3)^4$ $(-3)^7$
9. Explain why $7^0 \cdot 7^5 = 7^5$ When you multiply you add exponents and any number raised to the zero power is $1 \times 7^5 = 7^5$.
10. The state of Alaska is approximately 5.7×10^5 square miles in area. There are about 2.79×10^7 square feet in a square mile. About how many square feet does the state of Alaska cover? Write your answer in scientific notation. 1.5903×10^{13} ft²

Name ______ Class ______ Date ______

✔ Checkpoint Quiz 2

Use with Lessons 7-3 through 7-4.

Simplify each expression.

1. $(4x)^{-2}$ $\frac{1}{16x^2}$
2. $(32^3)^{12}$ 32^{36}
3. $(6a^4)^3$ $216a^{12}$
4. $y^0 \cdot y^2 \cdot y^4$ y^6
5. $\frac{(5y)^8}{(5y)^3}$ $(5y)^5$ or $3{,}125y^5$
6. $\frac{h^{-t}}{h^{-4t}}$ h^{3t}
7. The radius of a circle is 8×10^{-2} m. Use the formula $A = \pi r^2$, using 3.14 for π, to find its area. Write your answer in scientific notation. 2.0096×10^{-2}
8. Write the number 7×10^{-7} in standard form. 0.0000007
9. Explain why 3.25×10^{-2} is greater then $\frac{1}{32}$. $\frac{1}{32}$ is 0.03125 as a decimal and 3.25×10^{-2} is 0.0325 and 0.0325 is greater than 0.03125.
10. Which is greater, 6×10^{-3} or $(6 \times 10^{-3})^2$? Explain. 6×10^{-3} is greater since $(6 \times 10^{-3})^2$ will have an exponent of -6 and be a smaller decimal value.

24 — Checkpoint Quizzes — Course 3 Chapter 7

Available in Spanish

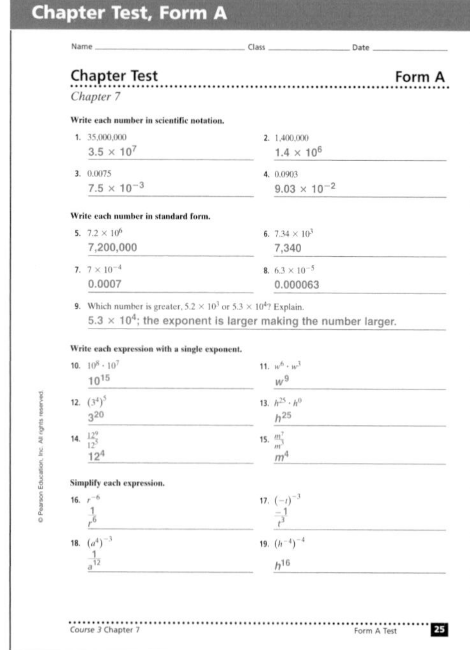

Chapter Test, Form A

Name ______ Class ______ Date ______

Chapter Test — Form A
Chapter 7

Write each number in scientific notation.

1. 35,000,000 — 3.5×10^7
2. 1,400,000 — 1.4×10^6
3. 0.0075 — 7.5×10^{-3}
4. 0.0903 — 9.03×10^{-2}

Write each number in standard form.

5. 7.2×10^6 — 7,200,000
6. 7.34×10^3 — 7,340
7. 7×10^{-4} — 0.0007
8. 6.3×10^{-5} — 0.000063
9. Which number is greater, 5.2×10^3 or 5.3×10^4? Explain. 5.3×10^4; the exponent is larger making the number larger.

Write each expression with a single exponent.

10. $10^8 \cdot 10^7$ — 10^{15}
11. $w^6 \cdot w^3$ — w^9
12. $(3^4)^5$ — 3^{20}
13. $h^{25} \cdot h^0$ — h^{25}
14. $\frac{12^9}{12^5}$ — 12^4
15. $\frac{m^7}{m^3}$ — m^4

Simplify each expression.

16. r^{-6} — $\frac{1}{r^6}$
17. $(-t)^{-3}$ — $\frac{-1}{t^3}$
18. $(a^4)^{-3}$ — $\frac{1}{a^{12}}$
19. $(h^{-4})^{-4}$ — h^{16}

Course 3 Chapter 7 — Form A Test — 25

Available in Spanish

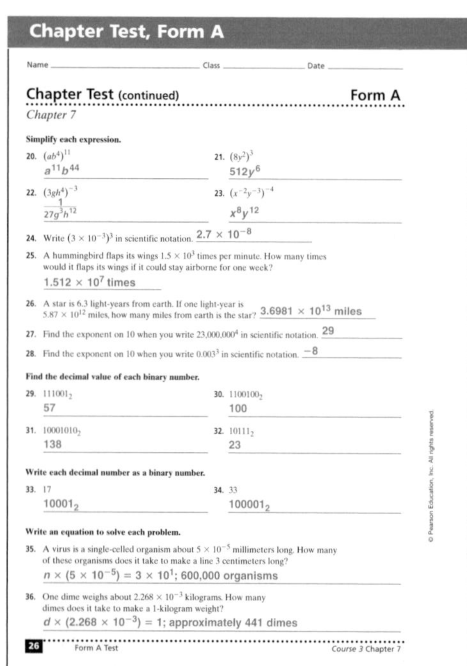

Chapter Test, Form A

Name ______ Class ______ Date ______

Chapter Test (continued) — Form A
Chapter 7

Simplify each expression.

20. $(ab^4)^{11}$ — $a^{11}b^{44}$
21. $(8y^2)^3$ — $512y^6$
22. $(3gh^4)^{-3}$ — $\frac{1}{27g^3h^{12}}$
23. $(x^{-2}y^{-3})^{-4}$ — x^8y^{12}
24. Write $(3 \times 10^{-3})^3$ in scientific notation. 2.7×10^{-8}
25. A hummingbird flaps its wings 1.5×10^3 times per minute. How many times would it flaps its wings if it could stay airborne for one week? 1.512×10^7 times
26. A star is 6.3 light-years from earth. If one light-year is 5.87×10^{12} miles, how many miles from earth is the star? 3.6981×10^{13} miles
27. Find the exponent on 10 when you write $23{,}000{,}000^4$ in scientific notation. 29
28. Find the exponent on 10 when you write 0.003^3 in scientific notation. -8

Find the decimal value of each binary number.

29. 111001_2 — 57
30. 1100100_2 — 100
31. 10001010_2 — 138
32. 10111_2 — 23

Write each decimal number as a binary number.

33. 17 — 10001_2
34. 33 — 100001_2

Write an equation to solve each problem.

35. A virus is a single-celled organism about 5×10^{-5} millimeters long. How many of these organisms does it take to make a line 3 centimeters long? $n \times (5 \times 10^{-5}) = 3 \times 10^1$; 600,000 organisms
36. One dime weighs about 2.268×10^{-3} kilograms. How many dimes does it take to make a 1-kilogram weight? $d \times (2.268 \times 10^{-3}) = 1$; approximately 441 dimes

26 — Form A Test — Course 3 Chapter 7

Available in Spanish

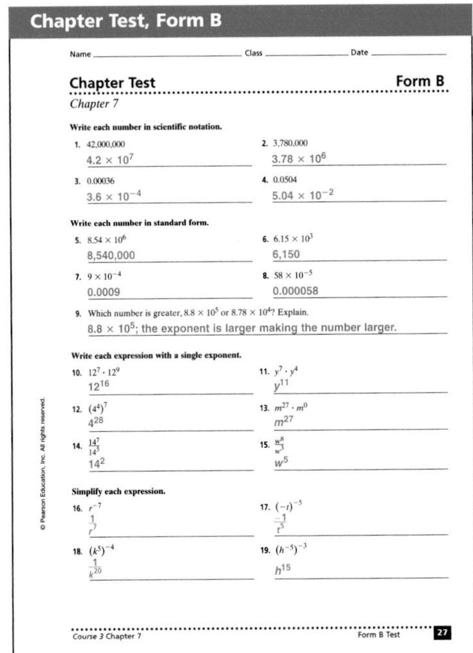

Chapter Test, Form B

Name ______________ Class ______________ Date ______________

Chapter Test — Form B

Chapter 7

Write each number in scientific notation.

1. 42,000,000 — 4.2×10^7
2. 3,780,000 — 3.78×10^6
3. 0.00036 — 3.6×10^{-4}
4. 0.0504 — 5.04×10^{-2}

Write each number in standard form.

5. 8.54×10^6 — 8,540,000
6. 6.15×10^3 — 6,150
7. 9×10^{-4} — 0.0009
8. 58×10^{-5} — 0.000058
9. Which number is greater, 8.8×10^5 or 8.78×10^4? Explain. — 8.8×10^5; the exponent is larger making the number larger.

Write each expression with a single exponent.

10. $12^7 \cdot 12^9$ — 12^{16}
11. $y^7 \cdot y^4$ — y^{11}
12. $(4^4)^7$ — 4^{28}
13. $m^{27} \cdot m^0$ — m^{27}
14. $\frac{14^7}{14^5}$ — 14^2
15. $\frac{w^8}{w^3}$ — w^5

Simplify each expression.

16. r^{-7} — $\frac{1}{r^7}$
17. $(-t)^{-5}$ — $\frac{-1}{t^5}$
18. $(k^5)^{-4}$ — $\frac{1}{k^{20}}$
19. $(h^{-5})^{-3}$ — h^{15}

Available in Spanish

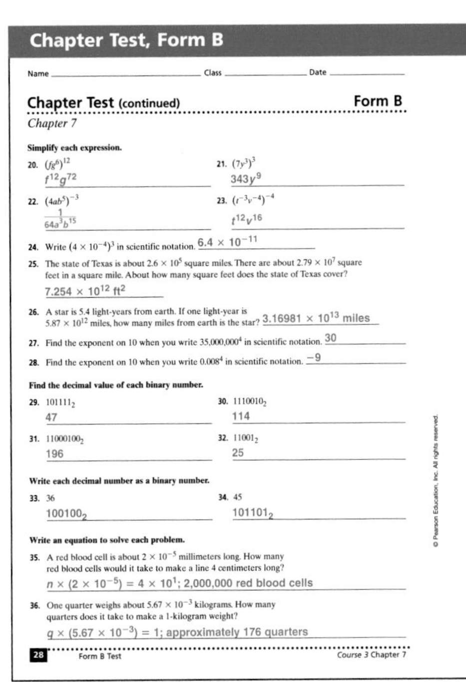

Chapter Test, Form B

Name ______________ Class ______________ Date ______________

Chapter Test (continued) — Form B

Chapter 7

Simplify each expression.

20. $(fg^6)^{12}$ — $f^{12}g^{72}$
21. $(7y^3)^3$ — $343y^9$
22. $(4ab^5)^{-3}$ — $\frac{1}{64a^3b^{15}}$
23. $(t^{-3}v^{-4})^{-4}$ — $t^{12}v^{16}$
24. Write $(4 \times 10^{-4})^3$ in scientific notation. 6.4×10^{-11}
25. The state of Texas is about 2.6×10^5 square miles. There are about 2.79×10^7 square feet in a square mile. About how many square feet does the state of Texas cover? 7.254×10^{12} ft^2
26. A star is 5.4 light-years from earth. If one light-year is 5.87×10^{12} miles, how many miles from earth is the star? 3.16981×10^{13} miles
27. Find the exponent on 10 when you write $35{,}000{,}000^4$ in scientific notation. 30
28. Find the exponent on 10 when you write 0.008^4 in scientific notation. −9

Find the decimal value of each binary number.

29. 101111_2 — 47
30. 1110010_2 — 114
31. 11000100_2 — 196
32. 11001_2 — 25

Write each decimal number as a binary number.

33. 36 — 100100_2
34. 45 — 101101_2

Write an equation to solve each problem.

35. A red blood cell is about 2×10^{-5} millimeters long. How many red blood cells would it take to make a line 4 centimeters long? $n \times (2 \times 10^{-5}) = 4 \times 10^1$; 2,000,000 red blood cells
36. One quarter weighs about 5.67×10^{-3} kilograms. How many quarters does it take to make a 1-kilogram weight? $q \times (5.67 \times 10^{-3}) = 1$; approximately 176 quarters

Available in Spanish

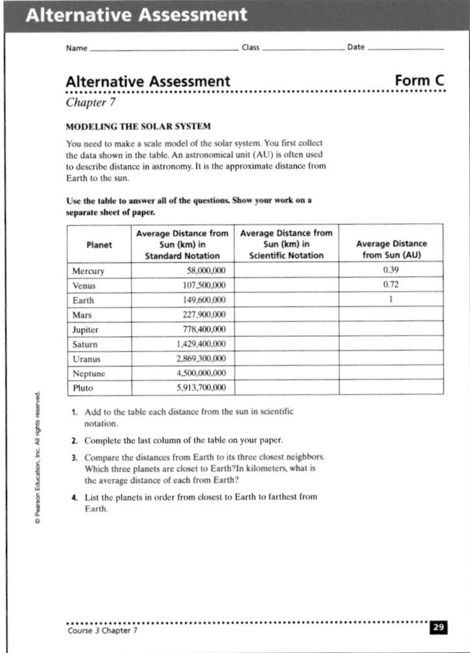

Alternative Assessment

Name ______________ Class ______________ Date ______________

Alternative Assessment — Form C

Chapter 7

MODELING THE SOLAR SYSTEM

You need to make a scale model of the solar system. You first collect the data shown in the table. An astronomical unit (AU) is often used to describe distance in astronomy. It is the approximate distance from Earth to the sun.

Use the table to answer all of the questions. Show your work on a separate sheet of paper.

Planet	Average Distance from Sun (km) in Standard Notation	Average Distance from Sun (km) in Scientific Notation	Average Distance from Sun (AU)
Mercury	58,000,000		0.39
Venus	107,500,000		0.72
Earth	149,600,000		1
Mars	227,900,000		
Jupiter	778,400,000		
Saturn	1,429,400,000		
Uranus	2,869,300,000		
Neptune	4,500,000,000		
Pluto	5,913,700,000		

1. Add to the table each distance from the sun in scientific notation.
2. Complete the last column of the table on your paper.
3. Compare the distances from Earth to its three closest neighbors. Which three planets are closet to Earth?In kilometers, what is the average distance of each from Earth?
4. List the planets in order from closest to Earth to farthest from Earth.

Available in Spanish

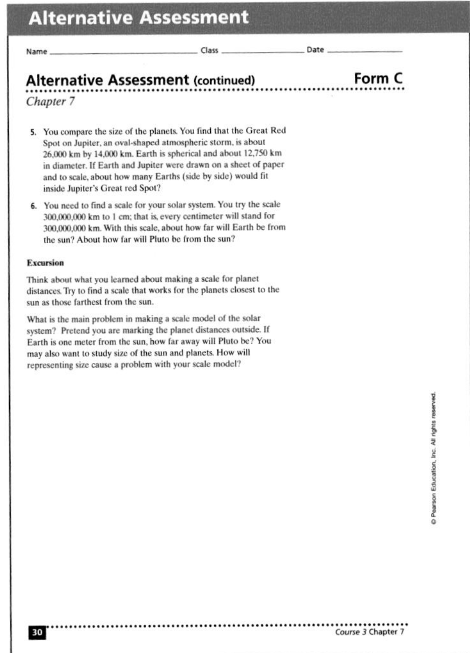

Alternative Assessment

Name ______________ Class ______________ Date ______________

Alternative Assessment (continued) — Form C

Chapter 7

5. You compare the size of the planets. You find that the Great Red Spot on Jupiter, an oval-shaped atmospheric storm, is about 26,000 km by 14,000 km. Earth is spherical and about 12,750 km in diameter. If Earth and Jupiter were drawn on a sheet of paper and to scale, about how many Earths (side by side) would fit inside Jupiter's Great red Spot?
6. You need to find a scale for your solar system. You try the scale 300,000,000 km to 1 cm; that is, every centimeter will stand for 300,000,000 km. With this scale, about how far will Earth be from the sun? About how far will Pluto be from the sun?

Excursion

Think about what you learned about making a scale for planet distances. Try to find a scale that works for the planets closest to the sun as those farthest from the sun.

What is the main problem in making a scale model of the solar system? Pretend you are marking the planet distances outside. If Earth is one meter from the sun, how far away will Pluto be? You may also want to study size of the sun and planets. How will representing size cause a problem with your scale model?

Available in Spanish

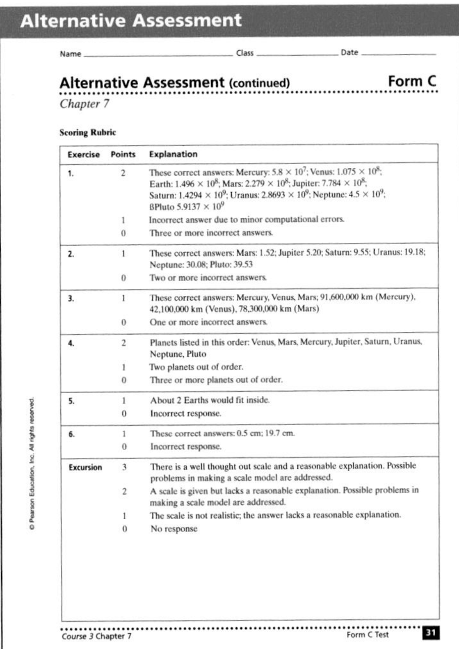

Alternative Assessment

Name ______________ Class ______________ Date ______________

Alternative Assessment (continued) — Form C

Chapter 7

Scoring Rubric

Exercise	Points	Explanation
1.	2	These correct answers: Mercury: 5.8×10^7; Venus: 1.075×10^8; Earth: 1.496×10^8; Mars: 2.279×10^8; Jupiter: 7.784×10^8; Saturn: 1.4294×10^9; Uranus: 2.8693×10^9; Neptune: 4.5×10^9; ßPluto 5.9137×10^9
	1	Incorrect answer due to minor computational errors.
	0	Three or more incorrect answers.
2.	1	These correct answers: Mars: 1.52; Jupiter 5.20; Saturn: 9.55; Uranus: 19.18; Neptune: 30.08; Pluto: 39.53
	0	Two or more incorrect answers.
3.	1	These correct answers: Mercury, Venus, Mars; 91,600,000 km (Mercury), 42,100,000 km (Venus), 78,300,000 km (Mars)
	0	One or more incorrect answers.
4.	2	Planets listed in this order: Venus, Mars, Mercury, Jupiter, Saturn, Uranus, Neptune, Pluto
	1	Two planets out of order.
	0	Three or more planets out of order.
5.	1	About 2 Earths would fit inside.
	0	Incorrect response.
6.	1	These correct answers: 0.5 cm; 19.7 cm.
	0	Incorrect response.
Excursion	3	There is a well thought out scale and a reasonable explanation. Possible problems in making a scale model are addressed.
	2	A scale is given but lacks a reasonable explanation. Possible problems in making a scale model are addressed.
	1	The scale is not realistic; the answer lacks a reasonable explanation.
	0	No response

Available in Spanish

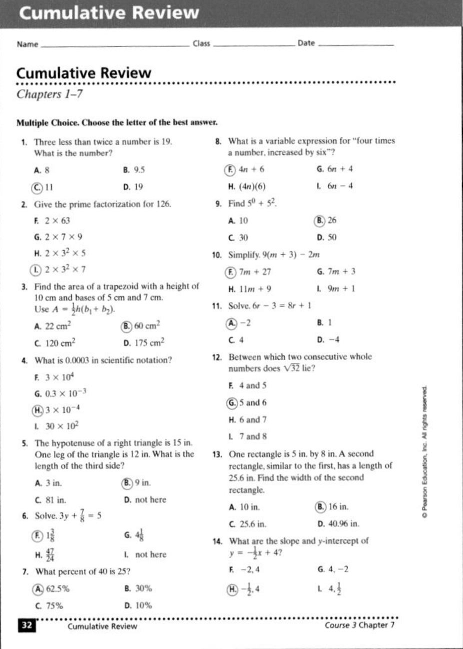

Cumulative Review

Name ______________ Class ______________ Date ______________

Cumulative Review

Chapters 1–7

Multiple Choice. Choose the letter of the best answer.

1. Three less than twice a number is 19. What is the number?
   A. 8 B. 9.5 **(C.) 11** D. 19
2. Give the prime factorization for 126.
   F. 2×63 G. $2 \times 7 \times 9$ H. $2 \times 3^2 \times 5$ **(I.) $2 \times 3^2 \times 7$**
3. Find the area of a trapezoid with a height of 10 cm and bases of 5 cm and 7 cm. Use $A = \frac{1}{2}h(b_1 + b_2)$.
   A. 22 cm^2 **(B.) 60 cm^2** C. 120 cm^2 D. 175 cm^2
4. What is 0.0003 in scientific notation?
   F. 3×10^4 G. 0.3×10^{-3} **(H.) 3×10^{-4}** I. 30×10^2
5. The hypotenuse of a right triangle is 15 in. One leg of the triangle is 12 in. What is the length of the third side?
   A. 3 in. **(B.) 9 in.** C. 81 in. D. not here
6. Solve. $3y + \frac{7}{8} = 5$
   (F.) $1\frac{3}{8}$ G. $4\frac{1}{8}$ H. $\frac{47}{24}$ I. not here
7. What percent of 40 is 25?
   (A.) 62.5% B. 30% C. 75% D. 10%
8. What is a variable expression for "four times a number, increased by six"?
   (F.) $4n + 6$ G. $6n + 4$ H. $(4n)(6)$ I. $6n - 4$
9. Find $5^0 + 5^2$.
   A. 10 **(B.) 26** C. 30 D. 50
10. Simplify. $9(m + 3) - 2m$
    (F.) $7m + 27$ G. $7m + 3$ H. $11m + 9$ I. $9m + 1$
11. Solve. $6r - 3 = 8r + 1$
    (A.) −2 B. 1 C. 4 D. −4
12. Between which two consecutive whole numbers does $\sqrt{32}$ lie?
    F. 4 and 5 **(G.) 5 and 6** H. 6 and 7 I. 7 and 8
13. One rectangle is 5 in. by 8 in. A second rectangle, similar to the first, has a length of 25.6 in. Find the width of the second rectangle.
    A. 10 in. **(B.) 16 in.** C. 25.6 in. D. 40.96 in.
14. What are the slope and y-intercept of $y = -\frac{1}{2}x + 4$?
    F. −2, 4 G. 4, −2 **(H.) $-\frac{1}{2}$, 4** I. 4, $\frac{1}{2}$

Available in Spanish

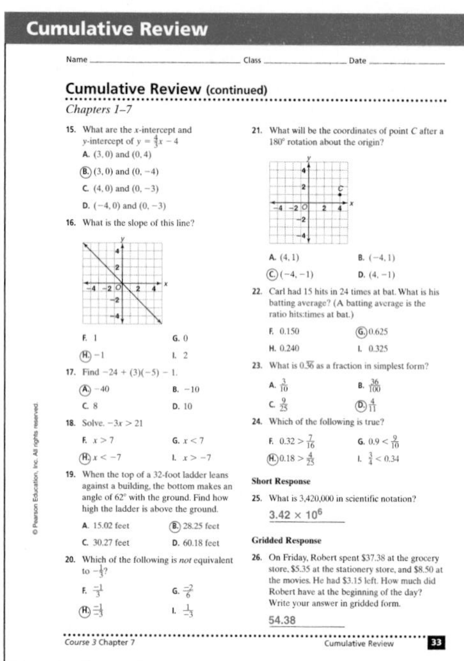

Cumulative Review

Name ______ Class ______ Date ______

Cumulative Review (continued)

Chapters 1–7

15. What are the x-intercept and y-intercept of $y = \frac{4}{3}x - 4$
 A. (3, 0) and (0, 4)
 (B.) (3, 0) and (0, −4)
 C. (4, 0) and (0, −3)
 D. (−4, 0) and (0, −3)

16. What is the slope of this line?
 F. 1 G. 0
 (H.) −1 I. 2

17. Find $-24 + (3)(-5) - 1$.
 (A.) −40 B. −10
 C. 8 D. 10

18. Solve. $-3x > 21$
 F. $x > 7$ G. $x < 7$
 (H.) $x < -7$ I. $x > -7$

19. When the top of a 32-foot ladder leans against a building, the bottom makes an angle of 62° with the ground. Find how high the ladder is above the ground.
 A. 15.02 feet (B.) 28.25 feet
 C. 30.27 feet D. 60.18 feet

20. Which of the following is *not* equivalent to $-\frac{1}{3}$?
 F. $\frac{-1}{3}$ G. $\frac{-2}{6}$
 (H.) $\frac{-1}{-3}$ I. $\frac{1}{-3}$

21. What will be the coordinates of point C after a 180° rotation about the origin?
 A. (4, 1) B. (−4, 1)
 (C.) (−4, −1) D. (4, −1)

22. Carl had 15 hits in 24 times at bat. What is his batting average? (A batting average is the ratio hits:times at bat.)
 F. 0.150 (G.) 0.625
 H. 0.240 I. 0.325

23. What is $0.\overline{36}$ as a fraction in simplest form?
 A. $\frac{3}{10}$ B. $\frac{36}{100}$
 C. $\frac{9}{25}$ (D.) $\frac{4}{11}$

24. Which of the following is true?
 F. $0.32 > \frac{7}{16}$ G. $0.9 < \frac{9}{10}$
 (H.) $0.18 > \frac{4}{25}$ I. $\frac{3}{4} < 0.34$

Short Response

25. What is 3,420,000 in scientific notation?
 3.42×10^6

Gridded Response

26. On Friday, Robert spent $37.38 at the grocery store, $5.35 at the stationery store, and $8.50 at the movies. He had $3.15 left. How much did Robert have at the beginning of the day? Write your answer in gridded form.
 54.38

Course 3 Chapter 7 Cumulative Review 33

Available in Spanish

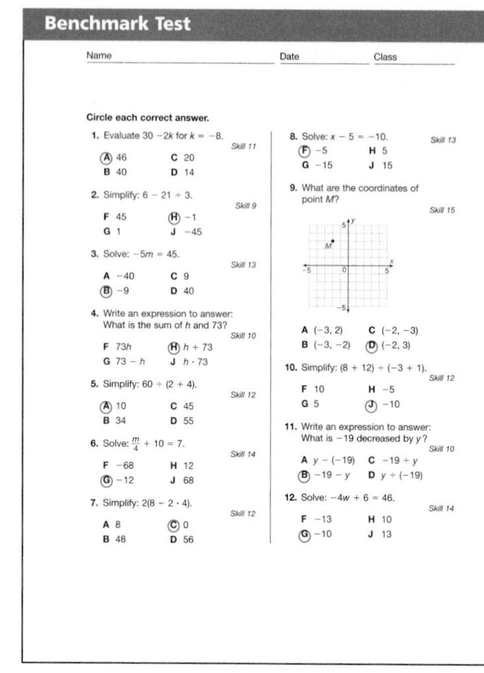

Benchmark Test

Name ______ Date ______ Class ______

Circle each correct answer.

1. Evaluate $30 - 2k$ for $k = -8$. *Skill 11*
 (A) 46 C 20
 B 40 D 14

2. Simplify: $6 - 21 \div 3$. *Skill 9*
 F 45 (H) −1
 G 1 J −45

3. Solve: $-5m = 45$. *Skill 13*
 A −40 C 9
 (B) −9 D 40

4. Write an expression to answer: What is the sum of h and 73? *Skill 10*
 F $73h$ (H) $h + 73$
 G $73 - h$ J $h \cdot 73$

5. Simplify: $60 \div (2 + 4)$. *Skill 12*
 (A) 10 C 45
 B 34 D 55

6. Solve: $\frac{m}{4} + 10 = 7$. *Skill 14*
 F −68 H 12
 (G) −12 J 68

7. Simplify: $2(8 - 2 \cdot 4)$. *Skill 12*
 A 8 (C) 0
 B 48 D 56

8. Solve: $x - 5 = -10$. *Skill 13*
 (F) −5 H 5
 G −15 J 15

9. What are the coordinates of point M? *Skill 15*
 A (−3, 2) C (−2, −3)
 B (−3, −2) (D) (−2, 3)

10. Simplify: $(8 + 12) \div (-3 + 1)$. *Skill 12*
 F 10 H −5
 G 5 (J) −10

11. Write an expression to answer: What is −19 decreased by y? *Skill 10*
 A $y - (-19)$ C $-19 \div y$
 (B) $-19 - y$ D $y \div (-19)$

12. Solve: $-4w + 6 = 46$. *Skill 14*
 F −13 H 10
 (G) −10 J 13

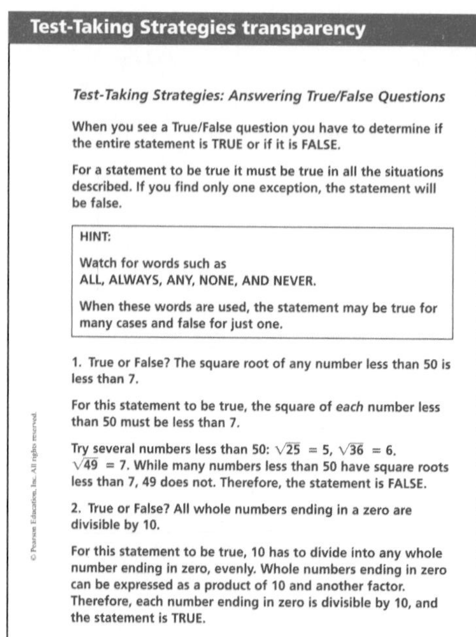

Test-Taking Strategies transparency

Test-Taking Strategies: Answering True/False Questions

When you see a True/False question you have to determine if the entire statement is TRUE or if it is FALSE.

For a statement to be true it must be true in all the situations described. If you find only one exception, the statement will be false.

> **HINT:**
>
> **Watch for words such as ALL, ALWAYS, ANY, NONE, AND NEVER.**
>
> **When these words are used, the statement may be true for many cases and false for just one.**

1. True or False? The square root of any number less than 50 is less than 7.

For this statement to be true, the square of *each* number less than 50 must be less than 7.

Try several numbers less than 50: $\sqrt{25} = 5$, $\sqrt{36} = 6$, $\sqrt{49} = 7$. While many numbers less than 50 have square roots less than 7, 49 does not. Therefore, the statement is FALSE.

2. True or False? All whole numbers ending in a zero are divisible by 10.

For this statement to be true, 10 has to divide into any whole number ending in zero, evenly. Whole numbers ending in zero can be expressed as a product of 10 and another factor. Therefore, each number ending in zero is divisible by 10, and the statement is TRUE.

Transparency 12

On PH Website

Test-Taking Strategies worksheet

Name ______ Class ______ Date ______

Chapter 7: Answering True/False Questions

Exercises

Determine whether each statement is true or false. Explain your answer.

1. True or False? When x is a positive integer, then 5^x is always positive.
 True; since 5 is positive, 5^x will also be positive.
2. True or False? The expression x^0 equals y^0 for all values of x and y.
 True; $x^0 = y^0 = 1$
3. True or False? The expression 5^8 always equals $5^4 \times 5^2$.
 False; $5^4 \times 5^2 = 5^6$
4. True or False? The expression x^3 is never smaller than x^2.
 False; if x is a fraction or a negative number then $x^3 < x^2$.
5. True or False? The expression $(s^{-5}t^{-4})^{-b}$ is equal to $s^{15}t^{12}$, when $b = -3$.
 True; if you substitute $b = -3$ into the expression the resulting expression is equal to $s^{15}t^{12}$.
6. True or False? The expression $(x - y)^2$ equals $x^2 - y^2$ when $x = 2$ and $y = 1$.
 False; when $x = 2$ and $y = 1$, then $(x - y)^2$ equals 1 and $x^2 - y^2$ equals 3.
7. True or False? The expression $\frac{9^8}{9^6}$ always equals 81.
 True; $\frac{9^8}{9^6} = 9^8 - 9^6 = 9^2$
8. True or False? The expression 9.8×10^{-4} is always greater than 6.4×10^{-3}.
 False; $9.8 \times 10^{-4} = 0.00098$, but $6.4 \times 10^{-3} = 0.0064$
9. True or False? The expression 11001_2 always equals $(1 \times 2^4) + (1 \times 2^3) + (1 \times 2^0)$.
 True; 11001_2 always equals $(1 \times 2^4) + (1 \times 2^3) + (1 \times 2^0)$
10. True or False? The expression 4×6^3 always equals $2^5 \times 3^3$.
 True; $4 \times 6^3 = 2^2 \times 2^3 \times 3^3 = 2^5 \times 3^3$
11. True or False? If $270{,}000 \times 21{,}000 = 5.67 \times 10^P$, then $P = 7$.
 False; $P = 9$

Test-Taking Strategies Course 3 31

Home Activities

in math class ...

We have been learning about exponents and powers. Here is a list of some of the skills and concepts we have studied.

- Scientific notation
- Operations with exponents
- Power rules
- Binary and base ten number systems

Home Activities

Here are some activities you can do with your child that use these math skills and concepts.

Have your child make a family tree of his or her direct ancestors that extends back to his or her great-grandparents. In the first generation of ancestors there are two parents, in the second generation there are four grandparents, and so on. Encourage your child to make a table showing the number of ancestors in each generation. Discuss the relationship between the number of the generation (1, 2, 3) and the number of ancestors in each generation (2, 4, 8). How many ancestors do you think there will be in the fourth generation?

Ask your child to factor the number of ancestors for each generation, and then to write each number as an exponent in simplest form. Your child should notice that there are 2^1 ancestors in the first generation, 2^2 ancestors in the second generation, and 2^3 ancestors in the third generation. Now how many ancestors do you think there will be in the fourth generation?

If your child concluded that there are 16 ancestors in the fourth generation each time the question was asked, discuss why both methods used to answer the question were correct. If your child did not answer the question correctly both times, discuss which method did not work and why.

There are, on average, 25 years in each generation. Ask your child questions such as: How many ancestors did you have in the generation in which Christopher Columbus discovered America? How many ancestors did you have in the generation in which George Washington was president of the United States?

Use with Chapter 7

Available in Spanish; Web Code: ack-5500

Interdisciplinary Activities

Name ______ ***Math and Science/Technology***

Doomsday Rock

Use decimals and scientific notation with astronomical distances.

Doomsday Rock Hurtling Toward Earth
Asteroid on Collision Course

Could these be real headlines, or are they just science fiction? The truth is, sooner or later an asteroid will collide with Earth. It's happened before—there are huge craters on Earth where asteroids have crashed—and it's likely to happen again. This may not happen for thousands of years or it may happen much sooner. And someday we may be able to spot incoming asteroids early enough to push them off course.

What are asteroids anyway? Asteroids are sometimes called minor planets. They are the "leftovers" of the rocky material which formed our solar system. Some are very small. Others are quite large, up to 1,000 km in diameter. All orbit the Sun. Most asteroids move in an orbit between the planets Mars and Jupiter. We don't have to worry about bumping into these. However, others have unusual orbits that cross the orbit of Earth. These are the asteroids we have to look out for.

In February, 1996, a spacecraft was launched by NASA to study the asteroid Eros. The spacecraft is called NEAR Shoemaker. NEAR stands for Near Earth Asteroid Rendezvous. The asteroid Eros is a potato-shaped rock twice the length of Manhattan Island. NEAR Shoemaker landed on the asteroid Eros in February 2000. Instruments aboard the spacecraft took photographs of Eros and collected data about it. The data provided scientists with clues about the composition and behavior of Eros.

Asteroids are chunks of rock that hurtle through space. They range in size from pebbles and boulders to about 1000 km in diameter. A large one crashing into Earth could do serious damage.

Scientists are unable to say whether it will collide with Earth at some distant point in the future. However, asteroids have collided with Earth in the past, and they will collide with Earth in the future.

1. What could be some of the dangers if an asteroid or part of an asteroid struck land on Earth?

Use with Chapter 7

Web Code: ack-5500

Interdisciplinary Activities

Name ______________________ ***Math and Science/Technology***

2. a. Asteroid Eros is 33 kilometers long. If there are 1.6 kilometers in 1 mile, how long is Eros in miles? Tell how you got your answer.

____

b. If Asteroid Eros is 8 miles in diameter, what is its diameter in kilometers?

____

c. How does the length of Eros compare with its diameter? Give your answer in miles.

____

3. a. Eros came close to Earth in 1931. It came within 24,135,000 kilometers of Earth. Round this distance to the nearest million.

____

b. Use scientific notation to express this distance.

____

4. Sometimes scientists express distance in space in astronomical units (AU), where the distance between Earth and the Sun is given as 1.00 AU. Asteroid Vesta is the third largest asteroid. It is 2.360 AU from the Sun.

a. Jupiter is 5.203 AU from the Sun. Saturn is 9.555 AU from the Sun and Mars is 1.524 AU from the Sun. Between which two planets is the Asteroid Vesta found?

____

b. Suppose other asteroids come within these distances from the Sun (in AU):

2.173; 0.9412; 1.6275; 0.8417

Which of these asteroids should we be worried about? Why?

____

5. A number of suggestions have been made about how to keep an asteroid that is on a collision course with Earth from hitting it. Do some research to find out what those suggestions are. Write a report of your findings on a separate sheet of paper. Explain which suggestion you would support and why.

____

Use with Chapter 7

Web Code: ack-5500

Algebra Readiness Puzzles

Name ______________ Class ______________ Date ______________

What a Difference a Base Makes — Puzzle 31

Exponents and Powers

Below are box scores for some sports. However, they are written in different bases. Find the winning team by rewriting each box score in base 10.

Examples:

$23_{\text{base }4} = 2 \times 4^1 + 3 \times 4^0 = 8 + 3 = 11$

$412_{\text{base }6} = 4 \times 6^2 + 1 \times 6^1 + 2 \times 6^0 = 4 \times 36 + 6 + 2 = 152$

Baseball

Cubs	vs	Orioles		Cubs	vs	Orioles
$13_{\text{base }5}$		$21_{\text{base }4}$		______		______
Reds	vs	Rangers		Reds	vs	Rangers
$20_{\text{base }3}$		$13_{\text{base }4}$		______		______

Basketball High School

Crusaders	vs	Cougars		Crusaders	vs	Cougars
$101_{\text{base }7}$		$45_{\text{base }7}$		______		______
Raiders	vs	Colonels		Raiders	vs	Colonels
$104_{\text{base }5}$		$42_{\text{base }7}$		______		______

Football

Steelers	vs	Chargers		Steelers	vs	Chargers
$12_{\text{base }5}$		$21_{\text{base }4}$		______		______
Bills	vs	Dolphins		Bills	vs	Dolphins
$130_{\text{base }4}$		$210_{\text{base }3}$		______		______

Softball

Champs	vs	Stallions		Champs	vs	Stallions
$14_{\text{base }5}$		$10_{\text{base }7}$		______		______
Stars	vs	Wizards		Stars	vs	Wizards
$10_{\text{base }3}$		$11_{\text{base }4}$		______		______

 Algebra Readiness Puzzles 31

Web Code: ack-5500

Algebra Readiness Puzzles

Name ______________ Class ______________ Date ______________

Choose and Divide — Puzzle 66

Each problem below is followed by 2 possible next steps. Ring the correct next step. Then finish simplifying.

1. $\frac{8x^4}{2x}$

   $\frac{8}{2} \cdot x^{4-1}$ $\quad$ $\frac{8}{2} \cdot x^{1-4}$

   ____

2. $\frac{-6x^5}{-3x^5}$

   $\frac{-6}{-3} \cdot x^{5+5}$ $\quad$ $\frac{-6}{-3} \cdot x^{5-5}$

   ____

3. $\frac{x^4}{5x^2}$

   $5 \cdot x^{4-2}$ $\quad$ $\frac{1}{5} \cdot x^{4-2}$

   ____

4. $\frac{10x^6y^2}{-2x^5y^2}$

   $\frac{10}{-2} \cdot x^{6-5}y^{2-2}$ $\quad$ $\frac{10}{2} \cdot x^{6-5}y^{2-2}$

   ____

5. $\frac{(3x)(4x)}{2x}$

   $\frac{(3+4)(x \cdot x)}{2x}$ $\quad$ $\frac{(3 \cdot 4)(x \cdot x)}{2x}$

   ____

   ____

6. $\frac{-6x^5y^4}{2y^2}$

   $\frac{-6}{2} \cdot x^5y^{4-2}$ $\quad$ $\frac{-6}{2} \cdot x^{2-4}$

   ____

   ____

66 Algebra Readiness Puzzles

Web Code: ack-5500

Chapter 7 Exponents and Powers

Chapter 7 Overview

In this chapter, students use scientific notation to express very large and very small numbers. They draw upon their understanding of simplifying expressions, and they apply what they learn here about the rules of exponents, to simplify expressions that contain exponents.

Reading Math
- Understanding Word Problems, p. 382
- **Vocabulary:** A complete list, plus exercises, in the Chapter Review, p. 398
- **Illustrated Glossary:** Examples for each vocabulary term, plus definitions in English and Spanish, on p. 735

Test-Taking Strategies
Answering True/False Questions, p. 397

Real-World Problem Solving
- **Strategies:** Write an Equation, p. 388–391
- **Real-World Snapshots:** Wild Exponents, pp. 402–403
- **Chapter Project:** One Small Step . . . , p. 699

www.PHSchool.com
Internet support includes:
- Self-grading Vocabulary and Chapter 7 Tests
- Activity Masters
- Chapter Project support
- Chapter Planner
- Ch. 7 Resources

Plus iTEXT

CHAPTER 7

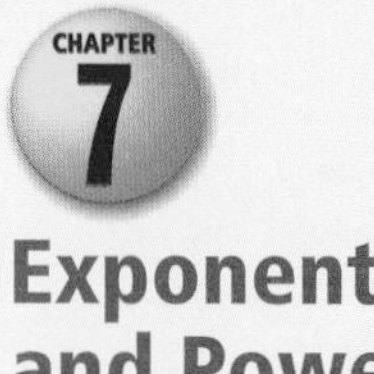

Exponents and Powers

Lessons

Key Vocabulary
- binary (p. 393)
- expanded form (p. 393)
- scientific notation (p. 366)

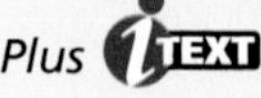

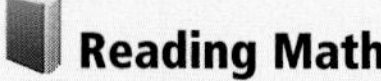

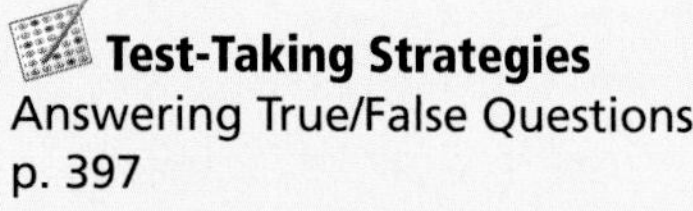

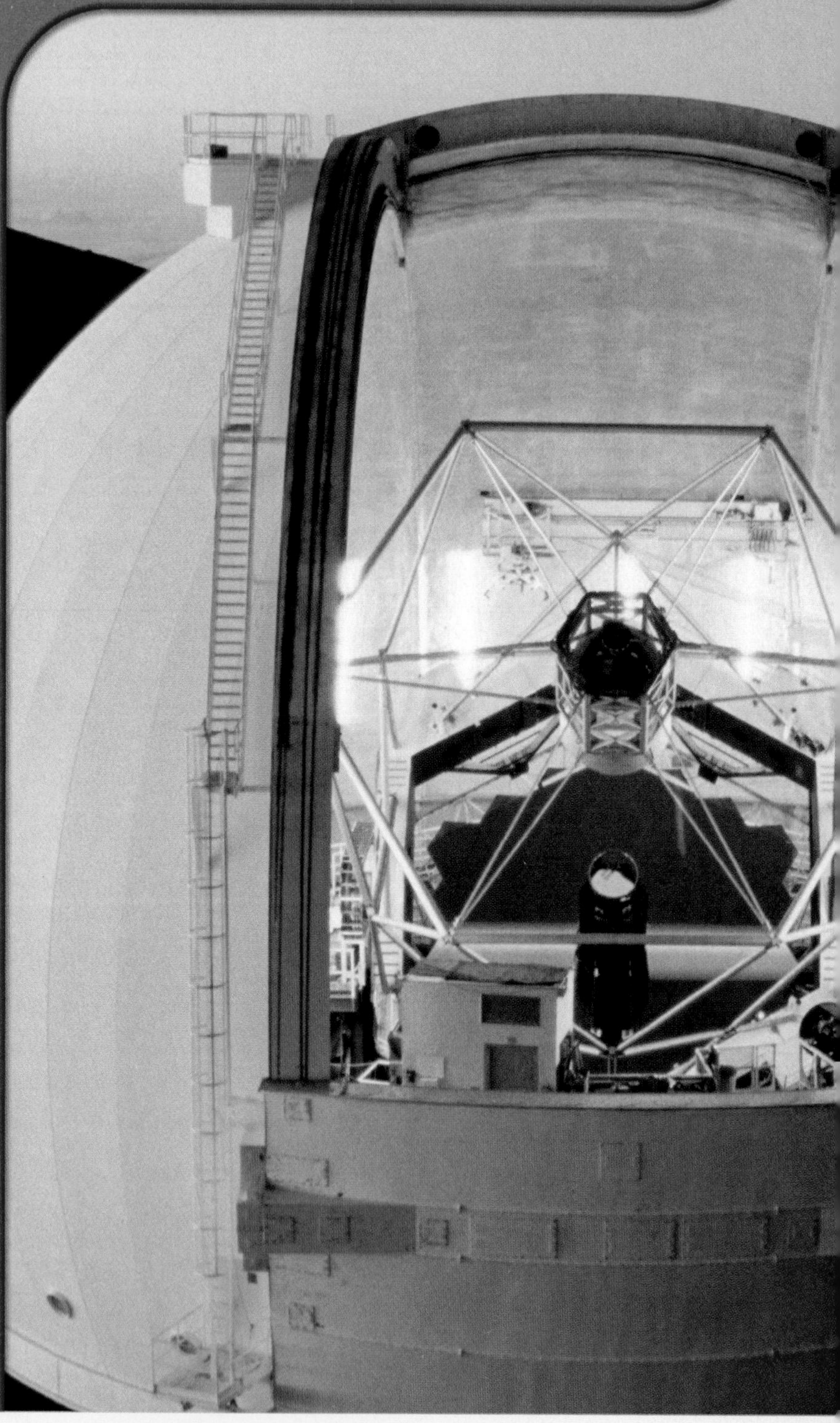

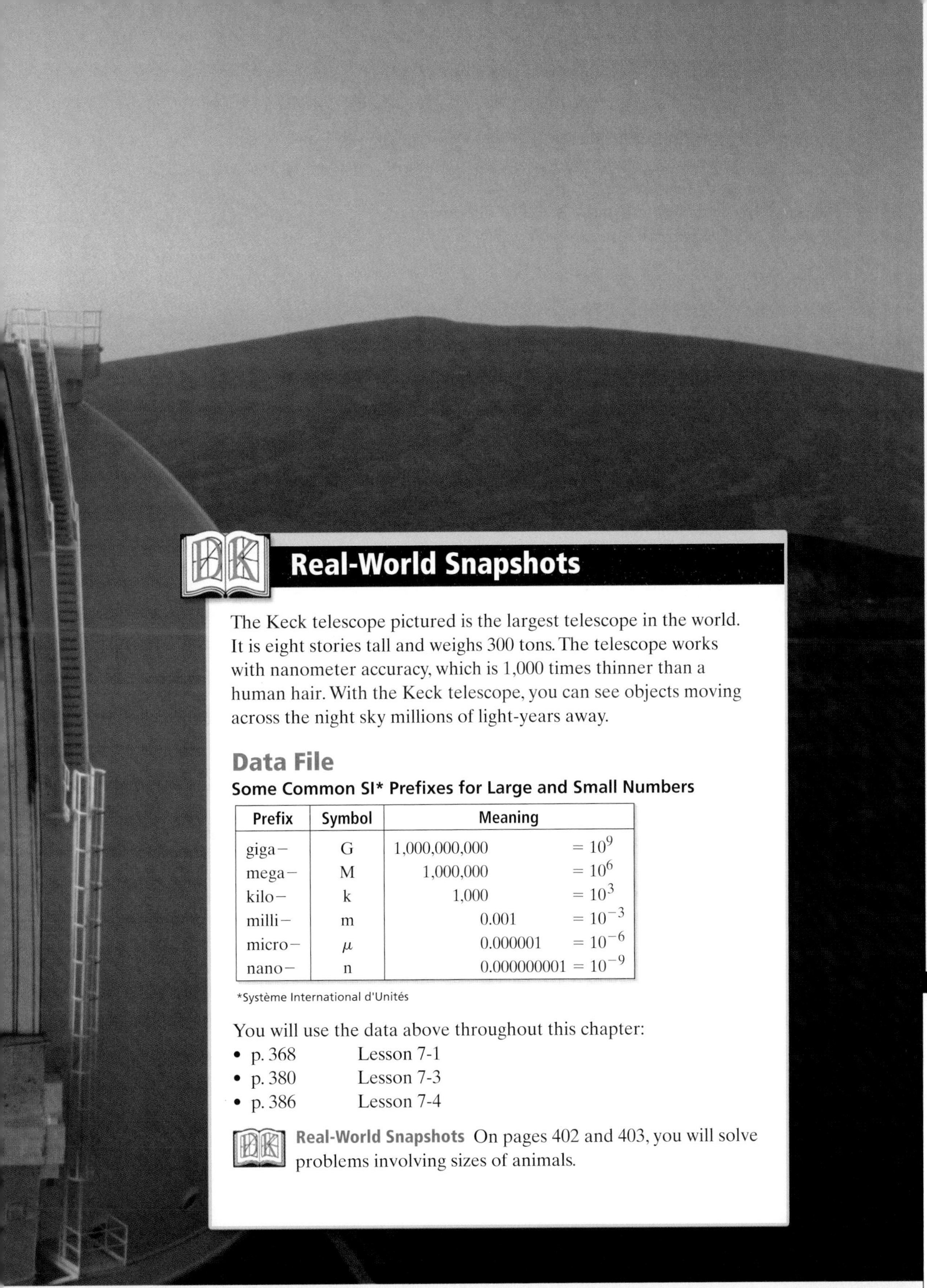

Real-World Snapshots

The Keck telescope pictured is the largest telescope in the world. It is eight stories tall and weighs 300 tons. The telescope works with nanometer accuracy, which is 1,000 times thinner than a human hair. With the Keck telescope, you can see objects moving across the night sky millions of light-years away.

Data File

Some Common SI* Prefixes for Large and Small Numbers

Prefix	Symbol	Meaning
giga–	G	1,000,000,000 $= 10^9$
mega–	M	1,000,000 $= 10^6$
kilo–	k	1,000 $= 10^3$
milli–	m	0.001 $= 10^{-3}$
micro–	μ	0.000001 $= 10^{-6}$
nano–	n	0.000000001 $= 10^{-9}$

*Système International d'Unités

You will use the data above throughout this chapter:

- p. 368 Lesson 7-1
- p. 380 Lesson 7-3
- p. 386 Lesson 7-4

Real-World Snapshots On pages 402 and 403, you will solve problems involving sizes of animals.

Teaching Notes

Activating Prior Knowledge
In this chapter, students build on their knowledge of decimal place value, of the order of operations, and of writing and simplifying expressions with exponents. Ask questions such as:

- *Simplify:* $2^2 + 3^3 + 1^4$. 32
- *What is the value of the digit 4 in the number 3.0641?* 4 thousandths
- *Use the order of operations. Solve:* $3^2 + 12 \times 5$. $9 + 60 = 69$

Real-World Snapshots
The data here will be used throughout the chapter. Have a volunteer read the opening sentences and the title of the chart, which contains information about some common prefixes for great and lesser numbers. Focus students on the data in the chart and ask:

- *Which prefix means "million"?* mega-
- *How many times greater than a millimeter is a kilometer?* one million
- *What would be the meaning of a number with the prefix "centi-"?* 0.01 (one hundredth)

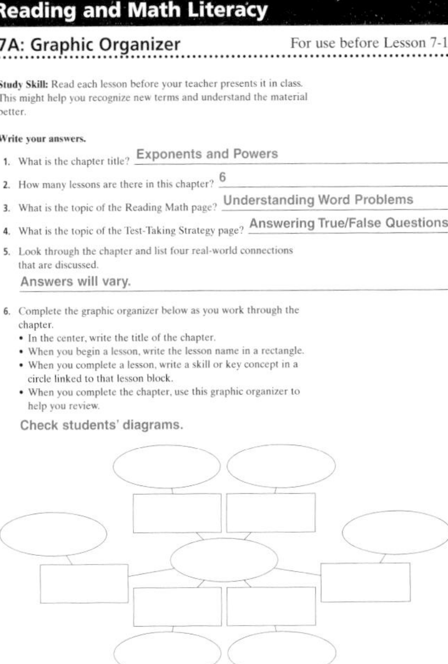

Reading and Math Literacy

7A: Graphic Organizer For use before Lesson 7-1

Study Skill: Read each lesson before your teacher presents it in class. This might help you recognize new terms and understand the material better.

Write your answers.

1. What is the chapter title? Exponents and Powers
2. How many lessons are there in this chapter? 6
3. What is the topic of the Reading Math page? Understanding Word Problems
4. What is the topic of the Test-Taking Strategy page? Answering True/False Questions
5. Look through the chapter and list four real-world connections that are discussed. Answers will vary.
6. Complete the graphic organizer below as you work through the chapter.
   - In the center, write the title of the chapter.
   - When you begin a lesson, write the lesson name in a rectangle.
   - When you complete a lesson, write a skill or key concept in a circle linked to that lesson block.
   - When you complete the chapter, use this graphic organizer to help you review.

Check students' diagrams.

Available in Spanish

Chapter 7: Exponents and Powers

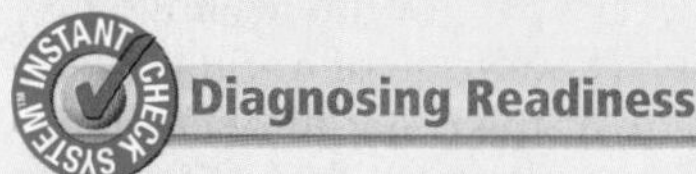

Students will find answers to these exercises in the back of their textbooks.

Prescribing Intervention
For intervention, direct students to:

Decimals and Place Value
Skills Handbook: Decimals and Place Value, p. 714.

Multiplying and Dividing by Powers of Ten
Skills Handbook: Multiplying and Dividing by Powers of Ten, p. 721.

Using Exponents
Lesson 1-7: Examples 1-2.
Extra Practice, p. 702.

Chapter 7 Preview

Where You've Been

- In Chapter 1, you learned how to write and simplify expressions with exponents. You also learned how to use the order of operations with exponents.

Where You're Going

- In Chapter 7, you will learn how to write very large and very small numbers using scientific notation.
- You will also learn how to simplify expressions using the rules of exponents.
- Applying what you learn, you will find the smallest object you can see at a certain distance through binoculars.

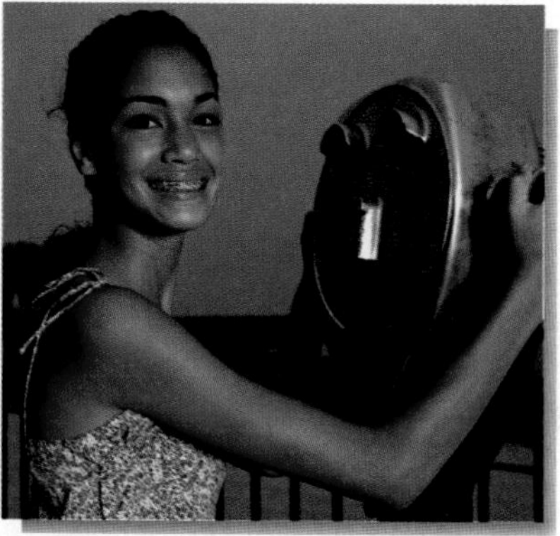

Binoculars are used to see distant objects.

Instant self-check online and on CD-ROM

Diagnosing Readiness

For help, go to the lesson in green.

Decimals and Place Value (Skills Handbook page 714)

Use the number 1,284,530.679. Write the value of each digit.

1. 3 3 tens **2.** 8 8 ten thousands **3.** 6 6 tenths **4.** 7 7 hundredths

Write each decimal in words.

5. 0.2 two tenths **6.** 0.05 five hundredths **7.** 1.34 one and thirty-four hundredths **8.** 2.09 two and nine hundredths

Multiplying and Dividing by Powers of Ten (Skills Handbook page 721)

Multiply or divide.

9. 45×100 4,500 **10.** $17 \times 1{,}000$ 17,000 **11.** $0.61 \div 10$ 0.061

12. $12 \div 10{,}000$ 0.0012 **13.** 56×0.1 5.6 **14.** 91.2×0.01 0.912

Using Exponents (Lesson 1-7)

Write using exponents.

15. $7 \cdot 7 \cdot 7 \cdot 7 \cdot 7$ 7^5 **16.** $5 \cdot 5 \cdot c \cdot c$ 5^2c^2 **17.** $a \cdot a \cdot b \cdot b \cdot b$ a^2b^3

18. $x \cdot y \cdot x \cdot y \cdot x$ x^3y^2 **19.** $(3x) \cdot (3x) \cdot (3x)$ $(3x)^3$ **20.** $c \cdot d \cdot e \cdot d \cdot e$ cd^2e^2

Simplify each expression.

21. 4^2 16 **22.** $(-4)^2$ 16 **23.** -4^2 −16

24. $-(-2)^5$ 32 **25.** 10^2 100 **26.** 10^3 1,000

7-1 Scientific Notation

What You'll Learn

To write numbers in standard form and scientific notation

To order numbers written in scientific notation

. . . And Why

To order the planets based on their distance from the sun, as in Example 3

✓ Check Skills You'll Need

For help, go to Skills Handbook page 721.

Multiply.

1. 2×10 20
2. $1.5 \times 1{,}000$ 1,500
3. 4.51×100 451
4. $2.39 \times 1{,}000{,}000$ 2,390,000
5. $1.803 \times 10{,}000$ 18,030
6. $7.6 \times 1{,}000$ 7,600
7. Explain how you would multiply 123.456 by 100. Move the decimal point 2 places to the right.

New Vocabulary

- scientific notation

OBJECTIVE 1

Standard Form and Scientific Notation

Interactive lesson includes instant self-check, tutorials, and activities.

Investigation: Multiplying by Powers of Ten

1. Copy and complete the following table.

$6.71 \times 10^6 = 6.71 \times 1{,}000{,}000 = \blacksquare$	6,710,000
$6.71 \times 10^5 = 6.71 \times 100{,}000 = \blacksquare$	671,000
$6.71 \times 10^4 = 6.71 \times 10{,}000 = \blacksquare$	67,100
$6.71 \times 10^3 = 6.71 \times \blacksquare = \blacksquare$	1,000; 6,710
$6.71 \times 10^2 = 6.71 \times 100 = \blacksquare$	671
$6.71 \times 10^1 = 6.71 \times \blacksquare = \blacksquare$	10; 67.1

2. **Patterns** What patterns do you see in your answers? See left.
3. Multiply 6.71 by 10^9. 6,710,000,000

2. Answers may vary. Sample: The exponent is the number of places the decimal point moves to the right.

Calculator Hint

2.59E11 on a calculator means 2.59×10^{11}.

Earth is roughly spherical in shape. Its volume is extremely large. Both of the numbers below indicate Earth's volume in cubic miles.

Scientific Notation		Standard Form
2.59×10^{11}	=	259,000,000,000

Scientific notation is a brief way to write very large or very small numbers.

7-1

1. Plan

Lesson Preview

✓ Check Skills You'll Need PowerPoint

Multiplying by Powers of Ten
Skills Handbook: Multiplying and Dividing by Powers of Ten, p. 721.

Lesson Resources

Teaching Resources
Practice, Reteaching, Enrichment

Reaching All Students
Practice Workbook 7-1
Spanish Practice Workbook 7-1
Guided Problem Solving 7-1
Hands-On Activities 4

Presentation Assistant Plus!
Transparencies
- Check Skills You'll Need 7-1
- Problem of the Day 7-1
- Additional Examples 7-1
- Student Edition Answers 7-1
- Lesson Quiz 7-1
- Classroom Aid 11

PH Presentation Pro CD-ROM 7-1

PRENTICE HALL ASSESSMENT SYSTEM
Computer Test Generator CD

Technology
Resource Pro® CD-ROM
Computer Test Generator CD
PH Presentation Pro CD-ROM

www.PHSchool.com
Student Site
- Teacher Web Code: ack-5500
- Self-grading Lesson Quiz

PH SuccessNet Teacher Center
- Lesson Planner
- Resources

Plus iText

Ongoing Assessment and Intervention

Before the Lesson
Diagnose prerequisite skills using:
- Check Skills You'll Need

During the Lesson
Monitor progress using:
- Check Understanding
- Additional Examples
- Test Prep

After the Lesson
Assess knowledge using:
- Lesson Quiz
- Computer Test Generator CD

2. Teach

Math Background

The "center" of decimal notation is the units place together with the decimal point. To the right of the decimal point is one-tenth; to the left of the decimal point is ten. A number is written in *scientific notation* when it is expressed as the product of $c \times 10^d$ where $1 \leq c < 10$ and d is an integer.

Teaching Notes

Investigation (Optional)
To make sure that students find the patterns in the table, have them describe what they see in each column. Point out the changes between each row. You may want to return to this pattern when students learn about the meaning of 10^0 and 10^{-1} in Lesson 7-3.

1 EXAMPLE Auditory Learners
Some students may find it helpful to quietly count the places aloud as they move the decimal point.

Tactile Learners
Have students make a set of index cards that includes fifteen cards: four cards with 0, nine cards with the digits 1–9, and one card with a decimal point. Have students use the cards to represent the numbers in Check Understanding 1. They can physically move the decimal point to express the numbers in scientific notation.

2 EXAMPLE Error Prevention
Some students may incorrectly find the exponent of 10 by counting all the digits or by counting just the zeros. Have them cover the first digit and count the remaining digits.

3 EXAMPLE Diversity
Explain that scientists all over the world use scientific notation to express the lesser and greater numbers that measure the physical world. Writing numbers in this form makes them easier to compare and to use for calculations.

Key Concepts — Scientific Notation

A number is in **scientific notation** if the first factor is greater than or equal to 1 and less than 10 and the second factor is a power of 10.

Examples 1×10^8 1.54×10^7 9.99×10^4

When you multiply a number by 10,000 or 10^4, the number's decimal point moves 4 places to the right.

$$35 \times 10^4 = 35 \times 10{,}000 = 350{,}000$$
$$3.428 \times 10^4 = 3.428 \times 10{,}000 = 34{,}280$$
$$0.00831 \times 10^4 = 0.00831 \times 10{,}000 = 83.1$$

Multiplying a number by 10^n, when n is positive, moves the decimal point n places to the right.

Real-World Connection
Hot gases above the sun's surface can reach up to 10^8 degrees Celsius.

1 EXAMPLE Writing in Standard Form

Science The temperature at the sun's core is about 1.55×10^6 degrees Celsius. Write the temperature in standard form.

$1.55 \times 10^6 = 1.550000.$ ← Move the decimal 6 places to the right. Insert zeros as necessary.
$= 1{,}550{,}000$

The temperature at the sun's core is 1,550,000°C.

Check Understanding 1 Write each number in standard form.
a. 3.05×10^5 305,000 **b.** 5×10^4 50,000 **c.** 2.1×10^2 210
d. Reasoning Explain why 1.55×10^6 does not have six zeros when it is written in standard form. Answers may vary. Sample: When you move the decimal point 6 places to the right, it takes 2 moves to get to the right of 0.55.

To write a number in scientific notation, determine the first factor. Then write the second factor as a power of 10.

2 EXAMPLE Writing in Scientific Notation

Computers Supercomputers can now reach speeds of over 35,600,000,000,000 mathematical operations per second. Write this number in scientific notation.

$35{,}600{,}000{,}000{,}000 = 3.5{,}600{,}000{,}000{,}000.$ ← The decimal point moves 13 places to the left.
$= 3.56 \times 10^{13}$ ← Use 13 as the exponent of 10.

The computer can do 3.56×10^{13} operations per second.

Check Understanding 2 **a.** Write 86,400,000 in scientific notation. 8.64×10^7
b. Reasoning When 123.4 and 654.321 are written in scientific notation, why will the exponents on 10 be the same? Answers may vary. Sample: The decimal point in each number needs to move 2 places to the left.

Reaching All Students

Below Level Multiply 7.9 by 10, 100, 1,000, and 10,000 and describe what happens to the location of the decimal point. 79, 790, 7,900, 79,000; moves as many places as there are zeros in the multiple of 10	**Advanced Learners** *How can you add $6 \times 10^3 + 4.2 \times 10^4$ without writing each number in standard form?* Sample: Change 4.2×10^4 to 42×10^3. Then add 42 + 6 to get 48×10^3.	**Inclusion** See note on page 367. **Diversity** See note on page 366.

OBJECTIVE

2 Ordering Numbers in Scientific Notation

To order numbers in scientific notation, first look at their exponents.

Average Distance from the Sun (km)	
Earth	1.496×10^8
Mars	2.279×10^8
Mercury	5.79×10^7
Saturn	1.427×10^9

3 EXAMPLE Ordering in Scientific Notation 

Astronomy Using the chart, order the planets from the least to the greatest distance from the sun.

10^7, 10^8, 10^8, 10^9 ← First, order the exponents from least to greatest.

1.496×10^8, 2.279×10^8 ← Compare any factors with the same power of 10.

$1.496 < 2.279$, so $1.496 \times 10^8 < 2.279 \times 10^8$.

5.79×10^7	Mercury	← Write the numbers in order from least to greatest.
1.496×10^8	Earth	
2.279×10^8	Mars	
1.427×10^9	Saturn	

The order of the planets is Mercury, Earth, Mars, and Saturn.

Check Understanding 3 a. Order this set of numbers from least to greatest. 5.6×10^{10}, 6.2×10^{10}, 9.2×10^{15}, 5.6×10^{21}

5.6×10^{10} 5.6×10^{21} 6.2×10^{10} 9.2×10^{15}

b. Reasoning Why is 1.4×10^5 greater than 9.8×10^4? The exponent of 10 is greater.

EXERCISES

For more practice, see *Extra Practice*.

A Practice by Example

Example 1 (page 366)

Write each number in standard form.

1. 3.2×10^3 3,200
2. 8.1×10^2 810
3. 2.39×10^2 239
4. 5.08×10^4 50,800
5. 8×10^2 800
6. 9.03×10^3 9,030
7. 5.8×10^5 580,000
8. 2.1×10^5 210,000
9. 4.1×10^8 410,000,000
10. 8.004×10^4 80,040
11. 1.004×10^5 100,400
12. 7.145×10^9 7,145,000,000

Example 2 (page 366)

Write each number in scientific notation.

13. 3,000 3×10^3
14. 17,200 1.72×10^4
15. 34,200 3.42×10^4
16. 180,000 1.8×10^5
17. 5,000,000 5×10^6
18. 2,000,000,000 2×10^9
19. 72,000 7.2×10^4
20. 250,100,000 2.501×10^8
21. **Space Travel** The most expensive rocket ever built, the *Saturn V*, cost \$25 billion to build. Write this number in scientific notation. 2.5×10^{10}

Technology Tip
Many calculators automatically display in scientific notation results that require more than 10 digits.

Inclusion
Watch for students who have difficulty reading small-type exponents or who cannot distinguish a comma from a decimal point.

Error Prevention!

To make it clear that you can order two numbers by using the powers of 10 alone (if the exponents are different), have students write these two numbers in standard notation: 1.1×10^3 and 9.9×10^2. Then have them compare them to show that the number times 10^3 is greater.

PowerPoint

Additional Examples

1. At one point, the distance from the Earth to the moon is 1.513431×10^{10} in. Write this number in standard form. 15,134,310,000
2. The diameter of the planet Jupiter is about 142,800 km. Write this number in scientific notation. 1.428×10^5
3. Order the planets from least to greatest in size according to these diameters (in km):

Mars	6.794×10^3
Mercury	4.88×10^3
Saturn	1.2×10^5
Neptune	4.86×10^4

Mercury, Mars, Neptune, Saturn

Closure

- Use an example to explain the differences between standard notation and scientific notation. Answers will vary but should include the fact that a number in scientific notation is the product of a number ≥ 1 and < 10 times a power of 10.
- *How do you compare the size of two numbers in scientific notation?* Sample: Compare the powers of 10. If the exponents are the same, then also compare the first number factors.

3. Practice

Assignment Guide

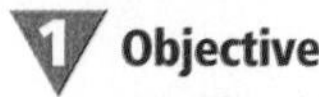 Objective 1

- A B Core 1–21, 31–43
- C Extension 44, 46

 Objective 2

- A B Core 22–30
- C Extension 45, 47

Test Prep 48–51
Mixed Review 52–61

Biology Connection
Exercise 31 Ask a volunteer to draw a diagram of an eye showing the retina.

Practice 7-1 — Scientific Notation

Write each number in scientific notation.

1. 45 — 4.5×10^1
2. 250 — 2.5×10^2
3. 90 — 9×10^1
4. 200 — 2×10^2
5. 670 — 6.7×10^2
6. 4,100 — 4.1×10^3
7. 500 — 5×10^2
8. 3,000 — 3×10^3
9. 43,200 — 4.32×10^4
10. 97,100 — 9.71×10^4
11. 38,050 — 3.805×10^4
12. 90,200 — 9.02×10^4
13. 480,000 — 4.8×10^5
14. 960,000 — 9.6×10^5
15. 8,750,000 — 8.75×10^6
16. 407,000 — 4.07×10^5

Write each number in standard form.

17. 3.1×10^1 — 31
18. 8.07×10^2 — 807
19. 4.96×10^3 — 4,960
20. 8.073×10^2 — 807.3
21. 4.501×10^4 — 45,010
22. 9.7×10^6 — 9,700,000
23. 8.3×10^7 — 83,000,000
24. 3.42×10^4 — 34,200
25. 2.86×10^5 — 286,000
26. 3.58×10^6 — 3,580,000
27. 8.1×10^1 — 81
28. 9.071×10^2 — 907.1
29. 4.83×10^9 — 4,830,000,000
30. 2.73×10^8 — 273,000,000
31. 2.57×10^5 — 257,000
32. 8.09×10^4 — 80,900

Order each set of numbers from least to greatest.

33. $8.9 \times 10^2, 6.3 \times 10^3, 2.1 \times 10^4, 7.8 \times 10^5$
    $8.9 \times 10^2, 6.3 \times 10^3, 2.1 \times 10^4, 7.8 \times 10^5$
34. $2.1 \times 10^4, 2.12 \times 10^3, 3.46 \times 10^5, 2.112 \times 10^2$
    $2.112 \times 10^2, 2.12 \times 10^3, 2.1 \times 10^4, 3.46 \times 10^5$
35. $8.93 \times 10^3, 7.8 \times 10^2, 7.84 \times 10^3, 8.915 \times 10^4$
    $7.8 \times 10^2, 7.84 \times 10^3, 8.93 \times 10^3, 8.915 \times 10^4$

Write each number in scientific notation.

36. The eye's retina contains about 130 million light-sensitive cells. 1.3×10^8 cells
37. A mulberry silkworm can spin a single thread that measures up to 3,900 ft in length. 3.9×10^3 ft

Reteaching 7-1 — Scientific Notation

To write a number such as 67,000 in *scientific notation,* move the decimal point to form a number between 1 and 10. The number of places moved shows which power of 10 to use.

- Write 67,000 in scientific notation.

  6.7 is between 1 and 10. So, move the decimal point in 67,000 to the left 4 places and multiply by 10^4.

  $67{,}000 = 6.7 \times 10^4$

To write scientific notation in *standard form,* look at the exponent. The exponent shows the number of places and the direction to move the decimal point.

- Write 8.5×10^5 in standard form.

  The exponent is positive 5, so move the decimal point 5 places to the right.

  $8.5 \times 10^5 = 850{,}000$

Write each number in scientific notation.

1. 6,500 — 6.5×10^3
2. 65,000 — 6.5×10^4
3. 6,520 — 6.52×10^3
4. 345 — 3.45×10^2
5. 29,100 — 2.91×10^4
6. 93,000,000 — 9.3×10^7
7. 200 — 2×10^2
8. 2,300 — 2.3×10^3
9. 23,000 — 2.3×10^4
10. 450 — 4.5×10^2
11. 90,000 — 9×10^4
12. 96,000 — 9.6×10^4

Write each number in standard form.

13. 4×10^4 — 40,000
14. 4×10^5 — 400,000
15. 3.6×10^3 — 3,600
16. 4.85×10^4 — 48,500
17. 4.05×10^2 — 405
18. 7.1×10^5 — 710,000
19. 4×10^2 — 400
20. 1.3×10^2 — 130
21. 7×10^1 — 70
22. 2.5×10^3 — 2,500
23. 1.81×10^3 — 1,810
24. 1.6×10^4 — 16,000
25. Jupiter is on the average 7.783×10^8 kilometers from the sun. 778,300,000 km

Which number is greater?

26. 5×10^2 or 2×10^5 — 2×10^5
27. 2.1×10^3 or 2.1×10^6 — 2.1×10^6
28. 6×10^{10} or 3×10^9 — 6×10^{10}
29. 3.6×10^1 or 3.6×10^3 — 3.6×10^3

Example 3 (page 367)

Order each set of numbers from least to greatest. 22–24. See below left.

22. 4.53×10^4, 3.27×10^3, 9.36×10^4
23. 7.3×10^{25}, 8.17×10^{21}, 8.29×10^{21}
24. 1.02×10^5, 1.2×10^4, 2.1×10^5

B Apply Your Skills

Number Sense **Which number is greater?**

25. 2×10^6 or 8×10^8 8×10^8
26. 4.1×10^4 or 4.0×10^5 4.0×10^5
27. 3.14×10^{99} or 3×10^{100} 3×10^{100}
28. 2×10^3 or 3×10^2 2×10^3
29. 182 thousand or 1.82×10^6 1.82×10^6
30. 400 thousand or 4×10^6 4×10^6

31. **Optometry** The eye's retina holds about 130 million light-sensitive cells. Write this number in scientific notation. 1.3×10^8

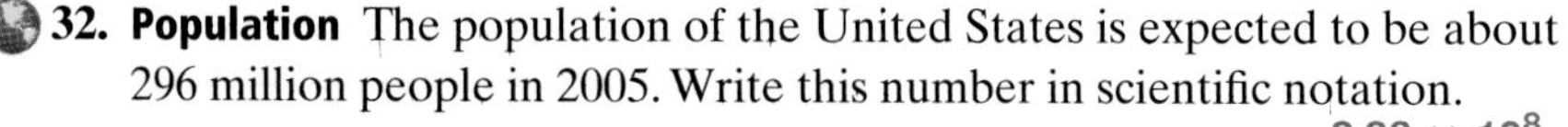

32. **Population** The population of the United States is expected to be about 296 million people in 2005. Write this number in scientific notation. 2.96×10^8

33. Error Analysis Explain why 492×10^5 is not in scientific notation. 492 is not between 1 and 10

34. **Astronomy** When the sun emits a solar flare, the blast wave travels through space at 3×10^6 km/h. Use the formula $d = r \cdot t$ to find how far it will go in 30 min. 1.5×10^6 km

GPS

Real-World Connection
Careers Optometrists use mathematics when they fit patients with glasses and contact lenses.

Find each value of n.

35. $4.812 \times 10^n = 481{,}200$ 5
36. $8{,}300 = 8.3 \times 10^n$ 3
37. $56{,}194 = n \times 10^4$ 5.6194
38. $245 = n \times 10^2$ 2.45
39. $1.0035 \times 10^n = 100{,}350{,}000$ 8
40. $3{,}000 = n \times 10^n$ 3
41. $5 \times 10^n = 50$ 1
42. $3 \times 10^5 = n$ 300,000

43. Data File, p. 363 When you take a 10-minute shower, you use about 2,000 kilocalories to heat 50 gallons of water. About how many Calories do you use in a 5-minute shower? Write the number in scientific notation. 1×10^6

C Challenge

44. Patterns Write each expression in scientific notation.
    a. $10^4 - 10^3$ 9×10^3
    b. $10^5 - 10^4$ 9×10^4
    c. $10^6 - 10^5$ 9×10^5
    d. $10^{29} - 10^{28}$ 9×10^{28}

45. **Writing in Math** A number written in scientific notation is multiplied by 100. Explain what happens to the power of 10. It increases by two.

46. The number 10^{100} is called a *googol*. Find the number of digits when a googol is written in standard form. 101 digits

47. Stretch Your Thinking Martina went shopping. She spent a fifth of what she had in her wallet and then a fifth of what remained. In all, she spent \$36. How much did she start with? \$100

22. 3.27×10^3, 4.53×10^4, 9.36×10^4
23. 8.17×10^{21}, 8.29×10^{21}, 7.3×10^{25}
24. 1.2×10^4, 1.02×10^5, 2.1×10^5

Use the Guided Problem Solving worksheet with Exercise 34.

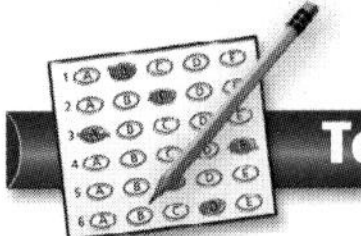

Test Prep

Reading Comprehension **Read the passage and answer the questions below.**

Languages of the World

What language do most people in the world speak? Although 341 million people speak English as their first language, it is not the most commonly spoken language in the world. Mandarin, a Chinese dialect, has the most native speakers. In 2001, about 874 million people spoke Mandarin worldwide. Hindi also has more native speakers in the world than English. Over 366 million people speak Hindi in 17 different countries.

51. [2] 380,000,000 m; 3.8×10^8 m
[1] only one correct answer

48. Use scientific notation to express the number of Mandarin speakers in the world. 8.74×10^8

49. What is the average number of people per country who speak Hindi in the countries where Hindi has native speakers? Express your answer in standard form. 22,000,000

Take It to the NET
Online lesson quiz at
www.PHSchool.com
Web Code: aca-0701

50. Which of the following is the same as the number of people who speak English as their first language? C

A. 3.41×10^6	**B.** 3.41×10^7
C. 3.41×10^8	**D.** 3.41×10^9

Short Response

51. The moon is about 380,000 km from Earth.
   a. Find the distance in meters.
   b. Write the distance in meters in scientific notation. See above left.

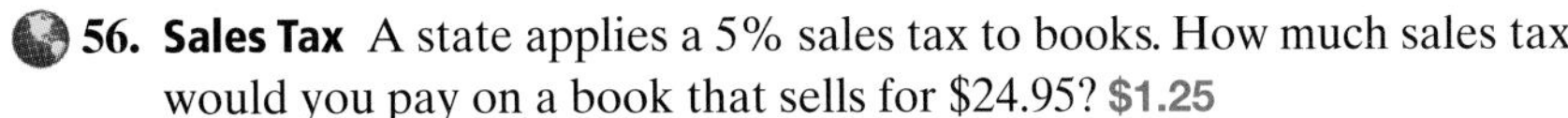

Mixed Review

Lesson 6-4 **Algebra** **Use an equation to solve each problem.**

52. What percent of 30 is 15? 50
53. 15 is what percent of 75? 20
54. 12 is 24% of what number? 50
55. What number is 8% of 200? 16

56. **Sales Tax** A state applies a 5% sales tax to books. How much sales tax would you pay on a book that sells for \$24.95? \$1.25

Lesson 6-1 **Write each percent as a decimal.**

57. 4% 0.04
58. 8.2% 0.082
59. 274% 2.74
60. 0.05% 0.0005

Lesson 5-5

61. **Algebra** A computer program can enlarge photos. The photo you want to enlarge is 3 inches wide by 5 inches high. The enlargement can be at most 11 inches high. How wide can the photo be?
at most 6.6 inches wide

4. Assess

PowerPoint **Lesson Quiz 7-1**

1. Write 7.304×10^2 in standard form. 730.4
2. Write 41,700,000,000 in scientific notation. 4.17×10^{10}
3. Order the following numbers from least to greatest.
   8.5×10^4
   2.9×10^6
   3×10^4
   3×10^4, 8.5×10^4, 2.9×10^6

Alternative Assessment

Each partner in a pair writes a positive integer with six to ten digits. Partner exchange papers and write six to ten zeros to the right of the number. Partners exchange papers again and write in scientific notation the number they see.

Test Prep

Resources
For additional practice with a variety of test item formats:
- Test Prep, p. 401
- Test-Taking Strategies, p. 397
- Test-Taking Strategies with Transparencies

Enrichment 7-1 Scientific Notation

Critical Thinking

A Russian cosmonaut spent 439 days in space, returning to the earth in March of 1995.

a. How many hours did he spend in space? Write your answer in standard notation.
b. How many minutes did he spend in space? Write this answer in scientific notation.

1. What are you asked to do? Find the number of hours and minutes in 439 days.
2. How can you find how many hours are in
   a. 2 days? 2×24 b. 439 days? 439×24
3. How can you find how many minutes are in
   a. 2 days? $2(60 \times 24)$ b. 439 days? $439(60 \times 24)$
4. How many hours did the cosmonaut spend in space? 10,536 hours
5. How many minutes did the cosmonaut spend in space? 632,160 minutes
6. Write the number of minutes in scientific notation. 6.3216×10^5
7. Why did you write the number of minutes in standard notation before writing it in scientific notation? The operations used to find the answer were performed on numbers written in standard notation; only one conversion needed to be done.
8. Kate's birthday is February 29. She was born in a leap year.
   a. How many days does she have to wait between birthdays? Write this answer in standard notation. 1,460 d
   b. How many minutes does she have to wait between birthdays? Write this answer in scientific notation. 2.1024×10^6 min

7-2

1. Plan

Lesson Preview

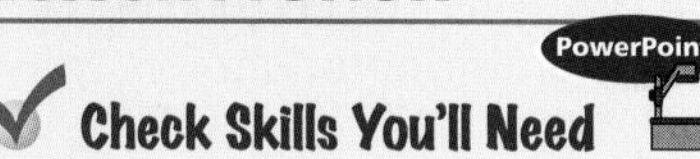

Check Skills You'll Need
Simplifying Expressions With Exponents
Lesson 1-7: Examples 2–3. Extra Practice, p. 702.

Lesson Resources

Teaching Resources
Practice, Reteaching, Enrichment
Checkpoint Quiz 1

Reaching All Students
Practice Workbook 7-2
Spanish Practice Workbook 7-2
Reading and Math Literacy 7B
Spanish Reading and Math Literacy 7B
Spanish Checkpoint Quiz 1
Guided Problem Solving 7-2

Presentation Assistant Plus!
Transparencies
- Check Skills You'll Need 7-2
- Problem of the Day 7-2
- Additional Examples 7-2
- Student Edition Answers 7-2
- Lesson Quiz 7-2
- Classroom Aid 11

PH Presentation Pro CD-ROM 7-2

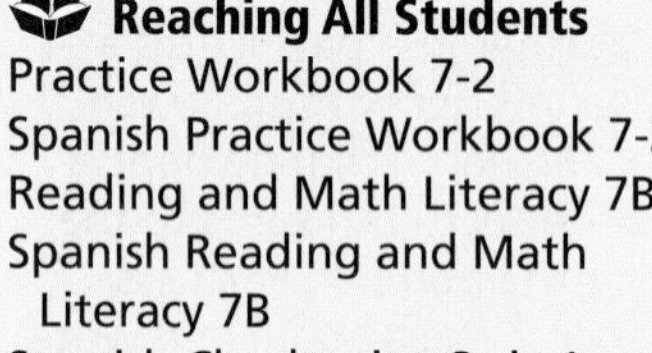

Checkpoint Quiz 1
Computer Test Generator CD

Technology
Resource Pro® CD-ROM
Computer Test Generator CD
PH Presentation Pro CD-ROM

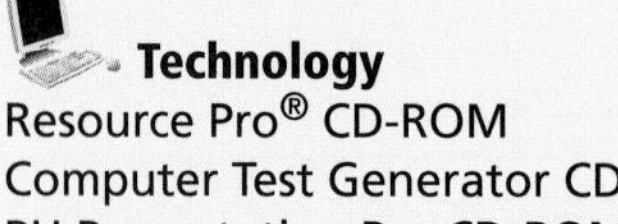

www.PHSchool.com
Student Site
- Teacher Web Code: ack-5500
- Self-grading Lesson Quiz

PH SuccessNet Teacher Center
- Lesson Planner
- Resources

Plus 

7-2 Exponents and Multiplication

What You'll Learn

To multiply powers with the same base

To multiply numbers in scientific notation

. . . And Why

To find how many feet are in a light-year, as in Example 3

Check Skills You'll Need

For help, go to Lesson 1-7.

Simplify each expression.

1. $2^3 \cdot 5^2$ 200
2. $(-3)^2$ 9
3. -3^2 −9
4. -1^4 −1
5. $(-1)^4$ 1
6. $3 \cdot 3^2$ 27
7. Explain why -4^4 is a negative number and $(-4)^4$ is a positive number. -4^4 means $-1 \cdot 4^4$, and $(-4)^4$ means $(-4)(-4)(-4)(-4)$.

 Interactive lesson includes instant self-check, tutorials, and activities.

OBJECTIVE 1

Multiplying Powers With the Same Base

Investigation: Exploring Exponents

1. Copy and complete the table below.

Exponent Form	Product as a Repeated Factor	Standard Form	Power of 2
$2^1 \cdot 2^1$	$2 \cdot 2$	4	2^2
$2^1 \cdot 2^2$	$2 \cdot 2 \cdot 2$ ■	8 ■	2^3 ■
$2^2 \cdot 2^2$	$2 \cdot 2 \cdot 2 \cdot 2$	16	2^4 ■
$2^2 \cdot 2^3$	■	32 ■	2^5 ■

$2 \cdot 2 \cdot 2 \cdot 2 \cdot 2$

2. Patterns For each row, what relationship do you see between the sum of the exponents for 2 in the first column and the exponent for 2 in the last column? The sum of the exponents in column 1 is equal to the exponent in column 4.

Need Help?
3^2 ← exponent
↑
base

In Lesson 1-7, you learned how to simplify expressions with exponents. In this lesson, you will learn how to simplify the products of powers that have the same base.

You can write the expression $3^2 \cdot 3^4$ using a single exponent.

$$3^2 \cdot 3^4 = (3 \cdot 3)(3 \cdot 3 \cdot 3 \cdot 3) = 3^6$$

The two factors of 3 together with four factors of 3 give a total of six factors of 3. Notice that the exponent 6 is equal to the sum of the exponents 2 and 4.

Ongoing Assessment and Intervention

Before the Lesson
Diagnose prerequisite skills using:
- Check Skills You'll Need

During the Lesson
Monitor progress using:
- Check Understanding
- Additional Examples
- Test Prep

After the Lesson
Assess knowledge using:
- Lesson Quiz
- Computer Test Generator CD
- Chapter Checkpoint 1 (p. 374)

You can use the following rule to simplify expressions that are the product of powers with the same base.

Test-Prep Tip
If you forget the exponent rules, writing out the factors may help.

Key Concepts **Multiplying Powers With the Same Base**

To multiply numbers or variables with the same base, add the exponents.

Arithmetic	Algebra
$3^2 \cdot 3^7 = 3^{(2+7)} = 3^9$	$a^m \cdot a^n = a^{(m+n)}$

1 EXAMPLE **Multiplying Powers**

Write each expression using a single exponent.

a. $(-2)^3 \cdot (-2)^5$

$(-2)^3 \cdot (-2)^5 = (-2)^{(3+5)}$ ← Add the exponents.

$= (-2)^8$ ← Simplify the exponent.

b. $a^1 \cdot a^4$

Add the exponents. → $a^1 \cdot a^4 = a^{(1+4)}$

Simplify the exponent. → $= a^5$

Check Understanding 1 Write each expression using a single exponent.

a. $6^2 \cdot 6^3$ 6^5 **b.** $(-4) \cdot (-4)^7$ $(-4)^8$ **c.** $m^1 \cdot m^{11}$ m^{12}

d. Reasoning Explain why you cannot write $5^3 \cdot 7^9$ as $(35)^{12}$. The bases are not the same.

OBJECTIVE

2 Multiplying Numbers in Scientific Notation

The rule for multiplying powers with the same base applies to multiplying numbers in scientific notation.

2 EXAMPLE **Multiplying Numbers in Scientific Notation**

Find the product $(5 \times 10^6)(9 \times 10^3)$. Write the result in scientific notation.

$(5 \times 10^6)(9 \times 10^3) = (5 \cdot 9) \times (10^6 \cdot 10^3)$ ← Use the Associative and Commutative properties.

$= 45 \times (10^6 \cdot 10^3)$ ← Multiply 5 and 9.

$= 45 \times 10^9$ ← Add the exponents for the powers of 10.

$= 4.5 \times 10^1 \times 10^9$ ← Write 45 in scientific notation.

$= 4.5 \times 10^{10}$ ← Add the exponents.

Check Understanding 2 Multiply. Write each result in scientific notation.

a. $(2 \times 10^6)(4 \times 10^3)$ 8×10^9 **b.** $(3 \times 10^5)(2 \times 10^8)$ 6×10^{13} **c.** $12(8 \times 10^{20})$ 9.6×10^{21}

You can multiply numbers in scientific notation to find solutions to real-world problems. Multiplying very large or very small numbers in scientific notation is easier than multiplying the same numbers in standard form.

Reaching All Students

Below Level Have students review the vocabulary for powers by naming the parts of 2^5 and finding the value. 2 is the base; 5 is the exponent; the value is 32.

Advanced Learners Have students prove that $\frac{2^7}{2^5} = 2^2$.

$\frac{2^7}{2^5} = \frac{2 \cdot 2 \cdot 2 \cdot 2 \cdot 2 \cdot 2 \cdot 2}{2 \cdot 2 \cdot 2 \cdot 2 \cdot 2} = \frac{2 \cdot 2}{1} = 2^2$

Inclusion
See note on page 371.
Auditory Learners
See note on page 371.

2. Teach

Math Background

Two exponential expressions with different exponents can be combined only when the bases are identical. So x^3 and y^2 cannot be combined unless you have values for the variables.

On the other hand, x^3 and x^2 can be multiplied (or divided) by adding (or subtracting) the exponents. But the quantities x^3 and x^2 cannot be added or subtracted.

Teaching Notes

Investigation (Optional)
Have students read aloud the expressions in the first and last columns of the table. This way they learn to say correctly, for example, "2 to the 1st power; 2 to the 2nd power, or 2 squared; 2 to the 3rd power, or 2 cubed."

Inclusion
Some students may think incorrectly that, for example, $2^2 \times 2^3$ should be 4^5. Have them write $(2 \times 2) \times (2 \times 2 \times 2)$ and compare it to $4 \times 4 \times 4 \times 4 \times 4$.

1 EXAMPLE Error Prevention!

Emphasize that adding the exponents is done *instead of* multiplying, so that you do not also multiply the bases. This means that the base remains unchanged and the two negatives are *not* multiplied.

2 EXAMPLE Auditory Learners

Ask a volunteer to explain why you multiply 5 and 9 but add the 6 and the 3. Sample: Adding the exponents is the way to multiply the powers.

PowerPoint

Additional Examples

1 Write each expression using a single exponent.

a. $(-3)^2 \cdot (-3)^4$ $(-3)^6$

b. $k^2 \cdot k^3$ k^5

2 Find the product $(3 \times 10^3)(7 \times 10^5)$. Write the result in scientific notation. 2.1×10^9

3 EXAMPLE Error Prevention!

Have students discuss whether a light year is a measure of time or of distance. distance

PowerPoint

Additional Examples

3 A light year is 5.9×10^{12} miles. A mile is 1.609×10^3 meters. How many meters are in a light year? Write your answer in scientific notation.
9.5×10^{15} m

Closure

- *How do you multiply powers with the same base?* Add the exponents.
- *What are the steps in multiplying numbers in scientific notation?* Sample: First, group the numbers and the powers of ten; second, multiply the numbers and multiply the powers by adding the exponents; third, write the product in scientific notation.

Einstein's famous formula, $E = mc^2$, relates energy, mass, and the speed of light.

3 EXAMPLE Real-World Problem Solving

Science A light-year, the distance light travels in one Earth year, is 5.9×10^{12} miles. A mile is 5.28×10^3 feet. How many feet are in a light-year? Write your answer in scientific notation.

$(5.9 \times 10^{12}) \cdot (5.28 \times 10^3)$ ← **Use dimensional analysis: mi $\cdot \frac{\text{ft}}{\text{mi}}$ = ft.**

$= (5.9 \cdot 5.28) \times (10^{12} \cdot 10^3)$ ← **Use the Associative and Commutative properties.**

$\approx 31.2 \times (10^{12} \times 10^3)$ ← **Multiply 5.9 and 5.28. Round to the nearest tenth.**

$= 31.2 \times 10^{15}$ ← **Add exponents of the powers of 10.**

$= 3.12 \times 10^1 \times 10^{15}$ ← **Write 31.1 in scientific notation.**

$= 3.12 \times 10^{16}$ ← **Add the exponents.**

There are about 3.12×10^{16} feet in a light-year.

Check Understanding 3 **a. Astronomy** The speed of light is 3.00×10^5 kilometers/second. Use the formula $d = r \cdot t$ to find the distance light travels in 3.6×10^3 seconds. 1.08×10^9 km

b. Mental Math Multiply 4.17×10^{20} by 10^3. 4.17×10^{23}

EXERCISES

For more practice, see *Extra Practice*.

A Practice by Example

Example 1 (page 371)

Write each expression using a single exponent.

1. $7^2 \cdot 7^8$ 7^{10} **2.** $(-2)^8 \cdot (-2)^3$ $(-2)^{11}$ **3.** $(-6)^2 \cdot (-6)^2$ $(-6)^4$ **4.** $4^5 \cdot 4^6$ 4^{11}

5. $y^3 \cdot y^5$ y^8 **6.** $m^{10} \cdot m^{100}$ m^{110} **7.** $3.4^3 \cdot 3.4^{10}$ 3.4^{13} **8.** $12^5 \cdot 12^{50}$ 12^{55}

9. $4.5^{10} \cdot 4.5^{10}$ 4.5^{20} **10.** $(-5)^5 \cdot (-5)$ $(-5)^6$ **11.** $0.4^5 \cdot 0.4^{10}$ 0.4^{15} **12.** $(2x) \cdot (2x)^2$ $(2x)^3$

Examples 2, 3 (pages 371, 372)

Multiply. Write each result in scientific notation.

13. $(2 \times 10^3)(4 \times 10^6)$ 8×10^9 **14.** $(7 \times 10^2)(9 \times 10^5)$ 6.3×10^8

15. $90(8 \times 10^9)$ 7.2×10^{11} **16.** $(3 \times 10^5)(5 \times 10^7)$ 1.5×10^{13}

17. $(9 \times 10^5)(5 \times 10^9)$ 4.5×10^{15} **18.** $(5.1 \times 10^4)(2 \times 10^7)$ 1.02×10^{12}

19. Earth Science There are about 4.8×10^{19} cubic feet of water on Earth. One cubic foot of water contains about 9.47×10^{26} water molecules. Approximately how many water molecules are there on Earth? about 4.55×10^{46} molecules

B Apply Your Skills

Use <, >, or = to complete each statement.

20. 4^6 ■ $4^3 \cdot 4^2$ > **21.** 36 ■ $6^2 \cdot 6^2$ < **22.** $2^3 \cdot 2^2$ ■ 4^5 < **23.** 5^{16} ■ $5^8 \cdot 5^2$ >

24. Double the number 3.4×10^{12}. Write the answer in scientific notation. 6.8×10^{12}

Real-World Connection

American Sign Language was developed in the early 1800s by Thomas Gallaudet.

Order each set of numbers from least to greatest. (*Hint:* Where necessary, first write numbers in scientific notation.)

25. 78×10^2, 6.3×10^3, 725 — 725, 6.3×10^3, 78×10^2

26. 39.8×10^5, 421×10^2, 285.6×10^4 — See below left.

27. 1.244×10^{12}, 24.45×10^{11}, 175.4×10^{10} — 1.244×10^{12}, 175.4×10^{10}, 24.45×10^{11}

28. Geography The Sahara Desert is about 3.5 million square miles in area. There are about 2.79×10^7 square feet in a square mile. About how many square feet does the Sahara Desert cover? Write your answer in scientific notation. 9.765×10^{13}

GPS

Write each expression using a single exponent for each base.

29. $4^x \cdot 4^t$ 4^{x+t} **30.** $3^m \cdot 3^n$ 3^{m+n} **31.** $1.5^8 \cdot 1.5^t$ 1.5^{8+t} **32.** $(-4)^x \cdot (-4)^y$ $(-4)^{x+y}$

33. $2^3 \cdot 2 \cdot 2^8$ 2^{12} **34.** $a^5 \cdot a^4 \cdot a$ a^{10} **35.** $9^{12} \cdot 9^6 \cdot 9^3$ 9^{21} **36.** $3^a \cdot 3^{2a} \cdot 3^{3a}$ 3^{6a}

37. $xy \cdot x^2y^3$ x^3y^4 **38.** $c^2d \cdot cd^3$ c^3d^4 **39.** $x \cdot x^3 \cdot x^5$ x^9 **40.** $3x^2 \cdot x^5 \cdot x$ $3x^8$

26. 421×10^2, 285.6×10^4, 39.8×10^5

41. Open-Ended Give three different ways to write 4^{12} as the product of two powers. Answers may vary. Sample: $4 \cdot 4^{11}$; $4^2 \cdot 4^{10}$; $4^6 \cdot 4^6$.

42. Error Analysis A student simplified $5^2 \cdot 5^4$ as 25^6. Explain the error. See below left.

Challenge

43. Science Einstein's Law states that $E = mc^2$. Find the value of E when $m = 1$ kilogram and $c = 3.00 \times 10^8$ meters per second. 9×10^{16} kg · m² per s²

42. Instead of just adding the exponents, he multiplied the bases and then added the exponents.

44. If $(h + h) \cdot (h \cdot h) = 16$, find the value of h. 2

45. Stretch Your Thinking In 10 seconds, a blade of a ceiling fan moves through 60 right angles. How many complete revolutions does the blade make in one minute? 90 revolutions

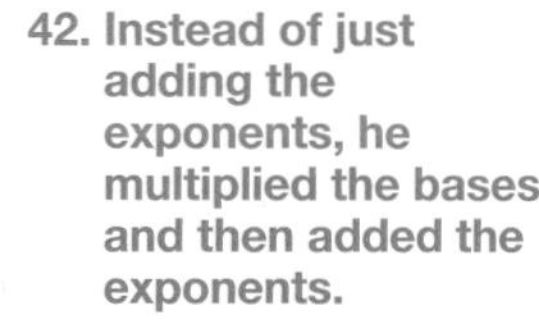

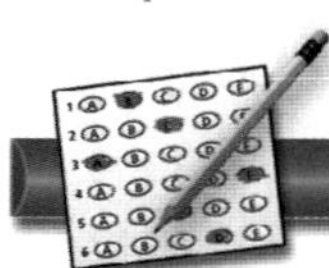

Test Prep

Multiple Choice

46. Which of the following is equal to 39×10^5? D

A. 3,900 B. 39,000 C. 390,000 D. 3,900,000

47. Computers store information in bits: 2^3 bits equals 1 byte, and 2^{10} bytes equals 1 kilobyte. How many bits are in 1 kilobyte? F

F. 2^{13} G. 2^{30} H. 4^{13} I. 4^{30}

Take It to the NET

Online lesson quiz at www.PHSchool.com

Web Code: aca-0702

48. Which of the following is equal to $(-b)^3 \cdot (-b)^{10}$? C

A. b^{13} B. b^{30} C. $(-b)^{13}$ D. $(-b)^{30}$

49. Which of the following is equal to $(3y)^a \cdot (3y)^{2a}$? G

F. $(3y)^{6a}$ G. $(3y)^{3a}$ H. $(9y^2)^{3a}$ I. $(6y)^{3a}$

Short Response

50. There are about 5×10^{10} white blood cells and about 500 times as many red blood cells in a human's bloodstream. **(a)** Write an equation to find the number of red blood cells. **(b)** Solve your equation. Express your answer in scientific notation. See margin.

50. [2] $r = 500(5 \times 10^{10})$; 2.5×10^{13}

[1] only one correct answer

Use the Guided Problem Solving worksheet with Exercise 28.

3. Practice

Assignment Guide

Objective 1

A B Core 1–12, 20–23, 29–42

C Extension 44

Objective 2

A B Core 13–19, 24–28

C Extension 43, 45

Test Prep 46–50

Mixed Review 51–63

Earth Science Connection

Exercise 19 Discuss major water sources such as glaciers and oceans.

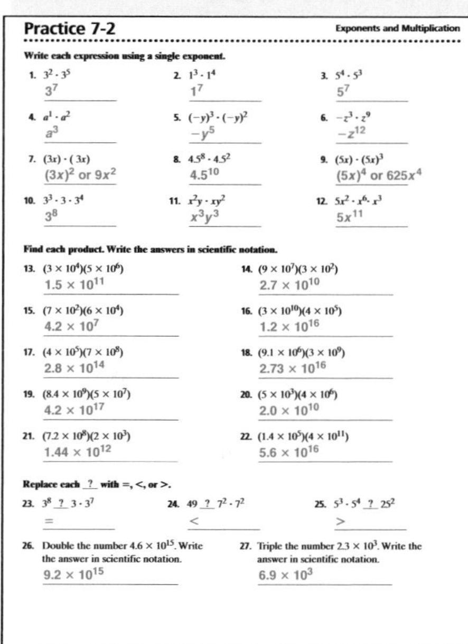

Practice 7-2 Exponents and Multiplication

Write each expression using a single exponent.

1. $3^2 \cdot 3^5$ 3^7
2. $1^3 \cdot 1^4$ 1^7
3. $5^4 \cdot 5^3$ 5^7
4. $a^1 \cdot a^2$ a^3
5. $(-y)^3 \cdot (-y)^2$ $-y^5$
6. $-z^3 \cdot z^9$ $-z^{12}$
7. $(3x) \cdot (3x)$ $(3x)^2$ or $9x^2$
8. $4.5^8 \cdot 4.5^2$ 4.5^{10}
9. $(5x) \cdot (5x)^3$ $(5x)^4$ or $625x^4$
10. $3^3 \cdot 3 \cdot 3^4$ 3^8
11. $x^2y \cdot xy^2$ x^3y^3
12. $5x^2 \cdot x^6 \cdot x^3$ $5x^{11}$

Find each product. Write the answers in scientific notation.

13. $(3 \times 10^4)(5 \times 10^6)$ 1.5×10^{11}
14. $(9 \times 10^7)(3 \times 10^2)$ 2.7×10^{10}
15. $(7 \times 10^2)(6 \times 10^4)$ 4.2×10^7
16. $(3 \times 10^{10})(4 \times 10^5)$ 1.2×10^{16}
17. $(4 \times 10^5)(7 \times 10^8)$ 2.8×10^{14}
18. $(9.1 \times 10^6)(3 \times 10^9)$ 2.73×10^{16}
19. $(8.4 \times 10^9)(5 \times 10^7)$ 4.2×10^{17}
20. $(5 \times 10^3)(4 \times 10^6)$ 2.0×10^{10}
21. $(7.2 \times 10^8)(2 \times 10^3)$ 1.44×10^{12}
22. $(1.4 \times 10^5)(4 \times 10^{11})$ 5.6×10^{16}

Replace each ? with =, <, or >.

23. 3^8 ? $3 \cdot 3^7$ $=$
24. 49 ? $7^2 \cdot 7^2$ $<$
25. $5^3 \cdot 5^4$? 25^2 $>$
26. Double the number 4.6×10^{15}. Write the answer in scientific notation. 9.2×10^{15}
27. Triple the number 2.3×10^3. Write the answer in scientific notation. 6.9×10^3

Reteaching 7-2 Exponents and Multiplication

- To multiply numbers or variables with the same base, add the exponents.

Simplify $3^2 \cdot 3^4$. $3^2 \cdot 3^4 = 3^{(2+4)} = 3^6$

Simplify $n^3 \cdot n^4$. $n^3 \cdot n^4 = n^{(3+4)} = n^7$

Simplify $-4^3 \cdot -4^5$. $-4^3 \cdot -4^5 = -4^{(3+5)} = -4^8$

- To multiply numbers in scientific notation.

Find the product $(5 \times 10^4)(7 \times 10^5)$. Write the result in scientific notation.

$(5 \times 10^4)(7 \times 10^5)$

$(5 \cdot 7)(10^4 \cdot 10^5)$ ← Use the Associative and Commutative properties.

$35 \times (10^4 \cdot 10^5)$ ← Multiply 5 and 7.

$35 \times 10^{4+5}$ ← Add the exponents for the powers of 10.

35×10^9

$3.5 \times 10^1 \times 10^9$ ← Write 35 in scientific notation.

3.5×10^{10} ← Add the exponents.

Write each expression using a single exponent.

1. $5^3 \cdot 5^4$ 5^7
2. $a^2 \cdot a^5$ a^7
3. $(-8)^4 \cdot (-8)^5$ $(-8)^9$
4. $n^6 \cdot n^2$ n^8
5. $m^3 \cdot m^6$ m^9
6. $(-7)^4 \cdot (-7)^2$ $(-7)^6$
7. $(-3)^2 \cdot (-3)^2$ $(-3)^4$
8. $2^5 \cdot 2^2$ 2^7
9. $c^5 \cdot c^3$ c^8
10. $7^5 \cdot 7^9$ 7^{14}
11. $n^3 \cdot n^{11}$ n^{14}
12. $3^5 \cdot 3^2$ 3^7

Find each product. Write the answer in scientific notation.

13. $(3 \times 10^4)(5 \times 10^3)$ 1.5×10^8
14. $(2 \times 10^3)(7 \times 10^6)$ 1.4×10^{10}
15. $(8 \times 10^2)(5 \times 10^2)$ 4.0×10^5
16. $(9 \times 10^4)(7 \times 10^4)$ 6.3×10^9
17. $(4 \times 10^2)(7 \times 10^5)$ 2.8×10^8
18. $(8 \times 10^3)(4 \times 10^5)$ 3.2×10^9

4. Assess

Lesson Quiz 7-2

1. Write $(-8)^4 \cdot (-8)^5$ using a single exponent. $(-8)^9$
2. Write the product of (8.2×10^6) and (5×10^2) in scientific notation. 4.1×10^9
3. The speed of light is 3.00×10^5 km/s. Find the distance light travels in 8×10^2 seconds. 2.4×10^8 km

Chapter Checkpoint

To check understanding of Lessons 7-1 to 7-2:

Checkpoint Quiz 1 (p. 374)

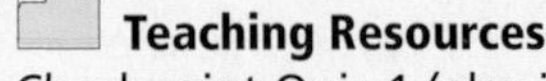

Teaching Resources
Checkpoint Quiz 1 (also in *Prentice Hall Assessment System*)

Reaching All Students
Reading and Math Literacy 7B

Spanish versions available

Exercise 49 Remind students that $a = 1a$.

Enrichment 7-2 — Exponents and Multiplication

Critical Thinking

Arrange each of the following numbers from greatest to least. Explain your answer.

a. 1.24×10^{-3} b. 2.24×10^{-2} c. 1.89×10^{-4} d. 2.6×10^{-2}

1. Are these numbers written in standard or scientific notation?
   scientific
2. Which of the numbers are positive?
   All of the numbers are positive.
3. Compare 10^{-4} and 10^{-3}. Which number is greater?
   $10^{-3} > 10^{-4}$
4. How can you use the exponents to compare powers of ten?
   The number having the larger exponent is the greater number.
5. Compare 1.6×10^{-2} and 2.6×10^{-2}. Which number is greater?
   2.6×10^{-2}
6. When the powers of 10 of two numbers written in scientific notation are the same, how can you compare the numbers?
   The number with the greater first factor is the greater number.
7. Use your insights from Exercises 2, 4, and 6 to order the numbers.
   $2.6 \times 10^{-2}, 2.24 \times 10^{-2}, 1.24 \times 10^{-3}, 1.89 \times 10^{-4}$
8. How could you have found the answer using a different method?
   Change all numbers to standard notation before comparing.
9. Arrange these numbers from least to greatest.
   a. 1.9×10^{-3} b. 2.5×10^{-4} c. 1.2×10^{-2} d. 2.8×10^{-4}
   $2.5 \times 10^{-4}, 2.8 \times 10^{-4}, 1.9 \times 10^{-3}, 1.2 \times 10^{-2}$

Mixed Review

Lesson 6-2 **Estimate each percent using decimals.** 51–53. Answers may vary. Samples are given.

51. 49% of 28 14 **52.** 18% of 45 9 **53.** 53% of 240 120

Estimate each percent using fractions. 54–56. Answers may vary. Samples are given.

54. 11% of 35 4 **55.** 29% of 150 45 **56.** 78% of 440 330

Lesson 5-9 **Algebra** **In each figure, use the sine or cosine ratios to find n to the nearest tenth.**

57. about 23

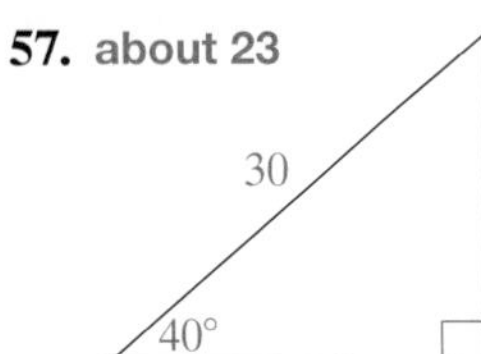

58. about 6.9

8, n, 60°

Lesson 5-1 **Choose a Method** **Use a calculator, paper and pencil, or mental math to find each unit rate.**

59. \$75 for 15 books \$5 per book **60.** 150 mi in 3.5 h 42.86 mi/h

61. \$150 for 250 lb \$.60 per lb **62.** 25 cents for 0.2 oz \$1.25 per oz

63. Consumer Issues A brand of cereal costs \$2.35 for 10.5 oz. Another brand costs \$1.95 for 8.2 oz. Find the unit price of each brand and determine which one is the better buy.
\$.22/oz; \$.24/oz; the first brand

Checkpoint Quiz 1 — Lessons 7-1 through 7-2

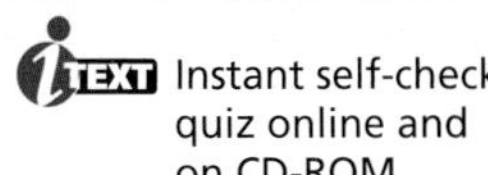

Instant self-check quiz online and on CD-ROM

Write each number in scientific notation.

1. 4,201,000,000 4.201×10^9 **2.** 4.8 million 4.8×10^6

3. 21 billion 2.1×10^{10} **4.** $7 \cdot (2 \times 10^8)$ 1.4×10^9

Write each expression using a single exponent.

5. $3^6 \cdot 3^8$ 3^{14} **6.** $t^4 \cdot t^8$ t^{12} **7.** $h^{4w} \cdot h^{2w}$ h^{6w} **8.** $(-9)^2 \cdot (-9)^3$ $(-9)^5$

9. Writing in Math Explain why $5 \cdot 5^t$ is equal to 5^{1+t}.
9. $5 \cdot 5^t = 5^1 \cdot 5^t$. Since the bases are the same, you add the exponents.

10. Football There are about 2.65×10^{32} possible ways a 30-player football team can form a line to run onto the field. When a thirty-first player is included, there will be about $31 \cdot (2.65 \times 10^{32})$ possible ways. Write this number in scientific notation. 8.215×10^{33}

Alternative Assessment

Each student in a pair writes a number in scientific notation. Partners then together find the product of their numbers.

Test Prep

Resources
For additional practice with a variety of test item formats:
- Test Prep, p. 401
- Test-Taking Strategies, p. 397
- Test-Taking Strategies with Transparencies

Technology Scientific Notation

For Use With Lesson 7-2

Calculators use scientific notation as a shorthand way to write very large numbers. If you enter a number with too many digits for a calculator to display, the calculator will use scientific notation to display the rounded number.

2346549887051 ENTER → 2.346549887E12 ← **The display shows the number rounded.**

The number in the display is $2.346549887 \times 10^{12}$. The 12 after the E is the exponent on 10.

You can use your calculator to simplify expressions in scientific notation.

1 EXAMPLE Multiplying Numbers in Scientific Notation

Use a calculator to find $(7.6 \times 10^6)(3.52 \times 10^3)$.

$(7.6 \times 10^6)(3.52 \times 10^3)$

7.6 EE 6 × 3.52 EE 3 ← **Use EE to enter the exponent of the power of 10.**

2.6752E10

The product is 2.6752×10^{10}.

2 EXAMPLE Adding Numbers in Scientific Notation

Use a calculator to find $(2.8 \times 10^{12}) + (4.9 \times 10^{15})$.

2.8 EE 12 + 4.9 EE 15

4.9028E15

The sum is 4.9028×10^{15}.

EXERCISES

Use a calculator to simplify. Write your answer in scientific notation.

1. $(3.5 \times 10^{12})(2.3 \times 10^9)$ 8.05×10^{21}

2. $(2.99 \times 10^{16})(4.36 \times 10^{12})$ 1.30364×10^{29}

3. $(2.75 \times 10^4)^2$ 7.5625×10^8

4. $(9.22 \times 10^{11})^3$ 7.8378×10^{35}

5. $(5.54 \times 10^6) + (1.38 \times 10^6)$ 6.92×10^6

6. $(4.02 \times 10^{13}) - (2.01 \times 10^{13})$ 2.01×10^{13}

7. **Mental Math** Simplify $10^{20} \cdot (1.56 \times 10^{15})$. Check your answer with a calculator. 1.56×10^{35}

8. Find the area of a square with side 1.5×10^4 mi. 2.25×10^8

Technology

Scientific Notation

Students have worked with exponents and scientific notation in the Lessons 7-1 and 7-2. In this feature, they are introduced to how to use a calculator to read, display, and calculate with numbers expressed in scientific notation.

Optional Materials

- any scientific or graphing calculator
- Classroom Aid 11

Teaching Notes

Discuss the opening information about how and when calculators will display a number in scientific notation. Invite students to enter additional great numbers into the display to verify this calculator feature.

English Learners
Review the meanings of the terms *shorthand* and *display* as they apply to the concepts in this feature.

1 EXAMPLE Inclusion

Review the rule for multiplying powers with the same base (add the exponents). Ask: *If $10^6 \times 10^3 = 10^9$, then why doesn't the calculator display the answer as the product of 7.6 and 3.52, or 26.752, times 10^9?* The first factor of a number in scientific notation must be greater than or equal to 1 and less than 10; 7.6×3.52 is greater than 10.

Error Prevention!

Remind students to be careful to enter the correct operation symbol when simplifying expressions with their calculators.

Exercises
Have students work in pairs on the exercises. Elicit from them that according to the order of operations, the *entire* expression within the parentheses is raised to a power of 2 in Exercise 3, and to a power of 3 in Exercise 4.

7-3

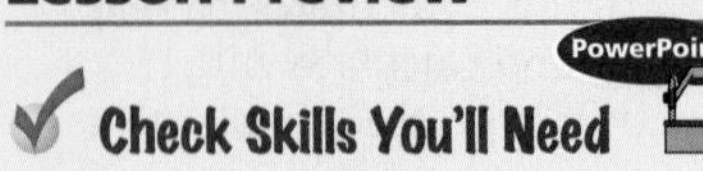

Lesson Preview

PowerPoint

✓ Check Skills You'll Need

Writing With Exponents
Lesson 1-7: Example 1. Extra Practice, p. 702.

Lesson Resources

Teaching Resources
Practice, Reteaching, Enrichment

Reaching All Students
Practice Workbook 7-3
Spanish Practice Workbook 7-3
Guided Problem Solving 7-3

Presentation Assistant Plus!
Transparencies
- Check Skills You'll Need 7-3
- Problem of the Day 7-3
- Additional Examples 7-3
- Student Edition Answers 7-3
- Lesson Quiz 7-3

PH Presentation Pro CD-ROM 7-3

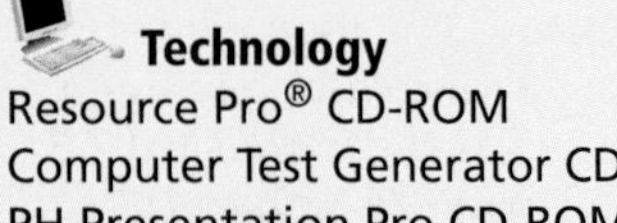

Computer Test Generator CD

Technology
Resource Pro® CD-ROM
Computer Test Generator CD
PH Presentation Pro CD-ROM

www.PHSchool.com
Student Site
- Teacher Web Code: ack-5500
- Algebra Readiness Puzzles 66
- Self-grading Lesson Quiz

PH SuccessNet Teacher Center
- Lesson Planner
- Resources

Plus iTEXT

7-3 Exponents and Division

What You'll Learn

To divide powers with the same base

To use negative or zero exponents

. . . And Why

To evaluate numbers in scientific notation, as in Example 6

✓ Check Skills You'll Need

For help, go to Lesson 1-7.

Write using exponents.

1. $7 \cdot 7 \cdot 7 \cdot 7$ 7^4

2. $4 \cdot 4 \cdot 4$ 4^3

3. $5 \cdot 5$ 5^2

4. $1 \cdot 1 \cdot 1 \cdot 1 \cdot 1$ 1^5

5. $3 \cdot 3 \cdot 3$ 3^3

6. $8 \cdot 8 \cdot 8 \cdot 8$ 8^4

7. Explain the relationship between a factor and an exponent.
An exponent tells how many times a number is used as a factor.

Interactive lesson includes instant self-check, tutorials, and activities.

OBJECTIVE 1

Dividing Powers With the Same Base

You can divide powers with the same base by writing out all the factors.

1 EXAMPLE Dividing Powers by Writing Factors

Need Help?
For help with exponents and factors, go to Lesson 1-7.

Write $\frac{7^5}{7^3}$ using a single exponent.

$\frac{7^5}{7^3} = \frac{7^1 \cdot 7^1 \cdot 7^1 \cdot 7 \cdot 7}{_1 7 \cdot _1 7 \cdot _1 7}$ ← Write out the factors in the numerator and denominator. Then divide the common factors.

$= \frac{7 \cdot 7}{1}$ ← Rewrite the numerator and denominator.

$= 7^2$ ← Write the result using exponents.

✓ **Check Understanding** 1 Write each expression using a single exponent.

a. $\frac{4^7}{4^5}$ 4^2

b. $\frac{10^5}{10^2}$ 10^3

c. $\frac{a^6}{a^5}$ a^1

Example 1 suggests the following rule.

Key Concepts — Dividing Powers With the Same Base

To divide nonzero numbers or variables with the same nonzero base, subtract the exponents.

Arithmetic	Algebra
$\frac{8^5}{8^3} = 8^{(5-3)} = 8^2$	$\frac{a^m}{a^n} = a^{(m-n)}$, where $a \neq 0$

Ongoing Assessment and Intervention

Before the Lesson
Diagnose prerequisite skills using:
- Check Skills You'll Need

During the Lesson
Monitor progress using:
- Check Understanding
- Additional Examples
- Test Prep

After the Lesson
Assess knowledge using:
- Lesson Quiz
- Computer Test Generator CD

2 EXAMPLE Dividing Powers by Subtracting Exponents

Write $\frac{m^{12}}{m^5}$ using a single exponent.

$\frac{m^{12}}{m^5} = m^{(12-5)}$ ← **Subtract exponents with the same base.**

$= m^7$ ← **Simplify.**

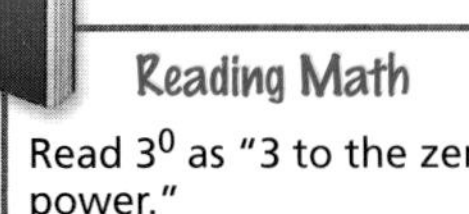

Check Understanding 2 Write each expression using a single exponent.

a. $\frac{w^8}{w^2}$ w^6 **b.** $\frac{t^{18}}{t^8}$ t^{10} **c.** $\frac{7^6}{7^3}$ 7^3

d. **Mental Math** Find the value of $\frac{123^5}{123^4}$. 123

OBJECTIVE

2 Using Zero or Negative Exponents

What does the exponent 0 mean? Consider finding the quotient $\frac{3^5}{3^5}$.

If you subtract exponents, $\frac{3^5}{3^5} = 3^{(5-5)}$
$= 3^0$

If you write factors, $\frac{3^5}{3^5} = \frac{\overset{1}{\cancel{3}} \cdot \overset{1}{\cancel{3}} \cdot \overset{1}{\cancel{3}} \cdot \overset{1}{\cancel{3}} \cdot \overset{1}{\cancel{3}}}{\underset{1}{\cancel{3}} \cdot \underset{1}{\cancel{3}} \cdot \underset{1}{\cancel{3}} \cdot \underset{1}{\cancel{3}} \cdot \underset{1}{\cancel{3}}}$
$= \frac{1}{1} = 1$

Reading Math
Read 3^0 as "3 to the zero power."

Notice that $\frac{3^5}{3^5} = 3^0$ and $\frac{3^5}{3^5} = 1$. This suggests the following rule.

Key Concepts **Zero as an Exponent**

For any nonzero number a, $a^0 = 1$.

Example $9^0 = 1$

3 EXAMPLE Expressions With a Zero Exponent

Simplify each expression.

a. $(-8)^0$
$(-8)^0 = 1$ ← **Simplify.**

b. m^0
$m^0 = 1$ ← **Simplify.**

Check Understanding 3 Simplify each expression.

a. $(-9)^0$ 1 **b.** $(2r)^0$ 1 **c.** $2r^0$ 2

d. **Reasoning** Is $(-1)^0$ a positive or a negative number? Explain.
Positive; any number to the power of zero is equal to one.

Reaching All Students

Below Level Write as a product of factors and find the value of $(-2)^2$, $(-2)^3$, -2^2, -2^3. $(-2)(-2) = 4$; $(-2)(-2)(-2) = -8$; $-(2)(2) = -4$; $-(2)(2)(2) = -8$	**Advanced Learners** Have students compare the value of $-x^0$ and $(-x)^0$. -1 and 1	**Inclusion** See note on page 378. **Alternative Method** See notes on page 377.

2. Teach

Math Background

Just as you can multiply powers with the same base by adding the exponents, you can divide powers with the same base by subtracting the exponents. Division of powers requires two important rules: For any nonzero number, x, $x^0 = 1$ and $x^{-1} = \frac{1}{x}$. Negative exponents can be used to write numbers which are less than 1 and greater than 0 in scientific notation. So, for example, 0.0035 is written as 3.5×10^{-3}.

Teaching Notes

1 EXAMPLE Alternative Method

Remind students how to multiply powers by having them find $2^3 \cdot 2^4$. Then ask:

- *Since $2^7 = 2^3 \cdot 2^4$, what must be the quotient of $2^7 \div 2^4$?* 2^3
- *What method does this suggest for dividing powers?* subtracting the exponents

2 EXAMPLE Error Prevention!

Remind students that subtracting exponents is the method for dividing powers, and that the numerical bases are *not* divided.

3 EXAMPLE Alternative Method

Have students add three more rows to the table on page 365 in Lesson 7-1. Discuss the patterns and the meaning of zero and negative exponents.

$6.71 \times 10^0 = 6.71 \times 1 = 6.71$

$6.71 \times 10^{-1} = 6.71 \times \frac{1}{10} = 0.671$

$6.71 \times 10^{-2} = 6.71 \times \frac{1}{100} = 0.0671$

PowerPoint

Additional Examples

1 Write $\frac{4^6}{4^3}$ using a single exponent. 4^3

2 Write $\frac{x^{14}}{x^9}$ using a single exponent. x^5

3 Simplify each expression.
a. $(-5)^0$ 1 b. y^0 1

4 EXAMPLE Inclusion

Some students may read 3^{-2} as $3 - 2$ or $3(-2)$. Have students read the problem aloud as "3 to the negative 2."

5 EXAMPLE Auditory Learners

Ask:
- *Is 7.14×10^{-3} a positive or a negative number?* positive
- *What does the exponent of −3 tell you about the number?* The number is between 0 and 1.

6 EXAMPLE Error Prevention!

Point out that it is the number of places the decimal point moves that you count, and *not* the number of zeros.

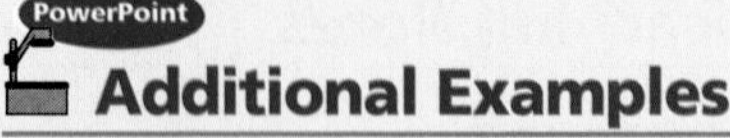

Additional Examples

4 Simplify each expression.
a. 2^{-3} $\frac{1}{8}$ b. $(p)^{-8}$ $\frac{1}{p^8}$

5 Among the microscopic possible fossils found on Mars, the largest are less than approximately 2.45×10^{-5} cm in size. Write this number in standard form. 0.0000245

6 Write 0.0000807 in scientific notation. 8.07×10^{-5}

Closure

- *How do you divide powers with the same base?* Subtract the exponents.
- *What is the meaning of a zero exponent and of a negative exponent? Explain.* Sample: Any nonzero number with a 0 exponent has a value of 1; any nonzero number with a negative exponent is equal to the reciprocal of that number with a positive exponent.

To understand negative exponents, consider finding the quotient $\frac{6^2}{6^5}$.

If you subtract exponents, $\frac{6^2}{6^5} = 6^{(2-5)} = 6^{-3}$.

If you write factors, $\frac{6^2}{6^5} = \frac{\overset{1}{\cancel{6}} \cdot \overset{1}{\cancel{6}}}{_1\cancel{6} \cdot {_1\cancel{6}} \cdot 6 \cdot 6 \cdot 6} = \frac{1}{6 \cdot 6 \cdot 6} = \frac{1}{6^3}$.

Notice that $\frac{6^2}{6^5} = 6^{-3}$ and $\frac{6^2}{6^5} = \frac{1}{6^3}$. This suggests the following rule.

Key Concepts **Negative Exponents**

For any nonzero number a and integer n, $a^{-n} = \frac{1}{a^n}$.

Example $8^{-5} = \frac{1}{8^5}$

To simplify an expression with negative exponents, first write the expression with a positive exponent.

4 EXAMPLE Expressions With Negative Exponents

Simplify each expression.

a. 3^{-2}

$3^{-2} = \frac{1}{3^2}$ ← Write the expression using a positive exponent. →

$= \frac{1}{9}$ ← Simplify.

b. $(y)^{-6}$

$(y)^{-6} = \frac{1}{y^6}$

Check Understanding 4 Simplify each expression.
a. 3^{-1} $\frac{1}{3}$ **b.** w^{-4} $\frac{1}{w^4}$ **c.** $(-2)^{-3}$ $-\frac{1}{8}$

Real-World Connection
A manicurist cleans, shapes, and polishes a customer's fingernails and toenails.

Numbers in scientific notation can have negative exponents. Multiplying a number by 10^n, when n is negative, moves the decimal point n places to the left.

5 EXAMPLE Real-World Problem Solving

Biology Fingernails grow about 1.23×10^{-2} centimeters per day. Write this number in standard form.

$1.23 \times 10^{-2} = .01.23$ ← A negative exponent indicates division. Move the decimal point 2 places to the left to make 1.23 less than 1.

Fingernails grow about 0.0123 centimeters per day.

Check Understanding 5 **a.** The diameter of a cell is 2.5×10^{-4} inches. Write this number in standard form. 0.00025

b. **Number Sense** Is 8.1×10^{-5} greater or less than 0? Explain. Greater; 81 millionths (0.000081) is greater than zero.

To write a number that is less than 1 in scientific notation, determine the first factor by moving the decimal point, then write the second factor as a negative power of ten.

6 EXAMPLE Writing Numbers in Scientific Notation

Write 0.0000076 in scientific notation.

$0.0000076 = 0.000007.6$ ← Move the decimal point 6 places to the right to get a factor greater than 1 but less than 10.

$= 7.6 \times 10^{-6}$ ← Since you moved the decimal 6 places, use -6 as the exponent of 10.

Check Understanding 6 **a.** Write 0.0000035 in scientific notation. 3.5×10^{-6}
b. Solve the equation $3.1 \times 10^{n} = 0.00031$. -4

3. Practice

Assignment Guide

Objective 1
A B Core 1–14, 33–40, 42
C Extension 63

Objective 2
A B Core 15–32, 41, 43–61
C Extension 62, 64–67

Test Prep 68–72
Mixed Review 73–78

Diversity
Exercise 27 Students may know ketchup as tomato sauce.

EXERCISES

For more practice, see *Extra Practice*.

A Practice by Example

Example 1 (page 376)

Write out all the factors of each expression. Then simplify using a single exponent. Exercise 1 has been started for you. 1–7. See margin.

1. $\frac{2^6}{2^5} = \frac{2 \cdot 2 \cdot 2 \cdot 2 \cdot 2 \cdot 2}{2 \cdot 2 \cdot 2 \cdot 2 \cdot 2}$ **2.** $\frac{3^4}{3^2}$ **3.** $\frac{8^5}{8^2}$

4. $\frac{6^7}{6^4}$ **5.** $\frac{13^5}{13^1}$ **6.** $\frac{(-3)^8}{(-3)^2}$ **7.** $\frac{(-4)^{10}}{(-4)^6}$

Example 2 (page 377)

Write each expression using a single exponent. Exercise 8 has been started for you.

8. $\frac{a^5}{a^3} = a^{(5-3)}$ a^2 **9.** $\frac{x^9}{x^5}$ x^4 **10.** $\frac{c^7}{c^2}$ c^5

11. $\frac{23^{12}}{23^8}$ 23^4 **12.** $\frac{135^{10}}{135^1}$ 135^9 **13.** $\frac{(-7)^{99}}{(-7)^{98}}$ $(-7)^1$ **14.** $\frac{(-9)^{32}}{(-9)^{15}}$ $(-9)^{17}$

Examples 3, 4 (pages 377, 378)

Simplify each expression.

15. 4^0 1 **16.** $(-3)^0$ 1 **17.** u^0 1 **18.** $(3t)^0$ 1

19. 10^{-2} $\frac{1}{100}$ **20.** b^{-6} $\frac{1}{b^6}$ **21.** x^{-4} $\frac{1}{x^4}$ **22.** 7^{-1} $\frac{1}{7}$

Example 5 (page 378)

Write each number in standard form.

23. 2.5×10^{-3} 0.0025 **24.** 5.12×10^{-5} 0.0000512 **25.** 1.05×10^{-2} 0.0105 **26.** 3.14×10^{-7} 0.000000314

27. Food A ketchup particle is about 9.5×10^{-5} cm. 0.000095 cm

28. Insects The shortest centipede is approximately 4.8×10^{-1} cm long. 0.48 cm

Example 6 (page 379)

Write each number in scientific notation.

29. 0.00581 5.81×10^{-3} **30.** 0.00105 1.05×10^{-3} **31.** 0.0000078 7.8×10^{-6} **32.** 0.000027 2.7×10^{-5}

1. $\frac{2 \cdot 2 \cdot 2 \cdot 2 \cdot 2 \cdot 2}{2 \cdot 2 \cdot 2 \cdot 2 \cdot 2} = 2^1$
2. $\frac{3 \cdot 3 \cdot 3 \cdot 3}{3 \cdot 3} = 3^2$
3. $\frac{8 \cdot 8 \cdot 8 \cdot 8 \cdot 8}{8 \cdot 8} = 8^3$
4. $\frac{6 \cdot 6 \cdot 6 \cdot 6 \cdot 6 \cdot 6 \cdot 6}{6 \cdot 6 \cdot 6 \cdot 6} = 6^3$
5. $\frac{13 \cdot 13 \cdot 13 \cdot 13 \cdot 13}{13} = 13^4$

6–7. See back of book.

Practice 7-3 Exponents and Division

Simplify each expression.

1. 8^{-2} $\frac{1}{64}$ 2. $(-3)^0$ 1 3. 5^{-1} $\frac{1}{5}$ 4. 18^0 1
5. 2^{-5} $\frac{1}{32}$ 6. 3^{-3} $\frac{1}{27}$ 7. 2^{-3} $\frac{1}{8}$ 8. 5^{-2} $\frac{1}{25}$
9. $\frac{4^4}{4}$ 64 10. $8^6 \div 8^8$ $\frac{1}{64}$ 11. $\frac{(-3)^6}{(-3)^8}$ $\frac{1}{9}$ 12. $\frac{8^4}{8^0}$ 4,096
13. $1^{15} \div 1^{18}$ 1 14. $7 \div 7^4$ $\frac{1}{343}$ 15. $\frac{(-4)^8}{(-4)^4}$ 256 16. $\frac{10^9}{10^{12}}$ $\frac{1}{1,000}$
17. $\frac{7^5}{7^3}$ 49 18. $8^4 \div 8^2$ 64 19. $\frac{(-3)^5}{(-3)^8}$ $-\frac{1}{27}$ 20. $\frac{6^7}{6^8}$ $\frac{1}{6}$
21. $\frac{b^{12}}{b^4}$ b^8 22. $\frac{g^9}{g^{15}}$ $\frac{1}{g^6}$ 23. $x^{16} \div x^7$ x^9 24. $v^{20} \div v^{25}$ $\frac{1}{v^5}$

Complete each equation.

25. $\frac{1}{3^5} = 3^{?}$ -5 26. $\frac{1}{(-2)^7} = -2^{?}$ -7 27. $\frac{1}{x^2} = x^{?}$ -2 28. $\frac{1}{-125} = (-5)^{?}$ -3
29. $\frac{1}{1,000} = 10^{?}$ -3 30. $\frac{5^{10}}{?} = 5^5$ 5^5 31. $\frac{z^{?}}{z^8} = z^{-3}$ 5 32. $\frac{q^5}{?} = q^{-7}$ q^{12}

Write each number in scientific notation.

33. 0.0007 7×10^{-4} 34. 0.00000001 10^{-8} 35. 0.000901 9.01×10^{-4}
36. 0.0000000091 9.1×10^{-9} 37. 0.0000000001 10^{-10} 38. 0.000032 3.2×10^{-5}

39. Write each term as a power of 4, and write the next three terms of the sequence 256, 64, 16, 4, . . .
$4^4, 4^3, 4^2, 4^1, \ldots; 4^0, 4^{-1}, 4^{-2}$, or $1, \frac{1}{4}, \frac{1}{16}$

Reteaching 7-3 Exponents and Division

To divide powers with the same base, subtract exponents.

$\frac{8^6}{8^4} = 8^{6-4} = 8^2 = 64$ $\frac{a^5}{a^3} = a^{5-3} = a^2$

- For any nonzero number a, $a^0 = 1$.

$3^0 = 1$ $(-6)^0 = 1$ $4t^0 = 4(1) = 4$

- For any nonzero number a and any integer n, $a^{-n} = \frac{1}{a^n}$.

$2^{-4} = \frac{1}{2^4} = \frac{1}{16}$ $3c^{-2} = \frac{3}{c^2}$ $\frac{5^3}{5^6} = 5^{3-6} = 5^{-3} = \frac{1}{5^3} = \frac{1}{125}$ $\frac{10z^3}{5z} = 2z^{3-1} = 2z^2$

Write each expression using a single exponent.

1. $\frac{6^5}{6^3} =$ 36 2. $(-4)^5 \div (-4)^3 =$ 16 3. $9^8 \div 9^6 =$ 81
4. $(-3)^{-2} =$ $\frac{1}{9}$ 5. $\frac{2^5}{2^7} =$ $\frac{1}{4}$ 6. $(-8)^0 =$ 1
7. $\frac{5^0}{5^2} =$ $\frac{1}{25}$ 8. $(-4)^{-3} =$ $-\frac{1}{64}$ 9. $\frac{(-6)^4}{(-6)^6} =$ $\frac{1}{36}$
10. $7^3 \div 7^5 =$ $\frac{1}{49}$ 11. $9^8 \div 9^{10} =$ $\frac{1}{81}$ 12. $\frac{2^7}{2^3} =$ 16

Simplify each expression. Use only positive exponents.

13. $w^8 \div w^3 =$ w^5 14. $x^6 \div x^1 =$ x^5 15. $\frac{d^7}{d^3} =$ d^4
16. $y^6 \div y^9 =$ $\frac{1}{y^3}$ 17. $a^{10} \div a^4 =$ a^6 18. $3m^6 \div m^2 =$ $3m^4$
19. $\frac{w^2}{w^6} =$ $\frac{1}{w^4}$ 20. $4c^5 \div c^8 =$ $\frac{4}{c^3}$ 21. $\frac{8x^2}{4x^5} =$ $\frac{2}{x^3}$
22. $8a^4 \div 2a^2 =$ $4a^2$ 23. $6w^2 \div 2w^5 =$ $\frac{3}{w^3}$ 24. $\frac{6x^6}{3x^9} =$ $\frac{2}{x^3}$

B Apply Your Skills

Complete each equation.

33. $\frac{4^{\blacksquare}}{4^2} = 4^{10}$ 12 34. $\frac{x^6}{x^{\blacksquare}} = x^4$ 2 35. $\frac{14x^5}{7x^3} = 2x^{\blacksquare}$ 2 36. $\frac{20^8}{20^{\blacksquare}} = 1$ 8

37. $\frac{1}{c^7} = c^{\blacksquare}$ −7 38. $\frac{1}{-8} = (-2)^{\blacksquare}$ −3 39. $\frac{1}{100} = 10^{\blacksquare}$ −2 40. $\frac{y^3}{y^{\blacksquare}} = y^{-9}$ 12

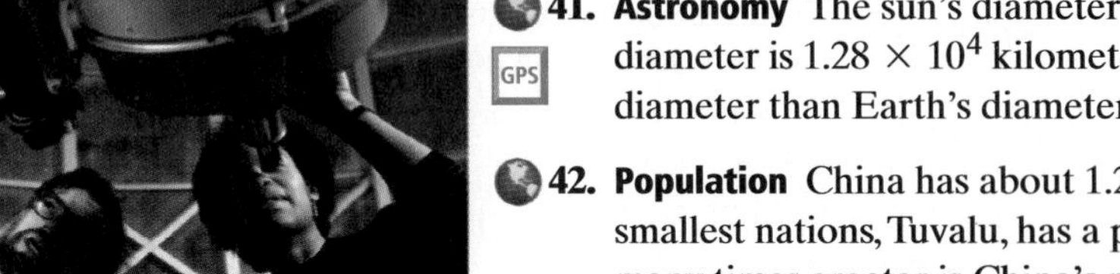

41. **Astronomy** The sun's diameter is 1.39×10^6 kilometers. Earth's diameter is 1.28×10^4 kilometers. How many times greater is the sun's diameter than Earth's diameter? 1.09×10^2 times greater

GPS

42. **Population** China has about 1.27×10^9 people. One of the world's smallest nations, Tuvalu, has a population of just 1.1×10^4 people. How many times greater is China's population than Tuvalu's? 1.15×10^5 times greater

Real-World Connection

Careers Astronomers often use scientific notation in their work with large numbers.

Use $w = -1$ and $x = 2$. Simplify each expression.

43. $(w + 4)^{-4}$ $\frac{1}{81}$ 44. x^w $\frac{1}{2}$ 45. -2^w $-\frac{1}{2}$ 46. $(2x)^{w+1}$ 1

47. $(x + 1)^w$ $\frac{1}{3}$ 48. $x^w + 1^w$ $\frac{3}{2}$ 49. $(4x)^w$ $\frac{1}{8}$ 50. $4^w \cdot x^w$ $\frac{1}{8}$

Number Sense **Which number is greater?**

51. 2.3×10^{-4} or 2.3×10^{-7} 2.3×10^{-4}

52. 1.04×10^{-5} or 0.00000104 1.04×10^{-5}

53. 0.0000123 or 1.23×10^{-4} 1.23×10^{-4}

54. $\frac{2}{100{,}000}$ or 0.000002 $\frac{2}{100{,}000}$

Writing in Math **Is each statement *true* or *false*? Explain your reasoning.**

55. $4^0 = 4^{-1}$ 56. $8^{-1} = (-8)^1$ 57. $2^1 \cdot 2^{-1} = 2^0$ 58. $(-2)^{-1} = 2$

55–58. See margin.

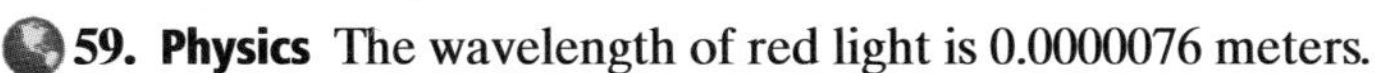

59. **Physics** The wavelength of red light is 0.0000076 meters.
   a. Write the number in scientific notation. 7.6×10^{-6}
   b. What is the wavelength in millimeters? 7.6×10^{-3}

Reading Math

For help with Exercise 60, see p. 382.

60. **Space Travel** In April 1983, the space probe *Pioneer 10* was 4.58×10^9 km from Earth. It sent radio signals that traveled at 3.00×10^5 km/s. How many hours did the signals take to reach Earth? 4.25 hrs

61. Data File, p. 363 Light travels at 3.00×10^5 kilometers per second. Find how many centimeters light travels in 1 nanosecond. 30 cm

C Challenge

62. Reasoning If you look through a powerful set of binoculars, you can see the diameter of a 1-inch ball from one mile away.
   a. Using these binoculars, what is the smallest diameter ball you can see if the ball is 5.58×10^8 miles away? 5.58×10^8 in.
   b. The diameter of Jupiter is 88,850 miles. Can you see Jupiter when it is 5.58×10^8 miles away? Explain. Yes, 5.58×10^8 in. is 8,807 mi. Since 88,850 is more than 8,807, you can see Jupiter.

63. Find the value of n for $5^{2n} = 5^9 \cdot 5^{n+1}$. 10

64. There are 2.2 pounds in a kilogram, and the mass of a nickel is about 5 grams. Find the number of pounds in $5.00 worth of nickels. 1.1 pounds

55. False; $4^0 = 1$ and $4^{-1} = \frac{1}{4}$.

56. False; $8^{-1} = \frac{1}{8}$ and $(-8)^1 = -8$.

57. True; $2^1 \cdot 2^{-1} = 2^{1+-1} = 2^0 = 1$.

58. False; $(-2)^{-1} = \frac{1}{-2} = -\frac{1}{2}$ and $-\frac{1}{2} \neq 2$.

Use the Guided Problem Solving worksheet with Exercise 41.

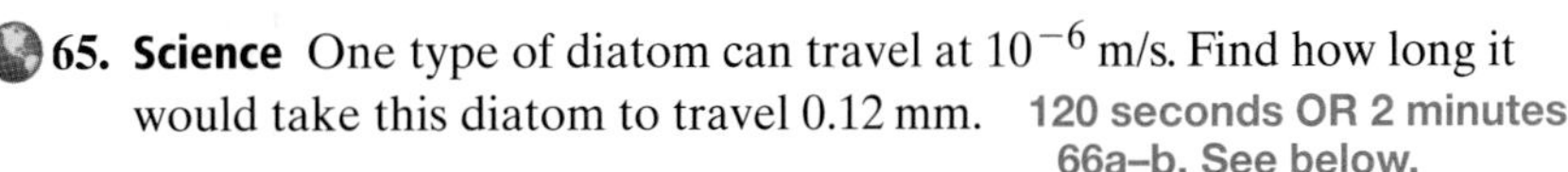

Real-World Connection

Diatoms are single-cell animals that live in both fresh and salt water.

65. Science One type of diatom can travel at 10^{-6} m/s. Find how long it would take this diatom to travel 0.12 mm. 120 seconds OR 2 minutes

66a–b. See below.

66. a. When is a^{-2} a negative number? A positive number? Zero?

b. When is a^{-3} a negative number? A positive number? Zero?

6 combinations

67. a. Stretch Your Thinking You have three tiles A, B, and C. How many three-letter combinations can be made using these tiles?

b. When the combinations are put in alphabetical order, ABC is first, and CBA is last. What "word" comes after ACB? BAC

66a. a^{-2} is positive for all nonzero numbers; a^{-2} cannot equal zero.
66b. a^{-3} is positive when a is positive, negative when a is negative, and cannot equal zero.

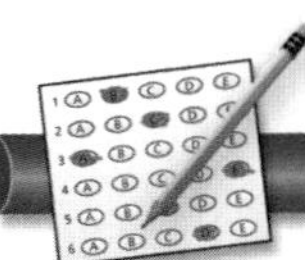

Test Prep

Multiple Choice

68. Write $7^5 \cdot 7^{10}$ using a single exponent. A

A. 7^{15} **B.** 7^{50} **C.** 49^{15} **D.** 49^{50}

69. Which of the following is equal to $\frac{3^6}{3^3}$? I

F. 1 **G.** 1^2 **H.** 3^2 **I.** 3^3

70. Which of the following is $\frac{5^h}{5}$ written using a single exponent? C

A. 1^h **B.** 5^h **C.** 5^{h-1} **D.** 5^{2h}

Take It to the NET
Online lesson quiz at **www.PHSchool.com**
Web Code: aca-0703

71. Which of the following is twice 8×10^{-6}? H

F. 1.6×20^{-6} **G.** 1.6×10^{-6} **H.** 0.000016 **I.** 0.00016

Short Response

72. Give an example of a number that is greater than 5×10^{-8} and less than 8×10^{-5}. Explain why your number satisfies the conditions.
See margin.

Mixed Review

Lesson 6-4

Algebra **Use an equation to solve each problem.**

73. What percent is 17 of 58? about 29.3%

74. 1.5 is 45% of what number? $3.\overline{3}$

75. What is 12.5% of 34.50? 4.3125

76. What percent is 22 of 222? about 9.9%

Lesson 5-9

77. When the top of a 24-foot ladder leans against a tree, the bottom makes an angle of 75° with the ground. Use the sine function to find how high the top of the ladder is above the ground. about 23.2 ft

78. Use the triangle at the right to find each trigonometric ratio as a fraction in simplest form.

a. sin P $\frac{12}{37}$ **b.** cos P $\frac{35}{37}$ **c.** cos Q $\frac{12}{37}$

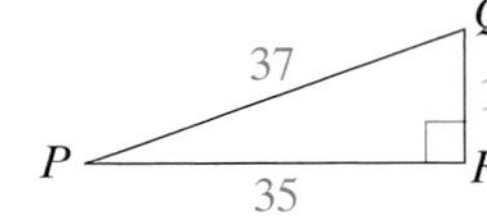

72. [2] Answers may vary. Sample: 8×10^{-6}; the exponent makes the value greater than 10^{-8} and less than 10^{-5}.
[1] correct answer without explanation

4. Assess

PowerPoint **Lesson Quiz 7-3**

1. Write $\frac{9^7}{9^4}$ using a single exponent. 9^3

Simplify each expression.

2. 6^0 1
3. 4^{-2} $\frac{1}{16}$
4. The diameter of a cell is 9×10^{-5} in. Write this number in standard form. 0.00009
5. Write 0.00084 in scientific notation. 8.4×10^{-4}

Alternative Assessment

Each student in a pair writes a number between 0 and 1 with at least 5 digits. Partners exchange papers and write the number using scientific notation.

Test Prep

Resources
For additional practice with a variety of test item formats:
- Test Prep, p. 401
- Test-Taking Strategies, p. 397
- Test-Taking Strategies with Transparencies

Exercise 70 Remind students that $5 = 5^1$.

Enrichment 7-3 Exponents and Division

Patterns in Numbers

1. You know that you add exponents when you multiply two expressions with the same base. For example: $7^2 \times 7^3 = 7^{2+3} = 7^5$. Make a conjecture about what you should do with the exponents when you divide expressions with the same base.
Check students' answers.

2. Study the example below. What is the value of $\frac{7 \times 7 \times 7}{7 \times 7 \times 7}$? 1
$7^7 \div 7^3 = \frac{7 \times 7 \times 7 \times 7 \times 7 \times 7 \times 7}{7 \times 7 \times 7} = 7 \times 7 \times 7 \times 7 \times \frac{7 \times 7 \times 7}{7 \times 7 \times 7}$
$= 7 \times 7 \times 7 \times 7$
$= 7^4$

3. Study and continue the pattern below.
$7^9 \div 7^3 = 7^{9-3} = 7^6 = 7 \times 7 \times 7 \times 7 \times 7 \times 7$
$7^9 \div 7^4 = 7^{9-4} = 7^5 = 7 \times 7 \times 7 \times 7 \times 7$
$7^9 \div 7^5 = 7^{9-5} = 7^4 = 7 \times 7 \times 7 \times 7$
$7^9 \div 7^6 = 7^{9-6} = 7^3 = 7 \times 7 \times 7$
$7^9 \div 7^7 = 7^{9-7} = 7^2 = 7 \times 7$
$7^9 \div 7^8 = 7^{9-8} = 7^1 = 7$

4. Describe the pattern that you see.
Sample answer: When you divide expressions with the same base, you subtract the exponents.

5. Extend the pattern for $7^9 \div 7^9$.
$7^9 \div 7^9 = \frac{7 \times 7 \times 7 \times 7 \times 7 \times 7 \times 7 \times 7 \times 7}{7 \times 7 \times 7 \times 7 \times 7 \times 7 \times 7 \times 7 \times 7} = 1$

6. What do you think a^0 means? Explain.
$a^0 = 1$. To get zero as an exponent, you are dividing a number by itself, such as $7^9 \div 7^9 = 7^{9-9} = 7^0 = 1$.

Reading Math

Understanding Word Problems

It is important for students to be able to use their understanding of scientific notation in real-world situations. In this feature, they apply the distance formula, using a calculator, to solve a problem involving the speed of radio signals.

Teaching Notes

Have a volunteer read aloud the Space Travel problem. Then guide students to notice how Juan uses a careful step-by-step problem-solving process to answer the question the problem asks.

Teaching Tip
Work through Juan's solution strategy, beginning with the key steps of identifying what he knows. As you discuss what Juan thinks and writes, elicit from students that different orders for the problem-solving steps are possible. For example, ask: *After Juan chooses a variable and substitutes for it, what could he do instead of dividing both sides of the equation by 3?* **Sample: Divide both sides by 10^5.**

As needed, allow pairs of students to work together for a few minutes to review and process all the steps in Juan's solution. Encourage students to explore alternate approaches to solving this problem.

Error Prevention!

Guide students to see that the problem asks for the number of *hours* the signal takes, not the number of seconds. Remind them to make sure they always answer the specific question a problem asks.

Inclusion
Remind students of the distance formula, helping them to fit the information in the problem into the $d = rt$ equation, as needed.

Exercises
Have students work independently on the exercises.

Reading Math: Understanding Word Problems

For Use With Page 380, Exercise 60

Read the problem below. Then follow along with Juan as he works through the problem. You can check your understanding with the exercises at the bottom of the page.

60. Space Travel In April 1983, the space probe *Pioneer 10* was 4.58×10^9 km from Earth. It sent radio signals that traveled at 3.00×10^5 km/s. How many hours did the signals take to reach Earth?

What Juan Thinks	What Juan Writes
I'll write down what I know.	rate = 3.00×10^5 km/s distance = 4.58×10^9 km
I can use the formula for distance.	distance = rate · time
I'll let t equal the time the signal traveled. Then I'll substitute into the distance formula.	Let t = time. $4.58 \times 10^9 = 3.00 \times 10^5 \cdot t$
I'll divide each side by 3. I'll divide and round to the nearest hundredth.	$\frac{4.58 \times 10^9}{3} = \frac{3.00 \times 10^5}{3} t$ $1.53 \times 10^9 = 10^5 t$
Now I'll divide each side by 10^5. I'll subtract the exponents since I'm dividing.	$1.53 \times 10^4 = t$
So, the time is 1.53×10^4 seconds. How many hours is that? I'll multiply by a conversion factor to cancel the common units.	$1.53 \times 10^4 \text{ seconds} \cdot \frac{1 \text{ hour}}{3{,}600 \text{ seconds}}$
Now I'll use a calculator to find $1.53 \times 10^4 \div 3{,}600$.	It will take 4.25 hours for the signals to get to Earth.

EXERCISES

1. **Geography** Light travels at a rate of 3.00×10^5 km/s. Find how long it will take light to travel from New York to Los Angeles. The straight-line distance between the two cities is about 4,000 km. **0.013 seconds**

2. **Animals** One of the slowest moving animals in the world is the three-toed sloth. It moves at about 7×10^{-2} mi/h. Find how many minutes it will take a sloth to go 10^{-3} miles. **about 0.857 minutes**

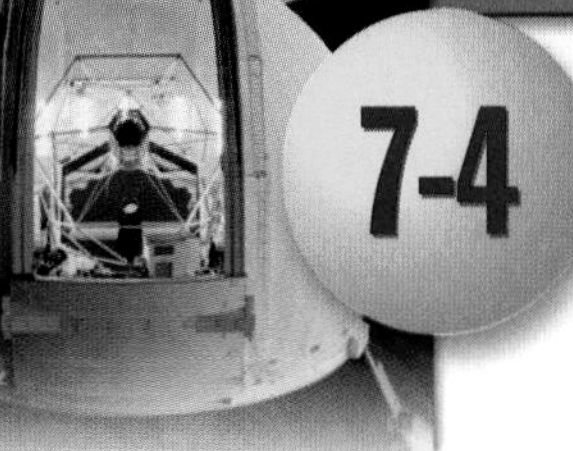

7-4 Power Rules

What You'll Learn

 To raise a power to a power

 To raise a product to a power

. . . And Why

To use power rules in science, as in Example 3

Check Skills You'll Need

For help, go to Lesson 7-2.

Write each expression using a single exponent.

1. $2^3 \cdot 2^3$ 2^6 **2.** $5^2 \cdot 5^2$ 5^4

3. $10^2 \cdot 10^2$ 10^4 **4.** $y^3 \cdot y^3$ y^6

5. $(-2)^5 \cdot (-2)^5$ $(-2)^{10}$ **6.** $(-2)^{10} \cdot (-2)^{10}$ $(-2)^{20}$

OBJECTIVE

 Interactive lesson includes instant self-check, tutorials, and activities.

1 Raising a Power to a Power

You can use the rule from Lesson 7-2 to simplify an expression like $(4^3)^2$.

$(4^3)^2 = 4^3 \cdot 4^3$ ← **Write two factors of 4^3.**

$= 4^{(3+3)}$ ← **Add the exponents.**

$= 4^6$ ← **Write the product as a power.**

Since $6 = 3 \cdot 2$, $(4^3)^2 = 4^{(3 \cdot 2)} = 4^6$. This result suggests the following rule for raising a power to a power.

Reading Math

The word *power* can be used in two ways. The expression a^n is a power. You can also read a^n as "*a* to the *n*th power."

Key Concepts: Raising a Power to a Power

To raise a power to a power, multiply the exponents.

Arithmetic	Algebra
$(2^5)^3 = 2^{(5 \cdot 3)} = 2^{15}$	$(a^m)^n = a^{(m \cdot n)}$, where m and n are integers.

1 EXAMPLE Raising a Power to a Power

Write each expression using a single exponent.

a. $(3^{-4})^5$

$= 3^{(-4 \cdot 5)}$ ← **Multiply the exponents.** →

$= 3^{-20}$ ← **Simplify the exponent.** →

b. $(x^{-2})^{-3}$

$= x^{(-2 \cdot -3)}$

$= x^6$

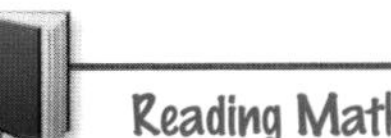

Check Understanding 1 Write each expression using a single exponent.

a. $(5^3)^{-2}$ 5^{-6} **b.** $(12^{-3})^{-2}$ 12^6 **c.** $(10^2)^9$ 10^{18}

d. Reasoning For $y > 1$, which is greater, $y^4 \cdot y^5$ or $(y^4)^5$? Explain. $(y^4)^5$; $y^4 \cdot y^5 = y^9$ and $(y^4)^5 = y^{20}$, and $y^{20} > y^9$.

Ongoing Assessment and Intervention

Before the Lesson
Diagnose prerequisite skills using:
- Check Skills You'll Need

During the Lesson
Monitor progress using:
- Check Understanding
- Additional Examples
- Test Prep

After the Lesson
Assess knowledge using:
- Lesson Quiz
- Computer Test Generator CD
- Chapter Checkpoint 2 (p. 387)

7-4

1. Plan

Lesson Preview

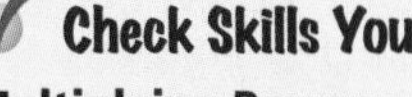

Multiplying Powers
Lesson 7-2: Example 1. Extra Practice, p. 708.

Lesson Resources

Teaching Resources
Practice, Reteaching, Enrichment
Checkpoint Quiz 2

Reaching All Students
Practice Workbook 7-4
Spanish Practice Workbook 7-4
Reading and Math Literacy 7C
Spanish Reading and Math Literacy 7C
Spanish Checkpoint Quiz 2
Guided Problem Solving 7-4
Technology Activities 43

Presentation Assistant Plus!
Transparencies
- Check Skills You'll Need 7-4
- Problem of the Day 7-4
- Additional Examples 7-4
- Student Edition Answers 7-4
- Lesson Quiz 7-4
- Classroom Aid 11

PH Presentation Pro CD-ROM 7-4

PRENTICE HALL ASSESSMENT SYSTEM

Checkpoint Quiz 2
Computer Test Generator CD

Technology
Resource Pro® CD-ROM
Computer Test Generator CD
PH Presentation Pro CD-ROM

www.PHSchool.com
Student Site
- Teacher Web Code: ack-5500
- Self-grading Lesson Quiz

PH SuccessNet Teacher Center
- Lesson Planner
- Resources

Plus 

2. Teach

Math Background

Since $a^3 \cdot a^3$ is a^6, it follows that $(a^3)^2$ is a^6. This example illustrates the rule that exponents are multiplied in order to raise a power to a power. Applying this rule means that $(2^3a^4)^2$ can be simplified to 2^6a^8 or $64a^8$.

Teaching Notes

Inclusion

Suggest that students recall the rules for $x^a \cdot x^b$ and $(x^a)^b$ by writing out the factors for $x^2 \cdot x^3$ and $(x^2)^3$. $(x \cdot x) \cdot (x \cdot x \cdot x)$ or x^5 and $(x \cdot x) \cdot (x \cdot x) \cdot (x \cdot x)$ or x^6

2 EXAMPLE Error Prevention!

Prepare students for algebra and help them distinguish between the meaning of $(ab)^2$ and $(a + b)^2$ by having them find the value for these two expressions using $a = 3$ and $b = 4$. Make sure they realize that you can raise each factor to the power but this does not work with a sum, since $(a + b)^2$ means $(a + b)(a + b)$ which is *not* the same as $a^2 + b^2$. For $a = 3$ and $b = 4$, $(ab)^2$ has a value of $(12)^2$ or 144, while $(a + b)^2$ has a value of $(7)^2$ or 49.

3 EXAMPLE Biology Connection

Ask a volunteer to explain which part of the eye is the pupil. The pupil is the round black opening in the center of the eye that is surrounded by a colored ring called the iris.

PowerPoint

Additional Examples

1. Write each expression using one base and one exponent.
   a. $(5^{-2})^3$ 5^{-6}
   b. $(y^{-4})^{-5}$ y^{20}
2. Simplify $(7p^5)^3$. $343p^{15}$
3. Use the formula for the area of a circle, $A = \pi r^2$, to find the area of a circle with a radius of 4×10^{-2} m. Write the answer in scientific notation. Use 3.14 for the value of π. 5.024×10^{-3} m^2

OBJECTIVE 2

Raising a Product to a Power

You can raise a product to a power using repeated multiplication.

$(2w)^3 = (2w) \cdot (2w) \cdot (2w)$ ← Write out the factors of the power.

$= 2 \cdot 2 \cdot 2 \cdot w \cdot w \cdot w$ ← Use the Commutative Property to rearrange the factors.

$= 2^3 \cdot w^3 = 2^3w^3$ ← Write the factors as a product.

Notice that $(2w)^3 = 2^3w^3$. This result suggests the following rule.

Key Concepts — Raising a Product to a Power

To raise a product to a power, raise each factor to the power.

Arithmetic	Algebra
$(3 \cdot 5)^2 = 3^2 \cdot 5^2$	$(ab)^m = a^mb^m$, where m is an integer.

2 EXAMPLE Raising a Product to a Power

Simplify $(3y^3)^2$.

$(3y^3)^2 = 3^2(y^3)^2$ ← Raise each factor to the second power.

$= 3^2y^6 = 9y^6$ ← Multiply the exponents. Simplify.

Check Understanding 2 Simplify each expression.
a. $(10x)^2$ $100x^2$ **b.** $(4u^5)^2$ $16u^{10}$ **c.** $(2a^3b)^3$ $8a^9b^3$

3 EXAMPLE Real-World Problem Solving

Science The pupil of a human eye is circular. In dim light, its radius is about 6×10^{-3} m. Use the formula for the area of a circle, $A = \pi r^2$, to find the area of the pupil. Write the answer in scientific notation. Use 3.14 for the value of π.

$A = \pi r^2$

$= 3.14 \cdot (6 \times 10^{-3})^2$ ← Substitute 6×10^{-3} for r.

$= 3.14 \cdot 6^2 \times (10^{-3})^2$ ← Raise the product to a power.

$= 3.14 \cdot 36 \times 10^{-6}$ ← Raise 10^{-3} to the second power.

$= 113.04 \times 10^{-6}$ ← Multiply 3.14 and 36.

$= 1.130 \times 10^{-4}$ ← Write in scientific notation.

The area of the pupil is about 1.13×10^{-4} m^2.

Check Understanding 3 Find the area of each circle with the given radius. Use the formula $A = \pi r^2$ and 3.14 for π.
a. $r = 1.3 \times 10^5$ m 5.3×10^{10} m^2 **b.** $r = 2.1 \times 10^{-5}$ cm 1.4×10^{-9} cm^2
c. Reasoning Is the square of 10^{-4} greater or less than 10^{-4}? Explain. less; $(10^{-4})^2 = 10^{-8}$; $10^{-8} < 10^{-4}$

Reaching All Students

Below Level	Advanced Learners	
Below Level Write in factored form and find the value of 2^5, $(-2)^5$, and -2^5. $2 \cdot 2 \cdot 2 \cdot 2 \cdot 2 = 32$; $-2 \cdot -2 \cdot -2 \cdot -2 \cdot -2 = -32$; $-(2 \cdot 2 \cdot 2 \cdot 2 \cdot 2) = -32$	**Advanced Learners** Write –340,000 in scientific notation $-(3.4 \times 10^5)$	**Inclusion** See note on page 384. **Error Prevention** See note on page 384.

More Than One Way

The Great Pyramid in Egypt contains about 2,300,000 blocks of stone and each block weighs about 5,000 pounds. About how many pounds of stone does the Great Pyramid contain?

Jasmine's Method

First, I will write each number in scientific notation.

Number of blocks: 2,300,000 = 2.3×10^6
Weight of each block: 5,000 lb = 5×10^3 lb

Now I'll multiply these numbers.

$(2.3 \times 10^6)(5 \times 10^3) = 11.5 \times 10^9$
$= 1.15 \times 10^{10}$

There are about 1.15×10^{10} pounds of stone.

Eric's Method

I'll use a calculator.

2,300,000 [×] 5,000 [ENTER] 1.15E10

The pyramid weighs about 1.15×10^{10} pounds.

Choose a Method

There are about 25 trillion red blood cells in a human body. If the typical mass of each cell is 10^{-10} grams, find the total mass of red blood cells in a human body. Explain why you chose the method you used.

2,500 grams; check students' methods.

Technology Tip
Jasmine's Method: Students might want to enter the factors in scientific notation. For example, on some calculators, you can enter 2.3, press [EE], and then enter the exponent of 6.

Eric's Method: Some calculators will actually show the answer as 1.15×10^{10}.

Closure

- *What is the difference between multiplying two powers and raising a power to a power?* Sample: To multiply two powers such as x^2 and x^3, you add the exponents to get x^5. To raise a power to a power, such as $(x^2)^3$, you multiply the exponents to get x^6.
- *How do you raise a product to a power?* Sample: Raise each factor to the power and simplify.

EXERCISES

For more practice, see *Extra Practice*.

A Practice by Example

Example 1 (page 383)

Write each expression using a single exponent.

1. $(3^3)^7$ 3^{21}
2. $(9^2)^{-5}$ 9^{-10}
3. $(h^2)^2$ h^4
4. $(y^{-3})^{-4}$ y^{12}
5. $(w^{-2})^{-6}$ w^{12}
6. $(7^2)^9$ 7^{18}
7. $(p^{-2})^{-1}$ p^2
8. $(r^2)^3$ r^6

Example 2 (page 384)

Algebra **Simplify each expression.**

9. $(3x)^2$ $9x^2$
10. $(y \cdot y^2)^5$ y^{15}
11. $(2x^2)^4$ $16x^8$
12. $(a^2b^3)^4$ a^8b^{12}
13. $(abc)^5$ $a^5b^5c^5$
14. $(10x^5)^2$ $100x^{10}$
15. $(10^5w)^2$ $10^{10}w^2$
16. $(y^2 \cdot 10^2)^4$ 10^8y^8

3. Practice

Assignment Guide

Objective 1

A B Core 1–8, 19–23, 25, 39–41

C Extension 43, 46

Objective 2

A B Core 9–18, 24, 26–38, 42

C Extension 44–45

Test Prep 47–51

Mixed Review 52–59

Geography Connection
Exercise 30 Have students locate Hawaii on a map.

Practice 7-4 — Power Rules

Write each expression using one base and one exponent.

1. $(5^3)^{-6}$ — 5^{-18}
2. $(-9^4)^{-2}$ — 9^{-8} or $(-9)^{-8}$
3. $(d^5)^6$ — d^{30}
4. $(8^{-3})^{-9}$ — 8^{27}
5. $(4^{-3}, 4^{-2}, 4^{-1})^{-4}$ — $4^{12}, 4^8, 4^4$
6. $(y^8)^{-6}$ — y^{-48}
7. $(v^3, v^6, v^9)^2$ — v^6, v^{12}, v^{18}
8. $(k^{-7})^{-5}$ — k^{35}
9. $((n^3)^2)^5$ — n^{30}
10. $((a^2)^2)^2$ — a^8

Simplify each expression.

11. $(xyz)^6$ — $x^6y^6z^6$
12. $(10^2 \cdot x^7)^3$ — $1{,}000{,}000x^{21}$
13. $(7y^8)^2$ — $49y^{16}$
14. $(t^2 \cdot t^4)^5$ — t^{30}
15. $(4g)^3$ — $64g^3$
16. $(x^5y^4)^8$ — $x^{40}y^{32}$

Use >, <, or = to complete each statement.

17. $7^3 \cdot 7^3$? $(7^3)^3$ — $<$
18. $(6^{-2} \cdot 6^5)^3$? $(6^3)^2$ — $>$
19. $(4^6)^0$? $4^6 \cdot 4^{-6}$ — $=$

20. Find the area of a square whose side is 3×10^4 millimeters. Write the answer in scientific notation. 9×10^8 mm²

21. As of October 29, 2002 the Ijen volcano had an active crater with a radius of 1,100 ft. Using the formula for a circle $A = \pi r^2$ and 3.14 for π, what is the area of the crater? 3.7994×10^6 ft²

Reteaching 7-4 — Power Rules

The expression x^n is a power. It can also be read as x to the nth power.

Raising a Power to a Power

To raise a power to a power, multiply exponents.

Arithmetic:
$(2^4)^6$
$= 2^{(4 \cdot 6)}$ ← Multiply the exponents.
$= 2^{24}$ ← Simplify the exponent.

Algebra:
$(a^x)^y$
$= a^{(x \cdot y)}$ ← Multiply the exponents.
$= a^{xy}$ ← Simplify the exponent.

$(x^{-3})^{-5}$
$= x^{(-3 \cdot -5)}$ ← Multiply the exponents.
$= x^{15}$ ← Simplify the exponent.

Raising a Product to a Power

To raise a product to a power, raise each factor to the power.

Arithmetic:
$(4 \cdot 7)^2$
$= 4^2 \cdot 7^2$ ← Raise each factor to the power.

Algebra:
$(xy)^a$
$= x^ay^a$ ← Raise each factor to the power.

$(4a^2)^3$
$= 4^3(a^2)^3$ ← Raise each factor to the power.
$= 4^3a^6$ ← Multiply the exponents.
$= 64a^6$ ← Simplify.

Write each expression using one base and one exponent.

1. $(6^2)^{-4}$ — 6^{-8}
2. $(y^6)^{-5}$ — y^{-30}
3. $(7^{-4})^{-5}$ — 7^{20}
4. $(x^b)^c$ — x^{bc}
5. $(5^9)^3$ — 5^{27}
6. $(a^{-3})^{-8}$ — a^{24}

Simplify each expression.

7. $(ht)^n$ — h^nt^n
8. $(5v)^2$ — $25v^2$
9. $(7p^4)^2$ — $49p^8$
10. $(3d^4f^2)^3$ — $27d^{12}f^6$
11. $(k^5j^4)^3$ — $k^{15}j^{12}$
12. $(2s^7u^6)^4$ — $16s^{28}u^{24}$

Use <, >, or = to complete each statement.

13. 2^5 ☐ $(2^3)^2$ — $<$
14. $(5^{-4})^2$ ☐ 5^{-8} — $=$
15. $(6 \cdot 4)^2$ ☐ 10^2 — $>$

Example 3 (page 384)

Write each answer in scientific notation.

17. **Geometry** Find the area of a square whose side is 7.1×10^3 centimeters. 5.0×10^7 cm²

18. **Geometry** Find the area of a circle with a radius of 4×10^{-6} inches. Use the formula $A = \pi r^2$ and 3.14 for π. 5.0×10^{-11} in.²

B Apply Your Skills

29. When multiplying powers with the same base, you add the exponents. When raising a power to a power, you multiply the exponents.

Use <, >, or = to complete each statement.

19. 5^5 ■ $(5^3)^2$ $<$
20. $8^2 \cdot 8^6$ ■ $(8^2)^2$ $>$
21. $(5^3)^0$ ■ $5^3 \cdot 5^{-3}$ $=$
22. $(5^3)^5$ ■ 5^8 $>$
23. $(7^{-3} \cdot 7^5)^3$ ■ $(7^2)^6$ $<$
24. 0^{12} ■ 12^0 $<$
25. $4^5 \cdot 4^6$ ■ $(4^5)^6$ $<$
26. $(-3)^4$ ■ -3^4 $>$
27. $(3 \cdot 4)^7$ ■ 12^7 $=$

28. **Computers** A megabyte is 2^{20} bytes. Use exponents to write 2^{20} in four different ways. Answers may vary. Sample: $2 \cdot 2^{19}$; $2^{10} \cdot 2^{10}$; $2^5 \cdot 2^{15}$; $2^2 \cdot 2^{18}$

29. **Writing in Math** Explain how multiplying powers with the same base is different from raising a power to a power. See above left.

30. **Volcanoes** A subdivision of the Kilauea Volcano in Hawaii erupted in 1967 and produced about 320,000 cubic meters of lava per day. Find the total amount of lava produced if the eruption lasted about 8.3 months. Assume there are 30 days in a month. 7.968×10^7 m³

GPS

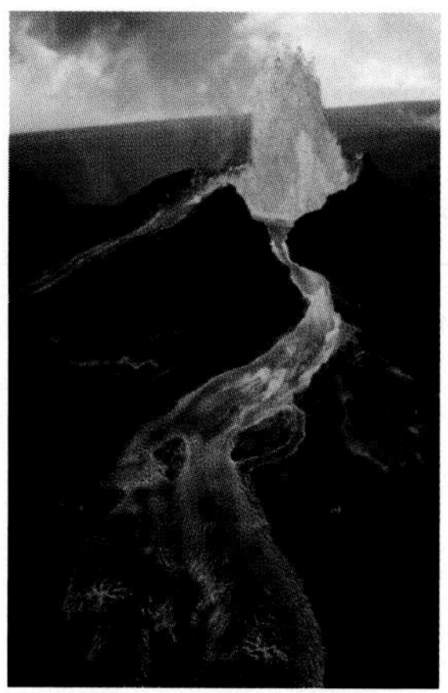

Real-World Connection

Hot lava from a volcano can reach a temperature of about 2,000°F.

Write each expression using a single exponent.

31. $(2^1 \cdot 2^2 \cdot 2^3)^2$ 2^{12}
32. $(3^{-2} \cdot 3^{-1} \cdot 3^0)^{-3}$ 3^9
33. $((5^2)^3)^2$ 5^{12}
34. $(y \cdot y^5 \cdot y^{10})^2$ y^{32}
35. $(a \cdot 10^{-1})^5$ $\left(\frac{a}{10}\right)^5$
36. $((m^1)^2)^4$ m^8

37. **Error Analysis** Beth thinks you can write $x^2 + x^2$ as $2x^2$. Clarissa thinks you can write $x^2 + x^2$ as x^4. Who is correct? Why? Beth is correct; $x^2 \cdot x^2 = x^4$, and $x^2 + x^2 = 2x^2$.

38. **Data File, p. 363** Convert 2.3 megawatts to watts. Use standard form. 2,300,000 watts

Simplify each expression.

39. $(a^b)^c$ a^{bc}
40. $(3u^2)^x$ 3^xu^{2x}
41. $(5^a \cdot 6^b)^x$ $5^{ax} \cdot 6^{bx}$

42. **Reasoning** Does $(2 + 3)^2 = 2^2 + 3^2$? Explain. No; $(2 + 3)^2 = 5^2 = 25$, and $2^2 + 3^2 = 4 + 9 = 13$.

C Challenge

43. A positive number is squared and the result is 25^{16}. Find the number, and write it as a power. 25^8

44. **Biology** The diameter of a human eyebrow hair is 8.0×10^{-5} m. Find the area of a cross section of an eyebrow hair. Use the formula $A = \pi r^2$ and 3.14 for π. 5.024×10^{-9} m²

45. **Astronomy** On January 1, 2004, Pluto will be about 2.9×10^9 miles from Earth. Light travels about 1.86×10^5 miles per second. Find how many hours it will take light to travel from Pluto to Earth. about 4.33 h

46. **Stretch Your Thinking** Arrange these numbers from least to greatest: $2^{222}, (2^{22})^2, (4)^{4^4}, (4^4)^{44}$ $(2^{22})^2, 2^{222}, (4^4)^{44}, (4)^{4^4}$

Use the Guided Problem Solving worksheet with Exercise 30.

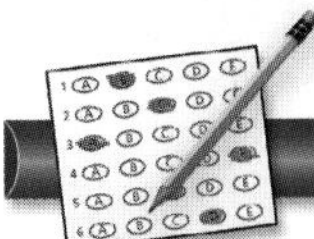

Test Prep

Multiple Choice

47. Find $(3.51 \times 10^{-4})^0$. C
A. 3.51×10^{-40} B. 0 C. 1 D. 3.51

48. The base of a crystal is a square with sides that measure 3×10^{-2} mm. Find the area of the base in square millimeters. G
F. 3×10^{-4} G. 9×10^{-4} H. 9×10^{-2} I. 9×10^{-1}

Take It to the NET
Online lesson quiz at **www.PHSchool.com**
Web Code: aca-0704

49. Which number is equal to 0.0625? B
A. 4×10^{-2} B. $(2^{-2})^2$ C. 6.25×10^{-1} D. $(4^{-2})^{-1}$

50. Which number is greater than $(35^3)^7$? I
F. 35^{10} G. 35^{21} H. $(35^7)^3$ I. 35^{37}

Extended Response

51. A square has a side length of 7×10^{-3} m. Find the perimeter and the area of the square. Write each answer in scientific notation. Show your work. See back of book.

Mixed Review

Lesson 7-2

Algebra **Write each expression using a single exponent.**

52. $15^{20} \cdot 15^2$ 15^{22} 53. $z^2 \cdot z^{12}$ z^{14} 54. $m^{10} \cdot m^{20}$ m^{30}

Lesson 6-9

Express each probability as a fraction and as a percent.

55. A letter chosen at random from the word V I D E O is a vowel. $\frac{3}{5}$; 60%

56. An integer chosen at random from the numbers 1 to 10 is prime. $\frac{2}{5}$; 40%

Lesson 6-1

Write each percent as a fraction in simplest form.

57. 20% $\frac{1}{5}$ 58. $33\frac{1}{3}\%$ $\frac{1}{3}$ 59. 1.75% $\frac{7}{400}$

Checkpoint Quiz 2 — Lessons 7-3 through 7-4

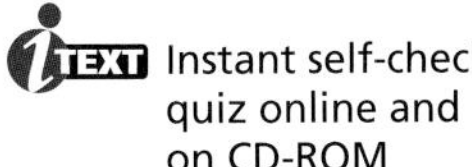

Instant self-check quiz online and on CD-ROM

Simplify each expression.

1. $(3x)^{-4}$ $\frac{1}{81x^4}$
2. $(26^2)^{20}$ 26^{40}
3. $(5b^3)^2$ $25b^6$
4. $m^0 \cdot m^1 \cdot m^{-2}$ $\frac{1}{m}$
5. $\frac{(3y)^{10}}{(3y)^{12}}$ $\frac{1}{9y^2}$
6. $\frac{a^{-b}}{a^{-3b}}$ a^{2b}
7. The radius of a circle is 6×10^{-3} m. Use the formula $A = \pi r^2$ and 3.14 for π to find its area. Write your answer in scientific notation. 1.1304×10^{-4} m^2
8. Write the number 4×10^{-8} in standard form. 0.00000004
9. **Reasoning** Explain why 2.25×10^{-3} is less than $\frac{1}{2}$. 0.00225 is less than 0.5.
10. Which is greater, 5×10^{-2} or $(5 \times 10^{-2})^2$? Explain. 5×10^{-2}; $0.05 > 0.0025$

4. Assess

Lesson Quiz 7-4

1. Write $(9^{-3})^8$ using a single exponent. 9^{-24}
2. Simplify $(2a^6)^3$. $8a^{18}$
3. Find the area of a circle whose radius is 5×10^{-7} m. Use 3.14 for π. 7.85×10^{-13} m^2

Chapter Checkpoint

To check understanding of Lessons 7-3 to 7-4:

Checkpoint Quiz 2 (p. 387)

Teaching Resources
Checkpoint Quiz 2 (also in *Prentice Hall Assessment System*)

Reaching All Students
Reading and Math Literacy 7C

Spanish versions available

Test Prep

Resources
For additional practice with a variety of test item formats:
- Test Prep, p. 401
- Test-Taking Strategies, p. 397
- Test-Taking Strategies with Transparencies

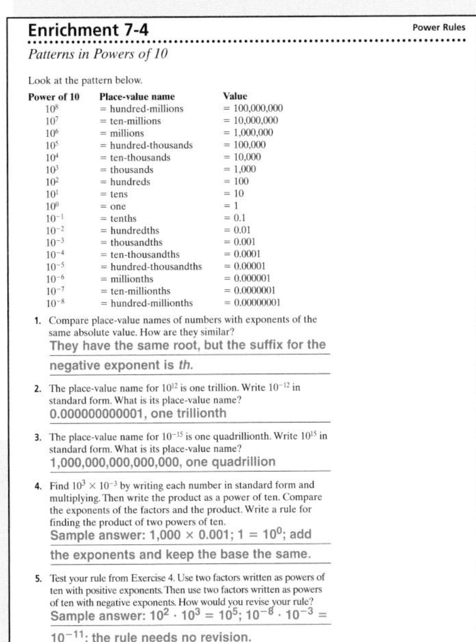

Enrichment 7-4 — Power Rules

Patterns in Powers of 10

Look at the pattern below.

Power of 10	Place-value name	Value
10^8	= hundred-millions	= 100,000,000
10^7	= ten-millions	= 10,000,000
10^6	= millions	= 1,000,000
10^5	= hundred-thousands	= 100,000
10^4	= ten-thousands	= 10,000
10^3	= thousands	= 1,000
10^2	= hundreds	= 100
10^1	= tens	= 10
10^0	= one	= 1
10^{-1}	= tenths	= 0.1
10^{-2}	= hundredths	= 0.01
10^{-3}	= thousandths	= 0.001
10^{-4}	= ten-thousandths	= 0.0001
10^{-5}	= hundred-thousandths	= 0.00001
10^{-6}	= millionths	= 0.000001
10^{-7}	= ten-millionths	= 0.0000001
10^{-8}	= hundred-millionths	= 0.00000001

1. Compare place-value names of numbers with exponents of the same absolute value. How are they similar?
They have the same root, but the suffix for the negative exponent is *th*.
2. The place-value name for 10^{12} is one trillion. Write 10^{-12} in standard form. What is its place-value name?
0.000000000001, one trillionth
3. The place-value name for 10^{-15} is one quadrillionth. Write 10^{15} in standard form. What is its place-value name?
1,000,000,000,000,000, one quadrillion
4. Find $10^3 \times 10^{-3}$ by writing each number in standard form and multiplying. Then write the product as a power of ten. Compare the exponents of the factors and the product. Write a rule for finding the product of two powers of ten.
Sample answer: $1{,}000 \times 0.001$; $1 = 10^0$; add the exponents and keep the base the same.
5. Test your rule from Exercise 4. Use two factors written as powers of ten with positive exponents. Then use two factors written as powers of ten with negative exponents. How would you revise your rule?
Sample answer: $10^2 \cdot 10^3 = 10^5$; $10^{-8} \cdot 10^{-3} = 10^{-11}$; the rule needs no revision.

Alternative Assessment

Each student in a pair writes an exponential expression. Partners exchange papers. Then they raise their partner's expression to the seventh power and simplify the expression.

7-5

1. Plan

Lesson Preview

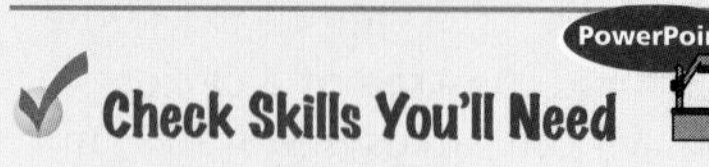

Check Skills You'll Need
Dividing Powers With the Same Base
Lesson 7-3: Examples 1–2. Extra Practice, p. 708.

Lesson Resources

Teaching Resources
Practice, Reteaching, Enrichment

Reaching All Students
Practice Workbook 7-5
Spanish Practice Workbook 7-5
Guided Problem Solving 7-5

Presentation Assistant Plus!
Transparencies
- Check Skills You'll Need 7-5
- Problem of the Day 7-5
- Additional Examples 7-5
- Student Edition Answers 7-5
- Lesson Quiz 7-5

PH Presentation Pro CD-ROM 7-5

Computer Test Generator CD

Technology
Resource Pro® CD-ROM
Computer Test Generator CD
PH Presentation Pro CD-ROM

www.PHSchool.com
Student Site
- Teacher Web Code: ack-5500
- Self-grading Lesson Quiz

PH SuccessNet Teacher Center
- Lesson Planner
- Resources

Plus iTEXT

7-5 Write an Equation

What You'll Learn

OBJECTIVE 1 To solve problems by writing equations

. . . And Why

To solve problems involving exponents, as in Example 1

Check Skills You'll Need

For help, go to Lesson 7-3.

Write each expression using a single exponent.

1. $\frac{a^9}{a^3}$ a^6
2. $\frac{10^{12}}{10^5}$ 10^7
3. $\frac{1.6^{11}}{1.6^6}$ 1.6^5
4. $\frac{10^5}{10^4}$ 10^1
5. $\frac{w^2}{w^6}$ w^{-4}
6. $\frac{d^3}{d^{10}}$ d^{-7}

iTEXT Interactive lesson includes instant self-check, tutorials, and activities.

OBJECTIVE 1 Solving Problems by Writing Equations

When to Use This Strategy You can use formulas and write equations to solve problems that include numbers written in scientific notation.

1 EXAMPLE Real-World Problem Solving

Real-World Connection
Space probes, like the *Pioneer 10,* are used to study the atmosphere of other planets.

Space Travel A space probe traveling at about 2×10^4 mi/h takes 760 days to reach Jupiter. Find the distance the probe travels.

Read and Understand The probe travels at 2×10^4 mi/h, and it takes 760 days to reach Jupiter. Your goal is to find the distance it travels.

Plan and Solve Use the formula $d = r \cdot t$ with the given information.

Words distance is rate times time

Let d = the distance the probe travels.

Equation $d = 2 \times 10^4 \cdot 760 \cdot 24$

$d = (2 \times 10^4) \cdot 18{,}240$ ← **Multiply 760 and 24.**
$= 36{,}480 \times 10^4$ ← **Multiply 2 and 18,240.**
$= 3.6480 \times 10^4 \times 10^4$ ← **Write 36,480 in scientific notation.**
$= 3.6480 \times 10^8$ ← **Add the exponents.**

The probe travels about 3.65×10^8 mi.

Look Back and Check The exponent on 10 for the distance is 8. This is larger than either of the exponents on 10 for the rate and time.

Check Understanding 1 Proxima Centauri is the nearest star to Earth, at 6×10^{12} mi away. How long will it take a space probe traveling at 18,000 mi/h to reach the star? $3.\overline{3} \times 10^8$ hours

Ongoing Assessment and Intervention

Before the Lesson
Diagnose prerequisite skills using:
- Check Skills You'll Need

During the Lesson
Monitor progress using:
- Check Understanding
- Additional Examples
- Test Prep

After the Lesson
Assess knowledge using:
- Lesson Quiz
- Computer Test Generator CD

 Real-World Problem Solving

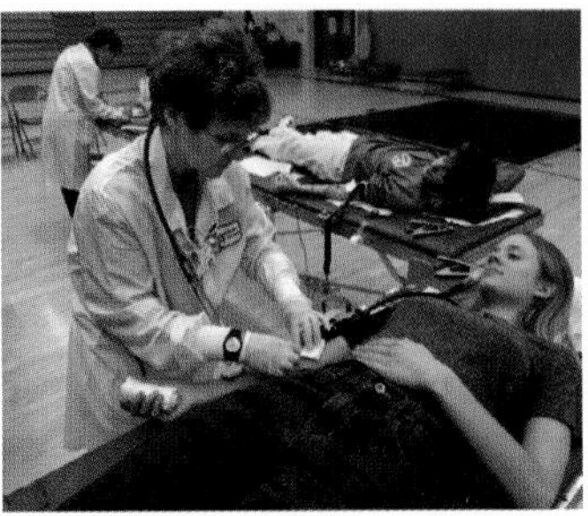

Real-World Connection

Each year about 4.5 million patients receive red blood cell transfusions.

SOURCE: America's Blood Centers

Circulatory System At any given moment, there are about 1×10^{13} red blood cells in a person's heart. If there are 5×10^{10} red blood cells in 1 milliliter of blood, how many milliliters of blood are in a person's heart?

Read and Understand There are 5×10^{10} red blood cells in 1 milliliter of blood and 1×10^{13} red blood cells in a person's heart. Your goal is to find the number of milliliters of blood in a person's heart.

Plan and Solve You can write an equation to solve this problem.

Words	milliliters of blood	times	red blood cells in a milliliter	is	total number of red blood cells
	Let b = the milliliters of blood.				
Equation	b	$\cdot$	5×10^{10}	$=$	1×10^{13}

$$b(5 \times 10^{10}) = 1 \times 10^{13}$$

$$\frac{b(5 \times 10^{10})}{5 \times 10^{10}} = \frac{1 \times 10^{13}}{5 \times 10^{10}} \quad \leftarrow \text{Divide each side by } 5.0 \times 10^{10}.$$

$$b = \frac{1}{5} \times \frac{10^{13}}{10^{10}} \quad \leftarrow \text{Use the Associative Property of Multiplication.}$$

$$b = 0.2 \times 10^{3} \quad \leftarrow \text{Divide. Subtract the exponents.}$$

$$b = 200 \quad \leftarrow \text{Write in standard form.}$$

There are about 200 milliliters of blood in a person's heart.

Look Back and Check Place the solution in the original equation.

$200(5 \times 10^{10}) = 1{,}000 \times 10^{10} = 1 \times 10^{13}$ ✔

 2 Light travels at 3.00×10^{8} m/s. How many seconds does a light ray take to travel 9×10^{6} m? 0.03 seconds

EXERCISES

For more practice, see *Extra Practice*.

A Practice by Example

Solve each problem by writing an equation. Check your answer.

Examples 1, 2 (pages 388, 389)

1. **Astronomy** The Milky Way Galaxy is about 5.879×10^{17} mi across, which is about 64 million times larger than the diameter of our solar system. Find the diameter of our solar system. 9.186×10^{9} mi

2. **Chemistry** If the mass of 6×10^{3} hydrogen atoms is 1.002×10^{-23} kg, what is the approximate mass of one hydrogen atom? 1.67×10^{-27} kg

Reaching All Students

Below Level Review dividing powers by finding the value of $2^7 \div 2^9$ and $(-3)^5 \div (-3)^3$. 2^{-2} or $\frac{1}{4}$; $(-3)^2$ or 9	**Advanced Learners** A space probe traveling at about 2×10^{4} mi/h travels a distance of 2.34×10^{6} mi. How many days does this take? 4.875 days	**Tactile Learners** See note on page 389. **Error Prevention** See note on page 389.

2. Teach

Professional Development

Math Background

When using the problem-solving steps of Read and Understand, Plan and Solve, and Look Back and Check, you can often write an equation as part of the planning step. The equation may be a familiar formula that relates the quantities in the problem.

Teaching Notes

1 EXAMPLE Error Prevention!

Ask: *Why is 760 multiplied by 24?* One day has 24 hours.

Science Connection
Have students locate Jupiter and Earth on a diagram of the planets.

Teaching Tip
Suggest that students determine the units for the answer before they begin to calculate.

2 EXAMPLE Tactile Learners

Pass around a container, such as a measuring cup or chemistry beaker, with metric measures marked on it. About one-eighth of a cup (or one fluid ounce) equals approximately 30 milliliters (or 30 cubic centimeters).

PowerPoint

Additional Examples

1. Sound travels at about 1.1×10^{3} ft/s. How far does a sound travel in 11s? 1.21×10^{4} ft

2. A certain blood sample contains 3×10^{12} red blood cells. If there are 5×10^{10} red blood cells in 1 milliliter of blood, about how many milliliters of blood are in this sample? 60 mL

Closure

What steps do you use to solve a problem by writing an equation? Sample: First read and understand the problem and identify the goal. Next use a formula or equation that applies and substitute for the known values. Then solve and check.

3. Practice

Assignment Guide

Objective 1

A B Core 1–10

C Extension 11–13

Test Prep 14–18

Mixed Review 19–30

Science Connection

Exercise 4 NASA stands for the National Aeronautics & Space Administration.

Practice 7-5

Problem Solving: Write an Equation

The top 10 United States counties with the greatest population are shown in the table.

Rank (of 3,141 counties)	County Name	State	Census Population April 1, 1990	Census Population April 1, 2000
1	Los Angeles County	CA	8.9×10^6	9.6×10^6
2	Cook County	IL	5.1×10^6	5.4×10^6
3	Harris County	TX	2.8×10^6	3.4×10^6
4	Maricopa County	AZ	2.1×10^6	3.1×10^6
5	Orange County	CA	2.4×10^6	2.8×10^6
6	San Diego County	CA	2.5×10^6	2.8×10^6
7	Kings County	NY	2.3×10^6	2.5×10^6
8	Miami-Dade County	FL	1.9×10^6	2.3×10^6
9	Queens County	NY	2.0×10^6	2.2×10^6
10	Dallas County	TX	1.9×10^6	2.2×10^6

Solve each problem by writing an equation. Check your answer.

1. In 1990, the population of Pima County in Arizona is about 4 times less than that of the population of Harris County in Texas. What was the population of Pima County in 1999?
   $4x = 2.8 \times 10^6$; about 7.0×10^5
2. In 2000, what was the difference in population between Cook County and Queens County?
   $x + 2.0 x 10^6 = 5.1 \times 10^6$; 3.1×10^6
3. About how many times larger was Los Angeles County than Cook County in 1990?
   $(5.1 \times 10^6)x = 8.9 \times 10^6$; about 1.75 times larger
4. In 2000, the population of Orange County in Florida was 896,344. How many more people lived in Miami-Dade County in 2000 than in Orange County?
   $x + 896{,}344 = 2.3 \times 10^6$; 1.4×10^6 more people lived in Miami Dade County than in Orange County in 2000.
5. The mayor of Kings County in New York expects the population to increase by about 10% from 2000 to 2010. How many people are predicted to populate that county in 2010?
   $x = 2.5 \times 10^6 + (0.10)2.5 \times 10^6$; about 2.75×10^6 people

Reteaching 7-5

Problem Solving: Write an Equation

You can write equations to help solve problems involving scientific notation.

The Pacific Ocean is about 6.4×10^7 square miles. It is about two times bigger than the size of the Atlantic Ocean. About how big is the Atlantic Ocean?

Read and Understand The Pacific Ocean has an area two times the size of the Atlantic Ocean. Your goal is to find the area of the Atlantic Ocean.

Plan and Solve You know the size of the Pacific Ocean. You can write an equation to solve for the size of the Atlantic Ocean.

Let x = the area of the Atlantic Ocean.

$$2x = 6.4 \times 10^7$$
$$x = \frac{6.4 \times 10^7}{2}$$
$$x = 3.2 \times 10^7$$

The Atlantic Ocean is about 3.2×10^7 square miles.

Look Back and Check Half of 6.4 is 3.2 and the exponent on 10 did not change. So the area of the Atlantic Ocean appears to be correct.

Solve each problem by writing an equation.

1. The Artic Ocean is about 5.4×10^6 square miles. The Indian Ocean is about 5 times the size of the Artic Ocean. About how big is the Indian Ocean?
   2.7×10^7 mi^2
2. The greatest depth of the Artic Ocean is about 1.8×10^5 ft. The greatest depth of the Pacific Ocean is about two times this amount. About how deep is the greatest depth of the Pacific Ocean?
   3.6×10^5 ft
3. Joe is 5 years older than Bijan. If the sum of their ages is 25, how old is each boy?
   Joe 15 Bijan 10
4. A chicken dinner costs $2.50 more than a spaghetti dinner. If the cost of both is $18.40, how much does each meal cost?
   Chicken $10.45 Spaghetti $7.95
5. Elaine sold twice as many T-shirts as Kim. How many did each girl sell if the total number of T-shirts sold was 27?
   Elaine 18 Kim 9
6. There are 5 more rows of corn than rows of peas in the garden. How many rows of each are there if there are 19 rows in all?
   Corn 12 Peas 7

Need Help?

- Reread the problem.
- Identify the key facts and details.
- Tell the problem in your own words.
- Try a different strategy.
- Check your work.

3. **Statistics** Population density is the number of people per square mile. The population density of India is about 8.05×10^2 people per square mile. The area of India is 1.27×10^6 square miles. What is the approximate population of India? 1.02×10^9 people

4. **Space Exploration** NASA scientists send a space probe outside of the solar system. The probe travels at a speed of about 2×10^5 mi/h. If Pluto is a minimum distance of 2.7×10^9 mi away from Earth, about how many days will it take the probe to reach Pluto? 563 days

B **Apply Your Skills**

Use any strategy to solve each problem. Show your work.

Strategies

Draw a Diagram
Look for a Pattern
Make a Graph
Make an Organized List
Make a Table
Simulate a Problem
Solve a Simpler Problem
Try, Check, and Revise
Use Logical Reasoning
Work Backward
Write an Equation

5. **Physics** The length of one type of atom is 1.57×10^{-8} in. Lined up end to end, how many atoms would make up a line 3 in. long? 1.91×10^8 atoms

6. GPS **Electricity** A refrigerator makes an electric field of 60 volts per meter (V/m). This field is 4 V/m less than four times the field made by a vacuum cleaner. Find the strength of the field a vacuum cleaner makes. 16 V/m

7. **Maps** You live at E Ave. and 2nd St. and your friend lives at G Ave. and 4th St. Using the roads, you can walk to your friend's house along many different routes. How many routes are four blocks long? 6 routes

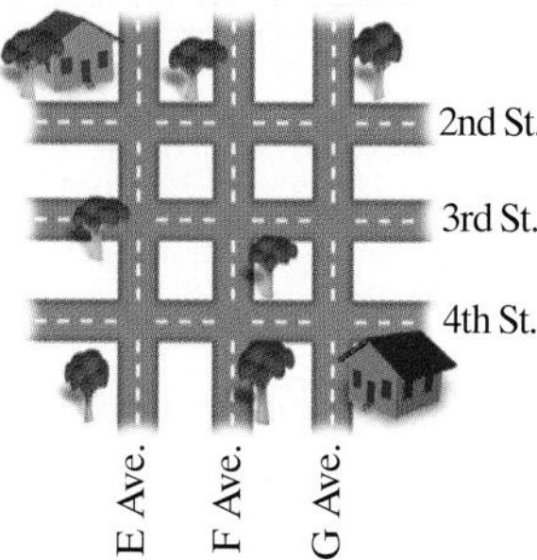

8. a. If you start with a number, subtract 8, multiply by one half, add 5, and then divide by 11, the result is 5. Find the number. 108
   b. **Writing in Math** What operations did you use to solve this problem? How are they related to the operations mentioned in the problem? See left.

b. Multiplication, subtraction, division, addition; they are inverse operations.

9. **Consumer Issues** Your brother paid $37.47 for two large skim boards like those at the right. One board was full price. The second was a used board and sold for half the price of the first board. How much did your brother pay for the used board? $12.49

10. **Patterns** The figure at the left shows a $3 \times 3 \times 3$ cube.
    a. How many $1 \times 1 \times 1$ cubes are there? 27 cubes
    b. How many $2 \times 2 \times 2$ cubes are there? 8 cubes
    c. How many cubes are there in all? 36 cubes
    d. How many cubes are there in a $4 \times 4 \times 4$ cube? 100 cubes

Use the Guided Problem Solving worksheet with Exercise 6.

C Challenge

11. **Probability** Without looking, you select one marble at a time from a bowl containing red, green, blue, and white marbles. There are a total of twenty marbles in the bowl. You stop when you have one marble of each color. What is the least number of marbles you have to select? What is the greatest? 4; 20

12. **Shopping** The local library sponsored a used-book sale to raise money. The books were priced at \$.60 for paperback books and \$1.00 for hardcover books. If the sales tax was 5% and your brother spent \$4.62, how many of each kind of book did he buy? 4 paperbacks and 2 hardcovers

13. **Stretch Your Thinking** A proper fraction is in lowest terms. Its two-digit numerator is a multiple of 7, and its two-digit denominator is a multiple of 8. The sum of the digits of its numerator is 3 greater than the sum of the digits of its denominator. What fraction is it? $\frac{49}{64}$

18. [2] Greater than 1; dividing by (4.5×10^{-6}) is the same as multiplying by (4.5×10^{6}). Since the numerator is greater than one, the product will also be greater than one.
[1] correct answer without explanation

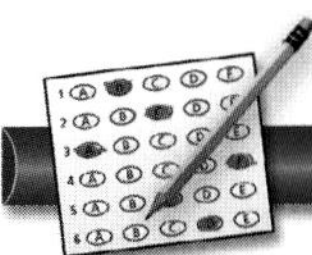

Test Prep

Multiple Choice

14. Evaluate $(a^2 \cdot b^3)^2$ for $a = 2$ and $b = 5$. C
A. 2.5×10^3 B. 2.5×10^4 C. 2.5×10^5 D. 2.5×10^6

15. What is the simplest form of $\frac{12b^{30}}{36b^{45}}$? H
F. $\frac{1}{3}b^{75}$ G. $\frac{1}{3b^{75}}$ H. $\frac{1}{3b^{15}}$ I. $\frac{1}{3}b^{15}$

Take It to the NET
Online lesson quiz at **www.PHSchool.com**
Web Code: aca-0705

16. What is 2.67×10^{-7} written in standard form? B
A. 0.00000267 B. 0.000000267 C. 26,700,000 D. 267,000,000

17. What is 245,000,000 written in scientific notation? H
F. 2.45×10^{-8} G. 24.5×10^{-8} H. 2.45×10^{8} I. 24.5×10^{8}

Short Response

18. Is $\frac{1.5 \times 10^5}{4.5 \times 10^{-6}}$ greater than or less than 1? Explain how you can tell without simplifying the expression. See above left.

Mixed Review

Lesson 7-4 **Algebra** **Write each expression using a single exponent.**

19. $(2^4)^3$ 2^{12} 20. $(4^{-2})^{-3}$ 4^6 21. $(r^3)^7$ r^{21} 22. $(x^5)^{-4}$ x^{-20}

23. $(10^3)^{-3}$ 10^{-9} 24. $(7^1)^1$ 7^1 25. $(m^2)^{100}$ m^{200} 26. $(3^2)^1$ 3^2

Lesson 6-9 **Express each probability as a fraction.** The last digit of a phone number can be 0, 1, 2, 3, 4, 5, 6, 7, 8, or 9. Suppose you pick a phone number at random and look at its last digit.

27. $P(6)$ $\frac{1}{10}$ 28. $P(\text{even number})$ $\frac{1}{2}$

29. $P(\text{prime number})$ $\frac{2}{5}$ 30. $P(\text{digit is less than 9})$ $\frac{9}{10}$

4. Assess

Lesson Quiz 7-5

Write an equation to solve each problem.

1. A space probe travels at 1.5×10^5 m/h. How far does it travel in 32 days? 1.152×10^8 m
2. Light travels at 3×10^8 m/s. How many seconds does a light ray take to travel 1.8×10^{11} m? 600 s

Alternative Assessment

Have students write an equation that could be used to solve Exercise 5 on p. 390.
$(1.57 \times 10^{-8})n = 3$

Test Prep

Resources
For additional practice with a variety of test item formats:
- Test Prep, p. 401
- Test-Taking Strategies, p. 397
- Test-Taking Strategies with Transparencies

Exercise 17 Remind students that the first factor must be greater than or equal to 1 and less than 10.

Enrichment 7-5 Problem Solving: Writing an Equation

Patterns in Data

The table shows the number of members of the U.S. House of Representatives according to the proportion of the population of some states to the total population of the United States. The apportioned population of the United States in the year 2000 was about 2.8×10^8 and the total number of representatives was 435.

State	Approximate Apportionment Population	Number of Apportioned Representatives Based on Census 2000
Alabama	4.5×10^6	7
Alaska	6.3×10^5	1
Arizona	5.1×10^6	8
Arkansas	2.7×10^6	4
California	3.4×10^7	53
Florida	1.6×10^7	25
Georgia	8.2×10^6	13

1. **Find the average number of people in each state per representative. Write your answer in scientific notation.**

Alabama	6.4×10^5	Alaska	6.3×10^5
Arizona	6.4×10^5	Arkansas	6.8×10^5
California	6.4×10^5	Florida	6.4×10^5
Georgia	6.3×10^5		

2. Find the average number of people in each state per representative in the entire United States.
6.4×10^5

3. What do you notice?
The averages per state are about the same.

4. Write and solve an equation to find the difference between the apportioned population of the United States in 2000 and the apportioned population of Arizona.
$2.8 \times 10^8 = 5.1 \times 10^6 + x$;
$x = 2.8 \times 10^8 - 0.051 \times 10^8$; $x = 2.749 \times 10^8$

5. Write and solve an equation to find the sum of the apportioned population of the Florida and Georgia in 2000.
$x - 1.6 \times 10^7 = 8.2 \times 10^6$;
$x = 1.6 \times 10^7 + 0.82 \times 10^7$; $x = 2.42 \times 10^7$

7-6

1. Plan

Lesson Preview

PowerPoint

 **Check Skills You'll Need**

Using the Order of Operations
Lesson 1-7: Example 3. Extra Practice, p. 702.

Lesson Resources

 **Teaching Resources**
Practice, Reteaching, Enrichment

 **Reaching All Students**
Practice Workbook 7-6
Spanish Practice Workbook 7-6
Guided Problem Solving 7-6

 **Presentation Assistant Plus!**
Transparencies
- Check Skills You'll Need 7-6
- Problem of the Day 7-6
- Additional Examples 7-6
- Student Edition Answers 7-6
- Lesson Quiz 7-6

PH Presentation Pro CD-ROM 7-6

Computer Test Generator CD

 **Technology**
Resource Pro® CD-ROM
Computer Test Generator CD
PH Presentation Pro CD-ROM

 **www.PHSchool.com**
Student Site
- Teacher Web Code: ack-5500
- Algebra Readiness Puzzles 31
- Self-grading Lesson Quiz

PH SuccessNet Teacher Center
- Lesson Planner
- Resources

Plus iTEXT

7-6 Number Systems

What You'll Learn

 To understand the base of a number system

. . . And Why

To learn how computers store numbers, as in Example 1

Check Skills You'll Need

For help, go to Lesson 1-7.

Simplify each expression.

1. $3 \cdot 10^2$ 300
2. $2 \cdot 10^2 + 5$ 205
3. $10^3 + 3 \cdot 10$ 1,030
4. $4 \cdot 10 + 6$ 46
5. $5 \cdot 10^3 + 5$ 5,005
6. $2^2 + 2$ 6
7. Evaluate the expression $2x^2 + x$ for $x = 10$. 210

New Vocabulary • expanded form • binary

OBJECTIVE

 Interactive lesson includes instant self-check, tutorials, and activities.

1 Understanding the Base of a Number System

Investigation: Modeling Number Systems

1–2. See back of book.

Light bulbs are packaged in the three packages at the left.

1. You work in the shipping department and fill orders for the light bulbs. You want to ship as many bulbs as possible using the least number of packages. For each of the following orders for light bulbs, how many of each kind of package do you ship?
   a. 20 b. 100 c. 161 d. 200
2. Super packages hold 216 bulbs. Find the least number of each kind of package you can use to fill each order.
   a. 300 b. 500 c. 600 d. 1,000
3. Explain the process you use to find how many of each kind of package you need to ship for any order of light bulbs. See left.

3. Answers may vary. Sample: Start with the largest package and use as many as you can; then move to the next smaller size.

When you watch the mileage on a car's odometer, the digit in the units place increases by 1 for every mile traveled.

The odometer works on a base-10 number system. The base-10 number system uses the 10 digits: 0, 1, 2, 3, 4, 5, 6, 7, 8, and 9. To get the next whole number after 9, you use the two digits 0 and 1 to make 10.

Ongoing Assessment and Intervention

Before the Lesson
Diagnose prerequisite skills using:
- Check Skills You'll Need

During the Lesson
Monitor progress using:
- Check Understanding
- Additional Examples
- Test Prep

After the Lesson
Assess knowledge using:
- Lesson Quiz
- Computer Test Generator CD

You can write the base-10 number 287 in standard form or expanded form.

Standard Form **Expanded Form**

$$287 = 200 + 80 + 7 = (2 \cdot 100) + (8 \cdot 10) + (7 \cdot 1)$$
$$= (2 \cdot 10^2) + (8 \cdot 10^1) + (7 \cdot 10^0)$$

The **expanded form** of a number shows the place value of each digit.

The **binary,** or base-2, number system uses the digits 0 and 1 with place values using powers of 2. Here is the binary number 10010_2 in standard form and expanded form.

Standard Form **Expanded Form**

$$10010_2 = (1 \cdot 2^4) + (0 \cdot 2^3) + (0 \cdot 2^2) + (1 \cdot 2^1) + (0 \cdot 2^0)$$

You read the binary number 10010_2 as "one, zero, zero, one, zero, base 2."

Real-World Connection Computer memories are made up of millions of transistors that can be switched on or off.

1 EXAMPLE The Decimal Value of a Binary Number

Real World

Computers Computers use binary numbers to store information. A binary digit represents an electrical circuit that is either on (1) or off (0). Six circuits with the switch settings on, on, on, on, off, on represent the binary number 111101_2. What is the decimal value of this number?

Write the binary number in expanded form.

$$111101_2 = (1 \cdot 2^5) + (1 \cdot 2^4) + (1 \cdot 2^3) + (1 \cdot 2^2) + (0 \cdot 2^1) + (1 \cdot 2^0)$$
$$= 32 + 16 + 8 + 4 + 0 + 1 \quad \leftarrow \text{Simplify within the parentheses.}$$
$$= 61 \quad \leftarrow \text{Add.}$$

The decimal value of 111101_2 is 61.

Check Understanding 1 Write the decimal value of each binary number.

a. 1101_2 13 **b.** 111_2 7 **c.** 10100_2 20

You can change decimal numbers into binary numbers.

2 EXAMPLE Changing a Decimal to a Binary Number

Need Help?

$2^0 = 1$	$2^1 = 2$
$2^2 = 4$	$2^3 = 8$
$2^4 = 16$	$2^5 = 32$

Write the decimal number 25 as a binary number.

Begin by writing 25 as the sum of powers of 2.

$$25 = 16 + 8 + 1 = 2^4 + 2^3 + 2^0 \quad \leftarrow \text{Use each power of 2 either once or not at all.}$$
$$= (1 \cdot 2^4) + (1 \cdot 2^3) + (0 \cdot 2^2) + (0 \cdot 2^1) + (1 \cdot 2^0) \quad \leftarrow \text{Use 1 if the power is used and 0 if the power is not used.}$$
$$= 11001_2 \quad \leftarrow \text{Use the digits 1 and 0 to write the binary number.}$$

The decimal 25 equals the binary number 11001_2.

Check Understanding 2 Write each decimal number as a binary number.

a. 9 1001_2 **b.** 17 10001_2 **c.** 28 11100_2

Reaching All Students

Below Level Have students write 3,245 in expanded form. $(3 \times 10^3) + (2 \times 10^2) + (4 \times 10^1) + (5 \times 10^0)$

Advanced Learners Have students work with a partner to make up digits with a value of 11 and 12 and use them to write a number in base-12.

English Learners See note on page 394.

Visual Learners See note on page 393.

2. Teach

Math Background

Our common number system is a base-10 system using the digits 0–9. A digit moved one decimal place to the left has a value 10 times greater than the original. Because computers are constructed with on or off switches, the binary, or base-2 system, is widely used in computer science. The binary system uses only the digits 0 and 1.

Teaching Notes

Investigation (Optional)

Ask:

- *What size package would you fill first?* largest one possible
- *When would you move to filling the next smaller size package?* when you can no longer fill completely the larger one

1 EXAMPLE Error Prevention!

Remind students that, just as the base-10 system has no digit for 10, the base-2 system has no digit for 2.

2 EXAMPLE Visual Learners

Have a row of students model a binary number, with each standing or sitting to represent 0 or 1. Ask other students to tell what the number would be in base-10.

Additional Examples

1. Write the decimal value of the binary number 110011_2. 51
2. Write the decimal number 34 as a binary number. 100010_2

Closure

Explain what it means to say that a number is written in the base-10 or the base-2 system. Sample: The base of a number system gives the value of the second place to the left of the decimal (the value of the first place to the left is always $(base)^0$ or 1). The value of all the other places are powers of that base. The base also tells how many digits are used.

3. Practice

Assignment Guide

Objective 1

- Ⓐ Ⓑ Core 1–22
- Ⓒ Extension 23–28

Test Prep 29–34

Mixed Review 35–47

English Learners
Exercises 25–28 *How might the "decimal" point be renamed for base-2 numbers?* Sample: bimal or binimal

Practice 7-6 — Number Systems

Write the decimal value for each binary number.

1. 11011_2 27
2. 100110_2 38
3. 10001_2 17
4. 11010_2 26
5. 110010_2 50
6. 110111_2 55
7. 110011_2 51
8. 11110_2 30
9. 11100_2 28
10. 1011001_2 89
11. 1101010_2 106
12. 10001111_2 143
13. 10001110_2 142
14. 1111111_2 127
15. 1001010_2 74

Write each decimal number as a binary number.

16. 14 1110_2
17. 22 10110_2
18. 58 111010_2
19. 63 111111_2
20. 86 1010110_2
21. 102 1100110_2
22. 65 1000001_2
23. 101 1100101_2

The base-5 number system uses the digits 0, 1, 2, 3, and 4 with place values using powers of 5. Write the decimal value for each base-5 number.

24. 123_5 38
25. 222_5 62
26. 431_5 116

The hexadecimal (base-6) number system uses the digits 0, 1, 2, 3, 4, and 5 with place values using powers of 6. Write the decimal value for each hexadecimal number.

27. 111_6 43
28. 214_6 82
29. 152_6 68

Reteaching 7-6 — Number Systems

The *binary*, or base-2 number system, uses the digits 0 and 1 with place values using powers of 2. Computers use binary numbers to store information.

- Finding the decimal value of a binary number

Find the decimal value of the binary number 1101_2.

$1101_2 = (1 \cdot 2^3) + (1 \cdot 2^2) + (0 \cdot 2^1) + (1 \cdot 2^0)$ ← Write the binary number in expanded form.
$= 8 + 4 + 0 + 1$ ← Simplify within the parentheses.
$= 13$ ← Add.

Find the decimal value of the binary number 110101_2.

$110101_2 = (1 \cdot 2^5) + (1 \cdot 2^4) + (0 \cdot 2^3) + (1 \cdot 2^2) + (0 \cdot 2^1) + (1 \cdot 2^0)$ ← Write the binary number in expanded form.
$= 32 + 16 + 0 + 4 + 0 + 1$ ← Simplify within the parentheses.
$= 53$ ← Add.

- Changing a decimal to a binary number

Write the decimal number 18 as a binary number.

Begin by completing a table of powers of 2.

2^7	2^6	2^5	2^4	2^3	2^2	2^1	2^0
128	64	32	16	8	4	2	1

Complete the table by using each power of 2 either once or not at all. Use a 1 if the power is used and a 0 if the power is not used.

2^7	2^6	2^5	2^4	2^3	2^2	2^1	2^0
128	64	32	16	8	4	2	1
			1	0	0	1	0

$18 = 16 + 2$ (Use the digits 1 and 0 to write the binary number.)
$18 = 10010_2$

Write the decimal value for each binary number.

1. $1111_2 =$ 15
2. $11100_2 =$ 28
3. $10111_2 =$ 23
4. $110101_2 =$ 53

Write each decimal number as a binary number.

5. 14 1110_2
6. 7 111_2
7. 33 100001_2
8. 22 10110_2

EXERCISES

For more practice, see *Extra Practice*.

Ⓐ Practice by Example

Example 1 (page 393)

Write the decimal value of each binary number. Exercise 1 is started for you.

1. $101_2 = 1 \cdot 2^2 + 0 \cdot 2^1 + 1 \cdot 2^0$ 5
2. 111_2 7
3. 1000_2 8
4. 1100_2 12
5. 1010_2 10

Example 2 (page 393)

Write each decimal number as a binary number. Exercise 6 is started for you.

6. $13 = 8 + 4 + 1$ 1101_2
7. 15 1111_2
8. 11 1011_2
9. 12 1100_2
10. 24 11000_2
11. 27 11011_2

Ⓑ Apply Your Skills

Computers **Find the decimal value for each switch setting.**

12. on, off, off 4
13. on, on, off 6
14. on, on, on, on 15

GPS 15. The greatest four-digit number in base 10 is 9,999.
   a. **Reasoning** What is the greatest four-digit number in base 2? 1111_2
   b. **Reasoning** What is the decimal value of the greatest four-digit number in base 2? 15

16. The red path in the tree diagram at the right represents the binary number 110_2. Find its decimal value. 6

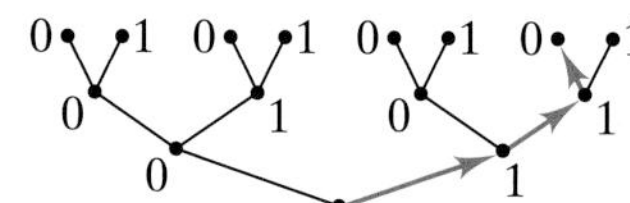

Write the decimal value of each base-3 number. The base-3 number system uses the digits 0, 1, and 2 with place values using powers of 3. Exercise 17 is started for you.

17. $102_3 = (1 \cdot 3^2) + (0 \cdot 3^1) + (2 \cdot 3^0) = 9 + 0 + 2$ 11
18. 21_3 7
19. 12_3 5
20. 221_3 25
21. 120_3 15

22. **Writing in Math** The digit 5 in the decimal number 351 is in the tens place. Explain why the digit 1 in the binary number 1000_2 is in the eights place. Its value is $1 \cdot 2^3$, which equals 8.

Ⓒ Challenge

23. When you multiply 10 by 1,011, you get the answer 10,110. Find the answer when you multiply 10_2 by 1011_2. Write the answer as a binary number. 10110_2

24. When you add 10 and 101, you get the answer 111. Find the answer when you add 10_2 and 101_2. Write the answer as a binary number. 111_2

Stretch Your Thinking **Write the decimal value of each base-2 number.** The base-2 number 1.1_2 equals $1 + \frac{1}{2}$.

25. 10.1_2 $2\frac{1}{2}$
26. 1.11_2 $1\frac{3}{4}$
27. 11.1_2 $3\frac{1}{2}$
28. 1.01_2 $1\frac{1}{4}$

Use the Guided Problem Solving worksheet with Exercise 15.

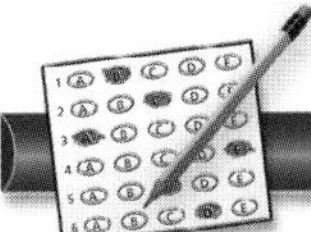

Test Prep

Gridded Response

29. What is the base-10 value of 110_2? 6

30. What is the base-10 value of 110010_2? 50

31. Write the digits of the binary number that equals 20. 10100

32. Write the digits of the binary number that equals 31. 11111

33. A computer stores the binary number 10111_2. What is the decimal value of the number? 23

34. When counting in base 2, write the digits of the binary number that comes after 1001_2. 1010

Take It to the NET
Online lesson quiz at **www.PHSchool.com**
Web Code: aca-0706

Mixed Review

Lesson 7-2 **Write each expression using a single exponent.**

35. $x^8 \cdot x^{10}$ x^{18} **36.** $3^{12} \cdot 3^8$ 3^{20} **37.** $(3y)^1 \cdot (3y)^2$ $27y^3$

Lesson 7-1 **Write each number in standard form.**

38. 2.97×10^3 2,970 **39.** 1.02×10^5 102,000 **40.** 8.11×10^4 81,000

Write each number in scientific notation.

41. 12,340,000 1.234×10^7 **42.** 18,000 1.8×10^4 **43.** 120,000,000 1.2×10^8

Lesson 6-5 **Find each percent of change. Round your answer to the nearest tenth of a percent where necessary.**

44. 25 to 26 4% increase **45.** 145 to 45 69% decrease **46.** 100 to 1000 900% increase **47.** 2.05 to 2.00 2.4% decrease

Math at Work

Video Game Programmers

Video game programmers need a strong background in mathematics and computer programming. They use logic to design their programs. Then they use algebra to write the detailed instructions that the computer understands. The result is a game that is fun for you to play.

Take It to the NET For more information about programming, go to **www.PHSchool.com**.
Web Code: acb-2031

4. Assess

Lesson Quiz 7-6

Write the decimal value of each binary number.

1. 1000110_2 70

2. 11011101_2 221

Write each decimal number as a binary number.

3. 54 110110_2

4. 29 11101_2

Alternative Assessment

Have students write a binary number with six digits. Then have them challenge a partner to write the decimal value for the number.

Test Prep

Resources

A sheet of blank grids is available in the *Test-Taking Strategies with Transparencies* booklet. Give copies of this sheet to students so they can practice filling in grids.

For additional practice with a variety of test item formats:

- Test Prep, p. 401
- Test-Taking Strategies, p. 397
- Test-Taking Strategies with Transparencies

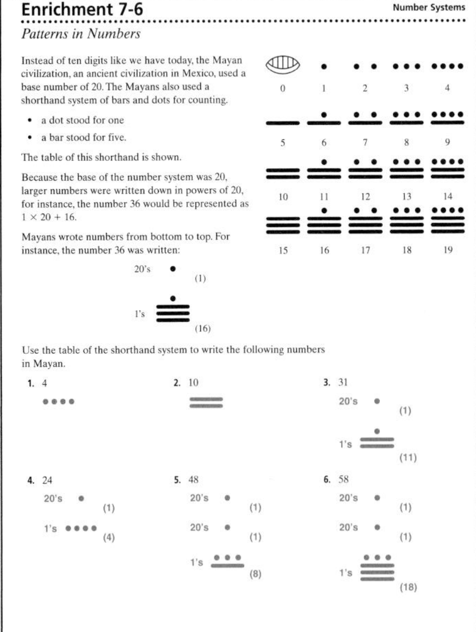

Enrichment 7-6 Number Systems

Patterns in Numbers

Instead of ten digits like we have today, the Mayan civilization, an ancient civilization in Mexico, used a base number of 20. The Mayans also used a shorthand system of bars and dots for counting.

- a dot stood for one
- a bar stood for five.

The table of this shorthand is shown.

0 1 2 3 4
5 6 7 8 9
10 11 12 13 14
15 16 17 18 19

Because the base of the number system was 20, larger numbers were written down in powers of 20, for instance, the number 36 would be represented as $1 \times 20 + 16$.

Mayans wrote numbers from bottom to top. For instance, the number 36 was written:

20's (1)
1's (16)

Use the table of the shorthand system to write the following numbers in Mayan.

1. 4 **2.** 10 **3.** 31 20's (1) 1's (11)

4. 24 20's (1) 1's (4) **5.** 48 20's (1) 20's (1) 1's (8) **6.** 58 20's (1) 20's (1) 1's (18)

Extension

Bar Codes

This extension introduces students to bar codes and to the unique way in which they are formed.

Teaching Notes

Although it is likely that all of your students are familiar with bar codes, most probably won't know very much about them. The UPC (Universal Product Code) bar codes were originally designed for food products to help supermarkets speed up the checkout process as well as to keep careful track of their inventory. The bar code system rapidly spread to all other retail items.

Teaching Tip

Go over the breakdown of the bar code. Point out that every product a manufacturer sells has a different 5-digit item code. A 12-ounce can of juice, for example, has a different item number from an 8-ounce can of the same juice.

Discuss how the last digit of the UPC code, the check digit, is used, and how it is determined. Work through the process with students.

Exercises

Have students work with partners on the exercises. Invite them to go through the steps for finding the check digit using the bar codes of sample products students have with them in class.

Extension Bar Codes

For Use With Lesson 7-6

Most products that you buy contain a bar code. Companies that use bar codes assign a different code to each of their products. Most bar codes consist of a 12-digit number.

- The first 6 digits identify the company.
- The next 5 digits identify the product.
- The last digit is called the check digit.

The check digit guarantees that the bar code is read correctly.

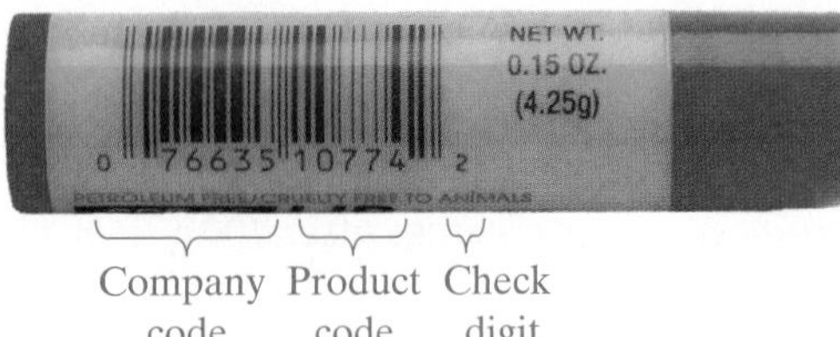

Company code Product code Check digit

EXAMPLE

Verify the check digit in the bar code above.

Step 1 Multiply all the digits in the odd positions by 3. Then multiply all the digits in the even positions by 1, and add the result.

$$(0 \cdot 3) + (7 \cdot 1) + (6 \cdot 3) + (6 \cdot 1) + (3 \cdot 3) + (5 \cdot 1) + (1 \cdot 3) + (0 \cdot 1) + (7 \cdot 3) + (7 \cdot 1) + (4 \cdot 3)$$
$$= 0 + 7 + 18 + 6 + 9 + 5 + 3 + 0 + 21 + 7 + 12$$
$$= 88$$

Step 2 Subtract the result in Step 1 from the next greatest multiple of 10.

$$90 - 88 = 2$$

The check digit is 2.

EXERCISES

For each bar code, determine if each check digit is correct.

1. 002361 00035 4 correct
2. 045000 54001 1 incorrect
3. 091000 00034 3 correct

Find the check digit for each 11-digit bar code.

4. 015000 40501 ■ 4
5. 023400 10024 ■ 8
6. 041000 32851 ■ 0

7. **Reasoning** A person manually enters a bar code but mistakenly interchanges two digits that are next to each other. Explain how the check digit will help detect the mistake.

7. The check digit would not be the same, because adjacent numbers have different multipliers.

8. What are the least and greatest check digits possible in a 12-digit bar code? 0; 9

Test-Taking Strategies

Answering True/False Questions

In true/false questions, all of the information in the statement must be true; otherwise the statement is false. Watch for words such as *all, always, none,* and *never*. When they are used, the statement may be true for many cases and false for just one.

1 EXAMPLE

True or false? The expression x^2 is always greater than x.

Try a few test values:

When $x = 2, x^2 = 4$, so $x^2 > x$.

When $x = 0, x^2 = 0$, so x^2 is *not* greater than x.

Since the statement used the word *always*, the statement is false.

2 EXAMPLE

A *counterexample* is an example that shows that a statement is false. Find a counterexample for the statement, "$x + 3$ is always positive." Suppose $x = -4$. Then $x + 3 = -4 + 3 = -1$, which is negative. So, $-4 + 3 = -1$ is a counterexample.

Real-World Connection

All cats have long tails.

Since Manx cats have short tails, the statement is false. This is a counterexample.

EXERCISES

Determine whether each statement is *true* or *false*. Explain your reasoning.

1. The expression $3h^2$ is always positive. False; if $h = 0$, the expression will equal zero, which is neither positive or negative.
2. If $60{,}000 \cdot 60{,}000 = 3.6 \times 10^k$, then $k = 8$. False; $k = 9$.
3. If n is a positive integer, then $3n$ is always less than 3^n. False; if $n = 1$, then $3(1) = 3$ and $3^1 = 3$, so the values are equal.
4. If w is a negative integer, then 4^w is always less than 0. False; when w is negative, the value of the expression is a fraction greater than zero and less than 1.

Find a counterexample for each statement.

5. All prime numbers are odd. False; 2 is both prime and even.
6. The expression $(w + x)^3$ equals $w^3 + x^3$ for all values of w and x. False; let $w = 2$ and $x = 3$. $(w + x)^3 = 5^3 = 125$, and $w^3 + x^3 = 35$.
7. The expression $a + b$ is always less than $a \cdot b$. False; let $a = 2$ and $b = 0$. $a + b = 2 + 0 = 2$, and $a \cdot b = 2 \cdot 0 = 0$. $2 \not< 0$.
8. The expression $c + d$ is always greater than $c - d$. False; let $c = 4$ and $d = -1$. $c + d = 4 + (-1) = 3$, and $c - d = 4 - (-1) = 5$. $3 \not> 5$.

Test-Taking Strategies

Answering True/False Questions

This page alerts students to the type of test question in which they need to determine whether a statement is or is not completely true. It gives pointers for how to successfully answer these questions.

Resources

Test-Taking Strategies with Transparencies
- Transparency 12
- Practice sheet, p. 31

Teaching Notes

Teaching Tip
Elicit from students that careful reading is essential for success on this kind of test question. Guide them to look for the key words provided at the top of the page.

Inclusion
Use a simple non-mathematical example to get across the concept that a statement is true if and only if there is *never* a case of it being false. Example: *All television actors fail when they try to become movie stars.*

Test-Taking Strategies With Transparencies

Chapter 7: Answering True/False Questions

Exercises

Determine whether each statement is true or false. Explain your answer.

1. True or False? When x is a positive integer, then 5^x is always positive.
   True; since 5 is positive, 5^x will also be positive.
2. True or False? The expression x^0 equals y^0 for all values of x and y.
   True; $x^0 = y^0 = 1$
3. True or False? The expression 5^8 always equals $5^4 \times 5^2$.
   False; $5^4 \times 5^2 = 5^6$
4. True or False? The expression x^3 is never smaller than x^2.
   False; if x is a fraction or a negative number then $x^3 < x^2$.
5. True or False? The expression $(s^{-5}t^{-4})^{-b}$ is equal to $s^{15}t^{12}$, when $b = -3$.
   True; if you substitute $b = -3$ into the expression the resulting expression is equal to $s^{15}t^{12}$.
6. True or False? The expression $(x - y)^2$ equals $x^2 - y^2$ when $x = 2$ and $y = 1$.
   False; when $x = 2$ and $y = 1$, then $(x - y)^2$ equals 1 and $x^2 - y^2$ equals 3.
7. True or False? The expression $\frac{9^8}{9^6}$ always equals 81.
   True; $\frac{9^8}{9^6} = 9^8 - 9^6 = 9^2$
8. True or False? The expression 9.8×10^{-4} is always greater than 6.4×10^{-3}.
   False; $9.8 \times 10^{-4} = 0.00098$, but $6.4 \times 10^{-3} = 0.0064$
9. True or False? The expression 11001_2 always equals $(1 \times 2^4) + (1 \times 2^3) + (1 \times 2^0)$.
   True; 11001_2 always equals $(1 \times 2^4) + (1 \times 2^3) + (1 \times 2^0)$
10. True or False? The expression 4×6^3 always equals $2^5 \times 3^3$.
    True; $4 \times 6^3 = 2^2 \times 2^3 \times 3^3 = 2^5 \times 3^3$
11. True or False? If $270{,}000 \times 21{,}000 = 5.67 \times 10^P$, then $P = 7$.
    False; $P = 9$

Resources

Student Edition
Extra Practice, Ch. 7, p. 708
English/Spanish Glossary, p. 735
Table of Symbols, p. 730

 **Reaching All Students**
Reading and Math Literacy 7D
Spanish Reading and Math Literacy 7D

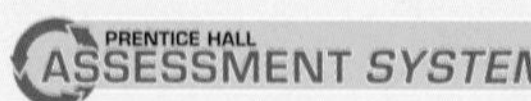

Test Preparation
- Chapter 7 practice in test formats

 **www.PHSchool.com**
Student Site
- Self-grading vocabulary test

PH SuccessNet Teacher Center
- Resources

Spanish Reading and Math Literacy

Reading and Math Literacy

7D: Vocabulary For use with the Chapter Review

Study Skill: Ask questions in class if you are unclear on a topic.

Match the term in Column A with its definition in Column B.

Column A		Column B
1. solution	F	A. figures that have the same shape and size
2. principal	L	B. the value that occurs most often in a data set
3. median	I	C. transformation that turns a figure about a fixed point
4. sample space	N	D. the change in *y* divided by the change in *x*
5. cosine	K	E. a mathematical statement that contains an equal sign
6. sine	P	F. the value of a variable that makes an equation true
7. outlier	R	G. A ratio comparing quantities that are measured in different units
8. congruent	A	H. transformation that flips a figure over a line
9. rotation	C	I. the middle value in a data set that has been ordered from least to greatest value
10. tangent	J	J. the ratio of the opposite side to the adjacent side of a right triangle
11. mode	B	K. the ratio of the adjacent side to the hypotenuse of a right triangle
12. prime	Q	L. the original deposit into a bank account
13. slope	D	M. tells how many times the base is used as a factor
14. rate	G	N. a collection of all the possible outcomes in an experiment
15. exponent	M	O. the longest side of a right triangle
16. mean	S	P. the ratio of the opposite side to the hypotenuse of a right triangle
17. reflection	H	Q. a number with exactly two factors, one and itself
18. equation	E	R. a data item that is much greater or less than the other items in the data set
19. hypotenuse	O	S. the sum of the data values in a set divided by the number of values in the set

Chapter Review

Vocabulary

binary (p. 393) **expanded form** (p. 393) **scientific notation** (p. 366)

 **Reading Math:** Understanding Vocabulary

Take It to the NET
Online vocabulary quiz at **www.PHSchool.com**
Web Code: acj-0751

Choose the correct vocabulary term to complete each sentence.

1. The number 10110_2 is an example of a(n) __?__ number. binary
2. __?__ is used when writing very large or very small numbers scientific notation
3. The __?__ of 459 is $4 \cdot 10^2 + 5 \cdot 10^1 + 9 \cdot 10^0$. expanded form
4. To find the decimal value of a binary number, you use __?__. expanded form
5. The number 3×10^2 is written in __?__. scientific notation

Skills and Concepts

7-1 Objectives
- To write numbers in standard form and scientific notation
- To order numbers written in scientific notation

A number is in **scientific notation** if the first factor is greater than or equal to 1 and less than 10 and the second factor is a power of 10.

Write each number in scientific notation.

6. 3,500 3.5×10^3
7. 801,000 8.01×10^5
8. 2,005 2.005×10^3
9. 8,104,000 8.104×10^6

Write each number in standard form.

10. 4.1×10^3 4,100
11. 1.03×10^8 103,000,000
12. 6×10^4 60,000
13. 5.005×10^9 5,005,000,000

Order each set of numbers from least to greatest.

14. $5.4 \times 10^5, 5.1 \times 10^6, 7 \times 10^3$
15. $4 \times 10^{12}, 9.1 \times 10^9, 9.9 \times 10^{12}$

14–15. See left.

14. 7×10^3, 5.4×10^5, 5.1×10^6
15. 9.1×10^9, 4×10^{12}, 9.9×10^{12}

7-2 and 7-3 Objectives
- To multiply powers with the same base
- To multiply numbers in scientific notation
- To divide powers with the same base
- To use negative or zero exponents

To multiply numbers with the same base, add the exponents. To divide numbers with the same base, subtract the exponents.

Write each expression using a single exponent. 17. $(-3)^{13}$ 18. 2.6^{24}

16. $8^{10} \cdot 8^9$ 8^{19}
17. $(-3)^4 \cdot (-3)^9$
18. $2.6^{12} \cdot 2.6^{12}$
19. $11^5 \cdot 11^6$ 11^{11}
20. $\frac{5^{10}}{5^7}$ 5^3
21. $\frac{(-8)^{12}}{(-8)^2}$ $(-8)^{10}$
22. $\frac{76^{11}}{76^5}$ 76^6
23. $\frac{1.8^6}{1.8^5}$ 1.8^1

Find each product. Write the answer in scientific notation.

24. $(3 \times 10^6) \cdot (2 \times 10^{12})$ 6×10^{18}
25. $5 \cdot (1.4 \times 10^6)$ 7×10^6
26. $(6 \times 10^9) \cdot (5 \times 10^4)$ 3×10^{14}
27. $(2.1 \times 10^7) \cdot (7 \times 10^{12})$ 1.47×10^{20}

Simplify each expression.

28. 5^0 1 **29.** 5^{-1} $\frac{1}{5}$ **30.** $(2ab)^0$ 1 **31.** $(-2)^{-3}$ $-\frac{1}{8}$

Write each number in standard form.

32. 4×10^{-3} 0.004 **33.** 1.9×10^{-6} 0.0000019 **34.** 6.01×10^{-4} 0.000601

Write each number in scientific notation.

35. 0.00002 2×10^{-5} **36.** 0.00105 1.05×10^{-3} **37.** 0.0115 1.15×10^{-2}

7-4 Objectives

- To raise a power to a power
- To raise a product to a power

To raise a power to a power, multiply the powers. To raise a product to a power, raise each factor to the power.

Write each expression using a single exponent.

38. $(5^2)^4$ 5^8 **39.** $(9^1)^{20}$ 9^{20} **40.** $(8^{-2})^{-3}$ 8^6 **41.** $(a^{-4})^2$ a^{-8} **42.** $(x^{20})^{-1}$ x^{-20}

43. $(a^4)^{10}$ a^{40} **44.** $(2^{10})^{-10}$ 2^{-100} **45.** $(333^{33})^3$ 333^{99} **46.** $(3^0)^8$ 3^0 **47.** $(w^5)^0$ w^0

Simplify each expression.

48. $(4x)^2$ $16x^2$ **49.** $(2n)^3$ $8n^3$ **50.** $(4 \times 10^9)^2$ 1.6×10^{19} **51.** $(2 \times 10^4)^3$ 8×10^{12} **52.** $(ab^5)^4$ a^4b^{20}

53. $(abc)^{14}$ $a^{14}b^{14}c^{14}$ **54.** $(3a^{-4})^2$ $9a^{-8}$ **55.** $(w^5x^{-5})^2$ $w^{10}x^{-10}$ **56.** $(6ab^3)^2$ $36a^2b^6$ **57.** $(2x^4y)^0$ 1

7-5 Objective

- To solve problems by writing equations

You can write and solve equations that involve scientific notation.

Solve each problem by writing an equation.

58. If you travel for 8 seconds at 2.5×10^4 centimeters per second, find how far you would go. 2×10^5 cm

59. Biology A person's body contains about 5 liters of blood. Each liter of blood contains about 5×10^{13} red blood cells. About how many red blood cells are there in a person's body? 2.5×10^{14} blood cells

---

7-6 Objective

- To understand the base of a number system

The base-10 number system uses the digits 0, 1, 2, 3, 4, 5, 6, 7, 8, and 9 and powers of 10. The **binary**, or base-2, number system uses the digits 0 and 1 and powers of 2. A number in **expanded form** shows the place value of each digit using powers of the base.

Write the decimal value for each binary number.

60. 101_2 5 **61.** 100_2 4 **62.** 1110_2 14 **63.** 1101_2 13

Write each decimal number as a binary number.

64. 7 111_2 **65.** 10 1010_2 **66.** 29 11101_2 **67.** 30 11110_2

Alternative Assessment Form C

Alternative Assessment **Form C**

Chapter 7

MODELING THE SOLAR SYSTEM

You need to make a scale model of the solar system. You first collect the data shown in the table. An astronomical unit (AU) is often used to describe distance in astronomy. It is the approximate distance from Earth to the sun.

Use the table to answer all of the questions. Show your work on a separate sheet of paper.

Planet	Average Distance from Sun (km) in Standard Notation	Average Distance from Sun (km) in Scientific Notation	Average Distance from Sun (AU)
Mercury	58,000,000		0.39
Venus	107,500,000		0.72
Earth	149,600,000		1
Mars	227,900,000		
Jupiter	778,400,000		
Saturn	1,429,400,000		
Uranus	2,869,300,000		
Neptune	4,500,000,000		
Pluto	5,913,700,000		

1. Add to the table each distance from the sun in scientific notation.
2. Complete the last column of the table on your paper.
3. Compare the distances from Earth to its three closest neighbors. Which three planets are closet to Earth?In kilometers, what is the average distance of each from Earth?
4. List the planets in order from closest to Earth to farthest from Earth.

Resources

 **Teaching Resources**
Ch. 7 Test, Forms A & B
Ch. 7 Alternative Assessment, Form C

Reaching All Students
Spanish Ch. 7 Test, Forms A & B
Spanish Ch. 7 Alternative Assessment, Form C

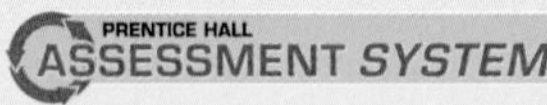

Assessment Resources
- Ch. 7 Test, Forms A & B
- Ch. 7 Alternative Assessment, Form C

Computer Test Generator CD
- Ch. 7 Instant Chapter Test™
- Make your own Ch.7 test

 **www.PHSchool.com**
Student Site
- Self-grading Ch. 7 test

PH SuccessNet Teacher Center
- Resources

Plus 

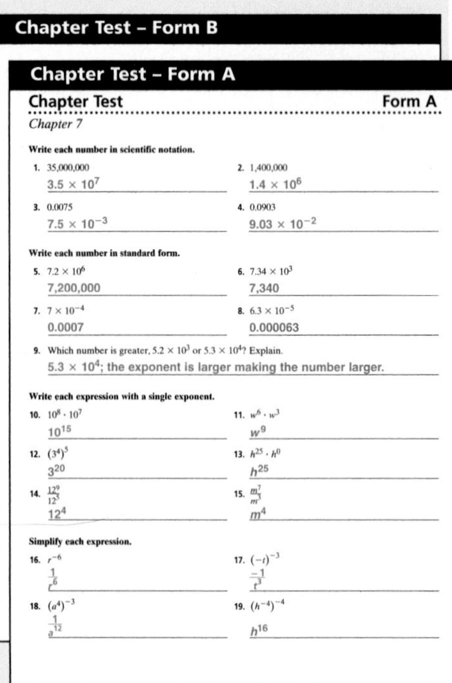

Chapter Test – Form B

Chapter Test – Form A

Chapter Test — Form A

Chapter 7

Write each number in scientific notation.

1. 35,000,000 — 3.5×10^7
2. 1,400,000 — 1.4×10^6
3. 0.0075 — 7.5×10^{-3}
4. 0.0903 — 9.03×10^{-2}

Write each number in standard form.

5. 7.2×10^6 — 7,200,000
6. 7.34×10^3 — 7,340
7. 7×10^{-4} — 0.0007
8. 6.3×10^{-5} — 0.000063
9. Which number is greater, 5.2×10^3 or 5.3×10^4? Explain. — 5.3×10^4; the exponent is larger making the number larger.

Write each expression with a single exponent.

10. $10^8 \cdot 10^7$ — 10^{15}
11. $w^6 \cdot w^3$ — w^9
12. $(3^4)^5$ — 3^{20}
13. $h^{25} \cdot h^0$ — h^{25}
14. $\frac{12^9}{12^5}$ — 12^4
15. $\frac{m^7}{m^3}$ — m^4

Simplify each expression.

16. r^{-6} — $\frac{1}{r^6}$
17. $(-t)^{-3}$ — $\frac{-1}{t^3}$
18. $(a^4)^{-3}$ — $\frac{1}{a^{12}}$
19. $(h^{-4})^{-4}$ — h^{16}

Chapter Test

Take It to the NET
Online chapter test at **www.PHSchool.com**
Web Code: aca-0752

Write each number in scientific notation.

1. 23,000,000 2.3×10^7
2. 1,500,000 1.5×10^6
3. 450,000,000 4.5×10^8
4. 0.00007 7.0×10^{-5}
5. 0.0089 8.9×10^{-3}
6. 0.0401 4.01×10^{-2}

Write each number in standard form.

7. 4.1×10^5 410,000
8. 8.02×10^4 80,200
9. 5×10^{-3} .005
10. 8.8×10^{-6} .0000088

11. **Number Sense** Which number is greater, 5×10^{-6} or 6×10^{-5}? Explain. 6×10^{-5}; $\frac{6}{100{,}000} > \frac{5}{1{,}000{,}000}$

Write each expression using a single exponent.

12. $10^7 \cdot 10^6$ 10^{13}
13. $a^5 \cdot a^2$ a^7
14. $t^{23} \cdot t^0$ t^{23}
15. $\frac{(-3)^5}{(-3)^2}$ $(-3)^3$
16. $\frac{14^8}{14^4}$ 14^4
17. $\frac{c^6}{c^2}$ c^4

Write each expression with a positive exponent.

18. w^{-5} $\frac{1}{w^5}$
19. $(-a)^{-8}$ $\frac{1}{(-a)^8}$
20. $(r^3)^{-2}$ $\frac{1}{r^6}$
21. $(d^{-3})^{-4}$ d^{12}
22. $(x^{-6})^3$ $\frac{1}{x^{18}}$
23. $(-y^{-2})^{-5}$ $(-y^{10})$

Simplify each expression.

24. $(2^2)^3$ 64
25. $(rs^5)^{10}$ $r^{10}s^{50}$
26. $(7p^3)^2$ $49p^6$
27. $(2cd^3)^{-2}$ $\frac{1}{4c^2d^6}$

28. Write $(4 \times 10^{-9})^2$ in scientific notation. 1.6×10^{-17}
29. **Biology** The human eye blinks about 6.25×10^6 times each year. About how many times has the eye of a 14-year-old blinked? Write the answer in scientific notation. See margin.
30. **Writing in Math** Write what you would say to a classmate who asked you to explain why 5^0 is equal to 1. See margin.
31. A googol is the large number 10^{100}. Write $\frac{1}{10^{100}}$ in scientific notation. 1×10^{-100}
32. **Science** Helium atoms are the smallest particles of any gas that exists. They are one tenth of a billionth of a meter in diameter. Write this number in scientific notation. 1×10^{-10}

Solve each problem by writing an equation.

33. **Biology** A *Euglena* is a single-celled organism about 2×10^{-3} inches long. How many of these organisms does it take to make a line 12 inches long? 6,000 organisms
34. One quarter has a mass of about 5.7×10^{-3} kilograms. How many quarters does it take to make a 1-kilogram mass? 175 quarters
35. **Science** The speed of light is about 3.00×10^5 kilometers per second.
    a. How many kilometers does light travel in 10^{-6} seconds? 3×10^{-1} km, or 0.3 km
    b. The distance from Earth to the moon is about 3.8×10^5 kilometers. How many seconds does it take a light ray to travel from the moon to Earth? 1.27 s
36. If $m^5 = 8$, what is the value of m^{10}? 64
37. The probability that 100 fair coins will show exactly 50 heads is about 8×10^{-2}. Write this number as a percent. 8%

Find the decimal value of each binary number.

38. 101010_2 42
39. 100100_2 36
40. 11011_2 27
41. 1110111_2 119

Write each decimal number as a binary number.

42. 14 1110_2
43. 16 10000_2
44. 31 11111_2

45. The first 4 multiples of 2 are 2, 4, 6, and 8. Write these numbers as binary numbers. 10_2; 100_2; 110_2; 1000_2

29. 8.75×10^7 times

30. Answers may vary. Sample: $\frac{5^{10}}{5^{10}} = 5^{10-10} = 5^0 = 1$, and $\frac{5^{10}}{5^{10}} = 1$.

Test Prep

Reading Comprehension **Read each passage and answer the questions that follow.**

Our Changing America The 1990 U.S. Census gave the populations of the four largest racial groups as White: 209,491,000; African American: 29,986,000; Latino: 22,354,000; and Asian American: 7,274,000. By 2000, the White population increased to 211,461,000, the African American population increased to 34,658,000, the Latino population increased to 35,306,000, and the Asian American population increased to 10,243,000. The entire population of the United States in 2000 was about 2.82×10^8 people.

1. How would you write the 2000 Latino population in scientific notation? B
   - A. $3 \times 10^8 + 5 \times 10^7 + 3 \times 10^6 + 6 \times 10^4$
   - B. 3.5306×10^7
   - C. 35.306×10^6
   - D. 3.5306×10^6

2. In 2000, about what percent of the population was non-white? H
   - F. 2.5 G. 7.5 H. 25 I. 75

3. What was the approximate percent of increase in the Asian American population from 1990 to 2000? C
   - A. 4 B. 29 C. 40 D. 71

4. About what percent of the population was Latino in 2000? G
   - F. 1.25 G. 12.5
   - H. 25 I. 1.25×10^7

Internet Protocol Addresses Each computer on a network has an Internet Protocol (IP) address. Each IP address consists of four numbers from 0 to 255 separated by periods. The address 150.214.23.5 is an example. To be read by a computer, each of the four numbers is converted into an 8-digit binary, or base-2, number. When necessary, zeros are put before the binary number to make each number eight digits long.

10010110.11010110.00010111.00000101

10010110	11010110	00010111	00000101
150	214	23	5

5. Write the base-10 numbers of the IP address 0010110001.00001011.00010010.00000101. A
   - A. 177.11.18.5 B. 177.13.18.5
   - C. 177.14.18.5 D. 177.15.18.5

6. The first eight digits of some IP addresses begin with the sequence 1110 . . . What is the base-10 value of 11100000? I
   - F. 216 G. 218 H. 222 I. 224

7. What are the base-2 numbers of the IP address 220.150.25.6? B
   - A. 11011100.10010110.00010001.00000110
   - B. 11011100.10010110.00011001.00000110
   - C. 11011100.10010110.00011101.00000110
   - D. 11011100.10010110.00011111.00000110

Test Prep

Students must be able to extract information from reading passages, answer multiple-choice questions, and construct responses in order to be successful in current state and national assessments.

Resources

Teaching Resources
Cumulative Review

Reaching All Students
Spanish Cumulative Review

Test Preparation
- Ch. 7 standardized test prep

Assessment Resources
- Cumulative Review

Computer Test Generator CD
- Standardized test prep

www.PHSchool.com
- Standardized test prep
- Resources

Plus 

Cumulative Review

Cumulative Review

Chapters 1–7

Multiple Choice. Choose the letter of the best answer.

1. Three less than twice a number is 19. What is the number?
   - A. 8 B. 9.5 (C) 11 D. 19
2. Give the prime factorization for 126.
   - F. 2×63
   - G. $2 \times 7 \times 9$
   - H. $2 \times 3^2 \times 5$
   - (I) $2 \times 3^2 \times 7$
3. Find the area of a trapezoid with a height of 10 cm and bases of 5 cm and 7 cm. Use $A = \frac{1}{2}h(b_1 + b_2)$.
   - A. 22 cm^2 (B) 60 cm^2 C. 120 cm^2 D. 175 cm^2
4. What is 0.0003 in scientific notation?
   - F. 3×10^4
   - G. 0.3×10^{-3}
   - (H) 3×10^{-4}
   - I. 30×10^2
5. The hypotenuse of a right triangle is 15 in. One leg of the triangle is 12 in. What is the length of the third side?
   - A. 3 in. (B) 9 in. C. 81 in. D. not here
6. Solve. $3y + \frac{7}{8} = 5$
   - (F) $1\frac{3}{8}$ G. $4\frac{1}{8}$ H. $\frac{47}{24}$ I. not here
7. What percent of 40 is 25?
   - (A) 62.5% B. 30% C. 75% D. 10%
8. What is a variable expression for "four times a number, increased by six"?
   - (F) $4n + 6$ G. $6n + 4$ H. $(4n)(6)$ I. $6n - 4$
9. Find $5^0 + 5^2$.
   - A. 10 (B) 26 C. 30 D. 50
10. Simplify. $9(m + 3) - 2m$
    - (F) $7m + 27$ G. $7m + 3$ H. $11m + 9$ I. $9m + 1$
11. Solve. $6r - 3 = 8r + 1$
    - (A) -2 B. 1 C. 4 D. -4
12. Between which two consecutive whole numbers does $\sqrt{32}$ lie?
    - F. 4 and 5
    - (G) 5 and 6
    - H. 6 and 7
    - I. 7 and 8
13. One rectangle is 5 in. by 8 in. A second rectangle, similar to the first, has a length of 25.6 in. Find the width of the second rectangle.
    - A. 10 in. (B) 16 in. C. 25.6 in. D. 40.96 in.
14. What are the slope and y-intercept of $y = -\frac{1}{2}x + 4$?
    - F. $-2, 4$ G. $4, -2$ (H) $-\frac{1}{2}, 4$ I. $4, \frac{1}{2}$

Wild Exponents

Students will use data from these two pages to complete the activities posed here in Put It All Together.

Activating Prior Knowledge
Have students brainstorm a list of the tallest, shortest, longest, heaviest, lightest, fastest, and slowest animals. Then have volunteers do research on this topic to compare the names on the list with actual animal data.

Teaching Notes

Have volunteers read aloud the opening paragraph with the information about various animals. Then discuss the data presented. Have a student explain and demonstrate how to express in standard form numbers written in scientific notation.

Science Connection
How do the giants of today's animal kingdom compare in size, weight, and speed with the dinosaurs and giant reptiles and mammals of the distant past? Have interested students find out. Ask them to share what they have learned with classmates. Invite them to present their findings in a table and graph.

Careers
What kinds of jobs are there, other than as pet store owners, zoo keepers, or veterinarians, for those wishing to work with or learn more about animals? What skills, interests, and aptitudes should those interested in the field possess? What education is required? Have them put together an annotated list of interesting job opportunities.

Wild Exponents

Applying Scientific Notation Would a giraffe 5.79×10^3 mm tall fit in your bedroom? Should you be afraid of a lobster that weighs 7.5×10^{-4} t? Could you outrun a rabbit that hopped 5.55×10^9 ft per decade? Scientific notation is convenient for expressing and comparing numbers, but it can also mislead you into thinking the numbers are wilder than they actually are. Often you can tame them by turning them back into a more familiar form.

Average Heights
Middle school boy: 156 cm
Middle school girl: 157 cm
Male giraffe: 530 cm
Female giraffe: 430 cm

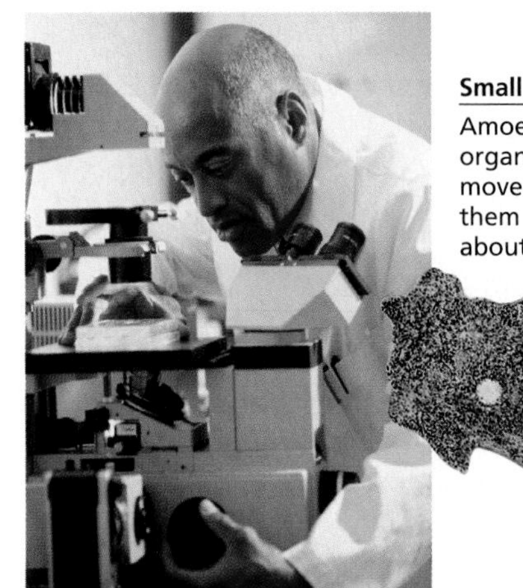

Small Packages
Amoebas, small, transparent organisms, flow outward to move. It's easy to overlook them because they're only about 0.003 mm long!

How Many Is That?
A blue whale can be 33.5 m long—about the length of 18 scuba divers, including their flippers.

Take It to the NET For more information about animals, go to **www.PHSchool.com**.
Web Code: ace-0753

1a. 5.79 m
b. 1.5 lb
c. 12 mi/h
2–3. Check students' work.

Put It All Together

1. **Warm Up** Use the information in the introductory paragraph.
   a. How tall is the giraffe in meters?
   b. How much does the lobster weigh in pounds?
   c. How fast does the rabbit hop in miles per hour?

The goal of this game is to identify an animal when given its common dimensions in uncommon ways.

What You'll Need

- 3 to 5 index cards per student
- **Research** Choose an animal for each card. Consider animals that range in size from microscopic to gigantic. Find three numerical facts about each animal.
- Convert each fact to scientific notation, using units of measure that make the animal look especially large or small. Some numbers should have positive exponents and others should have negative exponents.
- Write these facts, or clues, on the front of the card.
- Illustrate the back of the card with a picture of the animal.

How to Play

2. Exchange cards with another student. Looking only at the clues, and *not* at the back of the card, change each into standard notation. Write your answers on a piece of paper.
3. Check your partner's answers while he or she checks yours. Correct any mistakes. Take turns asking questions about each animal until you guess what it is.

Sample Card (Zebra)

Who Am I?

1. Shoulder height up to 1.5×10^{-2} km
2. Weight up to 4×10^{5} g
3. Adult female has 1×10^{0} foal per year.

Length Conversions
1 micron = 1×10^{-6} m
1 mm = 1×10^{-3} m
1 km = 1×10^{3} m
1 ft = 3.048×10^{-1} m
1 mi = 5.28×10^{3} ft
1 light-year = 5.879×10^{12} mi

Weight Conversions
1 mg = 1×10^{-3} g
1 kg = 1×10^{3} g
1 kg = 2.2 lb
1 oz = 28.35 g
1 lb = 16 oz
1 t = 2×10^{3} lb

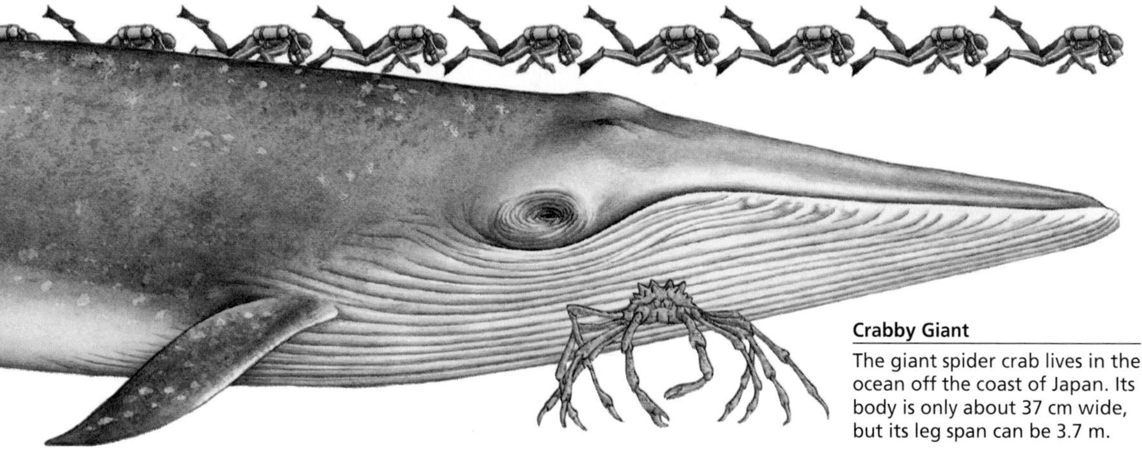

Crabby Giant

The giant spider crab lives in the ocean off the coast of Japan. Its body is only about 37 cm wide, but its leg span can be 3.7 m.

Put It All Together

Work through the Warm Up exercises together. Then discuss the rules and goals of the game that students will play. You may wish to have students work in pairs to create their cards. Refer all students to the conversion charts.

Teaching Tip
Using the sample card for the zebra as a guide, emphasize the importance of using the correct language when describing characteristics of a particular kind of animal. Point out, for instance, that a *foal* is a baby zebra.

Visual Learners
Invite students to tape photos of the animals on the back of the cards instead of creating drawings of them.

Inclusion
As needed, have students help one another compute with or convert the numbers expressed in scientific notation, particularly with those containing negative powers of ten. Review the abbreviations for the different customary units of measure.

CHAPTER 8

Geometry

Chapter at a Glance

8-1 Pairs of Angles
pp. 407–412

Objectives

1. Using Adjacent Angles and Vertical Angles
2. Using Supplementary Angles and Complementary Angles

New Vocabulary
adjacent angles, vertical angles, supplementary, complementary, perpendicular lines

Optional Materials
protractor

NCTM Standards
1, 2, 3, 4, 6, 7, 8, 9, 10

Local Standards

8-2 Angles and Parallel Lines
pp. 413–418

Objectives

1. Angles Formed by Parallel Lines
2. Identifying Parallel Lines

New Vocabulary
transversal, corresponding angles, alternate interior angles

Optional Materials
protractor

NCTM Standards
1, 2, 3, 4, 6, 7, 8, 9, 10

Local Standards

8-3 Congruent Polygons
pp. 420–425

Objectives

1. Identifying Congruent Parts
2. Identifying Congruent Triangles

New Vocabulary
congruent polygons

NCTM Standards
1, 2, 3, 4, 6, 7, 8, 9, 10

Local Standards

8-4 Problem Solving
Solving a Simpler Problem and Look for a Pattern
pp. 426–429

Objectives

1. Solving a Problem by Combining Strategies

NCTM Standards
1, 3, 6, 7, 8, 9, 10

Local Standards

✓ Checkpoint Quiz 1

8-5 Classifying Triangles and Quadrilaterals
pp. 430–433

Objectives

1. Classifying Triangles and Quadrilaterals

New Vocabulary
acute triangle, obtuse triangle, right triangle, equilateral triangle, isosceles triangle, scalene triangle, quadrilateral, parallelogram, trapezoid, rhombus, rectangle, square

NCTM Standards
1, 3, 6, 7, 8, 9, 10

Local Standards

8-6 Angles and Polygons
pp. 436–439

Objectives

1. Finding the Angle Measures of a Polygon

New Vocabulary
regular polygon

NCTM Standards
1, 2, 3, 4, 6, 7, 8, 9, 10

Local Standards

8-7 Areas of Polygons
pp. 441–446

Objectives

1. Finding the Areas of Polygons

New Vocabulary
area

NCTM Standards
1, 2, 3, 4, 6, 7, 8, 9, 10

Local Standards

8-8 Circumferences and Areas of Circles
pp. 447–452

Objectives

1. Finding the Circumference of a Circle
2. Finding the Areas of a Circle

NCTM Standards
1, 2, 3, 4, 5, 6, 7, 8, 9, 10

Local Standards

8-9 Constructions
pp. 454–459

Objectives

1. Constructing Congruent Segments and Angles
2. Constructing Bisectors

New Vocabulary
compass, midpoint, segment bisector, perpendicular bisector, angle bisector

Optional Materials
compass, straightedge

NCTM Standards
1, 3, 4, 6, 7, 8, 9, 10

Local Standards

✓ Checkpoint Quiz 2

Reaching All Students
Additional Instructional Options in Chapter 8

Reading and Math Literacy

Reading Math
- Connecting Ideas With Concept Maps, p. 434
- Reading Math hints, pp. 422, 430, 431, 438, 447, 456
- Reading Comprehension, p. 418
- Understanding Vocabulary, p. 462

Writing in Math
- Writing to Compare, p. 453
- Daily Writing Practice, pp. 411, 416, 424, 428, 433, 438, 445, 446, 450, 453, 458, 464

Above Level

Challenge exercises
- pp. 411, 417, 425, 429, 433, 439, 446, 451, 458

Extension
- Parallel and Perpendicular Lines, p. 419
- Tessellations, p. 440

Hands-On and Technology

Investigations
- Exploring Pairs of Angles, p. 407
- Exploring Parallel Lines, p. 413
- Sum of the Angles of a Polygon, p. 435

Technology
- Geometry Software and Constructions, p. 460

Activities and Projects

Real-World Snapshots
- Applying Geometry, pp. 466-467

Chapter Project
- Great Escape, p. 699

Test Prep

Daily Test Prep
- pp. 412, 418, 425, 429, 433, 439, 446, 452, 458

Test-Taking Strategies
- Drawing a Diagram, p. 461

Test Prep
- Cumulative Review (Chapters 1–8), p. 465

Chapter Assessment

Checkpoint Quiz
- pp. 429, 459

Chapter Review
- pp. 462–463

Chapter Test
- p. 464

Pacing Options

This chart suggests pacing only for the core lessons and their parts. It is provided as a possible guide. It will help you determine how much time you have in your schedule to cover the additional features and assessment, as described at the left.

Day	Traditional 45-minute class periods	Block 90-minute class periods
1	8-1 ▼1	8-1 ▼1 ▼2
2	8-1 ▼2	8-2 ▼1 ▼2
3	8-2 ▼1	8-3 ▼1 ▼2 8-4 ▼1
4	8-2 ▼2	8-5 ▼1 8-6 ▼1
5	8-3 ▼1 ▼2	8-7 ▼1 8-8 ▼1 ▼2
6	8-4 ▼1	8-9 ▼1 ▼2
7	8-5 ▼1	
8	8-6 ▼1	
9	8-7 ▼1	
10	8-8 ▼1	
11	8-8 ▼2	
12	8-9 ▼1	
13	8-9 ▼2	
14		
15		

NCTM STANDARDS 2000

1	Number and Operations	6	Problem Solving
2	Algebra	7	Reasoning and Proof
3	Geometry	8	Communication
4	Measurement	9	Connections
5	Data Analysis and Probability	10	Representation

Math Background

Skills Trace

BEFORE Chapter 8

Course 2 introduced properties of geometric figures and finding areas of polygons.

DURING Chapter 8

Course 3 reviews and extends properties of two-dimensional geometric figures including basic constructions.

AFTER Chapter 8

Throughout this course students solve real-world problems using geometric figures.

8-1 Pairs of Angles

Math Understandings

- A pair of angles can be supplementary or complementary even though they are not adjacent, or even in the same figure.
- Two lines that intersect to form equal adjacent angles are perpendicular.

Adjacent angles (for example: ∠1 and ∠2; ∠2 and ∠3; ∠3 and ∠4; ∠1 and ∠4 in the figure below) have a common vertex and a common side, but no common interior points. **Vertical angles**, (for example: ∠1 and ∠3; ∠2 and ∠4 in the figure) are formed by two intersecting lines and are opposite each other. Vertical angles are congruent.

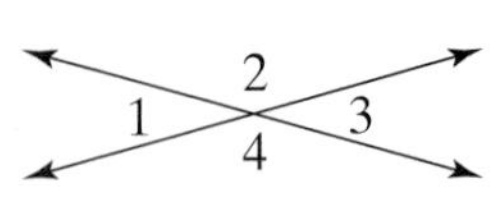

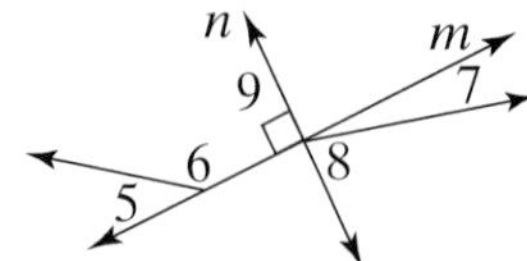

If the sum of the measures of two angles is 180°, the angles are **supplementary** (for example: ∠1 and ∠2; ∠2 and ∠3; ∠3 and ∠4; ∠1 and ∠4; ∠5 and ∠6 in the figure above). If the sum of the measures of two angles is 90°, the angles are **complementary** (for example: ∠7 and ∠8 in the figure above). **Perpendicular lines** (for example: lines *m* and *n* in the figure above) are two lines that intersect to form a right angle.

8-2 Angles and Parallel Lines

Math Understandings

- A transversal can also intersect two lines that are not parallel to each other.
- If you know that corresponding angles or alternate interior angles are congruent, then you can be sure the lines intersected by the transversal are parallel.

A line that intersects two other lines at different points is a **transversal**. Corresponding angles lie on the same side of the transversal and in corresponding positions. **Alternate interior angles** lie within a pair of lines and on opposite sides of the transversal.

Transversals and Parallel Lines

When a transversal intersects two parallel lines,

- corresponding angles are congruent, and
- alternate interior angles are congruent.

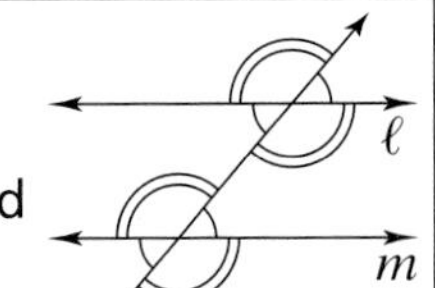

8-3 Congruent Polygons

Math Understandings

- When two polygons are congruent, you can slide, flip, or turn one so that it fits exactly on top of the other one.
- The matching angles and sides of congruent polygons are called corresponding parts. When you name congruent polygons, you always list the corresponding vertices in the same order.
- The order of the angles and sides is important in determining whether two triangles are congruent.

Congruent polygons are polygons with the same size and shape. The tick marks in a diagram identify congruent sides. The arcs identify congruent angles.

Showing Triangles Are Congruent

To demonstrate that two triangles are congruent, show that the following parts of one triangle are congruent to the corresponding parts of the other triangle.

(SSS) (SAS)

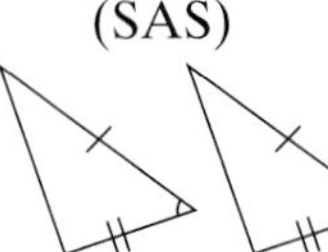

(ASA)

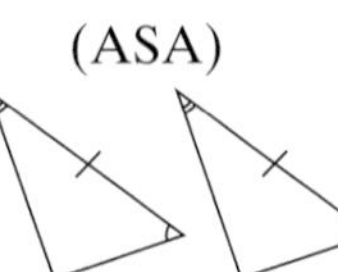

Solve a Simpler Problem and Look for a Pattern

If you read a problem, and it seems to require many steps, you may be able to use the strategy of *solve a simpler problem* first. Then *look for a pattern*. Use the pattern to solve the original problem. When you make a conjecture based on a pattern, you are using *inductive reasoning.* Since patterns may not always continue, it is important to check results whenever possible.

Classifying Triangles and Quadrilaterals Angles and Polygons

Math Understandings

- You can classify triangles and quadrilaterals by their angle measures or by the number of congruent sides.

When a quadrilateral has more than one name, use the one that describes the quadrilateral most precisely.

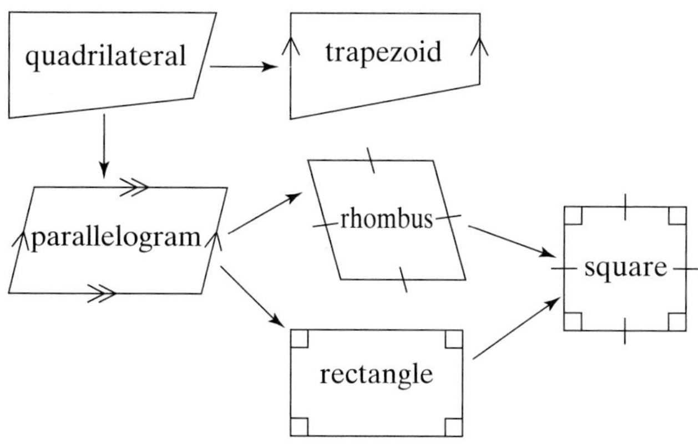

For a polygon with *n* sides, the **sum of the measures** of the interior angles is $(n - 2)180°$. A **regular polygon** is a polygon with all the sides congruent and all the angles congruent. You can find the measure of each angle of a regular polygon by dividing the sum of the angle measures by the number of angles.

8-7
8-8

Areas of Polygons Circumferences and Areas of Circles

Math Understandings

- The area of a figure is the number of square units it encloses.
- The circumference of a circle is the distance around the circle, or its perimeter.

Areas of Polygons and Circles

Rectangle	$A = bh$	
Parallelogram	$A = bh$	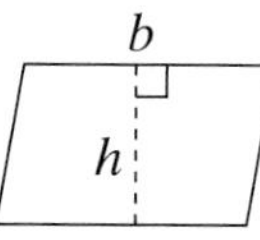
Triangle	$A = \frac{1}{2}bh$	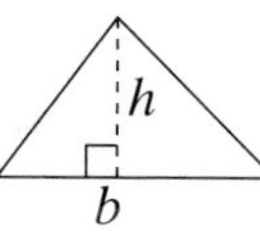
Trapezoid	$A = \frac{1}{2}h(b_1 + b_2)$	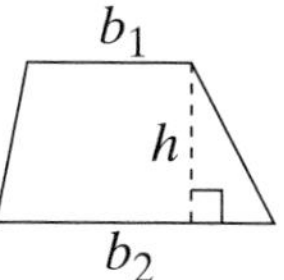
Circle	$A = \pi r^2$ $C = \pi d$ or $C = 2\pi r$	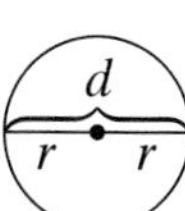

8-9

Constructions

Math Understandings

- Not all lines that bisect a line segment are perpendicular bisectors.

A **compass** is a tool used to draw circles and parts of circles called arcs. A straightedge, the only other tool used for classic geometric constructions, has no measurement markings.

Additional Professional Development Opportunities

Chapter 8 Math Background notes: pp. 408, 414, 421, 427, 431, 437, 442, 448, 455

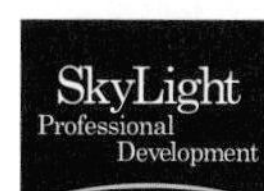

Additional resources available from SkyLight Professional Development:

On-site courses, workshops, summer institutes. Online courses and chat rooms. Videocassettes and books. Visit www.skylightedu.com.

Ongoing Assessment and Intervention

The *Prentice Hall Mathematics* program provides many options for assessment in the Student Edition, Teacher's Edition, and teaching resources. From these options you may choose instructional materials that are appropriate for your students and that support your district's curriculum requirements.

Daily Assessment

Instant Check System™ in Chapter 8

Allows students to check their own learning before, during, and after each lesson.

Diagnosing Readiness before the chapter (p. 406)

Check Skills You'll Need exercises in each lesson (pp. 407, 413, 420, 426, 430, 436, 441, 447, 454)

Check Understanding questions with each Example (pp. 408, 409, 414, 415, 421, 422, 427, 430, 431, 436, 437, 442, 443, 448, 449, 455, 456, 457)

Checkpoint Quiz (pp. 429, 459)

Formal Assessment

Assessment in the Student Text and in Additional Resources

Assess student progress throughout the Course 2 textbook and with blackline masters and CD-ROM.

Student Edition

- Chapter 8 Review, with Vocabulary, Skills, and Concepts Review, pp. 462–463
- Chapter 8 Test, p. 464

Assessment Resources

- Checkpoint Quizzes 1 & 2
- Chapter Test, forms A & B
- Chapter Alternative Assessment

Spanish versions available.

Computer Test Generator CD-ROM

- Instant Chapter Tests™—pre-made tests with items that vary every time you print.
- Online Testing allows you to give tests online and receive progress reports.
- Prepare students by making tests based on standardized test objectives.

Algebra Readiness Tests

- Includes Basic Skills Tests and Concept-Readiness Tests.
- Assess understanding of skills and concepts needed for success in algebra.

Intervention

Skills Intervention Kit

Online Intervention

Integrated within the iText, this online intervention system includes diagnostic tests and prescribed remediation, plus reports to track student mastery.

A *complete* system for the student who is struggling with course-level work

Eight intervention units cover core skills and allow you to:

- **Diagnose** students' gaps in basic skills
- **Prescribe** an individualized course of study
- **Monitor** student progress

Includes print workbooks, tutorial CD-ROM, teacher editions, progress folders, and more. *Available in Spanish.*

How to Use with Chapter 8

8-1	Geometry, Skill 1
8-2	Geometry, Skill 3
8-3	Geometry, Skill 10
8-5	Geometry, Skills 7, 9
8-6	Geometry, Skill 8
8-7	Measurement, Skills 8–10
8-8	Measurement, Skills 13–14
8-9	Geometry, Skill 3

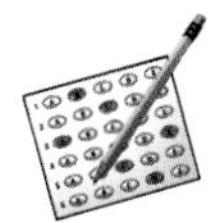

Standardized Test Preparation

The *Prentice Hall Mathematics* program integrates preparation for high-stakes standardized tests in every lesson of the Student Edition and continues this support in the Prentice Hall Assessment System.

Test Prep

In Student Text, Chapter 8

Teaches students strategies and gives them practice with all the test item formats they will encounter on high-stakes tests.

Test Prep exercises in each lesson (pp. 412, 418, 425, 429, 433, 439, 446, 452, 458)

Test-Taking Strategies Drawing a Diagram, p. 461

Test Prep (p. 465: Cumulative Review, Chapters 1–8)

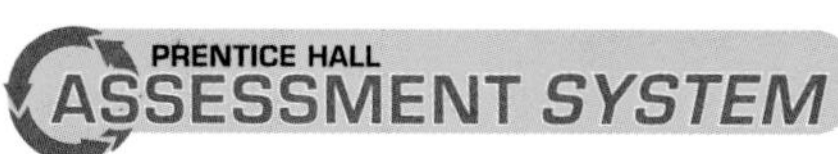

PRENTICE HALL
ASSESSMENT SYSTEM

A three-step approach to preparing students for high stakes, national, and state exams.

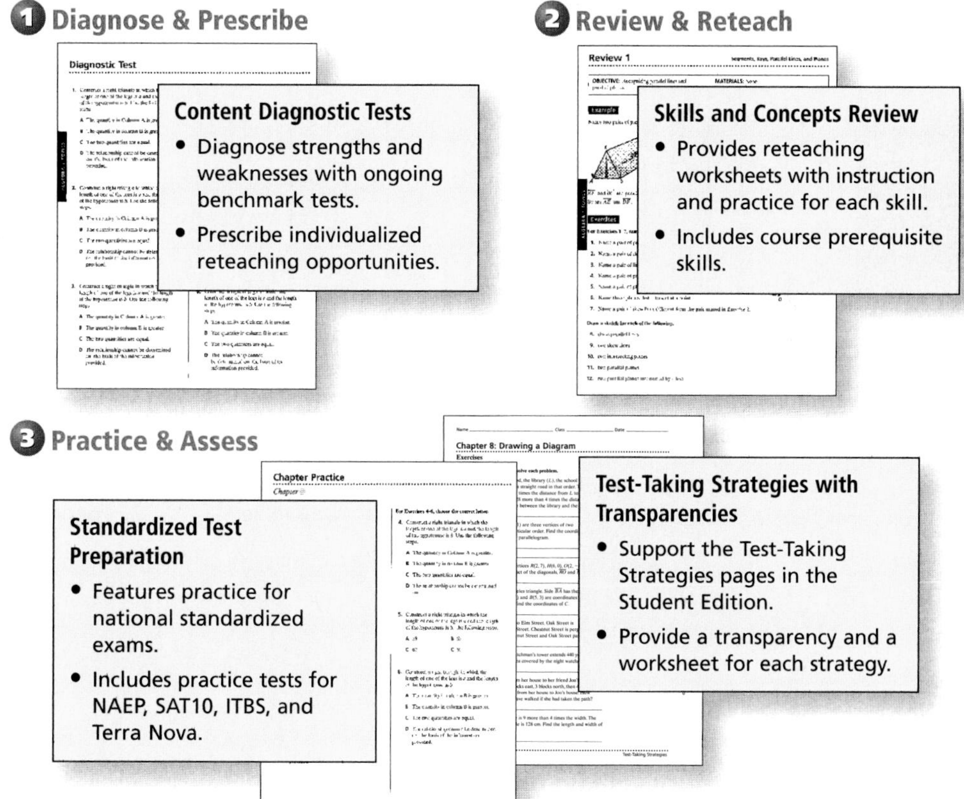

1 Diagnose & Prescribe
Content Diagnostic Tests
• Diagnose strengths and weaknesses with ongoing benchmark tests.
• Prescribe individualized reteaching opportunities.
2 Review & Reteach
Skills and Concepts Review
• Provides reteaching worksheets with instruction and practice for each skill.
• Includes course prerequisite skills.
3 Practice & Assess
Standardized Test Preparation
• Features practice for national standardized exams.
• Includes practice tests for NAEP, SAT10, ITBS, and Terra Nova.
Test-Taking Strategies with Transparencies
• Support the Test-Taking Strategies pages in the Student Edition.
• Provide a transparency and a worksheet for each strategy.

Correlation to Standardized Tests

Lesson		NAEP	Terra Nova		ITBS	SAT10	Local Test
			CAT6	CTBS			
8-1	Pairs of Angles	G1c, G3b, G3g	■	■			
8-2	Angles and Parallel Lines	G3b, G3g	■	■		■	
8-3	Congruent Polygons	G2e		■			
8-4	Solve a Simpler Problem and Look for a Pattern						
8-5	Classifying Triangles and Quadrilaterals	G3f		■		■	
8-6	Angles and Polygons	G3f					
8-7	Areas of Polygons	M1h	■	■	■	■	
8-8	Circumferences and Areas of Circles	M1h	■	■		■	
8-9	Constructions	G3b					

NAEP National Assessment of Educational Progress
CAT6/Terra Nova California Achievement Test, 6th Ed.
CTBS/Terra Nova Comprehensive Test of Basic Skills
ITBS Iowa Test of Basic Skills, Form M.
SAT10 Stanford Achievement Test, 10th Ed.

Program Resources

	Resources in Grab & Go™ Files				Resources for Reaching All Students				Spanish Resources			Presentation Assistant Plus! Transparencies					Presentation Assistant Plus!
	Practice	Reteach	Enrich	Checkpt Quiz	Reading & Math Literacy	Technology Activities	Hands-On Activities	Guided Problem Solving	Practice	Reading & Math Literacy	Checkpt Quiz	Skills Check	Problem of the Day	Additional Examples	Answers to Exercises	Lesson Quiz	Prentice Hall Presentation Pro CD-ROM
8-1	■	■	■		■			■	■	■		■	■	■	■	■	■
8-2	■	■	■			■		■	■			■	■	■	■	■	■
8-3	■	■	■			■		■	■			■	■	■	■	■	■
8-4	■	■	■	■	■		■	■	■	■	■	■	■	■	■	■	■
8-5	■	■	■				■	■	■			■	■	■	■	■	■
8-6	■	■	■				■	■	■			■	■	■	■	■	■
8-7	■	■	■				■	■	■			■	■	■	■	■	■
8-8	■	■	■				■	■	■			■	■	■	■	■	■
8-9	■	■	■	■	■		■	■	■	■	■	■	■	■	■	■	■
For the Chapter	Chapter Projects, Chapter Tests, Alternative Assessment, Cumulative Review, Cumulative Assessment				**On web site only:** Home Activities, Interdisciplinary Activities, Algebra Readiness Puzzles				Spanish Chapter Tests, Alternative Assessment, Cumulative Review, Cumulative Assessment			Classroom Aid Transparencies					

Also available for use with the chapter:

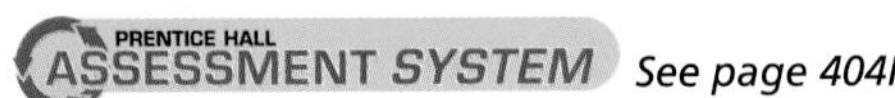

See page 404F.

- Practice Workbook
- Solution Key
- MathNotes folder

- For teacher support and access to student Web materials, use the Web Code abk-5500.
- For additional online and technology resources, *see below.*

Technology

Online and on CD-ROM

Complete Interactive Student Text online and on CD-ROM—with instant feedback assessment, tutorial help, dynamic activities, instructional and real-world videos, audio, and additional practice.

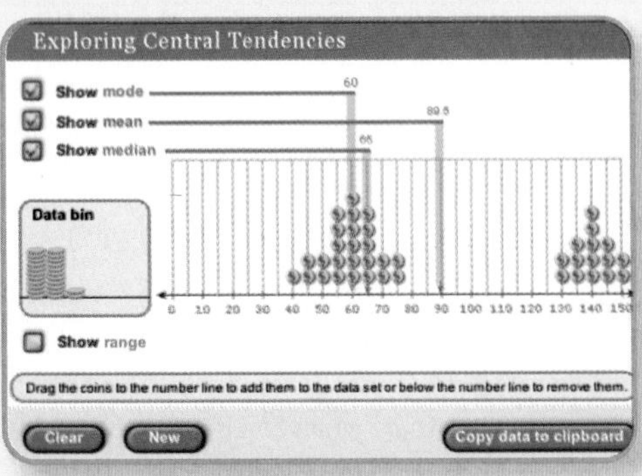

www.PHSchool.com For Students

Use Web codes for easy access to online activities, chapter projects, self-grading lesson quizzes, chapter tests, vocabulary quizzes, updated data sources, graphing calculator procedures, and more.

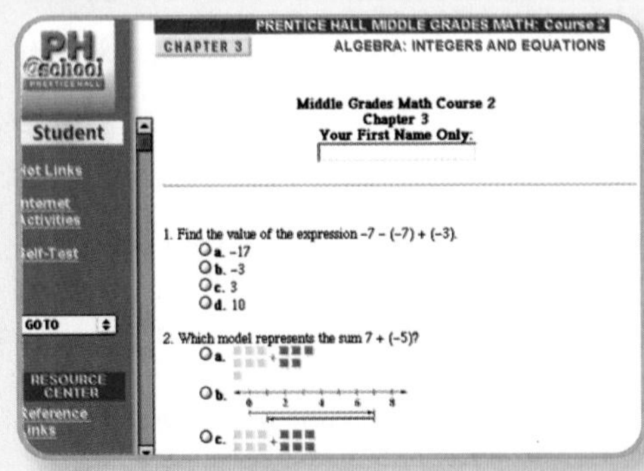

PH SuccessNet For Teachers

Online lesson planning with built-in state correlations, all the teaching resources, complete reference library, your own calendar and Teacher Web page, professional development, and more.

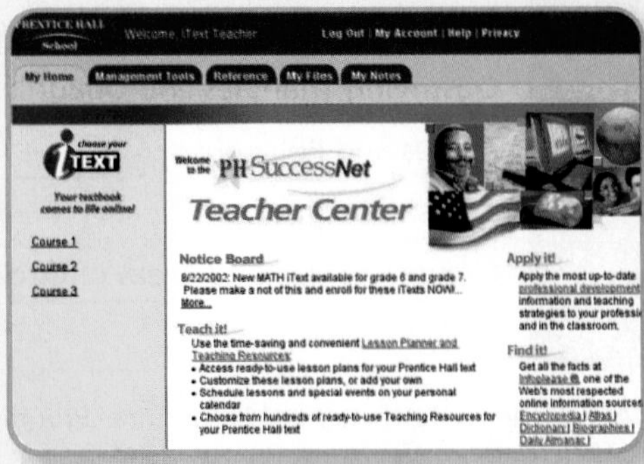

Presentation Assistant Plus!

The *Prentice Hall Presentation Assistant Plus!* provides you with the material you need to teach a lesson from beginning to end. Two easy-to-use formats—Transparencies and PowerPoint®—allow you to present a lesson the way you are most comfortable.

Transparencies

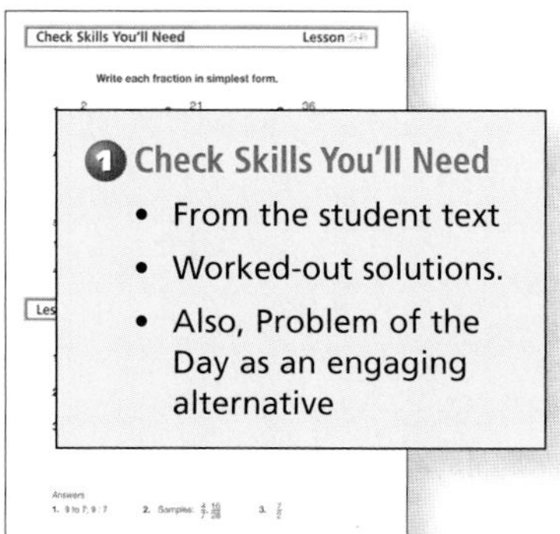

1 Check Skills You'll Need

- From the student text
- Worked-out solutions.
- Also, Problem of the Day as an engaging alternative

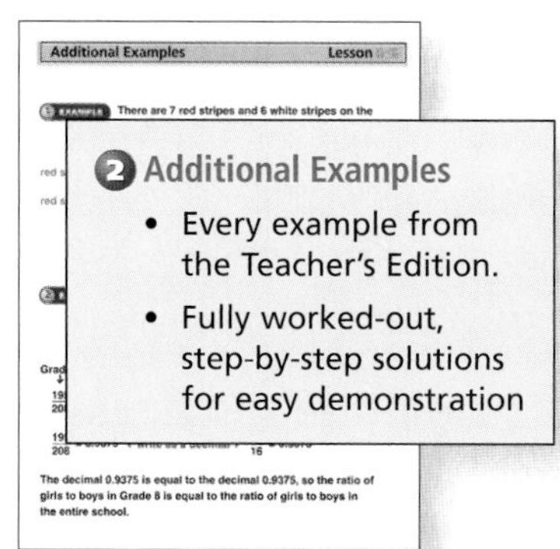

2 Additional Examples

- Every example from the Teacher's Edition.
- Fully worked-out, step-by-step solutions for easy demonstration

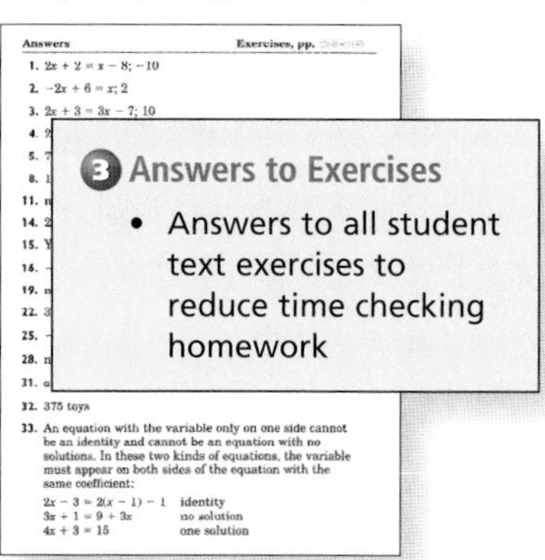

3 Answers to Exercises

- Answers to all student text exercises to reduce time checking homework

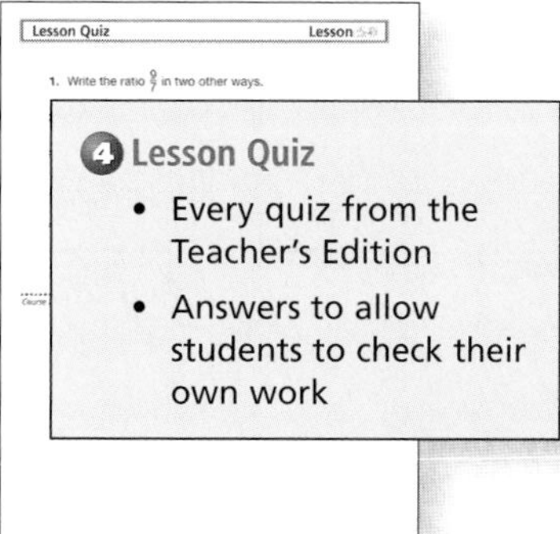

4 Lesson Quiz

- Every quiz from the Teacher's Edition
- Answers to allow students to check their own work

Throughout the Teacher's Edition, this symbol indicates material that is available in the Presentation Assistant Plus!

PowerPoint Prentice Hall Presentation Pro CD-ROM

- Includes all Transparencies.
- Conveniently organized by lesson so you can easily 1 Introduce, 2 Teach, 3 Check Homework, and 4 Assess each lesson.
- Animated examples allow step-by-step instruction at your own pace.
- Easy to edit so you can create custom presentations.

Teaching Chapter 8 Using Presentation Assistant Plus!

	1 Introduce	2 Teach	3 Check Homework	4 Assess
	Check Skills You'll Need	Additional Examples	Student Edition Answers	Lesson Quiz
8-1	p. 60	pp. 135–136	✔	p. 60
8-2	p. 61	p. 137	✔	p. 61
8-3	p. 62	pp.138–139	✔	p. 62
8-4	p. 63	pp.140–141	✔	p. 63
8-5	p. 64	p. 142	✔	p. 64
8-6	p. 65	pp. 143–144	✔	p. 65
8-7	p. 66	pp. 145–146	✔	p. 66
8-8	p. 67	pp. 147–148	✔	p. 67
8-9	p. 68	pp. 149–152	✔	p. 68

Prentice Hall Presentation Pro

CD-ROM with dynamic PowerPoint® presentations for every lesson. Helps you introduce and develop concepts, check homework, and assess progress. Part of Presentation Assistant Plus! *(See above.)*

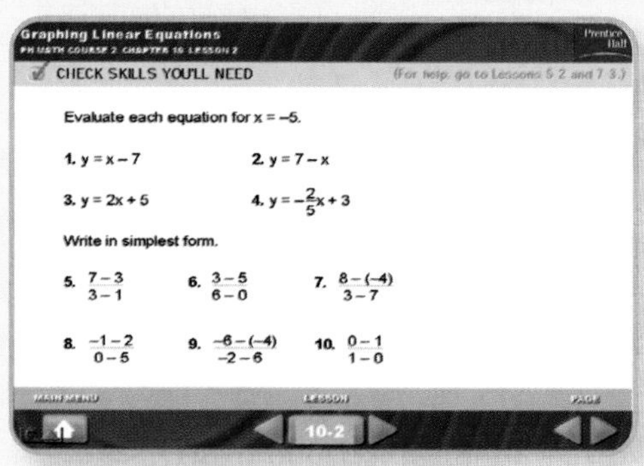

Computer Test Generator

CD-ROM to create practice sheets and tests for course objectives and standardized tests. Includes Instant Chapter Tests™, online testing, and student reports. Part of the PH Assessment System. *(See page 404F.)*

Resource Pro® with Planning Express®

CD-ROM with a lesson planning tool that allows you to import state and local objectives. Includes electronic versions of all the teaching resources.

Chapter Resources

Reading and Math Support

Reading and Math Literacy Masters

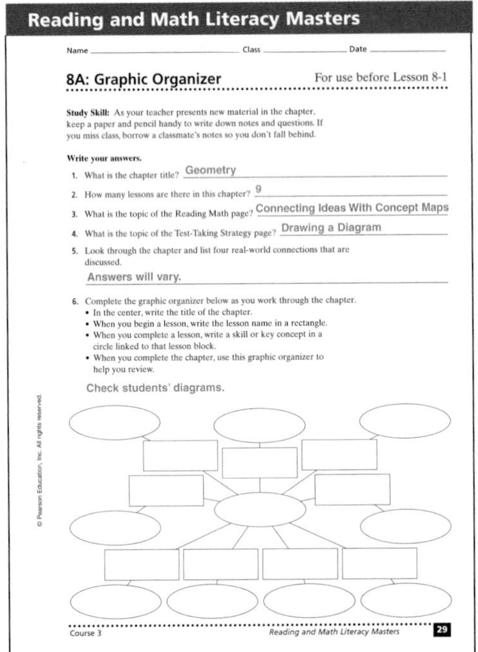

Name ____ Class ____ Date ____

8A: Graphic Organizer For use before Lesson 8-1

Study Skill: As your teacher presents new material in the chapter, keep a paper and pencil handy to write down notes and questions. If you miss class, borrow a classmate's notes so you don't fall behind.

Write your answers.

1. What is the chapter title? Geometry
2. How many lessons are there in this chapter? 9
3. What is the topic of the Reading Math page? Connecting Ideas With Concept Maps
4. What is the topic of the Test-Taking Strategy page? Drawing a Diagram
5. Look through the chapter and list four real-world connections that are discussed. Answers will vary.
6. Complete the graphic organizer below as you work through the chapter.
   - In the center, write the title of the chapter.
   - When you begin a lesson, write the lesson name in a rectangle.
   - When you complete a lesson, write a skill or key concept in a circle linked to that lesson block.
   - When you complete the chapter, use this graphic organizer to help you review.

Check students' diagrams.

© Pearson Education, Inc. All rights reserved.

Course 3 Reading and Math Literacy Masters 29

Available in Spanish

Reading and Math Literacy Masters

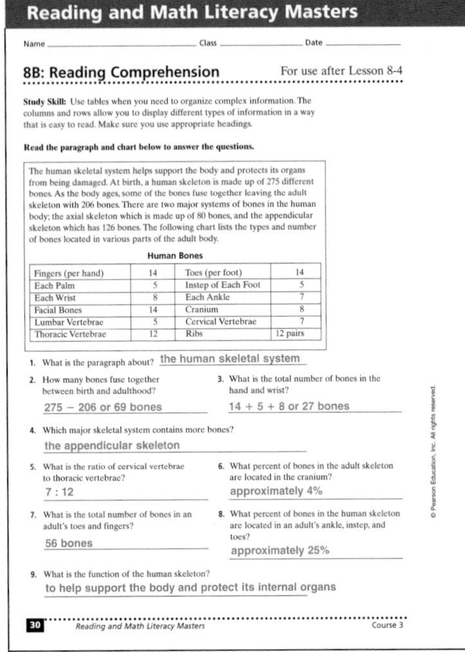

Name ____ Class ____ Date ____

8B: Reading Comprehension For use after Lesson 8-4

Study Skill: Use tables when you need to organize complex information. The columns and rows allow you to display different types of information in a way that is easy to read. Make sure you use appropriate headings.

Read the paragraph and chart below to answer the questions.

The human skeletal system helps support the body and protects its organs from being damaged. At birth, a human skeleton is made up of 275 different bones. As the body ages, some of the bones fuse together leaving the adult skeleton with 206 bones. There are two major systems of bones in the human body; the axial skeleton which is made up of 80 bones, and the appendicular skeleton which has 126 bones. The following chart lists the types and number of bones located in various parts of the adult body.

Human Bones

Fingers (per hand)	14	Toes (per foot)	14
Each Palm	5	Instep of Each Foot	5
Each Wrist	8	Each Ankle	7
Facial Bones	14	Cranium	8
Lumbar Vertebrae	5	Cervical Vertebrae	7
Thoracic Vertebrae	12	Ribs	12 pairs

1. What is the paragraph about? the human skeletal system
2. How many bones fuse together between birth and adulthood? 275 − 206 or 69 bones
3. What is the total number of bones in the hand and wrist? 14 + 5 + 8 or 27 bones
4. Which major skeletal system contains more bones? the appendicular skeleton
5. What is the ratio of cervical vertebrae to thoracic vertebrae? 7 : 12
6. What percent of bones in the adult skeleton are located in the cranium? approximately 4%
7. What is the total number of bones in an adult's toes and fingers? 56 bones
8. What percent of bones in the human skeleton are located in an adult's ankle, instep, and toes? approximately 25%
9. What is the function of the human skeleton? to help support the body and protect its internal organs

© Pearson Education, Inc. All rights reserved.

30 Reading and Math Literacy Masters Course 3

Available in Spanish

Reading and Math Literacy Masters

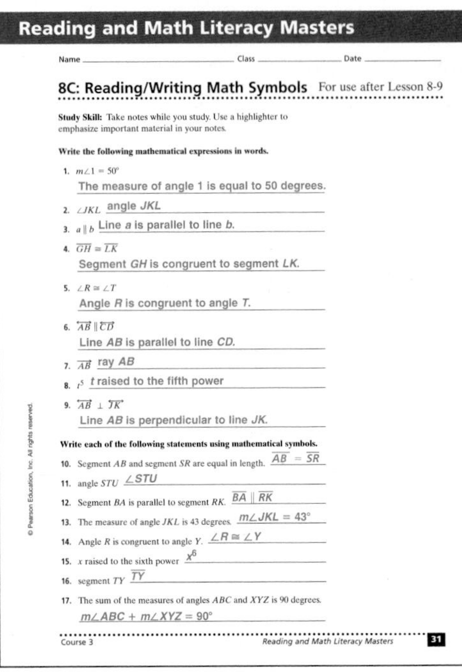

Name ____ Class ____ Date ____

8C: Reading/Writing Math Symbols For use after Lesson 8-9

Study Skill: Take notes while you study. Use a highlighter to emphasize important material in your notes.

Write the following mathematical expressions in words.

1. $m\angle 1 = 50°$ The measure of angle 1 is equal to 50 degrees.
2. $\angle JKL$ angle JKL
3. $a \parallel b$ Line a is parallel to line b.
4. $\overline{GH} \cong \overline{LK}$ Segment GH is congruent to segment LK.
5. $\angle R \cong \angle T$ Angle R is congruent to angle T.
6. $\overleftrightarrow{AB} \parallel \overleftrightarrow{CD}$ Line AB is parallel to line CD.
7. $\overrightarrow{AB}$ ray AB
8. t^5 t raised to the fifth power
9. $\overleftrightarrow{AB} \perp \overleftrightarrow{JK}$ Line AB is perpendicular to line JK.

Write each of the following statements using mathematical symbols.

10. Segment AB and segment SR are equal in length. $\overline{AB} = \overline{SR}$
11. angle STU $\angle STU$
12. Segment BA is parallel to segment RK. $\overline{BA} \parallel \overline{RK}$
13. The measure of angle JKL is 43 degrees. $m\angle JKL = 43°$
14. Angle R is congruent to angle Y. $\angle R \cong \angle Y$
15. x raised to the sixth power x^6
16. segment TY $\overline{TY}$
17. The sum of the measures of angles ABC and XYZ is 90 degrees. $m\angle ABC + m\angle XYZ = 90°$

© Pearson Education, Inc. All rights reserved.

Course 3 Reading and Math Literacy Masters 31

Available in Spanish

Reading and Math Literacy Masters

Name ____ Class ____ Date ____

8D: Vocabulary For use with the Chapter Review

Study Skill: As you read through a new lesson, write new vocabulary words and the definitions on index cards.

Complete the crossword puzzle below. For help, use the glossary in your textbook.

Here are the words you will use to complete this crossword puzzle.

right	square	trapezoid	vertical	tessellation
equilateral	supplementary	scalene	acute	isosceles
circumference	regular	complementary	obtuse	quadrilateral
adjacent	rectangle	transversal		parallelogram

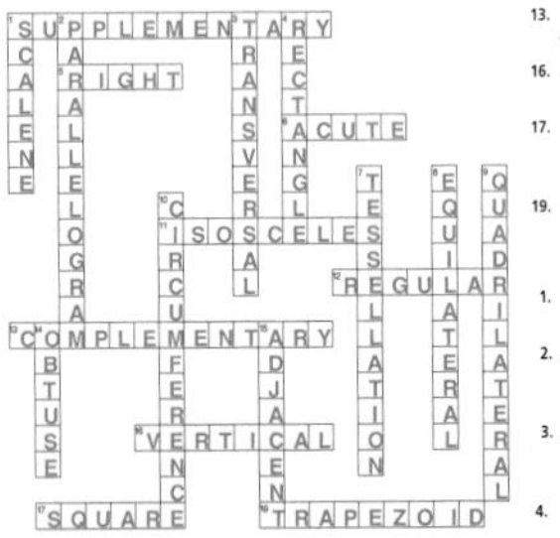

ACROSS

1. two angles whose sum is 180 degrees
5. a triangle with one angle measuring 90 degrees
6. a triangle with angles each measuring less than 90 degrees
11. a triangle with at least two sides congruent
12. a polygon in which all the sides are congruent
13. two angles whose sum is 90 degrees
16. a type of angle formed by intersecting lines
17. a parallelogram with four right angles and four congruent sides
19. a quadrilateral with exactly one pair of parallel sides

DOWN

1. a triangle with no congruent sides
2. a quadrilateral with two pairs of opposite sides that are parallel
3. a line that intersects two other lines in different points
4. a parallelogram with four right angles
7. a repeated geometric pattern that covers a plane with no gaps or overlaps
8. a triangle with three congruent sides
9. a polygon with four sides
10. the distance around a circle
14. a triangle with one angle larger than 90 degrees
15. two angles that shares a vertex and a side but have no common interior points

© Pearson Education, Inc. All rights reserved.

32 Reading and Math Literacy Masters Course 3

Available in Spanish

Problem Solving

Guided Problem Solving Masters

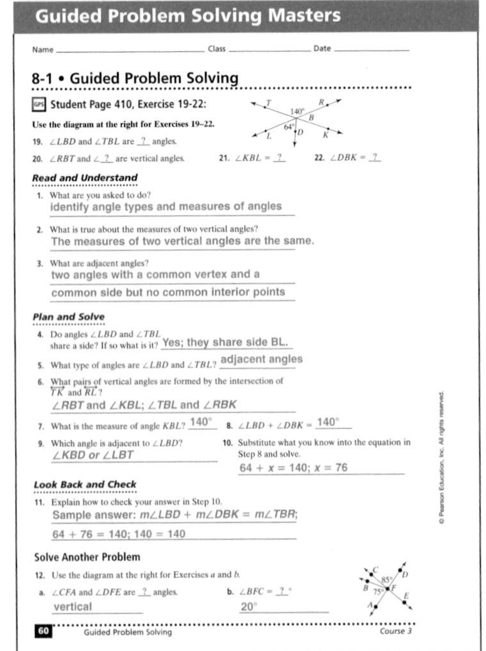

Name ____ Class ____ Date ____

8-1 • Guided Problem Solving

Student Page 410, Exercise 19-22:

Use the diagram at the right for Exercises 19–22.

19. $\angle LBD$ and $\angle TBL$ are _?_ angles.
20. $\angle RBT$ and $\angle$ _?_ are vertical angles.
21. $\angle KBL$ = _?_
22. $\angle DBK$ = _?_

Read and Understand

1. What are you asked to do? identify angle types and measures of angles
2. What is true about the measures of two vertical angles? The measures of two vertical angles are the same.
3. What are adjacent angles? two angles with a common vertex and a common side but no common interior points

Plan and Solve

4. Do angles $\angle LBD$ and $\angle TBL$ share a side? If so what is it? Yes; they share side BL.
5. What type of angles are $\angle LBD$ and $\angle TBL$? adjacent angles
6. What pairs of vertical angles are formed by the intersection of $\overleftrightarrow{TK}$ and $\overleftrightarrow{RL}$? $\angle RBT$ and $\angle KBL$; $\angle TBL$ and $\angle RBK$
7. What is the measure of angle KBL? 140°
8. $\angle LBD + \angle DBK$ = 140°
9. Which angle is adjacent to $\angle LBD$? $\angle KBD$ or $\angle LBT$
10. Substitute what you know into the equation in Step 8 and solve. $64 + x = 140$; $x = 76$

Look Back and Check

11. Explain how to check your answer in Step 10. Sample answer: $m\angle LBD + m\angle DBK = m\angle TBR$; $64 + 76 = 140$; $140 = 140$

Solve Another Problem

12. Use the diagram at the right for Exercises a and b.
   a. $\angle CFA$ and $\angle DFE$ are _?_ angles. vertical
   b. $\angle BFC$ = _?_° 20°

© Pearson Education, Inc. All rights reserved.

60 Guided Problem Solving Course 3

Guided Problem Solving Masters

Name ____ Class ____ Date ____

8-2 • Guided Problem Solving

Student Page 416, Exercise 20:

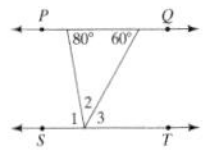

a. In the diagram at the right, $\overleftrightarrow{PQ} \parallel \overleftrightarrow{ST}$. Find the measure of each numbered angle.

b. What is the sum of the angle measures of the triangle?

Read and Understand

1. What are alternate interior angles? Alternate interior angles lie within a pair of lines and on opposite sides of a transversal.
2. What are you asked to do? Find the measure of each numbered angle.

Plan and Solve

3. Use angle 1 and angle 3 to name two pairs of alternate interior angles. angle 1 and the 80° angle; angle 3 and the 60° angle
4. What is true of the measure of alternate interior angles? The measures are the same.
5. What is the measure of angle 1? 80°
6. What is the measure of angle 3? 60°
7. What type of angle do angles 1, 2 and 3 form? straight
8. How many degrees are in a straight angle? 180°
9. Use the information from Steps 5 and 6 to help find the measure of angle 2. $180 - (80 + 60) = 40°$
10. What is the sum of the angle measures in the triangle? 180°

Look Back and Check

11. Explain your answer from Step 10. Sample answer: $80 + 60 + 40 = 180°$, the number of degrees in a triangle.

Solve Another Problem

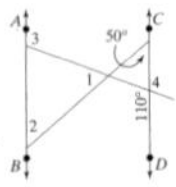

12. In the diagram, $\overleftrightarrow{AB} \parallel \overleftrightarrow{CD}$. Find the measure of each numbered angle. $m\angle 2 = 50°$; $m\angle 3 = m\angle 4 = 110°$; $m\angle 1 = 60°$

© Pearson Education, Inc. All rights reserved.

Course 3 Guided Problem Solving 61

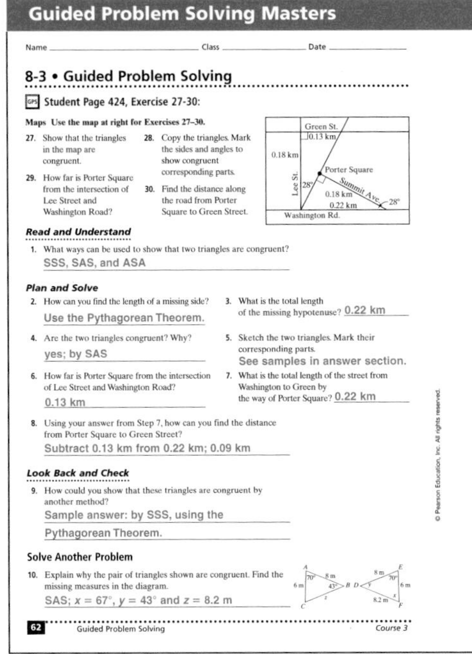

Guided Problem Solving Masters

Name ______________ Class ______ Date ______

8-3 • Guided Problem Solving

Student Page 424, Exercise 27-30:

Maps Use the map at right for Exercises 27–30.

27. Show that the triangles in the map are congruent.
28. Copy the triangles. Mark the sides and angles to show congruent corresponding parts.
29. How far is Porter Square from the intersection of Lee Street and Washington Road?
30. Find the distance along the road from Porter Square to Green Street.

Read and Understand

1. What ways can be used to show that two triangles are congruent? SSS, SAS, and ASA

Plan and Solve

2. How can you find the length of a missing side? Use the Pythagorean Theorem.
3. What is the total length of the missing hypotenuse? 0.22 km
4. Are the two triangles congruent? Why? yes; by SAS
5. Sketch the two triangles. Mark their corresponding parts. See samples in answer section.
6. How far is Porter Square from the intersection of Lee Street and Washington Road? 0.13 km
7. What is the total length of the street from Washington to Green by the way of Porter Square? 0.22 km
8. Using your answer from Step 7, how can you find the distance from Porter Square to Green Street? Subtract 0.13 km from 0.22 km; 0.09 km

Look Back and Check

9. How could you show that these triangles are congruent by another method? Sample answer: by SSS, using the Pythagorean Theorem.

Solve Another Problem

10. Explain why the pair of triangles shown are congruent. Find the missing measures in the diagram. SAS; $x = 67°$, $y = 43°$ and $z = 8.2$ m

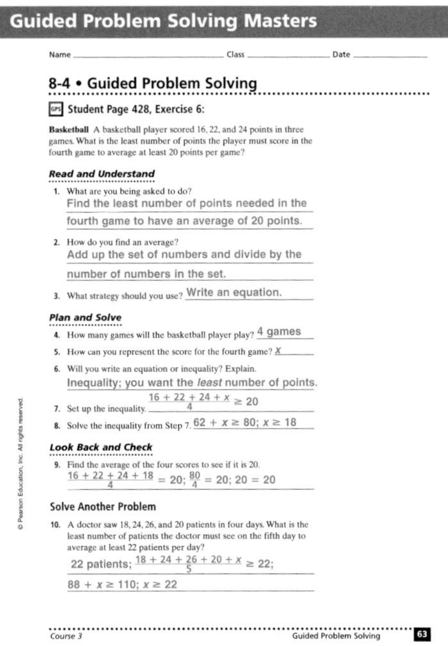

Guided Problem Solving Masters

Name ______________ Class ______ Date ______

8-4 • Guided Problem Solving

Student Page 428, Exercise 6:

Basketball A basketball player scored 16, 22, and 24 points in three games. What is the least number of points the player must score in the fourth game to average at least 20 points per game?

Read and Understand

1. What are you being asked to do? Find the least number of points needed in the fourth game to have an average of 20 points.
2. How do you find an average? Add up the set of numbers and divide by the number of numbers in the set.
3. What strategy should you use? Write an equation.

Plan and Solve

4. How many games will the basketball player play? 4 games
5. How can you represent the score for the fourth game? x
6. Will you write an equation or inequality? Explain. Inequality; you want the *least* number of points.
7. Set up the inequality. $\frac{16 + 22 + 24 + x}{4} \geq 20$
8. Solve the inequality from Step 7. $62 + x \geq 80$; $x \geq 18$

Look Back and Check

9. Find the average of the four scores to see if it is 20. $\frac{16 + 22 + 24 + 18}{4} = 20$; $\frac{80}{4} = 20$; $20 = 20$

Solve Another Problem

10. A doctor saw 18, 24, 26, and 20 patients in four days. What is the least number of patients the doctor must see on the fifth day to average at least 22 patients per day? 22 patients; $\frac{18 + 24 + 26 + 20 + x}{5} \geq 22$; $88 + x \geq 110$; $x \geq 22$

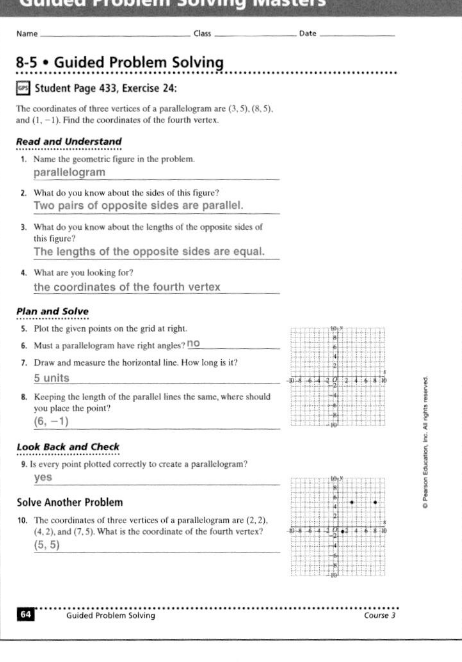

Guided Problem Solving Masters

Name ______________ Class ______ Date ______

8-5 • Guided Problem Solving

Student Page 433, Exercise 24:

The coordinates of three vertices of a parallelogram are (3, 5), (8, 5), and (1, −1). Find the coordinates of the fourth vertex.

Read and Understand

1. Name the geometric figure in the problem. parallelogram
2. What do you know about the sides of this figure? Two pairs of opposite sides are parallel.
3. What do you know about the lengths of the opposite sides of this figure? The lengths of the opposite sides are equal.
4. What are you looking for? the coordinates of the fourth vertex

Plan and Solve

5. Plot the given points on the grid at right.
6. Must a parallelogram have right angles? no
7. Draw and measure the horizontal line. How long is it? 5 units
8. Keeping the length of the parallel lines the same, where should you place the point? (6, −1)

Look Back and Check

9. Is every point plotted correctly to create a parallelogram? yes

Solve Another Problem

10. The coordinates of three vertices of a parallelogram are (2, 2), (4, 2), and (7, 5). What is the coordinate of the fourth vertex? (5, 5)

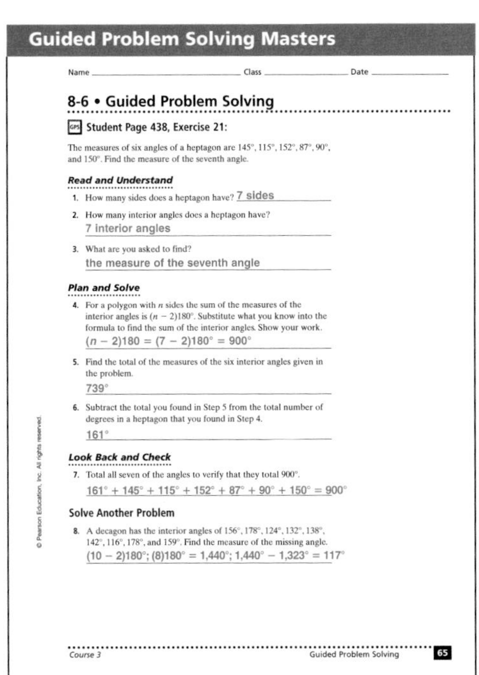

Guided Problem Solving Masters

Name ______________ Class ______ Date ______

8-6 • Guided Problem Solving

Student Page 438, Exercise 21:

The measures of six angles of a heptagon are 145°, 115°, 152°, 87°, 90°, and 150°. Find the measure of the seventh angle.

Read and Understand

1. How many sides does a heptagon have? 7 sides
2. How many interior angles does a heptagon have? 7 interior angles
3. What are you asked to find? the measure of the seventh angle

Plan and Solve

4. For a polygon with n sides the sum of the measures of the interior angles is $(n - 2)180°$. Substitute what you know into the formula to find the sum of the interior angles. Show your work. $(n - 2)180 = (7 - 2)180° = 900°$
5. Find the total of the measures of the six interior angles given in the problem. 739°
6. Subtract the total you found in Step 5 from the total number of degrees in a heptagon that you found in Step 4. 161°

Look Back and Check

7. Total all seven of the angles to verify that they total 900°. $161° + 145° + 115° + 152° + 87° + 90° + 150° = 900°$

Solve Another Problem

8. A decagon has the interior angles of 156°, 178°, 124°, 132°, 138°, 142°, 116°, 178°, and 159°. Find the measure of the missing angle. $(10 - 2)180°$; $(8)180° = 1{,}440°$; $1{,}440° - 1{,}323° = 117°$

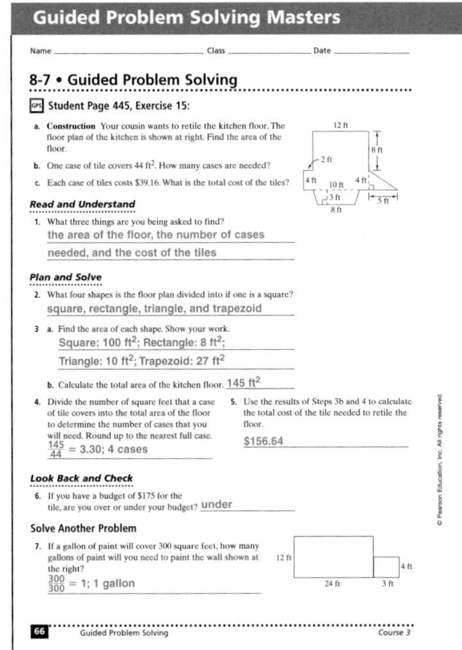

Guided Problem Solving Masters

Name ______________ Class ______ Date ______

8-7 • Guided Problem Solving

Student Page 445, Exercise 15:

a. **Construction** Your cousin wants to retile the kitchen floor. The floor plan of the kitchen is shown at right. Find the area of the floor.

b. One case of tile covers 44 ft². How many cases are needed?

c. Each case of tiles costs $39.16. What is the total cost of the tiles?

Read and Understand

1. What three things are you being asked to find? the area of the floor, the number of cases needed, and the cost of the tiles

Plan and Solve

2. What four shapes is the floor plan divided into if one is a square? square, rectangle, triangle, and trapezoid
3. a. Find the area of each shape. Show your work. Square: 100 ft²; Rectangle: 8 ft²; Triangle: 10 ft²; Trapezoid: 27 ft²
   b. Calculate the total area of the kitchen floor. 145 ft²
4. Divide the number of square feet that a case of tile covers into the total area of the floor to determine the number of cases that you will need. Round up to the nearest full case. $\frac{145}{44} = 3.30$; 4 cases
5. Use the results of Steps 3b and 4 to calculate the total cost of the tile needed to retile the floor. $156.64

Look Back and Check

6. If you have a budget of $175 for the tile, are you over or under your budget? under

Solve Another Problem

7. If a gallon of paint will cover 300 square feet, how many gallons of paint will you need to paint the wall shown at the right? $\frac{300}{300} = 1$; 1 gallon

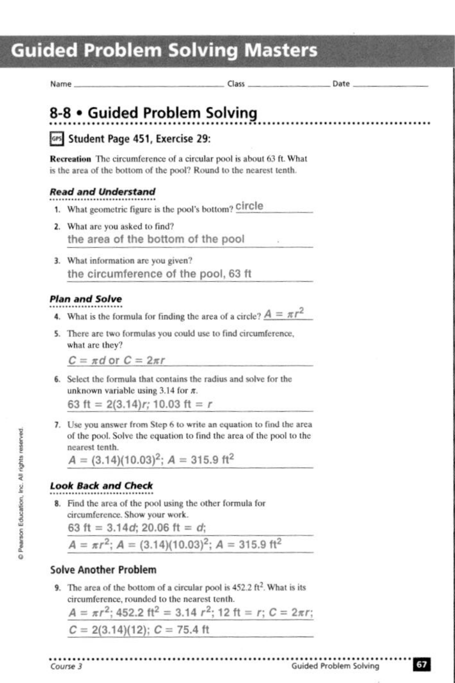

Guided Problem Solving Masters

Name ______________ Class ______ Date ______

8-8 • Guided Problem Solving

Student Page 451, Exercise 29:

Recreation The circumference of a circular pool is about 63 ft. What is the area of the bottom of the pool? Round to the nearest tenth.

Read and Understand

1. What geometric figure is the pool's bottom? circle
2. What are you asked to find? the area of the bottom of the pool
3. What information are you given? the circumference of the pool, 63 ft

Plan and Solve

4. What is the formula for finding the area of a circle? $A = \pi r^2$
5. There are two formulas you could use to find circumference, what are they? $C = \pi d$ or $C = 2\pi r$
6. Select the formula that contains the radius and solve for the unknown variable using 3.14 for π. $63 \text{ ft} = 2(3.14)r$; $10.03 \text{ ft} = r$
7. Use you answer from Step 6 to write an equation to find the area of the pool. Solve the equation to find the area of the pool to the nearest tenth. $A = (3.14)(10.03)^2$; $A = 315.9 \text{ ft}^2$

Look Back and Check

8. Find the area of the pool using the other formula for circumference. Show your work. $63 \text{ ft} = 3.14d$; $20.06 \text{ ft} = d$; $A = \pi r^2$; $A = (3.14)(10.03)^2$; $A = 315.9 \text{ ft}^2$

Solve Another Problem

9. The area of the bottom of a circular pool is 452.2 ft². What is its circumference, rounded to the nearest tenth. $A = \pi r^2$; $452.2 \text{ ft}^2 = 3.14 r^2$; $12 \text{ ft} = r$; $C = 2\pi r$; $C = 2(3.14)(12)$; $C = 75.4$ ft

Activities and Projects

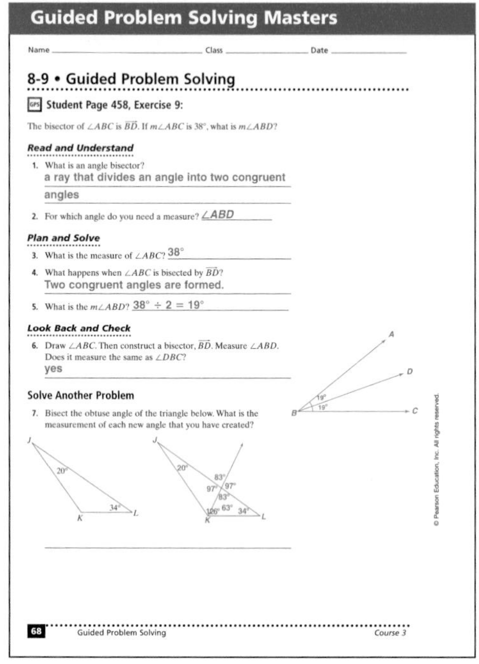

Guided Problem Solving Masters

Name ______________ Class ______________ Date ______________

8-9 • Guided Problem Solving

GPS **Student Page 458, Exercise 9:**

The bisector of $\angle ABC$ is $\overrightarrow{BD}$. If $m\angle ABC$ is 38°, what is $m\angle ABD$?

Read and Understand

1. What is an angle bisector?
   a ray that divides an angle into two congruent angles
2. For which angle do you need a measure? $\angle ABD$

Plan and Solve

3. What is the measure of $\angle ABC$? 38°
4. What happens when $\angle ABC$ is bisected by $\overrightarrow{BD}$?
   Two congruent angles are formed.
5. What is the $m\angle ABD$? $38° \div 2 = 19°$

Look Back and Check

6. Draw $\angle ABC$. Then construct a bisector, $\overrightarrow{BD}$. Measure $\angle ABD$. Does it measure the same as $\angle DBC$?
   yes

Solve Another Problem

7. Bisect the obtuse angle of the triangle below. What is the measurement of each new angle that you have created?

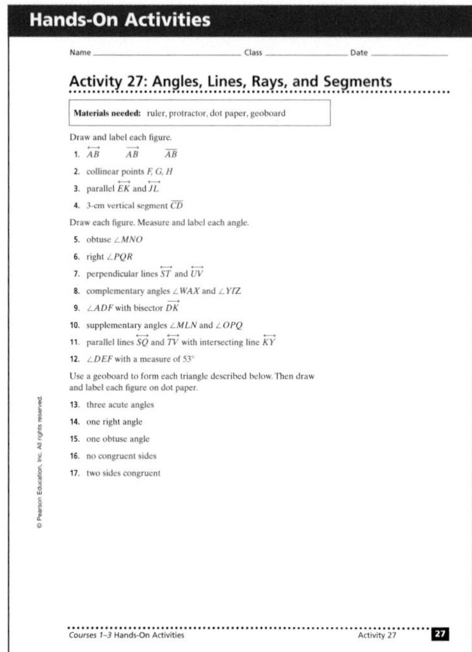

Hands-On Activities

Name ______________ Class ______________ Date ______________

Activity 27: Angles, Lines, Rays, and Segments

Materials needed: ruler, protractor, dot paper, geoboard

Draw and label each figure.

1. $\overleftrightarrow{AB}$ $\overrightarrow{AB}$ $\overline{AB}$
2. collinear points F, G, H
3. parallel $\overleftrightarrow{EK}$ and $\overleftrightarrow{JL}$
4. 3-cm vertical segment $\overline{CD}$

Draw each figure. Measure and label each angle.

5. obtuse $\angle MNO$
6. right $\angle PQR$
7. perpendicular lines $\overleftrightarrow{ST}$ and $\overleftrightarrow{UV}$
8. complementary angles $\angle WAX$ and $\angle YIZ$
9. $\angle ADF$ with bisector $\overrightarrow{DK}$
10. supplementary angles $\angle MLN$ and $\angle OPQ$
11. parallel lines $\overleftrightarrow{SQ}$ and $\overleftrightarrow{TV}$ with intersecting line $\overleftrightarrow{KY}$
12. $\angle DEF$ with a measure of 53°

Use a geoboard to form each triangle described below. Then draw and label each figure on dot paper.

13. three acute angles
14. one right angle
15. one obtuse angle
16. no congruent sides
17. two sides congruent

Sample page; see p. G for complete list.

Hands-On Activities

Name ______________ Class ______________ Date ______________

Activity 36: Area and Perimeter

Materials needed: paper, yardstick, ruler, measuring tape

1. Copy the table below.

	Length	Width	Perimeter	Area
Desk				
Classroom				

2. a. Use the measuring device that you were given to measure the length and width of your desk. Round to the nearest eighth of an inch.
   b. Write the measurements in the table. Calculate the perimeter and area of your desk. Record your calculations in the table.
   c. Compare the entries in the table with those of the person next to you. Are your desks the same size? Are your results the same? Name three factors that might cause different results.
3. Now measure the length and width of your classroom. You should do this with a partner.
   a. Fill in the classroom measurements in your table.
   b. Calculate the perimeter and area and compare your results.
4. You and your partner should find two more objects in the classroom to measure. Then, calculate the perimeter and area of each object. Compare your results.
5. a. Explain what the perimeter of an object is and how you calculate it.
   b. Explain what the area of an object is.
   c. Would you calculate perimeter or area to determine the amount of carpet needed to cover the floor of your classroom? Explain.

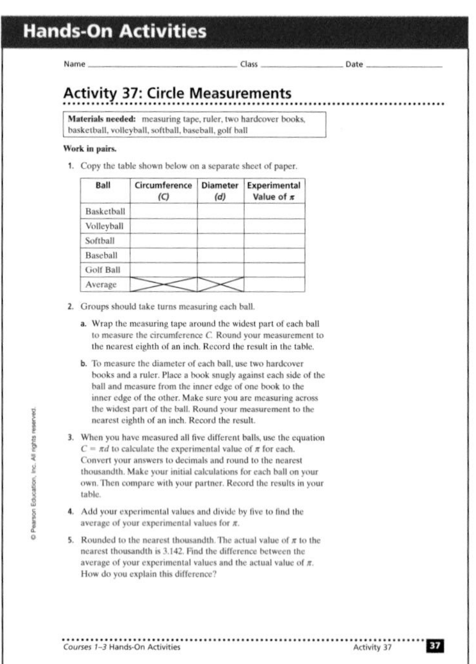

Hands-On Activities

Name ______________ Class ______________ Date ______________

Activity 37: Circle Measurements

Materials needed: measuring tape, ruler, two hardcover books, basketball, volleyball, softball, baseball, golf ball

Work in pairs.

1. Copy the table shown below on a separate sheet of paper.

Ball	Circumference (*C*)	Diameter (*d*)	Experimental Value of π
Basketball			
Volleyball			
Softball			
Baseball			
Golf Ball			
Average	X	X	

2. Groups should take turns measuring each ball.
   a. Wrap the measuring tape around the widest part of each ball to measure the circumference C. Round your measurement to the nearest eighth of an inch. Record the result in the table.
   b. To measure the diameter of each ball, use two hardcover books and a ruler. Place a book snugly against each side of the ball and measure from the inner edge of one book to the inner edge of the other. Make sure you are measuring across the widest part of the ball. Round your measurement to the nearest eighth of an inch. Record the result.
3. When you have measured all five different balls, use the equation $C = \pi d$ to calculate the experimental value of π for each. Convert your answers to decimals and round to the nearest thousandth. Make your initial calculations for each ball on your own. Then compare with your partner. Record the results in your table.
4. Add your experimental values and divide by five to find the average of your experimental values for π.
5. Rounded to the nearest thousandth. The actual value of π to the nearest thousandth is 3.142. Find the difference between the average of your experimental values and the actual value of π. How do you explain this difference?

Technology Activities

Name ______________ Class ______________ Date ______________

Exploring Parallel Lines — Activity 44

Use your geometry software to do this activity.

Example: Plot the following points: $A(-3, 3)$, $B(3, 3)$, $C(-3, 1)$, $D(3, 1)$, $E(-2, 4)$, $F(4, -1)$ and construct $\overline{AB}$ and $\overline{CD}$. Is $\overline{AB} \parallel \overline{CD}$?

① Pull down the **Graph** menu and select **Show Grid.**

② Pull down the **Graph** menu again and see if there is a check mark next to **Snap Points.** If there is no check mark, select **Snap Points.**

③ Plot and label these points: $A(-3, 3)$, $B(3, 3)$, $C(-3, 1)$, $D(3, 1)$, $E(-2, 4)$, $F(4, -1)$.

④ Highlight points A and B only, and then pull down the **Construct** menu and select **Segment.** You now have $\overline{AB}$. Use the same procedure to construct $\overline{CD}$.

⑤ Highlight only points F and E. Pull down the **Construct** menu and select **Segment.** You now have $\overline{EF}$ as a transversal of $\overline{AB}$ and $\overline{CD}$.

⑥ Pull down the **Graph** menu and select **Snap Points** to uncheck this selection.

⑦ Place point G at the intersection of $\overline{AB}$ and $\overline{EF}$. When your pointer is in the correct place, both lines will appear in color. Place point H at the intersection of $\overline{EF}$ and $\overline{CD}$.

⑧ Highlight, in order, only points A, G, and H. Pull down the **Measure** menu and select **Angle.** The measurement of $\angle AGH$ is displayed in the corner of the screen.

⑨ Highlight only points G, H, and D. Pull down the **Measure** menu and select **Angle.** The measurement of $\angle GHD$ is displayed in the corner of the screen.

⑩ Since $\angle AGH$ and $\angle GHD$ are alternate interior angles, and they are equal, $\overline{AB} \parallel \overline{CD}$. Manipulate $\overline{AB}$ and $\overline{CD}$ and verify that the angles remain equal. *Note:* the measures of the angles may differ by less than 1 degree because of the width of the drawing objects.

Exercises

Plot the points and construct the given segments. Measure the alternate interior angles to find out whether the segments are parallel.

1. $A(3, 4)$, $B(6, 1)$, $C(1, 2)$, $D(4, -2)$, $E(5, 4)$, $F(2, -2)$ and construct $\overline{AB}$ and $\overline{CD}$. Determine whether $\overline{AB} \parallel \overline{CD}$.
2. $Q(-4, 3)$, $R(-3, -3)$, $S(-7, 1)$, $T(-6, -4)$, $U(-2, 2)$, $V(-7, -4)$ and construct $\overline{QR}$ and $\overline{ST}$. Determine whether $\overline{QR} \parallel \overline{ST}$.

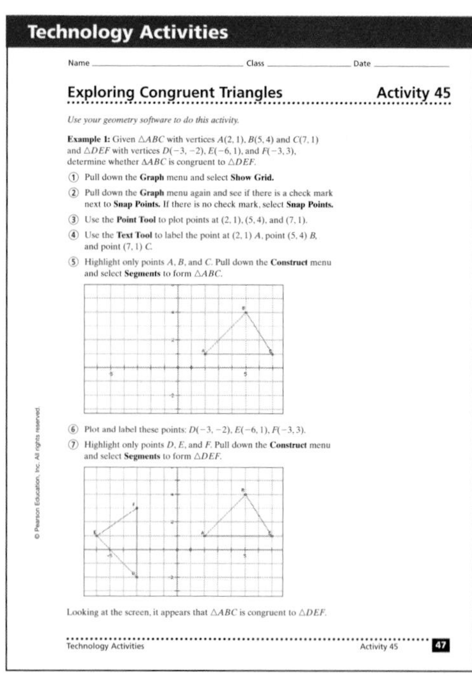

Technology Activities

Name ______________ Class ______________ Date ______________

Exploring Congruent Triangles — Activity 45

Use your geometry software to do this activity.

Example 1: Given $\triangle ABC$ with vertices $A(2, 1)$, $B(5, 4)$ and $C(7, 1)$ and $\triangle DEF$ with vertices $D(-3, -2)$, $E(-6, 1)$, and $F(-3, 3)$, determine whether $\triangle ABC$ is congruent to $\triangle DEF$.

① Pull down the **Graph** menu and select **Show Grid.**

② Pull down the **Graph** menu again and see if there is a check mark next to **Snap Points.** If there is no check mark, select **Snap Points.**

③ Use the **Point Tool** to plot points at (2, 1), (5, 4), and (7, 1).

④ Use the **Text Tool** to label the point at (2, 1) A, point (5, 4) B, and point (7, 1) C.

⑤ Highlight only points A, B, and C. Pull down the **Construct** menu and select **Segments** to form $\triangle ABC$.

⑥ Plot and label these points: $D(-3, -2)$, $E(-6, 1)$, $F(-3, 3)$.

⑦ Highlight only points D, E, and F. Pull down the **Construct** menu and select **Segments** to form $\triangle DEF$.

Looking at the screen, it appears that $\triangle ABC$ is congruent to $\triangle DEF$.

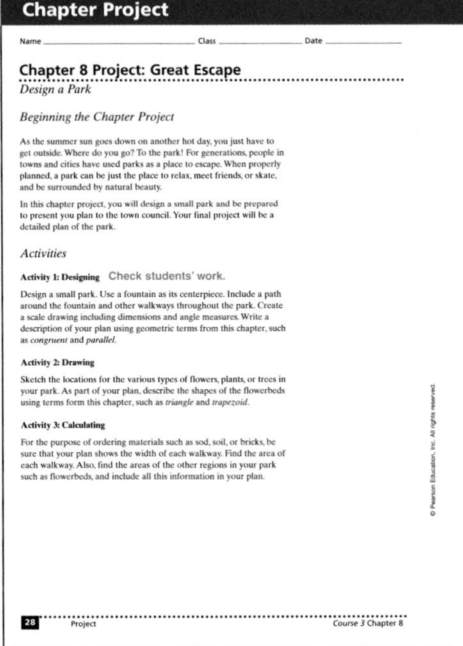

Chapter Project

Name ______________ Class ______________ Date ______________

Chapter 8 Project: Great Escape

Design a Park

Beginning the Chapter Project

As the summer sun goes down on another hot day, you just have to get outside. Where do you go? To the park! For generations, people in towns and cities have used parks as a place to escape. When properly planned, a park can be just the place to relax, meet friends, or skate, and be surrounded by natural beauty.

In this chapter project, you will design a small park and be prepared to present you plan to the town council. Your final project will be a detailed plan of the park.

Activities

Activity 1: Designing Check students' work.

Design a small park. Use a fountain as its centerpiece. Include a path around the fountain and other walkways throughout the park. Create a scale drawing including dimensions and angle measures. Write a description of your plan using geometric terms from this chapter, such as *congruent* and *parallel*.

Activity 2: Drawing

Sketch the locations for the various types of flowers, plants, or trees in your park. As part of your plan, describe the shapes of the flowerbeds using terms form this chapter, such as *triangle* and *trapezoid*.

Activity 3: Calculating

For the purpose of ordering materials such as sod, soil, or bricks, be sure that your plan shows the width of each walkway. Find the area of each walkway. Also, find the areas of the other regions in your park such as flowerbeds, and include all this information in your plan.

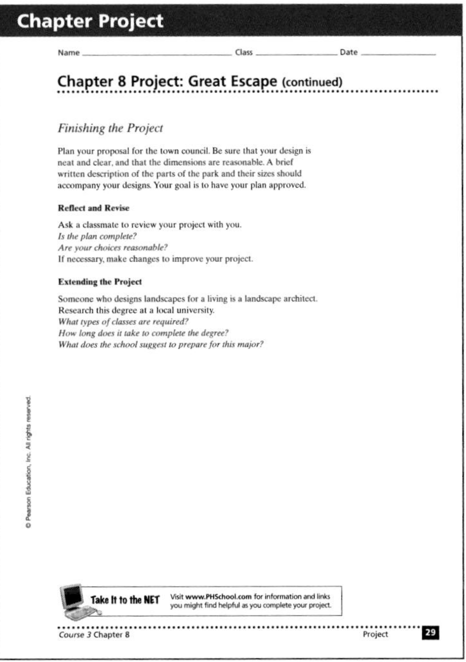

Chapter Project

Name ______________ Class ______________ Date ______________

Chapter 8 Project: Great Escape (continued)

Finishing the Project

Plan your proposal for the town council. Be sure that your design is neat and clear, and that the dimensions are reasonable. A brief written description of the parts of the park and their sizes should accompany your designs. Your goal is to have your plan approved.

Reflect and Revise

Ask a classmate to review your project with you.
Is the plan complete?
Are your choices reasonable?
If necessary, make changes to improve your project.

Extending the Project

Someone who designs landscapes for a living is a landscape architect. Research this degree at a local university.
What types of classes are required?
How long does it take to complete the degree?
What does the school suggest to prepare for this major?

Take It to the NET Visit www.PHSchool.com for information and links you might find helpful as you complete your project.

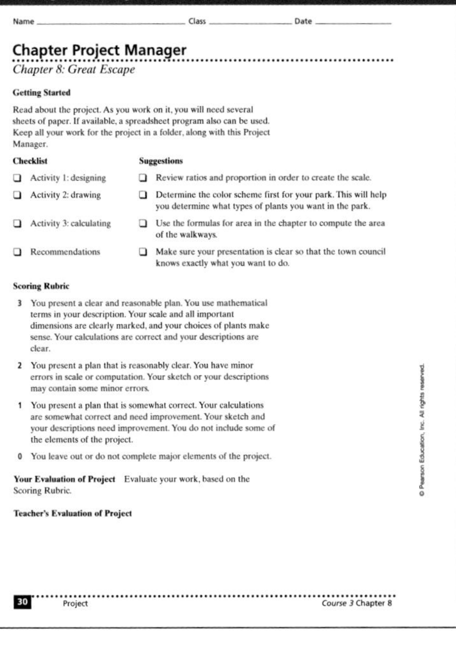

Chapter Project

Name ______________ Class ______________ Date ______________

Chapter Project Manager

Chapter 8: Great Escape

Getting Started

Read about the project. As you work on it, you will need several sheets of paper. If available, a spreadsheet program also can be used. Keep all your work for the project in a folder, along with this Project Manager.

Checklist	Suggestions
❑ Activity 1: designing	❑ Review ratios and proportion in order to create the scale.
❑ Activity 2: drawing	❑ Determine the color scheme first for your park. This will help you determine what types of plants you want in the park.
❑ Activity 3: calculating	❑ Use the formulas for area in the chapter to compute the area of the walkways.
❑ Recommendations	❑ Make sure your presentation is clear so that the town council knows exactly what you want to do.

Scoring Rubric

3 You present a clear and reasonable plan. You use mathematical terms in your description. Your scale and all important dimensions are clearly marked, and your choices of plants make sense. Your calculations are correct and your descriptions are clear.

2 You present a plan that is reasonably clear. You have minor errors in scale or computation. Your sketch or your descriptions may contain some minor errors.

1 You present a plan that is somewhat correct. Your calculations are somewhat correct and need improvement. Your sketch and your descriptions need improvement. You do not include some of the elements of the project.

0 You leave out or do not complete major elements of the project.

Your Evaluation of Project Evaluate your work, based on the Scoring Rubric.

Teacher's Evaluation of Project

Chapter Project

Name ______________ Class ______________ Date ______________

Chapter Project Teacher Notes

Chapter 8: Great Escape

About the Project Students will apply their knowledge of area and patterns in geometry to design their own format garden in a town park.

Introducing the Project

Ask students:

- Have you ever been to a formal garden?
- What do you remember about it?
- Have you seen any pictures of famous gardens? What do the gardens have in common?
- What makes a garden enjoyable? What would you think about when designing a garden?

Activity 1: Designing

Have students first sketch their plans on grid paper. This will help them organize their garden and help keep its contents in proportion. Students can use a compass, protractor, and straightedge to keep their design neat.

Activity 2: Drawing

Students may want to visit a local park to get ideas for shapes and sizes of flowerbeds.

Activity 3: Calculating

Have students research the dimensions of different styles of bricks and calculate how many are needed for their bricked walkways or flowerbed trims.

Finishing the Project

You may wish to plan a project day on which students share their completed projects. Have students review their methods for designing and building their scale models.

Take It to the NET Visit www.PHSchool.com for information, student links, and teacher support for this project.

Transparencies

Problem of the Day

Problem of the Day — Lesson 8-1

Five consecutive multiples of 6 have a sum of 270. What are they?

Answer

42, 48, 54, 60, 66

Problem of the Day — Lesson 8-2

For every 5 western videos rented, the store rents 8 sports videos. If the store rents 48 sports videos, then how many western videos did they rent?

Answer

30

Problem of the Day — Lesson 8-3

At a factory, workers cut rolls of copper coils 50 m long. How many rolls can they make with 1,200 m of copper coil?

Answer

24

Problem of the Day

Problem of the Day — Lesson 8-4

Barbara scored a 42, 96, 88, 67, 96, 71, and an 84 on her math tests this fall. When her parents asked her about her math average, Barbara replied, "It's a 96." Explain and evaluate her answer.

Answer

Barbara gave the correct mode, but her mean and median scores were quite a bit lower.

Problem of the Day — Lesson 8-5

A developer has 30 acres. He divides the land into 0.75-acre lots. How many lots does he have?

Answer

40

Problem of the Day — Lesson 8-6

Jamal's normal pulse rate is 72 beats per minute. When he swims, this rate increases by 50 beats per minute. How many times does his heart beat during a five-minute swim?

Answer

610

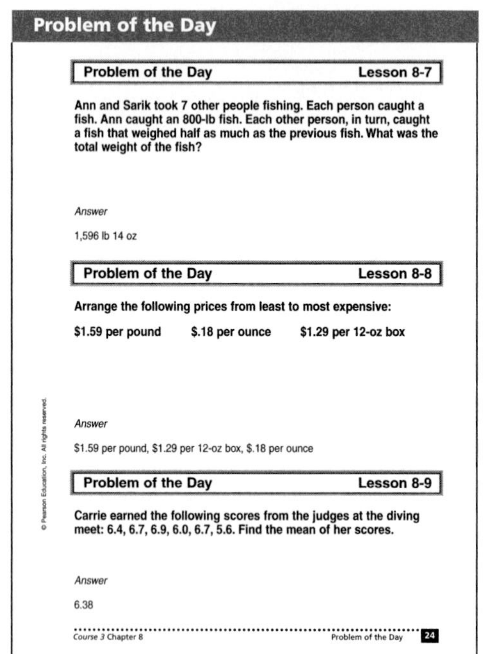

Problem of the Day

Problem of the Day — Lesson 8-7

Ann and Sarik took 7 other people fishing. Each person caught a fish. Ann caught an 800-lb fish. Each other person, in turn, caught a fish that weighed half as much as the previous fish. What was the total weight of the fish?

Answer

1,596 lb 14 oz

Problem of the Day — Lesson 8-8

Arrange the following prices from least to most expensive:

\$1.59 per pound　　\$.18 per ounce　　\$1.29 per 12-oz box

Answer

\$1.59 per pound, \$1.29 per 12-oz box, \$.18 per ounce

Problem of the Day — Lesson 8-9

Carrie earned the following scores from the judges at the diving meet: 6.4, 6.7, 6.9, 6.0, 6.7, 5.6. Find the mean of her scores.

Answer

6.38

Course 3 Chapter 8　　Problem of the Day　　24

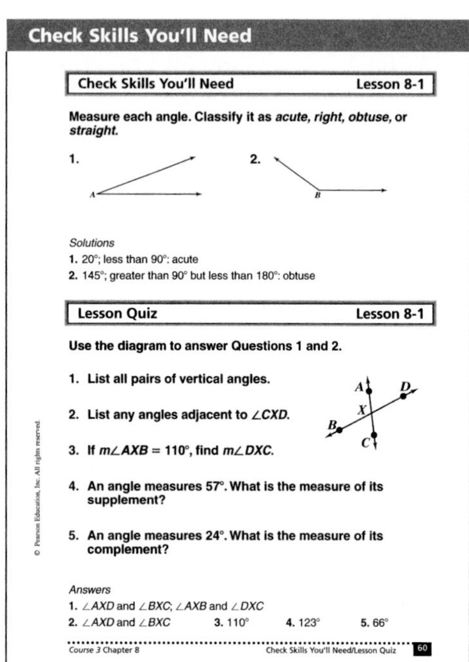

Check Skills You'll Need

Check Skills You'll Need — Lesson 8-1

Measure each angle. Classify it as *acute, right, obtuse,* or *straight.*

1.　　2.

Solutions

1. 20°; less than 90°: acute
2. 145°; greater than 90° but less than 180°: obtuse

Lesson Quiz — Lesson 8-1

Use the diagram to answer Questions 1 and 2.

1. **List all pairs of vertical angles.**
2. **List any angles adjacent to ∠CXD.**
3. **If m∠AXB = 110°, find m∠DXC.**
4. **An angle measures 57°. What is the measure of its supplement?**
5. **An angle measures 24°. What is the measure of its complement?**

Answers

1. ∠AXD and ∠BXC; ∠AXB and ∠DXC
2. ∠AXD and ∠BXC　3. 110°　4. 123°　5. 66°

Course 3 Chapter 8　　Check Skills You'll Need/Lesson Quiz　　60

Sample page; see p. H for complete list.

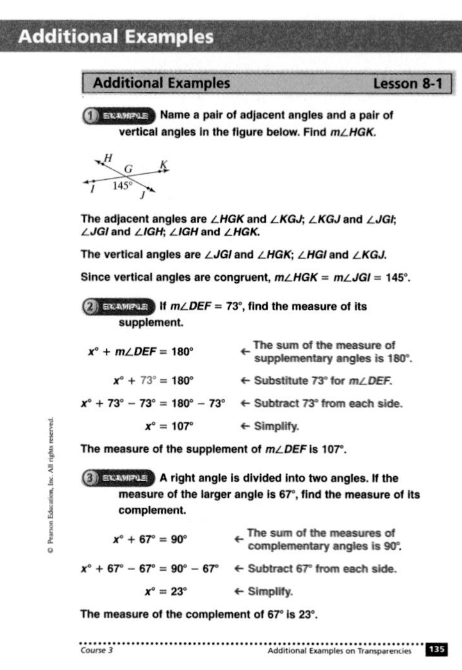

Additional Examples

Additional Examples — Lesson 8-1

1 EXAMPLE Name a pair of adjacent angles and a pair of vertical angles in the figure below. Find m∠HGK.

The adjacent angles are ∠HGK and ∠KGJ; ∠KGJ and ∠JGI; ∠JGI and ∠IGH; ∠IGH and ∠HGK.

The vertical angles are ∠JGI and ∠HGK; ∠HGI and ∠KGJ.

Since vertical angles are congruent, m∠HGK = m∠JGI = 145°.

2 EXAMPLE If m∠DEF = 73°, find the measure of its supplement.

$x° + m\angle DEF = 180°$　← The sum of the measure of supplementary angles is 180°.

$x° + 73° = 180°$　← Substitute 73° for m∠DEF.

$x° + 73° - 73° = 180° - 73°$　← Subtract 73° from each side.

$x° = 107°$　← Simplify.

The measure of the supplement of m∠DEF is 107°.

3 EXAMPLE A right angle is divided into two angles. If the measure of the larger angle is 67°, find the measure of its complement.

$x° + 67° = 90°$　← The sum of the measures of complementary angles is 90°.

$x° + 67° - 67° = 90° - 67°$　← Subtract 67° from each side.

$x° = 23°$　← Simplify.

The measure of the complement of 67° is 23°.

Course 3　　Additional Examples on Transparencies　　135

Sample page; see p. H for complete list.

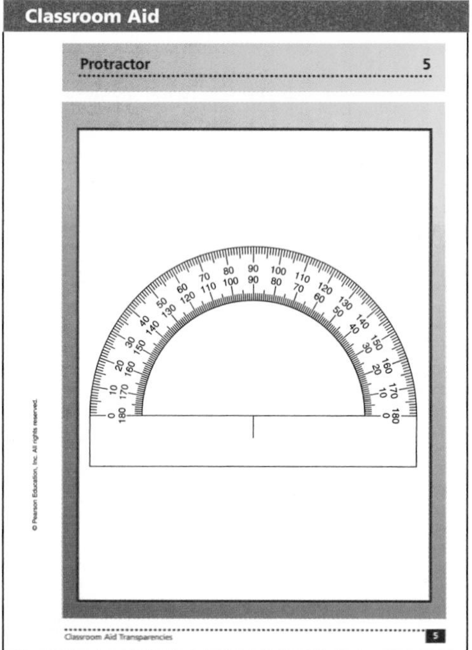

Classroom Aid

Protractor　　5

Classroom Aid Transparencies　　5

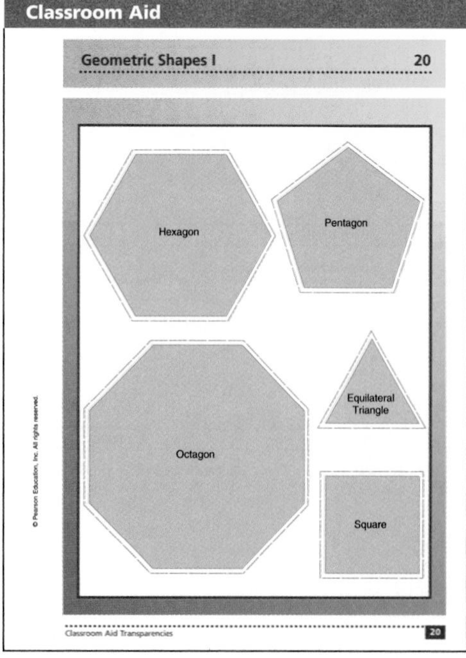

Classroom Aid

Geometric Shapes I　　20

Classroom Aid Transparencies　　20

Sample pages.

Student Edition Answers

Answers for Lesson *On Your Own* Exercises

1. Sample: 1 : 4, 1 to 4, $\frac{1}{4}$　**2.** Sample: 24 to 25, 24 : 25, $\frac{24}{25}$　**3.** 12 to 4, $\frac{12}{4}$

4. 8 : 10, $\frac{8}{10}$　**5.** 5 to 4, 5 : 4　**6.** 13 to 8, $\frac{13}{8}$

7. 21 to 28, $\frac{21}{28}$　**8.** 8 to 18, 8 : 18　**9.** B

10a. 7 : 15, 7 to 15, $\frac{7}{15}$
b. 7 : 8, 7 to 8, $\frac{7}{8}$

11a. 23 : 19, 23 to 19, $\frac{23}{19}$
b. 19 : 42, 19 to 42, $\frac{19}{42}$

12. No; the new ratio is 16 : 11.

13. 0.9　**14.** 3.6　**15.** 2.7　**16.** 0.7

17. 0.5　**18.** 1.0

19a. 225 : 3, 455 : 7
b. 75, 65
c. Answers may vary. Sample: Train A travels 75 mi/h while Train B travels 65 mi/h

20a. $\frac{13}{18}$
b. $\frac{169}{324}$
c. The ratio of areas is the square of the ratio of sides.

21–26. Answers may vary. Samples are given.

21. 13 : 27, 78 : 162　**22.** 6 to 22, 3 to 11

23. $\frac{106}{50}, \frac{53}{25}$　**24.** $\frac{7}{1}, \frac{14}{2}$　**25.** $\frac{9}{18}, \frac{3}{6}$

26. 2 : 12, 3 : 18　**27.** 5 : 2　**28.** 1 to 9

29. $\frac{1}{50}$　**30.** 4 to 1　**31.** 1 : 2

32. $\frac{1}{3}$　**33.** 25 to 1

34a. 101 and 107
b. 7 : 12

35a. 8 : 4
b. 10 qt antifreeze, 5 qt water

Course 2 Chapter 6

Sample page; see p. H for complete list.

Assessment

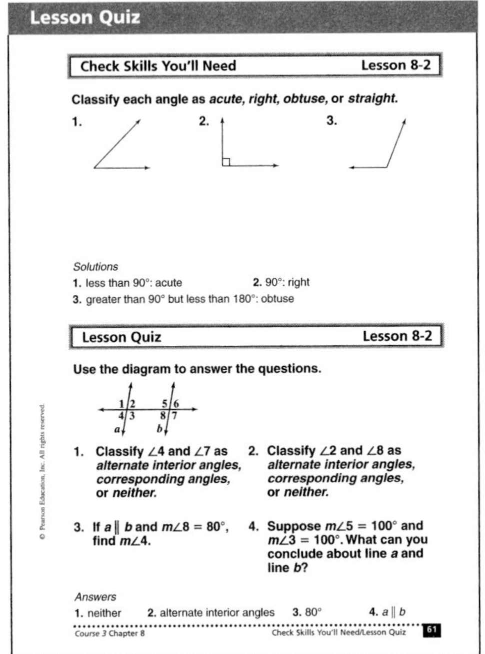

Lesson Quiz

Check Skills You'll Need — **Lesson 8-2**

Classify each angle as *acute, right, obtuse,* or *straight*.

1. 2. 3.

Solutions
1. less than 90°: acute 2. 90°: right
3. greater than 90° but less than 180°: obtuse

Lesson Quiz — **Lesson 8-2**

Use the diagram to answer the questions.

1. Classify ∠4 and ∠7 as *alternate interior angles, corresponding angles,* or *neither.*
2. Classify ∠2 and ∠8 as *alternate interior angles, corresponding angles,* or *neither.*
3. If *a* ∥ *b* and m∠8 = 80°, find m∠4.
4. Suppose m∠5 = 100° and m∠3 = 100°. What can you conclude about line *a* and line *b*?

Answers
1. neither 2. alternate interior angles 3. 80° 4. *a* ∥ *b*

© Pearson Education, Inc. All rights reserved.

Course 3 Chapter 8 — Check Skills You'll Need/Lesson Quiz — 61

Sample page; see p. H for complete list.

Checkpoint Quizzes

Name ______ Class ______ Date ______

✔ Checkpoint Quiz 1

Use with Lessons 8-1 through 8-4.

In the diagram at the right, s ∥ t. Identify the following angles.

1. four pairs of corresponding angles
∠1, ∠8; ∠4, ∠5; ∠3, ∠6; ∠2, ∠7
2. two pairs of vertical angles
any two pairs of ∠1, ∠3 or ∠2, ∠4 or ∠6, ∠8 or ∠5, ∠7
3. the supplements of ∠3
∠2, ∠4, ∠5, and ∠7
4. If m∠8 is 72°, find m∠5 and m∠6.
m∠5 = 108°, m∠6 = 72°

In the diagram at the right, quadrilateral *QRST* ≅ *WXYZ*. Complete the following.

5. ∠S ≅ ∠Y
6. ∠X ≅ ∠R
7. m∠Q = 35°
8. $\overline{QT}$ ≅ $\overline{WZ}$
9. A store has a sale on baseballs: one for $3.50, two for $7, three for $10.25, four for $13.25, and so on. How much will six baseballs cost?
$18.50

Name ______ Class ______ Date ______

✔ Checkpoint Quiz 2

Use with Lessons 8-5 through 8-9.

Draw and label a figure to fit each description.

1. isosceles acute triangle
Check students' drawings.
2. rectangle that is not a square
Check students' drawings.
3. What is the sum of the measures of the angles of a regular polygon with 5 sides? with 10 sides?
540°; 1,440°

Find the circumference and area of a circle with the given radius or diameter. Round to the nearest tenth.

4. d = 2.4 in.
7.5 in.; 4.5 in.²
5. r = 2.4 ft
15.1 ft; 18.1 ft²
6. r = 10.2 cm
64.1 cm; 326.9 cm²

© Pearson Education, Inc. All rights reserved.

32 — Checkpoint Quizzes — Course 3 Chapter 8

Available in Spanish

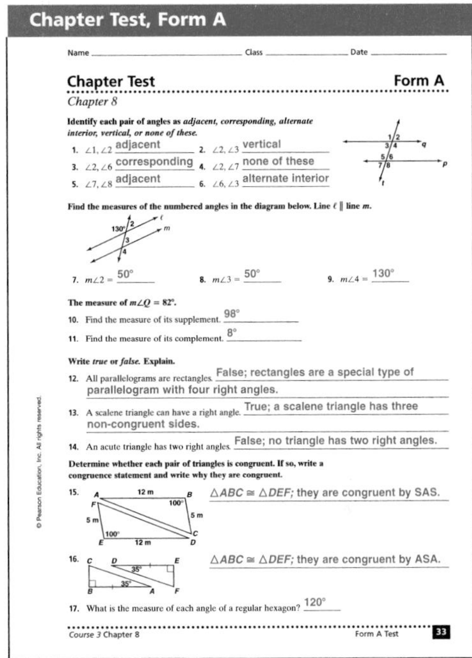

Chapter Test, Form A

Name ______ Class ______ Date ______

Chapter Test — **Form A**

Chapter 8

Identify each pair of angles as *adjacent, corresponding, alternate interior, vertical, or none of these.*

1. ∠1, ∠2 adjacent
2. ∠2, ∠3 vertical
3. ∠2, ∠6 corresponding
4. ∠2, ∠7 none of these
5. ∠7, ∠8 adjacent
6. ∠6, ∠3 alternate interior

Find the measures of the numbered angles in the diagram below. Line ℓ ∥ line *m*.

7. m∠2 = 50°
8. m∠3 = 50°
9. m∠4 = 130°

The measure of m∠Q = 82°.

10. Find the measure of its supplement. 98°
11. Find the measure of its complement. 8°

Write *true* or *false*. Explain.

12. All parallelograms are rectangles. False; rectangles are a special type of parallelogram with four right angles.
13. A scalene triangle can have a right angle. True; a scalene triangle has three non-congruent sides.
14. An acute triangle has two right angles. False; no triangle has two right angles.

Determine whether each pair of triangles is congruent. If so, write a congruence statement and write why they are congruent.

15. △ABC ≅ △DEF; they are congruent by SAS.
16. △ABC ≅ △DEF; they are congruent by ASA.
17. What is the measure of each angle of a regular hexagon? 120°

© Pearson Education, Inc. All rights reserved.

Course 3 Chapter 8 — Form A Test — 33

Available in Spanish

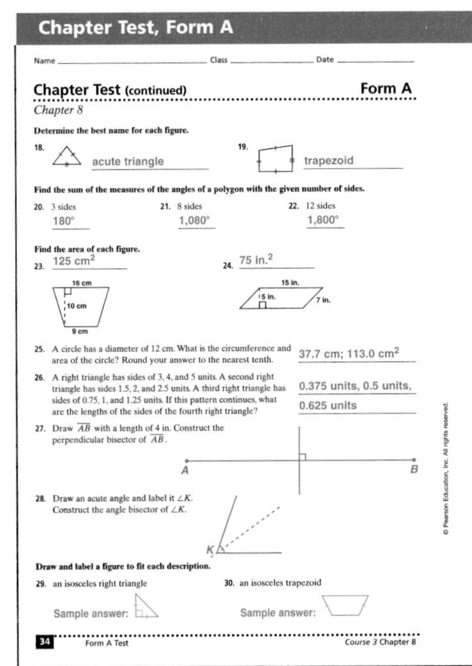

Chapter Test, Form A

Name ______ Class ______ Date ______

Chapter Test (continued) — **Form A**

Chapter 8

Determine the best name for each figure.

18. acute triangle
19. trapezoid

Find the sum of the measures of the angles of a polygon with the given number of sides.

20. 3 sides 180°
21. 8 sides 1,080°
22. 12 sides 1,800°

Find the area of each figure.

23. 125 cm²
24. 75 in.²

25. A circle has a diameter of 12 cm. What is the circumference and area of the circle? Round your answer to the nearest tenth. 37.7 cm; 113.0 cm²
26. A right triangle has sides of 3, 4, and 5 units. A second right triangle has sides 1.5, 2, and 2.5 units. A third right triangle has sides of 0.75, 1, and 1.25 units. If this pattern continues, what are the lengths of the sides of the fourth right triangle? 0.375 units, 0.5 units, 0.625 units
27. Draw $\overline{AB}$ with a length of 4 in. Construct the perpendicular bisector of $\overline{AB}$.
28. Draw an acute angle and label it ∠K. Construct the angle bisector of ∠K.

Draw and label a figure to fit each description.

29. an isosceles right triangle Sample answer:
30. an isosceles trapezoid Sample answer:

© Pearson Education, Inc. All rights reserved.

34 — Form A Test — Course 3 Chapter 8

Available in Spanish

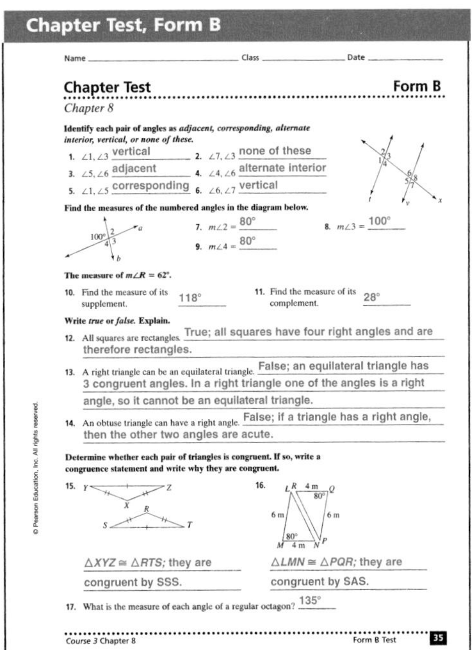

Chapter Test, Form B

Name ______ Class ______ Date ______

Chapter Test — **Form B**

Chapter 8

Identify each pair of angles as *adjacent, corresponding, alternate interior, vertical, or none of these.*

1. ∠1, ∠3 vertical
2. ∠7, ∠3 none of these
3. ∠5, ∠6 adjacent
4. ∠4, ∠6 alternate interior
5. ∠1, ∠5 corresponding
6. ∠6, ∠7 vertical

Find the measures of the numbered angles in the diagram below.

7. m∠2 = 80°
8. m∠3 = 100°
9. m∠4 = 80°

The measure of m∠R = 62°.

10. Find the measure of its supplement. 118°
11. Find the measure of its complement. 28°

Write *true* or *false*. Explain.

12. All squares are rectangles. True; all squares have four right angles and are therefore rectangles.
13. A right triangle can be an equilateral triangle. False; an equilateral triangle has 3 congruent angles. In a right triangle one of the angles is a right angle, so it cannot be an equilateral triangle.
14. An obtuse triangle can have a right angle. False; if a triangle has a right angle, then the other two angles are acute.

Determine whether each pair of triangles is congruent. If so, write a congruence statement and write why they are congruent.

15. △XYZ ≅ △RTS; they are congruent by SSS.
16. △LMN ≅ △PQR; they are congruent by SAS.
17. What is the measure of each angle of a regular octagon? 135°

© Pearson Education, Inc. All rights reserved.

Course 3 Chapter 8 — Form B Test — 35

Available in Spanish

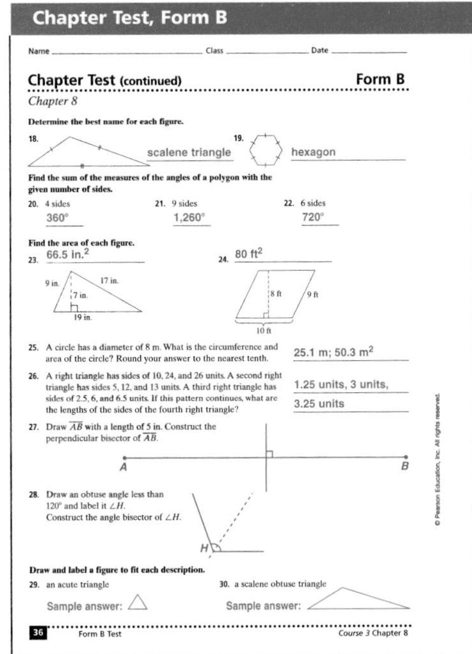

Chapter Test, Form B

Name ______ Class ______ Date ______

Chapter Test (continued) — **Form B**

Chapter 8

Determine the best name for each figure.

18. scalene triangle
19. hexagon

Find the sum of the measures of the angles of a polygon with the given number of sides.

20. 4 sides 360°
21. 9 sides 1,260°
22. 6 sides 720°

Find the area of each figure.

23. 66.5 in.²
24. 80 ft²

25. A circle has a diameter of 8 m. What is the circumference and area of the circle? Round your answer to the nearest tenth. 25.1 m; 50.3 m²
26. A right triangle has sides of 10, 24, and 26 units. A second right triangle has sides 5, 12, and 13 units. A third right triangle has sides of 2.5, 6, and 6.5 units. If this pattern continues, what are the lengths of the sides of the fourth right triangle? 1.25 units, 3 units, 3.25 units
27. Draw $\overline{AB}$ with a length of 5 in. Construct the perpendicular bisector of $\overline{AB}$.
28. Draw an obtuse angle less than 120° and label it ∠H. Construct the angle bisector of ∠H.

Draw and label a figure to fit each description.

29. an acute triangle Sample answer:
30. a scalene obtuse triangle Sample answer:

© Pearson Education, Inc. All rights reserved.

36 — Form B Test — Course 3 Chapter 8

Available in Spanish

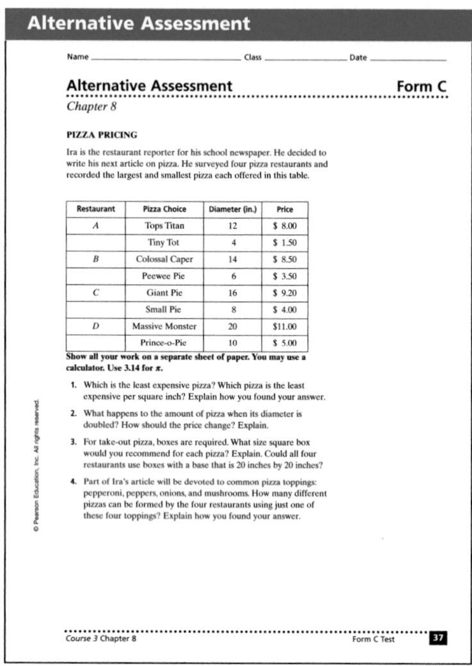

Alternative Assessment

Name ______ Class ______ Date ______

Alternative Assessment — Form C

Chapter 8

PIZZA PRICING

Ira is the restaurant reporter for his school newspaper. He decided to write his next article on pizza. He surveyed four pizza restaurants and recorded the largest and smallest pizza each offered in this table.

Restaurant	Pizza Choice	Diameter (in.)	Price
A	Tops Titan	12	$ 8.00
	Tiny Tot	4	$ 1.50
B	Colossal Caper	14	$ 8.50
	Peewee Pie	6	$ 3.50
C	Giant Pie	16	$ 9.20
	Small Pie	8	$ 4.00
D	Massive Monster	20	$11.00
	Prince-o-Pie	10	$ 5.00

Show all your work on a separate sheet of paper. You may use a calculator. Use 3.14 for π.

1. Which is the least expensive pizza? Which pizza is the least expensive per square inch? Explain how you found your answer.
2. What happens to the amount of pizza when its diameter is doubled? How should the price change? Explain.
3. For take-out pizza, boxes are required. What size square box would you recommend for each pizza? Explain. Could all four restaurants use boxes with a base that is 20 inches by 20 inches?
4. Part of Ira's article will be devoted to common pizza toppings: pepperoni, peppers, onions, and mushrooms. How many different pizzas can be formed by the four restaurants using just one of these four toppings? Explain how you found your answer.

Course 3 Chapter 8 · Form C Test · 37

Available in Spanish

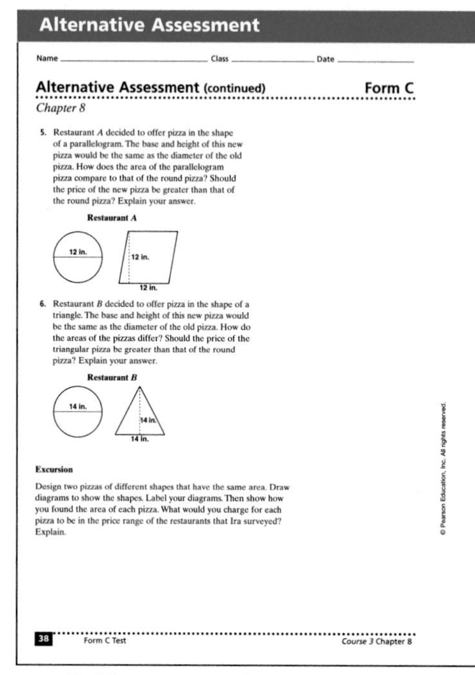

Alternative Assessment

Name ______ Class ______ Date ______

Alternative Assessment (continued) — Form C

Chapter 8

5. Restaurant *A* decided to offer pizza in the shape of a parallelogram. The base and height of this new pizza would be the same as the diameter of the old pizza. How does the area of the parallelogram pizza compare to that of the round pizza? Should the price of the new pizza be greater than that of the round pizza? Explain your answer.

6. Restaurant *B* decided to offer pizza in the shape of a triangle. The base and height of this new pizza would be the same as the diameter of the old pizza. How do the areas of the pizzas differ? Should the price of the triangular pizza be greater than that of the round pizza? Explain your answer.

Excursion

Design two pizzas of different shapes that have the same area. Draw diagrams to show the shapes. Label your diagrams. Then show how you found the area of each pizza. What would you charge for each pizza to be in the price range of the restaurants that Ira surveyed? Explain.

38 · Form C Test · Course 3 Chapter 8

Available in Spanish

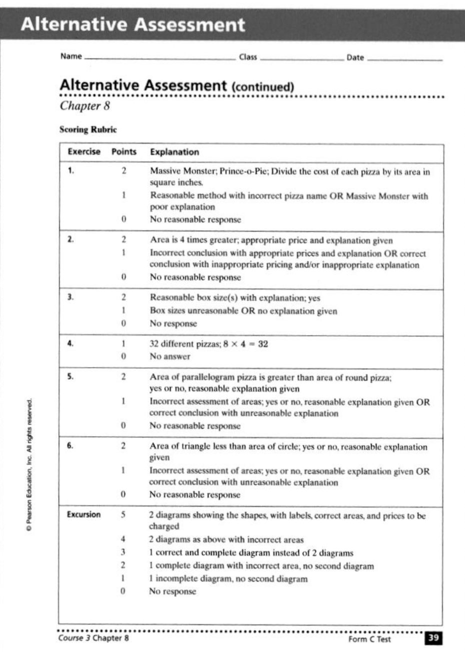

Alternative Assessment

Name ______ Class ______ Date ______

Alternative Assessment (continued)

Chapter 8

Scoring Rubric

Exercise	Points	Explanation
1.	2	Massive Monster; Prince-o-Pie; Divide the cost of each pizza by its area in square inches.
	1	Reasonable method with incorrect pizza name OR Massive Monster with poor explanation
	0	No reasonable response
2.	2	Area is 4 times greater; appropriate price and explanation given
	1	Incorrect conclusion with appropriate prices and explanation OR correct conclusion with inappropriate pricing and/or inappropriate explanation
	0	No reasonable response
3.	2	Reasonable box size(s) with explanation; yes
	1	Box sizes unreasonable OR no explanation given
	0	No response
4.	1	32 different pizzas; 8 × 4 = 32
	0	No answer
5.	2	Area of parallelogram pizza is greater than area of round pizza; yes or no, reasonable explanation given
	1	Incorrect assessment of areas; yes or no, reasonable explanation given OR correct conclusion with unreasonable explanation
	0	No reasonable response
6.	2	Area of triangle less than area of circle; yes or no, reasonable explanation given
	1	Incorrect assessment of areas; yes or no, reasonable explanation given OR correct conclusion with unreasonable explanation
	0	No reasonable response
Excursion	5	2 diagrams showing the shapes, with labels, correct areas, and prices to be charged
	4	2 diagrams as above with incorrect areas
	3	1 correct and complete diagram instead of 2 diagrams
	2	1 complete diagram with incorrect area, no second diagram
	1	1 incomplete diagram, no second diagram
	0	No response

Course 3 Chapter 8 · Form C Test · 39

Available in Spanish

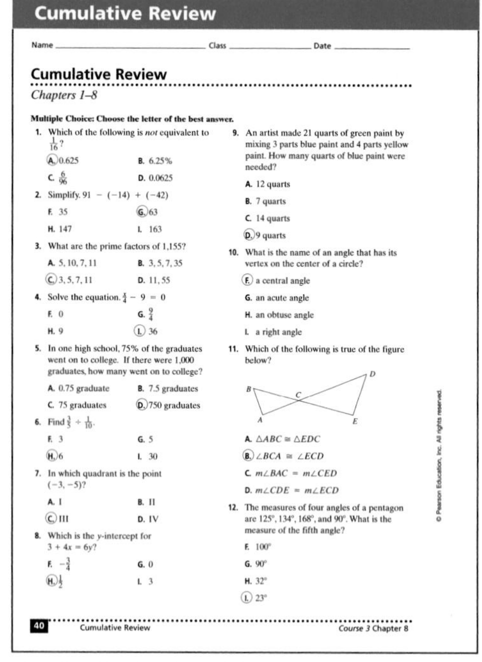

Cumulative Review

Name ______ Class ______ Date ______

Cumulative Review

Chapters 1–8

Multiple Choice: Choose the letter of the best answer.

1. Which of the following is *not* equivalent to $\frac{1}{16}$?
   Ⓐ 0.625 B. 6.25% C. $\frac{6}{96}$ D. 0.0625
2. Simplify. $91 - (-14) + (-42)$
   F. 35 Ⓖ 63 H. 147 I. 163
3. What are the prime factors of 1,155?
   A. 5, 10, 7, 11 B. 3, 5, 7, 35 Ⓒ 3, 5, 7, 11 D. 11, 55
4. Solve the equation. $\frac{x}{4} - 9 = 0$
   F. 0 G. $\frac{9}{4}$ H. 9 Ⓘ 36
5. In one high school, 75% of the graduates went on to college. If there were 1,000 graduates, how many went on to college?
   A. 0.75 graduate B. 7.5 graduates C. 75 graduates Ⓓ 750 graduates
6. Find $\frac{3}{5} \div \frac{1}{10}$.
   F. 3 G. 5 Ⓗ 6 I. 30
7. In which quadrant is the point $(-3, -5)$?
   A. I B. II Ⓒ III D. IV
8. Which is the y-intercept for $3 + 4x = 6y$?
   F. $-\frac{3}{4}$ G. 0 Ⓗ $\frac{1}{2}$ I. 3
9. An artist made 21 quarts of green paint by mixing 3 parts blue paint and 4 parts yellow paint. How many quarts of blue paint were needed?
   A. 12 quarts B. 7 quarts C. 14 quarts Ⓓ 9 quarts
10. What is the name of an angle that has its vertex on the center of a circle?
    Ⓕ a central angle G. an acute angle H. an obtuse angle I. a right angle
11. Which of the following is true of the figure below?

    A. $\triangle ABC \cong \triangle EDC$ Ⓑ $\angle BCA \cong \angle ECD$ C. $m\angle BAC = m\angle CED$ D. $m\angle CDE = m\angle ECD$
12. The measures of four angles of a pentagon are 125°, 134°, 168°, and 90°. What is the measure of the fifth angle?
    F. 100° G. 90° H. 32° Ⓘ 23°

40 · Cumulative Review · Course 3 Chapter 8

Available in Spanish

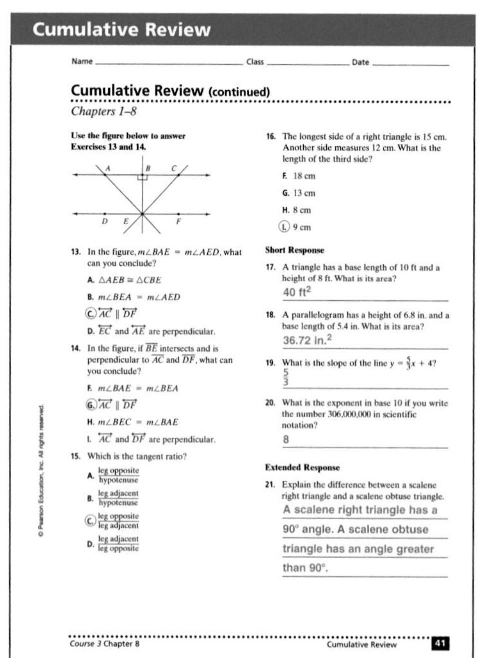

Cumulative Review

Name ______ Class ______ Date ______

Cumulative Review (continued)

Chapters 1–8

Use the figure below to answer Exercises 13 and 14.

13. In the figure, $m\angle BAE = m\angle AED$, what can you conclude?
    A. $\triangle AEB \cong \triangle CBE$ B. $m\angle BEA = m\angle AED$ Ⓒ $\overleftrightarrow{AC} \parallel \overleftrightarrow{DF}$ D. $\overleftrightarrow{EC}$ and $\overleftrightarrow{AE}$ are perpendicular.
14. In the figure, if $\overline{BE}$ intersects and is perpendicular to $\overline{AC}$ and $\overline{DF}$, what can you conclude?
    F. $m\angle BAE = m\angle BEA$ Ⓖ $\overleftrightarrow{AC} \parallel \overleftrightarrow{DF}$ H. $m\angle BEC = m\angle BAE$ I. $\overleftrightarrow{AC}$ and $\overleftrightarrow{DF}$ are perpendicular.
15. Which is the tangent ratio?
    A. $\frac{\text{leg opposite}}{\text{hypotenuse}}$ B. $\frac{\text{leg adjacent}}{\text{hypotenuse}}$ Ⓒ $\frac{\text{leg opposite}}{\text{leg adjacent}}$ D. $\frac{\text{leg adjacent}}{\text{leg opposite}}$
16. The longest side of a right triangle is 15 cm. Another side measures 12 cm. What is the length of the third side?
    F. 18 cm G. 13 cm H. 8 cm Ⓘ 9 cm

Short Response

17. A triangle has a base length of 10 ft and a height of 8 ft. What is its area?
    40 ft^2
18. A parallelogram has a height of 6.8 in. and a base length of 5.4 in. What is its area?
    36.72 in.^{2}
19. What is the slope of the line $y = \frac{5}{3}x + 4$?
    $\frac{5}{3}$
20. What is the exponent in base 10 if you write the number 306,000,000 in scientific notation?
    8

Extended Response

21. Explain the difference between a scalene right triangle and a scalene obtuse triangle.
    A scalene right triangle has a 90° angle. A scalene obtuse triangle has an angle greater than 90°.

Course 3 Chapter 8 · Cumulative Review · 41

Available in Spanish

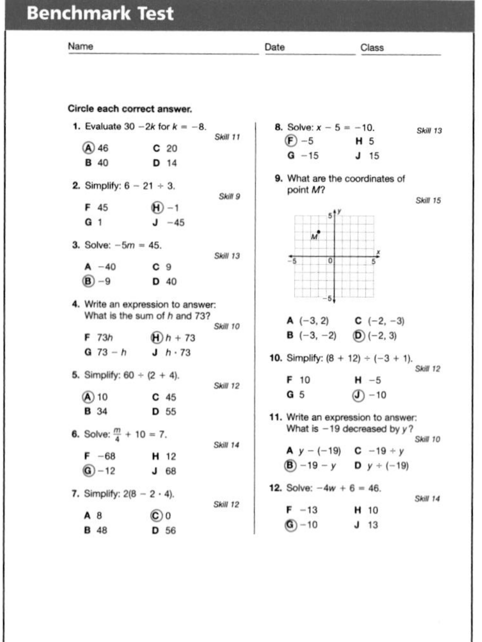

Benchmark Test

Name ______ Date ______ Class ______

Circle each correct answer.

1. Evaluate $30 - 2k$ for $k = -8$. *Skill 11*
   Ⓐ 46 C 20 B 40 D 14
2. Simplify: $6 - 21 \div 3$. *Skill 9*
   F 45 Ⓗ −1 G 1 J −45
3. Solve: $-5m = 45$. *Skill 13*
   A −40 C 9 Ⓑ −9 D 40
4. Write an expression to answer: What is the sum of h and 73? *Skill 10*
   F $73h$ Ⓗ $h + 73$ G $73 - h$ J $h \cdot 73$
5. Simplify: $60 \div (2 + 4)$. *Skill 12*
   Ⓐ 10 C 45 B 34 D 55
6. Solve: $\frac{m}{4} + 10 = 7$. *Skill 14*
   F −68 H 12 Ⓖ −12 J 68
7. Simplify: $2(8 - 2 \cdot 4)$. *Skill 12*
   A 8 Ⓒ 0 B 48 D 56
8. Solve: $x - 5 = -10$. *Skill 13*
   Ⓕ −5 H 5 G −15 J 15
9. What are the coordinates of point M? *Skill 15*

   A (−3, 2) C (−2, −3) B (−3, −2) Ⓓ (−2, 3)
10. Simplify: $(8 + 12) \div (-3 + 1)$. *Skill 12*
    F 10 H −5 G 5 Ⓙ −10
11. Write an expression to answer: What is −19 decreased by y? *Skill 10*
    A $y - (-19)$ C $-19 \div y$ Ⓑ $-19 - y$ D $y \div (-19)$
12. Solve: $-4w + 6 = 46$. *Skill 14*
    F −13 H 10 Ⓖ −10 J 13

On PH Website

Test-Taking Strategies transparency

Test-Taking Strategies: Drawing a Diagram

A diagram can help you see how to solve a problem.

Example A square quilt has 6 in. by 6 in. fabric squares. The outside perimeter is 144 in. How many squares are on the quilt perimeter?

A. 144 B. 36 C. 24 D. 20

Each side must be 144 ÷ 4 = 36 in.

Let one unit on graph paper represent 6 in.

There must be 36 ÷ 6 = 6 squares on each side.

Draw a diagram, and count the perimeter squares.

The answer is 20, or choice D.

Use a diagram to find the answer. Explain your reasoning.

1. Tess wants to fence in her garden, which is 5 ft long and 4 ft wide. She will put a post at each corner and at every foot. How many fence posts will she need?

   A. 14 B. 20 C. 18 D. 19

2. What is the area of the shaded square in the figure?

   F. 50 cm^2
   G. 100 cm^2
   H. 200 cm^2
   I. 400 cm^2

20 cm

20 cm

Transparency 9

Test-Taking Strategies worksheet

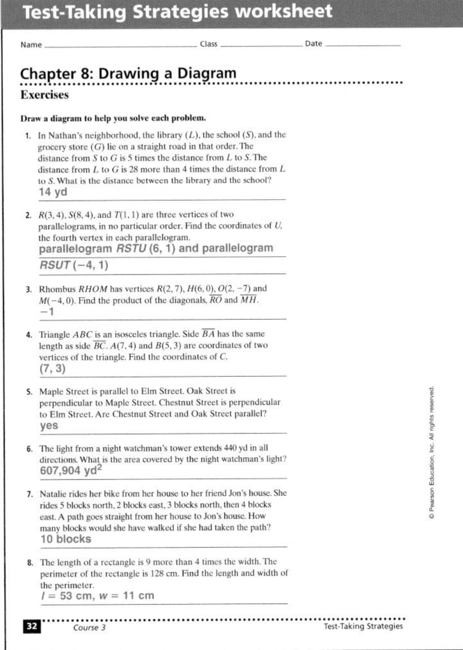

Name ____________ Class ____________ Date ____________

Chapter 8: Drawing a Diagram

Exercises

Draw a diagram to help you solve each problem.

1. In Nathan's neighborhood, the library (L), the school (S), and the grocery store (G) lie on a straight road in that order. The distance from S to G is 5 times the distance from L to S. The distance from L to G is 28 more than 4 times the distance from L to S. What is the distance between the library and the school?
   14 yd
2. $R(3, 4)$, $S(8, 4)$, and $T(1, 1)$ are three vertices of two parallelograms, in no particular order. Find the coordinates of U, the fourth vertex in each parallelogram.
   parallelogram *RSTU* (6, 1) and parallelogram *RSUT* (−4, 1)
3. Rhombus $RHOM$ has vertices $R(2, 7)$, $H(6, 0)$, $O(2, -7)$ and $M(-4, 0)$. Find the product of the diagonals, $\overline{RO}$ and $\overline{MH}$.
   −1
4. Triangle ABC is an isosceles triangle. Side $\overline{BA}$ has the same length as side $\overline{BC}$. $A(7, 4)$ and $B(5, 3)$ are coordinates of two vertices of the triangle. Find the coordinates of C.
   (7, 3)
5. Maple Street is parallel to Elm Street. Oak Street is perpendicular to Maple Street. Chestnut Street is perpendicular to Elm Street. Are Chestnut Street and Oak Street parallel?
   yes
6. The light from a night watchman's tower extends 440 yd in all directions. What is the area covered by the night watchman's light?
   607,904 yd^2
7. Natalie rides her bike from her house to her friend Jon's house. She rides 5 blocks north, 2 blocks east, 3 blocks north, then 4 blocks east. A path goes straight from her house to Jon's house. How many blocks would she have walked if she had taken the path?
   10 blocks
8. The length of a rectangle is 9 more than 4 times the width. The perimeter of the rectangle is 128 cm. Find the length and width of the perimeter.
   l = 53 cm, w = 11 cm

32 Course 3 Test-Taking Strategies

Home Activities

in math class ...

We have been learning about geometry and measurement.
Here is a list of some of the skills and concepts we have studied.

- Lines and angles
- Parallel and perpendicular lines
- Polygons
- 3-D views

Home Activities

Here are some activities you can do with your child that use these math skills and concepts.

Find some building blocks. Have your child build a small structure using 6–10 blocks. Then have your child observe the structure from above, from the front, and from the right side, each time drawing his or her observation. You and your child can, without the other one seeing, create your own structures and draw your own top, front, and right-side views. Exchange the three views, and see if you can recreate each other's structure. A sample structure with the top, front, and right-side views is shown.

Sample Structure Top Front Right Side

If building blocks are not available, you might try to draw structures and have your child draw the different views.

Use with Chapter 8

Available in Spanish; Web Code: ack-5500

Interdisciplinary Activities

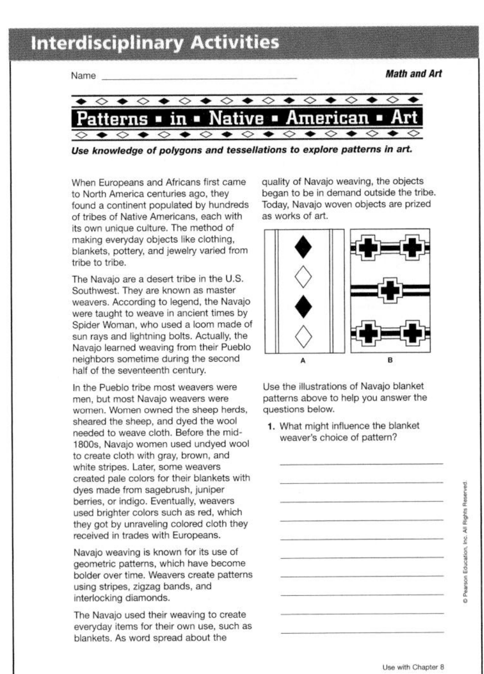

Name ____________ **Math and Art**

Patterns ▪ in ▪ Native ▪ American ▪ Art

Use knowledge of polygons and tessellations to explore patterns in art.

When Europeans and Africans first came to North America centuries ago, they found a continent populated by hundreds of tribes of Native Americans, each with its own unique culture. The method of making everyday objects like clothing, blankets, pottery, and jewelry varied from tribe to tribe.

The Navajo are a desert tribe in the U.S. Southwest. They are known as master weavers. According to legend, the Navajo were taught to weave in ancient times by Spider Woman, who used a loom made of sun rays and lightning bolts. Actually, the Navajo learned weaving from their Pueblo neighbors sometime during the second half of the seventeenth century.

In the Pueblo tribe most weavers were men, but most Navajo weavers were women. Women owned the sheep herds, sheared the sheep, and dyed the wool needed to weave cloth. Before the mid-1800s, Navajo women used undyed wool to create cloth with gray, brown, and white stripes. Later, some weavers created pale colors for their blankets with dyes made from sagebrush, juniper berries, or indigo. Eventually, weavers used brighter colors such as red, which they got by unraveling colored cloth they received in trades with Europeans.

Navajo weaving is known for its use of geometric patterns, which have become bolder over time. Weavers create patterns using stripes, zigzag bands, and interlocking diamonds.

The Navajo used their weaving to create everyday items for their own use, such as blankets. As word spread about the quality of Navajo weaving, the objects began to be in demand outside the tribe. Today, Navajo woven objects are prized as works of art.

A B

Use the illustrations of Navajo blanket patterns above to help you answer the questions below.

1. What might influence the blanket weaver's choice of pattern?

Use with Chapter 8

Web Code: ack-5500

Interdisciplinary Activities

Name ____________ **Math and Art**

2. Look at the diamond pattern in "A". What type of transformation has created it? Explain.
3. a. Examine the pattern in "B" above. If the cross-like figures were rotated 45° about their center, would the pattern stay the same? Explain.
   b. How about if they were rotated 90°?
4. Are either of the Navajo blanket patterns tessellations? Explain your answer.
5. Consider the regular polygons below. Which of them could you use to create a tessellation? Which could not be used? Cut out similar figures and try fitting them together to test your ideas.

   Triangle Square Pentagon Hexagon

6. Create a tessellation using an octagon. Will the octagon tessellate by itself or must another type of polygon be used with it? Draw the resulting tessellation.
7. Design a pattern for a blanket. It should be a tessellation that involves at least two of the regular polygons in item 5 above. The polygons can be of any size and color. Share your designs with your classmates.

Use with Chapter 8

Web Code: ack-5500

Algebra Readiness Puzzles

Name ____________ Class ____________ Date ____________

Angle Scramble! **Puzzle 32**

Geometry

r t p q m n 1 2 3 4 5 6 60° 10 40° 30° 110° 8 9 70° 11 12 70° 28 7 14 15 18 19 13 16 17 20 21 22 23 24 25 26 27 40°

Given:

Line p is parallel to line q.

Line m is parallel to line n.

Line r is parallel to line t.

1. Find the angle measures for angles 1 through 28.

$m\angle 1 =$	$m\angle 2 =$	$m\angle 3 =$	$m\angle 4 =$	$m\angle 5 =$	$m\angle 6 =$	$m\angle 7 =$
$m\angle 8 =$	$m\angle 9 =$	$m\angle 10 =$	$m\angle 11 =$	$m\angle 12 =$	$m\angle 13 =$	$m\angle 14 =$
$m\angle 15 =$	$m\angle 16 =$	$m\angle 17 =$	$m\angle 18 =$	$m\angle 19 =$	$m\angle 20 =$	$m\angle 21 =$
$m\angle 22 =$	$m\angle 23 =$	$m\angle 24 =$	$m\angle 25 =$	$m\angle 26 =$	$m\angle 27 =$	$m\angle 28 =$

2. How many triangles are formed by these lines? ____________
3. How many quadrilaterals can be identified? ____________
4. Find another angle that is congruent to $\angle 2$. ____________
5. Name a pair of vertical angles.

32 Algebra Readiness Puzzles

Web Code: ack-5500

Geometry

Chapter 8 Overview

In this chapter, students solve problems by learning and using the properties of pairs of angles, of parallel lines, and of polygons and circles. In addition, they find the areas of parallelograms, triangles, trapezoids, and circles. They also make constructions.

Reading Math
- Connecting Ideas With Concept Maps, p. 434
- **Vocabulary:** A complete list, plus exercises, in the Chapter Review, p. 462
- **Illustrated Glossary:** Examples for each vocabulary term, plus definitions in English and Spanish, on p. 735

Writing in Math
Writing to Compare, p. 453

Test-Taking Strategies
Drawing a Diagram, p. 461

Real-World Problem Solving
- **Strategies:** Solve a Simpler Problem and Look for a Pattern, p. 426–429
- **Real-World Snapshots:** You Can't Get There From Here, pp. 466–467
- **Chapter Project:** Great Escape, p. 699

www.PHSchool.com
Internet support includes:
- Self-grading Vocabulary and Chapter 8 Tests
- Activity Masters
- Chapter Project support
- Chapter Planner
- Ch. 8 Resources

Plus iTEXT

CHAPTER 8

Geometry

Lessons

Key Vocabulary

- acute triangle (p. 430)
- adjacent angles (p. 407)
- angle bisector (p. 457)
- complementary (p. 408)
- congruent polygons (p. 420)
- isosceles triangle (p. 430)
- midpoint (p. 456)
- obtuse triangle (p. 430)
- parallelogram (p. 431)
- perpendicular lines (p. 409)
- regular polygon (p. 437)
- rhombus (p. 431)
- scalene triangle (p. 430)
- supplementary (p. 408)
- transversal (p. 414)
- trapezoid (p. 431)
- vertical angles (p. 408)

404

Real-World Snapshots

Many sails are triangular in shape. Some sails, like the one at the right, have a right angle.

Sailors change the position of their sails, depending on the direction of the wind, to move their boats.

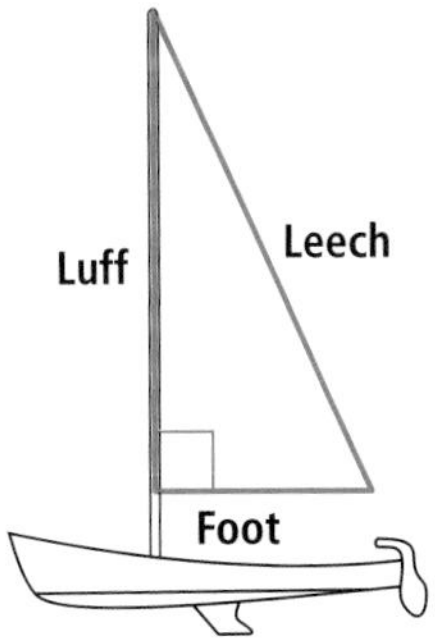

Luff
Leech
Foot

Data File

Sail Dimensions for Sailboats

Sailboat	Luff (feet)	Foot (feet)	Leech (feet)
Laser	16.67	10.54	18
470	18.87	10.5	20.55
Soling	27.89	10.5	29.92
Finn	18.7	10.73	19.75

You will use the data above throughout this chapter:

- p. 433 Lesson 8-5
- p. 445 Lesson 8-7

Real-World Snapshots On pages 466 and 467, you will solve problems about sailing.

Teaching Notes

Activating Prior Knowledge
In this chapter, students build on their knowledge of geometric concepts and of applying formulas to solve problems. Ask questions such as:

- *An angle measures 28°. What kind of angle is it?* acute angle
- *What is the perimeter of the square 14 cm on a side?* 56 cm
- *What is the area of the square 14 cm on a side?* 196 cm^2

Real-World Snapshots
The data here will be used throughout the chapter. Have a volunteer read the opening sentences about sails and the title of the chart, which contains information about dimensions of sails. Focus students on the data in the chart and ask:

- *What is the length of the luff on the sail of a Finn?* 18.7 ft
- *Which of the sail dimensions represents the hypotenuse of the triangular sail?* the leech
- *Which of the sailboats has the largest sail?* the Soling

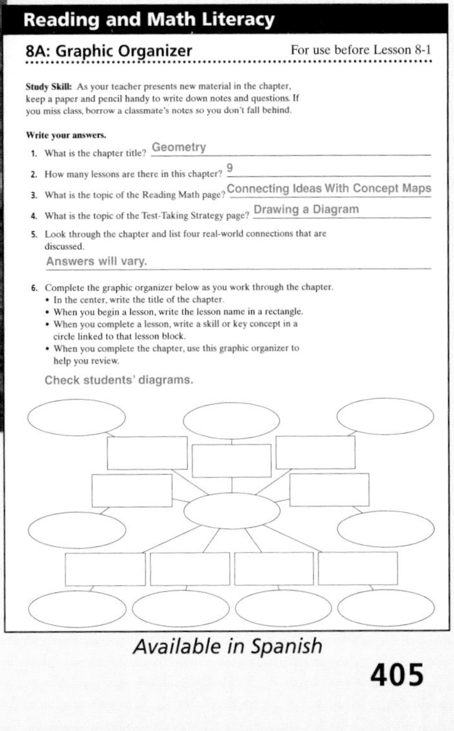

Reading and Math Literacy

8A: Graphic Organizer For use before Lesson 8-1

Study Skill: As your teacher presents new material in the chapter, keep a paper and pencil handy to write down notes and questions. If you miss class, borrow a classmate's notes so you don't fall behind.

Write your answers.

1. What is the chapter title? Geometry
2. How many lessons are there in this chapter? 9
3. What is the topic of the Reading Math page? Connecting Ideas With Concept Maps
4. What is the topic of the Test-Taking Strategy page? Drawing a Diagram
5. Look through the chapter and list four real-world connections that are discussed.
   Answers will vary.
6. Complete the graphic organizer below as you work through the chapter.
   - In the center, write the title of the chapter.
   - When you begin a lesson, write the lesson name in a rectangle.
   - When you complete a lesson, write a skill or key concept in a circle linked to that lesson block.
   - When you complete the chapter, use this graphic organizer to help you review.

   Check students' diagrams.

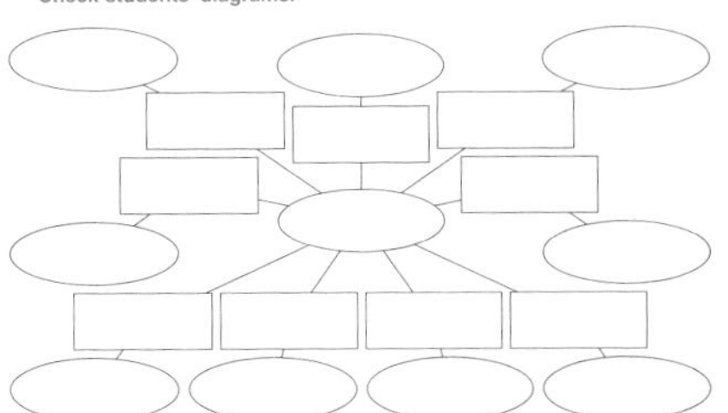

Available in Spanish

Chapter 8: Geometry

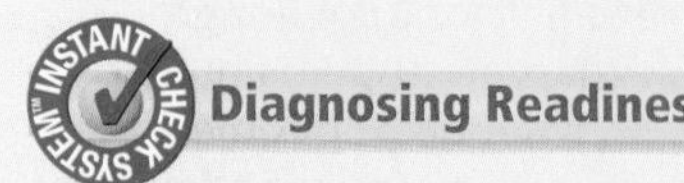

Students will find answers to these exercises in the back of their textbooks.

Prescribing Intervention
For intervention, direct students to:

Classifying Angles
Skills Handbook: Classifying Angles, p. 726.

Solving One-Step Equations
Lesson 2-1: Examples 1–4.
Extra Practice, p. 703.

Using Formulas to Solve Problems
Lesson 4-6: Example 1.
Extra Practice, p. 705.

Chapter 8 Preview

Where You've Been

- In chapter 4, you learned to use formulas to solve problems.

Where You're Going

- In Chapter 8, you will learn to use properties of pairs of angles, parallel lines, and figures to solve problems.
- You will also learn to find the areas of parallelograms, triangles, trapezoids, and circles, and to make constructions.
- Applying what you learn, you will calculate the area of different regions of a basketball court.

An NBA basketball court is 94 ft by 50 ft. A college or high school court is 84 ft by 50 ft. A middle school court is 74 ft by 42 ft.

Instant self-check online and on CD-ROM

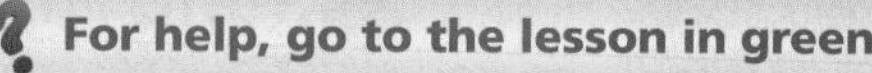

Diagnosing Readiness
For help, go to the lesson in green.

Classifying Angles (Skills Handbook page 726)

Measure each angle. Classify it as *acute, right, obtuse,* or *straight.*

1. 110° obtuse

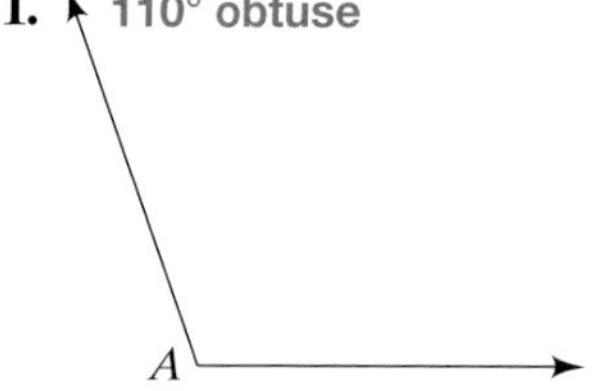

2. 35° acute

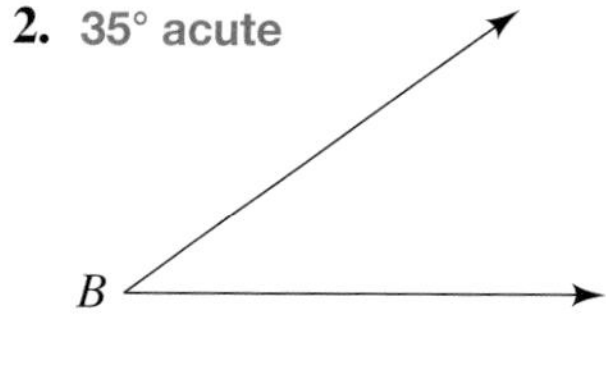

3. 90° right

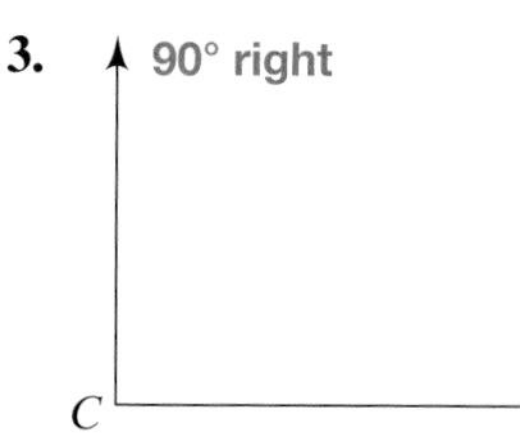

Solving One-Step Equations (Lesson 2-1)

Solve each equation.

4. $25 = 17 + m$ 8
5. $b + 13 = -56$ −69
6. $44 + s = 41$ −3
7. $-10 = p - 22$ 12
8. $4.2g = -63$ −15
9. $-16 = -14k$ $1\frac{1}{7}$
10. $\frac{w}{3.5} = 24$ 84
11. $5.1 = \frac{c}{-7}$ −35.7

Using Formulas to Solve Problems (Lesson 4-6)

Find the area of each figure.

12.

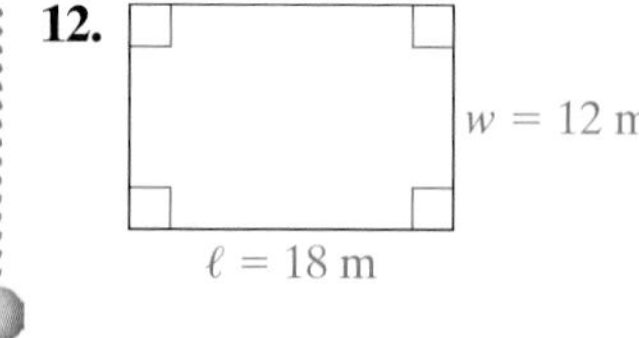

216 m^2

13.

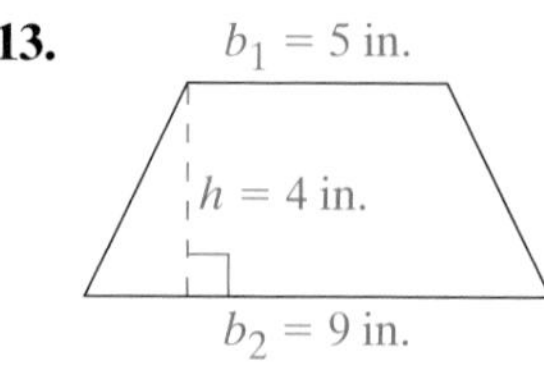

28 $in.^2$

14.

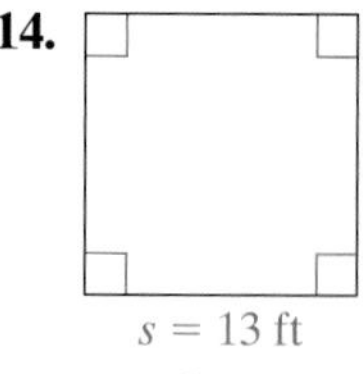

169 ft^2

8-1 Pairs of Angles

What You'll Learn

OBJECTIVE 1 To use adjacent and vertical angles

OBJECTIVE 2 To use supplementary and complementary angles

. . . And Why

To identify pairs of angles on city maps, as in Example 1

Check Skills You'll Need

For help, go to Skills Handbook page 726.

Measure each angle. Classify it as *acute, right, obtuse,* or *straight.*

1. 20°; acute

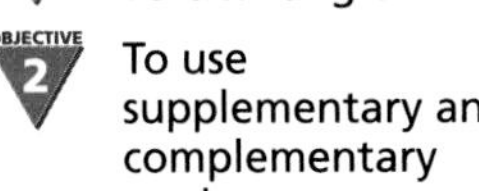

2. 145°; obtuse

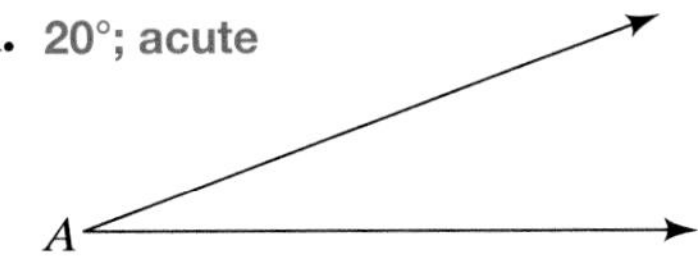

New Vocabulary

- adjacent angles
- vertical angles
- supplementary
- complementary
- perpendicular lines

Interactive lesson includes instant self-check, tutorials, and activities.

OBJECTIVE 1

Using Adjacent Angles and Vertical Angles

Investigation: Exploring Pairs of Angles

1–3. Check students' work.

1. Draw two intersecting lines. Number the angles as shown at the right.
2. Measure the angles in your drawing. Record the results.
3. Complete three trials for different pairs of intersecting lines.
4. Use the measures for each pair of intersecting lines. See left.
   a. Compare $m\angle 1$ and $m\angle 3$. Then compare $m\angle 2$ and $m\angle 4$.
   b. **Patterns** Make a conjecture about these pairs of angles.
5. Use the measures for each pair of intersecting lines.
   a. Find the sum of $m\angle 1$ and $m\angle 2$. 180°
   b. Find the sum of $m\angle 2$ and $m\angle 3$. 180°
   c. **Patterns** Make a conjecture about these pairs of angles. See left.

4a. $m\angle 1 = m\angle 3$; $m\angle 2 = m\angle 4$

4b. If two lines intersect each other, they form two pairs of angles with equal measures.

5c. Answers may vary. Sample: The sum of the measures of angles with a common side formed by the intersection of two lines is 180°.

When two lines intersect, they form special pairs of angles.

Adjacent angles have a common vertex and a common side, but no common interior points.

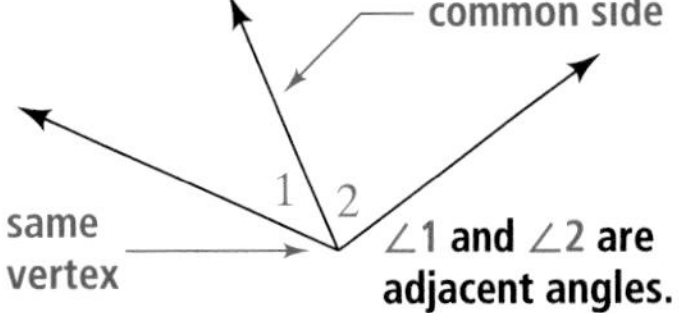

Need Help?
The vertex of an angle is the common endpoint of its two rays.

8-1

1. Plan

Lesson Preview

Check Skills You'll Need
Classifying and Measuring Angles
Skills Handbook: Classifying and Measuring Angles, p. 726.

Lesson Resources

Optional Materials
- protractor

Teaching Resources
Practice, Reteaching, Enrichment

Reaching All Students
Practice Workbook 8-1
Spanish Practice Workbook 8-1
Guided Problem Solving 8-1

Presentation Assistant Plus!
Transparencies
- Check Skills You'll Need 8-1
- Problem of the Day 8-1
- Additional Examples 8-1
- Student Edition Answers 8-1
- Lesson Quiz 8-1
- Classroom Aid 5

PH Presentation Pro CD-ROM 8-1

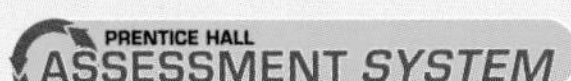

Computer Test Generator CD

Technology
Resource Pro® CD-ROM
Computer Test Generator CD
PH Presentation Pro CD-ROM

www.PHSchool.com
Student Site
- Teacher Web Code: ack-5500
- Self-grading Lesson Quiz

PH SuccessNet Teacher Center
- Lesson Planner
- Resources

Plus 

Ongoing Assessment and Intervention

Before the Lesson
Diagnose prerequisite skills using:
- Check Skills You'll Need

During the Lesson
Monitor progress using:
- Check Understanding
- Additional Examples
- Test Prep

After the Lesson
Assess knowledge using:
- Lesson Quiz
- Computer Test Generator CD

2. Teach

Math Background

When two straight lines intersect, both pairs of opposite angles (the pair marked ∠1 and ∠2, and the pair marked ∠3 and ∠4) are called *vertical angles*, and the two angles in each pair are congruent.

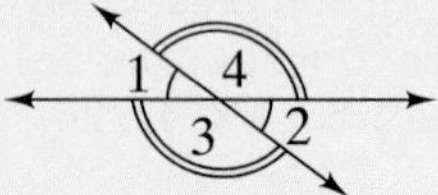

In the figure, ∠1 and ∠4 are *adjacent angles* because they share a vertex and a common side, but they do not have common interior points. In the figure, ∠1 and ∠4 are *supplementary angles* because their sum is a straight line, or 180°. In this figure, there are a total of four different pairs of adjacent and supplementary angles.

Teaching Notes

Investigation (Optional)
Remind students that the notation *m*∠1 is read as "the measure of angle one." It is correct to say that ∠1 is congruent to ∠3, while *m*∠1 is equal to *m*∠3.

English Learners
Define *adjacent* as "next to." Have students identify items in the classroom that are adjacent to each other.

1 EXAMPLE Tactile Learners
Have students use rulers, pencils, or other straight objects to model angles that are adjacent or vertical.

2 EXAMPLE Inclusion
Some students may incorrectly think that there is a relationship between the *x* used in *x*° and the *X* used in ∠*XYZ*. Explain that *x*° is just a variable used as a placeholder to find the measure of the supplement.

3 EXAMPLE Teaching Tip
Have students develop and share memory aids to help them remember that complementary angles add to a right angle (or 90°) while supplementary angles add to a straight line (or 180°).

In the diagrams below, ∠3 and ∠4 are *not* adjacent angles.

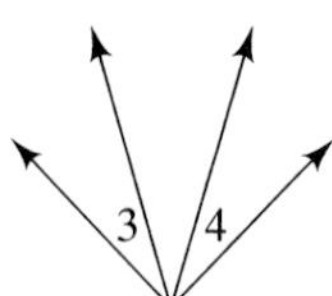

The angles share a vertex but not a side.

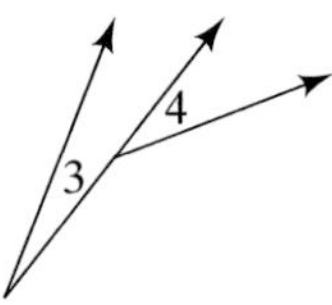

The angles share a side but not a vertex.

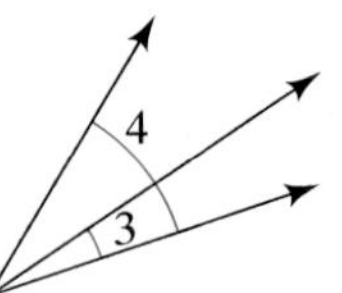

The angles have common interior points.

Vertical angles are formed by two intersecting lines and are opposite each other. Vertical angles have the same measure, so they are congruent.

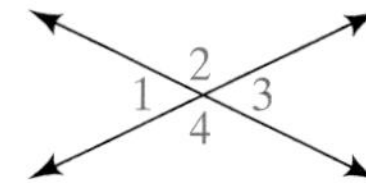

← ∠1 and ∠3 are vertical angles; *m*∠1 = *m*∠3.
∠2 and ∠4 are vertical angles; *m*∠2 = *m*∠4.

1 EXAMPLE Adjacent Angles and Vertical Angles

City Planning Identify a pair of adjacent angles and a pair of vertical angles in the photo of San Francisco. Find *m*∠*JBT*.

∠*DBJ* and ∠*JBT* are adjacent angles.
∠*DBY* and ∠*JBT* are vertical angles.

Since vertical angles are congruent, *m*∠*JBT* = *m*∠*DBY* = 80°.

1a. Vertical angles: ∠*DBJ* and ∠*YBT*; adjacent angles may vary. Sample: ∠*DBJ* and ∠*DBY*

a. Name another pair of vertical angles and another pair of adjacent angles in the photo.

b. Reasoning Suppose *m*∠*YBT* = 100°. Find *m*∠*DBJ*. Explain your answer. 100°; vertical angles are congruent.

OBJECTIVE

2 Using Supplementary Angles and Complementary Angles

Need Help?
You can name the angle below in three ways.

A, 1, B, C

∠1, ∠*B*, ∠*ABC*

If the sum of the measures of two angles is 180°, the angles are **supplementary.**

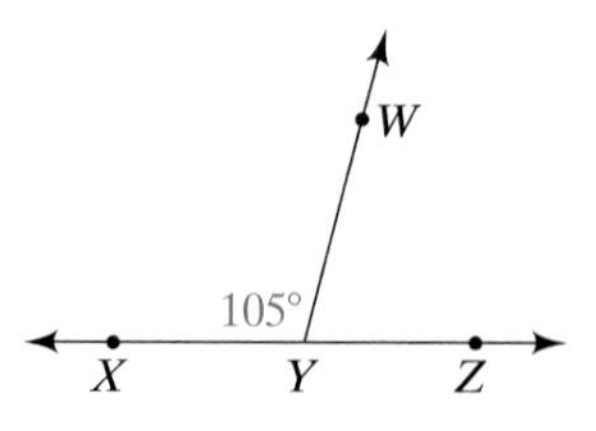

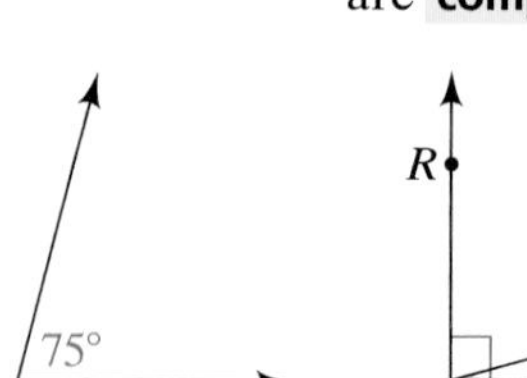

∠*C* and ∠*WYZ* are both supplements of ∠*XYW*.

If the sum of the measures of two angles is 90°, the angles are **complementary.**

R, V, 15°, S, T

∠*C* and ∠*VSR* are both complements of ∠*VST*.

Reaching All Students

Below Level Have students use protractors to review measuring and drawing angles including right angles and straight angles.	**Advanced Learners** Have students explore to find the angles formed by the diagonals of a square, or any parallelogram with four equal sides (rhombus). right angles	**English Learners** See note on page 408. **Inclusion** See note on page 408.

You can solve equations to find supplementary and complementary angles.

2 EXAMPLE Finding Supplementary Angles

Algebra Suppose $m\angle BCD = 121°$. Find the measure of its supplement.

$x° + m\angle BCD = 180°$ ← **The sum of the measures of supplementary angles is 180°.**

$x° + 121° = 180°$ ← **Substitute 121° for $m\angle BCD$.**

$x° + 121° - 121° = 180° - 121°$ ← **Subtract 121° from each side.**

$x° = 59°$ ← **Simplify.**

The measure of the supplement of $\angle BCD$ is 59°.

Check Understanding 2 Find the measure of the supplement of each angle.
a. 47° 133° **b.** 135° 45° **c.** 86° 94°

Perpendicular lines are two lines that intersect to form a right angle. Recall that a right angle has 90 degrees.

3 EXAMPLE Finding Complementary Angles

Algebra In the diagram at the left, $\overleftrightarrow{AB}$ is perpendicular to $\overleftrightarrow{BC}$. Find the measure of the complement of $\angle DBC$.

$x° + m\angle DBC = 90°$ ← **The sum of the measures of complementary angles is 90°.**

$x° + 42° = 90°$ ← **Substitute 42° for $m\angle BCD$.**

$x° + 42° - 42° = 90° - 42°$ ← **Subtract 42° from each side.**

$x° = 48°$ ← **Simplify.**

The measure of the complement of $\angle DBC$ is 48°.

Check Understanding 3 Find the measure of the complement of each angle.
a. 36° 54° **b.** 74° 16° **c.** 63° 27°
d. Reasoning Does every angle have a complement? Explain.
No; obtuse angles do not have complements.

You can use pairs of angles to find the measures of angles formed by intersecting lines.

4 EXAMPLE Finding Angle Measures

In the diagram at the left, $m\angle 5 = 58°$. Find the measures of $\angle 1$ and $\angle 2$.

$m\angle 1 + 58° = 90°$ ← **$\angle 1$ and $\angle 5$ are complementary.**

$m\angle 1 = 32°$ ← **Subtract 58° from each side.**

$m\angle 2 = m\angle 1 = 32°$ ← **$\angle 1$ and $\angle 2$ are vertical angles.**

Check Understanding 4 Find the measures of $\angle 3$ and $\angle 4$ in the diagram in Example 4. 58°; 90°

4 EXAMPLE Tactile Learners

Have students use a corner of a sheet of paper as a 90° angle and then cut the angle to divide it into an angle of 58° and another angle. Then have them verify that the smaller angle measures 32°.

PowerPoint

Additional Examples

1 Name a pair of adjacent angles and a pair of vertical angles in the figure below. Find $m\angle HGK$.

adj. angles: $\angle HGK$ and $\angle KGJ$; $\angle KGJ$ and $\angle JGI$; $\angle JGI$ and $\angle IGH$; $\angle IGH$ and $\angle HGK$; vert. angles: $\angle HGI$ and $\angle KGJ$; $\angle HGK$ and $\angle JGI$. $m\angle HGK = 145°$

2 If $m\angle DEF = 73°$, find the measure of its supplement. 107°

3 A right angle is divided into two angles. If the measure of the larger angle is 67°, find the measure of its complement. 23°

4 In this figure, if $m\angle DKH = 73°$, find the measures of $\angle GKJ$ and $\angle JKF$. 17°; 73°

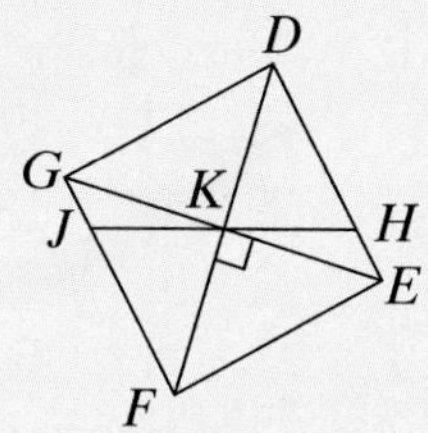

Closure

- *What are adjacent angles and vertical angles?* Sample: Adjacent angles share a vertex and a side, but no interior points. Vertical angles are a pair of non-adjacent angles formed by two intersecting lines.
- *What are supplementary angles and complementary angles?* Sample: Supplementary angles are two angles with measures that add to 180°, and complementary angles are two angles with measures that add to 90°.

3. Practice

Assignment Guide

1 Objective 1

A B Core 1–3, 19–20, 25–27

C Extension 37

2 Objective 2

A B Core 4–18, 21–24, 28–36

C Extension 38–41

Test Prep 42–45

Mixed Review 46–50

Practice 8-1 — Pairs of Angles

Name a pair of vertical angles and a pair of adjacent angles in each figure. Find $m\angle 1$.

1. 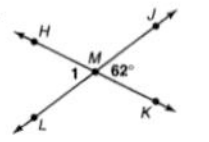 Sample answer: vertical $\angle HML$, $\angle JMK$; adjacent $\angle HML$, $\angle JMH$; $m\angle 1 = 62°$
2. 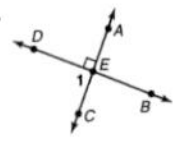 Sample answer: vertical $\angle DEA$, $\angle CEB$; adjacent $\angle DEA$, $\angle AEB$; $m\angle 1 = 90°$
3. 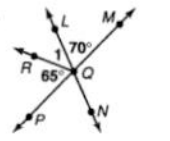 Sample answer: vertical $\angle LQM$, $\angle PQN$; adjacent $\angle PQR$, $\angle RQL$; $m\angle 1 = 45°$
4. 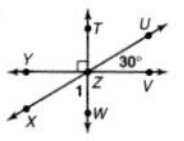 Sample answer: vertical $\angle XZY$, $\angle UZV$; adjacent $\angle XZY$, $\angle YZT$; $m\angle 1 = 60°$

Find the measure of the supplement and the complement of each angle.

5. 10° — 170°, 80°
6. 38° — 142°, 52°
7. 42.5° — 137.5°, 47.5°
8. $n°$ — $180 - n°$, $90 - n°$

Use the diagram at the right for Exercises 9–14. Decide whether each statement below is true or false.

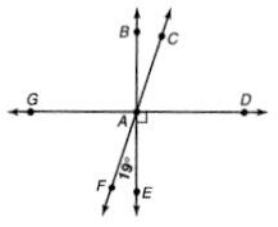

9. $\angle GAF$ and $\angle BAC$ are vertical angles. false
10. $\angle EAF$ and $\angle EAD$ are adjacent angles. true
11. $\angle CAD$ is a supplement of $\angle DAF$. true
12. $\angle CAD$ is a complement of $\angle EAF$. true
13. $m\angle GAC = 90°$ false
14. $m\angle DAF = 109°$ true

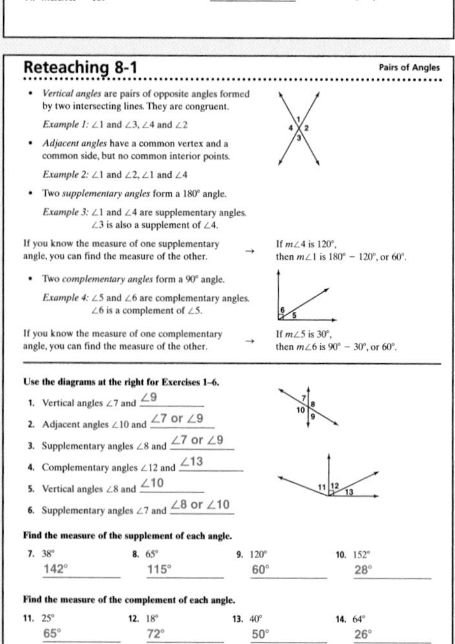

Reteaching 8-1 — Pairs of Angles

- *Vertical angles* are pairs of opposite angles formed by two intersecting lines. They are congruent.
  Example 1: $\angle 1$ and $\angle 3$, $\angle 4$ and $\angle 2$
- *Adjacent angles* have a common vertex and a common side, but no common interior points.
  Example 2: $\angle 1$ and $\angle 2$, $\angle 1$ and $\angle 4$
- Two *supplementary angles* form a 180° angle.
  Example 3: $\angle 1$ and $\angle 4$ are supplementary angles. $\angle 3$ is also a supplement of $\angle 4$.

If you know the measure of one supplementary angle, you can find the measure of the other. → If $m\angle 4$ is 120°, then $m\angle 1$ is 180° − 120°, or 60°.

- Two *complementary angles* form a 90° angle.
  Example 4: $\angle 5$ and $\angle 6$ are complementary angles. $\angle 6$ is a complement of $\angle 5$.

If you know the measure of one complementary angle, you can find the measure of the other. → If $m\angle 5$ is 30°, then $m\angle 6$ is 90° − 30°, or 60°.

Use the diagrams at the right for Exercises 1–6.

1. Vertical angles $\angle 7$ and $\angle 9$
2. Adjacent angles $\angle 10$ and $\angle 7$ or $\angle 9$
3. Supplementary angles $\angle 8$ and $\angle 7$ or $\angle 9$
4. Complementary angles $\angle 12$ and $\angle 13$
5. Vertical angles $\angle 8$ and $\angle 10$
6. Supplementary angles $\angle 7$ and $\angle 8$ or $\angle 10$

Find the measure of the supplement of each angle.

7. 38° — 142°
8. 65° — 115°
9. 120° — 60°
10. 152° — 28°

Find the measure of the complement of each angle.

11. 25° — 65°
12. 18° — 72°
13. 40° — 50°
14. 64° — 26°

EXERCISES

For more practice, see *Extra Practice*.

A Practice by Example

Example 1 (page 408)

Name a pair of vertical angles and a pair of adjacent angles in each figure. Find $m\angle 1$. 1–3. See margin.

1. 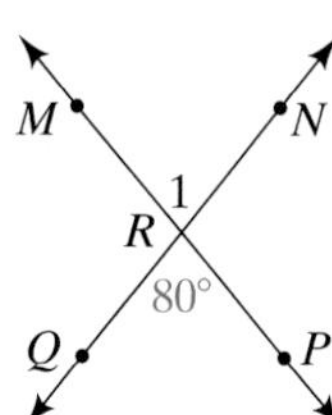

2. 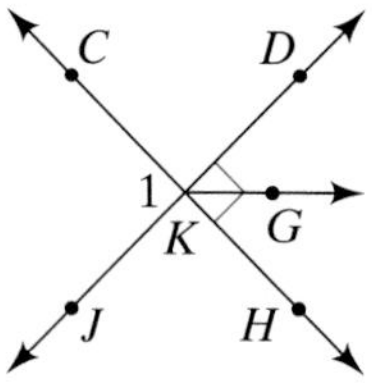 C, D, K, 1, G, J, H

3. 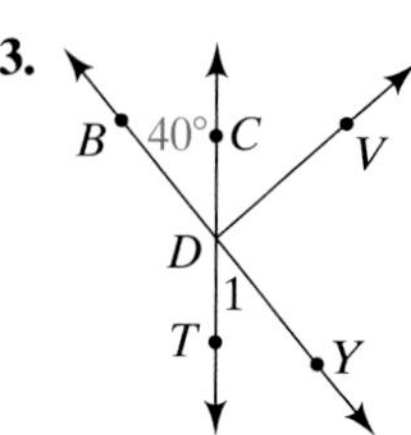

Example 2 (page 409)

Find the measure of the supplement of each angle. Exercise 4 has been started for you.

4. 74° 106°
   $x° + 74° = 180°$
5. 24° 156°
6. 145° 35°
7. 39° 141°
8. 116° 64°
9. 158° 22°

Example 3 (page 409)

Find the measure of the complement of each angle. Exercise 10 has been started for you.

10. 39° 51°
    $x° + 39° = 90°$
11. 87° 3°
12. 43° 47°
13. 21° 69°
14. 5° 85°
15. 56° 34°

Example 4 (page 409)

Find the measure of each numbered angle. 16–18. See margin.

16. 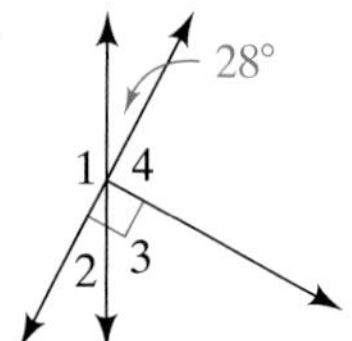

17. 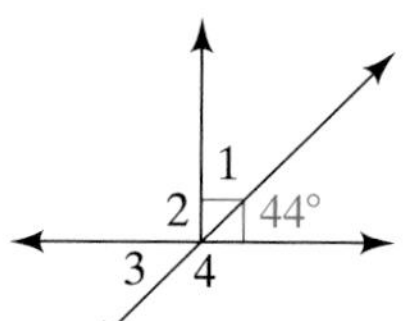

18. 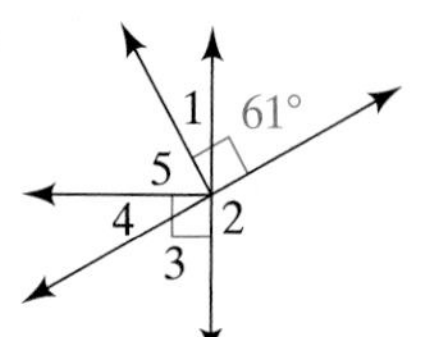

B Apply Your Skills

GPS **Use the diagram at the right for Exercises 19–22.**

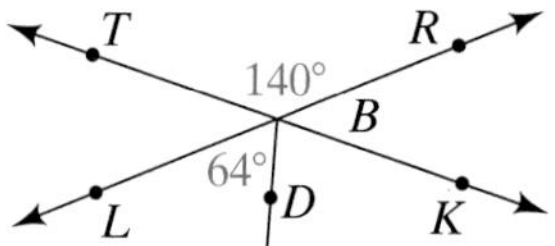

T R 140° B 64° D L K

19. $\angle LBD$ and $\angle TBL$ are __?__ angles. adjacent
20. $\angle RBT$ and $\angle$ __?__ are vertical angles. $\angle LBK$
21. $m\angle KBL = \blacksquare°$ 140°
22. $m\angle DBK = \blacksquare°$ 76°

23a–b. Check students' work.

23. a. **Open-Ended** Draw a pair of adjacent supplementary angles.
    b. Use a protractor. Draw a pair of supplementary angles that are not adjacent. Label each angle measure.

See left.

24. a. **Algebra** Write a formula to find the complement of an angle $x°$.
    b. Write a formula to find the supplement of an angle $y°$.

24a. $90° - x°$ = complement x
b. $180° - y°$ = supplement y

Use the Guided Problem Solving worksheet with Exercise 19–22.

1-3. Answers may vary. Samples are given.

1. $\angle MRQ$ and $\angle NRP$; $\angle NRP$ and $\angle QRP$; 80°
2. $\angle CKJ$ and $\angle DKH$; $\angle CKG$ and $\angle GKH$; 90°
3. $\angle BDC$ and $\angle TDY$; $\angle CDV$ and $\angle VDY$; 40°

16. $m\angle 1 = 152°$; $m\angle 2 = 28°$; $m\angle 3 = 62°$; $m\angle 4 = 90°$
17. $m\angle 1 = 46°$; $m\angle 2 = 90°$; $m\angle 3 = 44°$; $m\angle 4 = 136°$
18. $m\angle 1 = 29°$; $m\angle 2 = 119°$; $m\angle 3 = 61°$; $m\angle 4 = 29°$; $m\angle 5 = 61°$

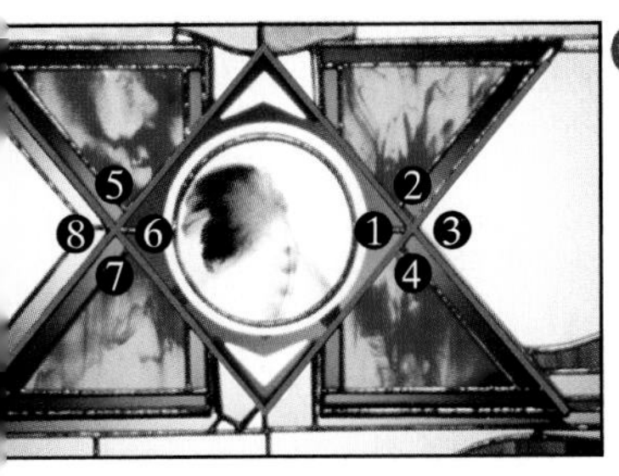

Windows Use the stained glass window for Exercises 25–28.
25–28. See below left.

25. Are $\angle 1$ and $\angle 7$ adjacent angles? Explain why or why not.

26. Are $\angle 2$ and $\angle 3$ vertical angles? Explain why or why not.

27. Name a pair of adjacent angles. Name a pair of vertical angles.

28. Suppose $m\angle 1 = m\angle 6$. Are $\angle 1$ and $\angle 5$ supplementary angles? Explain why or why not.

25. No; they do not share a common side.

26. No; they are not formed by two intersecting lines.

27. Answers may vary. Sample: $\angle 1$ and $\angle 2$; $\angle 5$ and $\angle 7$

28. Yes; $\angle 5$ is supplementary to $\angle 6$. Since $m\angle 1 = m\angle 6$, $\angle 1$ and $\angle 5$ are supplementary angles.

Find the measure of the complement and the supplement of each angle. If there is no complement, write *no complement*.

29. 32° 58°; 148°
30. 42.3° 47.7°; 137.7°
31. 85.9° 4.1°; 94.1°

32. 91° no complement; 89°
33. 139.5° no complement; 40.5°
34. 179° no complement; 1°

35. Maps A map of the Chicago area is shown at the right.

a. Find the measure of the acute angle formed by Route 43 and Northwest Highway. 50°

b. If you travel from Harwood Heights on Route 43 and turn right onto Northwest Highway, how many degrees do you turn? 130°

Route 43 is perpendicular to Devon Avenue. Northwest Highway and Devon Avenue intersect at 40° angles.

36. a. **Writing in Math** Can two supplementary angles have the same measure? Explain.

b. Can two complementary angles have the same measure? Explain.

36a. Yes; two right angles are supplementary and have measures of 90°.

b. Yes; two 45° angles are complementary and have equal measures.

Challenge

Algebra Write an equation for each pair of angles. Then solve for x.

37.

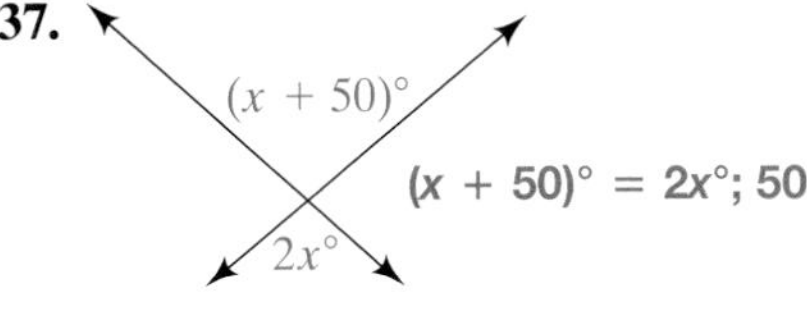

$(x + 50)° = 2x°$; 50

38.

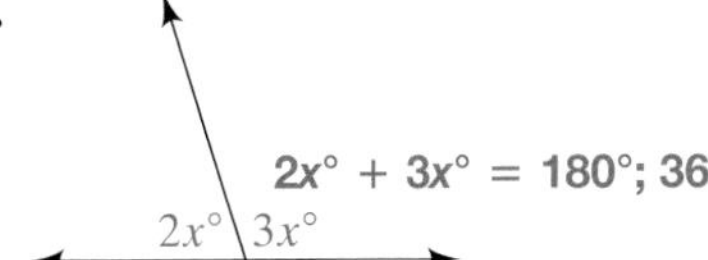

$2x° + 3x° = 180°$; 36

39.

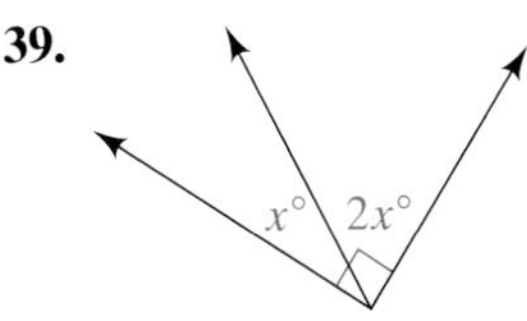

$x° + 2x° = 90°$; 30

40.

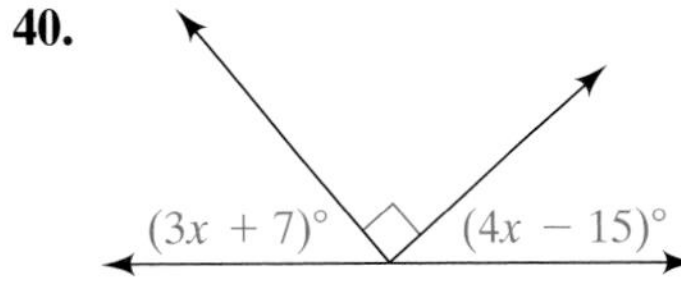

$(3x + 7)° + (4x - 15)° + 90° = 180°$; 14

41. Stretch Your Thinking Kira, Irene, and Tim bought 24 CDs at a recent sale. Kira bought 2 fewer than twice the number of CDs that Irene bought. Irene bought 2 more than half as many as Tim bought. How many CDs did each person buy? Kira: 10, Irene: 6, Tim: 8

Error Prevention!

Exercise 4–15 Only pairs of angles can be supplementary or complementary.

4. Assess

Lesson Quiz 8-1

Use the diagram to answer Questions 1 and 2.

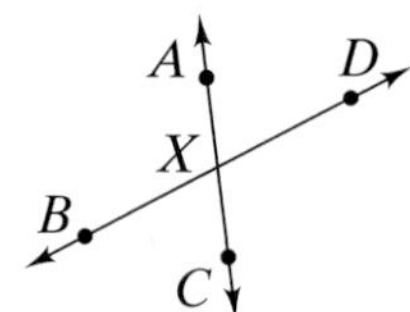

1. List all pairs of vertical angles. $\angle AXD$ and $\angle BXC$; $\angle AXB$ and $\angle DXC$
2. List any angles adjacent to $\angle CXD$. $\angle AXD$ and $\angle BXC$
3. If $m\angle AXB = 110°$, find $m\angle DXC$. 110°
4. An angle measures 57°. What is the measure of its supplement? 123°
5. An angle measures 24°. What is the measure of its complement? 66°

Test Prep

Resources

For additional practice with a variety of test item formats:

- Test Prep, p. 465
- Test-Taking Strategies, p. 461
- Test-Taking Strategies with Transparencies

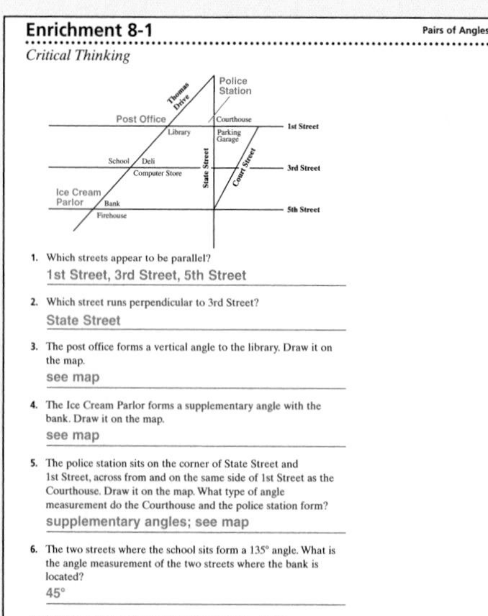

Enrichment 8-1 Pairs of Angles

Critical Thinking

1. Which streets appear to be parallel? 1st Street, 3rd Street, 5th Street
2. Which street runs perpendicular to 3rd Street? State Street
3. The post office forms a vertical angle to the library. Draw it on the map. see map
4. The Ice Cream Parlor forms a supplementary angle with the bank. Draw it on the map. see map
5. The police station sits on the corner of State Street and 1st Street, across from and on the same side of 1st Street as the Courthouse. Draw it on the map. What type of angle measurement do the Courthouse and the police station form? supplementary angles; see map
6. The two streets where the school sits form a 135° angle. What is the angle measurement of the two streets where the bank is located? 45°
7. Which place or places are located on the same angle measurement as the firehouse? Computer Store, School, Ice Cream Parlor, Post Office, and Library

Test Prep

Multiple Choice

42. Which angle is a supplement of $\angle WYZ$? B
    A. $\angle XYW$ B. $\angle JYZ$
    C. $\angle XYZ$ D. $\angle JYX$

43. What is the measure of $\angle 1$? H
    F. 35° G. 55°
    H. 65° I. 125°

44. Which angle is congruent to $\angle XYW$? A
    A. $\angle JYK$ B. $\angle ZYJ$
    C. $\angle JYX$ D. $\angle WYK$

Z, X, 1, 55°, J, Y, W, 120°, K

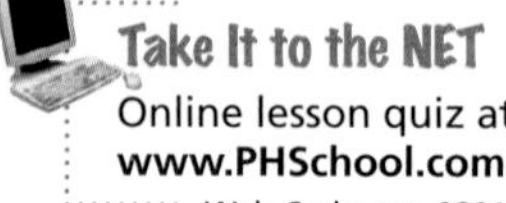

Take It to the NET Online lesson quiz at **www.PHSchool.com** Web Code: aca-0801

Short Response

45. Is it possible for two vertical angles to be complementary angles? Explain your answer. See margin.

Mixed Review

Lesson 7-2 **Multiply. Write each answer in scientific notation.**

46. $(4 \times 10^2) \cdot (2 \times 10^5)$ 8×10^7
47. $(7 \times 10^4) \cdot (6 \times 10^3)$ 4.2×10^8
48. $(9 \times 10^6) \cdot (3 \times 10^2)$ 2.7×10^9
49. $(5 \times 10^5) \cdot (1.9 \times 10^7)$ 9.5×10^{12}

Lesson 6-6

50. **Shopping** A department store is having its annual 30%-off sale. A winter jacket is on sale for \$63. What was the regular price of the jacket? \$90

Math at Work

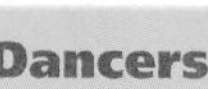

Dancers

Dancers combine music, rhythmical movement, stories, and expression in an art form known as dance.

Modern dance allows for freedom of movement and self-expression. Other types of dance include folk, classical ballet, ethnic, tap, and jazz.

You might wonder how math applies to dance. Dancers often perform as a group. The choreography, or the arranged movements of the dance, often consists of repeated steps. Knowledge of patterns helps dancers memorize the steps and synchronize with the other dancers.

Take It to the NET For more information about dance, go to **www.PHSchool.com**. Web Code: acb-2031

Alternative Assessment

Have students find the measure of the complement and supplement of a 39° angle. 51°; 141°

45. [2] Yes; since vertical angles are congruent, and complementary angles have a sum of 90°, the two angles must be 45°.
[1] correct answer without explanation

8-2 Angles and Parallel Lines

What You'll Learn

 To find the measures of angles formed by parallel lines

 To identify parallel lines

. . . And Why

To identify pairs of angles in architecture, as in Exercise 18

✓ Check Skills You'll Need

For help, go to Skills Handbook page 726.

Classify each angle as *acute, right, obtuse,* or *straight.*

1. acute
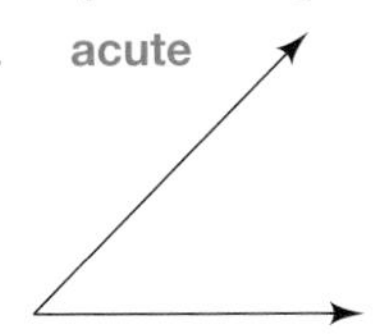
2. right
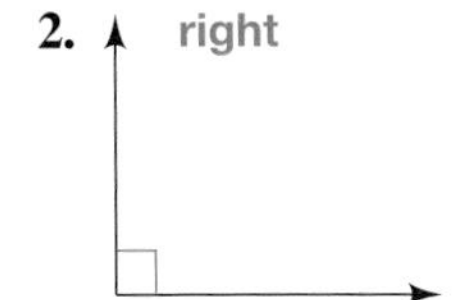
3. obtuse
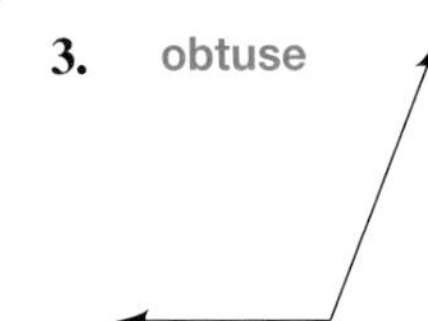

New Vocabulary

- transversal
- corresponding angles
- alternate interior angles

OBJECTIVE 1

Interactive lesson includes instant self-check, tutorials, and activities.

Angles Formed by Parallel Lines

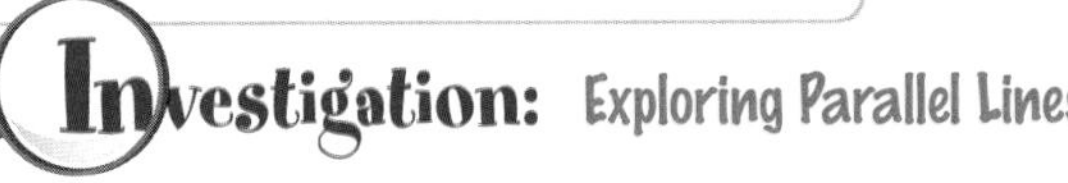

Investigation: Exploring Parallel Lines

Navigation The pilot of a ship uses a navigational tool called a *parallel rule* to plot routes on charts. Recall that parallel lines lie in the same plane and do not intersect. In the diagram below, *m* is parallel to *t*, and *r* is parallel to *s*.

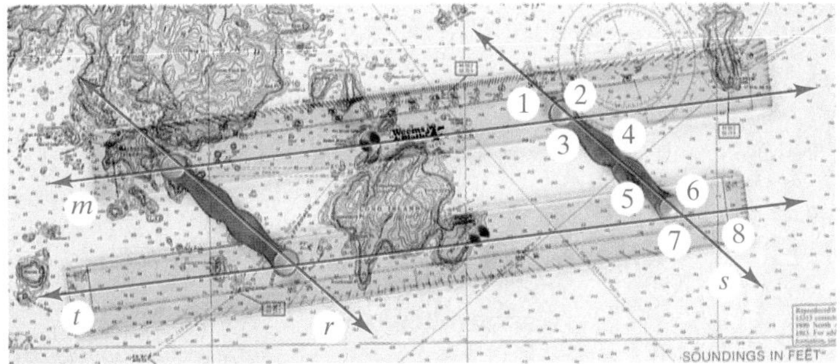

1–3. See left.

1. Use a protractor. Find the measures of the numbered angles.
2. Identify all the congruent pairs of angles.
3. Make a conjecture about the angles formed when a line intersects two parallel lines.
4. Check your conjecture by measuring other angles in the diagram. Check students' work.

1. $m\angle 1 = 47°$; $m\angle 2 = 133°$; $m\angle 3 = 133°$; $m\angle 4 = 47°$; $m\angle 5 = 47°$; $m\angle 6 = 133°$; $m\angle 7 = 133°$; $m\angle 8 = 47°$
2. $\angle 1 \cong \angle 4 \cong \angle 5 \cong \angle 8$; $\angle 2 \cong \angle 3 \cong \angle 6 \cong \angle 7$
3. Answers may vary. Sample: Four angles will have the same measure, and the other four angles will be supplements of those angles.

Ongoing Assessment and Intervention

Before the Lesson
Diagnose prerequisite skills using:
- Check Skills You'll Need

During the Lesson
Monitor progress using:
- Check Understanding
- Additional Examples
- Test Prep

After the Lesson
Assess knowledge using:
- Lesson Quiz
- Computer Test Generator CD

8-2

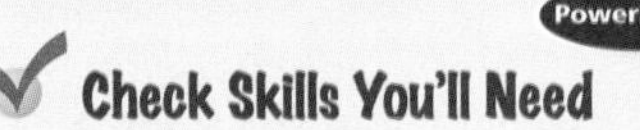

1. Plan

Lesson Preview

PowerPoint

✓ Check Skills You'll Need

Classifying Angles
Skills Handbook: Classifying and Measuring Angles, p. 726.

Lesson Resources

Optional Materials
- protractor

Teaching Resources
Practice, Reteaching, Enrichment

Reaching All Students
Practice Workbook 8-2
Spanish Practice Workbook 8-2
Guided Problem Solving 8-2
Technology Activities 44

Presentation Assistant Plus!
Transparencies
- Check Skills You'll Need 8-2
- Problem of the Day 8-2
- Additional Examples 8-2
- Student Edition Answers 8-2
- Lesson Quiz 8-2

PH Presentation Pro CD-ROM 8-2

PRENTICE HALL ASSESSMENT SYSTEM

Computer Test Generator CD

Technology
Resource Pro® CD-ROM
Computer Test Generator CD
PH Presentation Pro CD-ROM

www.PHSchool.com
Student Site
- Teacher Web Code: ack-5500
- Self-grading Lesson Quiz

PH SuccessNet Teacher Center
- Lesson Planner
- Resources

Plus 

2. Teach

Math Background

A straight line (or *transversal)* that intersects two other straight lines, whether or not the two lines are parallel, forms corresponding angles. *Corresponding angles* lie on the same side of the transversal in matching positions. *Alternate interior angles* lie between the two lines but on opposite sides of the transversal.

In the special case when the two lines intersected by a transversal are *parallel*, then the pairs of alternate interior angles are congruent, and the pairs of corresponding angles are congruent. Conversely, if two lines are intersected so that these angle pairs are congruent, the lines must be parallel.

Teaching Notes

Investigation (Optional)
To accurately measure each of the angles, students need to extend the sides of some angles. They can align the edge of a piece of paper with the side of an angle, thereby extending the side of an angle without writing in their text.

1 EXAMPLE English Learners
Have students explain and demonstrate the meaning of the words *interior*, *alternate*, and *corresponding* both with angles formed by a transversal and in other contexts in the classroom.

Tactile Learners
Have students use rulers, pencils, or other straight objects to physically model lines in a plane that are parallel and lines that are not parallel.

2 EXAMPLE Inclusion
Ask:
- *$m\angle 2 + m\angle 5 = ?$* 180°
- *$m\angle 1 + m\angle 4 = ?$* 180°
- *Therefore, since $m\angle 1 = m\angle 2$, what must be true about $m\angle 4$ and $m\angle 5$?* $m\angle 4 = m\angle 5$

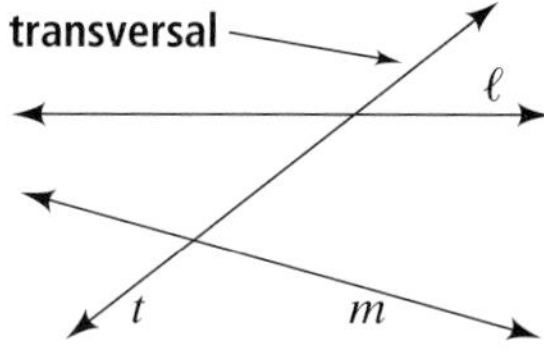

A line that intersects two other lines at different points is a **transversal.**

Some pairs of angles formed by two lines and a transversal have special names.

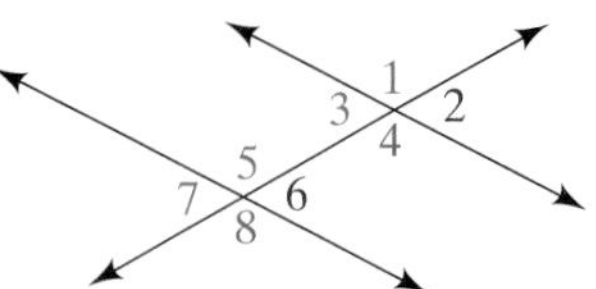

Corresponding angles lie on the same side of the transversal and in corresponding positions.
$\angle 1$ and $\angle 5$ $\angle 2$ and $\angle 6$
$\angle 3$ and $\angle 7$ $\angle 4$ and $\angle 8$

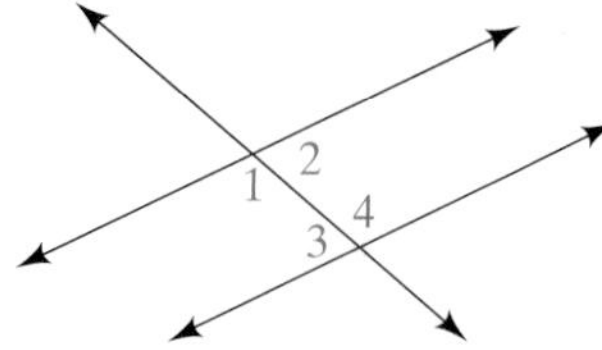

Alternate interior angles lie within a pair of lines and on opposite sides of the transversal.
$\angle 1$ and $\angle 4$ $\angle 2$ and $\angle 3$

1 EXAMPLE Identifying Angles Formed by Parallel Lines

Need Help?
Recall that parallel lines lie in the same plane and do not intersect.

Identify a pair of corresponding angles and a pair of alternate interior angles.

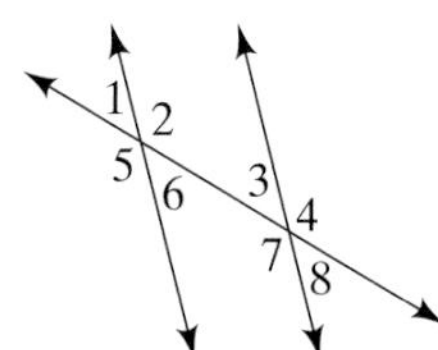

$\angle 1$ and $\angle 3$ are corresponding angles.

$\angle 2$ and $\angle 7$ are alternate interior angles.

Check Understanding 1 Use the diagram in Example 1. Identify each pair of angles as *corresponding*, *alternate interior*, or *neither*.

a. $\angle 3, \angle 6$ alternate interior **b.** $\angle 5, \angle 7$ corresponding **c.** $\angle 1, \angle 8$ neither

Key Concepts **Transversals and Parallel Lines**

When a transversal intersects two parallel lines,
- corresponding angles are congruent, and
- alternate interior angles are congruent.

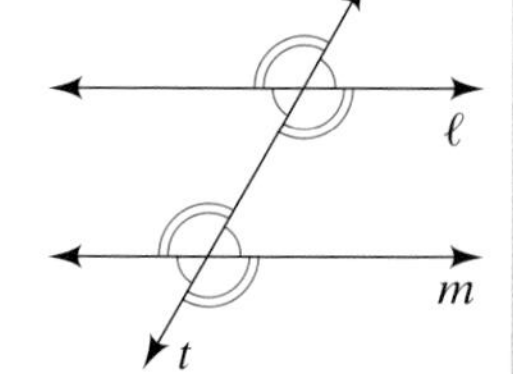

2 EXAMPLE Finding Angle Measures

In the diagram at the right, r is parallel to s, and $m\angle 1 = 63°$. Find $m\angle 2$ and $m\angle 3$.

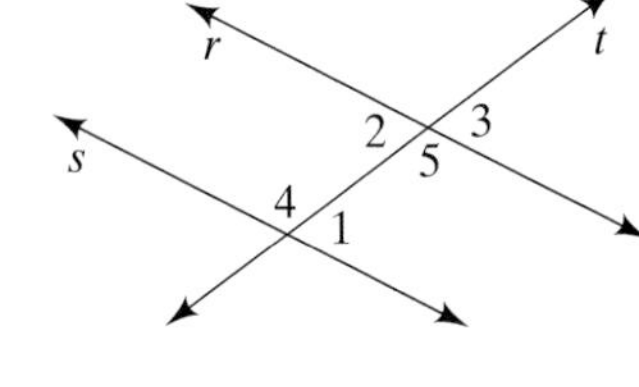

$m\angle 2 = m\angle 1 = 63°$ ← Alternate interior angles are congruent.

$m\angle 3 = m\angle 1 = 63°$ ← Corresponding angles are congruent.

Check Understanding 2 **a.** In the diagram for Example 2, $m\angle 4 = 117°$. Find $m\angle 5$. 117°

b. Reasoning Explain how you could find $m\angle 4$ using the information given in Example 2. Since $m\angle 1 = 63°$ and $m\angle 4 + m\angle 1 = 180°$, then $m\angle 4 = 117°$.

Reaching All Students

Below Level Have students work in pairs to draw and identify parallel and non-parallel lines, right angles, acute angles, and obtuse angles.	**Advanced Learners** Draw two perpendicular lines intersected by a transversal. Describe how the corresponding angles are related. In each corresponding pair, one angle is 90° larger than the other.	**English Learners** See note on page 414. **Inclusion** See note on page 414.

OBJECTIVE

2 Identifying Parallel Lines

When a transversal intersects two parallel lines, some pairs of angles are congruent. The reverse is also true. If the corresponding angles or the alternate interior angles are congruent, the lines are parallel.

If $\overleftrightarrow{AB}$ is parallel to $\overleftrightarrow{CD}$, you write $\overleftrightarrow{AB} \parallel \overleftrightarrow{CD}$.

3 EXAMPLE Identifying Parallel Lines

In the diagram at the right, $m\angle 1 = 60°$, $m\angle 2 = 60°$, and $m\angle 3 = 60°$. Explain why both pairs of opposite sides of *LMNP* are parallel.

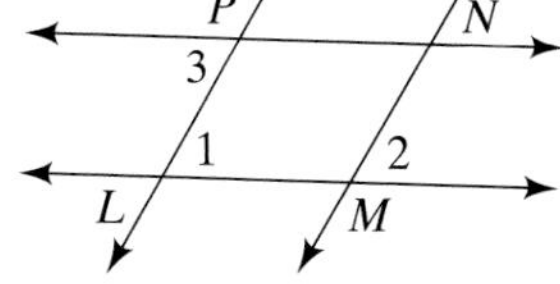

$\overleftrightarrow{LP} \parallel \overleftrightarrow{MN}$ because $\angle 1$ and $\angle 2$ are congruent corresponding angles.

$\overleftrightarrow{LM} \parallel \overleftrightarrow{PN}$ because $\angle 1$ and $\angle 3$ are congruent alternate interior angles.

Check Understanding 3 Transversal t is perpendicular to lines ℓ and m. Explain why $\ell \parallel m$.

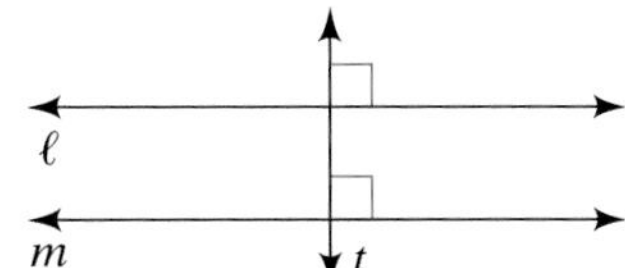

3. The right angles are ≅ corresponding angles, so $\ell \parallel m$.

The reasoning used in Example 3 is called *deductive reasoning*. Deductive reasoning is the logical process of drawing conclusions from given facts.

EXERCISES

For more practice, see *Extra Practice*.

A Practice by Example

1–6. See margin.

Example 1 (page 414)

Identify each pair of angles as *corresponding*, *alternate interior*, or *neither*.

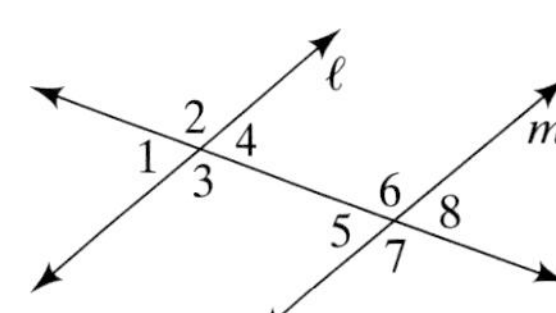

1. $\angle 6, \angle 3$
2. $\angle 8, \angle 4$
3. $\angle 2, \angle 1$
4. $\angle 2, \angle 4$
5. $\angle 1, \angle 5$
6. $\angle 2, \angle 7$
7. $\angle 3, \angle 5$ corresponding
8. $\angle 4, \angle 3$ neither

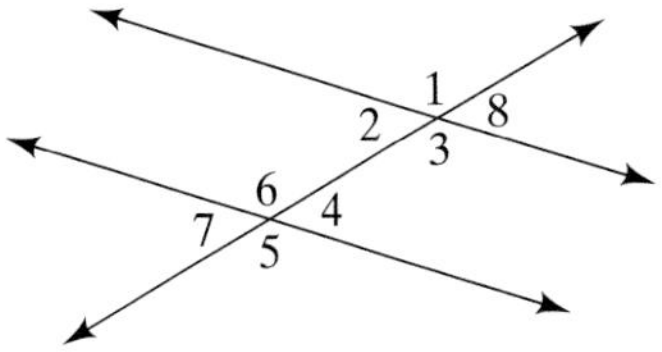

Example 2 (page 414)

In the diagram at the right, $\ell \parallel m$. If $m\angle 3 = 122°$, find the measure of each angle.

9. $\angle 4$ 58°
10. $\angle 2$ 122°
11. $\angle 6$ 122°
12. $\angle 7$ 122°
13. $\angle 8$ 58°
14. $\angle 5$ 58°

1. alternate interior
2. corresponding
3. neither
4. alternate interior
5. neither
6. corresponding

3 EXAMPLE Geometry

Explain that two lines may look parallel, but you cannot assume that they are actually parallel unless the problem states it or you prove that they must be parallel.

PowerPoint

Additional Examples

Use the diagram for Additional Examples 1 and 2.

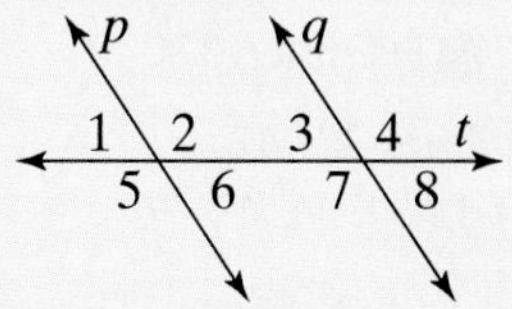

1. Identify each pair of corresponding angles and each pair of alternate interior angles. Corresponding: $\angle 1$ and $\angle 3$, $\angle 2$ and $\angle 4$, $\angle 5$ and $\angle 7$, $\angle 6$ and $\angle 8$; Alternate interior: $\angle 2$ and $\angle 7$, $\angle 3$ and $\angle 6$
2. If p is parallel to q, and $m\angle 3 = 56°$, find $m\angle 6$ and $m\angle 1$. 56°; 56°
3. In the diagram below, $m\angle 5 = 80°$, $m\angle 6 = 80°$, and $m\angle 7 = 80°$. Explain why p and q are parallel and why s and t are parallel.

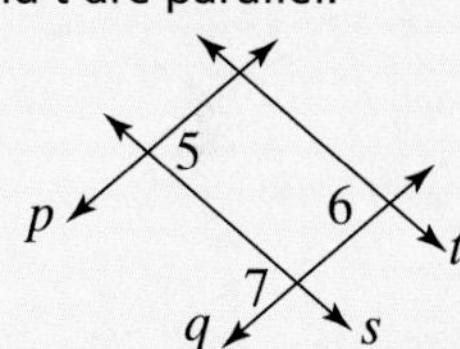

$p \parallel q$ because $\angle 5$ and $\angle 7$ are congruent alternate interior angles; $s \parallel t$ because $\angle 6$ and $\angle 7$ are congruent corresponding angles.

Closure

- *What angles are formed when a transversal intersects two parallel lines? Which of these angles are congruent?* Sample: corresponding angles and alternate interior angles; both are congruent
- *What are two ways to prove that two lines intersected by a transversal are parallel?* Sample: Prove either that a pair of corresponding angles or a pair of alternate interior angles are congruent.

Objective 1

A B Core 1–14, 18–25, 27–28, 33–34

C Extension 35–36

Objective 2

A B Core 15–17, 26, 29–32

C Extension 37

Test Prep 38–42

Mixed Review 43–55

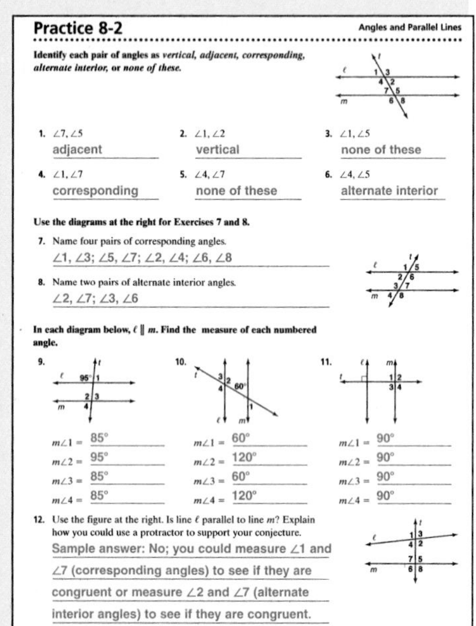

Practice 8-2 — Angles and Parallel Lines

Identify each pair of angles as *vertical, adjacent, corresponding, alternate interior,* or *none of these.*

1. ∠7, ∠5 — adjacent
2. ∠1, ∠2 — vertical
3. ∠1, ∠5 — none of these
4. ∠1, ∠7 — corresponding
5. ∠4, ∠7 — none of these
6. ∠4, ∠5 — alternate interior

Use the diagrams at the right for Exercises 7 and 8.

7. Name four pairs of corresponding angles. ∠1, ∠3; ∠5, ∠7; ∠2, ∠4; ∠6, ∠8
8. Name two pairs of alternate interior angles. ∠2, ∠7; ∠3, ∠6

In each diagram below, ℓ ∥ m. Find the measure of each numbered angle.

9. m∠1 = 85°; m∠2 = 95°; m∠3 = 85°; m∠4 = 85°

10. m∠1 = 60°; m∠2 = 120°; m∠3 = 60°; m∠4 = 120°

11. m∠1 = 90°; m∠2 = 90°; m∠3 = 90°; m∠4 = 90°

12. Use the figure at the right. Is line ℓ parallel to line m? Explain how you could use a protractor to support your conjecture. Sample answer: No; you could measure ∠1 and ∠7 (corresponding angles) to see if they are congruent or measure ∠2 and ∠7 (alternate interior angles) to see if they are congruent.

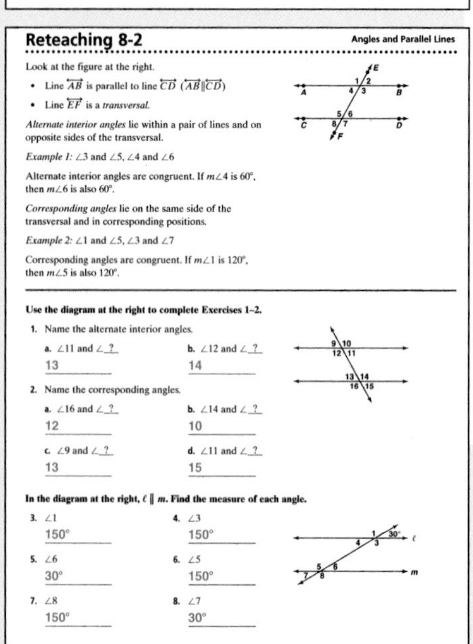

Reteaching 8-2 — Angles and Parallel Lines

Look at the figure at the right.

- Line $\overleftrightarrow{AB}$ is parallel to line $\overleftrightarrow{CD}$ ($\overleftrightarrow{AB} \parallel \overleftrightarrow{CD}$)
- Line $\overleftrightarrow{EF}$ is a *transversal.*

Alternate interior angles lie within a pair of lines and on opposite sides of the transversal.

Example 1: ∠3 and ∠5, ∠4 and ∠6

Alternate interior angles are congruent. If m∠4 is 60°, then m∠6 is also 60°.

Corresponding angles lie on the same side of the transversal and in corresponding positions.

Example 2: ∠1 and ∠5, ∠3 and ∠7

Corresponding angles are congruent. If m∠1 is 120°, then m∠5 is also 120°.

Use the diagram at the right to complete Exercises 1–2.

1. Name the alternate interior angles.
   a. ∠11 and ∠ ? — 13
   b. ∠12 and ∠ ? — 14
2. Name the corresponding angles.
   a. ∠16 and ∠ ? — 12
   b. ∠14 and ∠ ? — 10
   c. ∠9 and ∠ ? — 13
   d. ∠11 and ∠ ? — 15

In the diagram at the right, ℓ ∥ m. Find the measure of each angle.

3. ∠1 — 150°
4. ∠3 — 150°
5. ∠6 — 30°
6. ∠5 — 150°
7. ∠8 — 150°
8. ∠7 — 30°

Example 3 (page 415)

For each diagram, explain why $a \parallel b$. 15–17. See margin.

15.

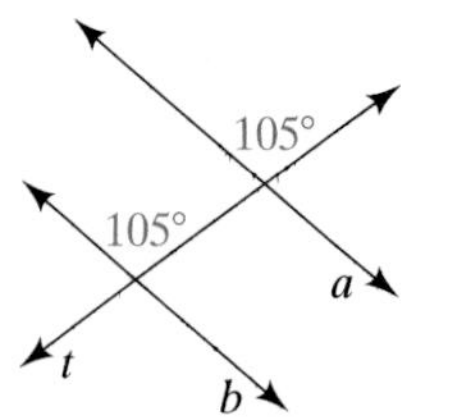

16.

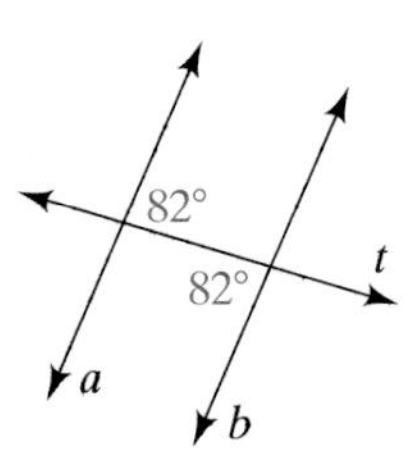

17.

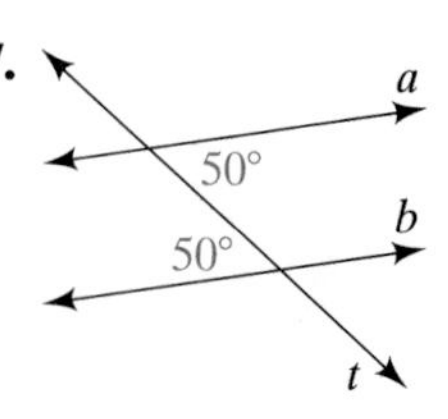

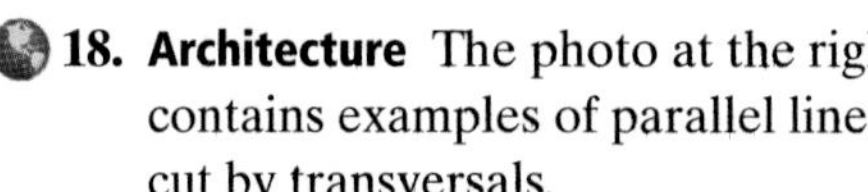

18. Architecture The photo at the right contains examples of parallel lines cut by transversals.

a. Name a pair of corresponding angles. ∠1 and ∠2

b. $a \parallel b$ and $m\angle 1 = 68°$. Find $m\angle 2$. 18b. 68°

c. $c \parallel d$ and $m\angle 3 = 42°$. Find $m\angle 4$. 18c. 138°

19. a. Writing in Math A transversal t cuts parallel lines m and n. If t is perpendicular to m, what is the relationship between lines t and n?

b. What are the measures of all the angles formed? Explain. See margin.

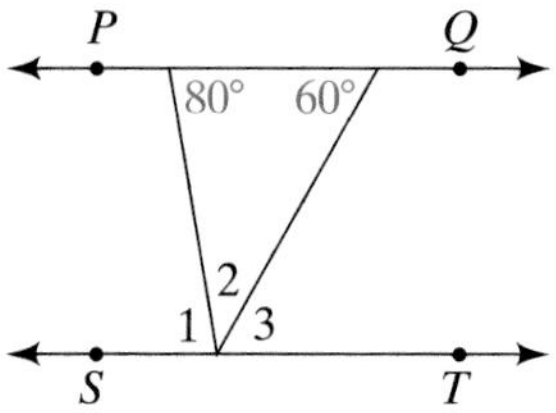

GPS **20. a.** In the diagram at the left, $\overleftrightarrow{PQ} \parallel \overleftrightarrow{ST}$. Find the measure of each numbered angle. See margin.

b. What is the sum of the angle measures of the triangle? 180°

In each diagram, $\ell \parallel m$. Find the measure of each numbered angle. 21–23. See below left.

21. **22.**

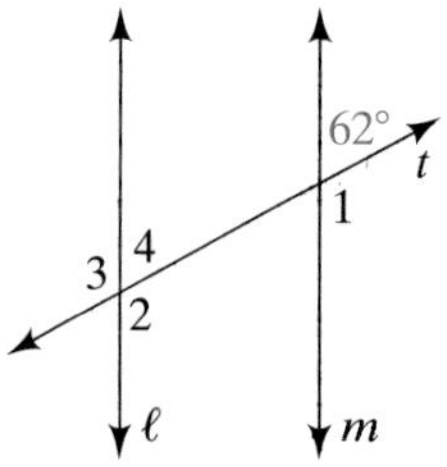

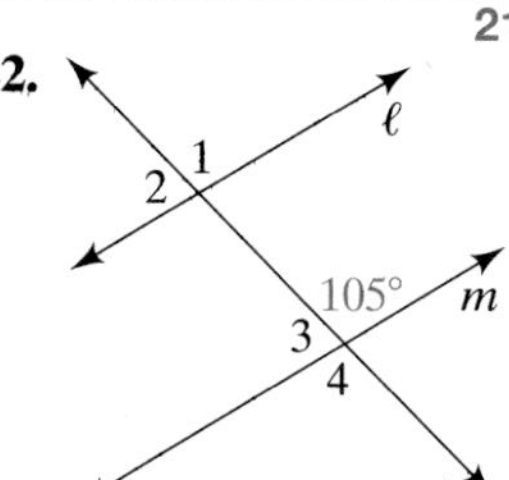

23.

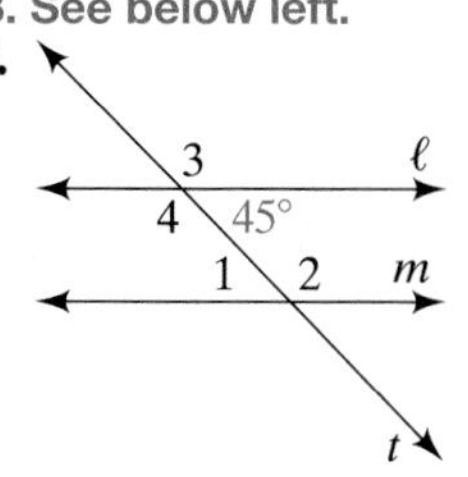

21. $m\angle 1 = 118°$; $m\angle 2 = 118°$; $m\angle 3 = 118°$; $m\angle 4 = 62°$

22. $m\angle 1 = 105°$; $m\angle 2 = 75°$; $m\angle 3 = 75°$; $m\angle 4 = 105°$

23. $m\angle 1 = 45°$; $m\angle 2 = 135°$; $m\angle 3 = 135°$; $m\angle 4 = 135°$

Reasoning **Determine whether each statement is *true* or *false*. Draw a diagram to justify your answer.**

24. A transversal is a line that crosses two other lines at different points. The two lines may or may not be parallel. true

25. Alternate interior angles are always congruent. false

26. Two lines are cut by a transversal. If the corresponding angles are *not* congruent, then the two lines are *not* parallel. true

27. Vertical angles are always congruent. true

Use the Guided Problem Solving worksheet with Exercise 20.

15. Corresponding angles are congruent.

16. Alternate interior angles are congruent.

17. Alternate interior angles are congruent.

19a. Lines t and n are perpendicular.

b. 90°; perpendicular lines form 90° angles.

20a. $m\angle 1 = 80°$; $m\angle 2 = 40°$; $m\angle 3 = 60°$

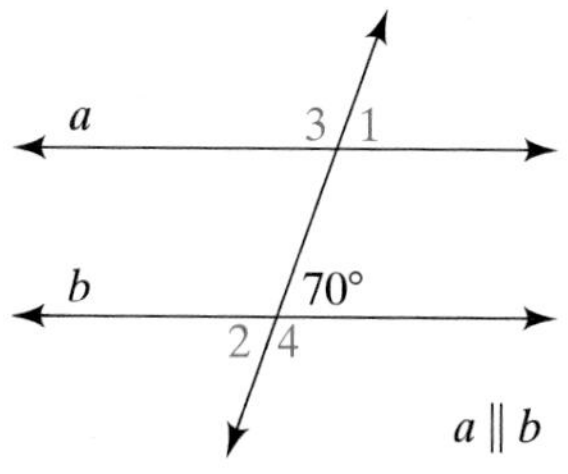

28. *Alternate exterior angles* lie outside a pair of lines and on opposite sides of a transversal. In the diagram at the left, ∠1 and ∠2 are alternate exterior angles of parallel lines. So are ∠3 and ∠4.
   a. Find the measures of ∠1 and ∠2. 70°; 70°
   b. Find the measures of ∠3 and ∠4. 110°; 110°
   c. What do you notice about the measures of alternate exterior angles of parallel lines? Explain. They are congruent; they are vertical angles of congruent alternate interior angles.

Determine which pairs of lines, if any, are parallel. Explain. 30–31. See left.

30. $y \parallel w$; corresponding angles are congruent.

31. $a \parallel b$; ∠1 is supplementary to a 110° angle, so its measure is 70°. Alternate interior angles are congruent.

29. 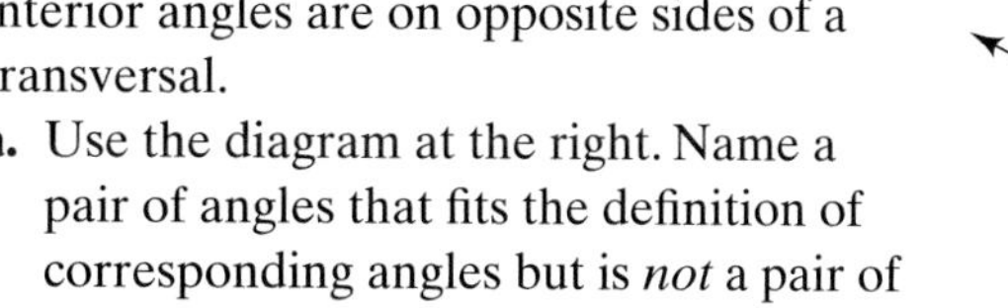

no parallel lines

30. 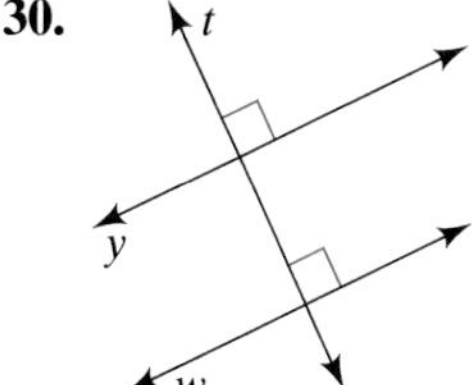

31. 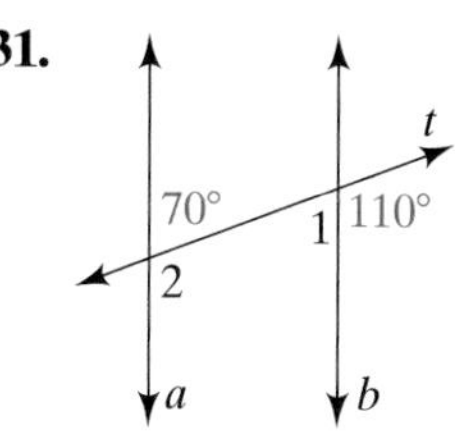

Jamaica

Flags **Use the flag of Jamaica at the left for Exercises 32 and 33.** 32–33. See below left.

32. Name two pairs of parallel lines and two transversals.

33. Name four pairs of alternate interior angles.

32. $\overleftrightarrow{AB} \parallel \overleftrightarrow{DC}$ and $\overleftrightarrow{AD} \parallel \overleftrightarrow{BC}$; $\overleftrightarrow{AC}$ and $\overleftrightarrow{DB}$

33. ∠1 and ∠5; ∠8 and ∠4; ∠7 and ∠3; ∠2 and ∠6

34a–b. Answers may vary. Samples are given.

34. **Reasoning** Corresponding angles are on the same side of a transversal. Alternate interior angles are on opposite sides of a transversal.

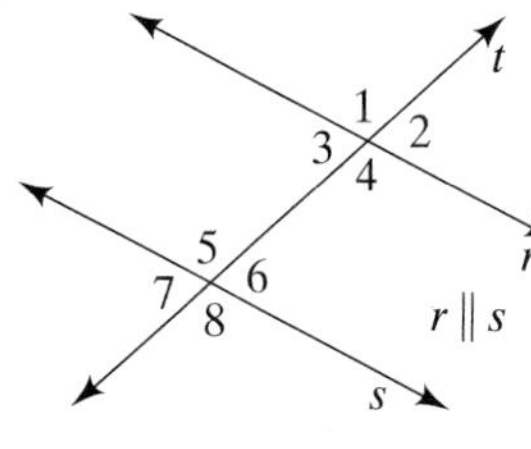

   a. Use the diagram at the right. Name a pair of angles that fits the definition of corresponding angles but is *not* a pair of corresponding angles. ∠1 and ∠7
   b. Name a pair of angles that fits the definition of alternate interior angles but is *not* a pair of alternate interior angles. ∠5 and ∠6

C Challenge

Algebra **In each diagram below, $p \parallel q$. Write and solve an equation to find the measures of ∠1 and ∠2.** 35–36. See margin.

35. 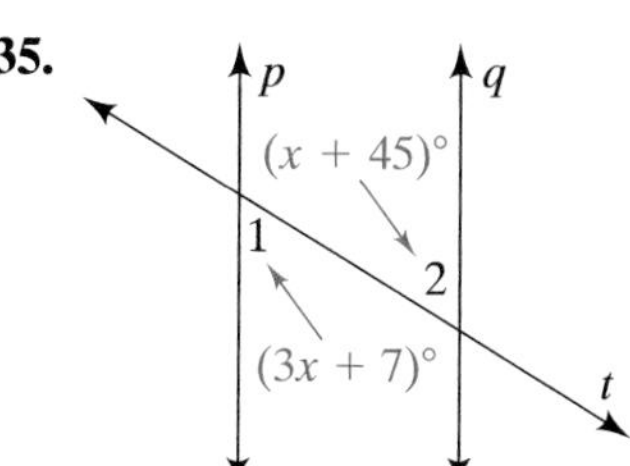

36. 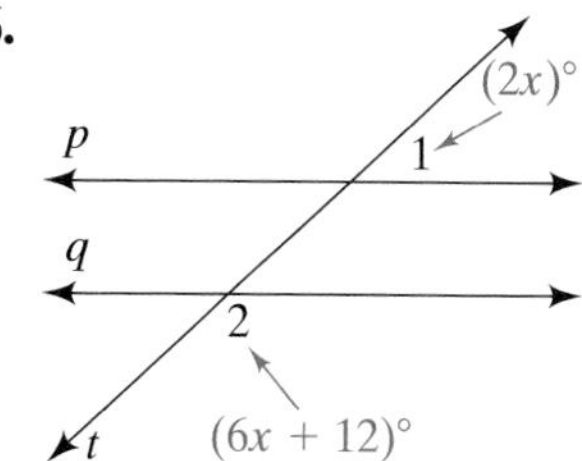

37. **Stretch Your Thinking** One number is 5 less than another number. The ratio of the first number to the second number is 5 to 6. What are the two numbers? 25 and 30

Error Prevention!

Exercise 19 Remind students that perpendicular lines meet with a 90° angle.

35. $(3x + 7)° = (x + 45)°$; $m\angle 1 = 64°$; $m\angle 2 = 64°$

36. $(2x)° + (6x + 12)° = 180°$; $m\angle 1 = 42°$; $m\angle 2 = 138°$

PowerPoint **Lesson Quiz 8-2**

Use the diagram to answer the questions.

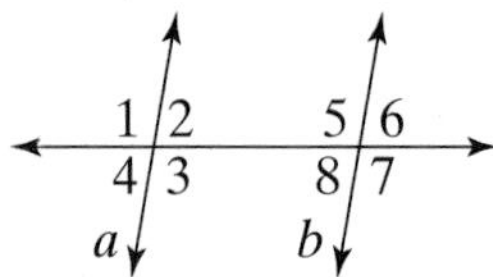

1. Classify ∠4 and ∠7 as *alternate interior angles*, *corresponding angles*, or *neither*. neither
2. Classify ∠2 and ∠8 as *alternate interior angles*, *corresponding angles*, or *neither*. alternate interior angles
3. If $a \parallel b$ and $m\angle 8 = 80°$, find $m\angle 4$. 80°
4. Suppose $m\angle 5 = 100°$ and $m\angle 3 = 100°$. What can you conclude about line *a* and line *b*? $a \parallel b$

Test Prep

Resources

For additional practice with a variety of test item formats:

- Test Prep, p. 465
- Test-Taking Strategies, p. 461
- Test-Taking Strategies with Transparencies

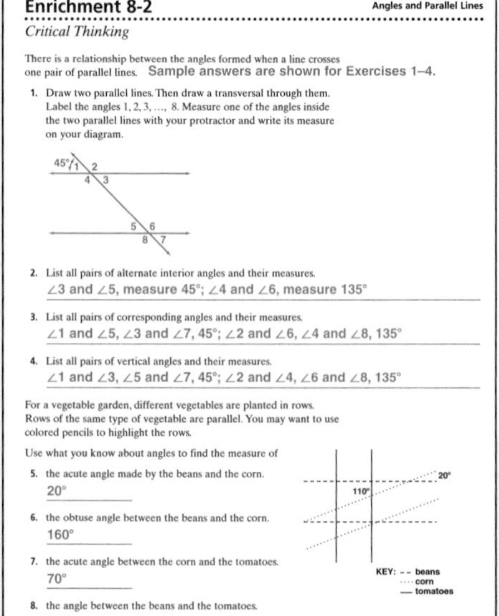

Enrichment 8-2 — Angles and Parallel Lines

Critical Thinking

There is a relationship between the angles formed when a line crosses one pair of parallel lines. Sample answers are shown for Exercises 1–4.

1. Draw two parallel lines. Then draw a transversal through them. Label the angles 1, 2, 3, ..., 8. Measure one of the angles inside the two parallel lines with your protractor and write its measure on your diagram.

   45° 1 2 4 3 5 6 8 7

2. List all pairs of alternate interior angles and their measures.
   ∠3 and ∠5, measure 45°; ∠4 and ∠6, measure 135°
3. List all pairs of corresponding angles and their measures.
   ∠1 and ∠5, ∠3 and ∠7, 45°; ∠2 and ∠6, ∠4 and ∠8, 135°
4. List all pairs of vertical angles and their measures.
   ∠1 and ∠3, ∠5 and ∠7, 45°; ∠2 and ∠4, ∠6 and ∠8, 135°

For a vegetable garden, different vegetables are planted in rows. Rows of the same type of vegetable are parallel. You may want to use colored pencils to highlight the rows.

Use what you know about angles to find the measure of

5. the acute angle made by the beans and the corn. 20°
6. the obtuse angle between the beans and the corn. 160°
7. the acute angle between the corn and the tomatoes. 70°
8. the angle between the beans and the tomatoes. 90°

110° 20° KEY: - - beans ···· corn — tomatoes

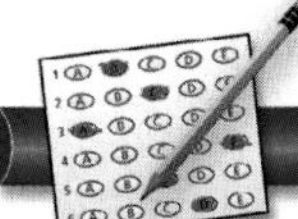

Test Prep

Reading Comprehension **Read the passage and answer the questions below.**

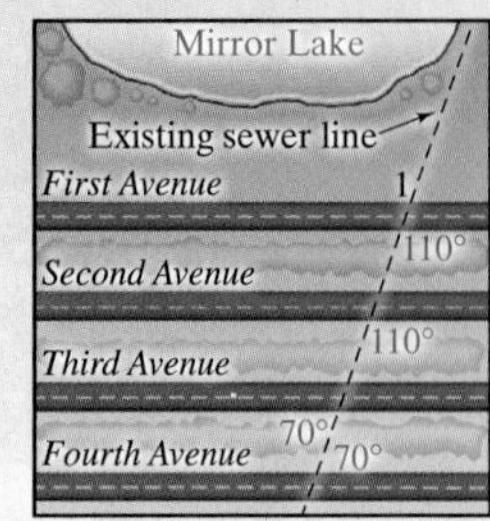

Subdivision Approved

The town has just approved the construction of a new subdivision near Mirror Lake. The subdivision will consist of forty houses on four parallel streets. According to the town engineer, special attention will be paid to the drainage system of the development. "We want to keep the lake clean. Town specifications require an additional sewer line for the new housing development."

38. Using the diagram, explain how you know that the streets in the plan are parallel. See margin.
39. What kind of angles are the two 70° angles marked on the diagram? alternate interior angles
40. Find $m\angle 1$. Explain your answer.

40. 110°; answers may vary. Sample: ∠1 and a 110° angle are vertical angles.

Multiple Choice

Take It to the NET
Online lesson quiz at **www.PHSchool.com**
Web Code: aca-0802

41. In the diagram at the right, $b \parallel c$. Which of the following statements is NOT true? D
    A. The measure of ∠2 is 98°.
    B. ∠2 and ∠6 are corresponding angles.
    C. The measure of ∠4 is 82°.
    D. ∠1 and ∠7 are alternate interior angles.

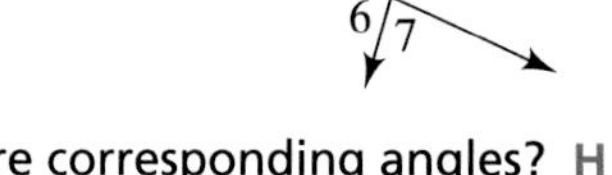

42. In the diagram above, ∠1 and what angle are corresponding angles? H
    F. ∠2 G. ∠3 H. ∠4 I. 98° angle

Mixed Review

Lesson 7-1 **Write each number in standard form.**

43. 7.24×10^2 724
44. 5.3×10^4 53,000
45. 6×10^6 6,000,000
46. 4.01×10^3 4,010
47. 2×10^5 200,000
48. 3.19×10^7 31,900,000

Lesson 6-7

49. **Savings** Suppose you invest between 1% and 16% of your weekly paycheck in one of your company's savings plans. Your weekly paycheck is $537. Find the minimum and maximum amounts you invest each week. $5.37; $85.92

Lesson 6-4 **Use an equation to find each percent.**

50. 23% of 55 12.65
51. 78% of 41 31.98
52. 14% of 36 5.04
53. 62% of 199 123.38
54. 3% of 250 7.5
55. 95% of 7 6.65

Alternative Assessment

Have students choose an exercise from Exercises 9–14 and explain how they reached their conclusions. Have them use the new terms in this lesson in their explanations.

38. Answers may vary. Sample: Since the complement of 70° is 110°, the measure of each corresponding angle is 110°. Since they are congruent, the streets are parallel.

Extension Parallel and Perpendicular Lines

For Use With Lesson 8-2

The slopes of parallel and perpendicular lines have special properties.

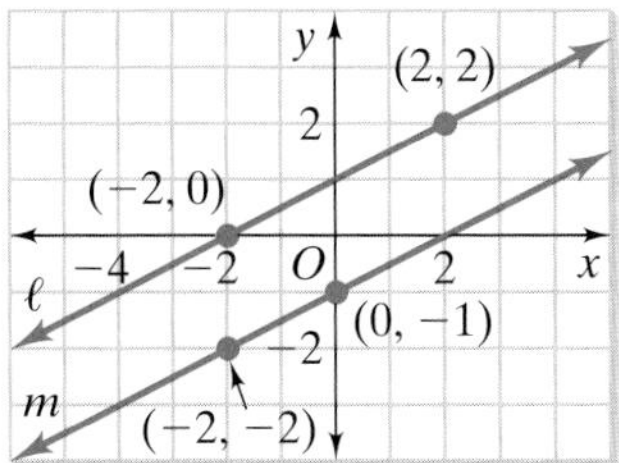

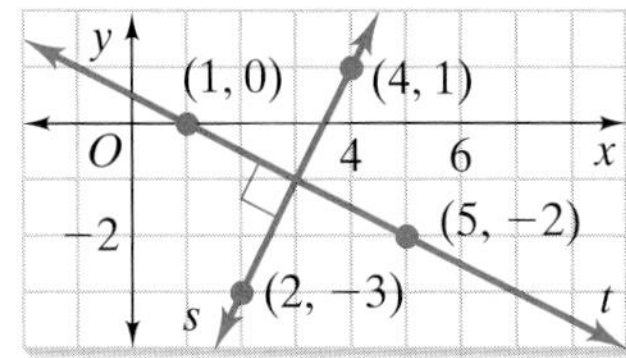

slope of $s = \frac{1-(-3)}{4-2} = \frac{4}{2} = \frac{2}{1}$

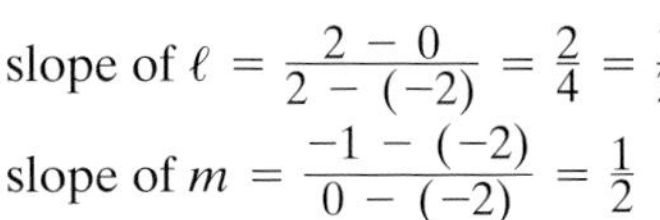

slope of $\ell = \frac{2-0}{2-(-2)} = \frac{2}{4} = \frac{1}{2}$

slope of $m = \frac{-1-(-2)}{0-(-2)} = \frac{1}{2}$

Parallel lines have the same slope.

slope of $t = \frac{-2-0}{5-1} = \frac{-2}{4} = -\frac{1}{2}$

product of slopes $= \frac{2}{1} \cdot \left(-\frac{1}{2}\right) = -1$

The product of the slopes of perpendicular lines is -1.

EXAMPLE

Given points $A(-5, -3)$ and $B(1, -1)$, find the slope of a line that is parallel to $\overleftrightarrow{AB}$ and the slope of a line that is perpendicular to $\overleftrightarrow{AB}$.

slope of $\overleftrightarrow{AB} = \frac{-1-(-3)}{1-(-5)} = \frac{2}{6} = \frac{1}{3}$

A line parallel to $\overleftrightarrow{AB}$ has a slope of $\frac{1}{3}$.

Let m be the slope of a line perpendicular to $\overleftrightarrow{AB}$.

$\frac{1}{3} \cdot m = -1$ ← **The product of the slopes of perpendicular lines is −1.**

$m = -3$ ← **Multiply each side by 3.**

A line perpendicular to $\overleftrightarrow{AB}$ has a slope of -3.

EXERCISES

Are lines with the given slopes *parallel, perpendicular,* or *neither*?

1. $\frac{2}{3}, -\frac{3}{2}$ perpendicular

2. $5, -5$ neither

3. $\frac{3}{4}, \frac{4}{3}$ neither

4. $\frac{1}{12}, -12$ perpendicular

5. $\frac{3}{9}, \frac{1}{3}$ parallel

Find the slope of a line that is parallel to $\overleftrightarrow{PQ}$ and a line that is perpendicular to $\overleftrightarrow{PQ}$.

6. $P(1, 2), Q(3, 4)$ 1; −1

7. $P(-5, 1), Q(-1, 2)$ $\frac{1}{4}$; −4

8. $P(3, -2), Q(-2, 1)$ $-\frac{3}{5}$; $\frac{5}{3}$

9. **Reasoning** If $a \parallel b$ and $b \parallel c$, how does a relate to c? Explain. See margin.

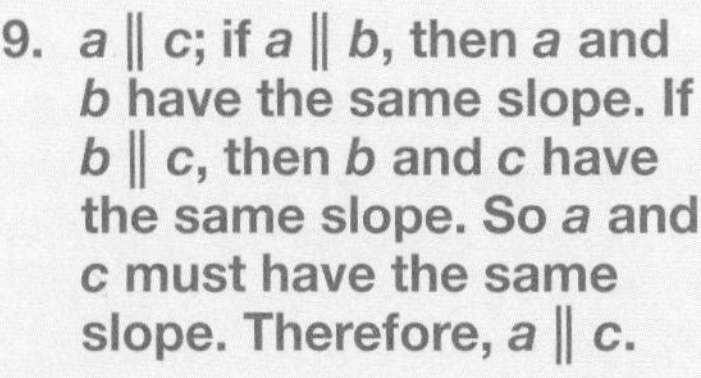

9. $a \parallel c$; if $a \parallel b$, then a and b have the same slope. If $b \parallel c$, then b and c have the same slope. So a and c must have the same slope. Therefore, $a \parallel c$.

Extension

Parallel and Perpendicular Lines

In Lesson 8-2, students identified parallel lines and found the measures of angles formed when lines intersect parallel lines. This feature focuses on the special properties of the slopes of parallel lines and of perpendicular lines.

Teaching Notes

Inclusion

Review the meaning of the slope of a line (change in vertical distance divided by change in horizontal distance, or rise over run). Elicit from students how to find slope (change in *y*-coordinate divided by change in *x*-coordinate). Remind them that the variable *m* is used to represent the slope of a line. Provide examples of lines with a positive slope and lines with a negative slope. Also review the meaning of perpendicular lines.

Teaching Tip

Work through the Example with the whole class. Ask volunteers to help set up the ratio and the equation. Write both on the board as students follow along at their seats. To check students' understanding, ask:

- *Suppose the slope of line AB = $-\frac{1}{5}$. What equation would you write to find the slope of a line perpendicular to AB?* $-\frac{1}{5}m = -1$
- *What would the slope of that line be?* $m = 5$

Exercises

Have students work in pairs on the exercises.

Exercises 6–8 Students can draw the lines on a coordinate grid.

Exercise 9 Encourage students to draw diagrams to support their conclusions.

8-3

1. Plan

Lesson Preview

Check Skills You'll Need

Identifying Similar Polygons
Lesson 5-5: Examples 1, 4.
Extra Practice, p. 706.

Lesson Resources

Teaching Resources
Practice, Reteaching, Enrichment

Reaching All Students
Practice Workbook 8-3
Spanish Practice Workbook 8-3
Guided Problem Solving 8-3
Technology Activities 45

Presentation Assistant Plus!
Transparencies
- Check Skills You'll Need 8-3
- Problem of the Day 8-3
- Additional Examples 8-3
- Student Edition Answers 8-3
- Lesson Quiz 8-3
- Classroom Aid 20–21

PH Presentation Pro CD-ROM 8-3

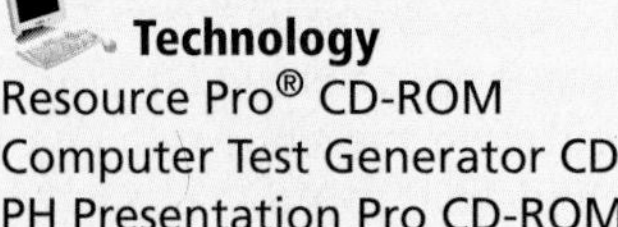

Computer Test Generator CD

Technology
Resource Pro® CD-ROM
Computer Test Generator CD
PH Presentation Pro CD-ROM

www.PHSchool.com
Student Site
- Teacher Web Code: ack-5500
- Self-grading Lesson Quiz

PH SuccessNet Teacher Center
- Lesson Planner
- Resources

Plus 

Check Skills You'll Need

1. Not similar; corresponding sides are not in proportion.

2–4. See back of book.

8-3 Congruent Polygons

What You'll Learn

To identify parts of congruent figures

To identify congruent triangles

. . . And Why

To use congruent figures to find distances, as in Example 2

Check Skills You'll Need

For help, go to Lesson 5-5.

1–4. See margin.

Tell whether each pair of polygons is similar. Explain why or why not.

1.

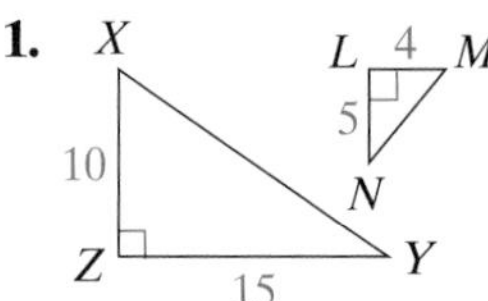

2.

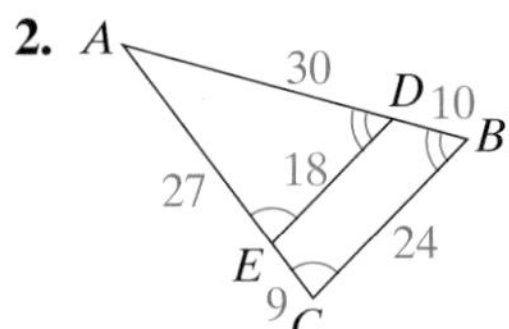

3.

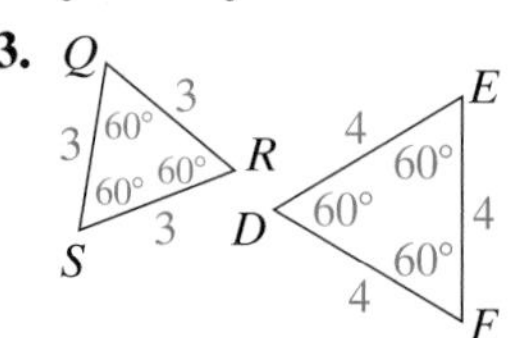

4. Explain how you determine whether two polygons are similar.

New Vocabulary
- congruent polygons

Interactive lesson includes instant self-check, tutorials, and activities.

OBJECTIVE 1

Identifying Congruent Parts

Congruent polygons are polygons with the same size and shape. The two yellow triangles in the photo of the bridge are congruent.

When two polygons are congruent, you can slide, flip, or turn one so that it fits exactly on top of the other one.

Need Help?
An angle is formed by two rays and a vertex.

The matching angles and sides of congruent polygons are called corresponding parts. Matching vertices are corresponding vertices. When you name congruent polygons, *always* list the corresponding vertices in the same order.

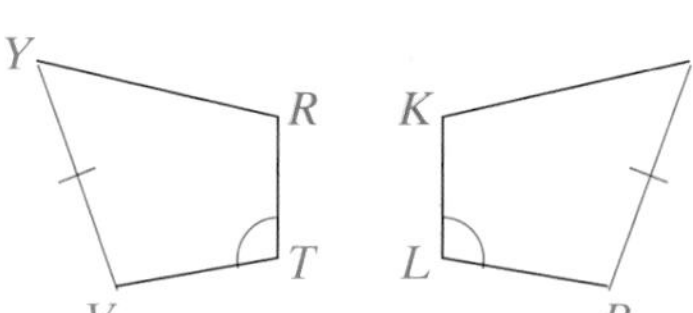

$\angle T$ corresponds to $\angle L$.
$\overline{YV}$ corresponds to $\overline{MP}$.
R corresponds to K.

$VTRY$ is congruent to $PLKM$. You can write quadrilateral $VTRY \cong$ quadrilateral $PLKM$, or $VTRY \cong PLKM$.

The tick marks in the diagram tell you which sides are congruent. The arcs tell you which angles are congruent.

Ongoing Assessment and Intervention

Before the Lesson
Diagnose prerequisite skills using:
- Check Skills You'll Need

During the Lesson
Monitor progress using:
- Check Understanding
- Additional Examples
- Test Prep

After the Lesson
Assess knowledge using:
- Lesson Quiz
- Computer Test Generator CD

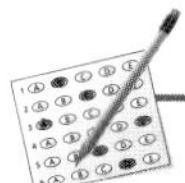

Test-Prep Tip

When writing congruence statements, copy the figures and mark the congruent parts.

1 EXAMPLE Identifying Congruent Parts

List the congruent parts of the two figures below. Then write a congruence statement.

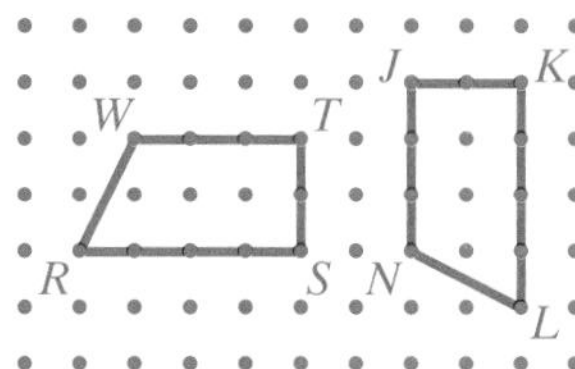

Congruent Angles	Congruent Sides
$\angle R \cong \angle L$	$\overline{RS} \cong \overline{LK}$
$\angle S \cong \angle K$	$\overline{ST} \cong \overline{KJ}$
$\angle T \cong \angle J$	$\overline{TW} \cong \overline{JN}$
$\angle W \cong \angle N$	$\overline{WR} \cong \overline{NL}$

Since $\angle R$ corresponds to $\angle L$, $\angle S$ corresponds to $\angle K$, $\angle T$ corresponds to $\angle J$, and $\angle W$ corresponds to $\angle N$, a congruence statement is $RSTW \cong LKJN$.

Check Understanding 1 **a.** List the congruent parts of the two triangles at the right. Then write a congruence statement. See left.

b. Reasoning Suppose $\triangle CJL \cong \triangle MYT$. List the congruent parts.

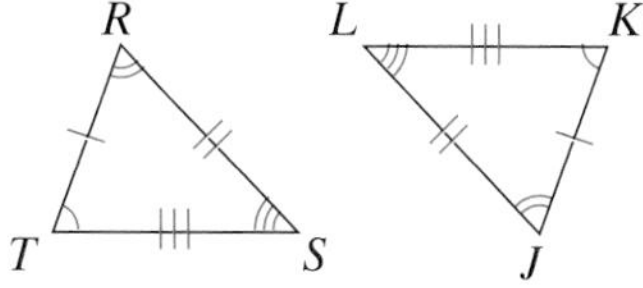

1a. $\angle T \cong \angle K$; $\angle R \cong \angle J$; $\angle S \cong \angle L$; $\overline{TR} \cong \overline{KJ}$; $\overline{RS} \cong \overline{JL}$; $\overline{ST} \cong \overline{LK}$; $\triangle TRS \cong \triangle KJL$

1 b. $\angle C \cong \angle M$; $\angle J \cong \angle Y$; $\angle L \cong \angle T$; $\overline{CJ} \cong \overline{MY}$; $\overline{JL} \cong \overline{YT}$; $\overline{LC} \cong \overline{TM}$

You can use the corresponding parts of congruent figures to find distances.

2 EXAMPLE Real-World Problem Solving

Surveying A surveyor drew the diagram at the right. A bridge will be built across the river from point A to point B. $\triangle ABC \cong \triangle EDC$. Find the distance AB.

Corresponding parts of congruent triangles are congruent. Since AB corresponds to ED, $AB = 82$ yd.

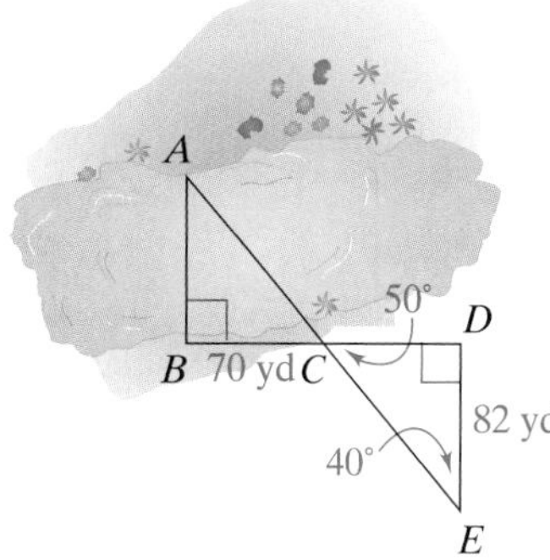

2d. Answers may vary. Sample: Corresponding vertices are not listed in the same order.

Check Understanding 2 Use the diagram in Example 2 to find each measurement.

a. CD 70 yd **b.** $m\angle A$ 40° **c.** $m\angle ACB$ 50°

d. Reasoning Explain why $\triangle ABC \cong \triangle CDE$ is not a correct congruence statement for the triangles in Example 2. See above left.

Reaching All Students

Below Level Use cut corners from a sheet of paper to explore and demonstrate similar triangles of different sizes.	**Advanced Learners** Have students find and share congruent figures in pictures and in classroom objects.	**Inclusion** See note on page 421. **Visual Learners** See note on page 421.

2. Teach

Math Background

Congruent polygons have exactly the same size and shape. Polygons are congruent if you can slide, turn, or flip them and make them coincide. This means that mirror images, or reflections, are congruent. The matching angles and sides of two polygons are called *corresponding parts.*

Teaching Notes

1 EXAMPLE Visual Learners

Have students draw the figures and use different colors to match the corresponding parts.

2 EXAMPLE Inclusion

Ask students to name the distances in the figure that can be directly measured and those that can only be measured indirectly. *BC, CD, DE,* and *EC* are on land and can be measured directly; *AB* and *AC* cannot be measured directly.

PowerPoint

Additional Examples

1 In the diagram below, list the congruent parts of the two figures. Then write a congruence statement.

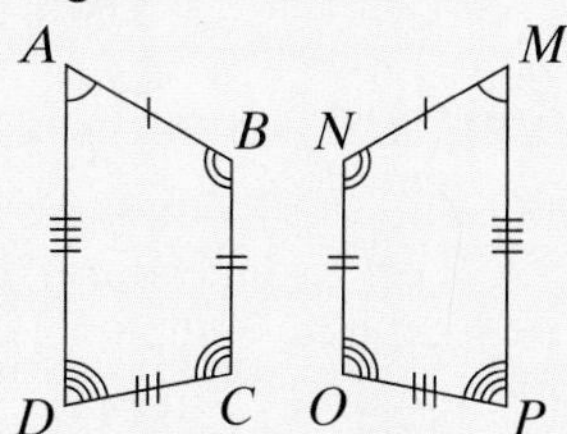

$\overline{AB} \cong \overline{MN}$; $\overline{BC} \cong \overline{NO}$; $\overline{CD} \cong \overline{OP}$; $\overline{DA} \cong \overline{PM}$; $\angle A \cong \angle M$; $\angle B \cong \angle N$; $\angle C \cong \angle O$; $\angle D \cong \angle P$; $ABCD \cong MNOP$

2 A surveyor drew the diagram below to find the distance from J to I across the canyon. $\triangle GHI \cong \triangle KJI$. What is the distance JI? 48 ft

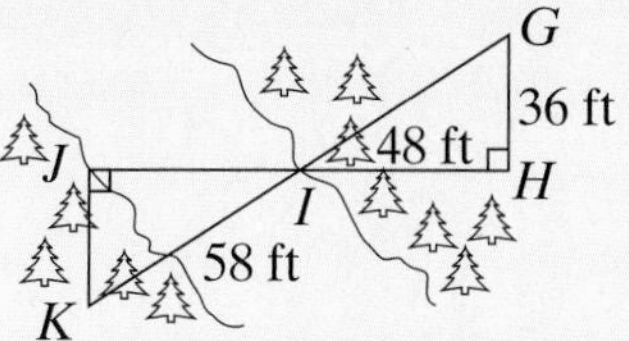

3 EXAMPLE Teaching Tip

Have students discuss how they can tell that the angle is included between the two sides or that the side is included between the two angles.

Error Prevention!

Watch for students who try to determine congruence by "eyeballing" a figure. Emphasize the importance of paying attention to the side and angle markings.

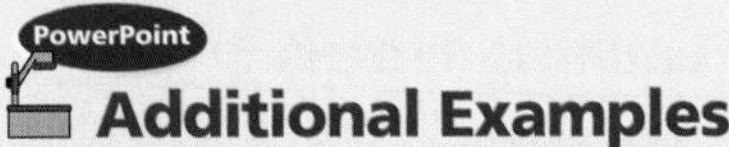

Additional Examples

3 Show that each pair of triangles is congruent.

a.

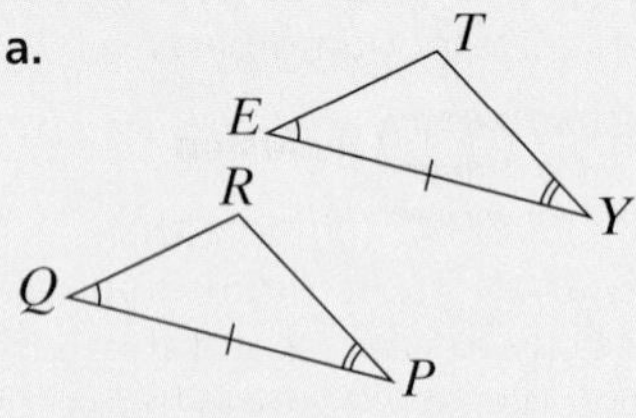

$\angle Q \cong \angle E$, $\overline{QP} \cong \overline{EY}$, $\angle P \cong \angle Y$; $\triangle QPR \cong \triangle EYT$; Angle-Side-Angle

b.

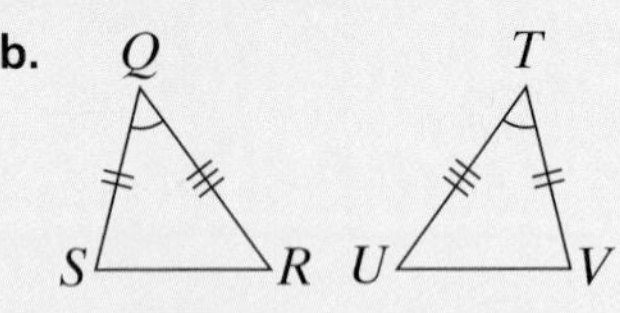

$\overline{SQ} \cong \overline{VT}$, $\angle Q \cong \angle T$, $\overline{QR} \cong \overline{TU}$; $\triangle SQR \cong \triangle VTU$; Side-Angle-Side

Closure

- Explain how to identify the parts of congruent figures that are congruent. Sample: The corresponding angles are congruent and the corresponding sides are congruent.
- Name three ways that you can demonstrate that two triangles are congruent. SSS, SAS, and ASA

OBJECTIVE

2 Identifying Congruent Triangles

You can use corresponding parts of triangles to show that two triangles are congruent. You do not need to know that *all* the corresponding parts are congruent to show congruent triangles.

Reading Math

The abbreviations SSS, SAS, and ASA are an easy way to remember how to show triangles are congruent.

Key Concepts **Showing Triangles Are Congruent**

To demonstrate that two triangles are congruent, show that the following parts of one triangle are congruent to the corresponding parts of the other triangle.

Side-Side-Side (SSS)	Side-Angle-Side (SAS)	Angle-Side-Angle (ASA)

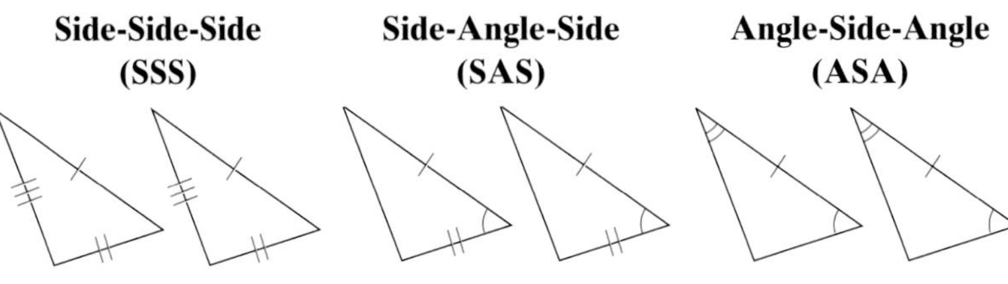

The order of the angles and sides is important in determining whether two triangles are congruent.

3 EXAMPLE Identifying Congruent Triangles

Show that each pair of triangles is congruent.

a.

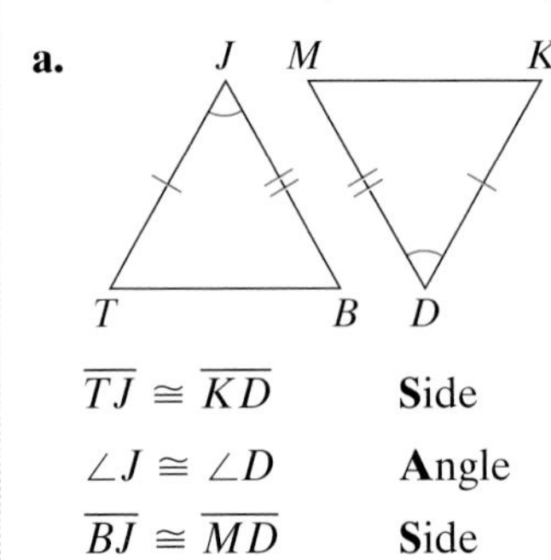

$\overline{TJ} \cong \overline{KD}$	**S**ide
$\angle J \cong \angle D$	**A**ngle
$\overline{BJ} \cong \overline{MD}$	**S**ide

$\triangle TJB \cong \triangle KDM$ by SAS.

b.

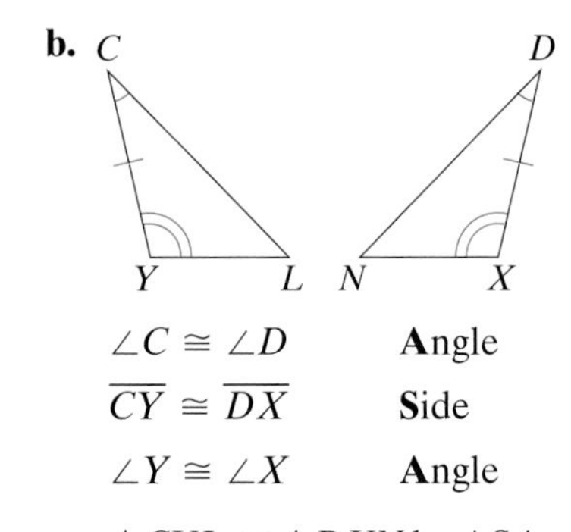

$\angle C \cong \angle D$	**A**ngle
$\overline{CY} \cong \overline{DX}$	**S**ide
$\angle Y \cong \angle X$	**A**ngle

$\triangle CYL \cong \triangle DXN$ by ASA.

Check Understanding 3 Show that each pair of triangles is congruent. 3a–b. See left.

3a. $\triangle XYZ \cong \triangle RQP$ by SSS

3b. $\triangle KLM \cong \triangle JLM$ by SAS

a.

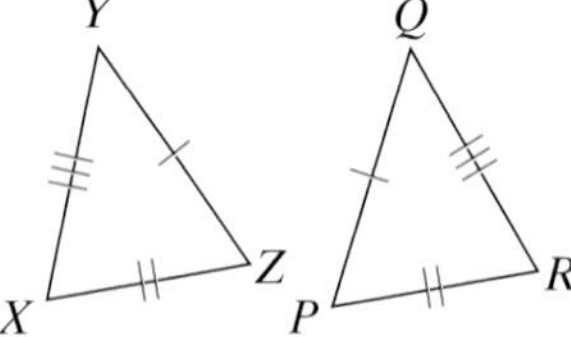

b.

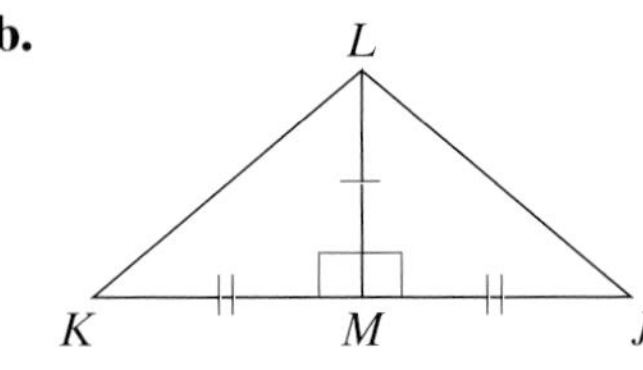

c. Reasoning Can you show two triangles are congruent by Angle-Angle-Angle? Draw figures to support your answer. no; $\triangle ABC \ncong \triangle DEF$

EXERCISES

For more practice, see *Extra Practice.*

A Practice by Example

Example 1 (page 421)

1. ∠Q ≅ ∠J; ∠C ≅ ∠E; ∠R ≅ ∠V; ∠Z ≅ ∠U; $\overline{RC} \cong \overline{VE}$; $\overline{CQ} \cong \overline{EJ}$; $\overline{QZ} \cong \overline{JU}$; $\overline{ZR} \cong \overline{UV}$; QCRZ ≅ JEVU

2. ∠W ≅ ∠T; ∠WOM ≅ ∠TOB; ∠M ≅ ∠B; ∠F ≅ ∠D; $\overline{WO} \cong \overline{TO}$; $\overline{OM} \cong \overline{OB}$; $\overline{MF} \cong \overline{BD}$; $\overline{FW} \cong \overline{DT}$; WOMF ≅ TOBD

3. ∠J ≅ ∠W; ∠K ≅ ∠T; ∠D ≅ ∠B; $\overline{JK} \cong \overline{WT}$; $\overline{KD} \cong \overline{TB}$; $\overline{DJ} \cong \overline{BW}$; △JKD ≅ △WTB

4. ∠CBR ≅ ∠YBD; ∠C ≅ ∠Y; ∠R ≅ ∠D; $\overline{BC} \cong \overline{BY}$; $\overline{CR} \cong \overline{YD}$; $\overline{RB} \cong \overline{DB}$; △BCR ≅ △BYD

Example 2 (page 421)

Example 3 (page 422)

5. ∠APK ≅ ∠SPK; ∠A ≅ ∠S; ∠L ≅ ∠N; ∠LKP ≅ ∠NKP; $\overline{PA} \cong \overline{PS}$; $\overline{AL} \cong \overline{SN}$; $\overline{LK} \cong \overline{NK}$; $\overline{KP} \cong \overline{KP}$; PALK ≅ PSNK

6. ∠H ≅ ∠V; ∠P ≅ ∠N; ∠HZP ≅ ∠VZN; $\overline{HP} \cong \overline{VN}$; $\overline{PZ} \cong \overline{NZ}$; $\overline{ZH} \cong \overline{ZV}$; △HPZ ≅ △VNZ

List the congruent parts of each pair of congruent figures. Then write a congruence statement.

1.
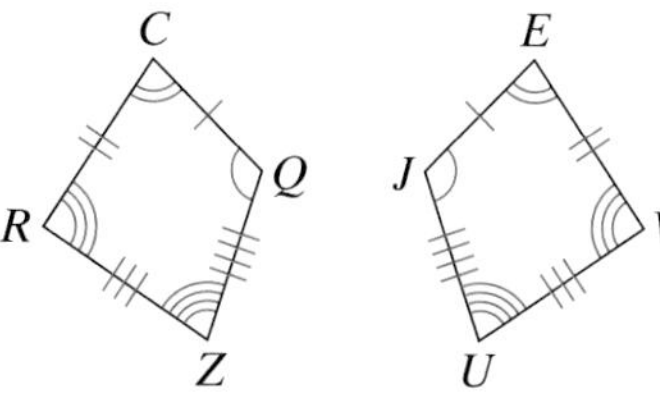

2.
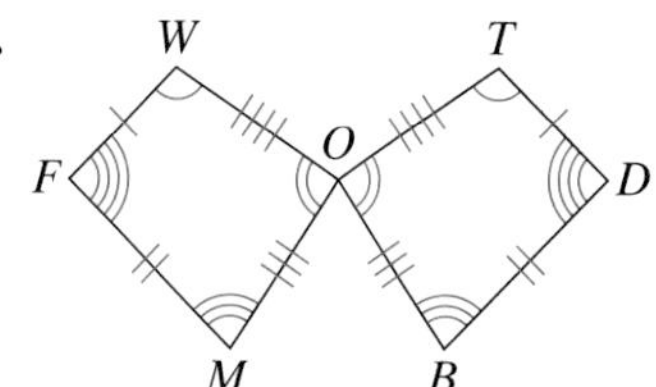

3.
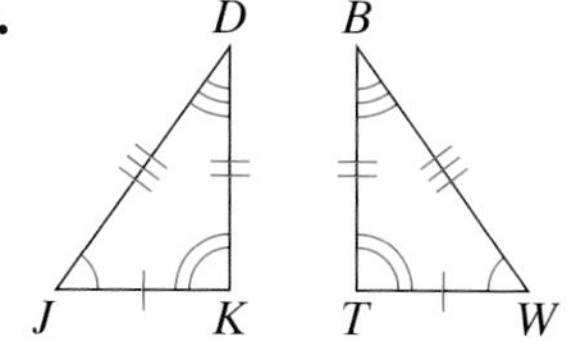

4.
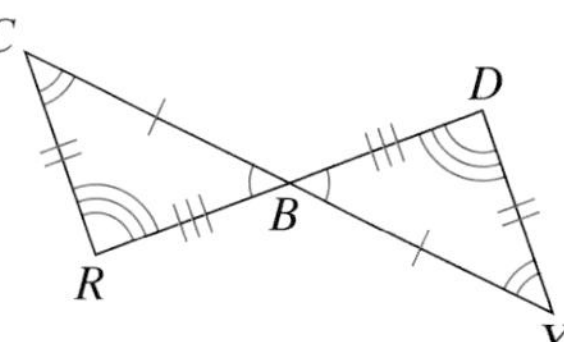

5.
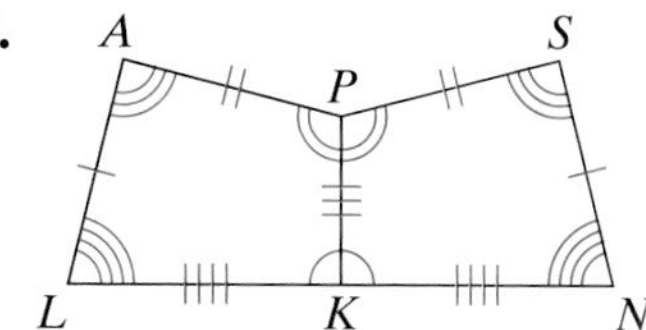

6.
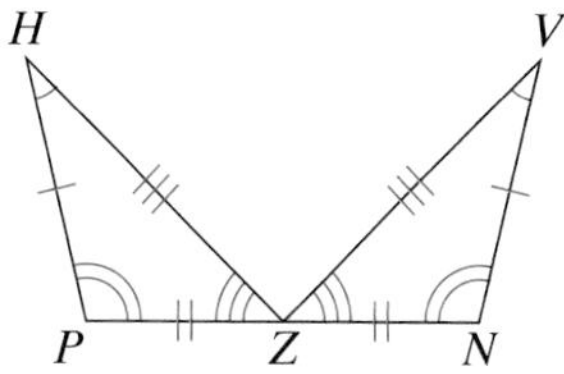

In the diagram, LMRC ≅ TXND. Find each measurement.

7. $m\angle N$ 104°
8. $m\angle T$ 86°
9. RM 0.9 cm
10. ND 1.6 cm
11. $m\angle C$ 62°
12. $m\angle M$ 108°
13. XT 1.4 cm
14. CL 1.7 cm

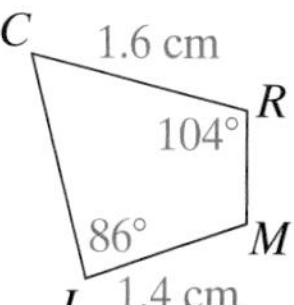

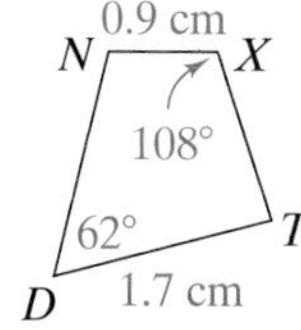

Show that each pair of triangles is congruent.

15. SAS
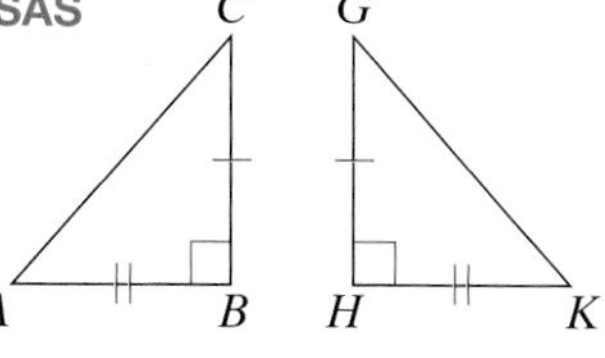

16. SSS
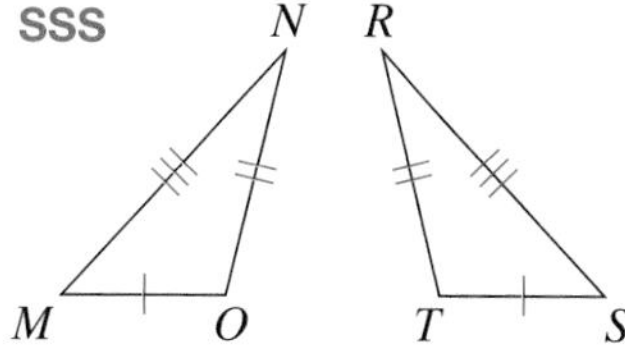

17. SAS
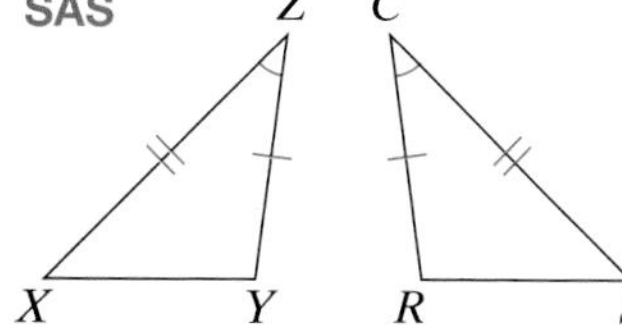

18. ASA
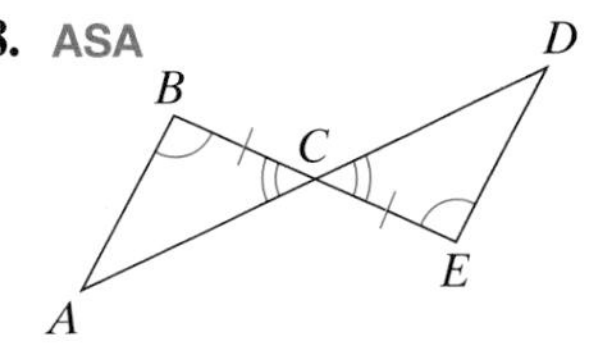

3. Practice

Assignment Guide

 Objective 1

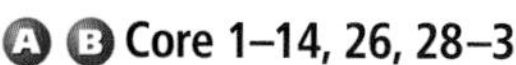 Core 1–14, 26, 28–30

 Objective 2

A B Core 15–25, 27

C Extension 31–34

Test Prep 35–38

Mixed Review 39–47

Auditory Learners

Exercises 7–14 Have students read these symbols aloud.

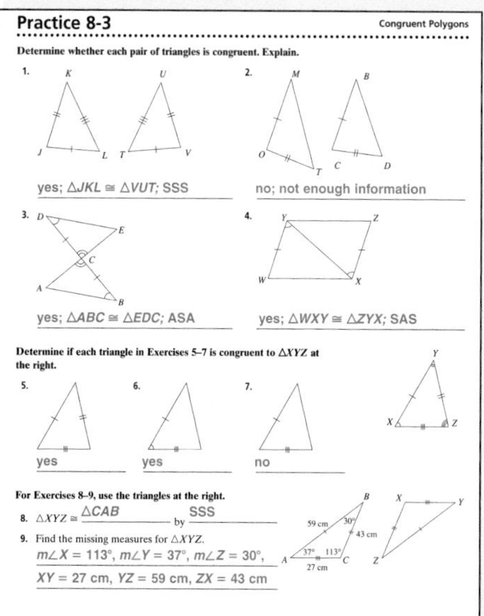

Practice 8-3 Congruent Polygons

Determine whether each pair of triangles is congruent. Explain.

1. yes; △JKL ≅ △VUT; SSS
2. no; not enough information
3. yes; △ABC ≅ △EDC; ASA
4. yes; △WXY ≅ △ZYX; SAS

Determine if each triangle in Exercises 5–7 is congruent to △XYZ at the right.

5. yes
6. yes
7. no

For Exercises 8–9, use the triangles at the right.

8. △XYZ ≅ △CAB by SSS
9. Find the missing measures for △XYZ. m∠X = 113°, m∠Y = 37°, m∠Z = 30°, XY = 27 cm, YZ = 59 cm, ZX = 43 cm

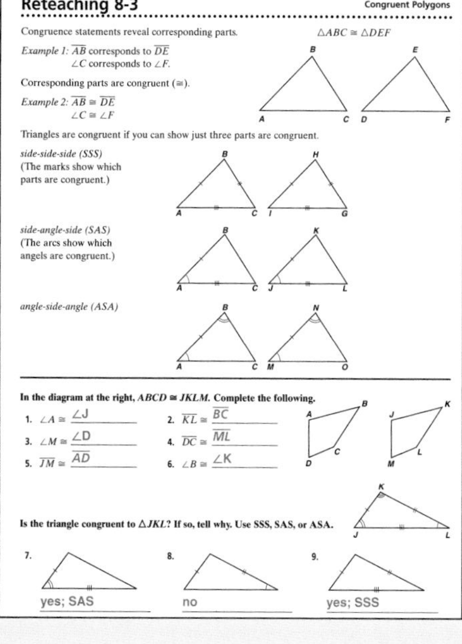

Reteaching 8-3 Congruent Polygons

Congruence statements reveal corresponding parts. △ABC ≅ △DEF

Example 1: $\overline{AB}$ corresponds to $\overline{DE}$. ∠C corresponds to ∠F.

Corresponding parts are congruent (≅).

Example 2: $\overline{AB} \cong \overline{DE}$, ∠C ≅ ∠F

Triangles are congruent if you can show just three parts are congruent.

side-side-side (SSS) (The marks show which parts are congruent.)

side-angle-side (SAS) (The arcs show which angles are congruent.)

angle-side-angle (ASA)

In the diagram at the right, ABCD ≅ JKLM. Complete the following.

1. ∠A ≅ ∠J
2. $\overline{KL} \cong \overline{BC}$
3. ∠M ≅ ∠D
4. $\overline{DC} \cong \overline{ML}$
5. $\overline{JM} \cong \overline{AD}$
6. ∠B ≅ ∠K

Is the triangle congruent to △JKL? If so, tell why. Use SSS, SAS, or ASA.

7. yes; SAS
8. no
9. yes; SSS

B Apply Your Skills

Determine whether each pair of triangles is congruent. Explain.

20. Answers may vary. Sample: Not congruent; the triangles have two pairs of congruent sides and a pair of congruent angles, but the angles are not included between the two sides.

19.

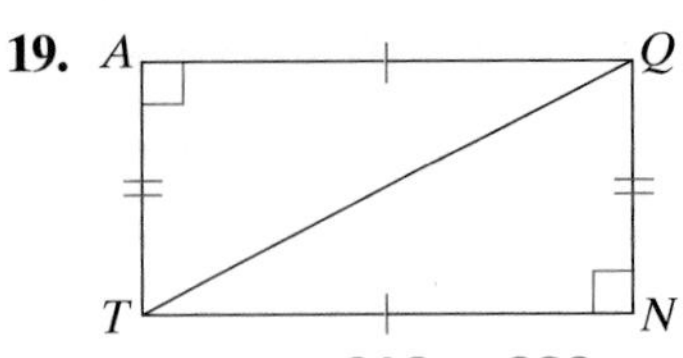

congruent; SAS or SSS

20.

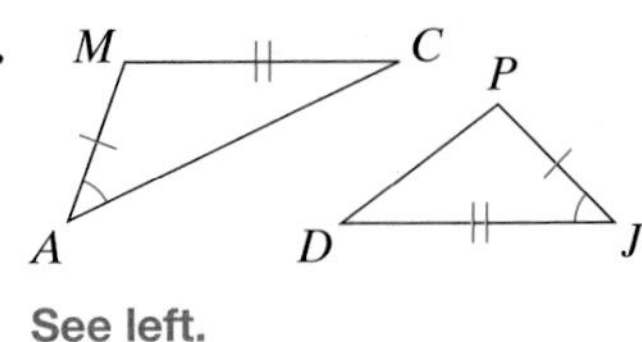

See left.

21. Construction Find a pair of congruent triangles in the photo. Draw them. Label your diagram and identify the congruent parts. Check students' work.

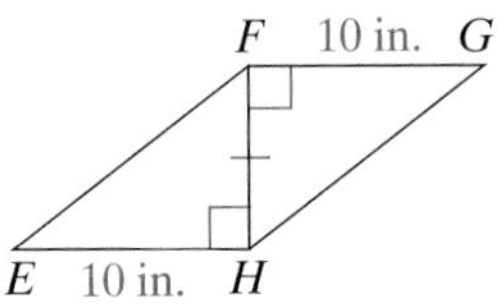

22. Error Analysis Your classmate says that $\triangle EFH \cong \triangle GFH$ in the diagram at the left by ASA. What is wrong with this statement? See margin.

23. Reasoning If a pair of triangles has two congruent angles and one congruent side, must the triangles be congruent? Explain using figures. See margin.

Show that each pair of triangles is congruent. Then find the missing measures in each diagram.

24. SAS; $x = 8$; $y° = 72°$; $z° = 59°$

25. SAS or ASA; $x = 4$; $y° = 30°$; $z° = 60°$

24.

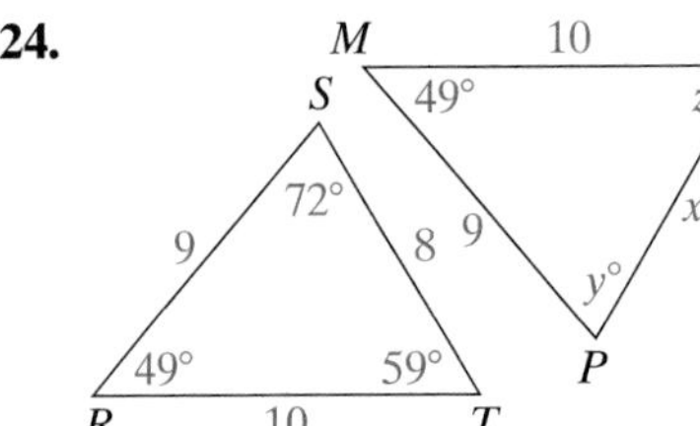

25.

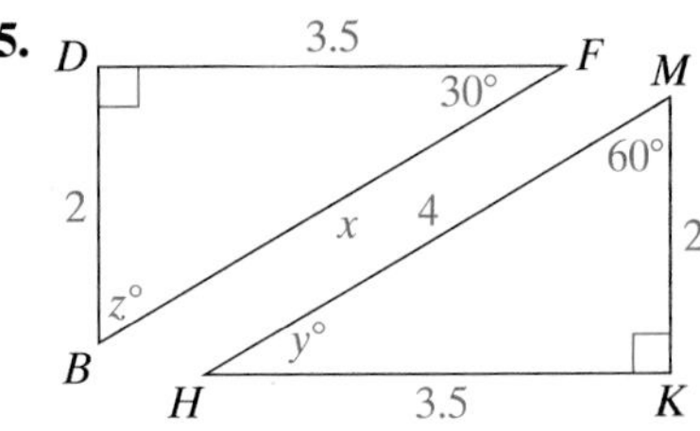

Need Help?
For help with similar figures, go to Lesson 5-5.

26. Writing in Math Explain the difference between similar triangles and congruent triangles. See margin.

Maps Use the map below for Exercises 27–30.

27. Show that the triangles in the map are congruent. ASA

28.

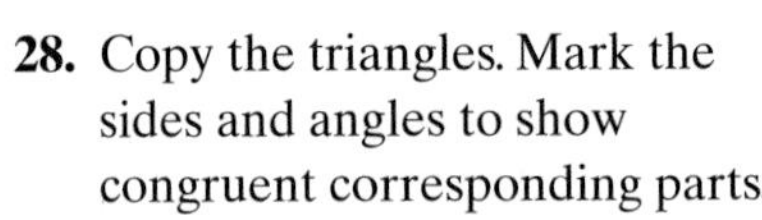

28. Copy the triangles. Mark the sides and angles to show congruent corresponding parts.

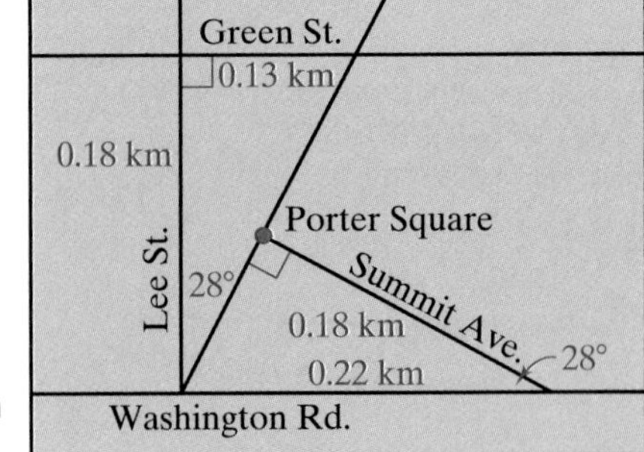

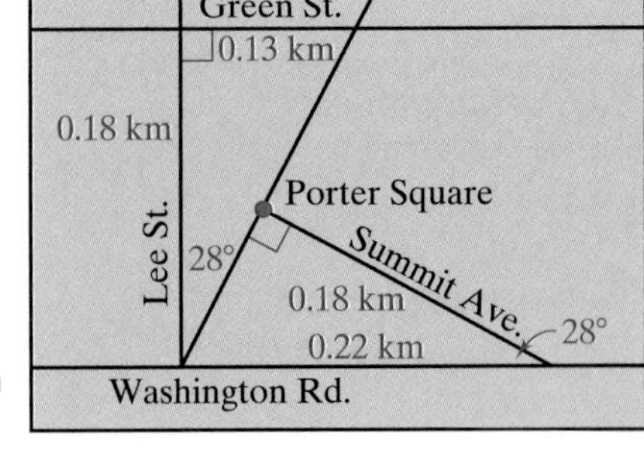

29. How far is Porter Square from the intersection of Lee Street and Washington Road? 0.13 km

30. Find the distance along the road from Porter Square to Green Street. 0.09 km

22. Corresponding vertices are not listed in the same order, and $\triangle EFH \cong \triangle GHF$ by SAS, not ASA.

23. Answers may vary. Sample: No; the corresponding side must be between the corresponding angles. $\triangle ABC \ncong \triangle DEF$

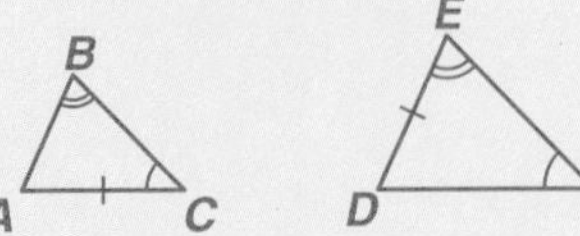

26. Answers may vary. Sample: Similar triangles have corresponding sides that are in proportion, while congruent triangles have corresponding sides that are congruent.

C Challenge

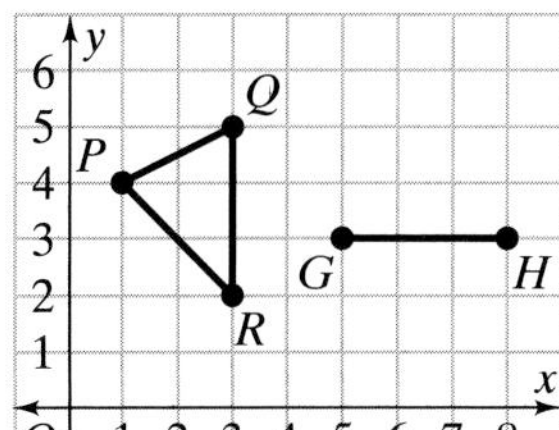

Use the graph at the left for Exercises 31 and 32.

31. Name the possible coordinates of a point F so that $\triangle PQR \cong \triangle FGH$. (6, 1) and (6, 5)

32. Name the possible coordinates of a point I so that $\triangle PQR \cong \triangle IHG$. (7, 1) and (7, 5)

Algebra **Show that each pair of triangles is congruent. Then find the missing measures in each diagram.**

33.

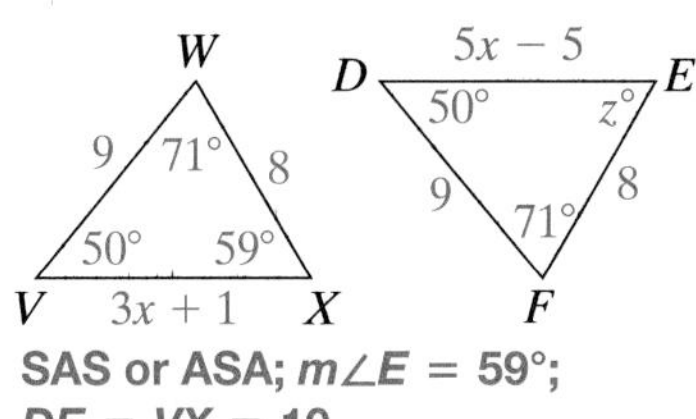

SAS or ASA; $m\angle E = 59°$; $DE = VX = 10$

34.

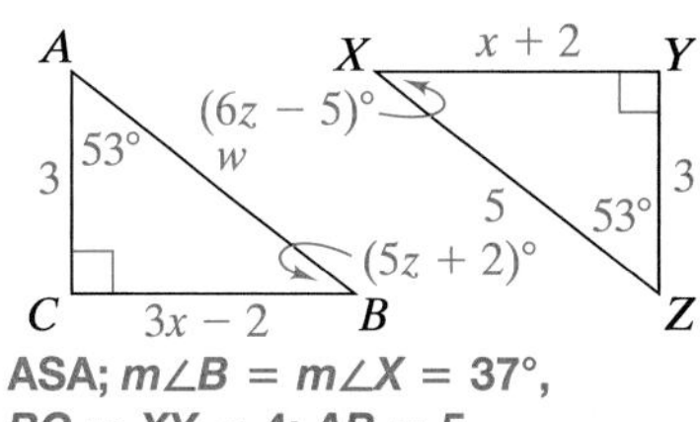

ASA; $m\angle B = m\angle X = 37°$, $BC = XY = 4$; $AB = 5$

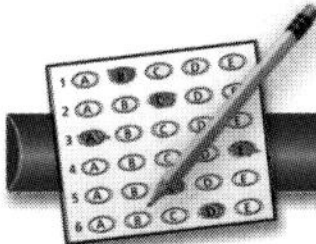

Test Prep

Multiple Choice

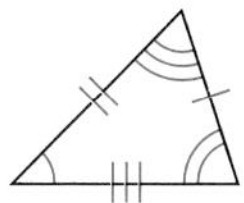

35. Which triangle is NOT necessarily congruent to the triangle at the left? C

A. 
B. 
C. 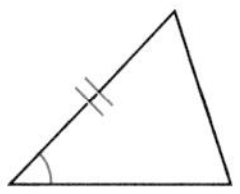
D. 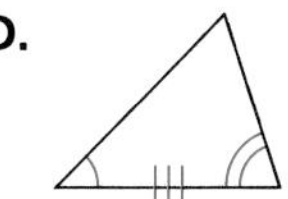

36. Sam wants to make $\triangle ABC$ congruent to $\triangle RST$. He has plotted points A and B on the grid at the right and needs to plot point C. Which ordered pair is a possible coordinate of point C? I

F. (6, 5) **G.** (5, 1)
H. (5, 6) **I.** (8, 5)

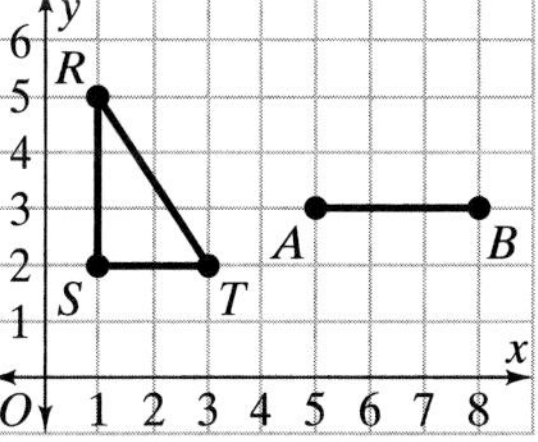

Take It to the NET
Online lesson quiz at **www.PHSchool.com**
Web Code: aca-0803

37. By which method is the pair of triangles at the right congruent? C

A. Side-Side-Side **B.** Angle-Angle-Side
C. Side-Angle-Side **D.** Angle-Side-Angle

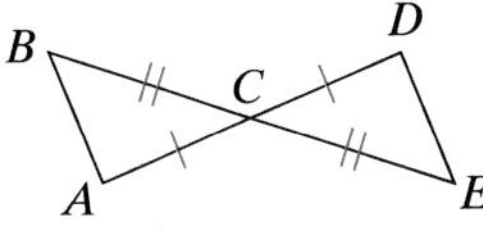

Short Response

38. Can you show that triangles are congruent by Side-Side-Angle? Explain using figures.
See back of book.

Mixed Review

Lesson 6-9

39. What is the probability of choosing a red ball from a box containing 10 white balls and 2 red balls? $\frac{1}{6}$

Lesson 6-1

Write each percent as a decimal.

40. 3.72% 0.0372 **41.** 180% 1.8 **42.** 0.015% 0.00015 **43.** 0.49% 0.0049

44. 15% 0.15 **45.** 0.24% 0.0024 **46.** 138.05% 1.3805 **47.** 0.004% 0.00004

Use the Guided Problem Solving worksheet with Exercise 27–30.

Alternative Assessment

In $\triangle FGH$ and $\triangle PQR$, $\overline{FH} \cong \overline{PR}$ and $\overline{GH} \cong \overline{QR}$. Ask what additional information is needed to prove $\triangle FGH \cong \triangle PQR$. $\overline{FG} \cong \overline{PQ}$ or $\angle FHG \cong \angle PRQ$

4. Assess

PowerPoint Lesson Quiz 8-3

Use $\triangle ABC$ and $\triangle XYZ$ to answer the questions.

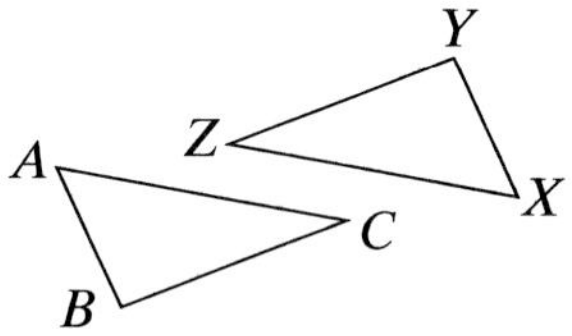

1. Suppose $\triangle ABC$ and $\triangle XYZ$ are congruent. If $AB = 5$ cm, $BC = 8$ cm, and $AC = 10$ cm, find XZ.
   10 cm
2. Suppose $\triangle ABC$ and $\triangle XYZ$ are congruent. What angle in $\triangle ABC$ is congruent to Y?
   $\angle B$
3. Suppose $\angle B \cong \angle Y$, $\angle A \cong \angle X$, and $\overline{AB} \cong \overline{XY}$. Why is $\triangle ABC \cong \triangle XYZ$?
   ASA

Test Prep

Resources

For additional practice with a variety of test item formats:
- Test Prep, p. 465
- Test-Taking Strategies, p. 461
- Test-Taking Strategies with Transparencies

Enrichment 8-3 Congruent Polygons

Visual Thinking

1. The following figure consists of four lines. $\overleftrightarrow{AB} \parallel \overleftrightarrow{CD}$. Explain why the two triangles are congruent. 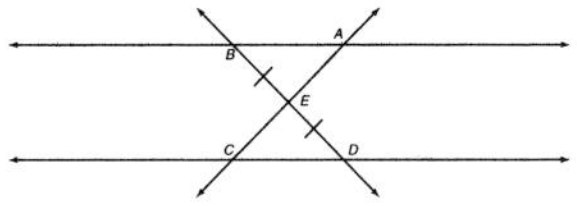
   Sample answer: $\angle ABE \cong \angle CDE$ by alt. int. angles, $\angle BEA \cong \angle CED$ by vert. angles, and $\triangle ABE \cong \triangle CDE$ by ASA.
2. $\overline{AB}$ and $\overline{CD}$ are diameters of the circle. Name a pair of congruent triangles. 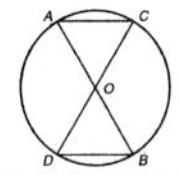
   Sample answer: $\triangle AOC \cong \triangle BOD$
3. $ABCD$ is a rectangle. Name a pair of congruent triangles. 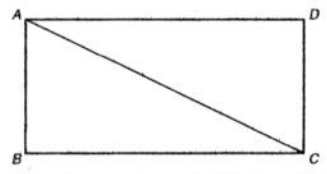
   Sample answer: $\triangle ABC \cong \triangle CDA$
4. $\triangle ABC \cong \triangle BAC$. What kind of triangle is $\triangle ABC$? Explain.
   Sample answer: $\overline{BC} \cong \overline{AC}$. They are corresponding sides of congruent triangles. $\triangle ABC$ is isosceles. Since the measure of $\angle BCA$ is not known, the triangle is not necessarily equilateral.
5. Explain why any two congruent triangles are similar.
   Sample answer: Since corresponding angles of congruent triangles are congruent and the similarity ratio is 1 for corresponding sides, congruent triangles are also similar.

8-4

1. Plan

Lesson Preview

Check Skills You'll Need

Writing and Simplifying Expressions With Exponents
Lesson 1-7: Examples 1–3. Extra Practice, p. 702.

Lesson Resources

Teaching Resources
Practice, Reteaching, Enrichment
Checkpoint Quiz 1

Reaching All Students
Practice Workbook 8-4
Spanish Practice Workbook 8-4
Reading and Math Literacy 8B
Spanish Reading and Math Literacy 8B
Spanish Checkpoint Quiz 1
Guided Problem Solving 8-4
Hands-On Activities 8

Presentation Assistant Plus!
Transparencies
- Check Skills You'll Need 8-4
- Problem of the Day 8-4
- Additional Examples 8-4
- Student Edition Answers 8-4
- Lesson Quiz 8-4

PH Presentation Pro CD-ROM 8-4

Checkpoint Quiz 1
Computer Test Generator CD

Technology
Resource Pro® CD-ROM
Computer Test Generator CD
PH Presentation Pro CD-ROM

www.PHSchool.com
Student Site
- Teacher Web Code: ack-5500
- Self-grading Lesson Quiz

PH SuccessNet Teacher Center
- Lesson Planner
- Resources

Plus 

Problem Solving

8-4 Solve a Simpler Problem and Look for a Pattern

What You'll Learn

OBJECTIVE 1 To solve a problem by combining strategies

. . . And Why

To combine effective strategies to solve a problem, as in Example 1

Check Skills You'll Need

 For help, go to Lesson 1-7.

Write using exponents.

1. $5 \cdot 5 \cdot 5 \cdot 5$ 5^4 **2.** $x \cdot x \cdot y \cdot y \cdot y$ x^2y^3 **3.** $8 \cdot m \cdot n \cdot m \cdot 8$ 8^2m^2n

Simplify each expression.

4. $6^2 + 3^3$ 63 **5.** $2^4 \cdot 4 + 7$ 71 **6.** $4^2 - 5^3 + 12$ −97

 Interactive lesson includes instant self-check, tutorials, and activities.

OBJECTIVE 1 Solving a Problem by Combining Strategies

When to Use These Strategies If you think solving a problem will require many steps, you may be able to ***solve a simpler problem*** first. Then ***look for a pattern.*** Use the pattern to solve the original problem.

1 EXAMPLE 

Human Pyramid A group in Spain built a human pyramid with ten levels. How many people were in the pyramid?

Read and Understand A human pyramid has ten levels. The goal is to find the total number of people needed to create the pyramid.

Plan and Solve You can solve a simpler problem by looking for a pattern in pyramids with fewer than ten levels.

Use a dot to represent each person. Create one-, two-, three-, and four-level pyramids. Then organize your information and look for a pattern.

Number of People	1	$1 + 2 = 3$	$1 + 2 + 3 = 6$	$1 + 2 + 3 + 4 = 10$

Make a conjecture about how to find the number of people in an n-level pyramid. The total number is the sum of the positive integers from 1 to n.

Ten levels: $1 + 2 + 3 + 4 + 5 + 6 + 7 + 8 + 9 + 10 = 55$ people

Look Back and Check To test your conjecture, draw a diagram of a five-level human pyramid.

Ongoing Assessment and Intervention

Before the Lesson
Diagnose prerequisite skills using:
- Check Skills You'll Need

During the Lesson
Monitor progress using:
- Check Understanding
- Additional Examples
- Test Prep

After the Lesson
Assess knowledge using:
- Lesson Quiz
- Computer Test Generator CD
- Chapter Checkpoint 1 (p. 429)

A new park will be in the shape of a 10-sided polygon like the one shown. The planners want a path between each pair of non-adjacent corners. How many paths will there be? 35 paths

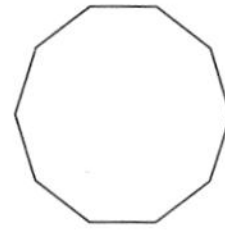

When you make a conjecture based on a pattern, you are using *inductive reasoning*. Since conjectures you make are not always true, check your results whenever possible.

2 EXAMPLE **Real-World Problem Solving**

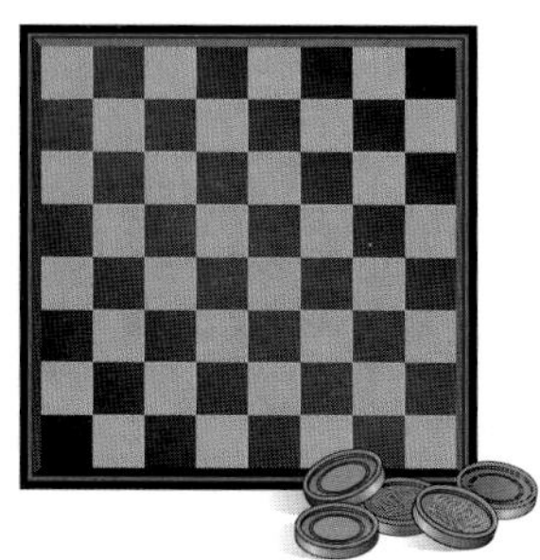

Checkers A standard checkerboard has 8 squares on each side. How many squares of different sizes are there on a standard (8×8) checkerboard?

Read and Understand The goal is to find the total number of squares on a checkerboard that are 1×1, 2×2, 3×3, 4×4, 5×5, 6×6, 7×7, or 8×8 in size.

Plan and Solve Solve a simpler problem similar to the given problem. Look for a pattern to help you solve the original problem.

Consider boards that are 1×1, 2×2, and 3×3. Then organize your data.

1 1×1 square

1 2×2 square
4 1×1 squares

1 3×3 square
4 2×2 squares
9 1×1 squares

Size of checkerboard	1×1	2×2	3×3
Number of squares	$1^2 = 1$	$1^2 + 2^2 = 5$	$1^2 + 2^2 + 3^2 = 14$

Using inductive reasoning, you can make this conjecture about the number of squares in a checkerboard with n squares on a side: the total number of squares is the sum of the squares of the positive integers from 1 to n.

Number of squares on an 8×8 checkerboard =

$$1^2 + 2^2 + 3^2 + 4^2 + 5^2 + 6^2 + 7^2 + 8^2 =$$

$$1 + 4 + 9 + 16 + 25 + 36 + 49 + 64 = 204 \text{ squares}$$

Look Back and Check To test your conjecture, draw a diagram of a 4×4 checkerboard.

Check Understanding 2

a. Find the number of small triangles in the figure. 25 triangles

b. How many small triangles will there be in the complete figure if you extend the figure to 10 rows? What about n rows? 100 triangles; n^2 triangles

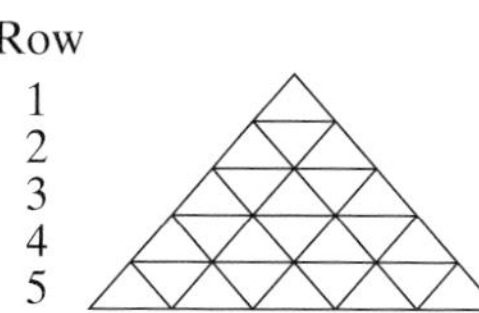

Reaching All Students

Below Level Have students review the meaning of exponents by writing 2^3 and 3^2 as the product of factors. $2 \cdot 2 \cdot 2$; $3 \cdot 3$	**Advanced Learners** How many different 1-inch line segments must you draw to make a standard (8×8) checkerboard that is 8 inches on a side? 144 line segments	**English Learners** See note on page 427. **Tactile Learners** See note on page 427.

2. Teach

Math Background

When a problem involves repetition and greater numbers, sometimes you can *solve a simpler problem* by beginning with lesser numbers and *look for a pattern*. Using this combination of strategies assumes that the pattern will continue as it began (*inductive reasoning*) and, in some cases, that assumption may not be true.

Teaching Notes

1 EXAMPLE English Learners

Pair English learners with fluent communicators. Encourage students to read and discuss the problem carefully, asking questions about words or phrases that are not clear.

2 EXAMPLE Tactile Learners

Have a few game boards available for students to handle. Have them sketch boards of various sizes on paper. They can use several colors to outline squares.

PowerPoint

Additional Examples

1. A meeting is attended by 8 people. Each person shakes hands once with every other person at the meeting. How many handshakes will there be? 28 handshakes

2. You place one grain of rice on the first square of a checkerboard, two grains on the next square, four on the next, and eight on the next (doubling each time). After you put 1,024 grains on a square, how many squares will have rice on them? 11 squares (from 2^0 to 2^{10})

Closure

What are some pairs of strategies that you could use to solve a problem? Samples: Solve a simpler problem AND look for a pattern; make a table AND write an equation; draw a diagram AND use logical reasoning.

3. Practice

Assignment Guide

Objective 1

Ⓐ Ⓑ Core 1–10

Ⓒ Extension 11

Test Prep 12–15

Mixed Review 16–23

Error Prevention!

Exercises 5–10 Have students Identify their strategies before they solve each exercise.

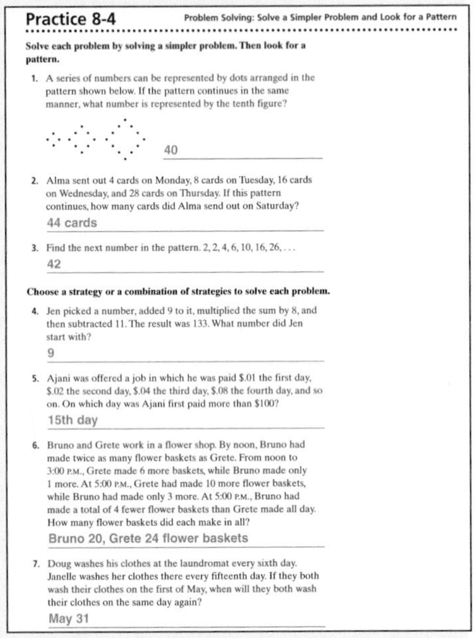

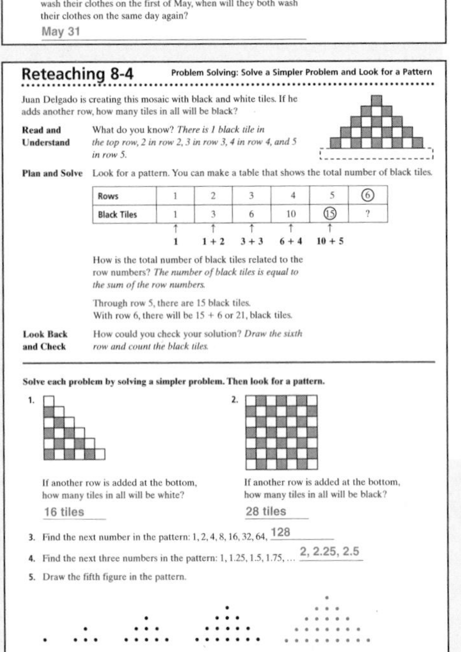

Practice 8-4 — Problem Solving: Solve a Simpler Problem and Look for a Pattern

Solve each problem by solving a simpler problem. Then look for a pattern.

1. A series of numbers can be represented by dots arranged in the pattern shown below. If the pattern continues in the same manner, what number is represented by the tenth figure?
   40
2. Alma sent out 4 cards on Monday, 8 cards on Tuesday, 16 cards on Wednesday, and 28 cards on Thursday. If this pattern continues, how many cards did Alma send out on Saturday?
   44 cards
3. Find the next number in the pattern. 2, 2, 4, 6, 10, 16, 26, . . .
   42

Choose a strategy or a combination of strategies to solve each problem.

4. Jen picked a number, added 9 to it, multiplied the sum by 8, and then subtracted 11. The result was 133. What number did Jen start with?
   9
5. Ajani was offered a job in which he was paid \$.01 the first day, \$.02 the second day, \$.04 the third day, \$.08 the fourth day, and so on. On which day was Ajani first paid more than \$100?
   15th day
6. Bruno and Grete work in a flower shop. By noon, Bruno had made twice as many flower baskets as Grete. From noon to 3:00 P.M., Grete made 6 more baskets, while Bruno made only 1 more. At 5:00 P.M., Grete had made 10 more flower baskets, while Bruno had made only 3 more. At 5:00 P.M., Bruno had made a total of 4 fewer flower baskets than Grete made all day. How many flower baskets did each make in all?
   Bruno 20, Grete 24 flower baskets
7. Doug washes his clothes at the laundromat every sixth day. Janelle washes her clothes there every fifteenth day. If they both wash their clothes on the first of May, when will they both wash their clothes on the same day again?
   May 31

Reteaching 8-4 — Problem Solving: Solve a Simpler Problem and Look for a Pattern

Juan Delgado is creating this mosaic with black and white tiles. If he adds another row, how many tiles in all will be black?

Read and Understand What do you know? *There is 1 black tile in the top row, 2 in row 2, 3 in row 3, 4 in row 4, and 5 in row 5.*

Plan and Solve Look for a pattern. You can make a table that shows the total number of black tiles.

Rows	1	2	3	4	5	⑥
Black Tiles	1	3	6	10	⑮	?
	1	1 + 2	3 + 3	6 + 4	10 + 5	

How is the total number of black tiles related to the row numbers? *The number of black tiles is equal to the sum of the row numbers.*

Through row 5, there are 15 black tiles.
With row 6, there will be 15 + 6 or 21, black tiles.

Look Back and Check How could you check your solution? *Draw the sixth row and count the black tiles.*

Solve each problem by solving a simpler problem. Then look for a pattern.

1. If another row is added at the bottom, how many tiles in all will be white?
   16 tiles
2. If another row is added at the bottom, how many tiles in all will be black?
   28 tiles
3. Find the next number in the pattern: 1, 2, 4, 8, 16, 32, 64, 128
4. Find the next three numbers in the pattern: 1, 1.25, 1.5, 1.75, … 2, 2.25, 2.5
5. Draw the fifth figure in the pattern.

EXERCISES

For more practice, see *Extra Practice.*

Ⓐ Practice by Example

Examples 1, 2 (pages 426, 427)

Need Help?
- Reread the problem.
- Identify the key facts and details.
- Tell the problem in your own words.
- Try a different strategy.
- Check your work.

Solve each problem by solving a simpler problem. Then look for a pattern.

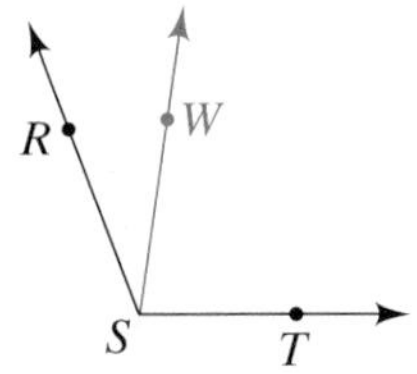

1. a. Onita drew $\overrightarrow{SW}$ in the interior of $\angle RST$. How many angles can she name? **3 angles**
   b. How many angles can Onita name after she draws five more rays? **28 angles**

2. **Chess** In a chess tournament, each participant plays one game against each of the other players. There are 20 participants. How many games will be played? **190 games**

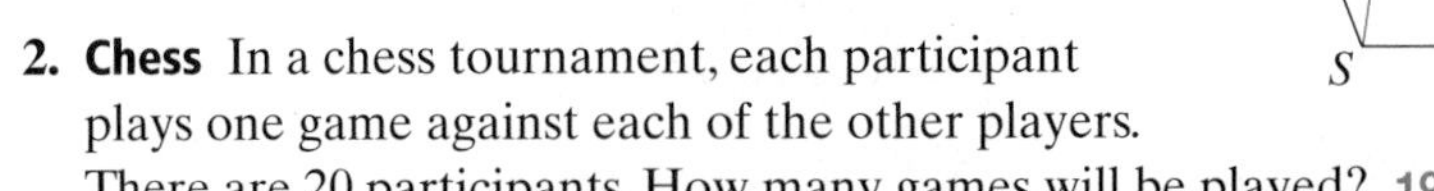

3. Draw the sixth figure in the pattern shown below. **See margin.**

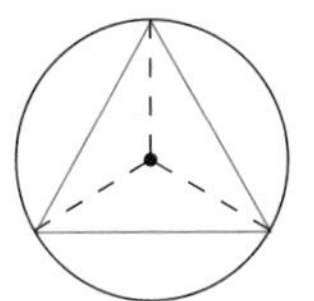 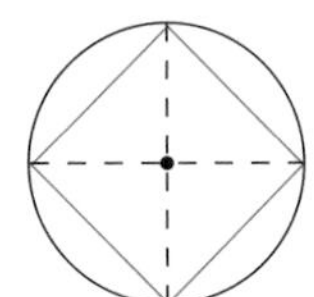 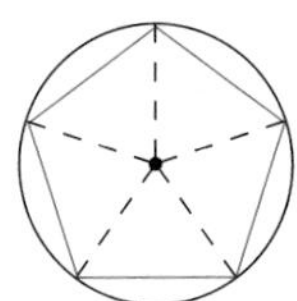

4. The houses on Hall Avenue are numbered with even numbers. Of the house numbers in order from 140 to 224, how many have at least one 6? **12**

Ⓑ Apply Your Skills

Use any strategy to solve each problem. Show your work.

5. **Consumer Issues** The Community Youth Club bought booster buttons at a wholesale price of 3 for \$1. They sold the buttons for \$.50 each. How much profit did the club make on the sale of 5 dozen buttons? **\$10**

6. **Basketball** A basketball player scored 16, 22, and 24 points in three games. What is the least number of points the player must score in the fourth game to average at least 20 points per game? **18 points**

7. **Writing in Math** Suppose you want to find the thickness of one sheet of paper. Describe the problem-solving strategy you would use. **See margin.**

Strategies

- Draw a Diagram
- Look for a Pattern
- Make a Graph
- Make an Organized List
- Make a Table
- Simulate a Problem
- Solve a Simpler Problem
- Try, Check, and Revise
- Use Logical Reasoning
- Work Backward
- Write an Equation

8. **Seating** The desks in a classroom are arranged in rows. Suppose your seat is the second from the right and the fourth from the left. You sit in the third row from the front and the fourth row from the back of the room. How many desks are in the room? **30 desks**

9. **Maps** Keats Drive is parallel to Byron Lane. Yeats Road is perpendicular to Melville Drive. Yeats Road is parallel to Byron Lane. Is Melville Drive parallel to Keats Drive? Explain. **See left.**

9. No; Keats ∥ Byron and Yeats ∥ Byron, so Keats ∥ Yeats. Melville ⊥ Yeats, so Melville ⊥ Keats.

10. **Baking** You need to bake a cake for 18 minutes, but you only have a 13-minute timer and an 8-minute timer. How can you bake the cake? **See margin.**

Use the Guided Problem Solving worksheet with Exercise 6.

3.

7. Answers may vary. Sample: Measure the thickness of 100 sheets of paper. Divide that number by 100.

10. Start both timers. When the 8-min timer goes off, put the cake in the oven and bake it for the 5 min remaining on the 13-min timer. When that timer goes off, reset it to bake the cake for another 13 min.

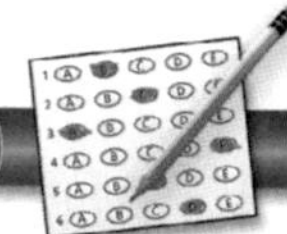

Challenge

11. **Stretch Your Thinking** An improper fraction is in lowest terms. Its two-digit numerator is a multiple of 4 and its two-digit denominator is a multiple of 7. The sum of the digits of the numerator is 11 greater than the sum of the digits of the denominator. What is the fraction? $\frac{68}{21}$

Test Prep

Multiple Choice

12. Which is equivalent to $\frac{12^7}{12^2}$? C

A. 3^5 B. 4^9 C. 12^5 D. 12^9

13. Which is equivalent to $\frac{6^{21}}{6^6}$? H

F. 3^{15} G. 2^{27} H. 6^{15} I. 6^{27}

14. Which is equivalent to $4^7 \cdot 4^{10}$? A

A. 4^{17} B. 2^{17} C. 4^3 D. 4^{-3}

Take It to the NET
Online lesson quiz at www.PHSchool.com
Web Code: aca-0804

Short Response

15. In 40 minutes, you can pick 3 qt of berries. If 4 people work at that rate, how long will it take to pick 15 qt? Justify your answer. See back of book.

Mixed Review

Lesson 7-4 **Algebra** **Simplify each expression.**

16. $(4m)^3$ $64m^3$ 17. $(7r^2s^3)^4$ $2{,}401r^8s^{12}$ 18. $(8a^9)^2$ $64a^{18}$ 19. $(x^2yz^3)^4$ $x^8y^4z^{12}$

20–23. Answers may vary. Samples are given.

Lesson 6-2 **Mental Math** **Estimate a 15% tip for each restaurant bill.**

20. \$28.35 \$4.50 21. \$64.82 \$9.60 22. \$13.97 2.10 23. \$108.16 \$16.50

Checkpoint Quiz 1 — Lessons 8-1 through 8-4

Instant self-check quiz online and on CD-ROM

Identify each pair of angles as *adjacent*, *corresponding*, *alternate interior*, or *vertical*.

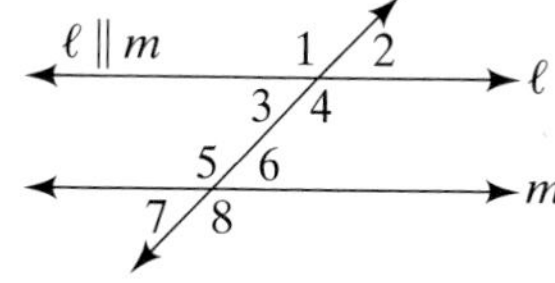

1. ∠6, ∠7 vertical
2. ∠4, ∠5 alternate interior
3. ∠2, ∠6 corresponding
4. ∠3, ∠4 adjacent

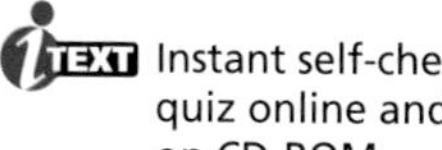

In the diagram at the left, $APKS \cong OFND$. Find each measurement.

5. $m\angle N$ 100° 6. $m\angle P$ 90° 7. PK 0.9 m 8. DO 1.6 m

9. Let $m\angle C = 67°$. Find the measures of the complement and the supplement. 23°; 113°

10. **Election** Four students are running for class president. How many different ways can they be listed on the ballot? 24 ways

4. Assess

Lesson Quiz 8-4

1. How many diagonals can a 15-sided polygon have? 90

Chapter Checkpoint

To check understanding of Lessons 8-1 to 8-4:

Checkpoint Quiz 1 (p. 429)

Teaching Resources
Checkpoint Quiz 1 (also in *Prentice Hall Assessment System*)

Reaching All Students
Reading and Math Literacy 8C

Spanish versions available

Test Prep

Resources
For additional practice with a variety of test item formats:
- Test Prep, p. 465
- Test-Taking Strategies, p. 461
- Test-Taking Strategies with Transparencies

Exercise 12 Suggest that students first evaluate the simpler problem, $\frac{2^7}{2^2}$.

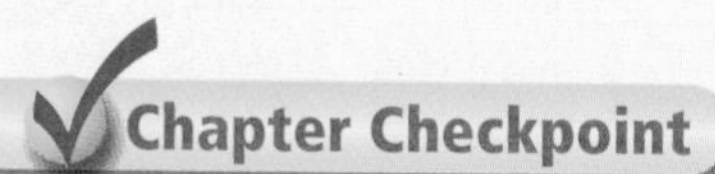

Enrichment 8-4 Problem Solving: Solve a Simpler Problem and Look for a Pattern
Visual Thinking

Analyze the shapes on the grid to find the pattern. Then complete the missing section in the center.

Describe the pattern.
Sample answer: The pattern is 1-2-2-1-2-1-1-2 and goes from left to right in odd rows and right to left in even rows.

Alternative Assessment

Each student writes a word problem that can be solved by identifying a pattern and solving a simpler problem. Students challenge classmates to solve the problem.

8-5

1. Plan

Lesson Preview

Check Skills You'll Need

Classifying Angles
Skills Handbook: Classifying and Measuring Angles, p. 726.

Lesson Resources

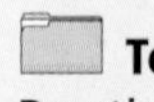

Teaching Resources
Practice, Reteaching, Enrichment

Reaching All Students
Practice Workbook 8-5
Spanish Practice Workbook 8-5
Guided Problem Solving 8-5
Hands-On Activities 29

Presentation Assistant Plus!
Transparencies
- Check Skills You'll Need 8-5
- Problem of the Day 8-5
- Additional Examples 8-5
- Student Edition Answers 8-5
- Lesson Quiz 8-5
- Classroom Aid 20–21

PH Presentation Pro CD-ROM 8-5

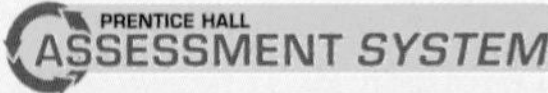

Computer Test Generator CD

Technology
Resource Pro® CD-ROM
Computer Test Generator CD
PH Presentation Pro CD-ROM

www.PHSchool.com
Student Site
- Teacher Web Code: ack-5500
- Algebra Readiness Puzzles 32
- Self-grading Lesson Quiz

PH SuccessNet Teacher Center
- Lesson Planner
- Resources

Plus 

8-5 Classifying Triangles and Quadrilaterals

What You'll Learn

To classify triangles and quadrilaterals

. . . And Why

To identify shapes in road signs, as in Example 1

Check Skills You'll Need

For help, go to Skills Handbook page 726.

Classify each angle as *acute, right, obtuse,* or *straight.*

1. 143° obtuse **2.** 52° acute **3.** 90° right **4.** 180 straight

New Vocabulary • acute triangle • obtuse triangle • right triangle • equilateral triangle • isosceles triangle • scalene triangle • quadrilateral • parallelogram • trapezoid • rhombus • rectangle • square

OBJECTIVE 1

Interactive lesson includes instant self-check, tutorials, and activities.

Classifying Triangles and Quadrilaterals

You can classify triangles by their angle measures or by the number of congruent sides.

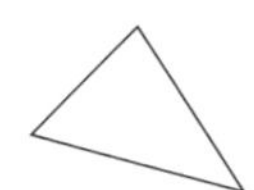

acute triangle
three acute angles

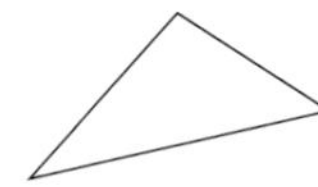

obtuse triangle
one obtuse angle

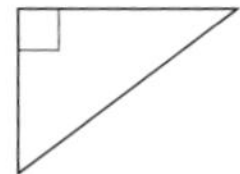

right triangle
one right angle

Reading Math
The prefix *equi* means "equal" or "the same." The word *equilateral* means "having equal sides."

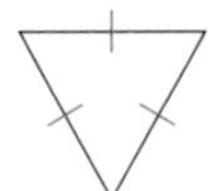

equilateral triangle
three congruent sides

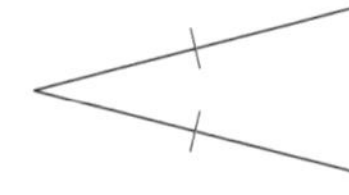

isosceles triangle
at least two congruent sides

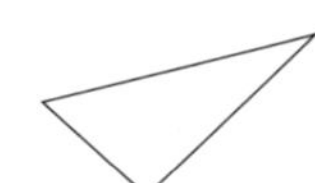

scalene triangle
no congruent sides

1 EXAMPLE Classifying Triangles

Real World

Signs Classify the triangle in the sign at the right by its sides and its angles.

The triangle has three sides that are not congruent and a right angle. It is a scalene right triangle.

Check Understanding 1 Classify each triangle by its sides and its angles.

a.

isosceles, obtuse

b.

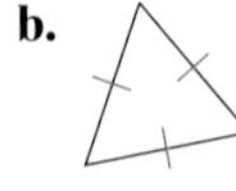

equilateral, acute

Ongoing Assessment and Intervention

Before the Lesson
Diagnose prerequisite skills using:
- Check Skills You'll Need

During the Lesson
Monitor progress using:
- Check Understanding
- Additional Examples
- Test Prep

After the Lesson
Assess knowledge using:
- Lesson Quiz
- Computer Test Generator CD

Quadrilateral comes from *quad*, meaning "four," and *latus*, meaning "side."

You can also classify quadrilaterals by their sides and angles. Arrowheads on the sides of quadrilaterals tell you which sides are parallel.

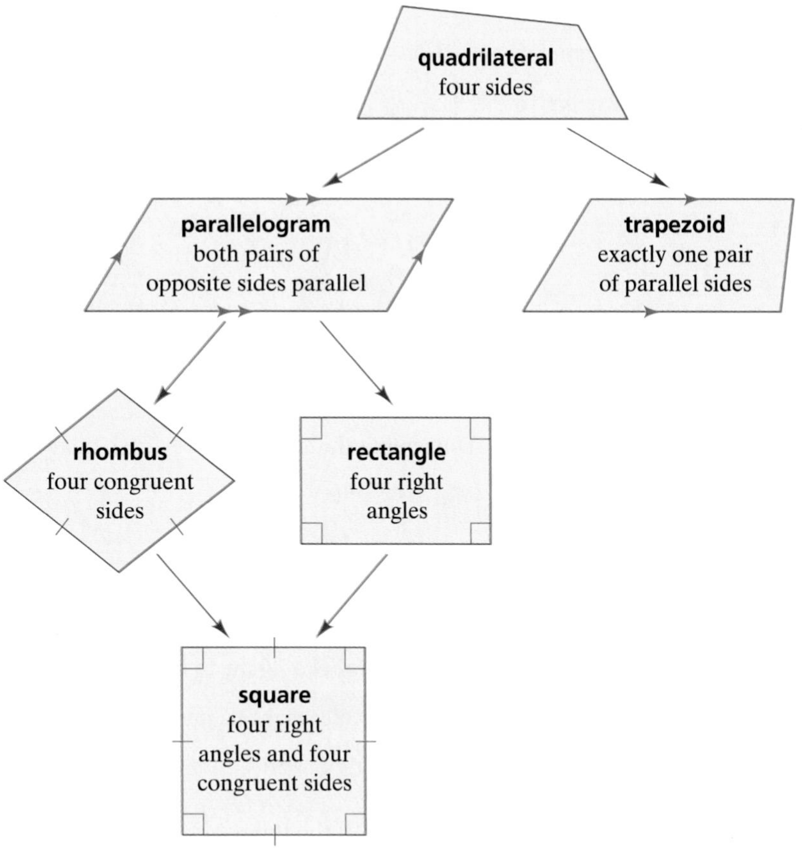

A quadrilateral can have more than one name. If it does, use the name that describes the quadrilateral most precisely. You name quadrilaterals by listing their vertices in consecutive order.

2 EXAMPLE Classifying Quadrilaterals by Sides and Angles

Determine the best name for quadrilateral *DGHJ*.

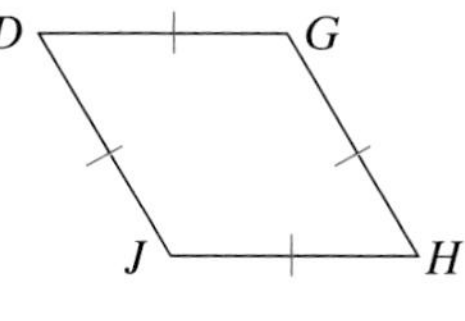

DGHJ is a quadrilateral and a parallelogram, but it is more precisely described as a rhombus. *DGHJ* has two pairs of opposite sides that are parallel and four sides that are congruent.

Check Understanding 2 Determine the best name for each quadrilateral.

a. 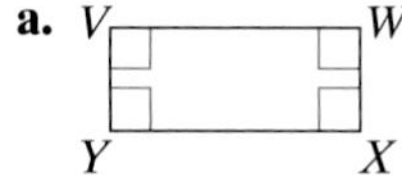

rectangle

b. 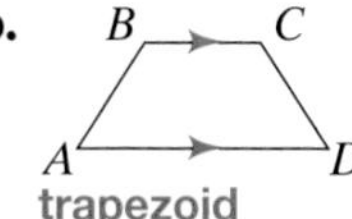

trapezoid

c. **Reasoning** Explain why *DGHJ* in Example 2 is not a square. See left.

2c. It does not have four right angles.

Reaching All Students

Below Level Have students draw a rhombus that is not a square.	**Advanced Learners** Have students explain how the angles formed by the diagonals of a rhombus differ from those of a rectangle that is not a rhombus. diagonals of rhombus form 90° angles	**Alternative Method** See note on page 431. **Tactile Learners** See note on page 431.

2. Teach

Math Background

Triangles can be classified by their greatest angle: acute (< 90°), obtuse (> 90°), or right (= 90°). Triangles can also be classified by how many congruent sides they have: scalene (0), isosceles (2), or equilateral (3). Quadrilaterals are classified by their sides and angles and may have more than one name. For example, a square is also a rhombus, a rectangle, and a parallelogram, but it is not a trapezoid.

Teaching Notes

1 EXAMPLE Alternative Method

Have students use protractors and rulers to explore whether it is possible to draw an equilateral triangle that is not equiangular. It is not possible.

2 EXAMPLE Tactile Learners

Have students model each quadrilateral on geoboards and give the best name for each. Have them identify all the other possible names.

PowerPoint

Additional Examples

1 Classify $\triangle LMN$ by its sides and angles.

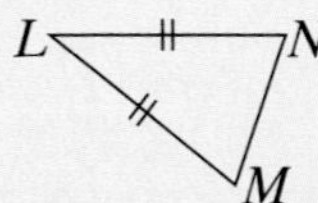

isosceles acute triangle

2 Determine the best name for quadrilateral *WXYZ*. Explain your choice.

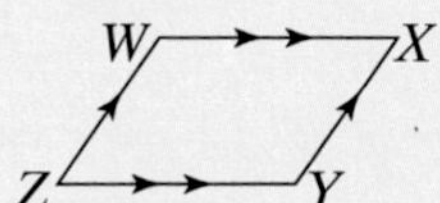

parallelogram; The opposite sides are parallel but adjacent sides are not equal.

Closure

How do you classify triangles and quadrilaterals? Sample: Triangles can be classified by their angles or by their congruent sides. Quadrilaterals are classified by sides and angles.

3. Practice

Assignment Guide

1 Objective 1

A B Core 1–25

C Extension 26–29

Test Prep 30–33

Mixed Review 34–44

Error Prevention!

Exercise 16 Explain that "exactly one pair" does *not* include two pairs, as in a parallelogram.

Practice 8-5 — Classifying Triangles and Quadrilaterals

Determine the best name for each quadrilateral. Explain your choice.

1. parallelogram; $\overline{JK} \cong \overline{LM}$; $\overline{KL} \cong \overline{MJ}$; $\angle J \cong \angle L$; $\angle K \cong \angle M$
2. rectangle; $\overline{UV} \cong \overline{TW}$; $\overline{UT} \cong \overline{VW}$; $\angle U \cong \angle V \cong \angle W \cong \angle T$
3. square; $\overline{AB} \cong \overline{BC} \cong \overline{CD} \cong \overline{DA}$; $\angle A \cong \angle B \cong \angle C \cong \angle D$
4. rectangle; 4 right angles and opposite sides congruent
5. square; 4 right angles and all sides congruent
6. rhombus; all sides congruent and opposite angles congruent
7. parallelogram; opposite sides congruent and parallel
8. square; 4 right angles and all sides congruent
9. $\triangle ABC \cong \triangle CDA$ parallelogram; opposite sides congruent and parallel

Classify each triangle by its sides and its angles. Explain your choice.

10. acute equilateral; all sides congruent
11. acute scalene; no sides congruent and all angles less than 90°
12. right scalene; right angle and no congruent sides

Reteaching 8-5 — Classifying Triangles and Quadrilaterals

A *quadrilateral* is a 4-sided polygon. A *triangle* is a 3-sided polygon.

QUADRILATERALS	TRIANGLES
A *parallelogram* is a quadrilateral with 2 pairs of parallel sides.	An *acute triangle* has 3 angles smaller than 90°.
A *trapezoid* is a quadrilateral with only 1 pair of parallel sides.	A *right triangle* has 1 angle of 90°.
A *rhombus* is a parallelogram with 4 congruent sides.	An *obtuse triangle* has 1 angle larger than 90°.
A *rectangle* is a parallelogram with 4 right angles.	An *equilateral triangle* has 3 congruent sides.
A *square* is a rectangle with 4 congruent sides or a rhombus with 4 right angles.	An *isosceles triangle* has at least 2 congruent sides.
	A *scalene triangle* has no congruent sides.

Name all the figures shown that fit each description. If none are shown, write *none*.

1. obtuse triangle $\triangle JKL$
2. parallelogram $QRST$, $DEFG$
3. right triangle $\triangle QRS$, $\triangle STQ$
4. rhombus $DEFG$
5. trapezoid none
6. isosceles triangle $\triangle ABC$
7. acute triangle $\triangle ABC$
8. rectangle $QRST$

EXERCISES

For more practice, see *Extra Practice*.

A Practice by Example

Example 1 (page 430)

Classify each triangle by its sides and its angles.

1. 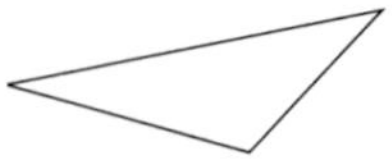 scalene, obtuse
2. 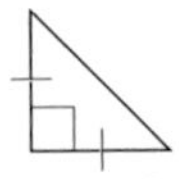 isosceles, right
3. 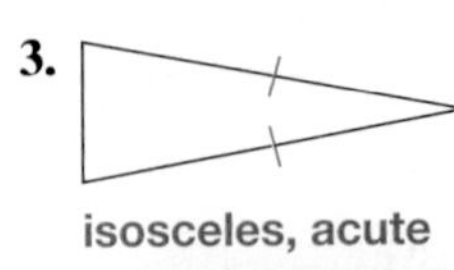 isosceles, acute
4.  equilateral, acute
5.  isosceles, obtuse
6.  scalene, right

Example 2 (page 431)

Determine the best name for each quadrilateral. Explain your choice. 7–10. See margin.

7. 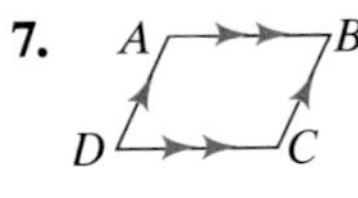
8. 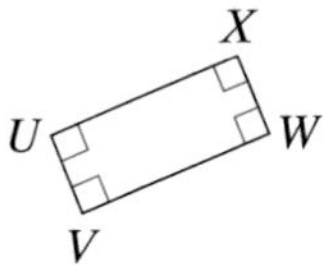
9. 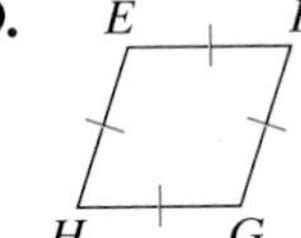
10.

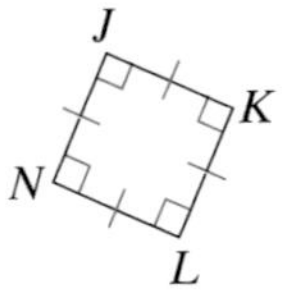

B Apply Your Skills

Draw and label a figure to fit each description. 11–14. Answers may vary. See margin for samples.

11. an isosceles right triangle
12. a trapezoid with a right angle
13. a rectangle with 4 congruent sides
14. a rhombus that is not a square

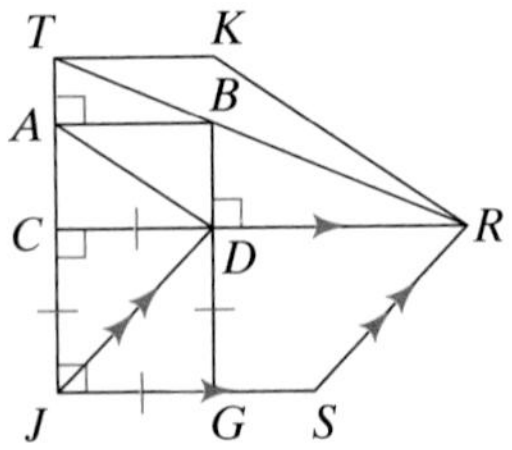

15. Name all the types of figures you see in the diagram at the left. Give an example of each. See back of book.

Exercise 15

Name all quadrilaterals that have each of these properties.

16. exactly one pair of parallel sides trapezoid
17. four right angles rectangle, square
18. four congruent sides rhombus, square
19. opposite angles congruent parallelogram, rhombus, rectangle, square

You can turn around *if-then* statements. This sometimes changes the meaning of a statement. Rewrite each of the following statements and determine if the result is still a true statement. 20–22. See left.

SAMPLE If a quadrilateral is a rhombus, then it is a parallelogram.

If a quadrilateral is a parallelogram, then it is a rhombus. This statement is not always true.

20. If a quadrilateral is a parallelogram, then it has two pairs of opposite sides that are parallel.
21. If a rectangle has four congruent sides, then it is a square.
22. If a triangle is equilateral, then it is an isosceles triangle.

20. If a quadrilateral has two pairs of opposite sides that are parallel, then it is a parallelogram; true.
21. If a rectangle is a square, then it has four congruent sides; true.
22. If a triangle is isosceles, then it is equilateral; not true.

GPS Use the Guided Problem Solving worksheet with Exercise 24.

7. parallelogram; both pairs of opposite sides parallel
8. rectangle; four right angles
9. rhombus; four congruent sides and two pairs of parallel sides
10. square; four right angles and four congruent sides
11. 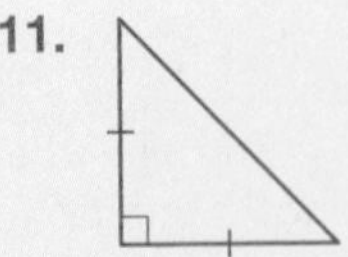
12. 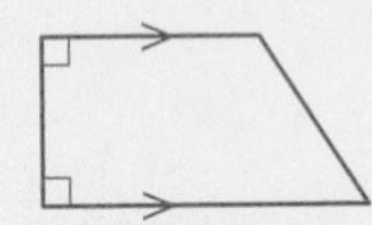

25. A square has four right angles like a rectangle and four congruent sides like a rhombus.

Challenge

23. **Data File, p. 405** Classify each sail as a type of triangle by its sides. all scalene triangles

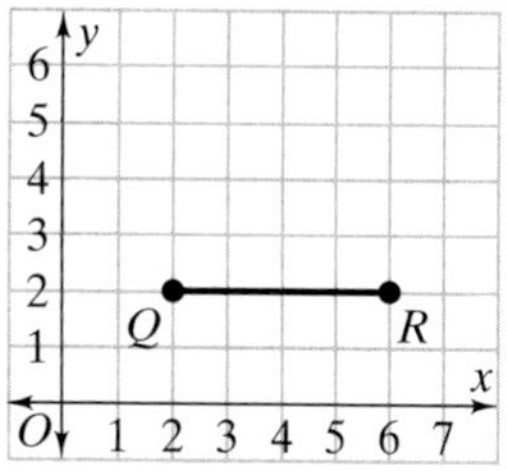

24. The coordinates of three vertices of a parallelogram are $(3, 5)$, $(8, 5)$, and $(1, -1)$. Find the coordinates for a fourth vertex. $(6, -1)$, $(-4, -1)$, or $(10, 11)$

25. **Writing in Math** Explain why a square is a rectangle and a rhombus. See left.

26. Draw a Venn diagram showing the relationships of quadrilaterals. See back of book.

27. Name the coordinates of P in the diagram at the left so that PQR fits each triangle description. 27a–c. Answers may vary. Samples are given.

a. isosceles obtuse (4, 3) b. scalene acute (5, 5) c. isosceles right (2, 6)

28. **Algebra** Equilateral triangles have congruent angles. Write and solve an equation to find the measure of an angle of an equilateral triangle. See left.

29. **Stretch Your Thinking** How does the area of one of the small triangles compare to the area of the large triangle at the right? The area of the small triangle is $\frac{1}{16}$ the area of the large triangle.

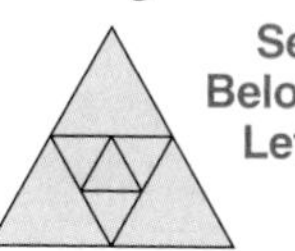

See Below Left.

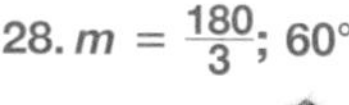

28. $m = \frac{180}{3}$; 60°

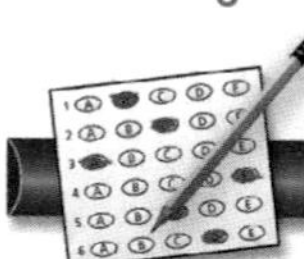

Test Prep

Multiple Choice

Take It to the NET
Online lesson quiz at **www.PHSchool.com**
Web Code: aca-0805

30. Which of the polygons listed CANNOT have four right angles? D
   A. rectangle B. rhombus C. square D. trapezoid

31. Which of the following statements is true? G
   F. All rectangles are squares.
   G. All squares are rhombuses.
   H. All parallelograms are rectangles.
   I. All trapezoids are isosceles.

32. Which triangle can have a 90° angle and two congruent sides? C
   A. obtuse B. scalene C. isosceles D. acute

Short Response

33. **(a)** Draw a parallelogram with four congruent sides but without a right angle. **(b)** What is another name for the figure? See margin.

Mixed Review

Lesson 7-3 **Simplify each expression.**

34. 5^{-3} $\frac{1}{125}$ 35. a^{-1} $\frac{1}{a}$ 36. $(-12)^0$ 1 37. b^0 1

Lesson 6-5 **Find each percent of change. Round to the nearest tenth of a percent. Label your answer *increase* or *decrease*.**

38. 500 to 450 10% decrease
39. 11 to 18 63.6% increase
40. 9.95 to 6.65 33.2% decrease
41. 12 to 13.52 12.7% increase
42. 85 to 7 91.8% decrease
43. 0.5 to 0.55 10% increase

Lesson 6-3

44. **Wedding** Suppose 86% of the people invited to a wedding attended. If 92 people went to the wedding, how many people were invited? 107 people

4. Assess

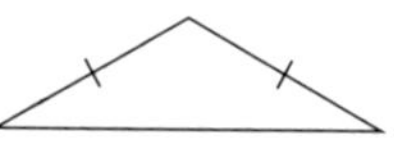

Lesson Quiz 8-5

1. Classify the triangle according to its angles and sides.

obtuse isosceles triangle

2. Determine the best name for the quadrilateral.

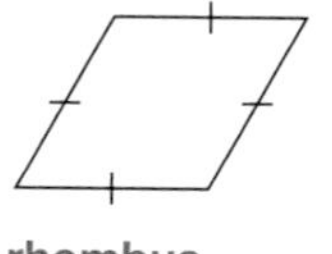

rhombus

Test Prep

Resources
For additional practice with a variety of test item formats:
- Test Prep, p. 465
- Test-Taking Strategies, p. 461
- Test-Taking Strategies with Transparencies

Exercise 33 Suggest that students draw the described figure.

33. [2] a.

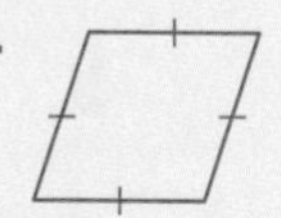

b. rhombus
[1] minor error in drawing OR incorrect name

13.

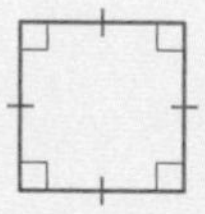

14.

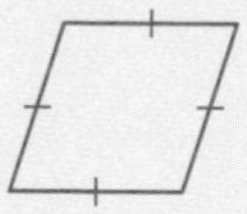

Alternative Assessment

One student in a small group draws a quadrilateral or triangle but does not show it to anyone. Other students in the group take turns asking about its characteristics. The first student who guesses the correct name of the figure draws the next figure.

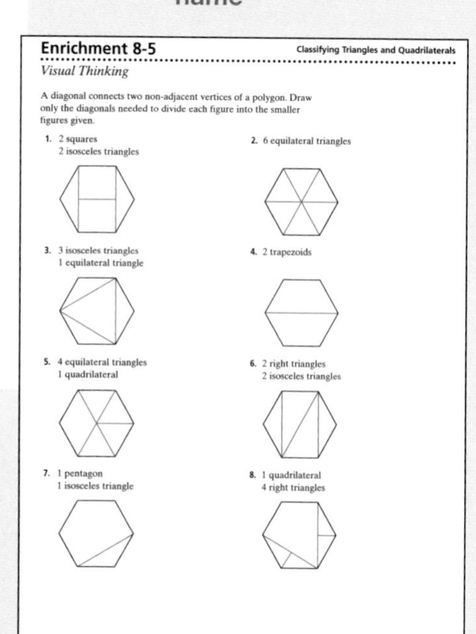

Enrichment 8-5 Classifying Triangles and Quadrilaterals
Visual Thinking

A diagonal connects two non-adjacent vertices of a polygon. Draw only the diagonals needed to divide each figure into the smaller figures given.

1. 2 squares, 2 isosceles triangles
2. 6 equilateral triangles
3. 3 isosceles triangles, 1 equilateral triangle
4. 2 trapezoids
5. 4 equilateral triangles, 1 quadrilateral
6. 2 right triangles, 2 isosceles triangles
7. 1 pentagon, 1 isosceles triangle
8. 1 quadrilateral, 4 right triangles

Connecting Ideas With Concept Maps

Graphic organizers provide visual representations of knowledge organized into patterns. They are valuable teaching tools that get students actively involved in their learning and help them to develop their critical-thinking skills. A concept map is a graphic organizer that shows the relationship between a main concept and supporting details. It is particularly useful for instruction in mathematics vocabulary, which is how it is used in Exercise 2.

Optional Materials

- Classroom Aid 1

Teaching Notes

Discuss with students what a concept map is and how they can use one to help them focus on, understand, and remember math ideas. Then go over the sample concept map in the Example on rules for working with exponents. Guide students to see the links between the main concept within the center rectangle and the supporting concepts within the ovals around it, linked to it by line segments.

English Learners
Graphic organizers are particularly helpful to English language learners. Have students work in small groups to discuss the concept map in the Example and to complete the exercises. You may wish to modify the map to meet the language needs of your students.

Exercises
Check students' maps. Invite volunteers to display their maps and to explain the choices they made. Invite students to suggest other kinds of graphic organizers they could use for the same purpose.

Connecting Ideas With Concept Maps

For Use With Lesson 8-5

Concept maps are visual tools that can help you relate different ideas and terms you have learned. Connecting new knowledge to existing knowledge is important in understanding mathematics.

To build a concept map, follow these steps:

- Place each concept or term inside a geometric shape.
- Draw lines connecting the concepts or terms that are related.

EXAMPLE

In Chapter 7, you learned about exponents and the rules for working with them. You can connect these ideas with the concept map below.

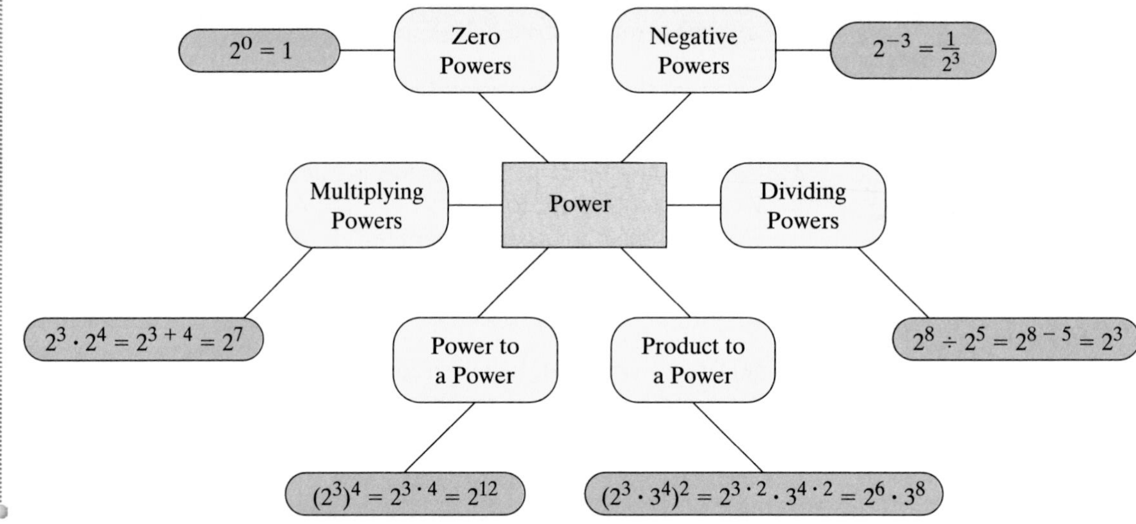

EXERCISES

1–2. See back of book.

1. Put the following properties from Chapter 2 in a concept map.

Properties of Equations	$6 = 3(2)$, so $6 - 4 = (3)(2) - 4$
Addition Property of Equality	$12 = 4(3)$, so $\frac{12}{2} = \frac{4(3)}{2}$
Subtraction Property of Equality	$6 = 3(2)$, so $6 + 4 = (3)(2) + 4$
Multiplication Property of Equality	$4 = \frac{12}{3}$, so $3(4) = 3\left(\frac{12}{3}\right)$
Division Property of Equality	

2. Use the terms from Lesson 8-5 that are related to different quadrilaterals. Make a concept map showing the relationships among the terms.

Investigation Sum of the Angles of a Polygon

For Use With Lesson 8-6

What is the sum of the measures of the angles of a polygon shaped like a STOP sign? You can find the answer by drawing diagonals from one vertex of the polygon.

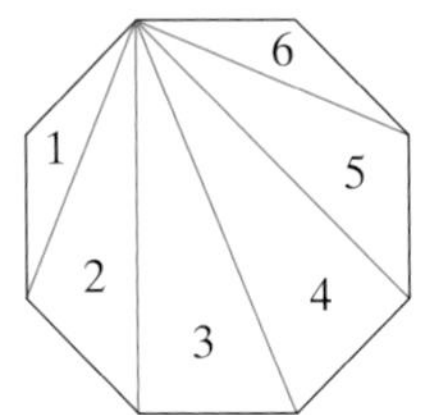

The diagonals form six triangles. The sum of the measures of all the angles of a triangle is 180°. The sum of the angles for a STOP sign is $6 \times 180° = 1{,}080°$.

Activity

You can develop a formula for finding the sum of the angles of a polygon.

1. Draw polygons with 4, 5, 6, and 7 sides. Then draw all the diagonals from one vertex of each figure. Count the number of triangles formed. Check students work.
2. Copy and complete the table below. See margin.

Number of Sides	Number of Triangles Formed	Sum of All Angle Measures
3	1	180°
■	■	■
■	■	■
■	■	■
■	■	■

3. a. **Patterns** Describe how the sum of the angle measures changes as the number of sides of a polygon increases by 1. The sum increases by 180°.
   b. **Reasoning** What relationship do you notice between the number of sides of a polygon and the number of triangles formed? Explain. 3b. The number of triangles is two less than the number of sides.
4. **Algebra** Write an expression for the sum of the angle measures of a polygon with n sides. $180(n - 2)$
5. a. An *exterior angle of a polygon* is an angle formed by a side and an extension of an adjacent side. ∠1, ∠2, ∠3, and ∠4 at the right are exterior angles of a polygon. Draw polygons with 3, 4, 5, and 6 sides. Then draw and measure the exterior angles of each polygon. 5a. Check students work.
   b. Find the sum of the measures of the exterior angles of each polygon. Record your information in a table. See margin.
   c. Make a conjecture about the sum of the exterior angles of a polygon. The sum of the exterior angles of a polygon is 360°.

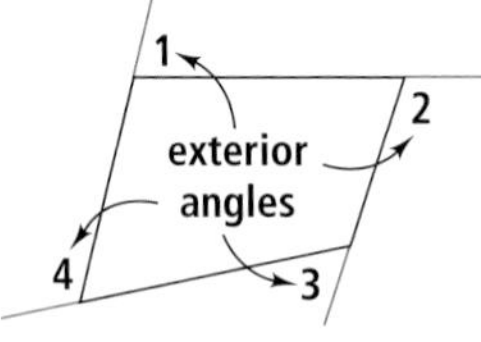

2.

Number of Sides	Number of Triangles Formed	Sum of All Angle Measures
3	1	180°
4	2	360°
5	3	540°
6	4	720°
7	5	900°

5b.

Number of Sides	Sum of Angles
3	360°
4	360°
5	360°
6	360°

Investigation

Sum of the Angles of a Polygon

In Lesson 8-6, students will apply a formula to find the angle measures of polygons. In this feature, they develop that formula through an activity.

Optional Materials

- straightedge
- protractor
- Classroom Aid 5

Teaching Notes

English Learners
Review the names and attributes of polygons, from triangles through nonagons. Also review the meanings of *diagonal* and *vertex*.

Teaching Tip
Invite a volunteer to use a straightedge to draw a hexagon. Then use a protractor to find the sum of the measures of all six angles. Compare findings with those obtained using the formula.

When students work on their tables, point out this easy way to multiply by 180: multiply by 9, double the result, write a zero to the right of the last digit.

Inclusion
After students have completed their drawings and tables, ask:

- *How many diagonals can you draw from one vertex of any quadrilateral?* 1
- *Of any pentagon?* 2
- *Of any hexagon?* 3
- *How many diagonals can you draw from a vertex of a 10-sided figure?* 7
- *A 20-sided figure?* 17
- *An n-sided figure?* $n - 3$

8-6

1. Plan

Lesson Preview

PowerPoint

Check Skills You'll Need

Solving One-Step Equations
Lesson 2-1: Examples 1–4. Extra Practice, p. 703.

Lesson Resources

Teaching Resources
Practice, Reteaching, Enrichment

Reaching All Students
Practice Workbook 8-6
Spanish Practice Workbook 8-6
Guided Problem Solving 8-6
Hands-On Activities 28–29

Presentation Assistant Plus!
Transparencies
- Check Skills You'll Need 8-6
- Problem of the Day 8-6
- Additional Examples 8-6
- Student Edition Answers 8-6
- Lesson Quiz 8-6
- Classroom Aid 1, 11, 20–21

PH Presentation Pro CD-ROM 8-6

Computer Test Generator CD

Technology
Resource Pro® CD-ROM
Computer Test Generator CD
PH Presentation Pro CD-ROM

www.PHSchool.com
Student Site
- Teacher Web Code: ack-5500
- Self-grading Lesson Quiz

PH SuccessNet Teacher Center
- Lesson Planner
- Resources

Plus iTEXT

8-6 Angles and Polygons

What You'll Learn

To find the angle measures of a polygon

. . . And Why

To use polygons in architecture, as in Example 3

Check Skills You'll Need

For help, go to Lesson 2-1.

Solve each equation.

1. $120 = 67 + a$ 53 **2.** $t - 35 = 14$ 49 **3.** $3r = -27$ −9

4. $\frac{x}{-6} = 11$ −66 **5.** $-42 + p = -8$ 34 **6.** $39 = 13y$ 3

New Vocabulary
- regular polygon

iTEXT Interactive lesson includes instant self-check, tutorials, and activities.

OBJECTIVE 1

Finding the Angle Measures of a Polygon

Here is a list of common polygons.

Polygon Name	Number of Sides	Polygon Name	Number of Sides
Triangle	3	Octagon	8
Quadrilateral	4	Nonagon	9
Pentagon	5	Decagon	10
Hexagon	6	Dodecagon	12
Heptagon	7		

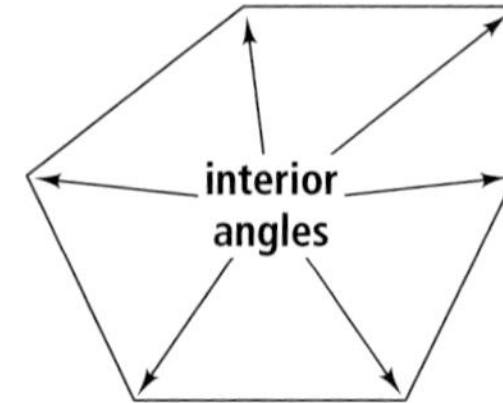

Interior angles are the angles inside a polygon at its vertices. You can find the sum of the measures of interior angles by using the number of sides of a polygon.

Key Concepts — Polygon Angle Sum

For a polygon with n sides, the sum of the measures of the interior angles is $(n - 2)180°$.

1 EXAMPLE The Sum of Angle Measures of a Polygon

Find the sum of the measures of the interior angles of a nonagon.

A nonagon has 9 sides.

$(n - 2)180° = (9 - 2)180°$ ← Substitute 9 for n.

$= 1{,}260°$ ← Simplify.

Check Understanding 1 Find the sum of the measures of the interior angles of a heptagon.
900°

Ongoing Assessment and Intervention

Before the Lesson
Diagnose prerequisite skills using:
- Check Skills You'll Need

During the Lesson
Monitor progress using:
- Check Understanding
- Additional Examples
- Test Prep

After the Lesson
Assess knowledge using:
- Lesson Quiz
- Computer Test Generator CD

You can find missing angle measures of a polygon.

2 EXAMPLE Angle Measures of a Polygon

Algebra Find the missing angle measure in the pentagon at the left.

Step 1 Find the sum of the measures of the interior angles of a pentagon.

$(n - 2)180° = (5 - 2)180°$ ← **Substitute 5 for *n*.**

$= 540°$ ← **Simplify.**

Step 2 Write an equation.

Let x = the missing angle measure.

$540° = 90° + 75° + 130° + 135° + x°$ ← **Write an equation.**

$540° = 430° + x°$ ← **Add.**

$110° = x°$ ← **Subtract 430° from each side.**

The missing angle measure is 110°.

Check Understanding 2 **a.** Find the missing angle measure in the figure at the right. 151°

b. Reasoning What is the name of the polygon at the right? hexagon

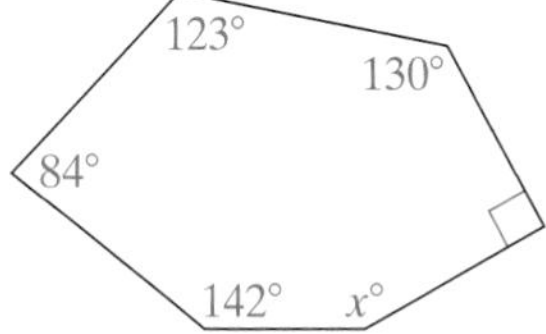

A **regular polygon** is a polygon with all the sides congruent and all the angles congruent.

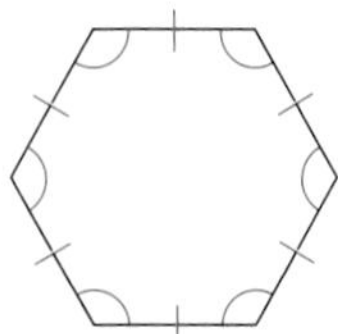

You can find the measure of each angle of a regular polygon by dividing the sum of the angle measures by the number of angles.

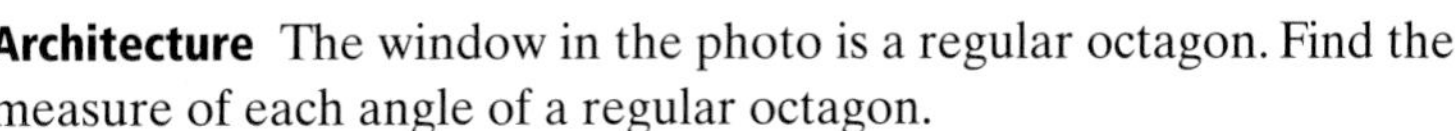

3 EXAMPLE Angle Measures of a Regular Polygon

Architecture The window in the photo is a regular octagon. Find the measure of each angle of a regular octagon.

Find the sum of the measures of the interior angles of the octagon.

$(n - 2)180° = (8 - 2)180°$ ← **Substitute 8 for *n*.**

$= 1{,}080°$ ← **Simplify.**

$1{,}080° \div 8 = 135°$ ← **Divide the sum by the number of angles.**

Each angle of a regular octagon has a measure of 135°.

Check Understanding 3 Find the measure of each angle of a regular polygon with the given number of sides.

a. 5 sides 108° **b.** 10 sides 144° **c.** 9 sides 140°

d. Reasoning What is another name for a regular quadrilateral? square

Reaching All Students

Below Level Have students make posters that show and name polygons with various numbers of sides.	Advanced Learners Have students use a compass and straightedge to construct a regular hexagon within a circle.	English Learners See note on page 437. Error Prevention See notes on pages 437 and 438.

2. Teach

Math Background

A polygon has an interior angle at each vertex. The sum of the measures of all the interior angles of a polygon with n sides is $(n - 2)(180°)$. A *regular polygon* has all sides congruent and all angles congruent, so the measure of each of its angles is $\frac{(n-2)(180°)}{n}$.

Teaching Notes

1 EXAMPLE Teaching Tip

Ask:

- *Is this formula the same if you write it as 180°(n − 2)?* yes
- *This is an example of what property?* Commutative Property of Multiplication

2 EXAMPLE English Learners

Ask students to write words, both in other languages and in English, that relate to the prefixes *tri-*, *quad-*, *hex-*, *oct-*, *non-*, and *dec-*.

3 EXAMPLE Error Prevention!

Caution students to divide by n and not by $n - 2$.

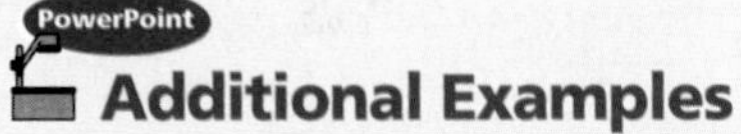

Additional Examples

1 Find the sum of the measures of the interior angles of an octagon. 1,080°

2 Find the missing angle measure in the hexagon. 122°

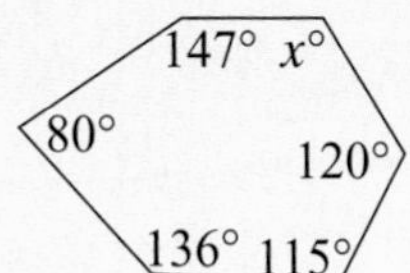

3 A design on a tile is in the shape of a regular nonagon. Find the measure of each angle. 140°

Closure

How do you find the interior angle measures of a polygon? Sample: To find the sum for a polygon of n sides, use $(n - 2)180°$. To find each angle in a regular polygon of n sides, divide the sum by n.

3. Practice

Assignment Guide

Objective 1

- A B Core 1–24
- C Extension 25–27

Test Prep 28–31
Mixed Review 32–41

Error Prevention!

Exercises 10–13 You cannot assume that an octagon, for example, is regular unless it is so stated in the problem.

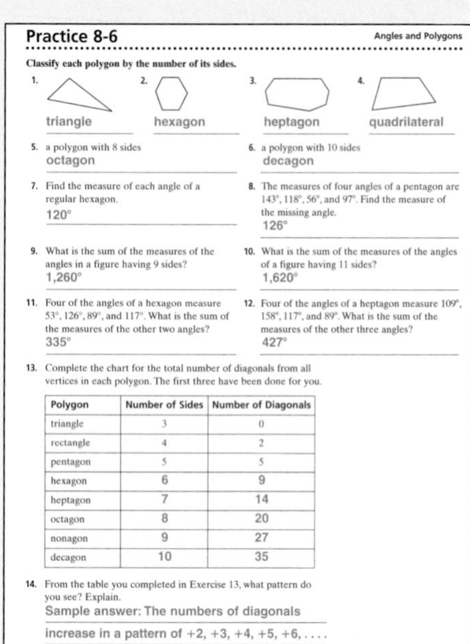

Practice 8-6 — Angles and Polygons

Classify each polygon by the number of its sides.

1. triangle
2. hexagon
3. heptagon
4. quadrilateral

5. a polygon with 8 sides
octagon

6. a polygon with 10 sides
decagon

7. Find the measure of each angle of a regular hexagon.
120°

8. The measures of four angles of a pentagon are 143°, 118°, 56°, and 97°. Find the measure of the missing angle.
126°

9. What is the sum of the measures of the angles in a figure having 9 sides?
1,260°

10. What is the sum of the measures of the angles of a figure having 11 sides?
1,620°

11. Four of the angles of a hexagon measure 53°, 126°, 89°, and 117°. What is the sum of the measures of the other two angles?
335°

12. Four of the angles of a heptagon measure 109°, 158°, 117°, and 89°. What is the sum of the measures of the other three angles?
427°

13. Complete the chart for the total number of diagonals from all vertices in each polygon. The first three have been done for you.

Polygon	Number of Sides	Number of Diagonals
triangle	3	0
rectangle	4	2
pentagon	5	5
hexagon	6	9
heptagon	7	14
octagon	8	20
nonagon	9	27
decagon	10	35

14. From the table you completed in Exercise 13, what pattern do you see? Explain.
Sample answer: The numbers of diagonals increase in a pattern of +2, +3, +4, +5, +6, ...

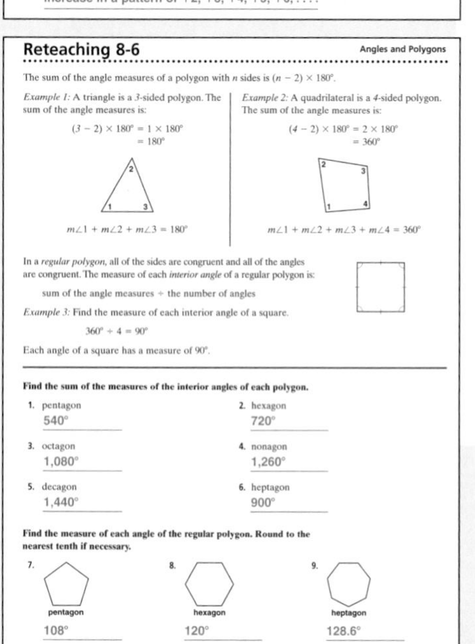

Reteaching 8-6 — Angles and Polygons

The sum of the angle measures of a polygon with n sides is $(n - 2) \times 180°$.

Example 1: A triangle is a 3-sided polygon. The sum of the angle measures is:

$(3 - 2) \times 180° = 1 \times 180° = 180°$

$m\angle 1 + m\angle 2 + m\angle 3 = 180°$

Example 2: A quadrilateral is a 4-sided polygon. The sum of the angle measures is:

$(4 - 2) \times 180° = 2 \times 180° = 360°$

$m\angle 1 + m\angle 2 + m\angle 3 + m\angle 4 = 360°$

In a *regular polygon,* all of the sides are congruent and all of the angles are congruent. The measure of each *interior angle* of a regular polygon is:

sum of the angle measures ÷ the number of angles

Example 3: Find the measure of each interior angle of a square.

$360° \div 4 = 90°$

Each angle of a square has a measure of 90°.

Find the sum of the measures of the interior angles of each polygon.

1. pentagon 540°
2. hexagon 720°
3. octagon 1,080°
4. nonagon 1,260°
5. decagon 1,440°
6. heptagon 900°

Find the measure of each angle of the regular polygon. Round to the nearest tenth if necessary.

7. pentagon 108°
8. hexagon 120°
9. heptagon 128.6°

EXERCISES

For more practice, see *Extra Practice.*

A Practice by Example

Example 1 (page 436)

Find the sum of the measures of the interior angles of each polygon. Exercise 1 has been started for you.

1. quadrilateral 360°
$(n - 2)180° = (4 - 2)180°$
2. octagon 1,080°
3. decagon 1,440°
4. hexagon 720°
5. triangle 180°
6. dodecagon 1,800°

Example 2 (page 437)

Algebra **Find the missing angle measure in each figure.**

7. 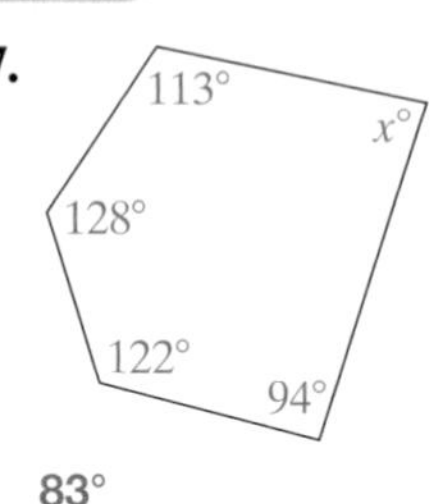

83°

8. 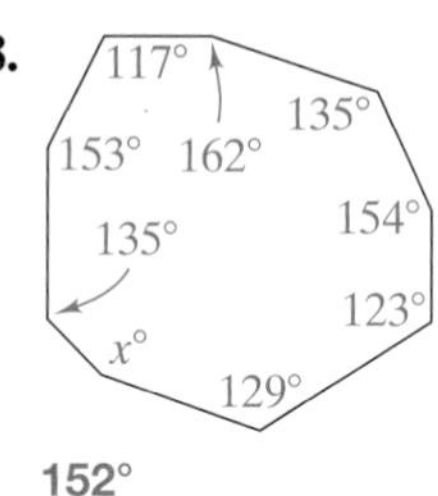

152°

9. 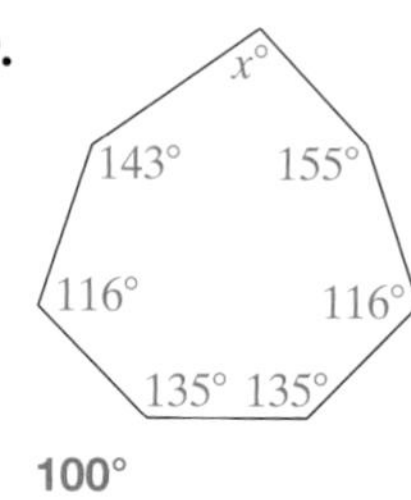

100°

Example 3 (page 437)

Find the measure of each angle of a regular polygon with the given number of sides.

10. 6 sides 120°
11. 18 sides 160°
12. 12 sides 150°
13. 15 sides 156°

B Apply Your Skills

Classify each polygon by the number of its sides.

14. 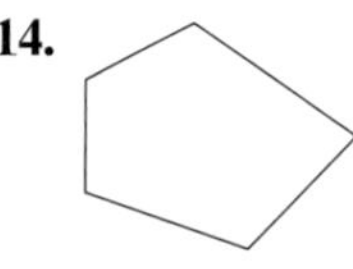 pentagon
15. 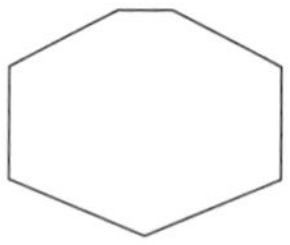 heptagon
16. 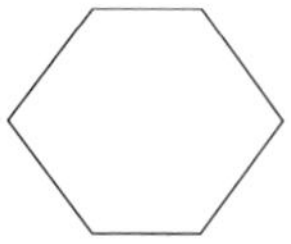 hexagon
17. 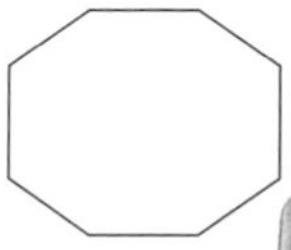  octagon

18. **Error Analysis** Jason knows the sum of angle measures of a hexagon is 720°. Since $12 = 2 \cdot 6$, he multiplies 720 by 2 to find the sum of the angle measures of a dodecagon. What is wrong with Jason's method? See left.

18. Answers may vary. Sample: The sum of the angle measures of a dodecagon is $(12 - 2)180°$, not $(6 - 2)180° \cdot 2$.

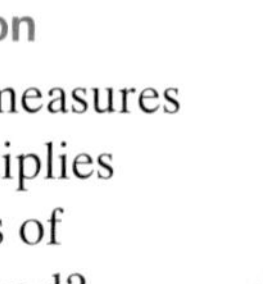

19. **Sports** In the diagram of the home plate at the right, $\angle 1 \cong \angle 2$. Find $m\angle 1$. 135°

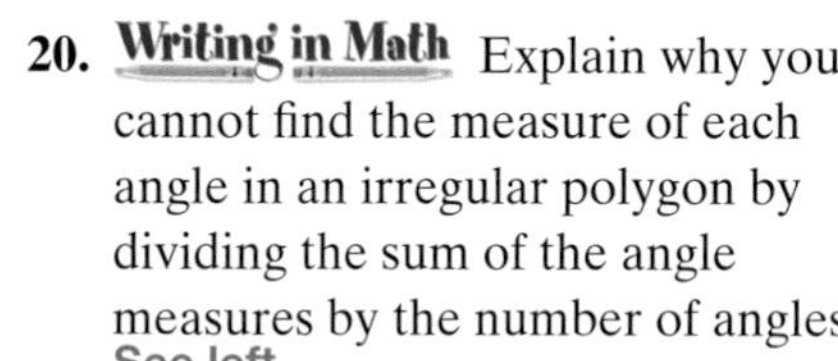

20. **Writing in Math** Explain why you cannot find the measure of each angle in an irregular polygon by dividing the sum of the angle measures by the number of angles. See left.

Reading Math

The prefix *ir* means "not." An irregular polygon is a polygon that is *not* regular.

20. The angles in an irregular polygon are not all congruent.

21. The measures of six angles of a heptagon are 145°, 115°, 152°, 87°, 90°, and 150°. Find the measure of the seventh angle. 161°

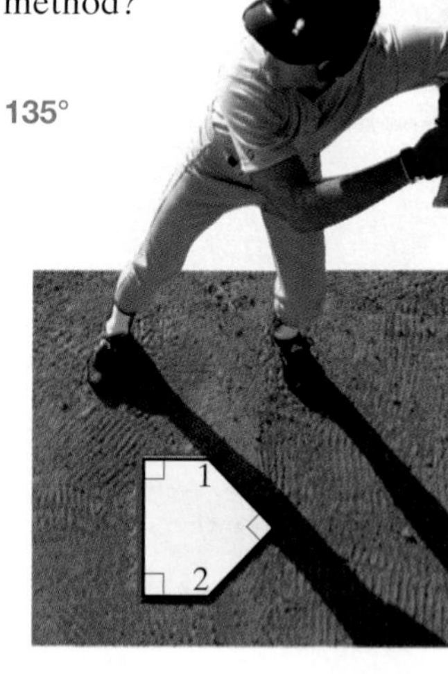

Use the Guided Problem Solving worksheet with Exercise 21.

22. $n° = 135°$

23. $a° = 105°$; $b° = 106°$

24. $x° = 86°$; $(x + 11)° = 97°$; $(x - 13)° = 73°$

Choose a Method **Use a calculator, paper and pencil, or mental math to find the missing measures.** 22–24. See left.

22.

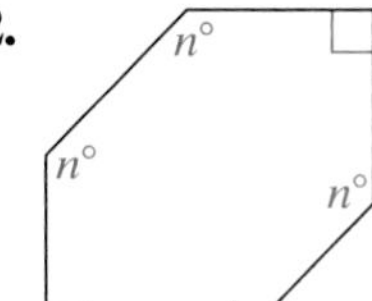

23.

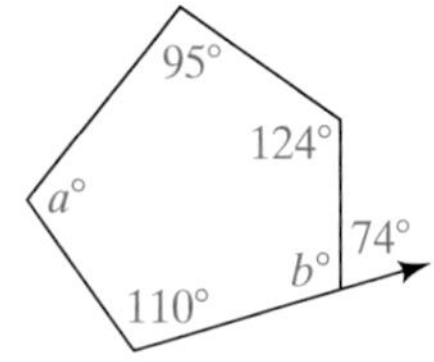

24.

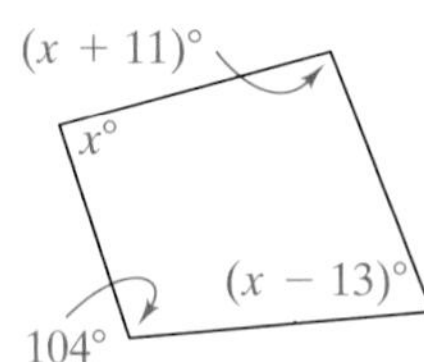

C Challenge

25. $\frac{3}{5}$, or 60%

25. Probability A polygon is chosen at random from five regular polygons with 3, 4, 5, 6, and 8 sides. What is the probability that the measure of an angle of the polygon she picks is a multiple of 30?

26. Algebra The sum of the angle measures of a pentagon is $4x - 65$. Write and solve an equation to find the value of x. $4x - 65 = 3(180)$; 151.25

27. Stretch Your Thinking Each edge of a cube is increased by 50%. What is the percent of increase of the surface area of the cube? 125%

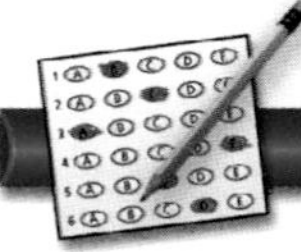

Test Prep

Multiple Choice

28. Which variable expression represents the measure of each angle of a regular polygon with n sides? D

A. $180°(n + 2)$ **B.** $180°(n - 2)$ **C.** $\frac{180°(n + 2)}{n}$ **D.** $\frac{180°(n - 2)}{n}$

Take It to the NET
Online lesson quiz at **www.PHSchool.com**
Web Code: aca-0806

29. An Australian 50-cent coin has 12 sides. What is the sum of the measures of the interior angles of the coin? G

F. 1,440° **G.** 1,800° **H.** 2,160° **I.** 2,520°

30. Which is NOT a possible angle measure of a regular polygon? B

A. 108° **B.** 130° **C.** 144° **D.** 150°

Short Response

31. The sum of the measures of the interior angles of a polygon is 1,800°. How many sides does the polygon have? Explain in words.
See margin.

Mixed Review

Lesson 8-5 **Name all quadrilaterals that have each property.**

32. two pairs of parallel sides parallelogram, rectangle, rhombus, square

33. four congruent angles rectangle, square

Lesson 8-1 **Find the measure of the supplement of each angle.**

34. 65° 115° **35.** 48° 132° **36.** 127° 53° **37.** 153° 27°

Lesson 7-6 **Write the decimal value of each binary number.**

38. 10_2 2 **39.** 110_2 6 **40.** 1011_2 11 **41.** 10001_2 17

31. [2] The polygon has 12 sides. Using the polygon angle sum formula, $(n - 2)180 = 1,800$. Divide each side of the equation by 180 to get $n - 2 = 10$. Add 2 to each side to get $n = 12$.

[1] minor computational error OR correct answer without explanation

4. Assess

Lesson Quiz 8-6

1. Find the sum of the measures of the interior angles of a polygon having 17 sides. 2,700°
2. Five angles of a hexagon measure 128°, 190°, 112°, 154°, and 90°. Find the measure of the missing angle. 46°
3. Find the measure of each angle of a regular polygon having 24 sides. 165°

Alternative Assessment

Nine angles of a decagon measure 150° each. Have students determine the measure of the missing angle. 90°

Test Prep

Resources

For additional practice with a variety of test item formats:

- Test Prep, p. 465
- Test-Taking Strategies, p. 461
- Test-Taking Strategies with Transparencies

Exercise 30 Suggest that students make a table of sides and angle measures that range from 60° to at least 150° to see which angle measure is not included.

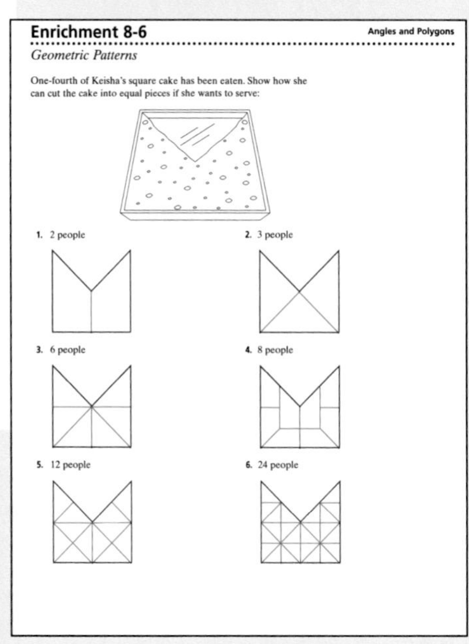

Enrichment 8-6 Angles and Polygons

Geometric Patterns

One-fourth of Keisha's square cake has been eaten. Show how she can cut the cake into equal pieces if she wants to serve:

1. 2 people
2. 3 people
3. 6 people
4. 8 people
5. 12 people
6. 24 people

Extension

Tessellations

This extension to Lesson 8-6 introduces students to tessellations, which are repeated arrangements of congruent polygonal regions that cover a plane with no gaps or overlaps.

Optional Materials

- graph paper
- scissors
- ruler
- Classroom Aid 2

Teaching Notes

Teaching Tip
Tell students that the term *tessellation* comes from the Latin word *tessella*, which is a small, square tile used in Roman mosaics. Show them examples of Escher's work, if available. Have students examine the drawings and try to identify the repeating patterns. Point out that a tessellation is called a *regular tessellation* if it is constructed solely of copies of regular polygons.

Tactile Learners
Have students cut out equilateral triangles to make the tessellation shown in the Example. Ask them to use the correct terminology (rotation, translation, or reflection) to describe how they are making the tessellation.

Exercises
Students can work individually on the exercises. Elicit from them that congruent triangles, congruent quadrilaterals, and congruent hexagons will tessellate a plane. Point out the "honeycomb" pattern created by the tessellation of regular hexagons.

6. The measure of an angle of a regular pentagon is not a factor of 360°.

Extension Tessellations

For Use With Lesson 8-6

A *tessellation* is a repeating pattern of congruent shapes that completely cover a plane without gaps or overlaps. The Dutch artist M. C. Escher (1898–1972) was famous for using tessellations in his art. Many of his designs, like the one at the right, are based on polygons that tessellate.

You can create a tessellation by repeatedly translating, rotating, or reflecting a figure.

EXAMPLE

Show how the figure at the right can form a tessellation.

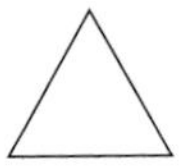

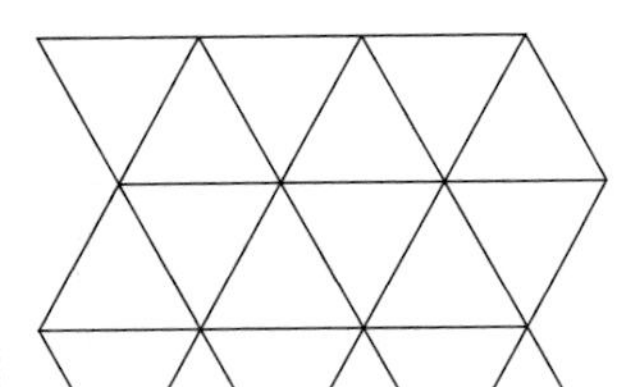

← Rotate, translate, and reflect the figure to cover the plane.

EXERCISES

Make multiple copies of each figure on graph paper. Determine whether each figure can form a tessellation. If it can, show the tessellation. 1–4. See margin.

1. 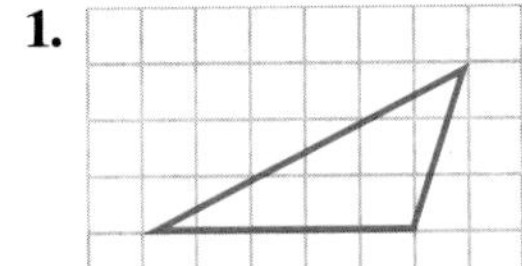
2. 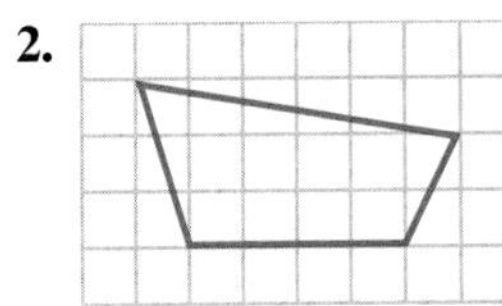
3. 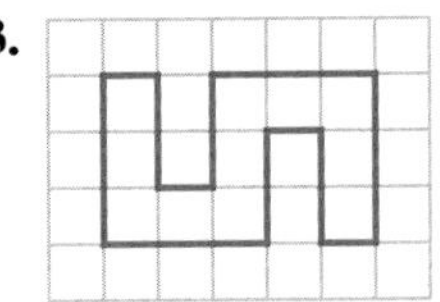
4. 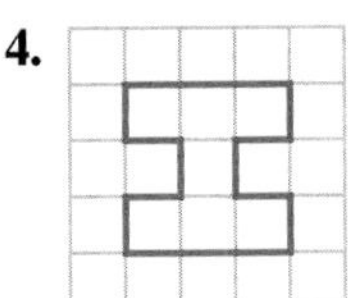

5. The diagrams below show how to create a repeating figure for a tessellation. Follow the steps shown to create your own tessellation. Check students' work.

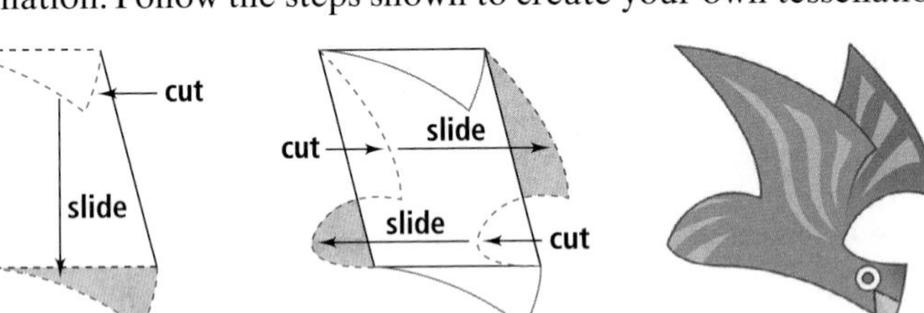

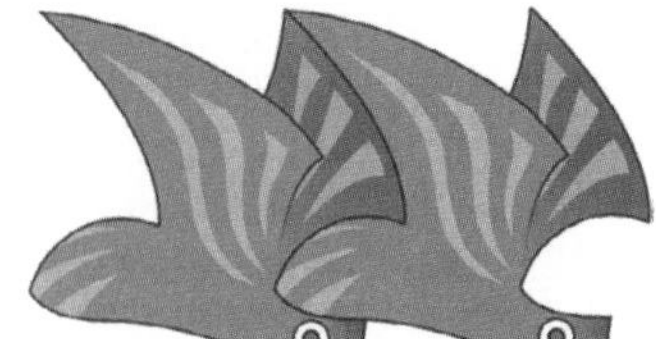

6. **Reasoning** You cannot form a tessellation with regular pentagons. Why? See margin.

7. **Open-Ended** Create and decorate a tessellation, starting with a square. Check students' work.

1. 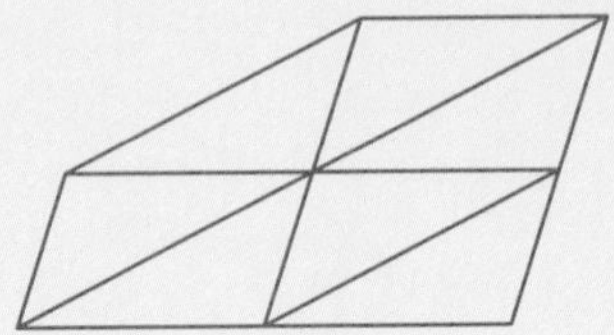

2. 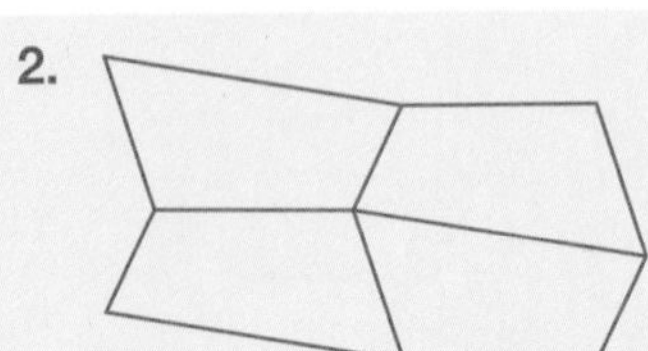

3. 

4. 

8-7 Areas of Polygons

What You'll Learn

To find the areas of polygons

. . . And Why

To calculate areas for a construction job, as in Example 2

Check Skills You'll Need

For help, go to Lesson 4-6.

Find the area of each figure.

1. 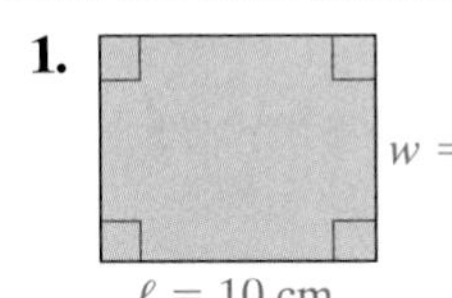

80 cm²

2. 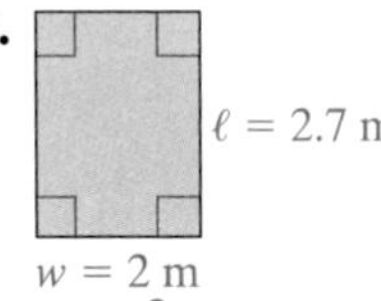

5.4 m²

3. s = 7 ft
49 ft²

New Vocabulary

• area

OBJECTIVE 1

Interactive lesson includes instant self-check, tutorials, and activities.

Finding the Areas of Polygons

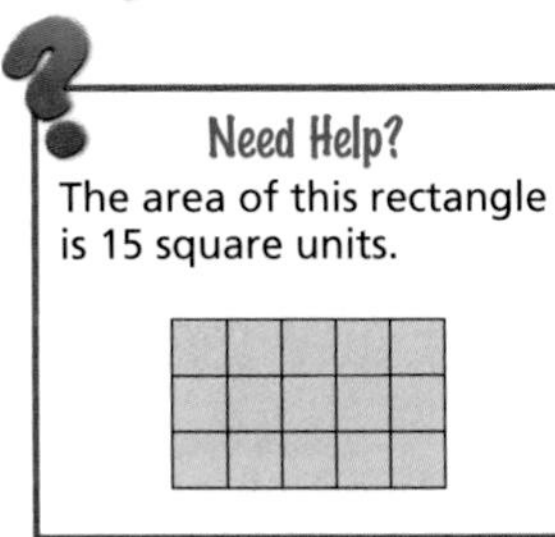

Need Help?
The area of this rectangle is 15 square units.

People who work in fields such as construction, crafts, and engineering use area to find the amounts of materials needed for a job. The **area** of a figure is the number of square units it encloses.

Recall that the formula for the area of a rectangle is $A = bh$, where b is the base and h is the height. The rectangle at the left has an area of 15 square units. The diagram below shows how a parallelogram can be rearranged to form a rectangle.

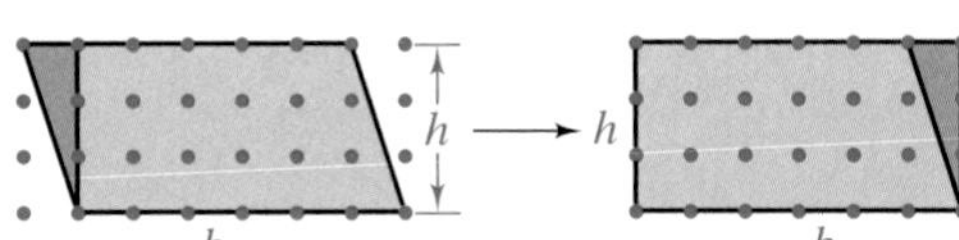

The formula for the area of a parallelogram is also $A = bh$. The height of a parallelogram is the perpendicular distance from one base to the other.

Key Concepts **Area of a Parallelogram**

The area of a parallelogram equals the product of any base length b and the corresponding height h.

$$A = bh$$

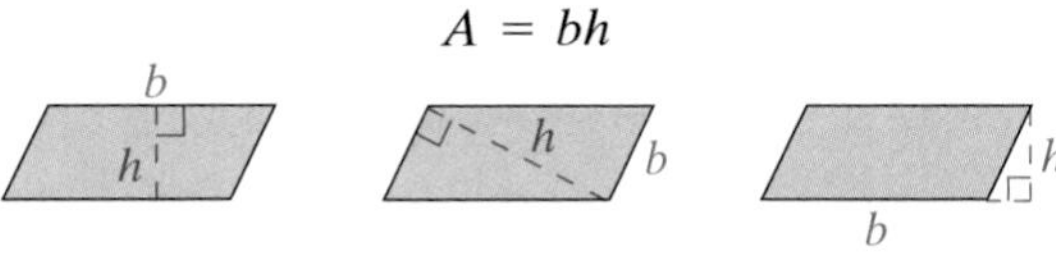

8-7

1. Plan

Lesson Preview

PowerPoint

Check Skills You'll Need
Using a Formula to Find Area
Lesson 4-6: Example 1.

Lesson Resources

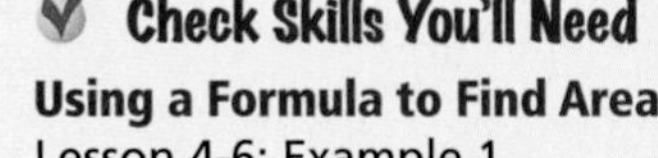

Teaching Resources
Practice, Reteaching, Enrichment

Reaching All Students
Practice Workbook 8-7
Spanish Practice Workbook 8-7
Guided Problem Solving 8-7
Hands-On Activities 32, 36

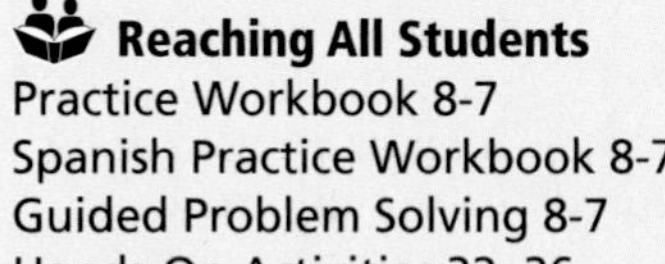

Presentation Assistant Plus!
Transparencies
- Check Skills You'll Need 8-7
- Problem of the Day 8-7
- Additional Examples 8-7
- Student Edition Answers 8-7
- Lesson Quiz 8-7

PH Presentation Pro CD-ROM 8-7

Computer Test Generator CD

Technology
Resource Pro® CD-ROM
Computer Test Generator CD
PH Presentation Pro CD-ROM

www.PHSchool.com
Student Site
- Teacher Web Code: ack-5500
- Self-grading Lesson Quiz

PH SuccessNet Teacher Center
- Lesson Planner
- Resources

Plus

Ongoing Assessment and Intervention

Before the Lesson
Diagnose prerequisite skills using:
- Check Skills You'll Need

During the Lesson
Monitor progress using:
- Check Understanding
- Additional Examples
- Test Prep

After the Lesson
Assess knowledge using:
- Lesson Quiz
- Computer Test Generator CD

2. Teach

Math Background

The area of a polygon is measured by finding the number of square units it encloses. For this reason, area is measured in square units, such as square inches (in.^{2}) or square meters (m^2).

To find the area of a rectangle or a parallelogram, use $A = bh$. For a triangle, use $A = \frac{1}{2}bh$. For a trapezoid, use $A = \frac{1}{2}h(b_1 + b_2)$.

Teaching Notes

Tactile Learners
Have students draw and cut out a parallelogram (that is not a rectangle). Then have them draw an altitude from one vertex perpendicular to the opposite side. Finally, have them cut off the triangle formed and move it to the other side, taping it in place to form a rectangle.

1 EXAMPLE Visual Learners
Have students work with a partner to draw a pair of parallel lines and measure the distance between the lines. Ask: *When you measure the distance, what angle is formed by the ruler and the lines?* a right angle

2 EXAMPLE Teaching Tip
Discuss the fact that every triangle has three heights, which may not be equal, but each specific height has a matching base. So no matter which pair of height, *h*, and matching base, *b*, you use, the area of a given triangle remains the same.

3 EXAMPLE Inclusion
Make sure that students understand the subscript, as in b_1 and b_2, names only two related variables and has no effect on the value of the variable. Contrast this to a superscript, as in b^2, which is an exponent and means $b \times b$.

1 EXAMPLE Finding the Area of a Parallelogram

Find the area of each parallelogram.

a.

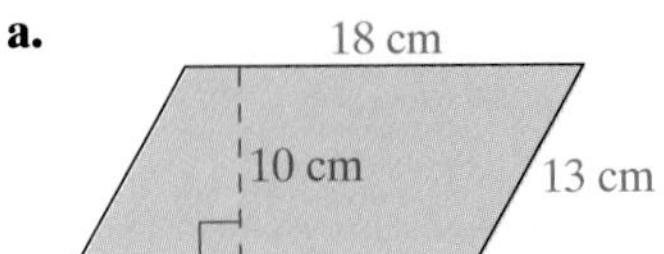

b.

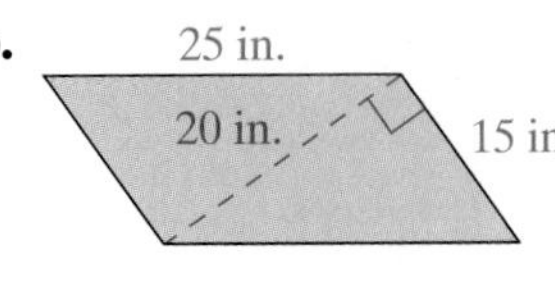

a.		b.
$A = bh$	← **Use the area of a parallelogram formula.** →	$A = bh$
$= (18)(10)$	← **Substitute for *b* and *h*.** →	$= (15)(20)$
$= 180$	← **Multiply.** →	$= 300$

✓ Check Understanding 1 Find the area of each parallelogram.

a.

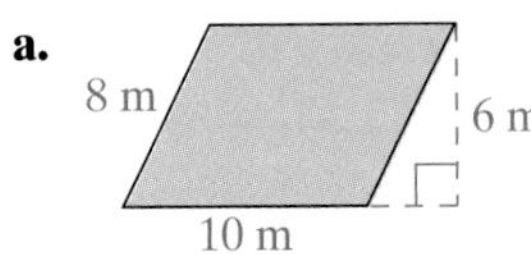

60 m^2

b.

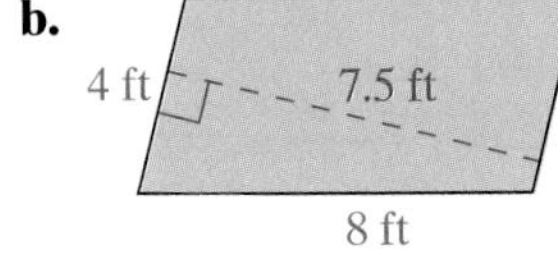

30 ft^2

A diagonal divides a parallelogram into two congruent triangles, as shown below. The area of each triangle is half the area of a parallelogram.

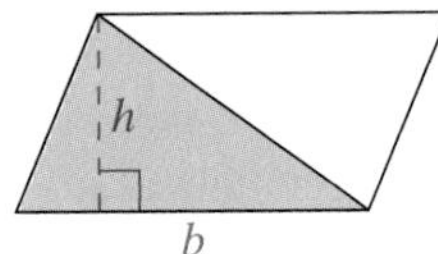

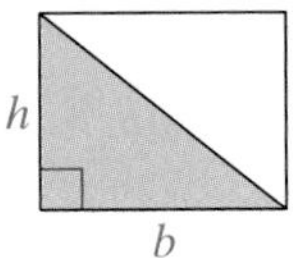

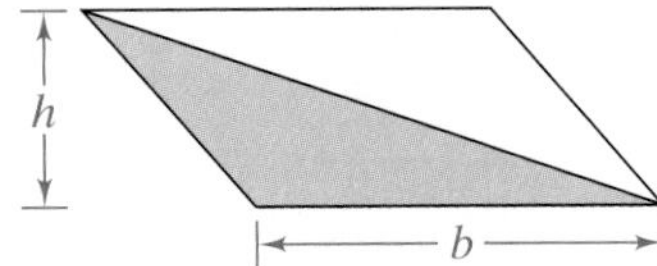

You can choose any side of a triangle to be the base. The height of a triangle is the perpendicular distance between the base and the vertex opposite the base.

Key Concepts — Area of a Triangle

The area of a triangle equals half the product of any base length *b* and the corresponding height *h*.

$$A = \frac{1}{2}bh$$

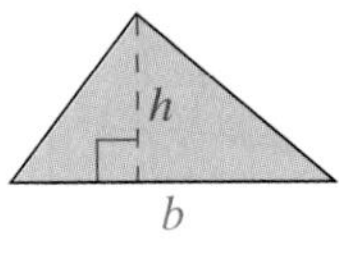

2 EXAMPLE Finding the Area of a Triangle

Construction A builder wants to cover the front triangular section of a townhouse with cedar shingles. Find the area of the triangle.

$A = \frac{1}{2}bh$ ← **Use the area of a triangle formula.**

$= \frac{1}{2} \cdot 24 \cdot 16$ ← **Substitute 24 for *b* and 16 for *h*.**

$= 192$ ← **Multiply.**

The area of the triangle is 192 ft^2.

Reaching All Students

Below Level Have students write any formulas they remember for finding the area of a rectangle and a square. Sample: $A = \ell w$; $A = bh$; $A = s^2$	**Advanced Learners** Ask students to develop a special formula for using the legs of a right triangle to find its area. Sample: $A = \frac{1}{2}(\text{leg}_1)(\text{leg}_2)$	**English Learners** See note on page 443. **Inclusion** See note on page 442.

Check Understanding 2 **a.** Find the area of the triangle at the right. **10.5 cm²**

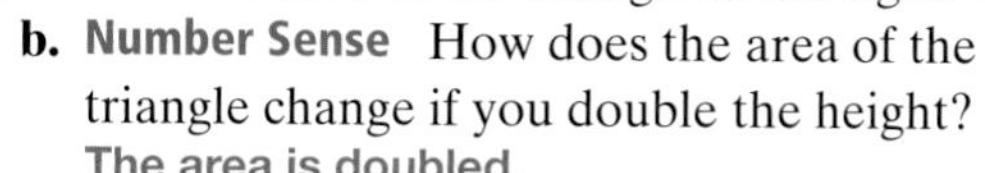

b. **Number Sense** How does the area of the triangle change if you double the height? **The area is doubled.**

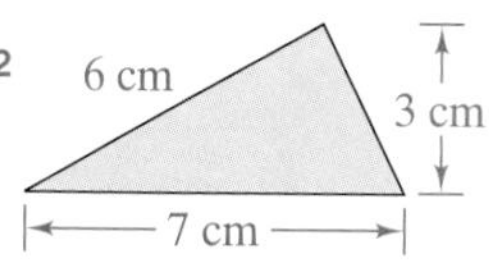

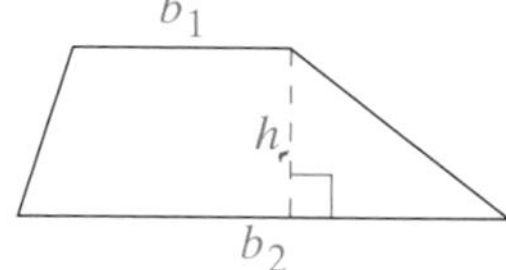

A trapezoid has two parallel sides, or bases, b_1 and b_2. The height h of a trapezoid is the perpendicular distance between the two bases.

You can arrange two congruent trapezoids to form a parallelogram.

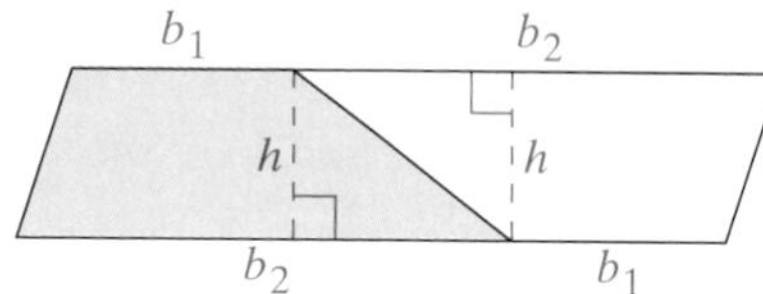

Area of parallelogram $= bh$ ← **Use the formula for the area of a parallelogram.**

$= (b_1 + b_2)h$ ← **Substitute for b and h. The base of the parallelogram is $b_1 + b_2$; the height is h.**

Area of trapezoid $= \frac{1}{2}(b_1 + b_2)h$ ← **The area of one of the trapezoids is half the area of the parallelogram.**

Key Concepts **Area of a Trapezoid**

The area of a trapezoid is one half the product of the height and the sum of the lengths of the bases.

$$A = \frac{1}{2}h(b_1 + b_2)$$

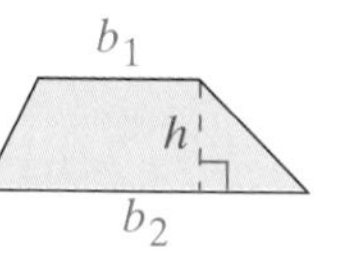

3 EXAMPLE Finding the Area of a Trapezoid

Find the area of the trapezoid at the right.

9 cm
3 cm
5 cm

$A = \frac{1}{2}h(b_1 + b_2)$ ← **Use the formula.**

$= \frac{1}{2}(3)(9 + 5)$ ← **Substitute 3 for h, 9 for b_1, and 5 for b_2.**

$= 21$ ← **Simplify.**

The area of the trapezoid is 21 cm².

Check Understanding 3 Find the area of each trapezoid.

a.

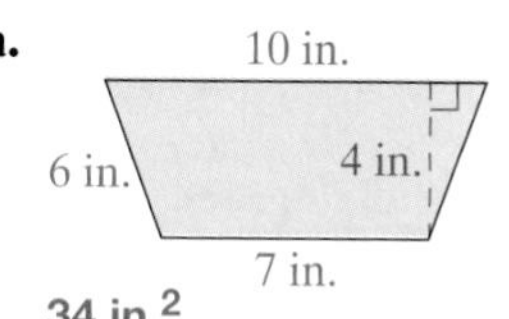

34 in.²

b.

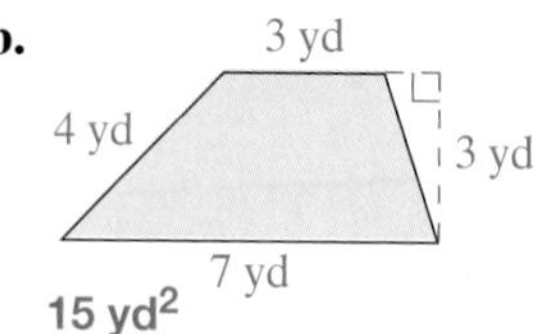

15 yd²

c. **Reasoning** When you are finding the area of a trapezoid, does it matter which base is b_1 and which is b_2? Explain.
No; addition is commutative.

English Learners
To make clear the differences between the various quadrilaterals, have students draw and label an example of a parallelogram (not a rectangle), a rectangle, and a trapezoid.

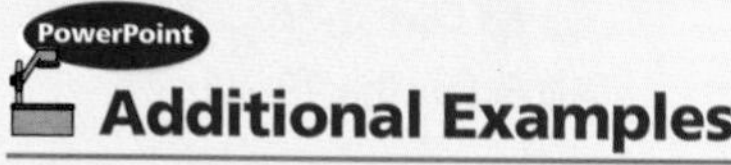

Additional Examples

1 Find the area of each parallelogram.

a.

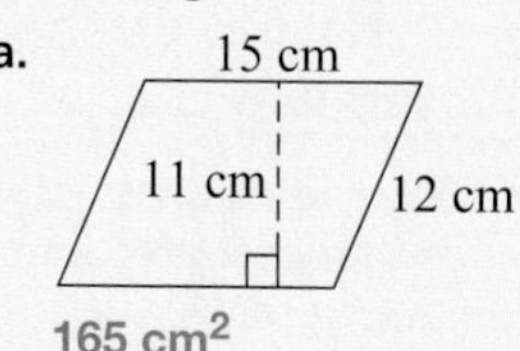

165 cm²

b.

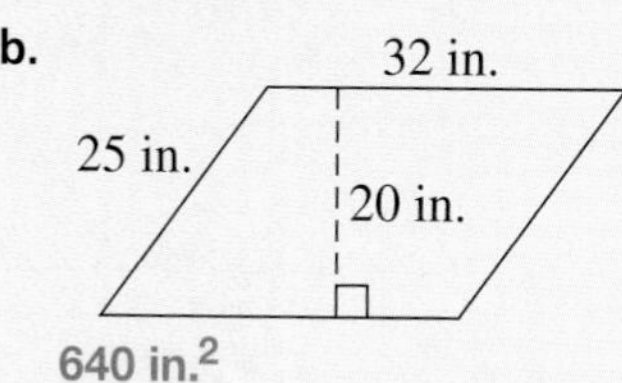

640 in.²

2 Find the area of the triangular part of the doghouse. **378 in.²**

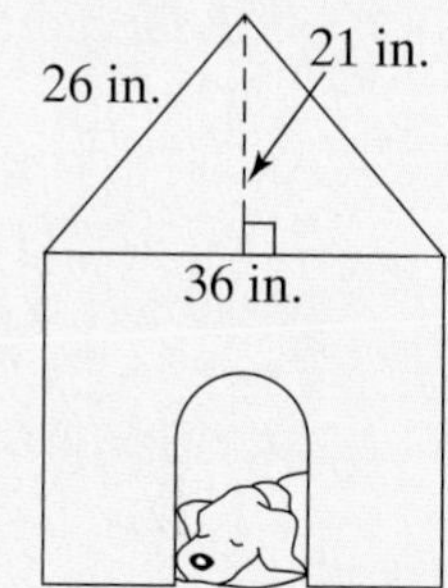

3 Find the area of the trapezoid. **35.2 in.²**

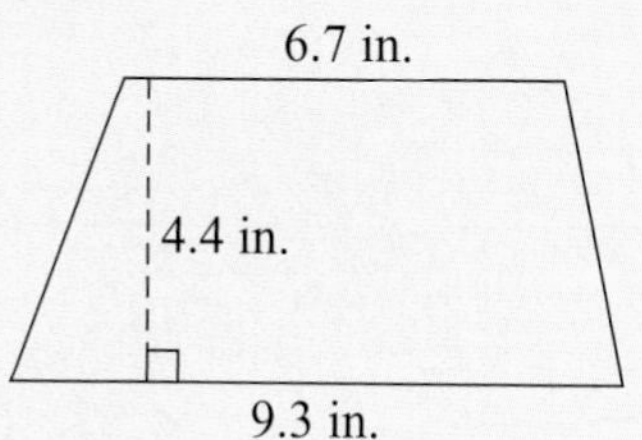

Closure

What formulas do you use to find the areas of rectangles, parallelograms, triangles, and trapezoids? **Sample: for a rectangle and for a parallelogram, $A = bh$; for a triangle, $A = \frac{1}{2}bh$; for a trapezoid, $A = \frac{1}{2}h(b_1 + b_2)$**

3. Practice

Assignment Guide

Objective 1

A B Core 1–18

C Extension 19–21

Test Prep 22–25

Mixed Review 26–30

Error Prevention!

Exercise 2 Some students may not realize that every rectangle is also a parallelogram.

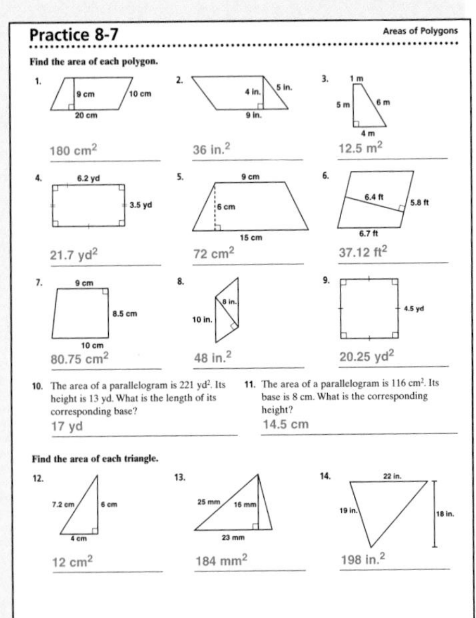

Practice 8-7 — Areas of Polygons

Find the area of each polygon.

1. 9 cm, 10 cm, 20 cm — 180 cm²
2. 4 in., 5 in., 9 in. — 36 in.²
3. 1 m, 5 m, 6 m, 4 m — 12.5 m²
4. 6.2 yd, 3.5 yd — 21.7 yd²
5. 9 cm, 6 cm, 15 cm — 72 cm²
6. 6.4 ft, 5.8 ft, 6.7 ft — 37.12 ft²
7. 9 cm, 8.5 cm, 10 cm — 80.75 cm²
8. 8 in., 10 in. — 48 in.²
9. 4.5 yd — 20.25 yd²
10. The area of a parallelogram is 221 yd². Its height is 13 yd. What is the length of its corresponding base? 17 yd
11. The area of a parallelogram is 116 cm². Its base is 8 cm. What is the corresponding height? 14.5 cm

Find the area of each triangle.

12. 7.2 cm, 6 cm, 4 cm — 12 cm²
13. 25 mm, 16 mm, 23 mm — 184 mm²
14. 22 in., 19 in., 18 in. — 198 in.²

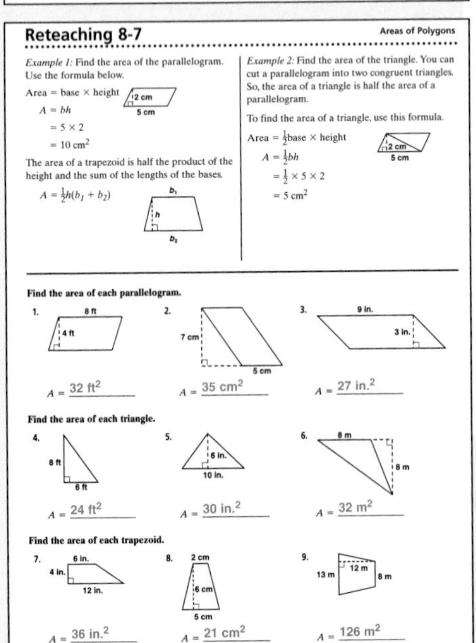

Reteaching 8-7 — Areas of Polygons

Example 1: Find the area of the parallelogram. Use the formula below.

Area = base × height (2 cm, 5 cm)

$A = bh$

$= 5 \times 2$

$= 10\text{ cm}^2$

The area of a trapezoid is half the product of the height and the sum of the lengths of the bases.

$A = \frac{1}{2}h(b_1 + b_2)$

Example 2: Find the area of the triangle. You can cut a parallelogram into two congruent triangles. So, the area of a triangle is half the area of a parallelogram.

To find the area of a triangle, use this formula.

Area = $\frac{1}{2}$base × height (2 cm, 5 cm)

$A = \frac{1}{2}bh$

$= \frac{1}{2} \times 5 \times 2$

$= 5\text{ cm}^2$

Find the area of each parallelogram.

1. 8 ft, 4 ft — A = 32 ft²
2. 7 cm, 5 cm — A = 35 cm²
3. 9 in., 3 in. — A = 27 in.²

Find the area of each triangle.

4. 8 ft, 6 ft — A = 24 ft²
5. 6 in., 10 in. — A = 30 in.²
6. 8 m, 8 m — A = 32 m²

Find the area of each trapezoid.

7. 6 in., 4 in., 12 in. — A = 36 in.²
8. 2 cm, 6 cm, 5 cm — A = 21 cm²
9. 12 m, 13 m, 8 m — A = 126 m²

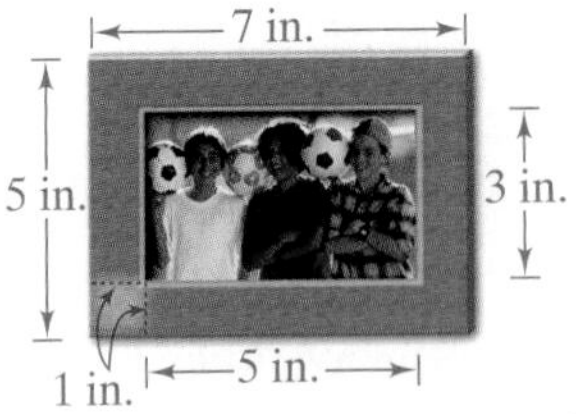

More Than One Way

Find the area of the picture frame at the left.

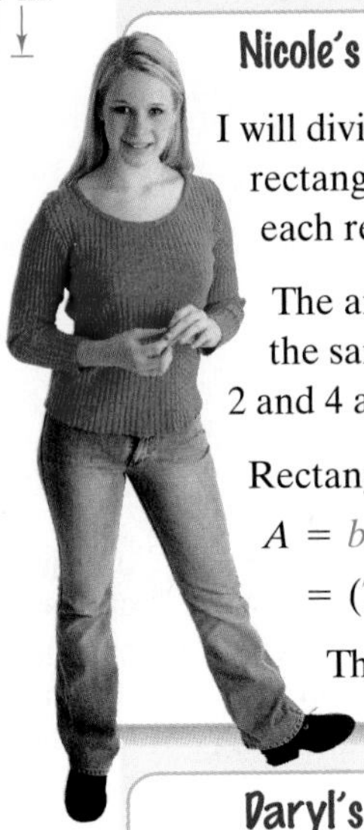

Nicole's Method

I will divide the frame into four rectangles. Then I will find the area of each rectangle and add them together.

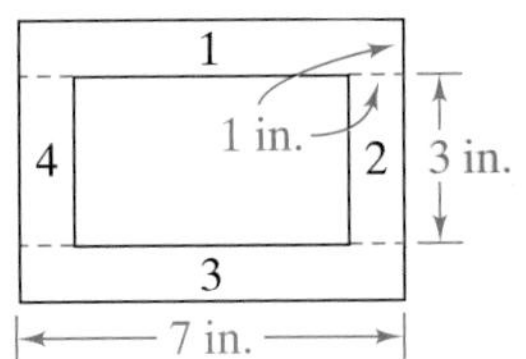

The areas of rectangles 1 and 3 are the same. The areas of rectangles 2 and 4 are the same.

Rectangles 1 and 3	Rectangles 2 and 4
$A = bh$	$A = bh$
$= (7)(1) = 7$	$= (1)(3) = 3$

The area of the frame is $2(7)\text{ in.}^2 + 2(3)\text{ in.}^2 = 20\text{ in.}^2$.

Daryl's Method

I will subtract the inner rectangle's area from the outer rectangle's area.

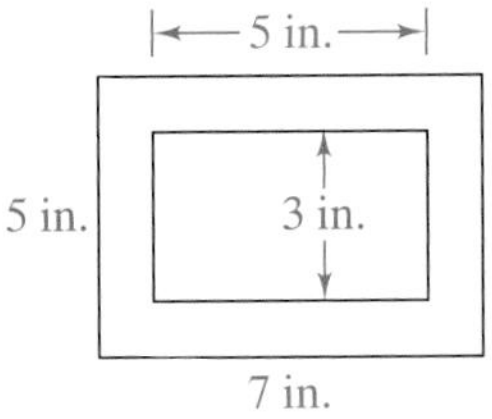

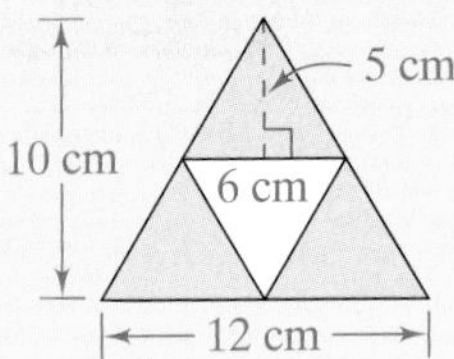

Outer Rectangle	Inner Rectangle
$A = bh$	$A = bh$
$= (7)(5) = 35$	$= (5)(3) = 15$

The area of the frame is $35\text{ in.}^2 - 15\text{ in.}^2 = 20\text{ in.}^2$.

Choose a Method

The four small triangles are congruent. Find the area of the shaded region. Explain why you chose the method you used.

10 cm, 5 cm, 6 cm, 12 cm

45 cm²; methods and explanations may vary.

EXERCISES

For more practice, see *Extra Practice*.

A Practice by Example

Example 1 (page 442)

Find the area of each parallelogram.

1.

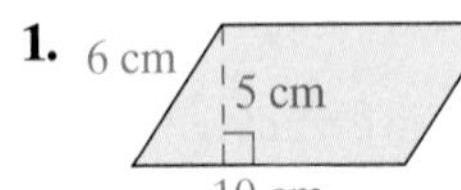

50 cm²

2.

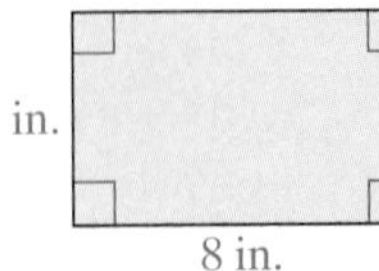

40 in.²

3.

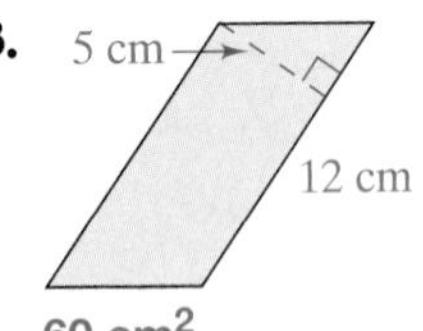

60 cm²

GPS Use the Guided Problem Solving worksheet with Exercise 15.

Example 2 (page 442)

Find the area of each triangle.

4. 5 in. 9.4 in. 8 in.

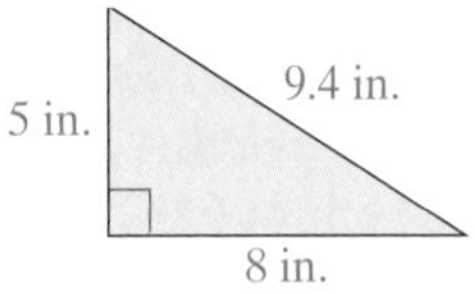

20 in.^{2}

5.

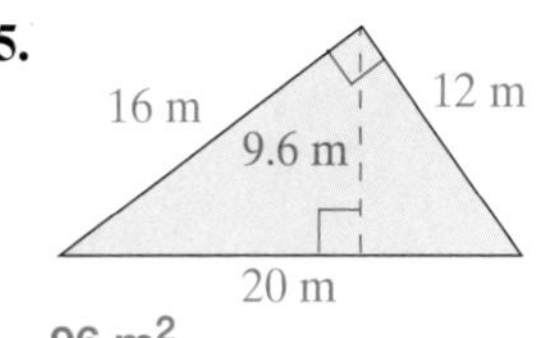

96 m^2

6.

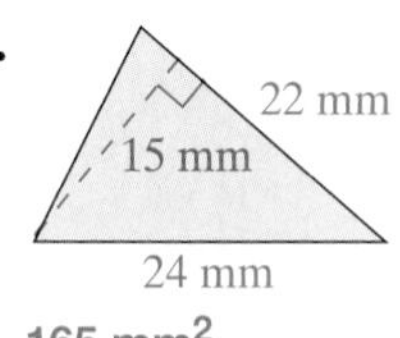

165 mm^2

Example 3 (page 443)

Find the area of each trapezoid.

7. 13 m 6 m 15 m

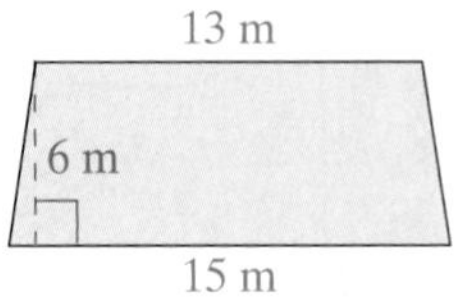

84 m^2

8.

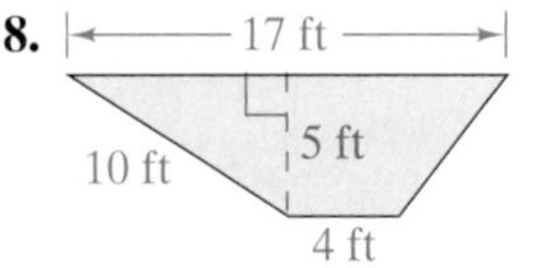

52.5 ft^2

9.

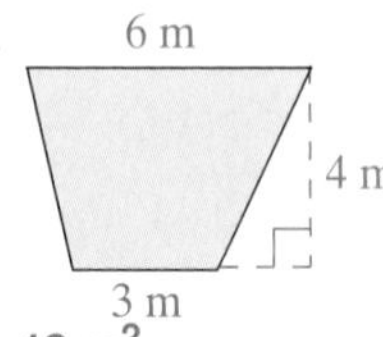

18 m^2

B Apply Your Skills

10. Engineering Planners are reviewing two plans for a new parking lot. One plan uses parallelograms for parking spaces and the other uses rectangles.

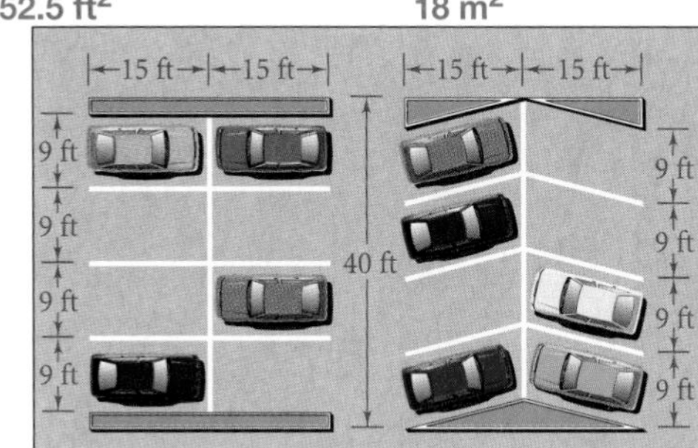

a. Find the area of a parking space in each plan. Each area is 135 ft^2

b. Find the total area of the unpaved sections in each plan. Each area is 120 ft^2.

c. **Writing in Math** Write a paragraph explaining why you would recommend one plan over the other. See left.

10c. Answers may vary. Sample: Each plan provides the same area for parking spaces and for grass. The rectangular parking-space plan allows cars to enter a space from two directions.

11. Data File, p. 405 Use the dimensions in the table to approximate the area of each sail. Assume each sail forms a right triangle.

11. Answers may vary. Sample: Laser: 85 ft^2; 470: 95 ft^2; Soling: 140 ft^2; Finn: 95 ft^2

Find the area of the parallelogram, the triangle, and the trapezoid.

12. 8.1 m 6 m

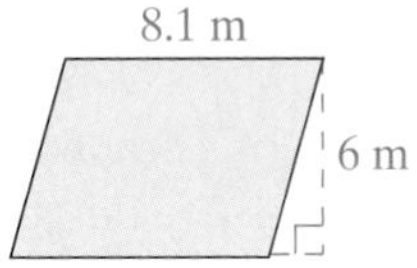

48.6 m^2

13.

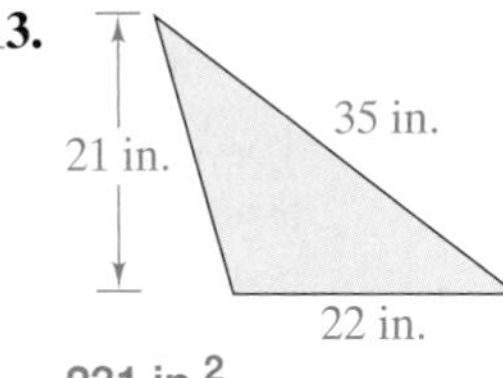

231 in.^{2}

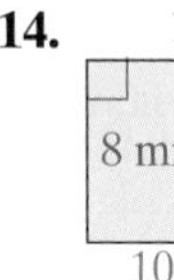

14. 15 mm 8 mm 10 mm

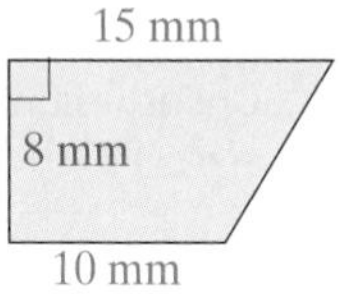

100 mm^2

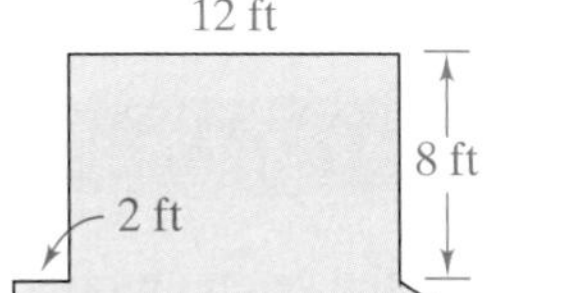

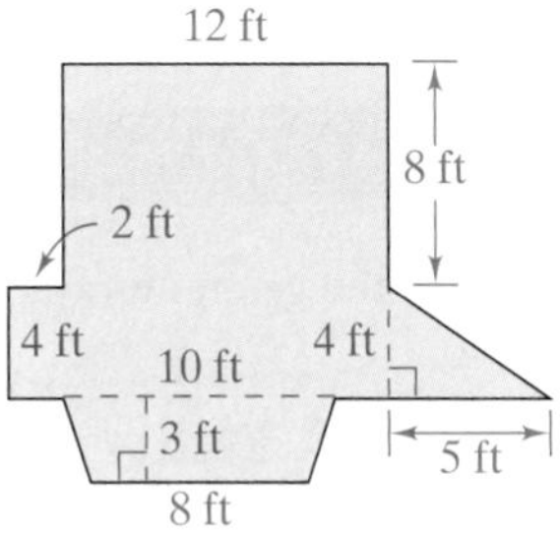

15. a. **Construction** Your cousin wants to retile the kitchen floor. The floor plan of the kitchen is shown at the left. Find the area of the floor. 189 ft^2

GPS

b. One case of tiles covers 44 ft^2. How many cases are needed? 5 cases

c. Each case of tiles costs \$39.16. What is the total cost of the tiles? \$195.80

16. Open-Ended Use graph paper to draw two different parallelograms with the same area. Identify the base length and corresponding height of each parallelogram. See margin.

17. Algebra A parallelogram has an area of 63 m^2. One base length is 18 m. What is the corresponding height? 3.5 m

16. Answers may vary. Sample:

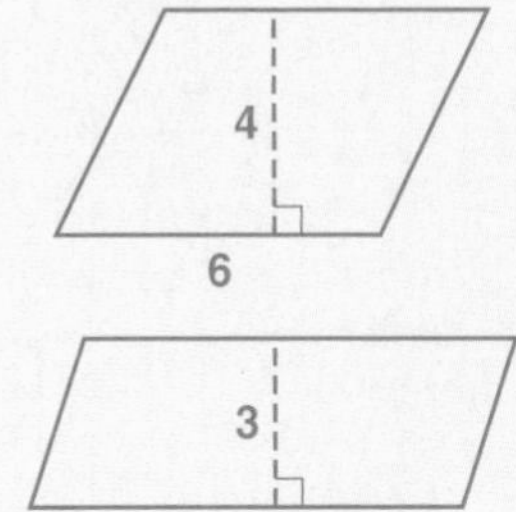

4. Assess

Lesson Quiz 8-7

Find the area of each.

1. 12 in.^{2}

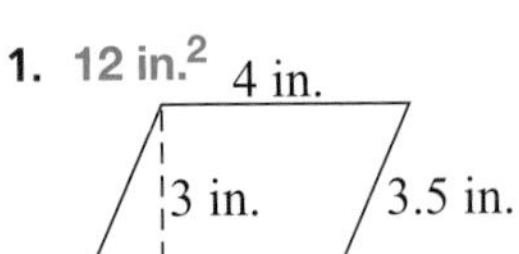

2. 14 cm^2

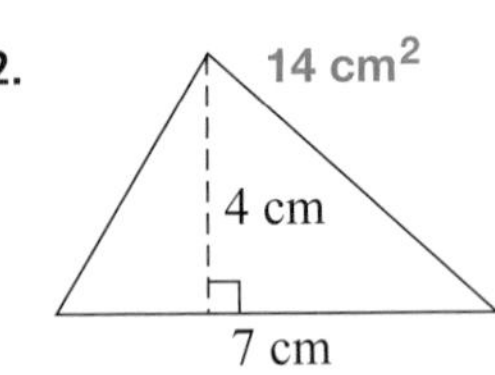

3. 56 ft^2

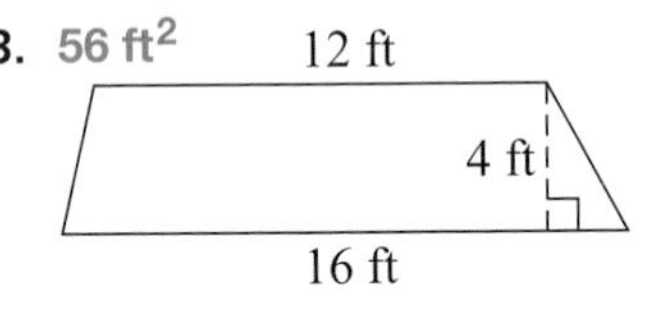

Test Prep

Resources

A sheet of blank grids is available in the *Test-Taking Strategies with Transparencies* booklet. Give copies of this sheet to students so they can practice filling in grids.

For additional practice with a variety of test item formats:

- Test Prep, p. 465
- Test-Taking Strategies, p. 461
- Test-Taking Strategies with Transparencies

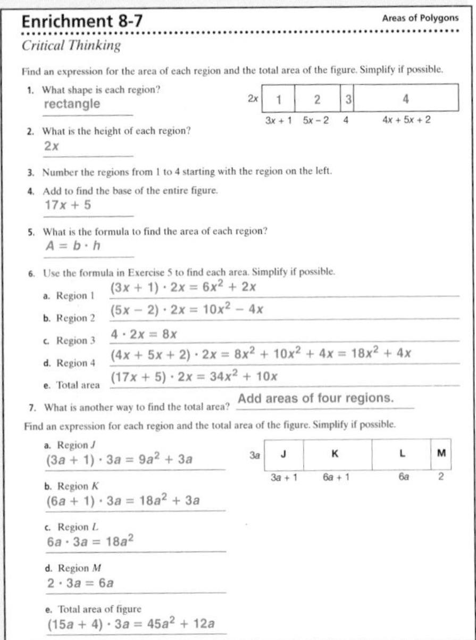

Enrichment 8-7 — Areas of Polygons

Critical Thinking

Find an expression for the area of each region and the total area of the figure. Simplify if possible.

1. What shape is each region? rectangle

2x	1	2	3	4
	3x + 1	5x − 2	4	4x + 5x + 2

2. What is the height of each region? $2x$
3. Number the regions from 1 to 4 starting with the region on the left.
4. Add to find the base of the entire figure. $17x + 5$
5. What is the formula to find the area of each region? $A = b \cdot h$
6. Use the formula in Exercise 5 to find each area. Simplify if possible.
   a. Region 1 $(3x + 1) \cdot 2x = 6x^2 + 2x$
   b. Region 2 $(5x - 2) \cdot 2x = 10x^2 - 4x$
   c. Region 3 $4 \cdot 2x = 8x$
   d. Region 4 $(4x + 5x + 2) \cdot 2x = 8x^2 + 10x^2 + 4x = 18x^2 + 4x$
   e. Total area $(17x + 5) \cdot 2x = 34x^2 + 10x$
7. What is another way to find the total area? Add areas of four regions.

Find an expression for each region and the total area of the figure. Simplify if possible.

3a	J	K	L	M
	3a + 1	6a + 1	6a	2

a. Region *J* $(3a + 1) \cdot 3a = 9a^2 + 3a$
b. Region *K* $(6a + 1) \cdot 3a = 18a^2 + 3a$
c. Region *L* $6a \cdot 3a = 18a^2$
d. Region *M* $2 \cdot 3a = 6a$
e. Total area of figure $(15a + 4) \cdot 3a = 45a^2 + 12a$

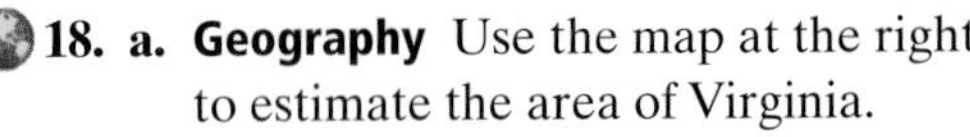

18a. Answers may vary. Sample: 104,000 km^2

18. a. **Geography** Use the map at the right to estimate the area of Virginia.
    b. **Research** Compare your estimate to the actual area of Virginia. The actual area is 109,624 km^2.

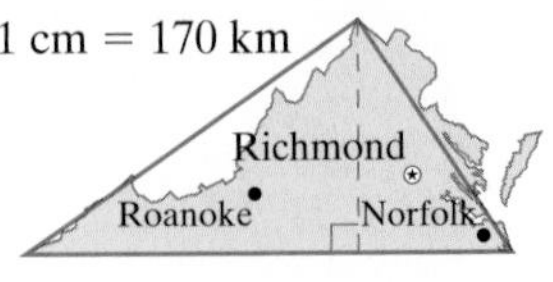

Challenge

Math in the Media **Use the cartoon below for Exercises 19 and 20.**

19. The area of a square is larger than the area of a triangle.

19. **Writing in Math** What does the cartoon suggest about the area of a square compared to the area of a triangle? See left.

20. The base and the height of a triangle are the same length as the side of a square. What is the ratio of the area of the triangle to the area of the square? 1 : 2

21. **Stretch Your Thinking** You have an acute angle in a right triangle. The cosine ratio is $\frac{4}{5}$. What is the sine ratio? $\frac{3}{5}$

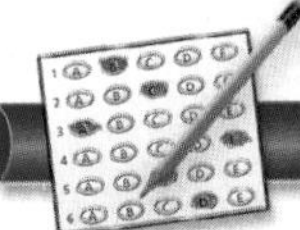

Test Prep

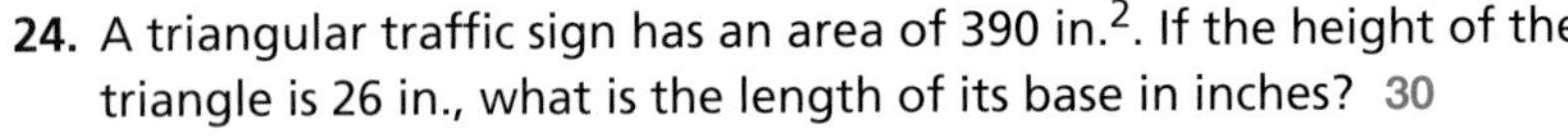

Gridded Response

22. What is the area in centimeters of a rectangle that is 13 cm by 5 cm? 65
23. What is the area of a triangle with a base of 7 and a height of 7? 24.5
24. A triangular traffic sign has an area of 390 in.^{2}. If the height of the triangle is 26 in., what is the length of its base in inches? 30
25. The length of one base of a trapezoid is 7 mm less than twice the length of the other base. The height of the trapezoid is 12 mm. The area of the trapezoid is 48 mm^2. Find the length in millimeters of the longer base. 5

Take It to the NET
Online lesson quiz at **www.PHSchool.com**
Web Code: aca-0807

Mixed Review

Lesson 8-6 **Find the measure of each angle of a regular polygon with the given number of sides.**

26. 3 sides 60° 27. 8 sides 135° 28. 16 sides 157.5° 29. 25 sides 165.6°

Lesson 6-8

30. Find the interest earned on \$685 at $2\frac{1}{2}$% simple interest for 3 years. \$51.38

Alternative Assessment

Each student in a pair draws and labels a parallelogram and a triangle on graph paper. Students trade papers with a partner and find the areas for each other's polygons.

8-8 Circumferences and Areas of Circles

What You'll Learn

 To find the circumference of a circle

 To find the area of a circle

. . . And Why

To compute the dimensions of sports equipment, as in Example 1

Check Skills You'll Need

For help, go to Lesson 4-6.

Find the area of each figure.

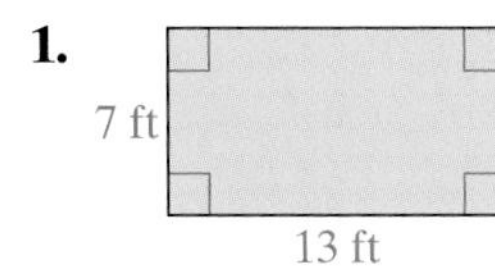

1. 7 ft by 13 ft rectangle — 91 ft^2

2. 3 in. by 3 in. square — 9 in.^{2}

3. 8 m by 4 m rectangle — 32 cm^2

4. Explain the difference between perimeter and area.
Perimeter is the distance around a figure. Area is the number of square units a figure encloses.

Interactive lesson includes instant self-check, tutorials, and activities.

OBJECTIVE 1 Finding the Circumference of a Circle

A basketball hoop has a diameter of 45 cm. To make a hoop, you need to know the distance around it.

In this lesson, you will learn to find the circumferences and areas of circles.

Circumference is the distance around the circle.

A ***radius*** is a segment that has one endpoint at the center and the other endpoint on the circle.

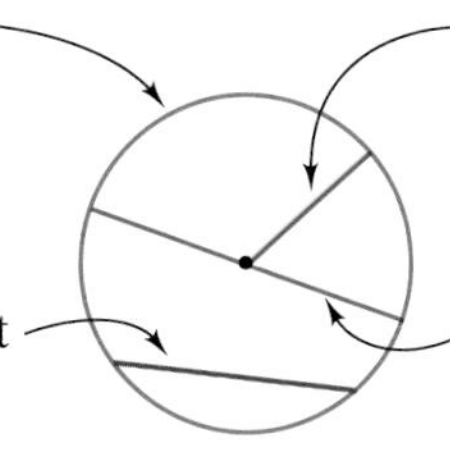

A ***chord*** is a segment with endpoints on the circle.

A ***diameter*** is a chord that passes through the center of the circle.

> **Reading Math**
> The symbol π is pronounced "pie."

Pi (π) is the special name for the ratio of the circumference C to the diameter d.

$$\pi = \frac{C}{d}$$

If you solve this equation for C, you get $C = \pi d$, a formula for the circumference of a circle. Approximate values for π are $\frac{22}{7}$ and 3.14.

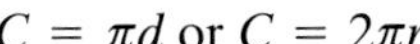

Key Concepts — Circumference of a Circle

The circumference of a circle is the product of π and the diameter d.

$$C = \pi d \text{ or } C = 2\pi r$$

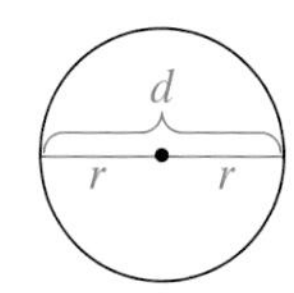

8-8

1. Plan

Lesson Preview

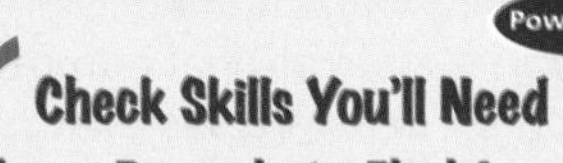

Check Skills You'll Need
Using a Formula to Find Area
Lesson 4-6: Example 1.

Lesson Resources

Teaching Resources
Practice, Reteaching, Enrichment

Reaching All Students
Practice Workbook 8-8
Spanish Practice Workbook 8-8
Guided Problem Solving 8-8
Hands-On Activities 37

Presentation Assistant Plus!
Transparencies
- Check Skills You'll Need 8-8
- Problem of the Day 8-8
- Additional Examples 8-8
- Student Edition Answers 8-8
- Lesson Quiz 8-8
- Classroom Aid 11

PH Presentation Pro CD-ROM 8-8

PRENTICE HALL ASSESSMENT SYSTEM

Computer Test Generator CD

Technology
Resource Pro® CD-ROM
Computer Test Generator CD
PH Presentation Pro CD-ROM

www.PHSchool.com
Student Site
- Teacher Web Code: ack-5500
- Self-grading Lesson Quiz

PH SuccessNet Teacher Center
- Lesson Planner
- Resources

Plus 

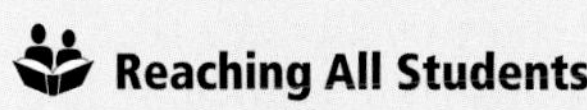

Ongoing Assessment and Intervention

Before the Lesson
Diagnose prerequisite skills using:
- Check Skills You'll Need

During the Lesson
Monitor progress using:
- Check Understanding
- Additional Examples
- Test Prep

After the Lesson
Assess knowledge using:
- Lesson Quiz
- Computer Test Generator CD

2. Teach

Math Background

In every circle, the ratio of the distance around (circumference) to the distance across (diameter) is a constant value named π, pi. This ratio is an irrational number that cannot be expressed exactly as the ratio of two integers. However, various approximate values for π, such as $\frac{22}{7}$ and 3.14, are used in problems to calculate approximate answers.

The diameter of a circle is twice the radius. The circumference, or perimeter, of a circle is a linear measure given by $C = \pi d$. The area or a circle is measured in square units and given by $A = \pi r^2$.

Teaching Notes

Teaching Tip
Have students compare these formulas for the perimeter of a square and its area: $P = 4s$ and $A = s^2$. Lead students to realize that area is in square units. The exponent 2 is read as "squared," so s^2 means "side squared."

1 EXAMPLE Alternative Method

Ask: *How could you rewrite the formula $C = \pi d$ using the radius?* $C = \pi(2r)$

2 EXAMPLE Error Prevention

Discuss the use of an approximate or rounded value for π. Help students see that calculated values using π will be "about" or an approximate value. If π is left as a symbol, the answer is exact.

English Learners
Review the vocabulary of circles. Verify that students understand each term by having them point out or draw examples of *radius*, *diameter*, *circumference*, and *area*.

3 EXAMPLE Visual Learners

To emphasize the difference between linear and area measures, have students use one color to trace the circumference of a circle and another color to shade the area.

Calculator Hint
If you use 3.14 for π in Example 1, the rounded result is 141.3, not 141.4. The calculator key π gives a more accurate value for π.

1 EXAMPLE Finding the Circumference of a Circle

Sports Equipment Find the circumference of the basketball hoop.

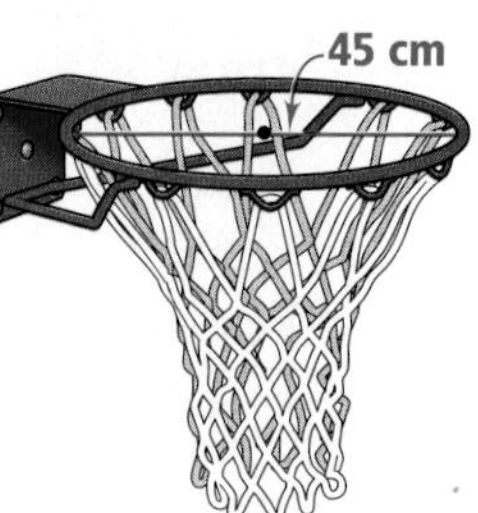

$C = \pi d$ ← **Use the formula for circumference.**

$= \pi(45)$ ← **Substitute 45 for d.**

π × 45 = 141.3716694 ← **Use a calculator.**

The circumference is about 141.4 cm.

Check Understanding 1 Find the circumference of each circle with the given radius or diameter. Round to the nearest tenth.

a. 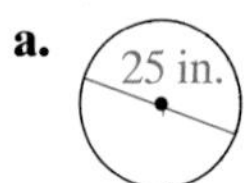

78.5 in.

b. 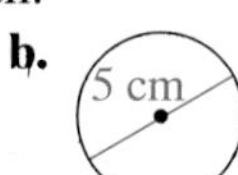

15.7 cm

c. 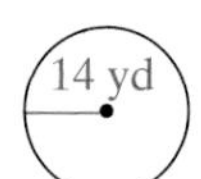

88.0 yd

d. **Reasoning** Show that the two formulas for circumference, $C = \pi d$ and $C = 2\pi r$, are equivalent. $d = 2r$, so $\pi d = 2\pi r$.

OBJECTIVE

2 Finding the Area of a Circle

If you cut a pizza into equal pieces and line the pieces up as shown below, the figure formed will resemble a parallelogram.

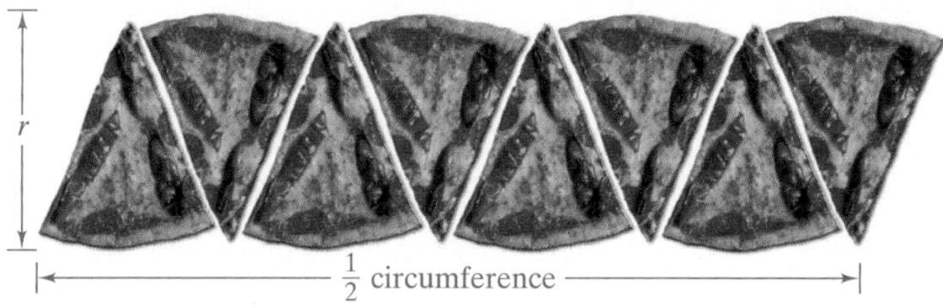

You can use the formula for the area of a parallelogram to find the formula for the area of a circle.

$A = b \cdot h$ ← **Use the formula for the area of a parallelogram.**

$= \frac{1}{2}C \cdot r$ ← **Substitute $\frac{1}{2}C$ for b and r for h.**

$= \frac{1}{2}(2\pi r) \cdot r$ ← **The circumference C of a circle is $2\pi r$.**

$= \pi r^2$ ← **Multiply.**

Key Concepts **Area of a Circle**

The area of a circle is the product of π and the square of the radius r.

$$A = \pi r^2$$

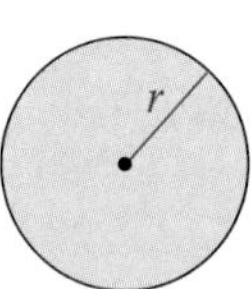

Reaching All Students

Below Level Review the meaning of *radius, diameter, circumference*, and *area*. Relate circumference of a circle to perimeter of a rectangle. Demonstrate by showing how a bug would "walk around each figure."	**Advanced Learners** Have students find the area of a circle whose circumference is 6π cm. $A = 9\pi$	**English Learners** See note on page 448. **Alternative Method** See note on page 448.

2 EXAMPLE Finding the Area of a Circle

Food The diameter of a large pizza is 14 inches. Find its area.

The radius of the pizza is 14 ÷ 2, or 7 in. Use the radius to find the area.

$A = \pi r^2$ ← **Use the formula for the area of a circle.**

$= \pi(7)^2$ ← **Substitute.**

π × 7 x^2 = 153.93804 ← **Use a calculator.**

The area of a large pizza is about 153.9 in.^{2}.

Check Understanding 2 Find the area of each circle with the given radius or diameter. Round to the nearest tenth.

a. $r = 4$ in. 50.3 in.^{2} **b.** $d = 16$ km 201.1 km^2 **c.** $r = 1.8$ km 10.2 km^2

d. **Number Sense** How does the area of a circle change if you halve the radius? The area would be $\frac{1}{4}$ of the original.

Sometimes you can find the area of an irregular figure by separating it into simpler figures.

3 EXAMPLE Finding the Area of an Irregular Figure

Mailbox Find the area of the front of the mailbox.

10 in.
7 in.
U.S. MAIL

You can separate the figure into a half circle and a rectangle.

Step 1 Find the area of the half circle.

Area of circle $= \pi r^2$

Area of half circle $= \frac{1}{2}\pi r^2$

$A = \frac{1}{2}\pi(5)^2$ ← **Substitute 5 for** ***r*****.**

≈ 39.3 ← **Multiply. Round to the nearest tenth.**

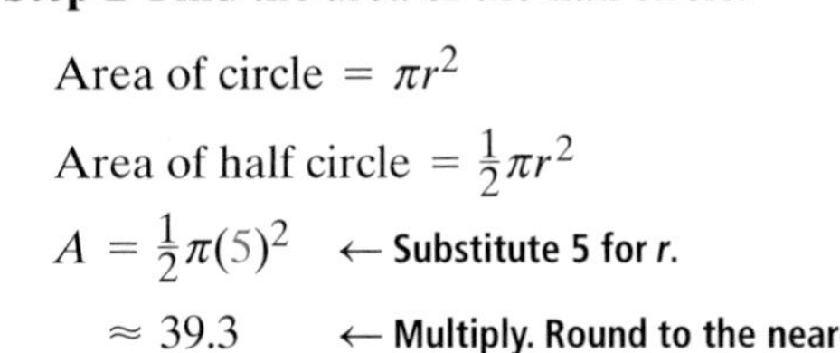

Step 2 Find the area of the rectangle.

Area of rectangle $= bh$

$A = 10 \cdot 7$ ← **Substitute 10 for** ***b*** **and 7 for** ***h*****.**

$= 70$ ← **Multiply.**

Step 3 Add the two areas.

The area of the front of the mailbox is about 39.3 in.^{2} + 70 in.^{2} = 109.3 in.^{2}.

Careers The U.S. Postal Service employs over 300,000 mail carriers to collect, sort, and deliver the mail.

Check Understanding 3 Find the area of each shaded region. Round to the nearest tenth.

a.

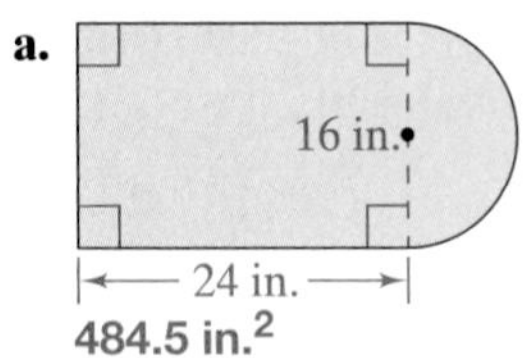

484.5 in.^{2}

b.

13.2 m
6.6 m
19.8 m

192.9 m^2

Additional Examples

1 The diameter of a tractor tire is 125 cm. Find the circumference. Round to the nearest tenth. 392.7 cm

2 The diameter of a small pizza is 24 cm. Find its area. Round to the nearest tenth. 452.4 cm^2

3 Find the area of the unshaded region of the square tile with a circle inside of it, as shown below. Round to the nearest tenth. 30.9 cm^2

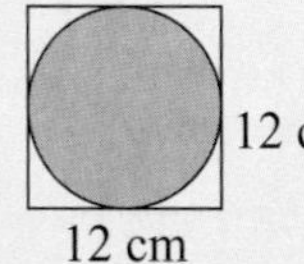

Closure

Compare the formulas for finding the circumference and area of a circle. Sample: The formula for the circumference, which is a linear measure, can use either the diameter, $C = \pi d$, or the radius, $C = \pi(2r)$. The area of a circle is measured in square units and the formula is $A = \pi r^2$. Both circumference and area use an approximate value for π in the calculations.

3. Practice

Assignment Guide

1 Objective 1

A B Core 1–6, 19–22, 25–28

2 Objective 2

A B Core 7–18, 23–24, 29–33

C Extension 34–37

Test Prep 38–41

Mixed Review 42–46

Error Prevention!

Exercise 7–12 Have students identify whether d or r is given.

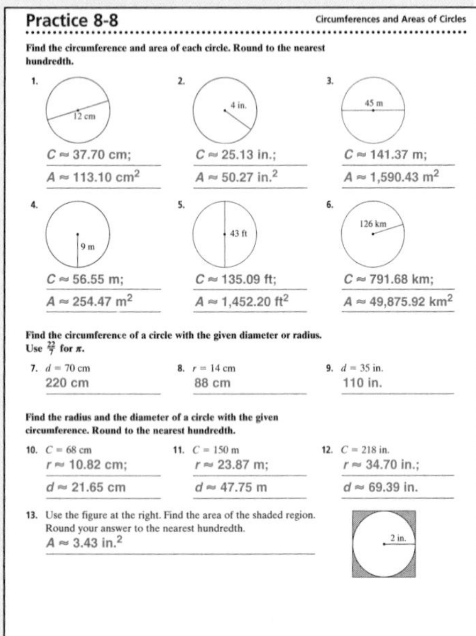

Practice 8-8 Circumferences and Areas of Circles

Find the circumference and area of each circle. Round to the nearest hundredth.

1. (12 cm) $C \approx$ 37.70 cm; $A \approx$ 113.10 cm²
2. (4 in.) $C \approx$ 25.13 in.; $A \approx$ 50.27 in.²
3. (45 m) $C \approx$ 141.37 m; $A \approx$ 1,590.43 m²
4. (9 m) $C \approx$ 56.55 m; $A \approx$ 254.47 m²
5. (43 ft) $C \approx$ 135.09 ft; $A \approx$ 1,452.20 ft²
6. (126 km) $C \approx$ 791.68 km; $A \approx$ 49,875.92 km²

Find the circumference of a circle with the given diameter or radius. Use $\frac{22}{7}$ for π.

7. d = 70 cm 220 cm
8. r = 14 cm 88 cm
9. d = 35 in. 110 in.

Find the radius and the diameter of a circle with the given circumference. Round to the nearest hundredth.

10. C = 68 cm $r \approx$ 10.82 cm; $d \approx$ 21.65 cm
11. C = 150 m $r \approx$ 23.87 m; $d \approx$ 47.75 m
12. C = 218 in. $r \approx$ 34.70 in.; $d \approx$ 69.39 in.

13. Use the figure at the right. Find the area of the shaded region. Round your answer to the nearest hundredth. $A \approx$ 3.43 in.²

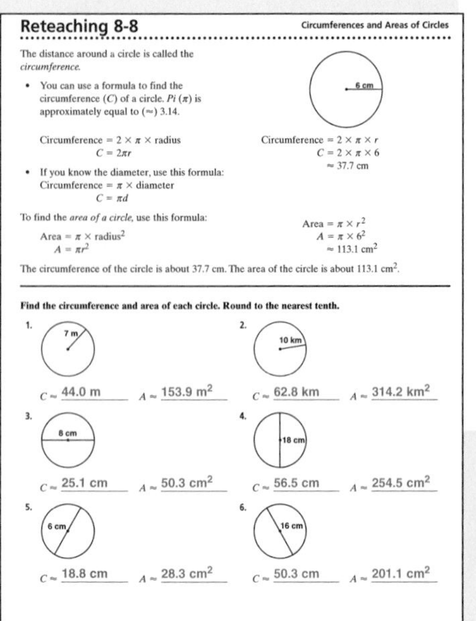

Reteaching 8-8 Circumferences and Areas of Circles

The distance around a circle is called the *circumference*.

- You can use a formula to find the circumference (C) of a circle. Pi (π) is approximately equal to ($\approx$) 3.14.

Circumference = 2 × π × radius
$C = 2\pi r$

Circumference = 2 × π × r
C = 2 × π × 6
$\approx$ 37.7 cm

- If you know the diameter, use this formula:
Circumference = π × diameter
$C = \pi d$

To find the *area of a circle*, use this formula:

Area = π × radius²
$A = \pi r^2$

Area = π × r^2
$A = \pi \times 6^2$
$\approx$ 113.1 cm²

The circumference of the circle is about 37.7 cm. The area of the circle is about 113.1 cm².

Find the circumference and area of each circle. Round to the nearest tenth.

1. (7 m) $C \approx$ 44.0 m $A \approx$ 153.9 m²
2. (10 km) $C \approx$ 62.8 km $A \approx$ 314.2 km²
3. (8 cm) $C \approx$ 25.1 cm $A \approx$ 50.3 cm²
4. (18 cm) $C \approx$ 56.5 cm $A \approx$ 254.5 cm²
5. (6 cm) $C \approx$ 18.8 cm $A \approx$ 28.3 cm²
6. (16 cm) $C \approx$ 50.3 cm $A \approx$ 201.1 cm²

EXERCISES

For more practice, see *Extra Practice*.

A Practice by Example

Example 1 (page 448)

Find the circumference of each circle with the given radius or diameter. Round to the nearest tenth. Exercise 1 has been started for you.

1. 37.7 m **2.** 15.7 ft

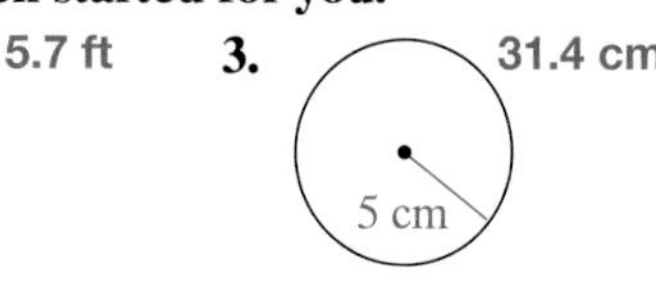

3. 31.4 cm

$C = \pi d = \pi(12)$

4. d = 9.2 in. 28.9 in. **5.** r = 4.5 cm 28.3 cm **6.** r = 17.6 mm 110.6 mm

Example 2 (page 449)

Find the area of each circle with the given radius or diameter. Round to the nearest tenth. Exercise 7 has been started for you.

7. r = 8 cm 201.1 cm² **8.** d = 22 in. 380.1 in.² **9.** r = 15 m 706.9 m²

$A = \pi r^2 = \pi(8)^2$

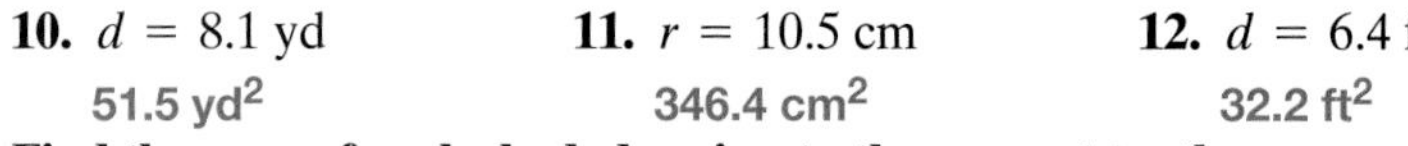

10. d = 8.1 yd 51.5 yd² **11.** r = 10.5 cm 346.4 cm² **12.** d = 6.4 ft 32.2 ft²

Example 3 (page 449)

Find the area of each shaded region to the nearest tenth.

13.

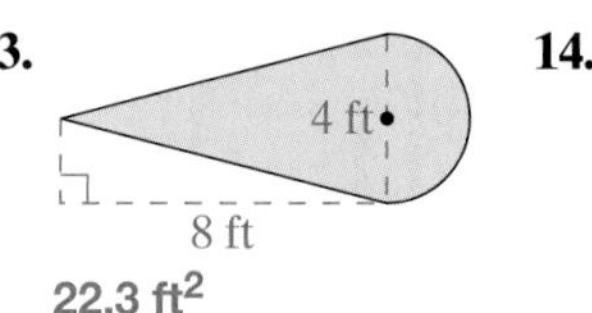

22.3 ft²

14.

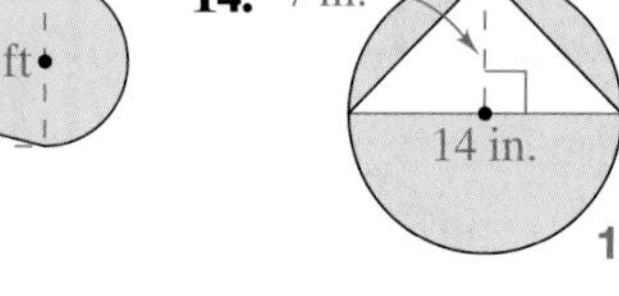

104.9 in.²

15.

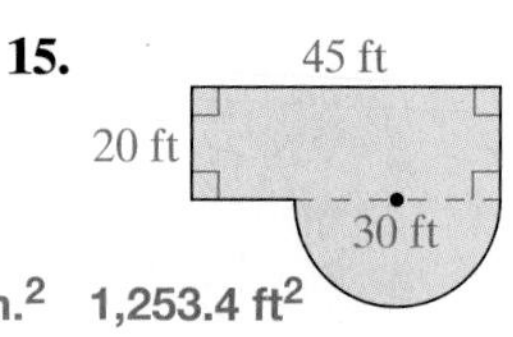

1,253.4 ft²

16.

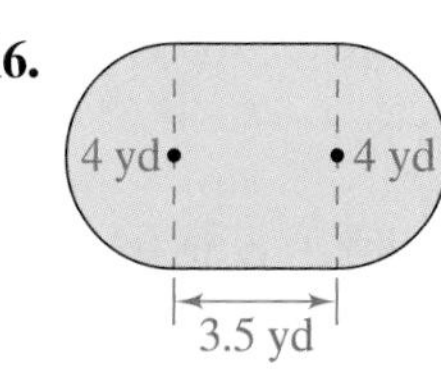

26.6 yd²

17.

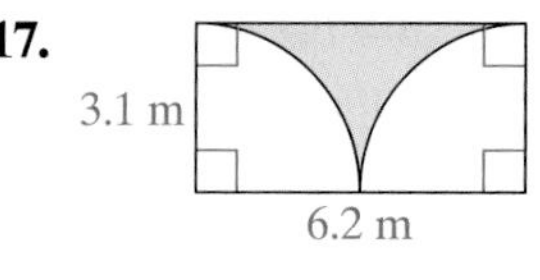

4.1 m²

18.

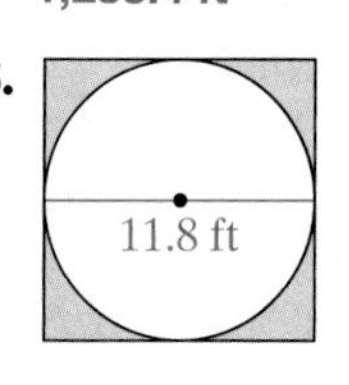

29.9 ft²

B Apply Your Skills

Mental Math **Find the circumference of a circle with the given radius or diameter. Use $\frac{22}{7}$ for π.**

19. d = 21 cm 66 cm **20.** r = 7 km 44 km **21.** r = 3.5 m 22 m **22.** d = 28 in. 88 in.

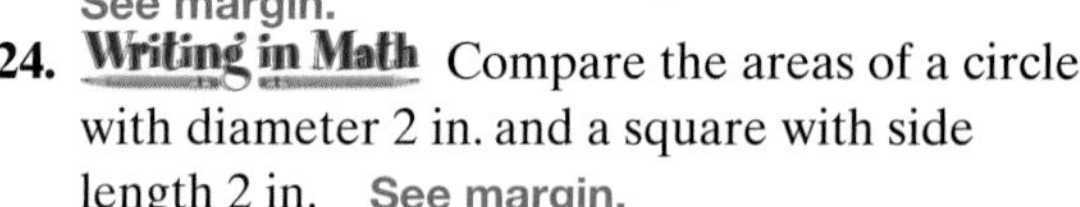

23. Find the area of the shaded ring to the nearest unit. Describe the method you used. See margin.

24. **Writing in Math** Compare the areas of a circle with diameter 2 in. and a square with side length 2 in. See margin.

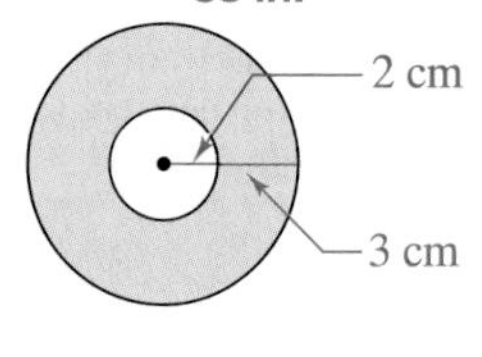

Writing in Math

For help with writing to compare, as in Exercise 24, go to p. 453.

Find the radius and diameter of each circle with the given circumference. Round to the nearest hundredth.

25. C = 22.35 cm 3.56 cm; 7.11 cm **26.** C = 1.71 in. 0.27 in.; 0.54 in. **27.** C = 150.94 ft 24.02 ft; 48.05 ft **28.** C = 62.83 m 10.00 m; 20.00 m

Use the Guided Problem Solving worksheet with Exercise 29.

23. 66 cm²; subtract the area of the smaller circle from the area of the larger circle.

24. The square, with an area of 4 in.², has a greater area than the circle, with an area of 3.14 in.².

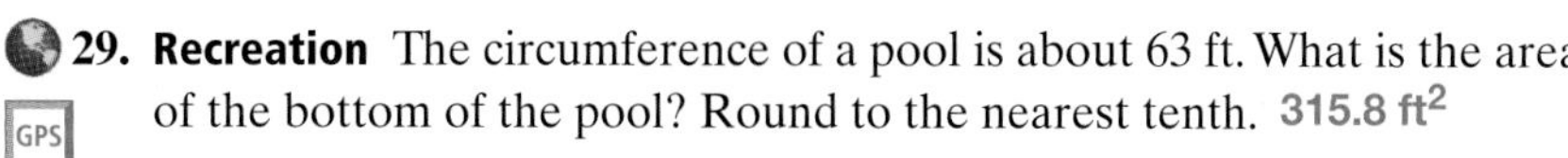

29. **Recreation** The circumference of a pool is about 63 ft. What is the area of the bottom of the pool? Round to the nearest tenth. 315.8 ft^2

GPS

30. **Number Sense** The ratio of the radii of two circles is 3 : 1.
   a. How do their circumferences compare? 3 : 1
   b. How do their areas compare? 9 : 1
   c. **Algebra** The ratio of the radii of two circles is $a:b$. Write the ratio of their circumferences and areas in terms of a and b $a : b; a^2 : b^2$

Use the diagram for Exercises 31–33. Round to the nearest tenth.

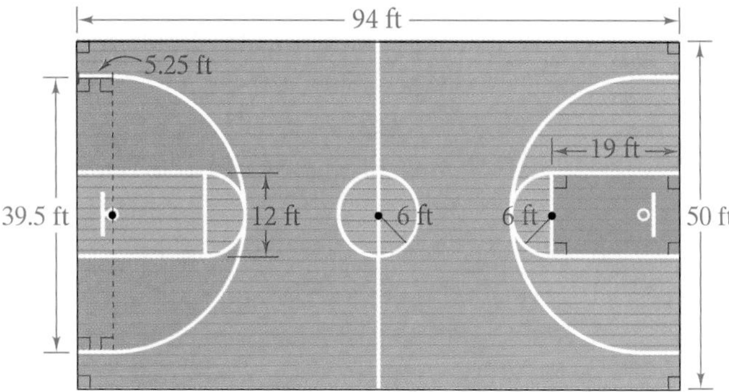

31. Find the area of the green shaded region. 228 ft^2

32. Find the area of the purple shaded region. 535.5 ft^2

33. Find the area of the blue shaded region. 2,946.7 ft^2

C Challenge

34. The area of a circle is 432 ft^2. Estimate its radius. Use 3 for π. 12 ft

35. a. **Estimation** Estimate the area of circle P at the right. Use 3 for π. 192 cm^2
   b. The area of the shaded wedge is about 64 cm^2. What percent of the area of circle P is the shaded wedge? Round to the nearest tenth of a percent. 33.3%

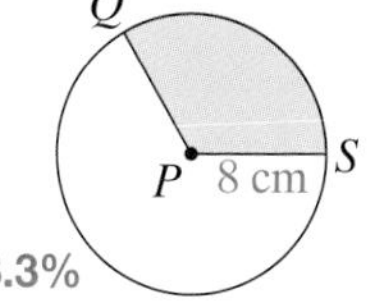

36. **Sleep** The circle graph below shows the average number of hours Americans sleep each night. The radius of the circle is 1.2 cm.

Average Number of Hours Americans Sleep Each Night

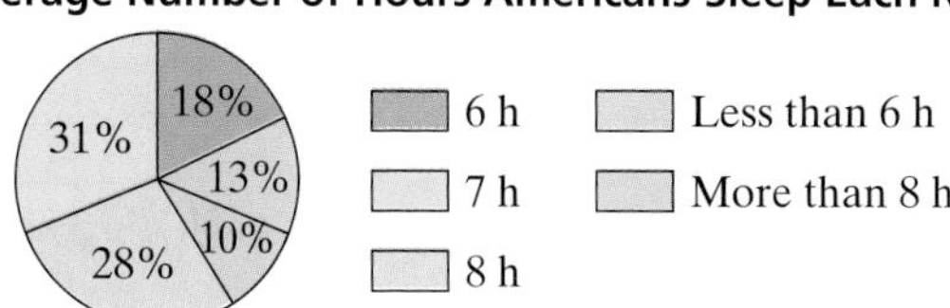

SOURCE: National Sleep Foundation

Need Help?
For help with percents, go to Lesson 6-3.

   a. Find the area of the circle. Round to the nearest tenth. about 4.5 cm^2
   b. Find the area of each wedge of the graph to the nearest hundredth. See left.

36b. 6 h: 0.81 cm^2; 7 h: 1.40 cm^2; 8 h: 1.26 cm^2; less than 6 h: 0.59 cm^2; more than 8 h: 0.45 cm^2

37. **Stretch Your Thinking** How many different lines can you draw to connect six points, no three of which lie on the same line? 15 lines

4. Assess

Lesson Quiz 8-8

Round to the nearest tenth.

1. Find the circumference and area of the circle. 18.8 km; 28.3 km^2

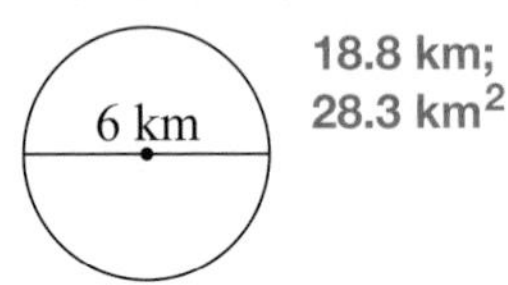

2. Find the area. 273.0 $in.^2$

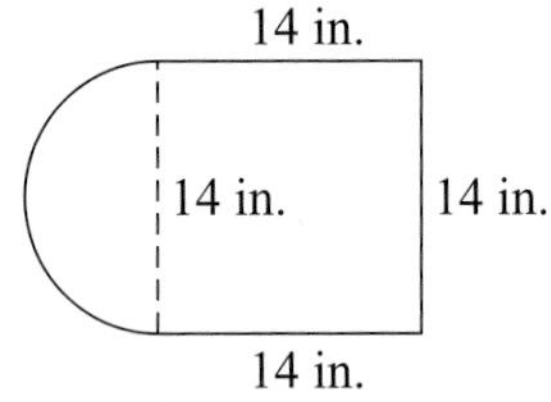

Alternative Assessment

Students use rulers to measure the diameter of a circular classroom object, such as a coin or a clock face. Then have them use formulas to find its circumference and area.

Test Prep

Resources

For additional practice with a variety of test item formats:

- Test Prep, p. 465
- Test-Taking Strategies, p. 461
- Test-Taking Strategies with Transparencies

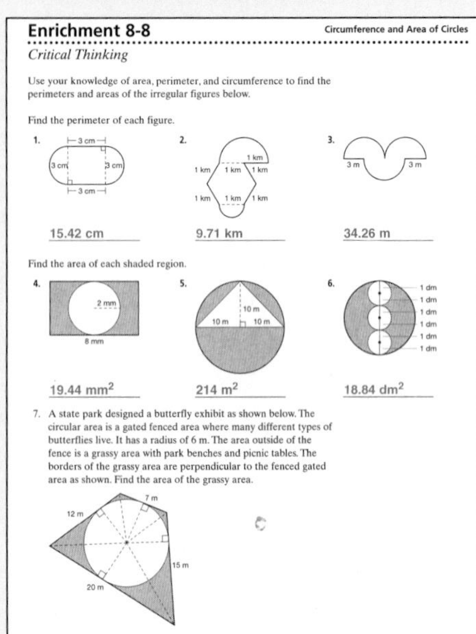

Enrichment 8-8 Circumference and Area of Circles

Critical Thinking

Use your knowledge of area, perimeter, and circumference to find the perimeters and areas of the irregular figures below.

Find the perimeter of each figure.

1. 15.42 cm
2. 9.71 km
3. 34.26 m

Find the area of each shaded region.

4. 19.44 mm^2
5. 214 m^2
6. 18.84 dm^2

7. A state park designed a butterfly exhibit as shown below. The circular area is a gated fenced area where many different types of butterflies live. It has a radius of 6 m. The area outside of the fence is a grassy area with park benches and picnic tables. The borders of the grassy area are perpendicular to the fenced gated area as shown. Find the area of the grassy area.

48.96 m

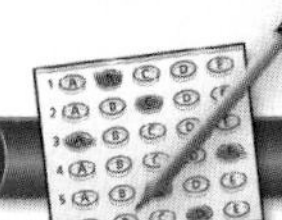

Test Prep

Multiple Choice

38. Which of the following figures has a perimeter that is about the same as the circumference of a circle with a radius of 10 in.? C

A. (10 in. by 10 in.) B. (4 in. by 10 in.) C. (15 in. by 20 in.) D.

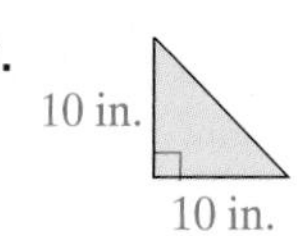

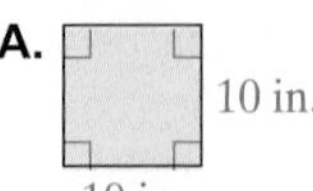

Take It to the NET
Online lesson quiz at **www.PHSchool.com**
Web Code: aca-0808

39. Which of the following is an expression for the area in square meters of the figure at the right? I

F. $4(4\pi) + 4$ G. 8π
H. $4 + 4\pi$ I. $2\pi + 2(2)$

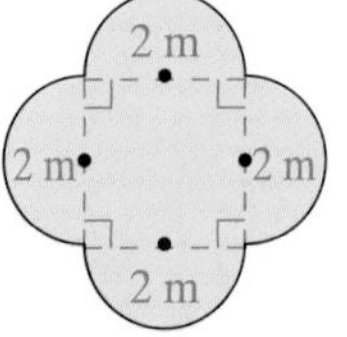

40. What is the approximate circumference of a circle with a radius of 5.2 in.? Use 3 for π. B

A. 15.6 in. B. 31.2 in. C. 40.6 in. D. 81.1 in.

Short Response

41. The running track and field shown at the right is composed of a rectangle and two semicircles. Estimate the area of the track and field. Use 3 for π. Explain. See margin.

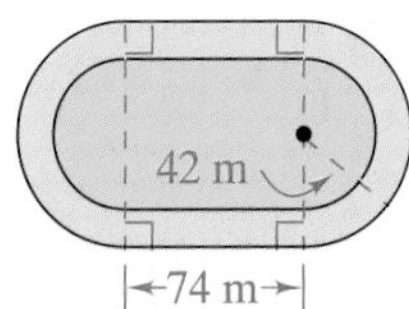

Mixed Review

Lesson 8-4

42. **Paper Folding** If you fold a sheet of paper in half, you get 2 rectangles. If you fold the paper in half again, you get 4 rectangles. How many times must you fold the paper in half before you get 64 rectangles? 6 times

Lesson 8-3

Show that each pair of triangles is congruent.

43.

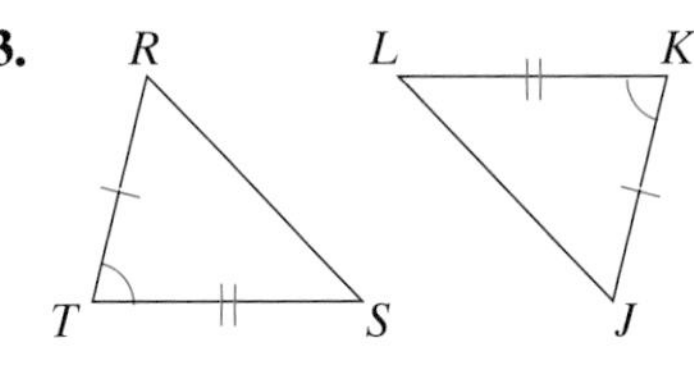

SAS

44. (Triangle PAM with AV perpendicular to PM at V)

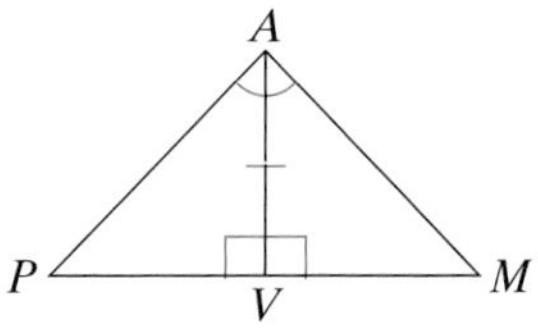

ASA

Lesson 8-2

Show that $c \parallel d$ in each diagram.

45. (Lines c and d cut by a transversal, angles 121° and 121°)

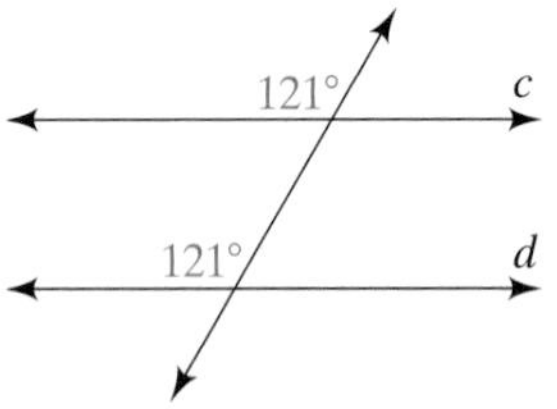

The corresponding angles are congruent.

46.

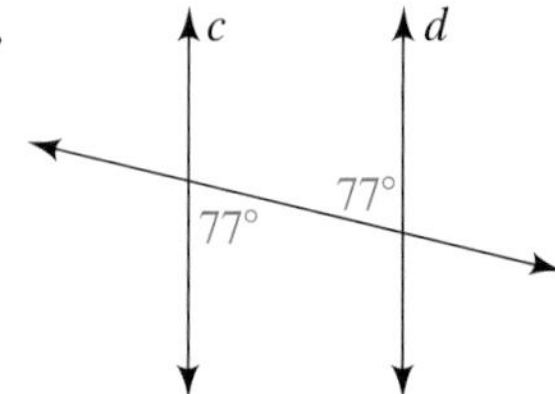

The alternate interior angles are congruent.

41. [2] Use 70 for 74 and 90 for 84 to avoid rounding in the same direction. Use 40 for 42. Substitute into a formula adding the area of a rectangle to the area of a circle.

$$A = \ell w + \pi r^2$$
$$= (70)(90) + 3(40)^2$$
$$= 6{,}300 + 4{,}800$$
$$= 11{,}100 \text{ m}^2$$

[1] minor computational error OR correct answer without explanation

Writing in Math — Writing to Compare

For Use With Exercise 24, page 450

When you are asked to compare two quantities, methods, or concepts, you should identify their similarities and their differences.

On page 450, you will find the following exercise:

24. **Writing in Math** Compare the areas of a circle with diameter 2 in. and a square with side length 2 in.

Here is one student's response.

> **Similarities:**
> The diameter of the circle is the same length as a side of the square.
>
> **Differences:**
> One is a circle; the other is a square. The two figures have different areas.
>
> Area of a circle $= \pi r^2 = \pi(1^2) = \pi(1) = \pi \approx 3.14$
>
> Area of a square $= s^2 = (2)^2 = 4$
>
> The area of the square is greater than the area of the circle.

EXERCISES

1–4. See margin.

1. Another student drew the diagram at the right to answer the problem above. Explain how the diagram compares the areas.

2 in.

2. Compare the areas of the three triangles.

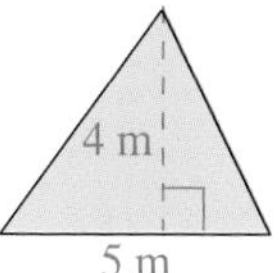

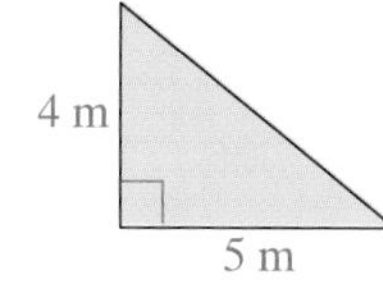

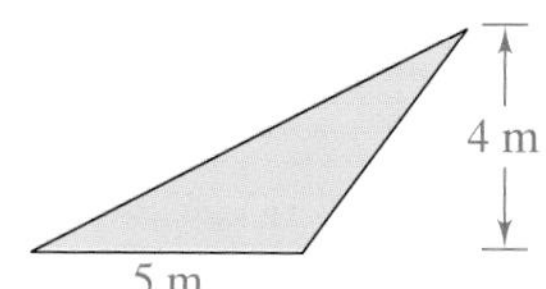

3. Compare two methods for finding the area of the trapezoid below.

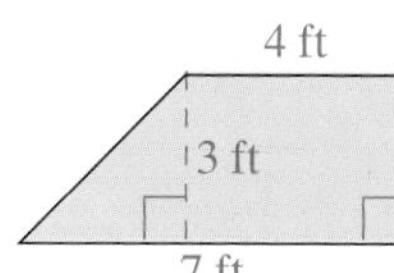

4. Compare the sum of $4\frac{1}{3}$ and $2\frac{5}{8}$ with the sum of $4.\overline{3}$ and 2.625.

Writing in Math

Writing to Compare

Students need to be able to write coherently when formulating and sharing their mathematical ideas and methods. This feature introduces them to the kind of expository writing in which they compare or contrast two things to point out or explain their similarities and differences.

Teaching Notes

Discuss with students the importance of being able to communicate mathematical ideas clearly, succinctly, and effectively.

Examine with students the response presented to the Writing in Math question. Guide students to see that the similarities and differences have been clearly identified and explained. Elicit that the comparison might have included a more precise identification of the difference in areas. Also, it might have been enhanced by including a sketch.

Inclusion
As needed, review the formulas for finding area of circles, triangles, and trapezoids.

Exercises
Have students work independently on the exercises. Then have them share their written comparisons within small groups. Ask students to adjust their responses based upon the group discussion. Guide them to look for ways to make their reasoning more explicit and concise.

1. Answers may vary. Sample: Since the circle fits inside the square, the area of the circle is smaller than the area of the square.

2. Similarities: The three triangles have the same base length and height. They all have an area of 10 m^2. Differences: The three triangles have different shapes.

3. Method 1: Use the formula for the area of a trapezoid. $\frac{1}{2}(b_1 + b_2)h = \frac{1}{2}(4 + 7)(3) = 16.5\ ft^2$ Method 2: Divide the trapezoid into a triangle and a rectangle. Find the area of each piece. Area of the triangle $= \frac{1}{2}(3)(3) = 4.5\ ft^2$. Area of the rectangle $= (3)(4) = 12\ ft^2$. Area of the trapezoid $= 4.5 + 12 = 16.5\ ft^2$. The area of the trapezoid is the same using either method.

4. See back of book.

8-9

1. Plan

Lesson Preview

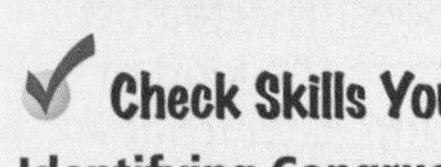

Check Skills You'll Need

Identifying Congruent Parts
Lesson 8-3: Example 1. Extra Practice, p. 709.

Lesson Resources

Optional Materials
- compass
- straightedge

Teaching Resources
Practice, Reteaching, Enrichment
Checkpoint Quiz 2

Reaching All Students
Practice Workbook 8-9
Spanish Practice Workbook 8-9
Reading and Math Literacy 8C
Spanish Reading and Math Literacy 8C
Spanish Checkpoint Quiz 2
Guided Problem Solving 8-9
Hands-On Activities 27

Presentation Assistant Plus!
Transparencies
- Check Skills You'll Need 8-9
- Problem of the Day 8-9
- Additional Examples 8-9
- Lesson Quiz 8-9

PH Presentation Pro CD-ROM 8-9

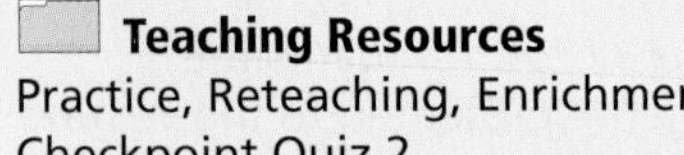

Checkpoint Quiz 2
Computer Test Generator CD

Technology
Resource Pro® CD-ROM
Computer Test Generator CD
PH Presentation Pro CD-ROM

www.PHSchool.com
Student Site
- Teacher Web Code: ack-5500
- Self-grading Lesson Quiz

PH SuccessNet Teacher Center
- Lesson Planner
- Resources

Plus 

8-9 Constructions

What You'll Learn

To construct congruent segments and angles

To construct bisectors

. . . And Why

To make precise drawings, as in Example 1

Check Skills You'll Need

For help, go to Lesson 8-3.

1–2. See below left.

List the congruent parts of each pair of congruent figures.

1. 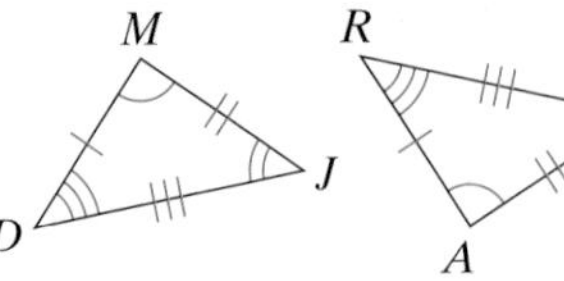

2. 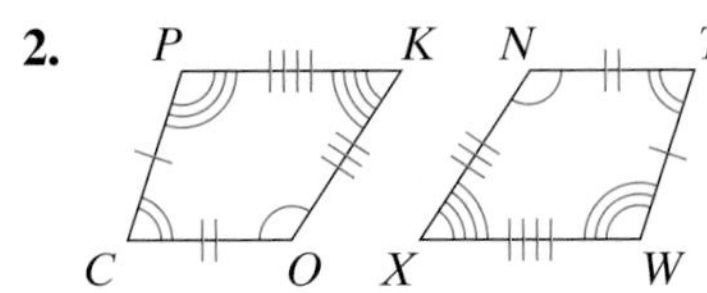

New Vocabulary
- compass
- midpoint
- segment bisector
- perpendicular bisector
- angle bisector

 Interactive lesson includes instant self-check, tutorials, and activities.

OBJECTIVE 1

Constructing Congruent Segments and Angles

Which segment at the left do you think is longer, $\overline{XY}$ or $\overline{UV}$?

Measure each segment. Although $\overline{UV}$ appears to be longer, $\overline{UV}$ and $\overline{XY}$ are actually the same length—that is, $\overline{UV} \cong \overline{XY}$. You can use a compass and a straightedge to construct congruent segments like these.

A **compass** is a tool used to draw circles and parts of circles called *arcs*. A straightedge is like a ruler, but it has no markings on it.

1. $\angle M \cong \angle A$; $\angle J \cong \angle U$; $\angle D \cong \angle R$; $\overline{MJ} \cong \overline{AU}$; $\overline{JD} \cong \overline{UR}$; $\overline{DM} \cong \overline{RA}$

2. $\angle P \cong \angle W$; $\angle K \cong \angle X$; $\angle O \cong \angle N$; $\angle C \cong \angle T$; $\overline{PK} \cong \overline{WX}$; $\overline{KO} \cong \overline{XN}$; $\overline{OC} \cong \overline{NT}$; $\overline{CP} \cong \overline{TW}$

1 EXAMPLE Constructing Congruent Segments

Construct segment $\overline{CD}$ congruent to $\overline{AB}$.

A ——— B

Step 1 Draw a ray with endpoint C.

C ———→

Step 2 Open the compass to the length of $\overline{AB}$.

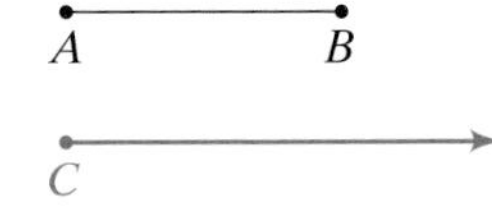

Step 3 Keep the compass open to the same width. Put the compass point on point C. Draw an arc that intersects the ray. Label the point of intersection D.

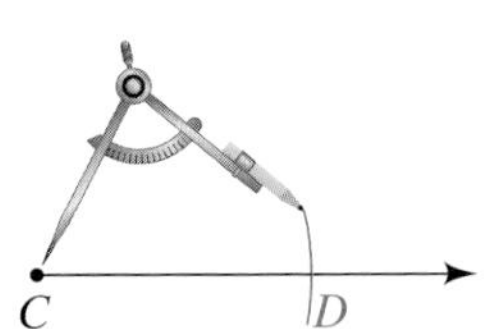

$\overline{CD}$ is congruent to $\overline{AB}$.

Ongoing Assessment and Intervention

Before the Lesson
Diagnose prerequisite skills using:
- Check Skills You'll Need

During the Lesson
Monitor progress using:
- Check Understanding
- Additional Examples
- Test Prep

After the Lesson
Assess knowledge using:
- Lesson Quiz
- Computer Test Generator CD
- Chapter Checkpoint 2 (p. 459)

Check Understanding 1 Draw a segment $\overline{TR}$ that is 25 mm long. Construct $\overline{SV}$ congruent to $\overline{TR}$. See below left.

You can also use a compass and straightedge to construct an angle congruent to a given angle.

2 EXAMPLE Constructing Congruent Angles

Construct $\angle S$ congruent to $\angle Y$.

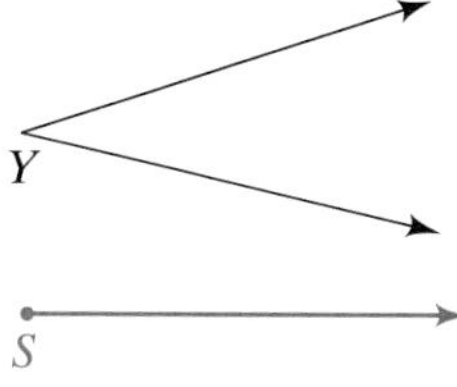

Step 1 Draw a ray with endpoint S.

Step 2 Put the compass tip at Y and draw an arc that intersects the sides of $\angle Y$. Label the points of intersection X and Z.

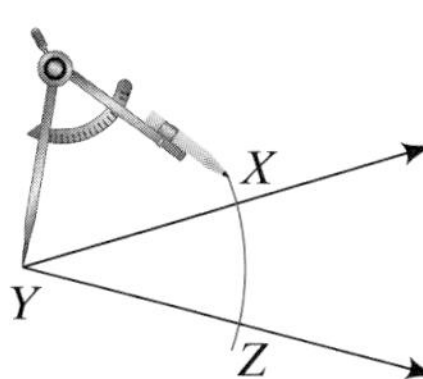

Step 3 Keep the compass open to the same width. Put the compass tip at S. Draw an arc that intersects the ray at a point T.

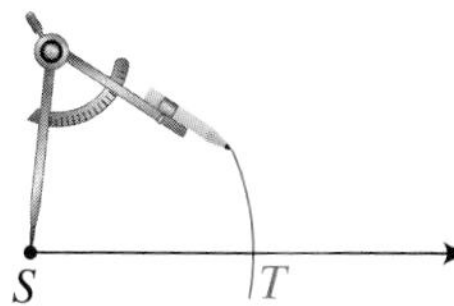

Step 4 Adjust the compass width so that the tip is at Z and the pencil is at X.

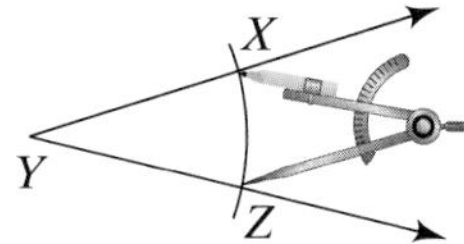

Step 5 Keep the compass open to the same width. Put the compass tip at T and draw an arc that intersects the first arc at point R.

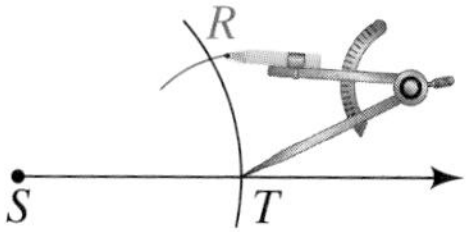

Step 6 Draw $\overrightarrow{SR}$.

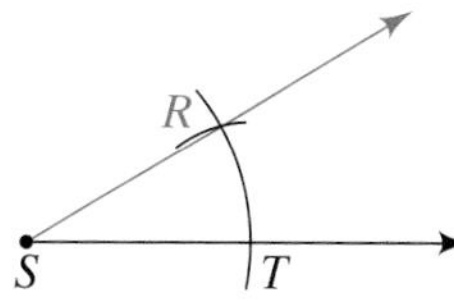

$\angle S$ is congruent to $\angle Y$.

Real-World Connection

Careers Marine pilots use compasses on maps to navigate ships in and out of harbors and through waterways.

1.

T 25 mm R

S V

Check Understanding 2 **a.** Draw an obtuse angle and label it $\angle F$. Then construct $\angle N$ congruent to $\angle F$. See back of book.

b. Reasoning Do you need to know the measure of an angle to construct a congruent angle? Explain. No; the construction copies the angle without measuring it.

2. Teach

Math Background

Euclid, the "father" of geometry, stated, in about 300 B.C., that formal geometric constructions be made with only an unmarked straightedge and a compass. Operating within these rules, you can construct many interesting figures without having to use a particular unit of measurement.

Teaching Notes

Tactile Learners
Have students practice using the compass by drawing circles and arcs until they are comfortable with changing the opening. Then they can produce carefully-drawn figures.

1 EXAMPLE Inclusion

Some students may have difficulty handling the compass and straightedge. Have them work with a partner who can help with the constructions.

2 EXAMPLE Teaching Tip

Ask: *Why do you draw the arc to find points X and Z and T?* This is so that you find the opening of both angles at the same distance from the vertex.

PowerPoint

Additional Examples

1. Use a ruler to draw a segment $\overline{KJ}$ that is 18 mm long. Construct $\overline{FG}$ congruent to $\overline{KJ}$.

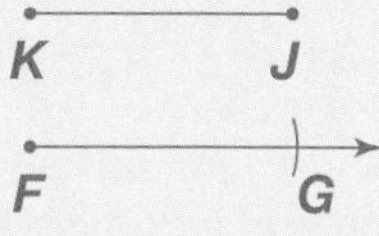

2. Use a protractor to draw a 40° angle and label it $\angle B$. Construct $\angle N$ congruent to $\angle B$.

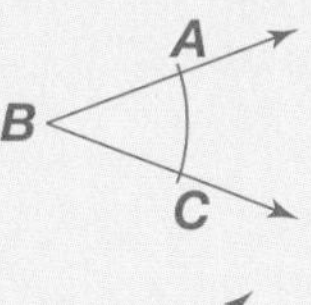

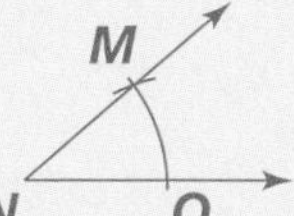

Reaching All Students

Below Level Review the meaning of *line*, *line segment*, *ray*, and *perpendicular*. Have students write the mathematical symbols for each.	**Advanced Learners** Have students construct an isosceles right triangle and verify that the acute angles are each 45°.	**Inclusion** See note on page 455. **Tactile Learners** See note on page 455.

Auditory Learners
Have students read aloud the statements in the figure above Example 3 to make sure that they say, for example, "line PQ is perpendicular to line segment GH," and so on.

4 EXAMPLE Teaching Tip

Ask: *What do you do if, in Step 2, the arcs do not intersect?* Open the compass wider and repeat Step 2.

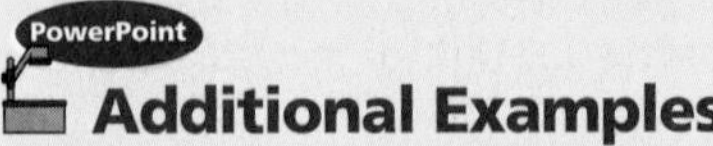

Additional Examples

3 Mark points *B* and *K* on a sheet of notebook paper. Then construct the perpendicular bisector of $\overline{BK}$.

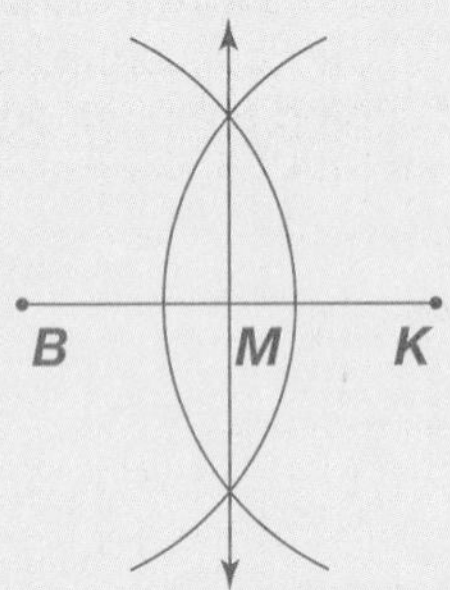

4 Use a protractor to draw a 80° angle and label it ∠*B*. Construct the angle bisector of ∠*B*.

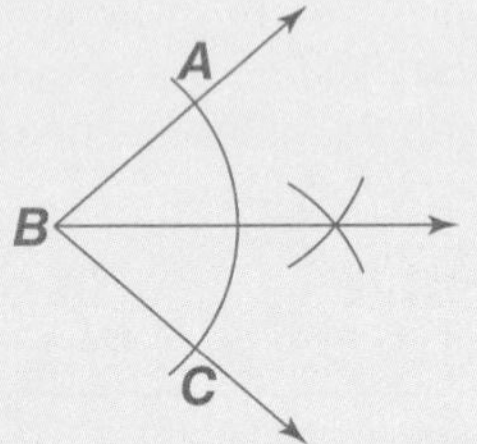

Closure

- *What tools can you use when you make a geometric construction?* an unmarked straightedge and a compass
- *In a construction, why do you leave your arcs and other compass marks visible instead of erasing them?* Sample: so someone else can see how you did the steps of the construction

OBJECTIVE

2 Constructing Bisectors

In addition to congruent figures, you can use a compass and a straightedge to construct bisectors.

Here are some important terms associated with bisectors and perpendicular lines.

Reading Math
The prefix *bi* means "two." A bicycle has two wheels. When you *bisect* a segment, you divide it into two congruent parts.

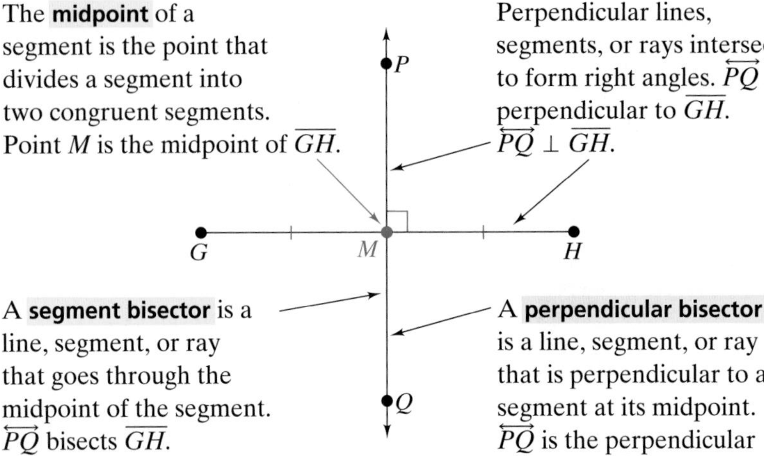

The **midpoint** of a segment is the point that divides a segment into two congruent segments. Point M is the midpoint of $\overline{GH}$.
Perpendicular lines, segments, or rays intersect to form right angles. $\overleftrightarrow{PQ}$ is perpendicular to $\overline{GH}$. $\overleftrightarrow{PQ} \perp \overline{GH}$.
P
G
M
H
Q
A **segment bisector** is a line, segment, or ray that goes through the midpoint of the segment. $\overleftrightarrow{PQ}$ bisects $\overline{GH}$.
A **perpendicular bisector** is a line, segment, or ray that is perpendicular to a segment at its midpoint. $\overleftrightarrow{PQ}$ is the perpendicular bisector of $\overline{GH}$.

3 EXAMPLE Constructing Perpendicular Bisectors

Construct the perpendicular bisector of $\overline{AB}$.

Step 1 Open the compass to more than half the length of $\overline{AB}$. Put the compass tip at A. Draw an arc intersecting $\overline{AB}$. Keep the compass open to the same width. Repeat with the compass tip at B.

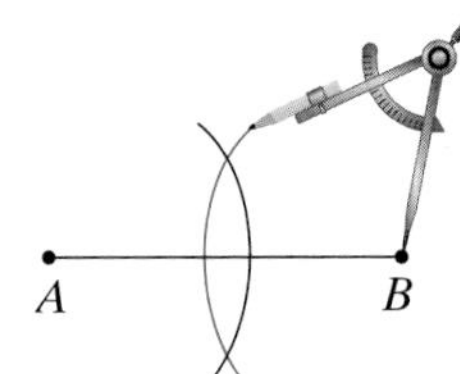

Step 2 Label the points of intersection of the arcs C and D. Draw $\overleftrightarrow{CD}$.

Step 3 Label the intersection of $\overline{AB}$ and $\overleftrightarrow{CD}$ point M.

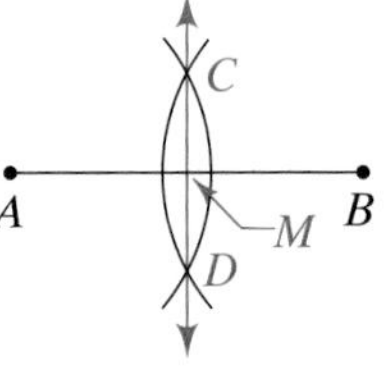

$\overleftrightarrow{CD}$ is the perpendicular bisector of $\overline{AB}$. Point M is the midpoint of $\overline{AB}$.

3a.

Check Understanding 3 **a.** Draw a segment that is 4 in. long. Construct the perpendicular bisector of the segment. See above left.

b. **Reasoning** Suppose $\overleftrightarrow{JK}$ is a segment bisector of $\overline{PR}$ at point Q. If $\overline{PQ}$ is 3 cm long, what is the length of $\overline{QR}$? 3 cm

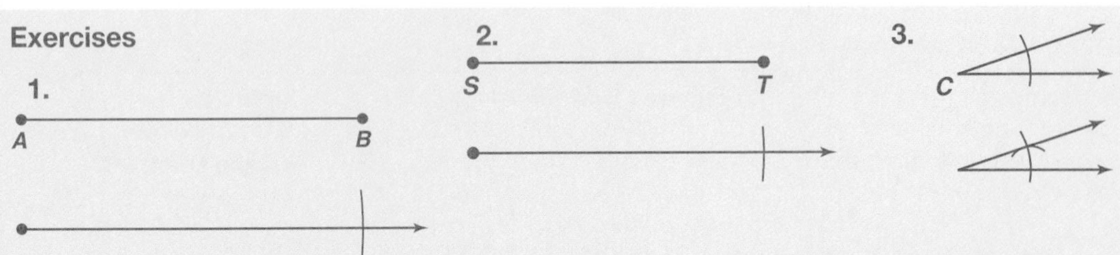

An **angle bisector** is a ray that divides an angle into two congruent angles.

4 EXAMPLE Constructing Angle Bisectors

Construct the angle bisector of $\angle P$ at the right.

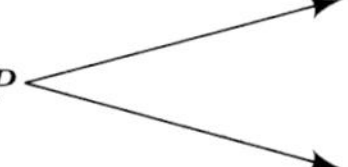

4a.

4b.

Step 1 Put the compass tip at $\angle P$. Draw an arc that intersects the sides of $\angle P$. Label the points of intersection S and T.

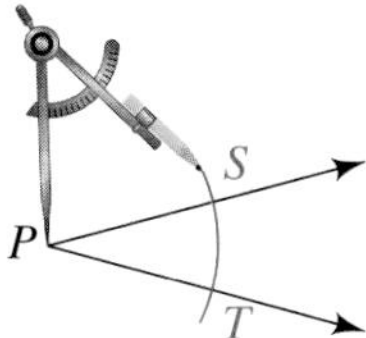

Step 2 Put the compass tip at S. Draw an arc. Keep the compass open to the same width. Repeat with the compass tip at T. Be sure the arcs intersect.

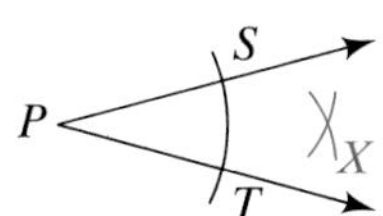

Step 3 Label the intersection of the arcs X. Draw $\overleftrightarrow{PX}$.

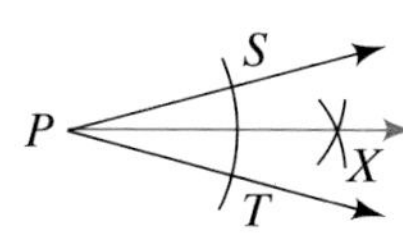

$\overleftrightarrow{PX}$ is the angle bisector of $\angle P$.

Check Understanding 4 **a.** Draw an acute angle. Construct its angle bisector. 4a–b. See above left.
b. Draw an obtuse angle. Construct its angle bisector.

EXERCISES

 For more practice, see *Extra Practice.*

A Practice by Example

Example 1 (page 454)

Copy each segment. Then construct a congruent segment. 1–2. See margin.

1. A B

2. S T

Example 2 (page 455)

Copy each angle. Then construct a congruent angle. 3–4. See margin.

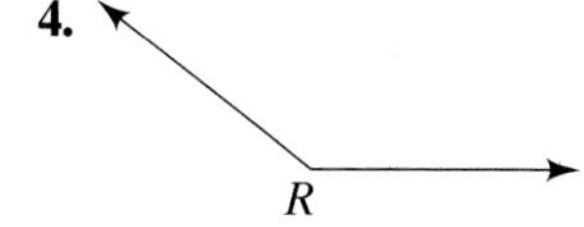

3. C

4. R

Example 3 (page 456)

Draw each segment. Then construct its perpendicular bisector. 5–6. See back of book.

5. a segment 5 in. long

6. a segment 10 cm long

Example 4 (page 457)

Draw each angle. Then construct its angle bisector. 7–8. See margin.

7. an obtuse angle

8. an acute angle

4.

R

7.

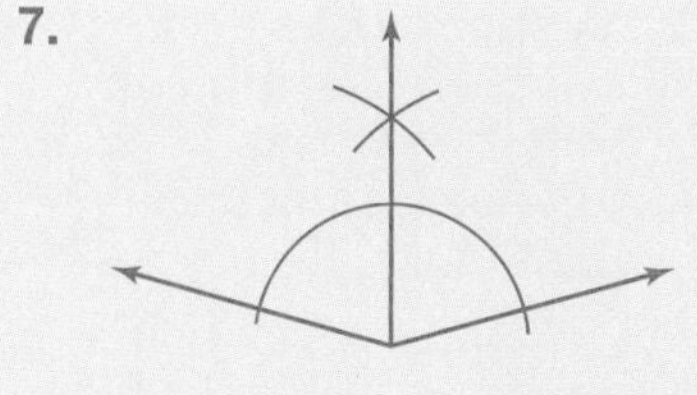

8.

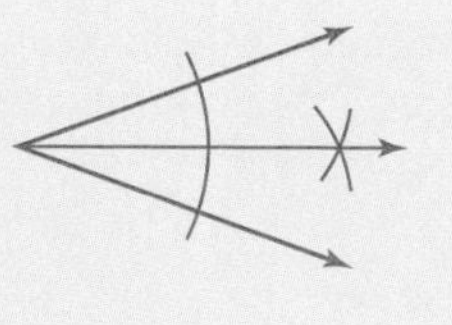

3. Practice

Assignment Guide

Objective 1

A B Core 1–4, 10–11, 13

Objective 2

A B Core 5–9, 12, 14–16

C Extension 17–20

Test Prep 21–24

Mixed Review 25–31

Error Prevention!

Exercises 1–8 Students should verify that their compass opening remains unchanged.

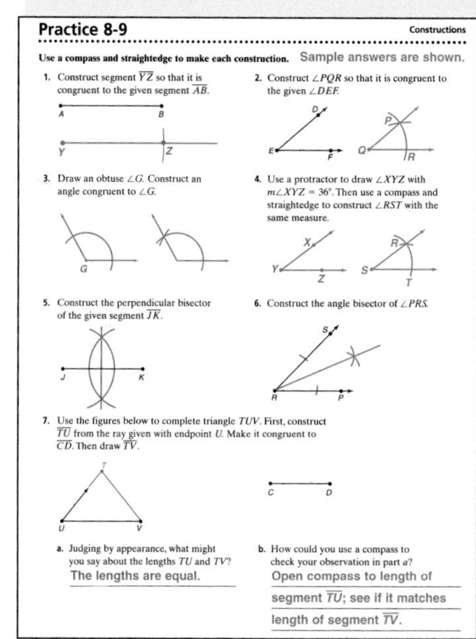

Practice 8-9 Constructions

Use a compass and straightedge to make each construction. Sample answers are shown.

1. Construct segment $\overline{YZ}$ so that it is congruent to the given segment $\overline{AB}$.
2. Construct $\angle PQR$ so that it is congruent to the given $\angle DEF$.
3. Draw an obtuse $\angle G$. Construct an angle congruent to $\angle G$.
4. Use a protractor to draw $\angle XYZ$ with $m\angle XYZ = 36°$. Then use a compass and straightedge to construct $\angle RST$ with the same measure.
5. Construct the perpendicular bisector of the given segment $\overline{JK}$.
6. Construct the angle bisector of $\angle PRS$.
7. Use the figures below to complete triangle TUV. First, construct $\overline{TU}$ from the ray given with endpoint U. Make it congruent to $\overline{CD}$. Then draw $\overline{TV}$.
   a. Judging by appearance, what might you say about the lengths TU and TV? The lengths are equal.
   b. How could you use a compass to check your observation in part *a*? Open compass to length of segment $\overline{TU}$; see if it matches length of segment $\overline{TV}$.

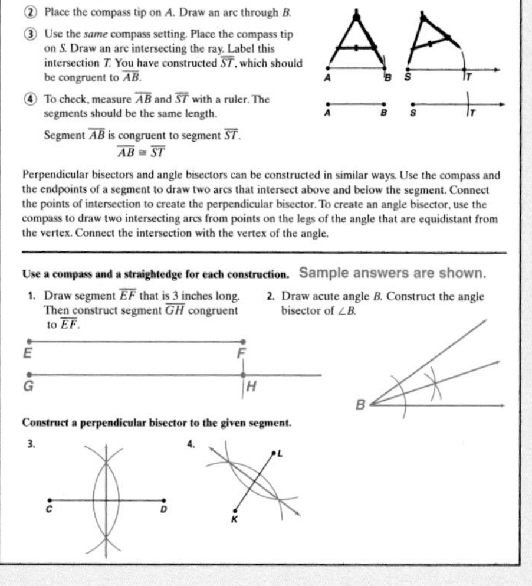

Reteaching 8-9 Constructions

Congruent segments are segments that have the same length. You can use a *compass* and a straightedge to construct one segment congruent to another segment.

① Start with segment $\overline{AB}$. Draw a ray with endpoint S that is longer than $\overline{AB}$.
② Place the compass tip on A. Draw an arc through B.
③ Use the *same* compass setting. Place the compass tip on S. Draw an arc intersecting the ray. Label this intersection T. You have constructed $\overline{ST}$, which should be congruent to $\overline{AB}$.
④ To check, measure $\overline{AB}$ and $\overline{ST}$ with a ruler. The segments should be the same length.

Segment $\overline{AB}$ is congruent to segment $\overline{ST}$.
$\overline{AB} \cong \overline{ST}$

Perpendicular bisectors and angle bisectors can be constructed in similar ways. Use the compass and the endpoints of a segment to draw two arcs that intersect above and below the segment. Connect the points of intersection to create the perpendicular bisector. To create an angle bisector, use the compass to draw two intersecting arcs from points on the legs of the angle that are equidistant from the vertex. Connect the intersection with the vertex of the angle.

Use a compass and a straightedge for each construction. Sample answers are shown.

1. Draw segment $\overline{EF}$ that is 3 inches long. Then construct segment $\overline{GH}$ congruent to $\overline{EF}$.
2. Draw acute angle B. Construct the angle bisector of $\angle B$.

Construct a perpendicular bisector to the given segment.

3.
4.

B Apply Your Skills  **9.** The bisector of $\angle ABC$ is $\overrightarrow{BD}$. If $m\angle ABC$ is 38°, what is $m\angle ABD$? 19°

10. Draw $\overline{MN}$ about 4 in. long. Then construct each segment.

a. $\overline{JK}$ twice as long as $\overline{MN}$ **b.** $\overline{CD}$ half as long as $\overline{MN}$

10a–b. See margin.

11. Draw a large triangle $\triangle ABC$. Construct a triangle congruent to $\triangle ABC$. Check students' work.

12. Reasoning How many midpoints does a segment have? How many segment bisectors? How many perpendicular bisectors? See margin.

13. Follow these steps to construct $\triangle EFG$ with all sides congruent to $\overline{XY}$.

Step 1 Draw a segment $\overline{XY}$. Use a compass to construct $\overline{EF} \cong \overline{XY}$.

Step 2 Using the same compass width, place the compass tip on point F and draw an arc above $\overline{EF}$.

Step 3 Using the same compass width, place the compass tip on point E and make another arc above $\overline{EF}$, intersecting the first arc. Label the intersection G.

Step 4 Draw $\overline{EG}$ and $\overline{GF}$ to form $\triangle EFG$. Check students' work.

14. a. Patterns Draw a large acute triangle. Construct the bisector of each angle. Describe the intersection of the three angle bisectors.

b. Repeat for an obtuse triangle. 14a–b. Check students' work.

c. Make a conjecture about the angle bisectors of any triangle. The angle bisectors intersect at the same point.

15c. The perpendicular bisectors intersect at the same point.

15. a. Patterns Draw a large acute triangle. Construct the perpendicular bisector of each side. Describe the intersection of the three bisectors.

b. Repeat for an obtuse triangle. 15a–b. Check students' work.

c. Make a conjecture about the perpendicular bisectors of any triangle.

16.  Describe how to construct a 45° angle. See margin.

C Challenge

Algebra For Exercises 17–19, $\overleftrightarrow{BD}$ is the angle bisector of $\angle ABC$. Write and solve an equation to find $m\angle ABC$. (*Hint:* Draw a diagram.)

17. $m\angle ABD = 4x, m\angle DBC = 3x + 15$ 120°

18. $m\angle ABC = 5x - 8, m\angle CBD = 2x + 1$ 42°

19. $m\angle DBA = 3x - 7, m\angle DBC = x + 9$ 34°

20. Stretch Your Thinking Using three 3's, write an expression that equals 4. $3\frac{3}{3}$

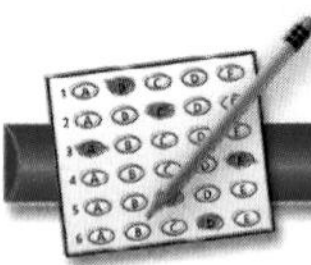

Test Prep

Multiple Choice

21. $\overrightarrow{KM}$ is the angle bisector of $\angle JKL$. If $m\angle JKM = 66°$, what is $m\angle JKL$? D

A. 22° **B.** 33° **C.** 66° **D.** 132°

22. Suppose you construct the perpendicular bisector of $\overline{AB}$ and label the midpoint C. You then bisect the congruent segments at points D and E. If $\overline{AB}$ is 48 cm long, what is the length of $\overline{CD}$? F

F. 12 cm **G.** 24 cm **H.** 36 cm **I.** 48 cm

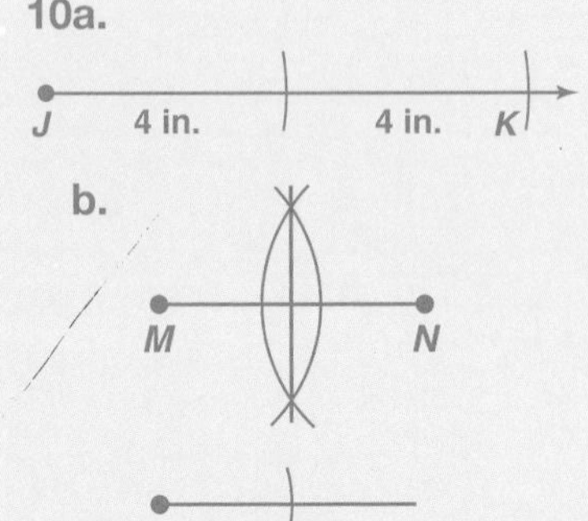

 Use the Guided Problem Solving worksheet with Exercise 9.

12. A segment has one midpoint, an infinite number of bisectors, and one perpendicular bisector.

16. Answers may vary. Sample: Draw a segment. Construct its perpendicular bisector. Then construct the angle bisector of one of the 90° angles formed.

Online lesson quiz at **www.PHSchool.com**
Web Code: aca-0809

23. The drawing below shows how to do which construction? C

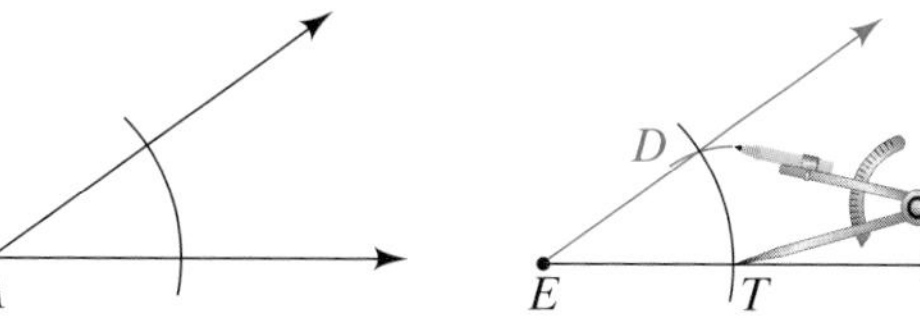

A. perpendicular lines
B. congruent segments
C. congruent angles
D. angle bisector

Extended Response

24. $\overleftrightarrow{PQ}$ bisects $\overline{ST}$ at point M. If $\overline{SM} = 5x - 4$ and $\overline{MT} = 3x + 8$, what is x? What is the length of $\overline{ST}$? Explain in words.
See back of book.

Mixed Review

Lesson 7-5

25. Astronomy Light travels at 3.00×10^8 m/s. How long does it take for light to travel 4.1×10^{16} m from the star Alpha Centauri to Earth? 1.37×10^8 s

Lesson 6-9

Probability **Find each probability if you spin the spinner once.** A spinner has 26 sections of equal size. Each section is labeled with a different letter of the alphabet. Express each probability as a fraction.

26. $P(\text{K})$ $\frac{1}{26}$
27. $P(\text{M, A, T, or H})$ $\frac{2}{13}$
28. $P(\text{a vowel})$ $\frac{5}{26}$
29. $P(\text{a consonant})$ $\frac{21}{26}$
30. $P(\text{a letter before G})$ $\frac{3}{13}$
31. $P(\text{a letter after Q})$ $\frac{9}{26}$

Checkpoint Quiz 2 — Lessons 8-5 through 8-9

Instant self-check quiz online and on CD-ROM

Determine the best name for each polygon. Then find the area. 1–3. See margin.

1.

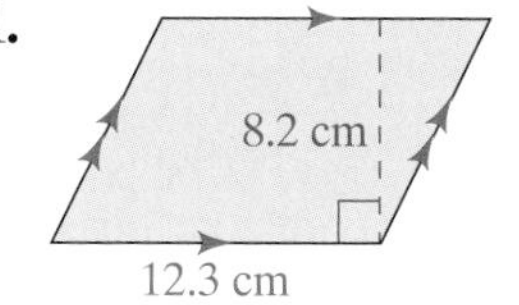

2.

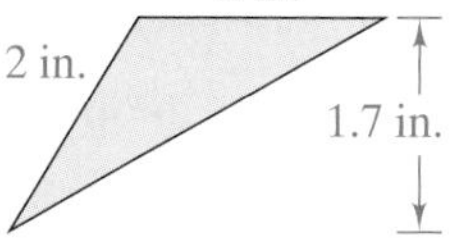

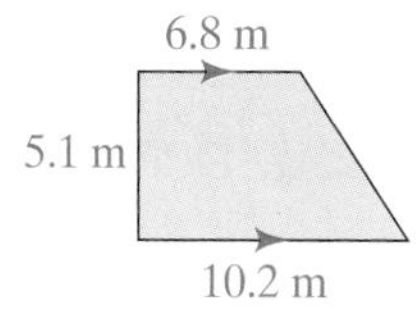

3. 6.8 m, 5.1 m, 10.2 m

143°, 109°, x°, 101°, 124°, 110°

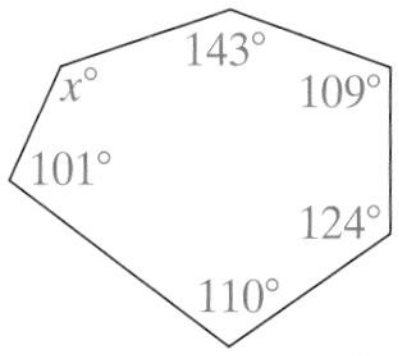

4. Find the missing angle measure in the figure at the left. 133°

Draw and label a figure to fit each description. 5–6. See back of book.

5. a scalene obtuse triangle
6. an equilateral triangle

Find the circumference and area of a circle with the given radius or diameter. Round to the nearest tenth.

7. $d = 2.3$ in. 7.2 in.; 4.2 in.^{2}
8. $r = 18.1$ ft 113.7 ft; 1,029.2 ft^2
9. $r = 6.5$ cm 40.8 cm; 132.7 cm^2

10. Draw an angle $\angle A$. Construct $\angle B$ congruent to $\angle A$.
See back of book.

4. Assess

1. Draw a segment $\overline{WX}$ that is 1 in. long. Construct $\overline{PQ}$ congruent to $\overline{WX}$.

2. Draw an acute angle and construct its angle bisector.

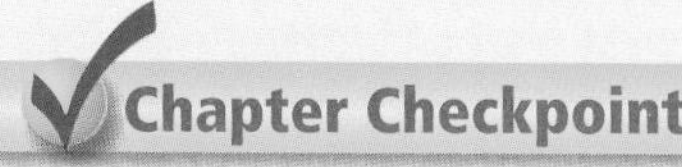

To check understanding of Lessons 8-5 to 8-9:

Checkpoint Quiz 2 (p. 459)

Teaching Resources
Checkpoint Quiz 2 (also in *Prentice Hall Assessment System*)

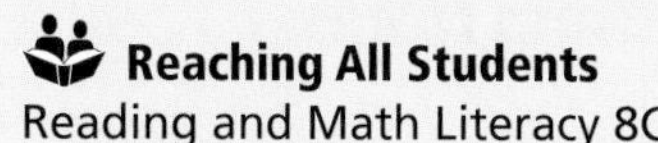
Reaching All Students
Reading and Math Literacy 8C

Spanish versions available

Checkpoint Quiz 2
1. parallelogram; 100.86 cm^2
2. obtuse isosceles triangle; 1.7 in.^{2}
3. trapezoid; 43.35 m^2

Enrichment 8-9 — Constructions

Geometric Tools

Draw an isosceles triangle with side lengths of 4 in. and 7 in. Determine the length of the third side. Is this the only possible isosceles triangle that has the side lengths 4 in. and 7 in.? Explain.

1. What defines an isosceles triangle?
Sample answer: 2 sides with equal lengths.
2. If only *one* side measures 4 in., what will be the measures of the other two sides?
7 in.; 7 in.
3. If only *one* side measures 7 in., what will be the measures of the other two sides?
4 in.; 4 in.
4. Use a compass and a ruler to draw one of the triangles on another sheet of paper. Draw a segment. Set the compass to one of your measures. Place the compass on each endpoint and draw two intersecting arcs above it. Connect the three points.
Check students' constructions
5. Measure the sides. One side should measure 4 in. and another side should measure 7 in. What is the measure of the third side?
7 in. or 4 in.
6. Repeat the procedure in Exercise 4 to draw different triangles. How many triangles can you draw? Explain.
2 triangles; Since two sides must be the same length, there are only two different combinations for the sides.
7. How can you use the relationship between the measures of the sides of a triangle to determine whether or not you can draw an isosceles triangle with any given measures?
Check that the sum of the measures of any two sides is greater than the measure of the third side.
8. Draw an isosceles triangle with side lengths of 2 cm and 5 cm. Determine the length of the third side. Is this the only possible isosceles triangle that has the side lengths 2 cm and 5 cm? Explain.
Sample answer: 2 cm, 5 cm, 5 cm; yes; only one triangle is possible.

Test Prep

Resources
For additional practice with a variety of test item formats:
- Test Prep, p. 465
- Test-Taking Strategies, p. 461
- Test-Taking Strategies with Transparencies

Alternative Assessment

Each student in a pair draws a line segment and trade papers with a partner. Partners construct a congruent segment and then find the perpendicular bisector of the original segment.

Geometry Software and Constructions

Learning about constructions in a computer-based environment can expand students' understanding of important geometric properties and procedures. In Lesson 8-9, students learned how to bisect angles and to construct perpendicular bisectors. In this activity, they use geometry software to continue their investigation of those two kinds of constructions and other constructions.

Resources

Students may use any dynamic geometry software application that can perform constructions and transformations.

Teaching Notes

Inclusion
Review, using sketches as needed, the meanings of the terms *perpendicular, bisector, midpoint, ray, intersections, vertex,* and *reflection*. Have students work in small groups with more advanced students who can demonstrate and help with key concepts and computer commands.

Teaching Tip
Have students work in small groups to complete the exercises. Have them share their constructions, methods, and conclusions with other groups.

Ask groups to prepare a written comparison that highlights the similarities and differences in the process of making constructions with and without a computer. Have groups share their findings.

Technology Geometry Software and Constructions

For Use With Lesson 8-9

Geometry software can make various types of constructions. You can use the *Construct* menu to create perpendicular bisectors and angle bisectors. You will notice that, once you have made a construction, the properties that you built into the construction will remain intact.

1 EXAMPLE

- Draw $\overline{AB}$. Highlight $\overline{AB}$ and use the *Construct* menu to construct the midpoint of $\overline{AB}$. Label this point C.
- Highlight $\overline{AB}$ and C and use the *Construct* menu to construct a perpendicular line through $\overline{AB}$ at C.

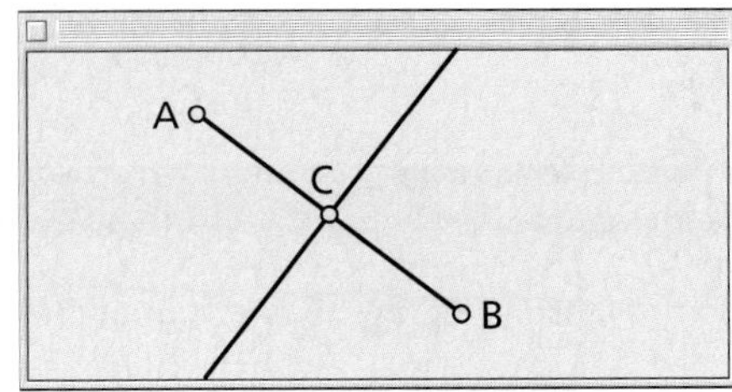

2 EXAMPLE

- Draw $\angle ABC$. Highlight all three vertices of $\angle ABC$, making sure that B is the second vertex highlighted.
- Use the *Construct* menu to create the angle bisector of $\angle ABC$.

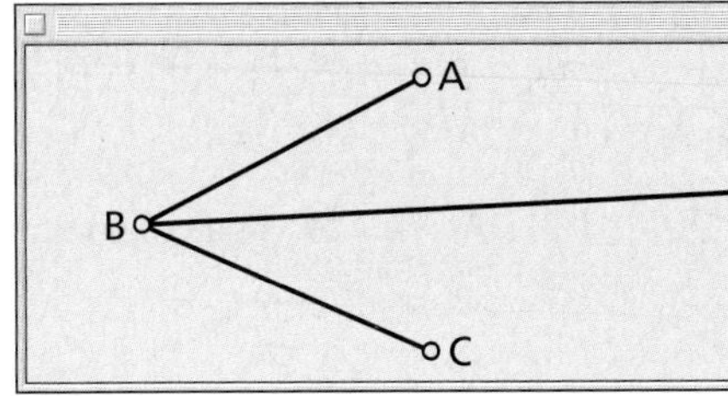

EXERCISES

1. Draw $\angle ABC$ and use *Construct* and *Angle Bisector* to create an angle whose measure is $\frac{1}{4}$ of $m\angle ABC$. Check students' work.

2. a. Draw $\overline{AB}$ and construct its midpoint D and its perpendicular bisector. Construct another point C on the perpendicular bisector. Draw $\overline{AC}$ and $\overline{BC}$. Check students' work.

b. What type of triangle is $\triangle ABC$? isosceles

c. Drag the vertices of $\triangle ABC$ and verify that your classification holds. Check students' work.

3. a. Draw $\overline{AB}$ and construct its perpendicular bisector as seen in the diagram. Construct point C on this perpendicular bisector and use the *Transform* menu to reflect C over $\overline{AB}$. Label this point D. Draw segments connecting points A, C, B, and D. Check students' work.

b. What type of quadrilateral is $ACBD$? rhombus

c. Drag the vertices of $ACBD$ to verify that your classification holds. Check students' work.

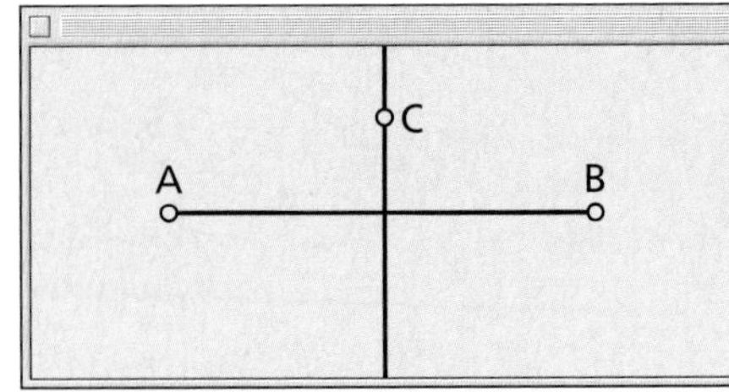

Test-Taking Strategies

Drawing a Diagram

Drawing a diagram using given information may help you solve a problem.

1 EXAMPLE

Three cars, A, B, and C, are parked in that order in the same row of a parking lot. The distance between B and C is twice the distance between A and B. The distance between A and C is 3 m more than the distance between B and C. Find the distance between A and B and the distance between B and C.

Let points A, B, and C represent the cars and x be the distance from A to B.

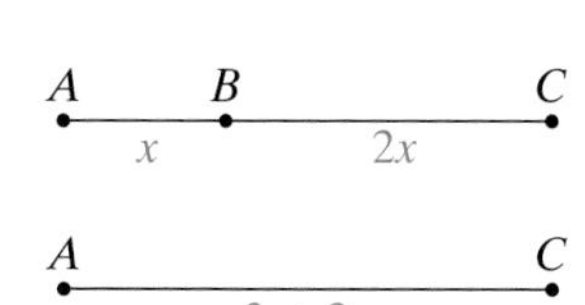

$x + 2x = 3 + 2x$ ← **Use the diagram to write an equation.**

$3x = 3 + 2x$ ← **Combine like terms.**

$3x - 2x = 3 + 2x - 2x$ ← **Subtract 2x from each side.**

$x = 3$ ← **Simplify.**

So, $AB = 3$ m and $BC = 2(3 \text{ m}) = 6$ m.

2 EXAMPLE

The points $D(-1, 1)$, $E(1, 4)$, and $F(5, -3)$ form a right triangle. Which two segments form the right angle of $\triangle DEF$?

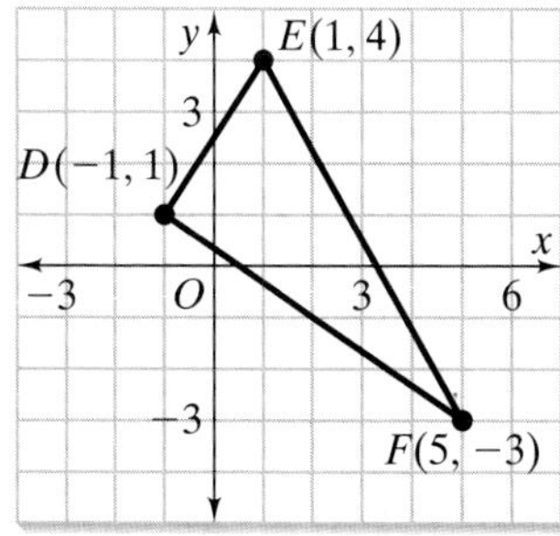

If two lines form a right angle, the product of their slopes is -1. When you draw a diagram, it looks like the right angle is at point D. Check to see whether the product of the slopes of $\overline{DE}$ and $\overline{DF}$ is -1.

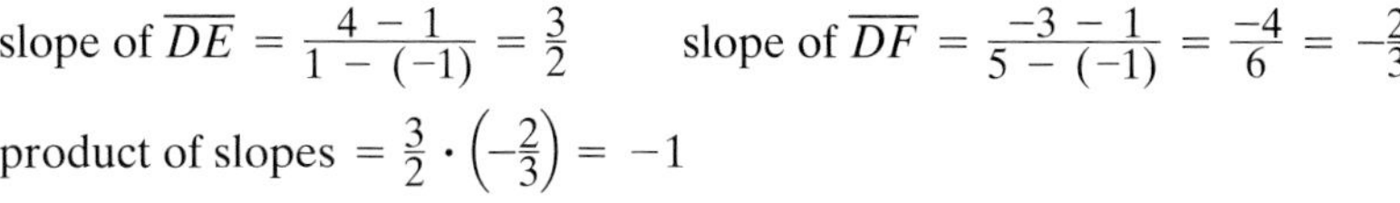

slope of $\overline{DE} = \frac{4 - 1}{1 - (-1)} = \frac{3}{2}$ slope of $\overline{DF} = \frac{-3 - 1}{5 - (-1)} = \frac{-4}{6} = -\frac{2}{3}$

product of slopes $= \frac{3}{2} \cdot \left(-\frac{2}{3}\right) = -1$

So, $\overline{DE}$ and $\overline{DF}$ form the right angle of $\triangle DEF$.

EXERCISES

Draw a diagram to solve each problem.

1. Jorge's house (J), Kate's house (K), and Lin's house (L) lie in that order on a straight road. The distance from K to L is 4 times the distance from J to K. The distance from J to L is 36 yd more than 3 times the distance from J to K. What is the distance from Jorge's house to Kate's? **18 yd**

2. $F(7, 1)$, $G(2, 1)$, $H(2, 6)$, and $I(7, 6)$ are the vertices of rectangle $FGHI$. Which sides are parallel to the x-axis? To the y-axis? **$\overline{GF}$ and $\overline{HI}$; $\overline{GH}$ and $\overline{FI}$ (vertices labeled clockwise)**

Test-Taking Strategies

Drawing a Diagram

This feature presents the effective test-taking strategy of drawing a diagram to help solve a problem.

Resources

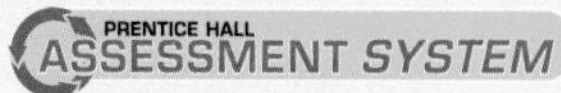

Test-Taking Strategies with Transparencies
- Transparency 9
- Practice master, p. 32

Teaching Notes

Discuss with students that sometimes drawing a diagram or a sketch can help them more clearly understand geometric relationships presented only in words.

Error Prevention!

Stress the importance of making a diagram that accurately represents the data provided. Guide students to reread the text after they have drawn their diagrams to make sure that they have presented the identical information.

2 EXAMPLE Inclusion

As students work through this example, help them draw upon their understanding of the relationship between slopes of perpendicular lines.

Test-Taking Strategies With Transparencies

Chapter 8: Drawing a Diagram

Exercises

Draw a diagram to help you solve each problem.

1. In Nathan's neighborhood, the library (L), the school (S), and the grocery store (G) lie on a straight road in that order. The distance from S to G is 5 times the distance from L to S. The distance from L to G is 28 more than 4 times the distance from L to S. What is the distance between the library and the school? 14 yd
2. $R(3, 4)$, $S(8, 4)$, and $T(1, 1)$ are three vertices of two parallelograms, in no particular order. Find the coordinates of U, the fourth vertex in each parallelogram. parallelogram $RSTU$ (6, 1) and parallelogram $RSUT$ (−4, 1)
3. Rhombus $RHOM$ has vertices $R(2, 7)$, $H(6, 0)$, $O(2, -7)$ and $M(-4, 0)$. Find the product of the diagonals, $\overline{RO}$ and $\overline{MH}$. −1
4. Triangle ABC is an isosceles triangle. Side $\overline{BA}$ has the same length as side $\overline{BC}$. $A(7, 4)$ and $B(5, 3)$ are coordinates of two vertices of the triangle. Find the coordinates of C. (7, 3)
5. Maple Street is parallel to Elm Street. Oak Street is perpendicular to Maple Street. Chestnut Street is perpendicular to Elm Street. Are Chestnut Street and Oak Street parallel? yes
6. The light from a night watchman's tower extends 440 yd in all directions. What is the area covered by the night watchman's light? 607,904 yd^2
7. Natalie rides her bike from her house to her friend Jon's house. She rides 5 blocks north, 2 blocks east, 3 blocks north, then 4 blocks east. A path goes straight from her house to Jon's house. How many blocks would she have walked if she had taken the path? 10 blocks
8. The length of a rectangle is 9 more than 4 times the width. The perimeter of the rectangle is 128 cm. Find the length and width of the perimeter. $l = 53$ cm, $w = 11$ cm

Resources

Student Edition
Extra Practice, Ch. 8, p. 709
English/Spanish Glossary, p. 735
Table of Symbols, p. 730

 **Reaching All Students**
Reading and Math Literacy 8D
Spanish Reading and Math Literacy 8D

Test Preparation
- Chapter 8 practice in test formats

www.PHSchool.com
Student Site
- Self-grading vocabulary test

PH SuccessNet Teacher Center
- Resources

Plus iTEXT

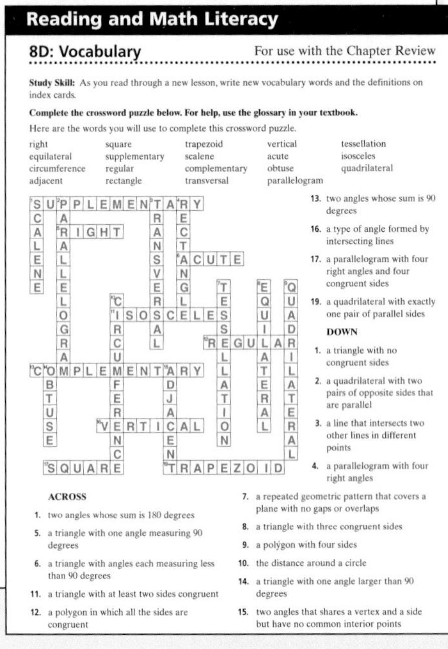

Spanish Reading and Math Literacy

Reading and Math Literacy

8D: Vocabulary — For use with the Chapter Review

Study Skill: As you read through a new lesson, write new vocabulary words and the definitions on index cards.

Complete the crossword puzzle below. For help, use the glossary in your textbook.

Here are the words you will use to complete this crossword puzzle.

right	square	trapezoid	vertical	tessellation
equilateral	supplementary	scalene	acute	isosceles
circumference	regular	complementary	obtuse	quadrilateral
adjacent	rectangle	transversal	parallelogram	

ACROSS

1. two angles whose sum is 180 degrees
5. a triangle with one angle measuring 90 degrees
6. a triangle with angles each measuring less than 90 degrees
11. a triangle with at least two sides congruent
12. a polygon in which all the sides are congruent
13. two angles whose sum is 90 degrees
16. a type of angle formed by intersecting lines
17. a parallelogram with four right angles and four congruent sides
19. a quadrilateral with exactly one pair of parallel sides

DOWN

1. a triangle with no congruent sides
2. a quadrilateral with two pairs of opposite sides that are parallel
3. a line that intersects two other lines in different points
4. a parallelogram with four right angles
7. a repeated geometric pattern that covers a plane with no gaps or overlaps
8. a triangle with three congruent sides
9. a polygon with four sides
10. the distance around a circle
14. a triangle with one angle larger than 90 degrees
15. two angles that shares a vertex and a side but have no common interior points

Chapter Review

Vocabulary

acute triangle (p. 430)
adjacent angles (p. 407)
alternate interior angles (p. 414)
angle bisector (p. 457)
area (p. 441)
compass (p. 454)
complementary (p. 408)
congruent polygons (p. 420)
corresponding angles (p. 414)
equilateral triangle (p. 430)
isosceles triangle (p. 430)
midpoint (p. 456)
obtuse triangle (p. 430)
parallelogram (p. 431)
perpendicular bisector (p. 456)
perpendicular lines (p. 409)
quadrilateral (p. 431)
rectangle (p. 431)
regular polygon (p. 437)
rhombus (p. 431)
right triangle (p. 430)
scalene triangle (p. 430)
segment bisector (p. 456)
square (p. 431)
supplementary (p. 408)
transversal (p. 414)
trapezoid (p. 431)
vertical angles (p. 408)

 **Reading Math:** Understanding Vocabulary

Choose the correct term to complete each sentence.

1. A (transversal/segment bisector) intersects two lines at different points. transversal
2. A triangle with no congruent sides is (isosceles/scalene). scalene
3. The measures of (complementary/supplementary) angles add up to 180°. supplementary
4. A (rhombus/trapezoid) has four congruent sides. rhombus
5. All the sides and angles of a (congruent/regular) polygon are congruent. regular

Take It to the NET
Online vocabulary quiz at www.PHSchool.com
Web Code: acj-0851

Skills and Concepts

8-1 and 8-2 Objectives
- To use adjacent and vertical angles
- To use supplementary and complementary angles
- To find the measures of angles formed by parallel lines
- To identify parallel lines

Vertical angles are congruent. The sum of the measures of a pair of **supplementary** angles is 180°. The sum of the measures of a pair of **complementary** angles is 90°.

If two parallel lines are cut by a **transversal**, the **corresponding angles** are congruent, and the **alternate interior angles** are congruent.

Find the measures of ∠1 and ∠2 in each diagram.

6. 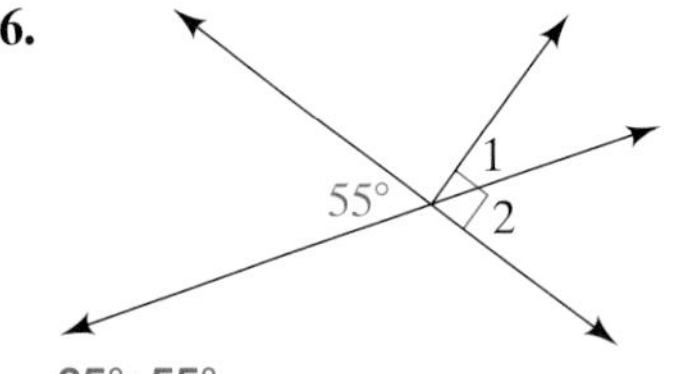

35°; 55°

7. 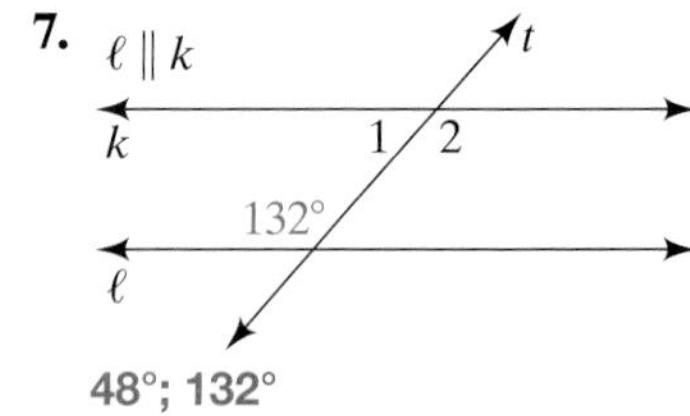

48°; 132°

8-4 Objective
- To solve a problem by combining strategies

You can solve problems by solving a simpler problem and using patterns.

8. **Books** Suppose you checked out a copy of the complete works of William Shakespeare from the library. It has 1,328 pages. How many pages in the book have at least one 7 in their number? 331 pages

8-3 and 8-5 Objectives

- To identify parts of congruent figures
- To identify congruent triangles
- To classify triangles and quadrilaterals

Congruent polygons have exactly the same size and shape. You can use SAS, ASA, or SSS to decide whether two triangles are congruent. You can classify triangles by angle measures or by the number of congruent sides. You can classify quadrilaterals by their sides and angles.

Write a congruence statement and show that the triangles are congruent.

9. 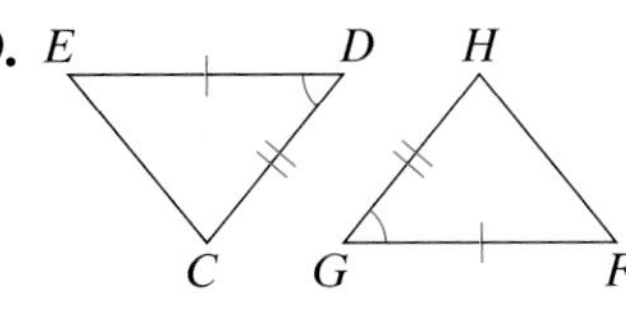

$\triangle CDE \cong \triangle HGF$; SAS

10. 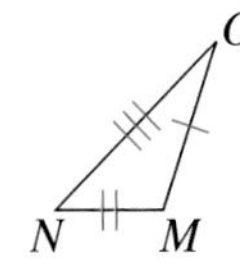

$\triangle JLK \cong \triangle OMN$; SSS

8-6 Objective

- To find the angle measures of a polygon

The sum of the measures of the interior angles of a polygon equals the product of 180° and two less than the number of sides. The measure of each angle of a **regular polygon** equals the sum of the angle measures divided by the number of angles.

Find the measure of each angle of a regular polygon with the given number of sides.

11. 6 120° **12.** 12 150° **13.** 18 160°

8-7 and 8-8 Objectives

- To find the areas of polygons
- To find the circumference of a circle
- To find the area of a circle

Area formulas:

parallelogram: $A = bh$ **triangle:** $A = \frac{1}{2}bh$

trapezoid: $A = \frac{1}{2}h(b_1 + b_2)$ **circle:** $A = \pi r^2$

The distance around a circle is the **circumference** of the circle.

$$C = \pi d \text{ or } C = 2\pi r.$$

Find the area of the parallelogram, the triangle, and the circle. If necessary, round to the nearest tenth.

14. 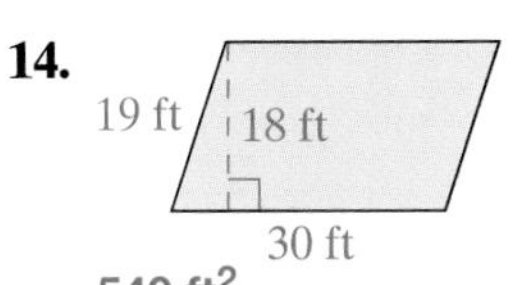

540 ft^2

15. 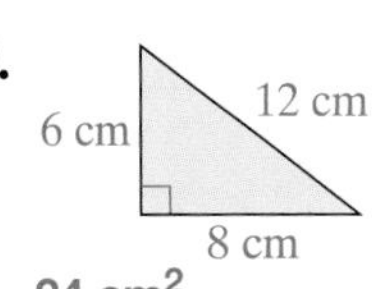

24 cm^2

16. 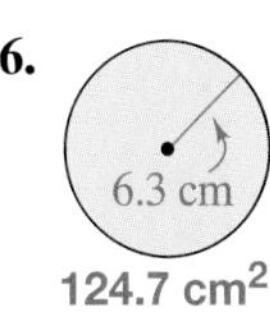

124.7 cm^2

8-9 Objectives

- To construct congruent segments and angles
- To construct bisectors

A **segment bisector** divides a segment into two congruent segments at the **midpoint.** An **angle bisector** divides an angle into two congruent angles.

17–18. See margin.

17. Use a ruler to draw $\overline{AB}$ with a length of 3.5 cm. Then construct $\overline{RS}$ congruent to $\overline{AB}$.

18. Use a protractor to draw angle $\angle P$ with a measure of 115°. Then construct its angle bisector.

17. 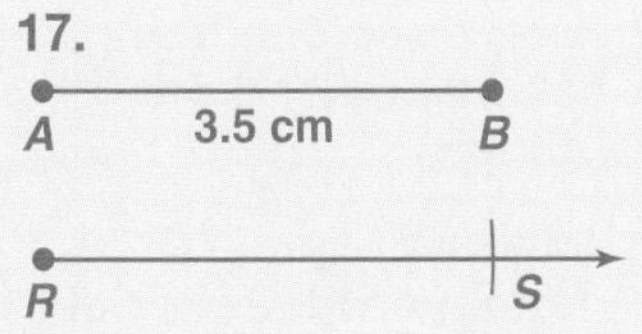

18. 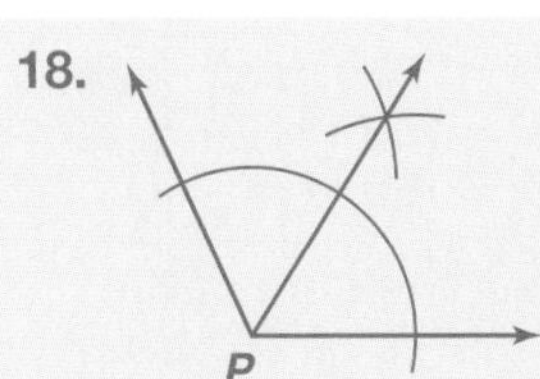

Alternative Assessment Form C

Alternative Assessment **Form C**

Chapter 8

PIZZA PRICING

Ira is the restaurant reporter for his school newspaper. He decided to write his next article on pizza. He surveyed four pizza restaurants and recorded the largest and smallest pizza each offered in this table.

Restaurant	Pizza Choice	Diameter (in.)	Price
A	Tops Titan	12	$ 8.00
	Tiny Tot	4	$ 1.50
B	Colossal Caper	14	$ 8.50
	Peewee Pie	6	$ 3.50
C	Giant Pie	16	$ 9.20
	Small Pie	8	$ 4.00
D	Massive Monster	20	$11.00
	Prince-o-Pie	10	$ 5.00

Show all your work on a separate sheet of paper. You may use a calculator. Use 3.14 for π.

1. Which is the least expensive pizza? Which pizza is the least expensive per square inch? Explain how you found your answer.
2. What happens to the amount of pizza when its diameter is doubled? How should the price change? Explain.
3. For take-out pizza, boxes are required. What size square box would you recommend for each pizza? Explain. Could all four restaurants use boxes with a base that is 20 inches by 20 inches?
4. Part of Ira's article will be devoted to common pizza toppings: pepperoni, peppers, onions, and mushrooms. How many different pizzas can be formed by the four restaurants using just one of these four toppings? Explain how you found your answer.

Resources

Teaching Resources
Ch. 8 Test, Forms A & B
Ch. 8 Alternative Assessment, Form C

Reaching All Students
Spanish Ch. 8 Test, Forms A & B
Spanish Ch. 8 Alternative Assessment, Form C

PRENTICE HALL ASSESSMENT SYSTEM

Assessment Resources
- Ch. 8 Test, Forms A & B
- Ch. 8 Alternative Assessment, Form C

Computer Test Generator CD
- Ch. 8 Instant Chapter Test™
- Make your own Ch. 8 test

www.PHSchool.com
Student Site
- Self-grading Ch. 8 test

PH SuccessNet Teacher Center
- Resources

Plus iText

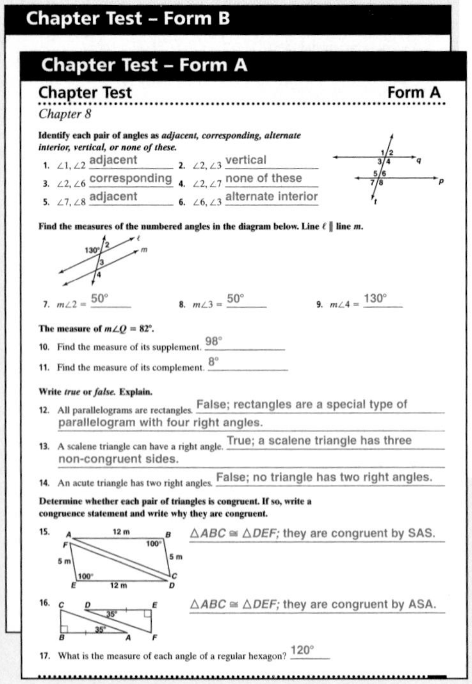

Chapter Test – Form B

Chapter Test – Form A

Chapter Test — Form A
Chapter 8

Identify each pair of angles as *adjacent, corresponding, alternate interior, vertical, or none of these.*

1. ∠1, ∠2 adjacent
2. ∠2, ∠3 vertical
3. ∠2, ∠6 corresponding
4. ∠2, ∠7 none of these
5. ∠7, ∠8 adjacent
6. ∠6, ∠3 alternate interior

Find the measures of the numbered angles in the diagram below. Line ℓ ∥ line m.

7. m∠2 = 50°
8. m∠3 = 50°
9. m∠4 = 130°

The measure of m∠Q = 82°.

10. Find the measure of its supplement. 98°
11. Find the measure of its complement. 8°

Write *true* or *false*. Explain.

12. All parallelograms are rectangles. False; rectangles are a special type of parallelogram with four right angles.
13. A scalene triangle can have a right angle. True; a scalene triangle has three non-congruent sides.
14. An acute triangle has two right angles. False; no triangle has two right angles.

Determine whether each pair of triangles is congruent. If so, write a congruence statement and write why they are congruent.

15. △ABC ≅ △DEF; they are congruent by SAS.
16. △ABC ≅ △DEF; they are congruent by ASA.
17. What is the measure of each angle of a regular hexagon? 120°

Chapter 8 Chapter Test

Take It to the NET
Online chapter test at **www.PHSchool.com**
Web Code: aca-0852

1a–f. See margin.

1. Identify each pair of angles in the diagram below as *adjacent, corresponding, alternate interior, vertical,* or *none of these.*
   a. ∠2, ∠4 **b.** ∠1, ∠5 **c.** ∠1, ∠3
   d. ∠3, ∠4 **e.** ∠4, ∠6 **f.** ∠3, ∠5

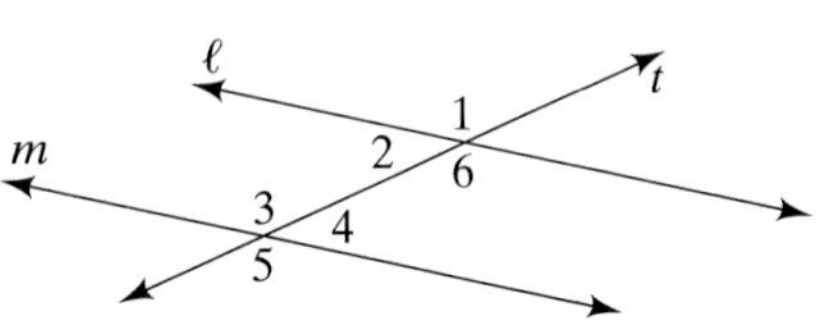

2. Find the measures of the numbered angles in the diagram below. See margin.

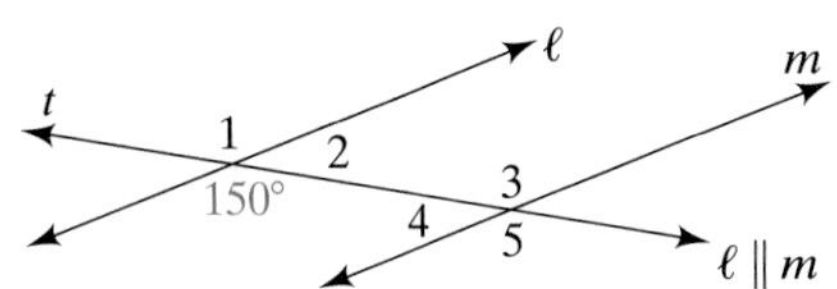

3. The measure of ∠D is 68°.
   a. Find the measure of its supplement. 112°
   b. Find the measure of its complement. 22°

4a–c. See margin.

4. **Reasoning** Write *true* or *false*. Explain.
   a. An obtuse triangle can be a right triangle.
   b. A scalene triangle can be an acute triangle.
   c. A rhombus can have four right angles.

5. Tell whether each pair of triangles is congruent. If so, write a congruence statement and tell how you know they are congruent.

a.

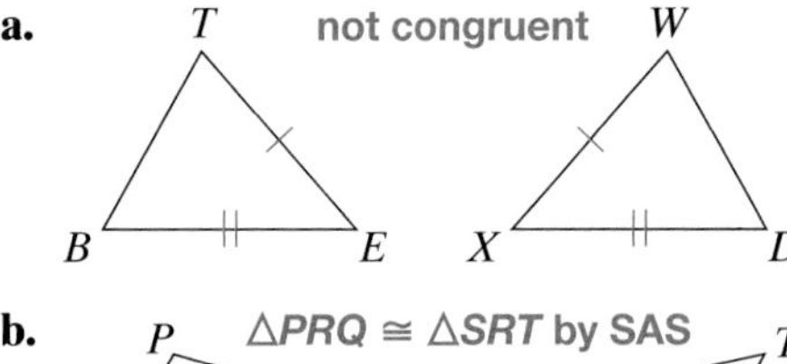

b.

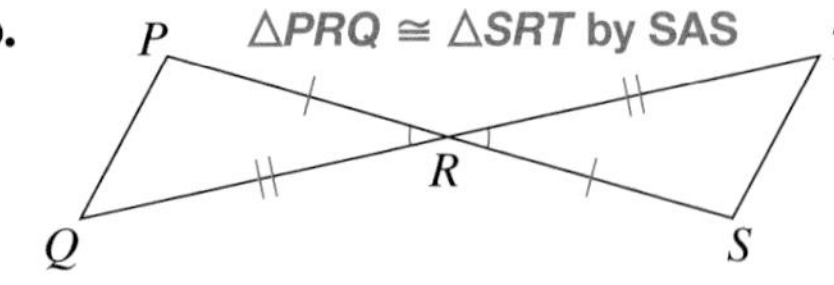

6. What is the measure of each angle of a regular pentagon? 108°

7. **Writing in Math** How are a rectangle and a parallelogram alike? How are they different? See back of book.

Determine the best name for each figure.

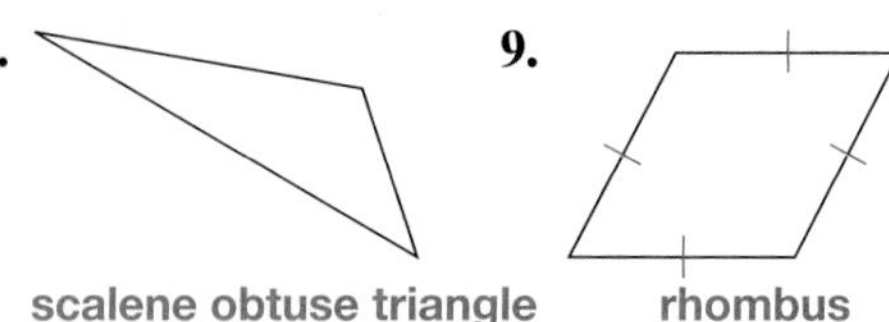

Draw and label a figure to fit each description.
10–13. See back of book.

10. a scalene right triangle
11. an equilateral triangle
12. a parallelogram that is not a rectangle
13. a rectangle that is a rhombus

Find the sum of the measures of the angles of a polygon with the given number of sides.

14. 4 sides 360°
15. 7 sides 900°
16. 15 sides 2,340°

17. **Savings** Every day you save two pennies more than you saved the day before. On the first day, you save one penny. How many pennies do you have after 100 days? 10,000 pennies

Find the area of the parallelogram and the triangle.

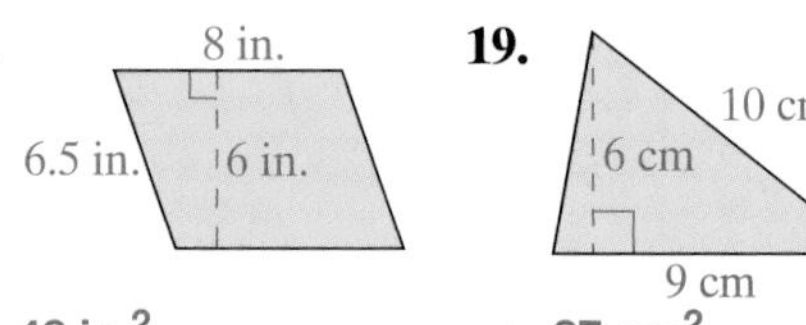

48 in.^{2} 27 cm^2

20. **Food** Find the circumference and area of a pancake with a diameter of 15 cm. Round your answer to the nearest tenth. 47.1 cm; 176.7 cm^2
21. Draw $\overline{AB}$ with a length of 5 in. Construct the perpendicular bisector of $\overline{AB}$. See back of book.
22. Draw an obtuse angle and label it ∠G. Construct ∠H congruent to ∠G. See back of book.

1a. alternate interior
b. none of these
c. corresponding
d. adjacent
e. none of these
f. vertical

2. $m\angle 1 = 150°$; $m\angle 2 = 30°$; $m\angle 3 = 150°$; $m\angle 4 = 30°$; $m\angle 5 = 150°$

4a. False; the sum of the measures of an obtuse angle and a right angle is greater than 180°.
b. True; a scalene triangle can be acute, right, or obtuse.
c. True; a square is a rhombus with four right angles.

Test Prep

Multiple Choice

For Exercises 1–10, choose the correct letter.

1. Which square root lies between the whole numbers 11 and 12? C
   A. $\sqrt{101}$ B. $\sqrt{120}$ C. $\sqrt{135}$ D. $\sqrt{144}$

2. Aleisha can read four pages in 12 min. Which proportion can she use to figure out how long it will take her to read an 18-page chapter? G
   F. $\frac{4}{12} = \frac{x}{18}$ G. $\frac{4}{18} = \frac{12}{x}$
   H. $\frac{12}{18} = \frac{4}{x}$ I. $\frac{4}{x} = \frac{18}{12}$

3. Write $3\frac{1}{2}\%$ as a fraction in simplest form. C
   A. $\frac{7}{2}$ B. $\frac{7}{20}$ C. $\frac{7}{200}$ D. $\frac{3.5}{100}$

4. What is the circumference of a circle with an area of 36π in.^{2}? G
   F. 6π in. G. 12π in.
   H. 18π in. I. 36π in.

5. Which power is equivalent to $5^3 \cdot 5^2$? A
   A. 5^5 B. 5^6
   C. 25^5 D. 25^6

6. Which is a pair of corresponding angles? I

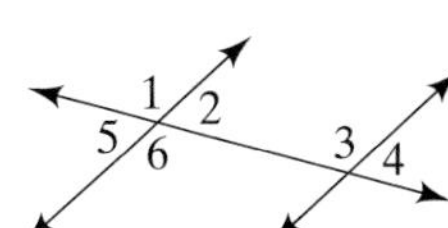

   F. ∠1 and ∠6 G. ∠3 and ∠6
   H. ∠1 and ∠4 I. ∠2 and ∠4

7. A job pays $160 for 25 hours. At this rate, what would it pay for 40 hours? B
   A. $216 B. $256
   C. $640 D. $1,000

8. Which algebraic expression is NOT equivalent to $2(x + 5)$? I
   F. $2(x) + 2(5)$ G. $(x + 5) + (x + 5)$
   H. $2(5 + x)$ I. $5 + 2x$

9. $S'(-3, -2)$ is the image after a translation of 6 units to the left and 2 units up. What are the coordinates of the original point? D
   A. (9, −2) B. (3, 2)
   C. (1, 2) D. (3, −4)

10. Choose the step you should complete first to construct $\overline{EF} \cong \overline{MN}$. G

M N

   F. Open the compass to the length of $\overline{MN}$.
   G. Draw a ray with endpoint E.
   H. Measure $\overline{MN}$ with a ruler.
   I. Draw points E and F.

Gridded Response

11. A painter needs 15 gallons of violet paint. The formula for mixing violet paint is 3 parts blue to 2 parts red. How many gallons of blue paint does the painter need? 9

Short Response

12. Farmer Hoyle usually takes the shortcut across his rectangular field. How much distance does he save by taking the shortcut instead of walking along two sides of the field? Justify your answer. See margin.

30 m
Shortcut
40 m

Extended Response

13. On the first day of gym class, students do 6 push-ups. The number of push-ups the students do will increase by 2 each time they come to class. 13a–b. See margin.
   a. Write an equation that represents the number of push-ups p the class does after c classes.
   b. How many push-ups will the class do on the ninth day of class? Justify your answer.

Item	1	2	3	4	5	6	7	8	9	10	11	12	13
Lesson	4-8	5-4	6-1	8-9	7-2	8-2	5-4	2-3	3-8	8-10	5-3	4-9	3-5

12. Let s = shortcut.
[2] $30^2 + 40^2 = s^2$
$900 + 1{,}600 = s^2$
$2{,}500 = s^2$
$50\text{ m} = s$
$30 + 40 = 70\text{ m}$
Farmer Hoyle saves $70 - 50$, or 20, m.
[1] minor computational error OR correct answer without work shown

Test Prep

Resources

Teaching Resources
Cumulative Review

Reaching All Students
Spanish Cumulative Review

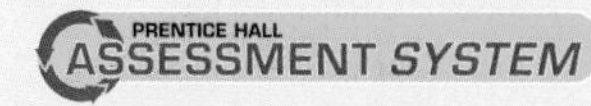

Test Preparation
- Ch. 8 standardized test prep

Assessment Resources
- Cumulative Review

Computer Test Generator CD
- Standardized test prep

www.PHSchool.com
- Standardized test prep
- Resources

Plus 

13. [4] a. $p = 6 + 2(c - 1)$
b. $p = 6 + 2(9 - 1)$
$= 6 + 2(8)$
$= 6 + 16$
$= 22$
[3] one minor computational error
[2] two minor computational errors
[1] correct answers without work shown

Cumulative Review

Cumulative Review

Chapters 1–8

Multiple Choice: Choose the letter of the best answer.

1. Which of the following is *not* equivalent to $\frac{1}{16}$?
   (A) 0.625 B. 6.25%
   C. $\frac{6}{96}$ D. 0.0625
2. Simplify. $91 - (-14) + (-42)$
   F. 35 (G) 63
   H. 147 I. 163
3. What are the prime factors of 1,155?
   A. 5, 10, 7, 11 B. 3, 5, 7, 35
   (C) 3, 5, 7, 11 D. 11, 55
4. Solve the equation. $\frac{x}{4} - 9 = 0$
   F. 0 G. $\frac{9}{4}$
   H. 9 (I) 36
5. In one high school, 75% of the graduates went on to college. If there were 1,000 graduates, how many went on to college?
   A. 0.75 graduate B. 7.5 graduates
   C. 75 graduates (D) 750 graduates
6. Find $\frac{3}{5} \div \frac{1}{10}$.
   F. 3 G. 5
   (H) 6 I. 30
7. In which quadrant is the point $(-3, -5)$?
   A. I B. II
   (C) III D. IV
8. Which is the y-intercept for $3 + 4x = 6y$?
   F. $-\frac{3}{4}$ G. 0
   (H) $\frac{1}{2}$ I. 3
9. An artist made 21 quarts of green paint by mixing 3 parts blue paint and 4 parts yellow paint. How many quarts of blue paint were needed?
   A. 12 quarts
   B. 7 quarts
   C. 14 quarts
   (D) 9 quarts
10. What is the name of an angle that has its vertex on the center of a circle?
    (F) a central angle
    G. an acute angle
    H. an obtuse angle
    I. a right angle
11. Which of the following is true of the figure below?

    B C D A E

    A. $\triangle ABC \cong \triangle EDC$
    (B) $\angle BCA \cong \angle ECD$
    C. $m\angle BAC = m\angle CED$
    D. $m\angle CDE = m\angle ECD$
12. The measures of four angles of a pentagon are 125°, 134°, 168°, and 90°. What is the measure of the fifth angle?
    F. 100°
    G. 90°
    H. 32°
    (I) 23°

Real-World Snapshots

You Can't Get There From Here

Students will use data from these two pages to answer the questions posed here in Put It All Together.

Activating Prior Knowledge
Have students share any experiences they have had sailing, either as passengers or as members of a crew. Ask them to explain why they think some people become very attached to sailing, despite all its rigors and dangers.

Teaching Notes

Have a student read aloud the opening paragraph about how sailboats must tack to travel into the direction of the wind.

Language Arts Connection
Tell students that sailing, both as a means of travel or commerce, and as a sport or recreational activity, comes with its own specialized vocabulary. Have interested students or groups of students prepare a sailing glossary. Invite them to include pictures to accompany the definitions, or even to make fully labeled drawings of sailboats to clarify some of these nautical terms.

History Connection
Invite interested students to learn about the history of sailing, from the earliest small craft to the sleek and swift vessels that ruled the seas before the age of steam.

Sports Connection
Any sailor worth his or her salt knows about the importance and many uses of knots, such as the tucked double overhand hitch knot shown on page 467. Invite curious students to learn about other kinds of knots sailors use. Challenge students to learn how to tie a few of these knots, and demonstrate their skills for classmates.

Real-World Snapshots

You Can't Get There From Here

Applying Geometry For a sailboat, the shortest distance between two points is not always a straight line. Sailboats cannot travel directly into the wind (upwind). They can head about 45° from the direction of the wind, but not closer. To get to a specific point upwind, the sailboat has to follow a zigzag course, as shown below. This is called tacking, and each diagonal length (or leg), is called a tack.

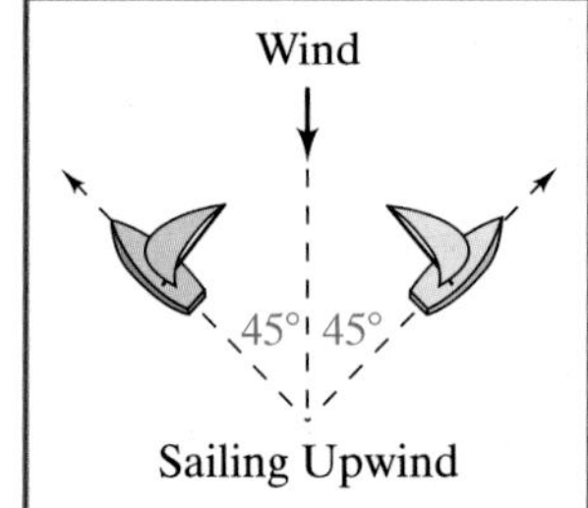

Sailing Upwind

Safe-Water Buoy
Buoys are floating aids that mark channels and warn sailors of obstructions in the water.

Put It All Together

Materials ruler, protractor

Three sailboats are racing upwind toward the finish line, 3 mi away. One crew tacks twice, another tacks three times, and the third crew tacks four times. Their courses create isosceles right triangles where they intersect the dashed lines.

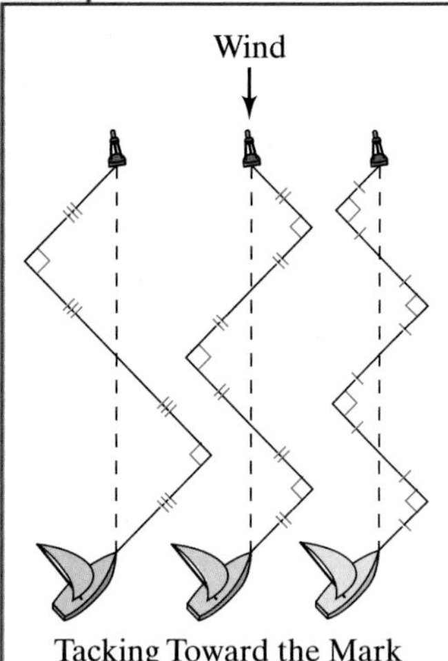

Tacking Toward the Mark

1. Copy the sailing diagram. For each course, find the length of the hypotenuse of each triangle.
2. **Writing in Math** In the triangle diagram below, point D is the midpoint of $\overline{BC}$, so $\overline{BD} \cong \overline{DC}$. Explain how you know that $\triangle ADC \cong \triangle ADB$.
3. **a.** Find the measures of the angles in $\triangle ABC$, $\triangle ADC$, and $\triangle ADB$. What do you notice?
   b. What are the measures of the three angles of an isosceles right triangle? Explain.
4. **a.** Suppose $DC = 100$ yd. How long is $\overline{AD}$? Explain.
   b. Reasoning Suppose the hypotenuse of $\triangle ABC$ measures 10 mi. How long is $\overline{AC}$? Explain.
5. **a.** Find the course length for each boat. Which boat follows the shortest course?
   b. Patterns If a boat tacks ten times, what will its course length be?
6. **Reasoning** Why might the skipper of a sailboat crew decide to tack more times? Fewer times?

B, A, D, C, 45°

1. green: 1.5 miles; red: 1 mile; blue: 0.75 mile
2. by SSS, because $\overline{AD}$ is congruent to itself

3a. All three triangles have angle measures of 45°, 45°, and 90°.
b. 45°, 45°, and 90°; when two legs of a right triangle are congruent, the vertex of the two congruent sides must be the 90° angle. The remaining angles are congruent, meaning each one must be half of (180 − 90°), or 45°.

Learning to Sail
Knotting ropes is one of the most important parts of sailing. A good knot is easy to fasten and unfasten but doesn't slip.
Trimming the Sails
Trimming the sails means adjusting them so that they receive the wind properly, so the boat moves easily and quickly across the water.
Tucked double overhand hitch knot
Take It to the NET For more information about sailing, go to www.PHSchool.com.
Web Code: ace-0853
467

4a. 100 yd; $\triangle CAD$ is an isosceles right triangle, so $DC = AD$. If $DC = 100$, then $AD = 100$.

b. approximately 7.07 mi; If $BC = 10$ miles, then $DC = 5$ miles and $AD = 5$ miles. Using the Pythagorean theorem, $AC = \sqrt{50} \approx 7.07$ miles.

5a. about 4.24 miles for all three courses

b. about 4.24 miles

6. Answers may vary. Sample: Sailors may tack to avoid obstacles and other boats, but might otherwise want to tack less because they lose some speed with each turn.

Put It All Together

Have students work in pairs to answer the questions. Guide them to record data as they measure and accumulate it.

Discuss what a right isosceles triangle is. Emphasize that every right triangle with 45° angles is an isosceles triangle. Make sure students understand how the diagram shows the different tackings the three crews make.

Inclusion
As needed, review the properties of and terminology associated with right triangles. Review the symbols for triangle, congruence, and line segment.

Exercise 4 In Chapter 5, students learned about the sine and cosine trigonometric ratios. You may wish to invite students to use the sine ratio to find the length of segment *AC* (or the length of the *entire* course, for that matter) and to explain how they did it.

Exercises 5–6 Discuss with students that each time a boat tacks, it loses speed.

CHAPTER 9

Geometry and Measurement

Chapter at a Glance

9-1 Solids
pp. 471–475

Objectives
1. Naming Solids
2. Recognizing Skew Lines

New Vocabulary
solids, prism, pyramid, cylinder, cone, polyhedron, skew lines

NCTM Standards
3, 6, 7, 8, 9, 10

Local Standards

9-2 Drawing Views of Solids
pp. 476–480

Objectives
1. Drawing a Base Plan
2. Drawing Top, Front, and Right Views

New Vocabulary
base plan, isometric view

Optional Materials
isometric dot paper, ruler

NCTM Standards
3, 6, 7, 8, 9, 10

Local Standards

9-3 Nets and Solids
pp. 481–485

Objectives
1. Identifying Nets of Solids

New Vocabulary
net

Optional Materials
graph paper, scissors, tape

NCTM Standards
3, 6, 7, 8, 9, 10

Local Standards

✓ Checkpoint Quiz 1

9-4 Surface Areas of Prisms and Cylinders
pp. 488–493

Objectives
1. Finding Surface Areas of Prisms
2. Finding Surface Areas of Cylinders

New Vocabulary
surface area, lateral area

NCTM Standards
1, 2, 3, 4, 6, 7, 8, 9, 10

Local Standards

9-5 Surface Areas of Pyramids and Cones
pp. 494–499

Objectives
1. Finding Surface Areas of Pyramids
2. Finding Surface Areas of Cones

New Vocabulary
slant height

NCTM Standards
1, 2, 3, 4, 6, 7, 8, 9, 10

Local Standards

9-6 Volumes of Prisms and Cylinders
pp. 500–505

Objectives
1. Finding Volumes of Prisms
2. Finding Volumes of Cylinders

New Vocabulary
volume

Optional Materials
unit cubes

NCTM Standards
1, 2, 3, 4, 6, 7, 8, 9, 10

Local Standards

9-7 Volumes of Pyramids and Cones
pp. 506–510

Objectives
1. Finding Volumes of Pyramids
2. Finding Volumes of Cones

NCTM Standards
1, 2, 3, 4, 6, 7, 8, 9, 10

Local Standards

9-8 Problem Solving: Draw a Diagram and Make a Table
pp. 512–515

Objectives
1. Solving a Problem by Combining Strategies

NCTM Standards
1, 2, 3, 4, 6, 7, 8, 9, 10

Local Standards

✓ Checkpoint Quiz 2

9-9 Exploring Similar Solids
pp. 517–521

Objectives
1. Finding Dimensions Using Proportions
2. Finding Surface Areas and Volumes of Similar Solids

New Vocabulary
similar solids

NCTM Standards
1, 2, 3, 4, 6, 7, 8, 9, 10

Local Standards

Reaching All Students

Additional Instructional Options in Chapter 9

Reading and Math Literacy

Reading Math

Using the Correct Formula, p. 516

Reading Math hints, pp. 471, 488, 502

Reading Comprehension, pp. 505, 527

Understanding Vocabulary, p. 524

Writing in Math

Daily Writing Practice, pp. 474, 479, 484, 487, 492, 498, 504, 509, 514, 520, 526

Above Level

Challenge exercises

pp. 475, 484, 494, 492, 498, 504, 510, 514, 521

Extension

Formulas for Spheres, p. 511

Significant Digits, p. 522

Hands-On and Technology

Investigations

Sketching Solids, p. 476

Creating Solids From Nets, p. 481

Precision and Greatest Possible Error, pp. 486-487

Looking at Rectangular Prisms, p. 500

Exploring Changing Dimensions, p. 518

Activities and Projects

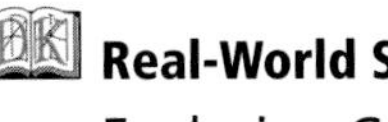

Real-World Snapshots

Exploring Geometry and Measurement, pp. 528-529

Chapter Project

A Better Way, p. 700

Test Prep

Daily Test Prep

pp. 475, 480, 485, 493, 499, 505, 510, 515, 521

Test-Taking Strategies

Eliminating Answers, p. 523

Test Prep

Reading Comprehension, p. 527

Chapter Assessment

Checkpoint Quiz

pp. 485, 515

Chapter Review

pp. 524–525

Chapter Test

p. 526

Pacing Options

This chart suggests pacing only for the core lessons and their parts. It is provided as a possible guide. It will help you determine how much time you have in your schedule to cover the additional features and assessment, as described at the left.

Day	Traditional 45-minute class periods	Block 90-minute class periods
1	9-1	9-1 9-2
2	9-2	9-2 9-3
3	9-2	9-4
4	9-3	9-5
5	9-4	9-6
6	9-4	9-7 9-8
7	9-5	9-9
8	9-5	
9	9-6	
10	9-6	
11	9-7	
12	9-8	
13	9-9	
14	9-9	
15		

NCTM STANDARDS 2000

1 Number and Operations
2 Algebra
3 Geometry
4 Measurement
5 Data Analysis and Probability
6 Problem Solving
7 Reasoning and Proof
8 Communication
9 Connections
10 Representation

Math Background

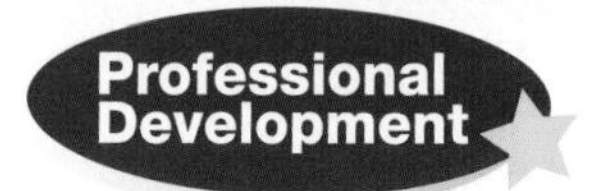

Skills Trace

BEFORE Chapter 9

Course 2 introduced basic three-dimensional figures.

DURING Chapter 9

Course 3 reviews and extends the study of three-dimensional figures to pyramids, cones, and similar solids.

AFTER Chapter 9

Throughout this course students solve problems that involve geometric reasoning.

9-1 Solids

Math Understandings

- Two-dimensional figures lie in a plane; three-dimensional figures lie in space, having length, width, and height.
- Prisms and pyramids have polygons, which are plane figures, for each face, and are polyhedrons; cylinders and cones have curved surfaces not in a plane and are not polyhedrons.

Solids, or three-dimensional figures, are objects that do not lie in a plane. A **polyhedron** is a solid with a polygon for each face.

Figure	Base(s)	Lateral face(s)
Prism	two parallel congruent polygons	parallelograms
Pyramid	exactly one polygon base	triangles
Cylinder	two parallel congruent circles	curved rectangle
Cone	exactly one circle, one vertex	curved surface

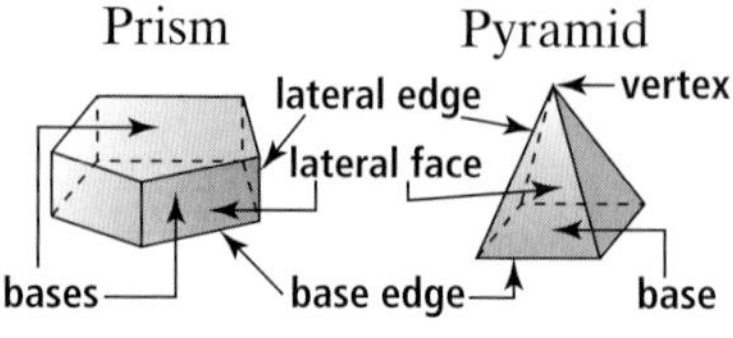

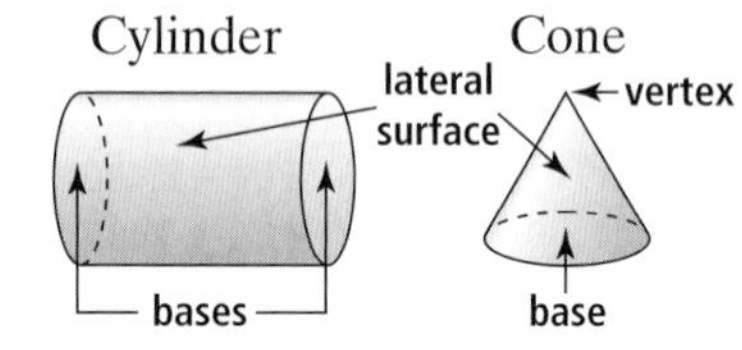

Cylinder
lateral surface
bases

Cone
vertex
base

Skew lines are lines that do not intersect and are not parallel. Unlike a pair of parallel lines or a pair of intersecting lines, skew lines do not lie in the same plane.

Drawing Views of Solids

Math Understandings

- Drawings in a plane can specify the exact shape of a solid by using drawings from different perspectives.
- An isometric view allows you to see the top, front, and right side of an object in the same drawing.

A **base plan** shows the shape of the base and indicates the height of each part of a solid. An **isometric view** is a corner view of a solid, usually drawn on isometric dot paper.

Nets and Solids

Math Understandings

- Nets for the same figure may be drawn in different configurations.

The **net** is a pattern that can be folded to form a solid. A net of a figure shows all the surfaces of that figure in one view.

9-4 Surface Areas of Prisms and Cylinders
9-5 Surface Areas of Pyramids and Cones

Math Understandings

- The surface area of a solid is the area of its net.
- The height of a pyramid is different from the height of its lateral faces.

The **surface area** of a solid is the sum of the areas of its surfaces. The lateral area is the portion of the surface area that is not the base(s). **Lateral area** is the sum of the areas of the lateral surfaces of a solid.

The height of a pyramid's lateral face is called the **slant height** and is indicated by the symbol ℓ. The four triangular faces of a square pyramid are congruent isosceles triangles.

Lateral Area and Surface Area

Prism

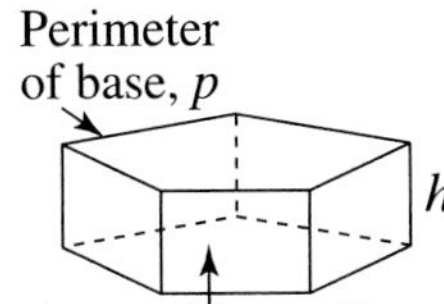

Lateral area
L.A. $= ph$
Surface area
S.A. $=$ L.A. $+ 2B$

Square Pyramid

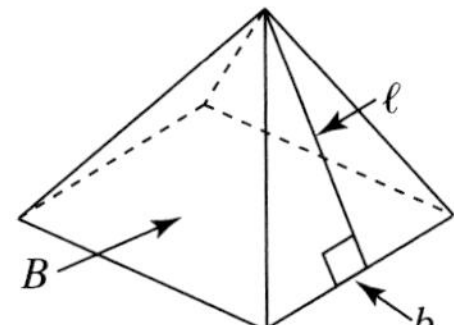

Lateral area
L.A. $= 4 \cdot (\frac{1}{2}b\ell) = 2b\ell$
Surface area
S.A. $=$ L.A. $+ B$

Cylinder

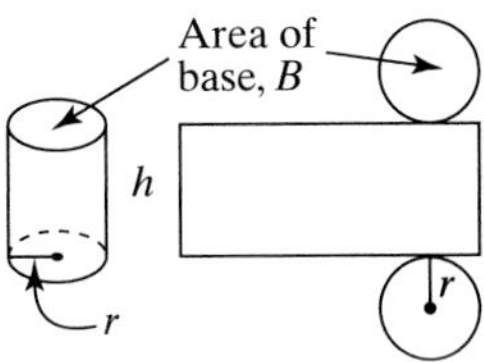

Lateral area
L.A. $= 2\pi rh$
Surface area
S.A. $=$ L.A. $+ 2B$

Cone

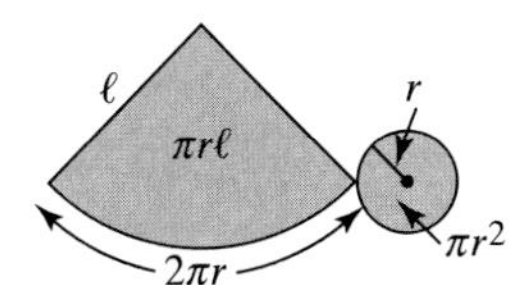

Lateral area
L.A. $= \frac{1}{2}(2\pi r)\ell = \pi r\ell$
Surface area
S.A. $=$ L.A. $+ B$

Volume

Prism or Cylinder

The volume *V* of a prism or a cylinder is the product of the base area *B* and the height *h*.

$V = Bh$

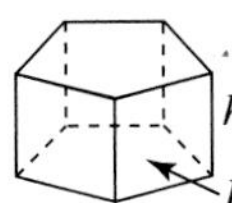

Square Pyramid or Cone

The volume *V* of a pyramid or cone is one third the product of the base area *B* and the height *h*.

$V = \frac{1}{3}Bh$

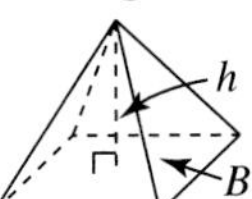

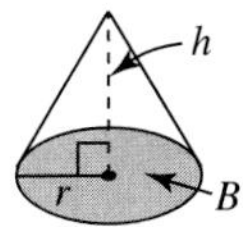

9-6 Volumes of Prisms and Cylinders
9-7 Volumes of Pyramids and Cones

Math Understandings

- Volume is an amount of three-dimensional space. You can also think of it as a measure of capacity.
- When you find the volume of a solid, the height is measured as perpendicular to the base.

Volume is the number of unit cubes, or cubic units, needed to fill a solid.

9-8 Draw a Diagram and Make a Table

You can *draw a diagram* to help you understand what a problem is asking. You can *make* a table to help you track of possible solutions.

9-9 Exploring Similar Solids

Math Understandings

- If you change each dimension of a solid by a given amount, the surface area changes by that amount squared, and the volume changes by that amount cubed.

Two solids are **similar solids** if they have the same shape and if all of their corresponding lengths are proportional. If the ratios of the corresponding dimensions of similar solids is $\frac{a}{b}$, then the ratio of their surface areas is $\frac{a^2}{b^2}$ and the ratio of their volumes is $\frac{a^3}{b^3}$.

Additional Professional Development Opportunities

Chapter 9 Math Background notes:
pp. 472, 477, 482, 489, 495, 501, 507, 513, 518

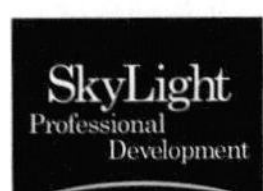

Additional resources available from SkyLight Professional Development:

On-site courses, workshops, summer institutes. Online courses and chat rooms. Videocassettes and books. Visit www.skylightedu.com.

Ongoing Assessment and Intervention

The *Prentice Hall Mathematics* program provides many options for assessment in the Student Edition, Teacher's Edition, and teaching resources. From these options you may choose instructional materials that are appropriate for your students and that support your district's curriculum requirements.

Daily Assessment

Instant Check System™ in Chapter 9

Allows students to check their own learning before, during, and after each lesson.

Diagnosing Readiness before the chapter (p. 470)

Check Skills You'll Need exercises in each lesson (pp. 471, 476, 481, 488, 494, 500, 506, 512, 517)

Check Understanding questions with each Example (pp. 472, 473, 477, 478, 482, 488, 489, 490, 491, 494, 495, 496, 501, 502, 507, 508, 513, 517, 519)

Checkpoint Quiz (pp. 485, 515)

Formal Assessment

Assessment in the Student Text and in Additional Resources

Assess student progress throughout the Course 2 textbook and with blackline masters and CD-ROM.

Student Edition
- Chapter 9 Review, with Vocabulary, Skills, and Concepts Review, pp. 524–525
- Chapter 9 Test, p. 526

Assessment Resources
- Checkpoint Quizzes 1 & 2
- Chapter Test, forms A & B
- Chapter Alternative Assessment

Spanish versions available.

Computer Test Generator CD-ROM
- Instant Chapter Tests™—pre-made tests with items that vary every time you print.
- Online Testing allows you to give tests online and receive progress reports.
- Prepare students by making tests based on standardized test objectives.

Algebra Readiness Tests
- Includes Basic Skills Tests and Concept-Readiness Tests.
- Assess understanding of skills and concepts needed for success in algebra.

Intervention

Skills Intervention Kit

Online Intervention

Integrated within the iText, this online intervention system includes diagnostic tests and prescribed remediation, plus reports to track student mastery.

A *complete* system for the student who is struggling with course-level work

Eight intervention units cover core skills and allow you to:
- **Diagnose** students' gaps in basic skills
- **Prescribe** an individualized course of study
- **Monitor** student progress

Includes print workbooks, tutorial CD-ROM, teacher editions, progress folders, and more. *Available in Spanish.*

How to Use with Chapter 9

9-1	Geometry, Skill 14
9-4	Measurement, Skills 15–16
9-6	Measurement, Skills 17, 21
9-9	Geometry, Skills 17, 21

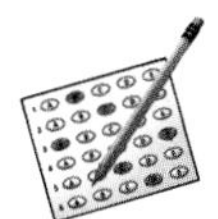

Standardized Test Preparation

The *Prentice Hall Mathematics* program integrates preparation for high-stakes standardized tests in every lesson of the Student Edition and continues this support in the Prentice Hall Assessment System.

Test Prep

In Student Text, Chapter 9

Teaches students strategies and gives them practice with all the test item formats they will encounter on high-stakes tests.

Test Prep exercises in each lesson (pp. 475, 480, 485, 493, 499, 505, 510, 515, 521)

Test-Taking Strategies Eliminating Answers, p. 523

Test Prep (p. 527: Reading Comprehension)

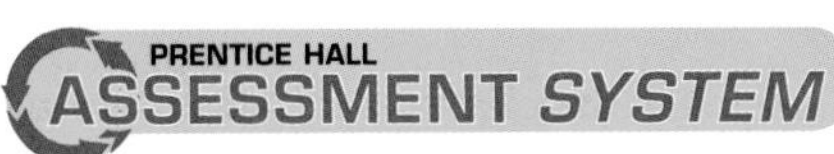
PRENTICE HALL
ASSESSMENT SYSTEM

A three-step approach to preparing students for high stakes, national, and state exams.

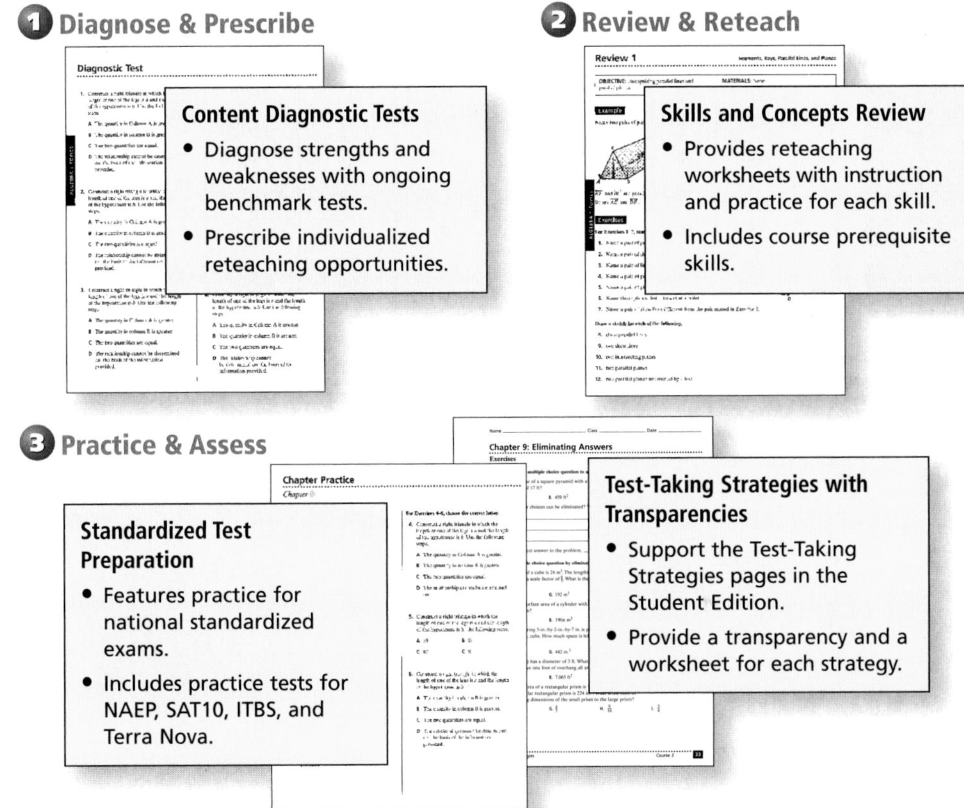
1 Diagnose & Prescribe
Diagnostic Test
Content Diagnostic Tests
• Diagnose strengths and weaknesses with ongoing benchmark tests.
• Prescribe individualized reteaching opportunities.
2 Review & Reteach
Review 1
Skills and Concepts Review
• Provides reteaching worksheets with instruction and practice for each skill.
• Includes course prerequisite skills.
3 Practice & Assess
Chapter Practice
Chapter 9: Eliminating Answers
Standardized Test Preparation
• Features practice for national standardized exams.
• Includes practice tests for NAEP, SAT10, ITBS, and Terra Nova.
Test-Taking Strategies with Transparencies
• Support the Test-Taking Strategies pages in the Student Edition.
• Provide a transparency and a worksheet for each strategy.

Correlation to Standardized Tests

Lesson		NAEP	Terra Nova CAT6	Terra Nova CTBS	ITBS	SAT10	Local Test
9-1	Solids	G1c, G1f	■	■			
9-2	Drawing Views of Solids	G1e, G1f	■				
9-3	Nets and Solids	G1e, G1f	■				
9-4	Surface Areas of Prisms and Cylinders	M1j		■			
9-5	Surface Areas of Pyramids and Cones	M1j		■			
9-6	Volumes of Prisms and Cylinders	M1j		■	■	■	
9-7	Volumes of Pyramids and Cones	M1j		■			
9-8	Draw a Diagram and Make a Table						
9-9	Exploring Similar Solids	M2b, M2c					

NAEP National Assessment of Educational Progress
CAT6/Terra Nova California Achievement Test, 6th Ed.
CTBS/Terra Nova Comprehensive Test of Basic Skills
ITBS Iowa Test of Basic Skills, Form M.
SAT10 Stanford Achievement Test, 10th Ed.

Program Resources

	Resources in Grab & Go™ Files				Resources for Reaching All Students				Spanish Resources			Presentation Assistant Plus! Transparencies					
	Practice	Reteach	Enrich	Checkpt Quiz	Reading & Math Literacy	Technology Activities	Hands-On Activities	Guided Problem Solving	Practice	Reading & Math Literacy	Checkpt Quiz	Skills Check	Problem of the Day	Additional Examples	Answers to Exercises	Lesson Quiz	Prentice Hall Presentation Pro CD-ROM
9-1	■	■	■		■		■	■	■	■		■	■	■	■	■	■
9-2	■	■	■				■	■	■			■	■	■	■	■	■
9-3	■	■	■	■	■	■		■	■	■	■	■	■	■	■	■	■
9-4	■	■	■				■	■	■			■	■	■	■	■	■
9-5	■	■	■			■		■	■			■	■	■	■	■	■
9-6	■	■	■				■	■	■			■	■	■	■	■	■
9-7	■	■	■			■		■	■			■	■	■	■	■	■
9-8	■	■	■	■	■			■	■	■	■	■	■	■	■	■	■
9-9	■	■	■					■	■			■	■	■	■	■	■
For the Chapter	Chapter Projects, Chapter Tests, Alternative Assessment, Cumulative Review, Cumulative Assessment				**On web site only:** Home Activities, Interdisciplinary Activities, Algebra Readiness Puzzles				Spanish Chapter Tests, Alternative Assessment, Cumulative Review, Cumulative Assessment			Classroom Aid Transparencies					

Also available for use with the chapter:

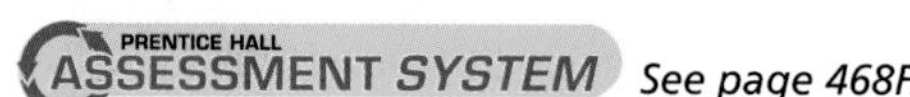

See page 468F.

- Practice Workbook
- Solution Key
- MathNotes folder

- For teacher support and access to student Web materials, use the Web Code abk-5500.
- For additional online and technology resources, *see below.*

Technology

Online and on CD-ROM

Complete Interactive Student Text online and on CD-ROM—with instant feedback assessment, tutorial help, dynamic activities, instructional and real-world videos, audio, and additional practice.

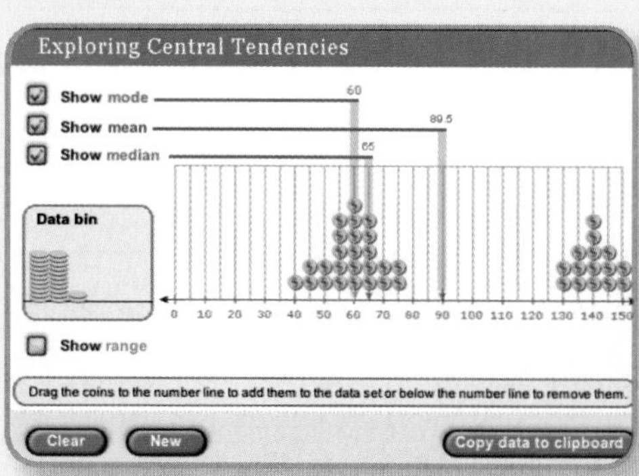

www.PHSchool.com For Students

Use Web codes for easy access to online activities, chapter projects, self-grading lesson quizzes, chapter tests, vocabulary quizzes, updated data sources, graphing calculator procedures, and more.

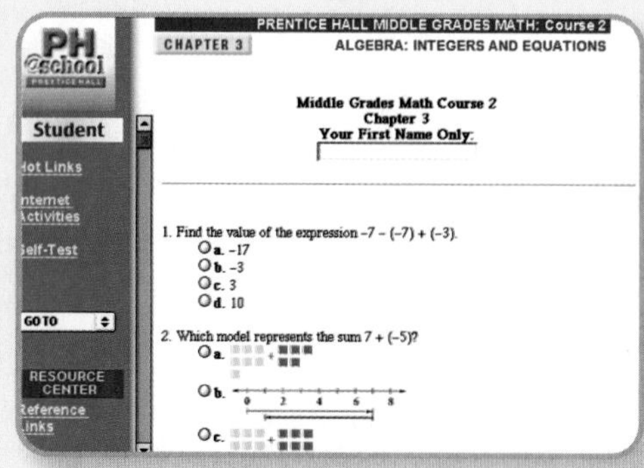

PH SuccessNet For Teachers

Online lesson planning with built-in state correlations, all the teaching resources, complete reference library, your own calendar and Teacher Web page, professional development, and more.

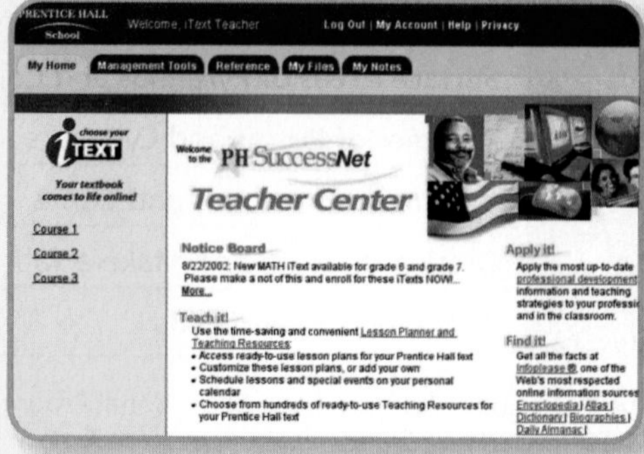

Presentation Assistant Plus!

The *Prentice Hall Presentation Assistant Plus!* provides you with the material you need to teach a lesson from beginning to end. Two easy-to-use formats—Transparencies and PowerPoint®—allow you to present a lesson the way you are most comfortable.

Transparencies

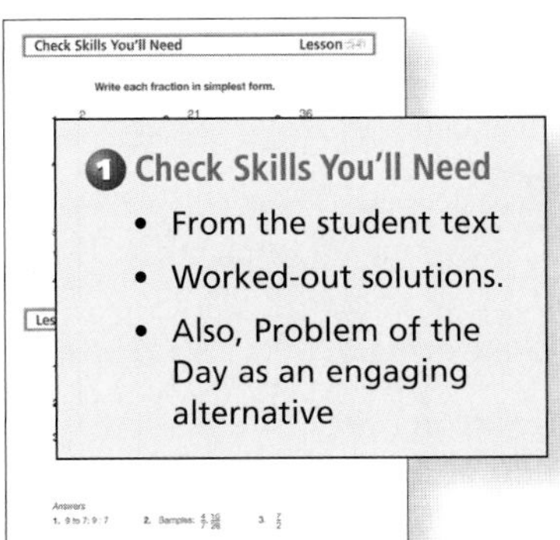

1 Check Skills You'll Need
- From the student text
- Worked-out solutions.
- Also, Problem of the Day as an engaging alternative

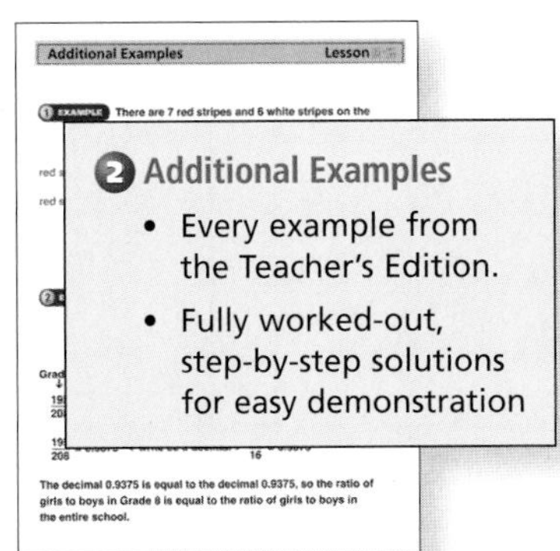

2 Additional Examples
- Every example from the Teacher's Edition.
- Fully worked-out, step-by-step solutions for easy demonstration

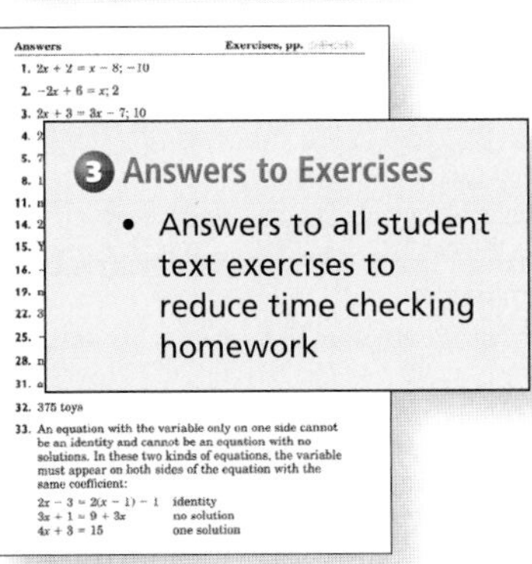

3 Answers to Exercises
- Answers to all student text exercises to reduce time checking homework

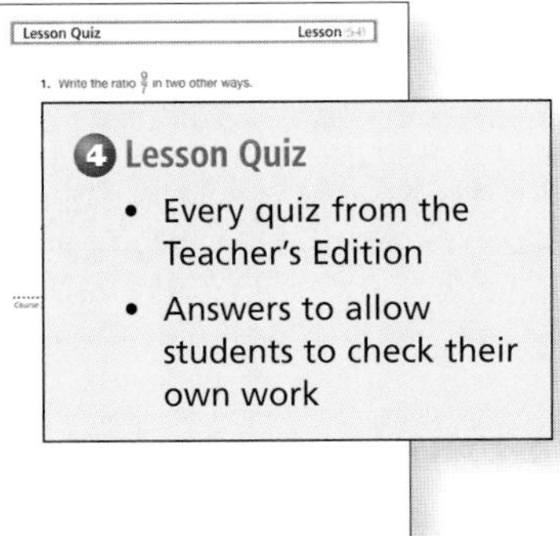

4 Lesson Quiz
- Every quiz from the Teacher's Edition
- Answers to allow students to check their own work

Throughout the Teacher's Edition, this symbol indicates material that is available in the Presentation Assistant Plus!

PowerPoint Prentice Hall Presentation Pro CD-ROM

- Includes all Transparencies.
- Conveniently organized by lesson so you can easily 1 Introduce, 2 Teach, 3 Check Homework, and 4 Assess each lesson.
- Animated examples allow step-by-step instruction at your own pace.
- Easy to edit so you can create custom presentations.

Teaching Chapter 9 Using Presentation Assistant Plus!

	1 Introduce	2 Teach	3 Check Homework	4 Assess
	Check Skills You'll Need	Additional Examples	Student Edition Answers	Lesson Quiz
9-1	p. 69	p. 153	✔	p. 69
9-2	p. 70	pp. 154–155	✔	p. 71
9-3	p. 72	p. 156	✔	p. 72
9-4	p. 73	pp. 157–158	✔	p. 73
9-5	p. 74	pp. 159–161	✔	p. 74
9-6	p. 75	pp. 162–163	✔	p. 75
9-7	p. 76	pp. 164–165	✔	p. 76
9-8	p. 77	pp. 166–167	✔	p. 77
9-9	p. 78	pp. 168–169	✔	p. 78

Prentice Hall Presentation Pro

CD-ROM with dynamic PowerPoint® presentations for every lesson. Helps you introduce and develop concepts, check homework, and assess progress. Part of Presentation Assistant Plus! *(See above.)*

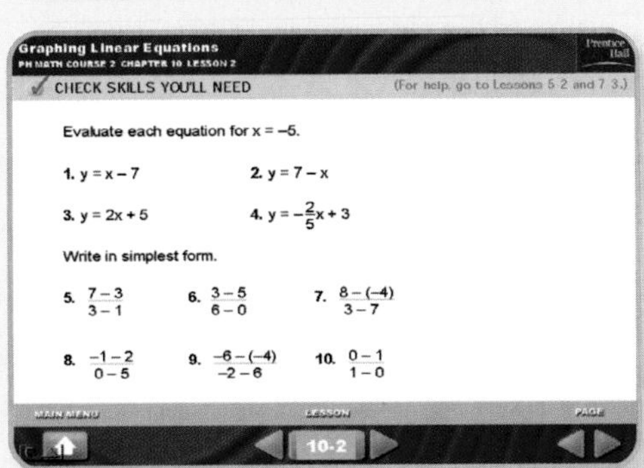

Computer Test Generator

CD-ROM to create practice sheets and tests for course objectives and standardized tests. Includes Instant Chapter Tests™, online testing, and student reports. Part of the PH Assessment System. *(See page 468F.)*

Resource Pro® with Planning Express®

CD-ROM with a lesson planning tool that allows you to import state and local objectives. Includes electronic versions of all the teaching resources.

Chapter Resources

Reading and Math Support

Reading and Math Literacy Masters

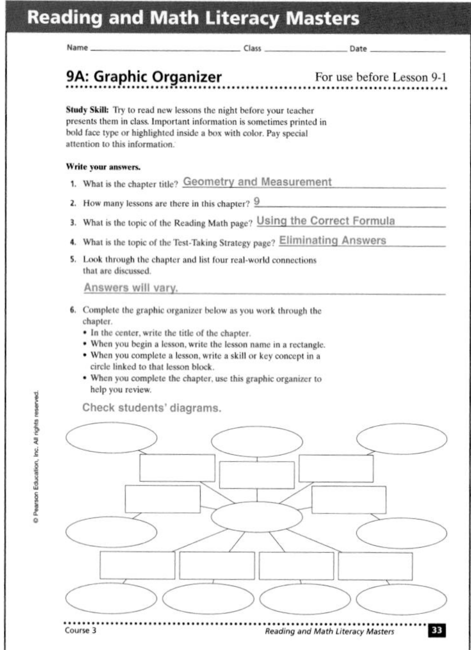

Name ____ Class ____ Date ____

9A: Graphic Organizer For use before Lesson 9-1

Study Skill: Try to read new lessons the night before your teacher presents them in class. Important information is sometimes printed in bold face type or highlighted inside a box with color. Pay special attention to this information.

Write your answers.

1. What is the chapter title? Geometry and Measurement
2. How many lessons are there in this chapter? 9
3. What is the topic of the Reading Math page? Using the Correct Formula
4. What is the topic of the Test-Taking Strategy page? Eliminating Answers
5. Look through the chapter and list four real-world connections that are discussed.
   Answers will vary.
6. Complete the graphic organizer below as you work through the chapter.
   - In the center, write the title of the chapter.
   - When you begin a lesson, write the lesson name in a rectangle.
   - When you complete a lesson, write a skill or key concept in a circle linked to that lesson block.
   - When you complete the chapter, use this graphic organizer to help you review.

   Check students' diagrams.

Available in Spanish

Reading and Math Literacy Masters

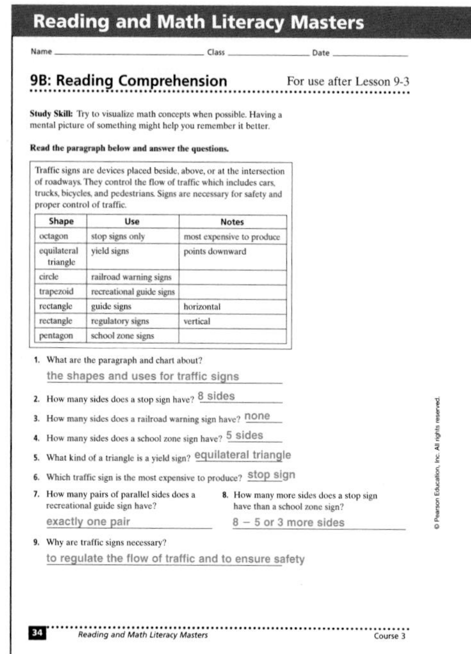

Name ____ Class ____ Date ____

9B: Reading Comprehension For use after Lesson 9-3

Study Skill: Try to visualize math concepts when possible. Having a mental picture of something might help you remember it better.

Read the paragraph below and answer the questions.

Traffic signs are devices placed beside, above, or at the intersection of roadways. They control the flow of traffic which includes cars, trucks, bicycles, and pedestrians. Signs are necessary for safety and proper control of traffic.

Shape	Use	Notes
octagon	stop signs only	most expensive to produce
equilateral triangle	yield signs	points downward
circle	railroad warning signs	
trapezoid	recreational guide signs	
rectangle	guide signs	horizontal
rectangle	regulatory signs	vertical
pentagon	school zone signs	

1. What are the paragraph and chart about? the shapes and uses for traffic signs
2. How many sides does a stop sign have? 8 sides
3. How many sides does a railroad warning sign have? none
4. How many sides does a school zone sign have? 5 sides
5. What kind of a triangle is a yield sign? equilateral triangle
6. Which traffic sign is the most expensive to produce? stop sign
7. How many pairs of parallel sides does a recreational guide sign have? exactly one pair
8. How many more sides does a stop sign have than a school zone sign? 8 − 5 or 3 more sides
9. Why are traffic signs necessary? to regulate the flow of traffic and to ensure safety

Available in Spanish

Reading and Math Literacy Masters

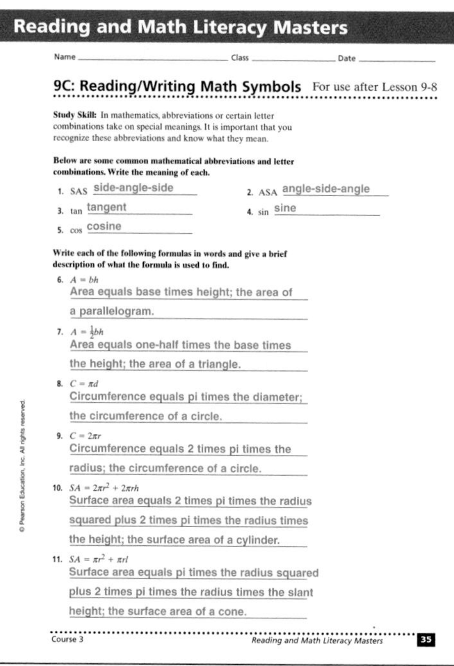

Name ____ Class ____ Date ____

9C: Reading/Writing Math Symbols For use after Lesson 9-8

Study Skill: In mathematics, abbreviations or certain letter combinations take on special meanings. It is important that you recognize these abbreviations and know what they mean.

Below are some common mathematical abbreviations and letter combinations. Write the meaning of each.

1. SAS side-angle-side
2. ASA angle-side-angle
3. tan tangent
4. sin sine
5. cos cosine

Write each of the following formulas in words and give a brief description of what the formula is used to find.

6. $A = bh$ Area equals base times height; the area of a parallelogram.
7. $A = \frac{1}{2}bh$ Area equals one-half times the base times the height; the area of a triangle.
8. $C = \pi d$ Circumference equals pi times the diameter; the circumference of a circle.
9. $C = 2\pi r$ Circumference equals 2 times pi times the radius; the circumference of a circle.
10. $SA = 2\pi r^2 + 2\pi rh$ Surface area equals 2 times pi times the radius squared plus 2 times pi times the radius times the height; the surface area of a cylinder.
11. $SA = \pi r^2 + \pi rl$ Surface area equals pi times the radius squared plus 2 times pi times the radius times the slant height; the surface area of a cone.

Available in Spanish

Reading and Math Literacy Masters

Name ____ Class ____ Date ____

9D: Vocabulary For use with the Chapter Review

Study Skill: Take a few minutes to relax before and after studying. Your mind will absorb and retain more information if you alternate studying with brief rest intervals.

Find and circle each of the words below in the puzzle. Words can be displayed forwards, backwards, up, down, or diagonally.

prism	pyramid	cylinder	cone
skew	polyhedron	space figures	obtuse
precision	isometric view	base plan	slant height
scale factor	tessellation	parallelogram	square
rectangle	rhombus	acute	straight

Q D R S N O I T A L L E S S E T H M
O R H V A W I X L R R U P M R E N B
N U O Q Z E J J E A S Y A P C W U G
O C M O J I I J E N R F P R I S M X
R Y B W R V X N E A O F B H S R Y M
D L U R L C V O M F S C A Z Q V A R
E I S E E I Y I B Z W K S A U S Z G
H N U C S R D E K F F S E K A L N Y
Y D R T U T J G B B Z T P W R A O Y
L E P A T E S T O H V R L D E N I B
O R B N B M T K F E S A A O D T S O
P U R G O O F A Q R H I N N G H I O
I C J L F S Z H K Z X G B S U E C P
C J X E J I C N P H J H U Y O I E V
N F I S X X N X L V E T U C A G R I
P A R A L L E L O G R A M E N H P V
X O N F S C A L E F A C T O R T Y R
A X J S E R U G I F E C A P S J I K

Available in Spanish

Problem Solving

Guided Problem Solving Masters

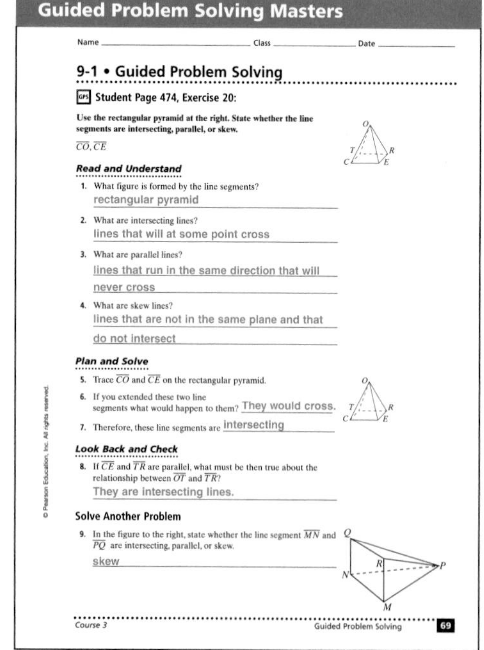

Name ____ Class ____ Date ____

9-1 • Guided Problem Solving

GPS Student Page 474, Exercise 20:

Use the rectangular pyramid at the right. State whether the line segments are intersecting, parallel, or skew.

$\overline{CO}, \overline{CE}$

Read and Understand

1. What figure is formed by the line segments? rectangular pyramid
2. What are intersecting lines? lines that will at some point cross
3. What are parallel lines? lines that run in the same direction that will never cross
4. What are skew lines? lines that are not in the same plane and that do not intersect

Plan and Solve

5. Trace $\overline{CO}$ and $\overline{CE}$ on the rectangular pyramid.
6. If you extended these two line segments what would happen to them? They would cross.
7. Therefore, these line segments are intersecting

Look Back and Check

8. If $\overline{CE}$ and $\overline{TR}$ are parallel, what must be then true about the relationship between $\overline{OT}$ and $\overline{TR}$? They are intersecting lines.

Solve Another Problem

9. In the figure to the right, state whether the line segment $\overline{MN}$ and $\overline{PQ}$ are intersecting, parallel, or skew. skew

Guided Problem Solving Masters

Name ____ Class ____ Date ____

9-2 • Guided Problem Solving

GPS Student Page 479, Exercise 8:

Draw a base plan for the set of stacked cubes.

Read and Understand

1. What are you asked to do? Draw a base plan for the stack of cubes.
2. What is a base plan? A base plan shows the shape of the base and indicates the height of each part of a solid.

Plan and Solve

3. Which of type of angles will be in your sketch? c
   a. Acute b. Obtuse c. Right
4. Which of these plans represents the base? b
5. What are the heights represented in the stack of cubes? 1, 2 and 3
6. Draw the base plan.

Look Back and Check

7. How can you check that your base plan is accurately sketched? Make sure that the front and right are labeled and the heights are correct.

Solve Another Problem

8. Draw a base plan for the set of stacked cubes.

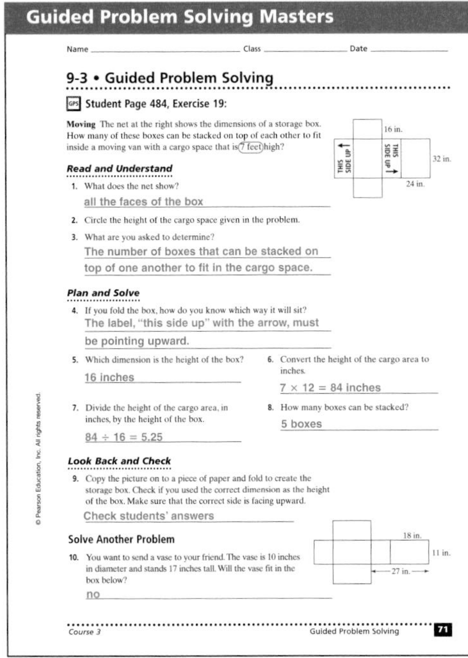

Guided Problem Solving Masters

Name ______ Class ______ Date ______

9-3 • Guided Problem Solving

GPS Student Page 484, Exercise 19:

Moving The net at the right shows the dimensions of a storage box. How many of these boxes can be stacked on top of each other to fit inside a moving van with a cargo space that is 7 feet high?

Read and Understand

1. What does the net show?
   all the faces of the box
2. Circle the height of the cargo space given in the problem.
3. What are you asked to determine?
   The number of boxes that can be stacked on top of one another to fit in the cargo space.

Plan and Solve

4. If you fold the box, how do you know which way it will sit?
   The label, "this side up" with the arrow, must be pointing upward.
5. Which dimension is the height of the box?
   16 inches
6. Convert the height of the cargo area to inches.
   $7 \times 12 = 84$ inches
7. Divide the height of the cargo area, in inches, by the height of the box.
   $84 \div 16 = 5.25$
8. How many boxes can be stacked?
   5 boxes

Look Back and Check

9. Copy the picture on to a piece of paper and fold to create the storage box. Check if you used the correct dimension as the height of the box. Make sure that the correct side is facing upward.
   Check students' answers

Solve Another Problem

10. You want to send a vase to your friend. The vase is 10 inches in diameter and stands 17 inches tall. Will the vase fit in the box below?
    no

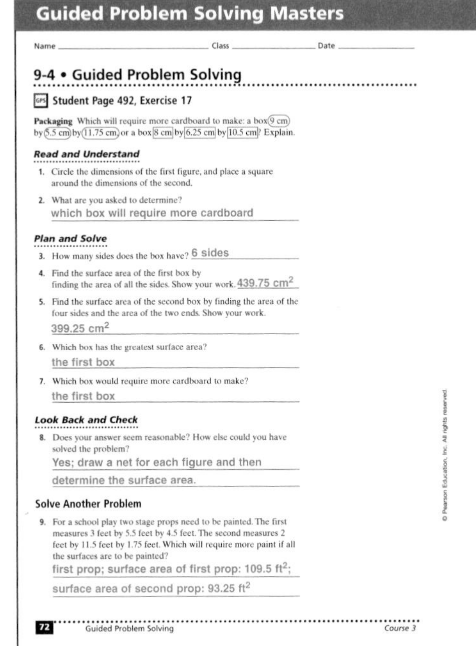

Guided Problem Solving Masters

Name ______ Class ______ Date ______

9-4 • Guided Problem Solving

GPS Student Page 492, Exercise 17

Packaging Which will require more cardboard to make: a box 9 cm by 5.5 cm by 11.75 cm, or a box 8 cm by 6.25 cm by 10.5 cm? Explain.

Read and Understand

1. Circle the dimensions of the first figure, and place a square around the dimensions of the second.
2. What are you asked to determine?
   which box will require more cardboard

Plan and Solve

3. How many sides does the box have? 6 sides
4. Find the surface area of the first box by finding the area of all the sides. Show your work. 439.75 cm^2
5. Find the surface area of the second box by finding the area of the four sides and the area of the two ends. Show your work.
   399.25 cm^2
6. Which box has the greatest surface area?
   the first box
7. Which box would require more cardboard to make?
   the first box

Look Back and Check

8. Does your answer seem reasonable? How else could you have solved the problem?
   Yes; draw a net for each figure and then determine the surface area.

Solve Another Problem

9. For a school play two stage props need to be painted. The first measures 3 feet by 5.5 feet by 4.5 feet. The second measures 2 feet by 11.5 feet by 1.75 feet. Which will require more paint if all the surfaces are to be painted?
   first prop; surface area of first prop: 109.5 ft^2; surface area of second prop: 93.25 ft^2

Guided Problem Solving Masters

Name ______ Class ______ Date ______

9-5 • Guided Problem Solving

GPS Student Page 498, Exercise 23:

Error Analysis A student tried to find the lateral area of the cone below. Explain his mistake at the right. Then find the correct solution.

8 cm
7 cm

$$\begin{aligned} L.A. &= \pi r l \\ &= \pi(8)(7) \\ &= 56\pi \\ &\approx 175.93 \\ &\approx 176 \text{ cm}^2 \end{aligned}$$

Read and Understand

1. Is the answer given correct? no
2. What are you asked to find?
   the student's mistake and the correct solution

Plan and Solve

3. Look at the first step of the student's solution. What is the mistake?
   Diameter is used instead of the radius.
4. What value should he have used? 4 cm
5. Solve the problem using the correct dimensions. Show your work.
   L.A. $= \pi r l = \pi(4)(7) = 28\pi \approx 87.92 \approx 88$ cm^2

Look Back and Check

6. How can you estimate to see if your answer is reasonable?
   Multiply the radius by the slant height by 3 (as an approximation for π). $(3)(4)(7) = 84$; 88 cm^2 is reasonable since it is close to the estimate of 84 cm^2.

Solve Another Problem

7. Find the lateral area of a cone with a diameter of 6 inches and slant height of 8 inches.
   L.A. $= \pi(3)(8) = 24\pi \approx 75$ cm^2

Guided Problem Solving Masters

Name ______ Class ______ Date ______

9-6 • Guided Problem Solving

GPS Student Page 504, Exercise 18:

Art Supplies An art supply store keeps roughly 240 boxes of crayons in its inventory.

a. If each box measures 6 in. by 2.5 in. by 4 in., how many cubic inches of storage space does the store need for the boxes of crayons?

b. One cubic foot is equal to (12 in.)^3, or 1,728 in.^{3}. Find the number of cubic feet necessary for storing 240 boxes of crayons.

Read and Understand

1. Circle the measures of the crayon boxes.
2. Underline how many boxes the art supply store has for inventory.

Plan and Solve

3. What formula will you use to find the volume of one box of crayons?
   $V = lwh$ or $V = Bh$
4. What is the volume of one box of crayons?
   $6 \times 2.5 \times 4 = 60$ in.^{3}
5. What operation will you use to find the volume of 240 boxes?
   multiplication
6. What is the volume of 240 boxes of crayons?
   $240 \times 60 = 14{,}400$ in.^{3}
7. How many cubic inches are in one cubic foot? 1,728 in.^{3}
8. How can you change cubic inches to cubic feet?
   Divide the total number of cubic inches by 1,728.
9. How many cubic feet are necessary for storaging 240 boxes of crayons? 8.333 ft^3

Look Back and Check

10. What is a way to check the problem? Use compatible numbers.

Solve Another Problem

11. A video store keeps approximately 350 boxes of storage cases in its inventory.

a. If each storage case measures 1 in. by 5.5 in. by 8.75 in., how many cubic inches of storage space does the store need for the boxes of storage cases? $1 \times 5.5 \times 8.75 = 48.125$ in.^{3}

b. Find the number of cubic feet necessary for storing 350 boxes of cases. $\frac{48.125 \times 350}{1{,}728} = 9.74$ ft^3

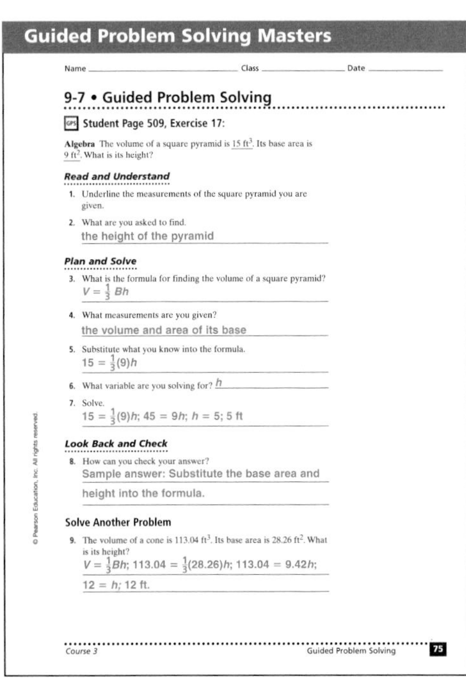

Guided Problem Solving Masters

Name ______ Class ______ Date ______

9-7 • Guided Problem Solving

GPS Student Page 509, Exercise 17:

Algebra The volume of a square pyramid is 15 ft^3. Its base area is 9 ft^2. What is its height?

Read and Understand

1. Underline the measurements of the square pyramid you are given.
2. What are you asked to find.
   the height of the pyramid

Plan and Solve

3. What is the formula for finding the volume of a square pyramid?
   $V = \frac{1}{3}Bh$
4. What measurements are you given?
   the volume and area of its base
5. Substitute what you know into the formula.
   $15 = \frac{1}{3}(9)h$
6. What variable are you solving for? h
7. Solve.
   $15 = \frac{1}{3}(9)h$; $45 = 9h$; $h = 5$; 5 ft

Look Back and Check

8. How can you check your answer?
   Sample answer: Substitute the base area and height into the formula.

Solve Another Problem

9. The volume of a cone is 113.04 ft^3. Its base area is 28.26 ft^2. What is its height?
   $V = \frac{1}{3}Bh$; $113.04 = \frac{1}{3}(28.26)h$; $113.04 = 9.42h$; $12 = h$; 12 ft.

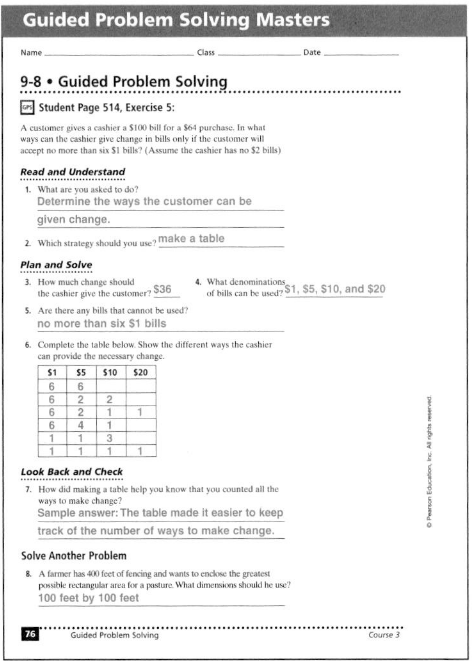

Guided Problem Solving Masters

Name ______ Class ______ Date ______

9-8 • Guided Problem Solving

GPS Student Page 514, Exercise 5:

A customer gives a cashier a \$100 bill for a \$64 purchase. In what ways can the cashier give change in bills only if the customer will accept no more than six \$1 bills? (Assume the cashier has no \$2 bills)

Read and Understand

1. What are you asked to do?
   Determine the ways the customer can be given change.
2. Which strategy should you use? make a table

Plan and Solve

3. How much change should the cashier give the customer? \$36
4. What denominations of bills can be used? \$1, \$5, \$10, and \$20
5. Are there any bills that cannot be used?
   no more than six \$1 bills
6. Complete the table below. Show the different ways the cashier can provide the necessary change.

\$1	\$5	\$10	\$20
6	6		
6	2	2	
6	2	1	1
6	4	1	
1	1	3	
1	1	1	1

Look Back and Check

7. How did making a table help you know that you counted all the ways to make change?
   Sample answer: The table made it easier to keep track of the number of ways to make change.

Solve Another Problem

8. A farmer has 400 feet of fencing and wants to enclose the greatest possible rectangular area for a pasture. What dimensions should he use?
   100 feet by 100 feet

Activities and Projects

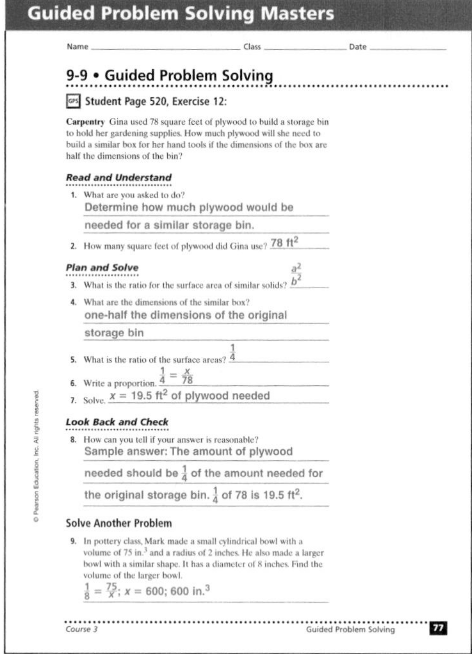

Guided Problem Solving Masters

Name ______ Class ______ Date ______

9-9 • Guided Problem Solving

Student Page 520, Exercise 12:

Carpentry Gina used 78 square feet of plywood to build a storage bin to hold her gardening supplies. How much plywood will she need to build a similar box for her hand tools if the dimensions of the box are half the dimensions of the bin?

Read and Understand

1. What are you asked to do? Determine how much plywood would be needed for a similar storage bin.
2. How many square feet of plywood did Gina use? 78 ft^2

Plan and Solve

3. What is the ratio for the surface area of similar solids? $\frac{a^2}{b^2}$
4. What are the dimensions of the similar box? one-half the dimensions of the original storage bin
5. What is the ratio of the surface areas? $\frac{1}{4}$
6. Write a proportion. $\frac{1}{4} = \frac{x}{78}$
7. Solve. $x = 19.5$ ft^2 of plywood needed

Look Back and Check

8. How can you tell if your answer is reasonable? Sample answer: The amount of plywood needed should be $\frac{1}{4}$ of the amount needed for the original storage bin. $\frac{1}{4}$ of 78 is 19.5 ft^2.

Solve Another Problem

9. In pottery class, Mark made a small cylindrical bowl with a volume of 75 in.^{3} and a radius of 2 inches. He also made a larger bowl with a similar shape. It has a diameter of 8 inches. Find the volume of the larger bowl. $\frac{1}{8} = \frac{75}{x}$; $x = 600$; 600 in.^{3}

Course 3 Guided Problem Solving 77

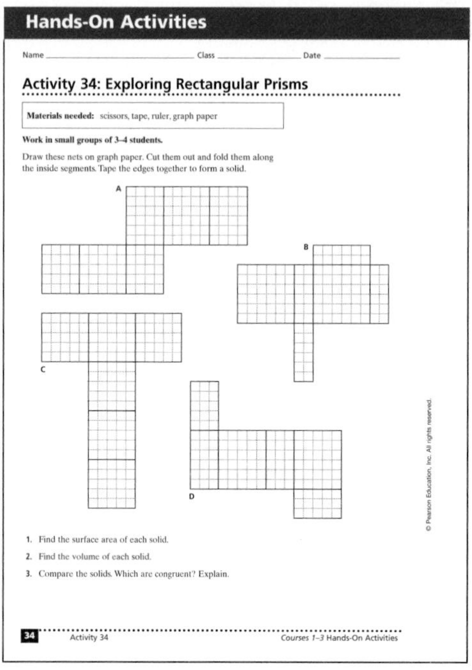

Hands-On Activities

Name ______ Class ______ Date ______

Activity 34: Exploring Rectangular Prisms

Materials needed: scissors, tape, ruler, graph paper

Work in small groups of 3–4 students.

Draw these nets on graph paper. Cut them out and fold them along the inside segments. Tape the edges together to form a solid.

1. Find the surface area of each solid.
2. Find the volume of each solid.
3. Compare the solids. Which are congruent? Explain.

34 Activity 34 Courses 1–3 Hands-On Activities

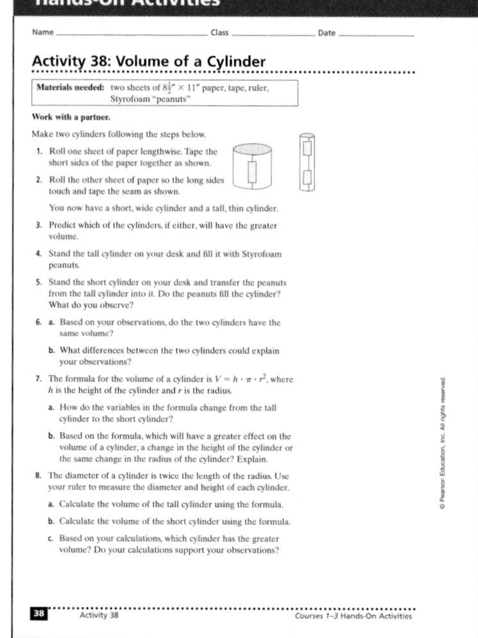

Hands-On Activities

Name ______ Class ______ Date ______

Activity 38: Volume of a Cylinder

Materials needed: two sheets of $8\frac{1}{2}$" × 11" paper, tape, ruler, Styrofoam "peanuts"

Work with a partner.

Make two cylinders following the steps below.

1. Roll one sheet of paper lengthwise. Tape the short sides of the paper together as shown.
2. Roll the other sheet of paper so the long sides touch and tape the seam as shown.
   You now have a short, wide cylinder and a tall, thin cylinder.
3. Predict which of the cylinders, if either, will have the greater volume.
4. Stand the tall cylinder on your desk and fill it with Styrofoam peanuts.
5. Stand the short cylinder on your desk and transfer the peanuts from the tall cylinder into it. Do the peanuts fill the cylinder? What do you observe?
6. a. Based on your observations, do the two cylinders have the same volume?
   b. What differences between the two cylinders could explain your observations?
7. The formula for the volume of a cylinder is $V = h \cdot \pi \cdot r^2$, where h is the height of the cylinder and r is the radius.
   a. How do the variables in the formula change from the tall cylinder to the short cylinder?
   b. Based on the formula, which will have a greater effect on the volume of a cylinder, a change in the height of the cylinder or the same change in the radius of the cylinder? Explain.
8. The diameter of a cylinder is twice the length of the radius. Use your ruler to measure the diameter and height of each cylinder.
   a. Calculate the volume of the tall cylinder using the formula.
   b. Calculate the volume of the short cylinder using the formula.
   c. Based on your calculations, which cylinder has the greater volume? Do your calculations support your observations?

38 Activity 38 Courses 1–3 Hands-On Activities

Sample page; see p. G for complete list.

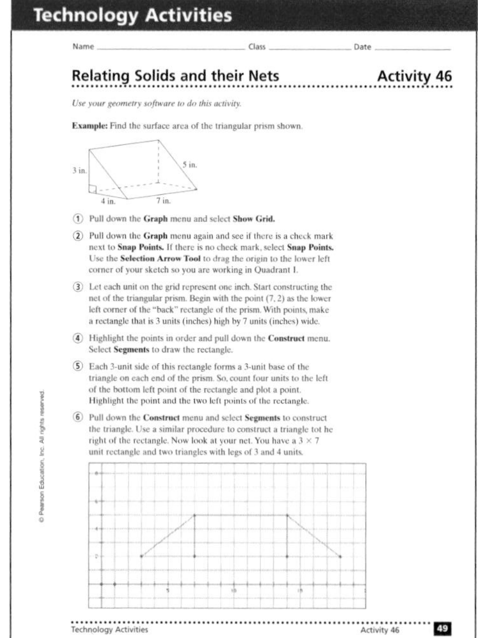

Technology Activities

Name ______ Class ______ Date ______

Relating Solids and their Nets **Activity 46**

Use your geometry software to do this activity.

Example: Find the surface area of the triangular prism shown.

① Pull down the **Graph** menu and select **Show Grid.**

② Pull down the **Graph** menu again and see if there is a check mark next to **Snap Points.** If there is no check mark, select **Snap Points.** Use the **Selection Arrow Tool** to drag the origin to the lower left corner of your sketch so you are working in Quadrant I.

③ Let each unit on the grid represent one inch. Start constructing the net of the triangular prism. Begin with the point (7, 2) as the lower left corner of the "back" rectangle of the prism. With points, make a rectangle that is 3 units (inches) high by 7 units (inches) wide.

④ Highlight the points in order and pull down the **Construct** menu. Select **Segments** to draw the rectangle.

⑤ Each 3-unit side of this rectangle forms a 3-unit base of the triangle on each end of the prism. So, count four units to the left of the bottom left point of the rectangle and plot a point. Highlight the point and the two left points of the rectangle.

⑥ Pull down the **Construct** menu and select **Segments** to construct the triangle. Use a similar procedure to construct a triangle tot he right of the rectangle. Now look at your net. You have a 3 × 7 unit rectangle and two triangles with legs of 3 and 4 units.

Technology Activities Activity 46 49

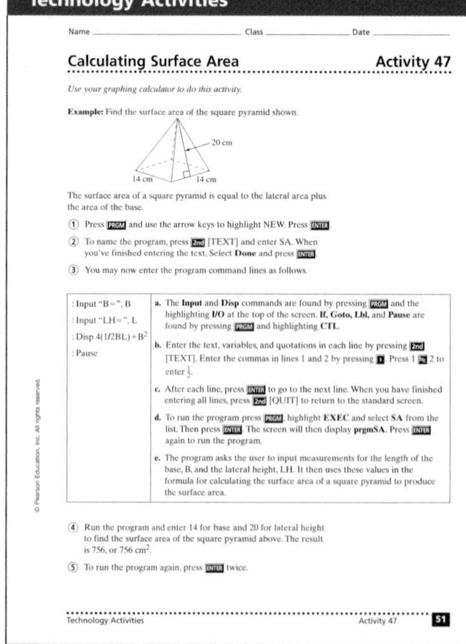

Technology Activities

Name ______ Class ______ Date ______

Calculating Surface Area **Activity 47**

Use your graphing calculator to do this activity.

Example: Find the surface area of the square pyramid shown.

The surface area of a square pyramid is equal to the lateral area plus the area of the base.

① Press PRGM and use the arrow keys to highlight NEW. Press ENTER

② To name the program, press 2nd [TEXT] and enter SA. When you've finished entering the text, Select **Done** and press ENTER

③ You may now enter the program command lines as follows.

:Input "B=", B :Input "LH=", L :Disp 4(1/2BL)+B^2 :Pause	a. The **Input** and **Disp** commands are found by pressing PRGM and the highlighting **I/O** at the top of the screen. **If, Goto, Lbl,** and **Pause** are found by pressing PRGM and highlighting **CTL**. b. Enter the text, variables, and quotations in each line by pressing 2nd [TEXT]. Enter the commas in lines 1 and 2 by pressing . Press 1 ÷ 2 to enter $\frac{1}{2}$. c. After each line, press ENTER to go to the next line. When you have finished entering all lines, press 2nd [QUIT] to return to the standard screen. d. To run the program press PRGM, highlight **EXEC** and select **SA** from the list. Then press ENTER. The screen will then display **prgmSA**. Press ENTER again to run the program. e. The program asks the user to input measurements for the length of the base, B, and the lateral height, LH. It then uses these values in the formula for calculating the surface area of a square pyramid to produce the surface area.

④ Run the program and enter 14 for base and 20 for lateral height to find the surface area of the square pyramid above. The result is 756, or 756 cm^2.

⑤ To run the program again, press ENTER twice.

Technology Activities Activity 47 51

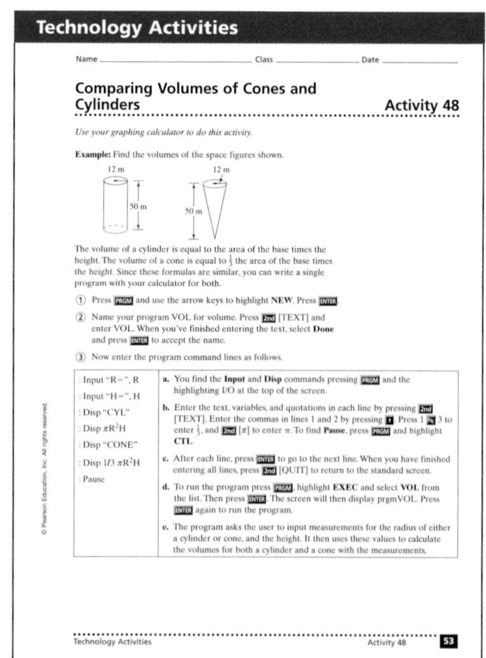

Technology Activities

Name ______ Class ______ Date ______

Comparing Volumes of Cones and Cylinders **Activity 48**

Use your graphing calculator to do this activity.

Example: Find the volumes of the space figures shown.

The volume of a cylinder is equal to the area of the base times the height. The volume of a cone is equal to $\frac{1}{3}$ the area of the base times the height. Since these formulas are similar, you can write a single program with your calculator for both.

① Press PRGM and use the arrow keys to highlight **NEW**. Press ENTER.

② Name your program VOL for volume. Press 2nd [TEXT] and enter VOL. When you've finished entering the text, select **Done** and press ENTER to accept the name.

③ Now enter the program command lines as follows.

:Input "R=", R :Input "H=", H :Disp "CYL" :Disp πR^{2}H :Disp "CONE" :Disp 1/3 πR^{2}H :Pause	a. You find the **Input** and **Disp** commands pressing PRGM and the highlighting I/O at the top of the screen. b. Enter the text, variables, and quotations in each line by pressing 2nd [TEXT]. Enter the commas in lines 1 and 2 by pressing . Press 1 ÷ 3 to enter $\frac{1}{3}$, and 2nd [π] to enter π. To find **Pause**, press PRGM and highlight **CTL**. c. After each line, press ENTER to go to the next line. When you have finished entering all lines, press 2nd [QUIT] to return to the standard screen. d. To run the program press PRGM, highlight **EXEC** and select **VOL** from the list. Then press ENTER. The screen will then display prgmVOL. Press ENTER again to run the program. e. The program asks the user to input measurements for the radius of either a cylinder or cone, and the height. It then uses these values to calculate the volumes for both a cylinder and a cone with the measurements.

Technology Activities Activity 48 53

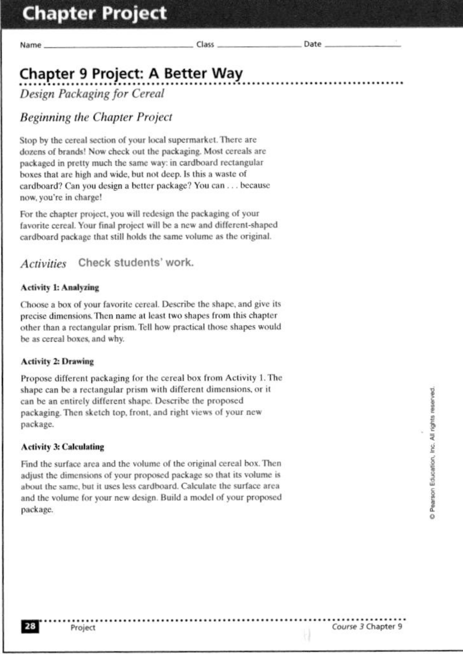

Chapter Project

Name ______________________ Class ______________ Date ______________

Chapter 9 Project: A Better Way

Design Packaging for Cereal

Beginning the Chapter Project

Stop by the cereal section of your local supermarket. There are dozens of brands! Now check out the packaging. Most cereals are packaged in pretty much the same way: in cardboard rectangular boxes that are high and wide, but not deep. Is this a waste of cardboard? Can you design a better package? You can . . . because now, you're in charge!

For the chapter project, you will redesign the packaging of your favorite cereal. Your final project will be a new and different-shaped cardboard package that still holds the same volume as the original.

Activities Check students' work.

Activity 1: Analyzing

Choose a box of your favorite cereal. Describe the shape, and give its precise dimensions. Then name at least two shapes from this chapter other than a rectangular prism. Tell how practical those shapes would be as cereal boxes, and why.

Activity 2: Drawing

Propose different packaging for the cereal box from Activity 1. The shape can be a rectangular prism with different dimensions, or it can be an entirely different shape. Describe the proposed packaging. Then sketch top, front, and right views of your new package.

Activity 3: Calculating

Find the surface area and the volume of the original cereal box. Then adjust the dimensions of your proposed package so that its volume is about the same, but it uses less cardboard. Calculate the surface area and the volume for your new design. Build a model of your proposed package.

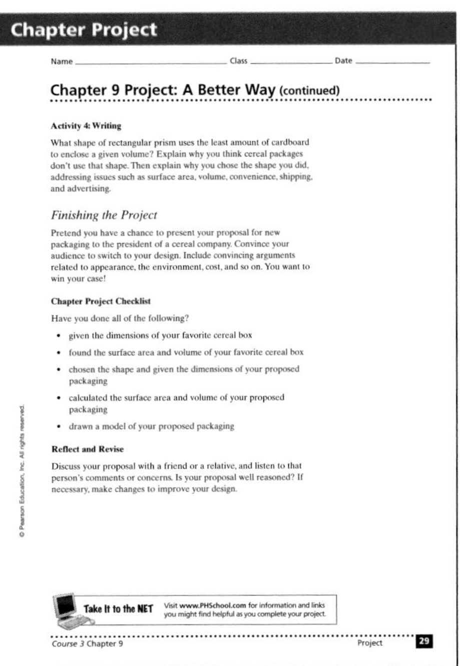

Chapter Project

Name ______________________ Class ______________ Date ______________

Chapter 9 Project: A Better Way (continued)

Activity 4: Writing

What shape of rectangular prism uses the least amount of cardboard to enclose a given volume? Explain why you think cereal packages don't use that shape. Then explain why you chose the shape you did, addressing issues such as surface area, volume, convenience, shipping, and advertising.

Finishing the Project

Pretend you have a chance to present your proposal for new packaging to the president of a cereal company. Convince your audience to switch to your design. Include convincing arguments related to appearance, the environment, cost, and so on. You want to win your case!

Chapter Project Checklist

Have you done all of the following?

- given the dimensions of your favorite cereal box
- found the surface area and volume of your favorite cereal box
- chosen the shape and given the dimensions of your proposed packaging
- calculated the surface area and volume of your proposed packaging
- drawn a model of your proposed packaging

Reflect and Revise

Discuss your proposal with a friend or a relative, and listen to that person's comments or concerns. Is your proposal well reasoned? If necessary, make changes to improve your design.

Take It to the NET Visit www.PHSchool.com for information and links you might find helpful as you complete your project.

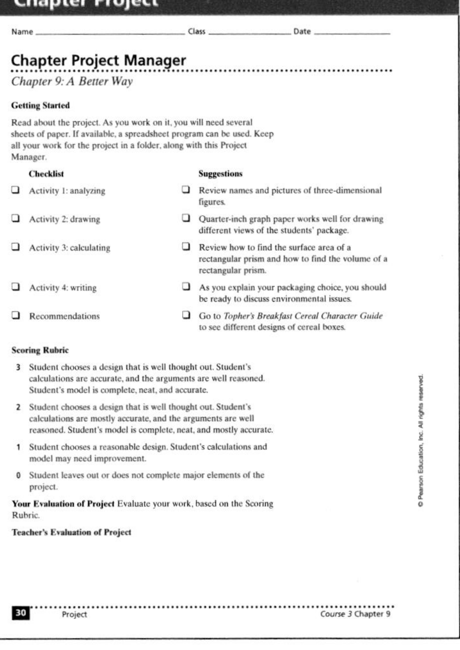

Chapter Project

Name ______________________ Class ______________ Date ______________

Chapter Project Manager

Chapter 9: A Better Way

Getting Started

Read about the project. As you work on it, you will need several sheets of paper. If available, a spreadsheet program can be used. Keep all your work for the project in a folder, along with this Project Manager.

Checklist	Suggestions
❑ Activity 1: analyzing	❑ Review names and pictures of three-dimensional figures.
❑ Activity 2: drawing	❑ Quarter-inch graph paper works well for drawing different views of the students' package.
❑ Activity 3: calculating	❑ Review how to find the surface area of a rectangular prism and how to find the volume of a rectangular prism.
❑ Activity 4: writing	❑ As you explain your packaging choice, you should be ready to discuss environmental issues.
❑ Recommendations	❑ Go to *Topher's Breakfast Cereal Character Guide* to see different designs of cereal boxes.

Scoring Rubric

3 Student chooses a design that is well thought out. Student's calculations are accurate, and the arguments are well reasoned. Student's model is complete, neat, and accurate.

2 Student chooses a design that is well thought out. Student's calculations are mostly accurate, and the arguments are well reasoned. Student's model is complete, neat, and mostly accurate.

1 Student chooses a reasonable design. Student's calculations and model may need improvement.

0 Student leaves out or does not complete major elements of the project.

Your Evaluation of Project Evaluate your work, based on the Scoring Rubric.

Teacher's Evaluation of Project

Chapter Project

Name ______________________ Class ______________ Date ______________

Chapter Project Teacher Notes

Chapter 9: A Better Way!

About the Project This project allows students to use their understanding of geometry and measurement to design packaging for their favorite cereal.

Introducing the Project

Ask students:

- How are cereal boxes alike? How are they different?
- What things would you want to keep in mind when designing a cereal box?
- How might you make a better box than those currently used?

Activity 1: Analyzing

Ask students why a rectangular prism is a practical package for a cereal box.

Activity 2: Drawing

Have students discuss what factors influence their choices. Such factors might include stacking ease, package attractiveness, or few folds.

Activity 3: Calculating

Pick five different space figures. Find dimensions that would make the volumes of all of them the same. Find the surface area from the dimensions. Ask students: Which one had the least surface area? Which one is the most practical to use as a cereal box? Which one is the best choice for the project?

Activity 4: Writing

Students may want to investigate different levels of thickness of cardboard cereal packages. Have students estimate the volume of their cereal box if the cardboard is 1 mm thick. How would a reduction in thickness by half affect the volume? What are the limits to the thinness of the cardboard? What other materials could they use for their package?

Finishing the Project

You may wish to plan a project day on which students share their completed projects. Encourage students to explain their process as well as their product.

Take It to the NET Visit www.PHSchool.com for information, student links, and teacher support for this project.

Transparencies

Problem of the Day

Problem of the Day — Lesson 9-1

On a bus, there are three times as many children as adults and twice as many girls as boys. If there are 8 girls on the bus, how many children are there? How many passengers?

Answers

12; 16

Problem of the Day — Lesson 9-2

Lucinda buys 12 gal of gasoline at $.95 per gallon. How much does the gas cost?

Answer

$11.40

Problem of the Day — Lesson 9-3

Round each number to the underlined digit.

a. 8<u>9</u>.63 **b.** <u>5</u>79,122 **c.** 0.834<u>7</u>6

Answers

a. 90 **b.** 600,000 **c.** 0.8348

Problem of the Day

Problem of the Day — Lesson 9-4

Forty-three boys and five girls tried out for the middle school football team. One-fourth of the students were dropped after the first day. Of those who were left, $\frac{1}{6}$ were dropped after the second day. Of those who remained, $\frac{4}{5}$ made the team. How many students made the team?

Answer

24

Problem of the Day — Lesson 9-5

The sum of 3 different one-digit numbers greater than 0 is 15. Two numbers are even, and one number is odd. Find all possible values for the numbers.

Answer

8, 6, 1; 8, 4, 3; 8, 2, 5; 6, 4, 5; 6, 2, 7; or 4, 2, 9

Problem of the Day — Lesson 9-6

Choose the symbol, $<$, $=$, or $>$ that makes each statement true.

a. $2\frac{5}{8} + 1 + 2\frac{3}{8} \ \underline{?} \ 4\frac{7}{8} + 1\frac{1}{8}$ **b.** $3\frac{5}{6} + 2\frac{1}{10} + \frac{9}{10} \ \underline{?} \ 4 + 3\frac{3}{4}$

Answers

a. $=$ **b.** $<$

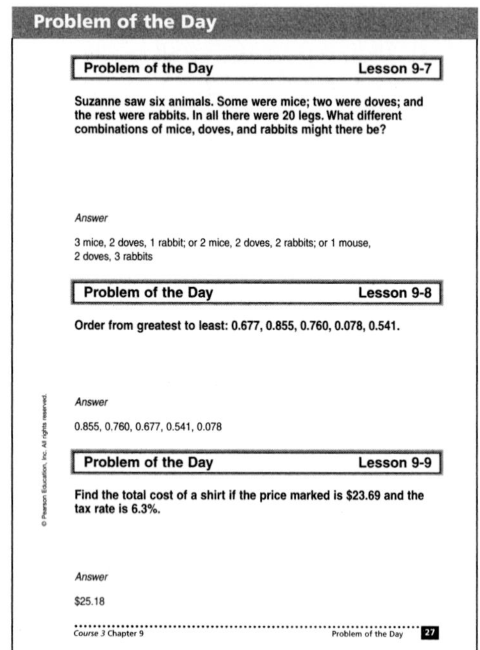

Problem of the Day

Problem of the Day — **Lesson 9-7**

Suzanne saw six animals. Some were mice; two were doves; and the rest were rabbits. In all there were 20 legs. What different combinations of mice, doves, and rabbits might there be?

Answer

3 mice, 2 doves, 1 rabbit; or 2 mice, 2 doves, 2 rabbits; or 1 mouse, 2 doves, 3 rabbits

Problem of the Day — **Lesson 9-8**

Order from greatest to least: 0.677, 0.855, 0.760, 0.078, 0.541.

Answer

0.855, 0.760, 0.677, 0.541, 0.078

Problem of the Day — **Lesson 9-9**

Find the total cost of a shirt if the price marked is \$23.69 and the tax rate is 6.3%.

Answer

\$25.18

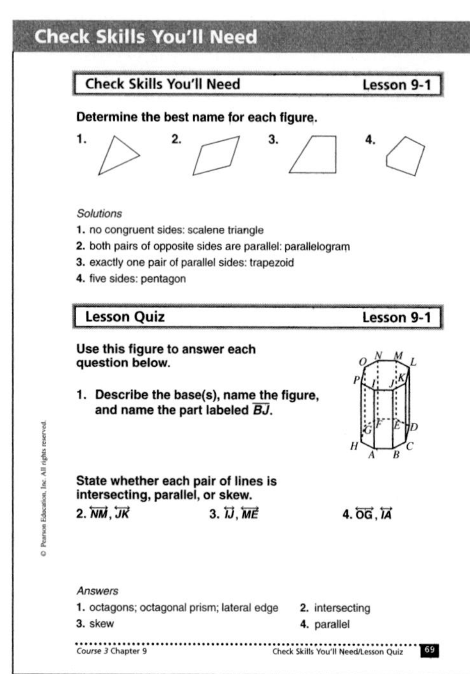

Check Skills You'll Need

Check Skills You'll Need — **Lesson 9-1**

Determine the best name for each figure.

1. **2.** **3.** **4.**

Solutions

1. no congruent sides: scalene triangle
2. both pairs of opposite sides are parallel: parallelogram
3. exactly one pair of parallel sides: trapezoid
4. five sides: pentagon

Lesson Quiz — **Lesson 9-1**

Use this figure to answer each question below.

1. Describe the base(s), name the figure, and name the part labeled $\overline{BJ}$.

State whether each pair of lines is intersecting, parallel, or skew.

2. $\overleftrightarrow{NM}$, $\overleftrightarrow{JK}$ **3.** $\overleftrightarrow{IJ}$, $\overleftrightarrow{ME}$ **4.** $\overleftrightarrow{OG}$, $\overleftrightarrow{IA}$

Answers

1. octagons; octagonal prism; lateral edge **2.** intersecting
3. skew **4.** parallel

Sample page; see p. H for complete list.

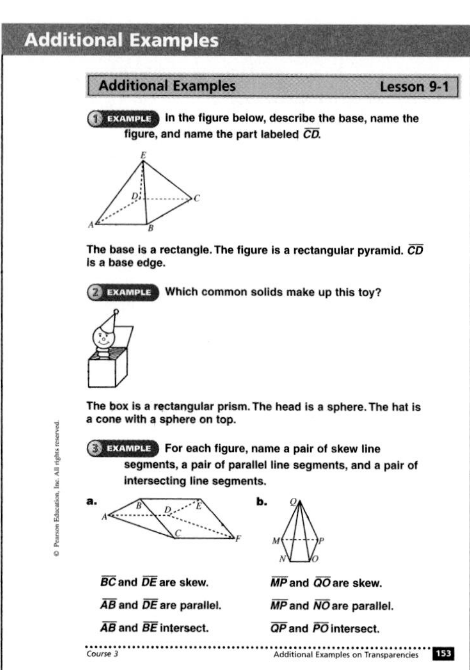

Additional Examples

Additional Examples — **Lesson 9-1**

1 EXAMPLE **In the figure below, describe the base, name the figure, and name the part labeled $\overline{CD}$.**

The base is a rectangle. The figure is a rectangular pyramid. $\overline{CD}$ is a base edge.

2 EXAMPLE **Which common solids make up this toy?**

The box is a rectangular prism. The head is a sphere. The hat is a cone with a sphere on top.

3 EXAMPLE **For each figure, name a pair of skew line segments, a pair of parallel line segments, and a pair of intersecting line segments.**

a. **b.**

$\overline{BC}$ and $\overline{DE}$ are skew. **$\overline{MP}$ and $\overline{QO}$ are skew.**
$\overline{AB}$ and $\overline{DE}$ are parallel. **$\overline{MP}$ and $\overline{NO}$ are parallel.**
$\overline{AB}$ and $\overline{BE}$ intersect. **$\overline{QP}$ and $\overline{PO}$ intersect.**

Sample page; see p. H for complete list.

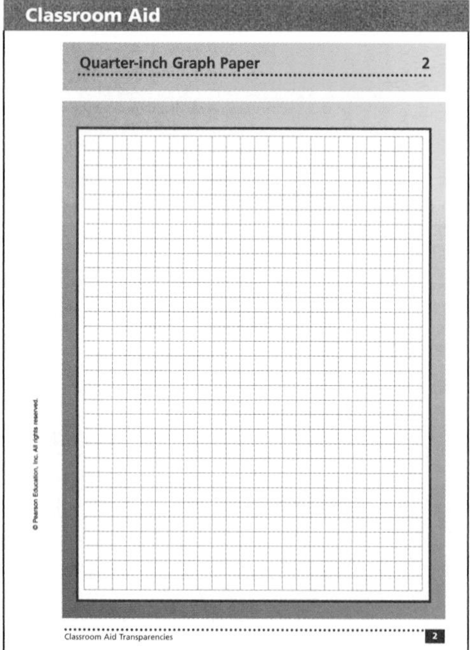

Classroom Aid

Quarter-inch Graph Paper 2

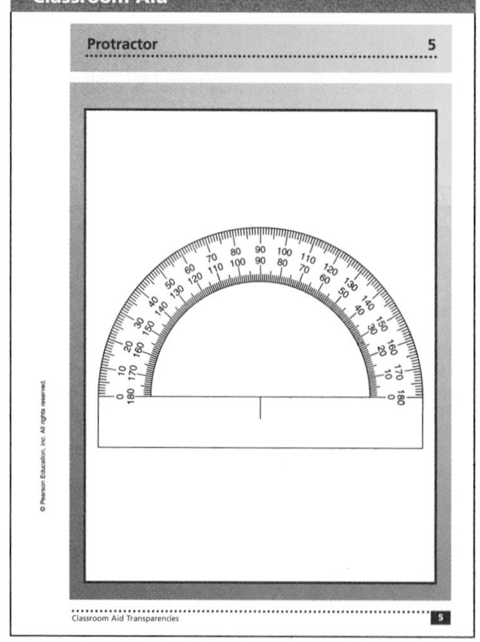

Classroom Aid

Protractor 5

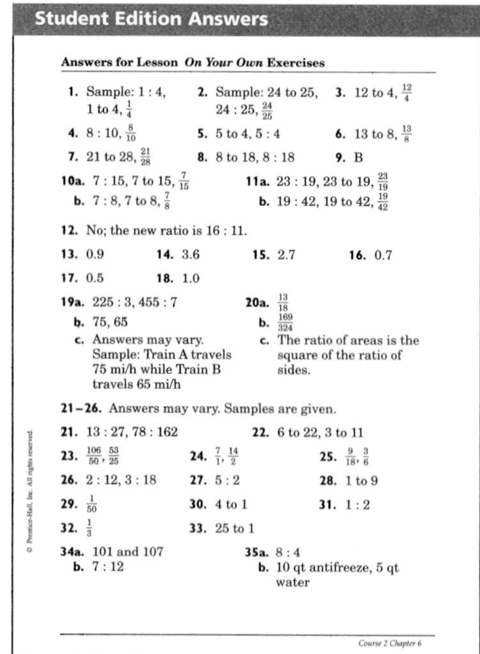

Student Edition Answers

Answers for Lesson *On Your Own* Exercises

1. Sample: 1 : 4, 1 to 4, $\frac{1}{4}$ **2.** Sample: 24 to 25, 24 : 25, $\frac{24}{25}$ **3.** 12 to 4, $\frac{12}{4}$
4. 8 : 10, $\frac{8}{10}$ **5.** 5 to 4, 5 : 4 **6.** 13 to 8, $\frac{13}{8}$
7. 21 to 28, $\frac{21}{28}$ **8.** 8 to 18, 8 : 18 **9.** B
10a. 7 : 15, 7 to 15, $\frac{7}{15}$ **11a.** 23 : 19, 23 to 19, $\frac{23}{19}$
b. 7 : 8, 7 to 8, $\frac{7}{8}$ **b.** 19 : 42, 19 to 42, $\frac{19}{42}$
12. No; the new ratio is 16 : 11.
13. 0.9 **14.** 3.6 **15.** 2.7 **16.** 0.7
17. 0.5 **18.** 1.0
19a. 225 : 3, 455 : 7 **20a.** $\frac{13}{18}$
b. 75, 65 **b.** $\frac{169}{324}$
c. Answers may vary. Sample: Train A travels 75 mi/h while Train B travels 65 mi/h **c.** The ratio of areas is the square of the ratio of sides.
21–26. Answers may vary. Samples are given.
21. 13 : 27, 78 : 162 **22.** 6 to 22, 3 to 11
23. $\frac{106}{50}$, $\frac{53}{25}$ **24.** $\frac{7}{1}$, $\frac{14}{2}$ **25.** $\frac{9}{18}$, $\frac{3}{6}$
26. 2 : 12, 3 : 18 **27.** 5 : 2 **28.** 1 to 9
29. $\frac{1}{50}$ **30.** 4 to 1 **31.** 1 : 2
32. $\frac{1}{3}$ **33.** 25 to 1
34a. 101 and 107 **35a.** 8 : 4
b. 7 : 12 **b.** 10 qt antifreeze, 5 qt water

Sample page; see p. H for complete list.

Assessment

Lesson Quiz

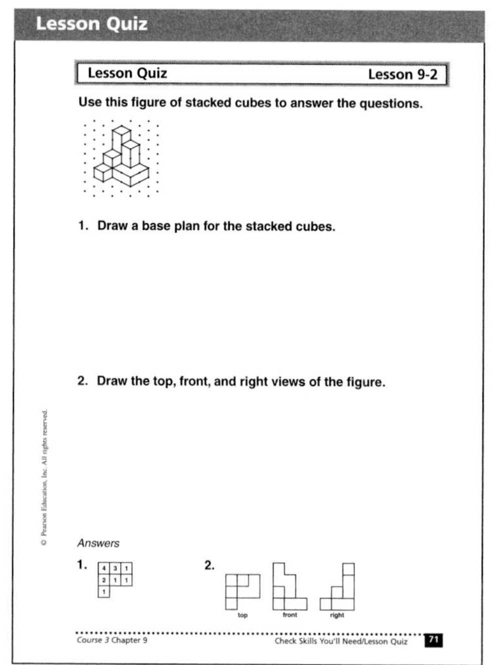

Lesson Quiz **Lesson 9-2**

Use this figure of stacked cubes to answer the questions.

1. **Draw a base plan for the stacked cubes.**

2. **Draw the top, front, and right views of the figure.**

Answers

1.

4	3	1
2	1	1
1		

2. top front right

Course 3 Chapter 9 Check Skills You'll Need/Lesson Quiz 71

Sample page; see p. H for complete list.

Checkpoint Quizzes

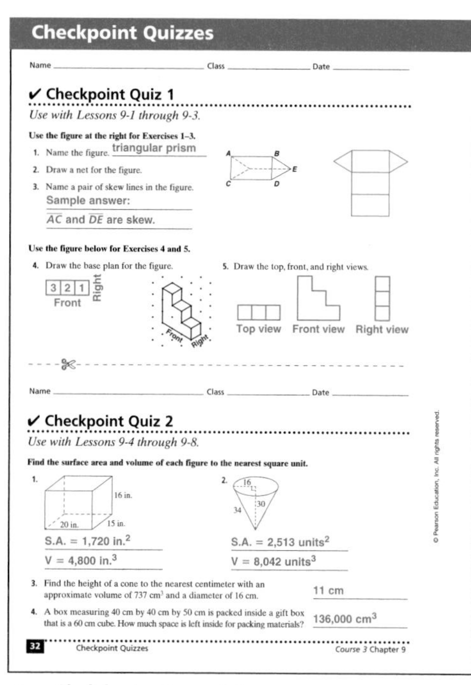

Name ________ Class ________ Date ________

✔ Checkpoint Quiz 1

Use with Lessons 9-1 through 9-3.

Use the figure at the right for Exercises 1–3.

1. Name the figure. triangular prism
2. Draw a net for the figure.
3. Name a pair of skew lines in the figure. Sample answer: $\overline{AC}$ and $\overline{DE}$ are skew.

Use the figure below for Exercises 4 and 5.

4. Draw the base plan for the figure. 3 2 1 Front Right
5. Draw the top, front, and right views. Top view Front view Right view

Name ________ Class ________ Date ________

✔ Checkpoint Quiz 2

Use with Lessons 9-4 through 9-8.

Find the surface area and volume of each figure to the nearest square unit.

1. S.A. = 1,720 in.^{2} V = 4,800 in.^{3}
2. S.A. = 2,513 units^2 V = 8,042 units^3
3. Find the height of a cone to the nearest centimeter with an approximate volume of 737 cm^3 and a diameter of 16 cm. 11 cm
4. A box measuring 40 cm by 40 cm by 50 cm is packed inside a gift box that is a 60 cm cube. How much space is left inside for packing materials? 136,000 cm^3

32 Checkpoint Quizzes Course 3 Chapter 9

Available in Spanish

Chapter Test, Form A

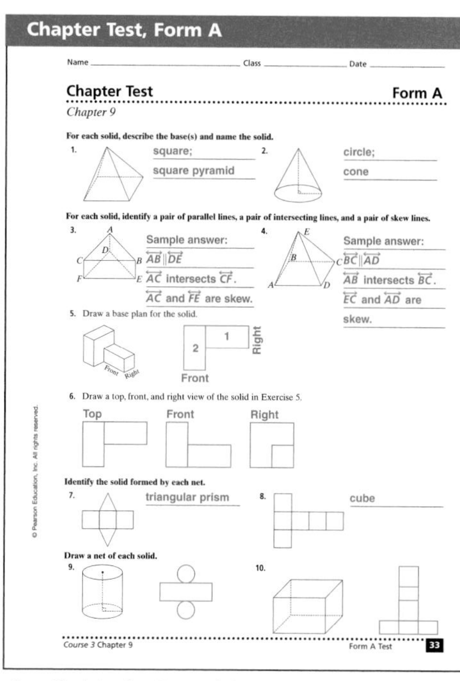

Name ________ Class ________ Date ________

Chapter Test **Form A**

Chapter 9

For each solid, describe the base(s) and name the solid.

1. square; square pyramid
2. circle; cone

For each solid, identify a pair of parallel lines, a pair of intersecting lines, and a pair of skew lines.

3. Sample answer: $\overleftrightarrow{AB} \parallel \overleftrightarrow{DE}$ $\overleftrightarrow{AC}$ intersects $\overleftrightarrow{CF}$. $\overleftrightarrow{AC}$ and $\overleftrightarrow{FE}$ are skew.
4. Sample answer: $\overleftrightarrow{BC} \parallel \overleftrightarrow{AD}$ $\overleftrightarrow{AB}$ intersects $\overleftrightarrow{BC}$. $\overleftrightarrow{EC}$ and $\overleftrightarrow{AD}$ are skew.
5. Draw a base plan for the solid. 1 2 Front Right
6. Draw a top, front, and right view of the solid in Exercise 5. Top Front Right

Identify the solid formed by each net.

7. triangular prism
8. cube

Draw a net of each solid.

9.
10.

Course 3 Chapter 9 Form A Test 33

Available in Spanish

Chapter Test, Form A

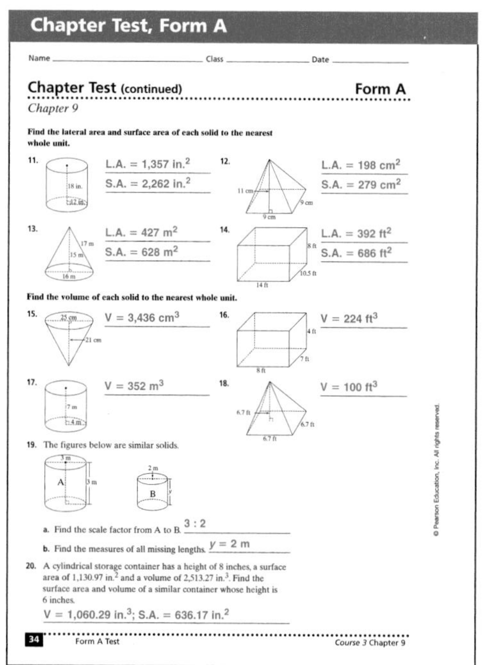

Name ________ Class ________ Date ________

Chapter Test (continued) **Form A**

Chapter 9

Find the lateral area and surface area of each solid to the nearest whole unit.

11. L.A. = 1,357 in.^{2} S.A. = 2,262 in.^{2}
12. L.A. = 198 cm^2 S.A. = 279 cm^2
13. L.A. = 427 m^2 S.A. = 628 m^2
14. L.A. = 392 ft^2 S.A. = 686 ft^2

Find the volume of each solid to the nearest whole unit.

15. V = 3,436 cm^3
16. V = 224 ft^3
17. V = 352 m^3
18. V = 100 ft^3
19. The figures below are similar solids.
   a. Find the scale factor from A to B. 3 : 2
   b. Find the measures of all missing lengths. y = 2 m
20. A cylindrical storage container has a height of 8 inches, a surface area of 1,130.97 in.^{2} and a volume of 2,513.27 in.^{3}. Find the surface area and volume of a similar container whose height is 6 inches. V = 1,060.29 in.^{3}; S.A. = 636.17 in.^{2}

34 Form A Test Course 3 Chapter 9

Available in Spanish

Chapter Test, Form B

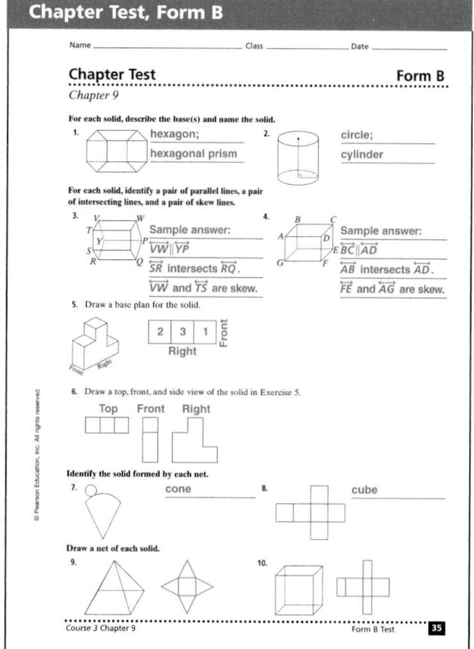

Name ________ Class ________ Date ________

Chapter Test **Form B**

Chapter 9

For each solid, describe the base(s) and name the solid.

1. hexagon; hexagonal prism
2. circle; cylinder

For each solid, identify a pair of parallel lines, a pair of intersecting lines, and a pair of skew lines.

3. Sample answer: $\overleftrightarrow{VW} \parallel \overleftrightarrow{YP}$ $\overleftrightarrow{SR}$ intersects $\overleftrightarrow{RQ}$. $\overleftrightarrow{VW}$ and $\overleftrightarrow{TS}$ are skew.
4. Sample answer: $\overleftrightarrow{BC} \parallel \overleftrightarrow{AD}$ $\overleftrightarrow{AB}$ intersects $\overleftrightarrow{AD}$. $\overleftrightarrow{FE}$ and $\overleftrightarrow{AG}$ are skew.
5. Draw a base plan for the solid. 2 3 1 Right Front
6. Draw a top, front, and side view of the solid in Exercise 5. Top Front Right

Identify the solid formed by each net.

7. cone
8. cube

Draw a net of each solid.

9.
10.

Course 3 Chapter 9 Form B Test 35

Available in Spanish

Chapter Test, Form B

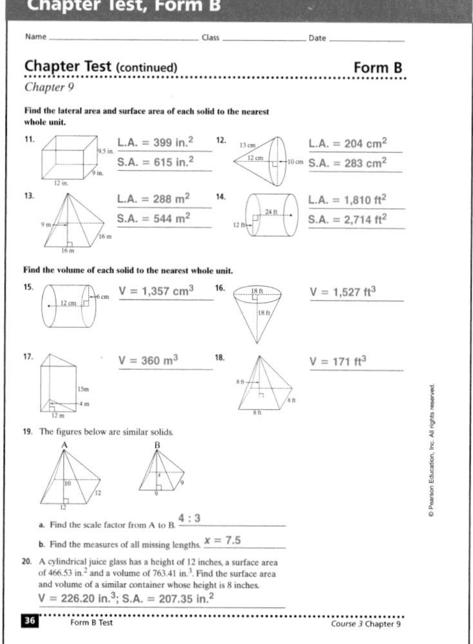

Name ________ Class ________ Date ________

Chapter Test (continued) **Form B**

Chapter 9

Find the lateral area and surface area of each solid to the nearest whole unit.

11. L.A. = 399 in.^{2} S.A. = 615 in.^{2}
12. L.A. = 204 cm^2 S.A. = 283 cm^2
13. L.A. = 288 m^2 S.A. = 544 m^2
14. L.A. = 1,810 ft^2 S.A. = 2,714 ft^2

Find the volume of each solid to the nearest whole unit.

15. V = 1,357 cm^3
16. V = 1,527 ft^3
17. V = 360 m^3
18. V = 171 ft^3
19. The figures below are similar solids.
   a. Find the scale factor from A to B. 4 : 3
   b. Find the measures of all missing lengths. x = 7.5
20. A cylindrical juice glass has a height of 12 inches, a surface area of 466.53 in.^{2} and a volume of 763.41 in.^{3}. Find the surface area and volume of a similar container whose height is 8 inches. V = 226.20 in.^{3}; S.A. = 207.35 in.^{2}

36 Form B Test Course 3 Chapter 9

Available in Spanish

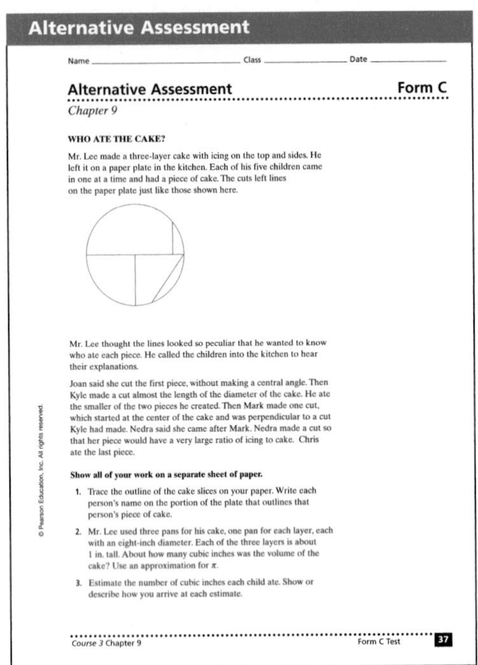

Alternative Assessment

Name ______ Class ______ Date ______

Alternative Assessment — Form C

Chapter 9

WHO ATE THE CAKE?

Mr. Lee made a three-layer cake with icing on the top and sides. He left it on a paper plate in the kitchen. Each of his five children came in one at a time and had a piece of cake. The cuts left lines on the paper plate just like those shown here.

Mr. Lee thought the lines looked so peculiar that he wanted to know who ate each piece. He called the children into the kitchen to hear their explanations.

Joan said she cut the first piece, without making a central angle. Then Kyle made a cut almost the length of the diameter of the cake. He ate the smaller of the two pieces he created. Then Mark made one cut, which started at the center of the cake and was perpendicular to a cut Kyle had made. Nedra said she came after Mark. Nedra made a cut so that her piece would have a very large ratio of icing to cake. Chris ate the last piece.

Show all of your work on a separate sheet of paper.

1. Trace the outline of the cake slices on your paper. Write each person's name on the portion of the plate that outlines that person's piece of cake.
2. Mr. Lee used three pans for his cake, one pan for each layer, each with an eight-inch diameter. Each of the three layers is about 1 in. tall. About how many cubic inches was the volume of the cake? Use an approximation for π.
3. Estimate the number of cubic inches each child ate. Show or describe how you arrive at each estimate.

Available in Spanish

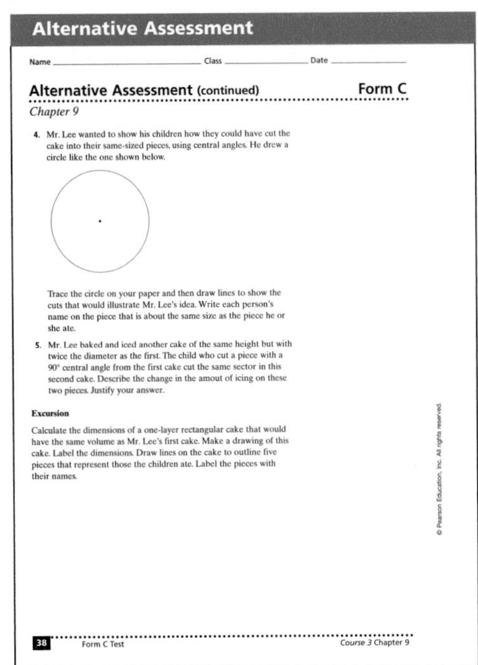

Alternative Assessment

Name ______ Class ______ Date ______

Alternative Assessment (continued) — Form C

Chapter 9

4. Mr. Lee wanted to show his children how they could have cut the cake into their same-sized pieces, using central angles. He drew a circle like the one shown below.

   Trace the circle on your paper and then draw lines to show the cuts that would illustrate Mr. Lee's idea. Write each person's name on the piece that is about the same size as the piece he or she ate.
5. Mr. Lee baked and iced another cake of the same height but with twice the diameter as the first. The child who cut a piece with a 90° central angle from the first cake cut the same sector in this second cake. Describe the change in the amout of icing on these two pieces. Justify your answer.

Excursion

Calculate the dimensions of a one-layer rectangular cake that would have the same volume as Mr. Lee's first cake. Make a drawing of this cake. Label the dimensions. Draw lines on the cake to outline five pieces that represent those the children ate. Label the pieces with their names.

Available in Spanish

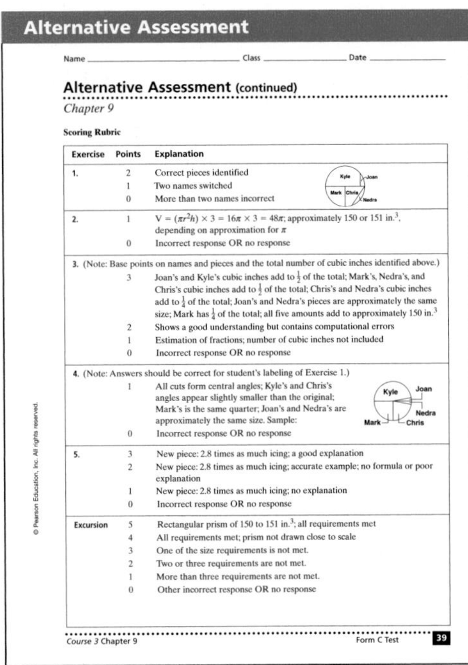

Alternative Assessment

Name ______ Class ______ Date ______

Alternative Assessment (continued)

Chapter 9

Scoring Rubric

Exercise	Points	Explanation
1.	2	Correct pieces identified
	1	Two names switched
	0	More than two names incorrect
2.	1	$V = (\pi r^2 h) \times 3 = 16\pi \times 3 = 48\pi$; approximately 150 or 151 in.³, depending on approximation for π
	0	Incorrect response OR no response
3. (Note: Base points on names and pieces and the total number of cubic inches identified above.)		
	3	Joan's and Kyle's cubic inches add to $\frac{1}{2}$ of the total; Mark's, Nedra's, and Chris's cubic inches add to $\frac{1}{2}$ of the total; Chris's and Nedra's cubic inches add to $\frac{1}{4}$ of the total; Joan's and Nedra's pieces are approximately the same size; Mark has $\frac{1}{4}$ of the total; all five amounts add to approximately 150 in.³
	2	Shows a good understanding but contains computational errors
	1	Estimation of fractions; number of cubic inches not included
	0	Incorrect response OR no response
4. (Note: Answers should be correct for student's labeling of Exercise 1.)		
	1	All cuts form central angles; Kyle's and Chris's angles appear slightly smaller than the original; Mark's is the same quarter; Joan's and Nedra's are approximately the same size. Sample:
	0	Incorrect response OR no response
5.	3	New piece: 2.8 times as much icing; a good explanation
	2	New piece: 2.8 times as much icing; accurate example; no formula or poor explanation
	1	New piece: 2.8 times as much icing; no explanation
	0	Incorrect response OR no response
Excursion	5	Rectangular prism of 150 to 151 in.³; all requirements met
	4	All requirements met; prism not drawn close to scale
	3	One of the size requirements is not met.
	2	Two or three requirements are not met.
	1	More than three requirements are not met.
	0	Other incorrect response OR no response

Available in Spanish

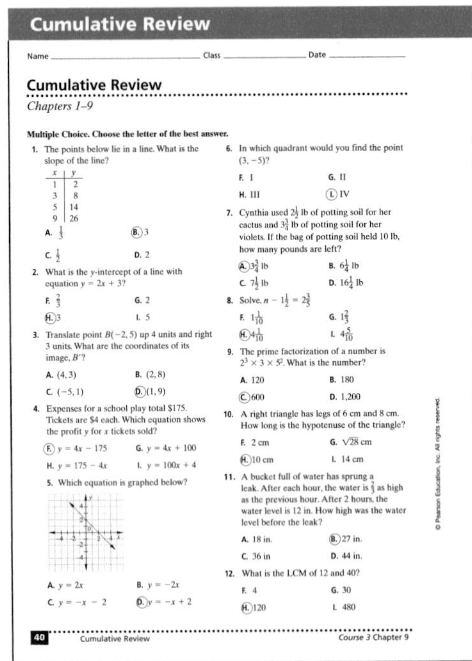

Cumulative Review

Name ______ Class ______ Date ______

Cumulative Review

Chapters 1–9

Multiple Choice. Choose the letter of the best answer.

1. The points below lie in a line. What is the slope of the line?

x	y
1	2
3	8
5	14
9	26

   A. $\frac{1}{3}$ B. 3 C. $\frac{1}{2}$ D. 2
2. What is the y-intercept of a line with equation $y = 2x + 3$?
   F. $\frac{2}{3}$ G. 2 H. 3 I. 5
3. Translate point $B(-2, 5)$ up 4 units and right 3 units. What are the coordinates of its image, B'?
   A. (4, 3) B. (2, 8) C. (−5, 1) D. (1, 9)
4. Expenses for a school play total $175. Tickets are $4 each. Which equation shows the profit y for x tickets sold?
   F. $y = 4x - 175$ G. $y = 4x + 100$ H. $y = 175 - 4x$ I. $y = 100x + 4$
5. Which equation is graphed below?
   A. $y = 2x$ B. $y = -2x$ C. $y = -x - 2$ D. $y = -x + 2$
6. In which quadrant would you find the point (3, −5)?
   F. I G. II H. III I. IV
7. Cynthia used $2\frac{1}{2}$ lb of potting soil for her cactus and $3\frac{3}{4}$ lb of potting soil for her violets. If the bag of potting soil held 10 lb, how many pounds are left?
   A. $3\frac{3}{4}$ lb B. $6\frac{1}{4}$ lb C. $7\frac{1}{2}$ lb D. $16\frac{1}{4}$ lb
8. Solve. $n - 1\frac{1}{2} = 2\frac{3}{5}$
   F. $1\frac{1}{10}$ G. $1\frac{2}{3}$ H. $4\frac{1}{10}$ I. $4\frac{5}{10}$
9. The prime factorization of a number is $2^3 \times 3 \times 5^2$. What is the number?
   A. 120 B. 180 C. 600 D. 1,200
10. A right triangle has legs of 6 cm and 8 cm. How long is the hypotenuse of the triangle?
   F. 2 cm G. $\sqrt{28}$ cm H. 10 cm I. 14 cm
11. A bucket full of water has sprung a leak. After each hour, the water is $\frac{2}{3}$ as high as the previous hour. After 2 hours, the water level is 12 in. How high was the water level before the leak?
   A. 18 in. B. 27 in. C. 36 in D. 44 in.
12. What is the LCM of 12 and 40?
   F. 4 G. 30 H. 120 I. 480

Available in Spanish

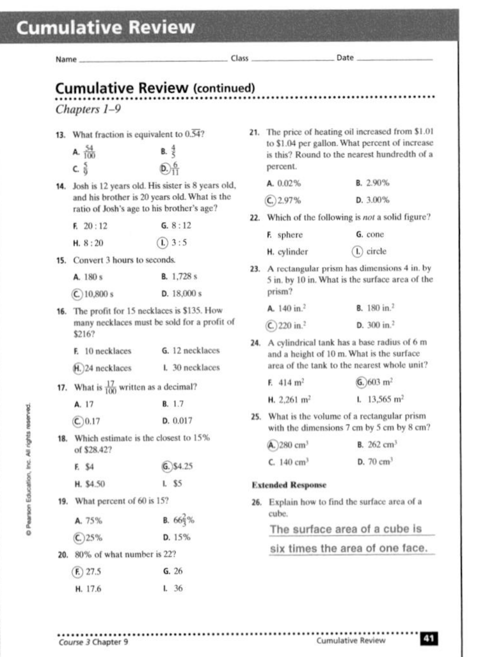

Cumulative Review

Name ______ Class ______ Date ______

Cumulative Review (continued)

Chapters 1–9

13. What fraction is equivalent to $0.\overline{54}$?
   A. $\frac{54}{100}$ B. $\frac{4}{5}$ C. $\frac{5}{9}$ D. $\frac{6}{11}$
14. Josh is 12 years old. His sister is 8 years old, and his brother is 20 years old. What is the ratio of Josh's age to his brother's age?
   F. 20 : 12 G. 8 : 12 H. 8 : 20 I. 3 : 5
15. Convert 3 hours to seconds.
   A. 180 s B. 1,728 s C. 10,800 s D. 18,000 s
16. The profit for 15 necklaces is $135. How many necklaces must be sold for a profit of $216?
   F. 10 necklaces G. 12 necklaces H. 24 necklaces I. 30 necklaces
17. What is $\frac{17}{100}$ written as a decimal?
   A. 17 B. 1.7 C. 0.17 D. 0.017
18. Which estimate is the closest to 15% of $28.42?
   F. $4 G. $4.25 H. $4.50 I. $5
19. What percent of 60 is 15?
   A. 75% B. $66\frac{2}{3}$% C. 25% D. 15%
20. 80% of what number is 22?
   F. 27.5 G. 26 H. 17.6 I. 36
21. The price of heating oil increased from $1.01 to $1.04 per gallon. What percent of increase is this? Round to the nearest hundredth of a percent.
   A. 0.02% B. 2.90% C. 2.97% D. 3.00%
22. Which of the following is *not* a solid figure?
   F. sphere G. cone H. cylinder I. circle
23. A rectangular prism has dimensions 4 in. by 5 in. by 10 in. What is the surface area of the prism?
   A. 140 in.² B. 180 in.² C. 220 in.² D. 300 in.²
24. A cylindrical tank has a base radius of 6 m and a height of 10 m. What is the surface area of the tank to the nearest whole unit?
   F. 414 m² G. 603 m² H. 2,261 m² I. 13,565 m²
25. What is the volume of a rectangular prism with the dimensions 7 cm by 5 cm by 8 cm?
   A. 280 cm³ B. 262 cm³ C. 140 cm³ D. 70 cm³

Extended Response

26. Explain how to find the surface area of a cube.
   The surface area of a cube is six times the area of one face.

Available in Spanish

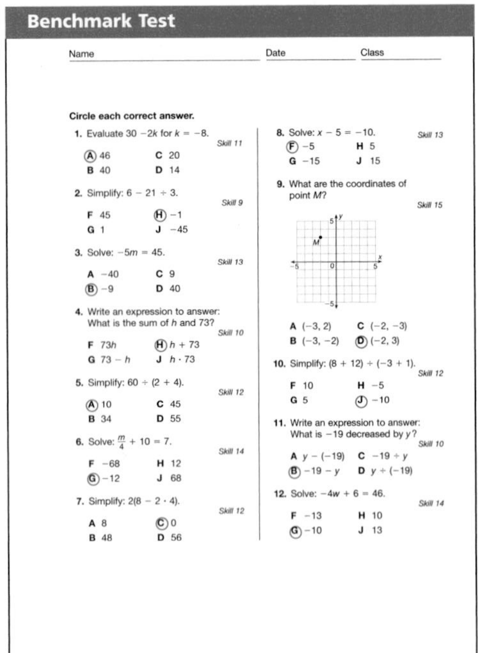

Benchmark Test

Name ______ Date ______ Class ______

Circle each correct answer.

1. Evaluate $30 - 2k$ for $k = -8$. *Skill 11*
   A 46 C 20 B 40 D 14
2. Simplify: $6 - 21 \div 3$. *Skill 9*
   F 45 H −1 G 1 J −45
3. Solve: $-5m = 45$. *Skill 13*
   A −40 C 9 B −9 D 40
4. Write an expression to answer: What is the sum of h and 73? *Skill 10*
   F $73h$ H $h + 73$ G $73 - h$ J $h \cdot 73$
5. Simplify: $60 \div (2 + 4)$. *Skill 12*
   A 10 C 45 B 34 D 55
6. Solve: $\frac{m}{4} + 10 = 7$. *Skill 14*
   F −68 H 12 G −12 J 68
7. Simplify: $2(8 - 2 \cdot 4)$. *Skill 12*
   A 8 C 0 B 48 D 56
8. Solve: $x - 5 = -10$. *Skill 13*
   F −5 H 5 G −15 J 15
9. What are the coordinates of point M? *Skill 15*
   A (−3, 2) C (−2, −3) B (−3, −2) D (−2, 3)
10. Simplify: $(8 + 12) \div (-3 + 1)$. *Skill 12*
   F 10 H −5 G 5 J −10
11. Write an expression to answer: What is −19 decreased by y? *Skill 10*
   A $y - (-19)$ C $-19 \div y$ B $-19 - y$ D $y \div (-19)$
12. Solve: $-4w + 6 = 46$. *Skill 14*
   F −13 H 10 G −10 J 13

On PH Website

Test-Taking Strategies transparency

Test-Taking Strategies: Eliminating Answers

When solving a multiple choice problem, first try to eliminate some of the answer choices.

Be sure to cross out answers you eliminate in the test booklet—*not* on the answer sheet.

Example The original price of a coat was $65. It was discounted 20% the day you bought it. How much money did you save?

A. $78 B. $52 C. $13 D. $5

Since $78 is more than the original amount, you can immediately eliminate choice A.

By estimating you can determine that $60 times 0.20 is greater than $5, so you can eliminate choice D.

Since the question is asking for how much you saved, you can eliminate choice B because you know by estimating that you did not save more than 50% of the original price.

The answer is choice C.

Identify two answer choices you can immediately eliminate. Then solve the problem.

1. There are 32 students in Wyatt's class. At least 75% of the students have been vaccinated against chicken pox. About how many students have not had this vaccination?
   A. 40 students B. 28 students
   C. 16 students D. 8 students

Eliminate choice A: There are only 32 students in the class. Eliminate choice B: By estimating you know that less than half the class has not had the vaccination. The answer is choice D.

Test-Taking Strategies worksheet

Name ____________ Class ____________ Date ____________

Chapter 9: Eliminating Answers

Exercises

Use the following multiple choice question to answer Exercises 1–2.

What is the volume of a square pyramid with a base edge length of 9 ft and a height of 17 ft?

A. 1,377 ft B. 459 ft^2 C. 306 ft^3 D. 459 ft^3

1. Which answer choices can be eliminated? Why?
   Sample answer: Answer choices A and B can be eliminated because volume should be measured in cubic feet. The answer is either choice C or choice D.
2. Find the correct answer to the problem. D

Solve each multiple choice question by eliminating answers.

3. The volume of a cube is 24 m^3. The lengths of the sides are increased by a scale factor of $\frac{6}{5}$. What is the volume of the new cube?
   (F.) 41.472 m^3 G. 192 m^3 H. 28.8 m^3 I. 34.56 m^3
4. What is the surface area of a cylinder with a radius of 5 cm and a height of 14 m?
   A. 710π m^3 B. 190π m^3 (C.) 190π m^2 D. 190 m^2
5. A box measuring 5-in.-by-2-in.-by-7 in. is packed inside a gift box that is an 8-in. cube. How much space is left inside for packing materials?
   F. 512 $in.^3$ (G.) 442 $in.^3$ H. 118 $in.^3$ I. 70 $in.^3$
6. A round table has a diameter of 3 ft. What size tablecloth is needed to have one foot of overhang all around the table?
   (A.) 19.625 ft^2 B. 7.065 ft^2 C. 15.7 ft^2 D. 12.56 ft^2
7. The surface area of a rectangular prism is 126 $in.^2$. The surface area of a similar rectangular prism is 224 $in.^2$. What is the ratio of corresponding dimensions of the small prism to the large prism?
   F. $\frac{16}{9}$ G. $\frac{4}{3}$ H. $\frac{9}{16}$ (I.) $\frac{3}{4}$

Home Activities

in math class ...

We have been learning about area and volume.
Here is a list of some of the skills and concepts we have studied.

- Perimeter and area of polygons
- Circles
- Surface area of prisms and cylinders
- Surface area of pyramids and cones
- Volume of rectangular prisms
- Volume of prisms and cylinders
- Volume of pyramids and cones

Home Activities

Here are some activities you can do with your child that use these math skills and concepts.

Suppose your child wanted some private space in your residence. You agree to give your child 40 feet of portable walls or screens. The private area has to be rectangular, and the portable walls must enclose four sides. Have your child determine the maximum area that can be enclosed. (maximum area: 100 square feet)

Suppose you limit your child to 60 square feet of private space. Since your child has to pay for the portable walls, have him or her determine the fewest number of feet of portable walls necessary to enclose the 60 square feet of space. (fewest number of feet: 32)

Available in Spanish; Web Code: ack-5500

Interdisciplinary Activities

Name ____________ ***Math and Science/Technology***

SHOPPING CENTER PUZZLES

Use calculation of perimeter and surface area to solve design problems in a shopping center.

There are more than 30,000 shopping centers in the United States. About 2,000 of them are completely enclosed centers called malls. Malls are fairly recent additions to the shopping scene. The first one opened in 1956 in Edina, Minnesota. The idea was to keep shoppers warm and dry in severe winter weather. Modern malls have expanded this idea to keep shoppers happy, comfortable, and amused, so they will stay and shop.

Chances are you've spent some time in a mall this month. In fact, a typical American probably spends at least two hours a month in a mall. Shopping center planners would like that amount of time to increase, because the more time you spend in a shopping center, the more money you are likely to spend. Shopping center planners study the way people shop and design malls to encourage people to spend their time there. For example, the designers know that most people won't walk more than 600 feet in a mall. If people think the walk down the mall is too long, they're less likely to visit. Mall planners break up a shopper's line of sight with fountains, trees, or bending corridors so shoppers can't see how far they really have to walk. Designers add food courts because research shows that shoppers who can snack will stay and shop longer. Researchers have even learned how fast most people walk past the store windows (about 4 feet per second), so store owners know they've got just a few seconds to grab your attention and get you inside.

Planning a mall requires more than psychology. It also involves architectural planning. Plants and trees in the mall must get enough light. The air conditioning system must be large enough to cool every space. The walkways must be strong enough to support the weight of crowds, furniture, and merchandise.

The diagram below shows the floorplan of a small mall. Use it to do calculations and solve planning problems.

900'
100'
300'
500'
N
W E
S

1. What are some of the things that mall designers would have to consider when planning a mall?

Web Code: ack-5500

Interdisciplinary Activities

Name ____________ ***Math and Science/Technology***

2. With the exception of the entrance, the mall designers have decided to plant trees every six feet around the outside of the mall. How many trees will they need?
3. The central walkway of the mall will be covered with marble tile. How much tile (in square feet) must be ordered to cover this area?
4. The owner of a store wants to give his walls and ceilings two coats of Mellow Yellow paint. He doesn't have to paint the wall that fronts on the mall corridor because it's glass. The store has ceilings that are 20 feet high. If each gallon of Mellow Yellow covers 400 square feet of surface, how many gallons of paint will he have to buy?
5. The shopping center planners would like to place a circular fountain halfway up the north-south corridor of the mall. If at least 20 feet will be needed for a walkway between the fountain and each wall nearby, what is the maximum area of the fountain? Use $\pi = 3.14$
6. If the shopping center costs $50 million to build, what is the cost per square foot? Round to the nearest dollar.
7. What occupations might be involved in planning a mall?
8. Visit a local mall. Make a floor plan of its corridors. In what ways is it similar to, or different from, the mall described in this activity?

Web Code: ack-5500

Algebra Readiness Puzzles

Name ____________ Class ____________ Date ____________

Solid Creations **Puzzle 33**

Geometry and Measurement

Jerry had to build five solid figures for a school project. He was allowed to use only the following two-dimensional shapes (not drawn to scale). Name the solid figures Jerry built. Then list which plane figures and how many he used to build each solid figure.

solid figures:

Web Code: ack-5500

Geometry and Measurement

Chapter 9 Overview

In this chapter, students continue their study of geometric concepts as they identify and draw different solid figures. They apply formulas to find the surface area and volume of prisms, pyramids, cylinders, and cones.

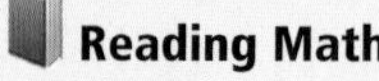

Reading Math
- Using the Correct Formula, p. 516
- **Vocabulary:** A complete list, plus exercises, in the Chapter Review, p. 524
- **Illustrated Glossary:** Examples for each vocabulary term, plus definitions in English and Spanish, on p. 735

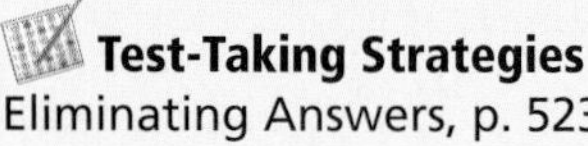

Test-Taking Strategies
Eliminating Answers, p. 523

Real-World Problem Solving
- **Strategies:** Draw a Diagram and Make a Table, p. 512–515
- **Real-World Snapshots:** For the Birds, pp. 528–529
- **Chapter Project:** A Better Way, p. 700

www.PHSchool.com
Internet support includes:
- Self-grading Vocabulary and Chapter 9 Tests
- Activity Masters
- Chapter Project support
- Chapter Planner
- Ch. 9 Resources

Plus iTEXT

Geometry and Measurement

Lessons

Key Vocabulary

- base plan (p. 477)
- cone (p. 471)
- cylinder (p. 471)
- isometric view (p. 477)
- lateral area (p. 489)
- net (p. 481)
- polyhedron (p. 471)
- prism (p. 471)
- pyramid (p. 471)
- similar solids (p. 517)
- skew lines (p. 473)
- slant height (p. 494)
- solids (p. 471)
- surface area (p. 488)
- volume (p. 500)

Real-World Snapshots

Scarlet ibises live in tropical and subtropical coastal marshes and swamps. Though native to South America, these birds have been seen as far north as southern Florida. Colonies of scarlet ibises build nests near water in low trees, on bushes, or among reeds.

Data File

Typical Measurements of Bird Species and Nest Sizes

Species	Typical Wingspan (in.)	Typical Length (in.)	Typical Nest Diameter (in.)
Bald Eagle	84	38.5	60
Red-Tailed Hawk	52	22	29
Scarlet Ibis	38	25	10
American Crow	36.5	17.5	24
Blue Jay	16	11	7.5
Ruby-Throated Hummingbird	4.25	3.5	1.5

SOURCES: *A Field Guide to the Birds' Nests: United States East of the Mississippi River*
Birds of North America

You will use the data above throughout this chapter:

- p. 509 Lesson 9-7
- p. 520 Lesson 9-9

Real-World Snapshots On pages 528 and 529, you will solve problems involving birds and wingspans.

Teaching Notes

Activating Prior Knowledge
In this chapter, students build on their knowledge of the properties of polygons and of how to use formulas to find the areas of parallelograms, triangles, trapezoids, and circles. They also draw upon their understanding of similarity and congruence when they explore similar solids. Ask questions such as:

- *What is the area of a trapezoid with bases of 10 in. and 12 in. and a height of 15 in.?* 165 in.^{2}
- *A right triangle has sides 3 m, 4 m, and 5 m. A triangle similar to it has a hypotenuse of 15 m. What are the lengths of its remaining sides?* 9 m and 12 m

Real-World Snapshots
The data here about bird species will be used throughout the chapter. Have a volunteer read the opening sentences and the title of the chart, which contains information about measurements of birds and their nests. Focus students on the data and ask:

- *Which bird is typically about 17.5 inches long?* American crow
- *Which bird's nest has an area of about 78 in.^{2}?* scarlet ibis
- *For which bird is the difference between wingspan and body length the least? Why?* ruby-throated hummingbird; it is by far the smallest bird listed.

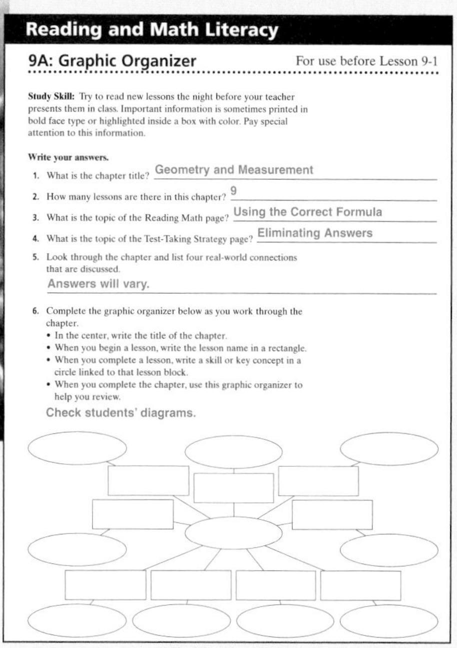

Reading and Math Literacy

9A: Graphic Organizer For use before Lesson 9-1

Study Skill: Try to read new lessons the night before your teacher presents them in class. Important information is sometimes printed in bold face type or highlighted inside a box with color. Pay special attention to this information.

Write your answers.

1. What is the chapter title? Geometry and Measurement
2. How many lessons are there in this chapter? 9
3. What is the topic of the Reading Math page? Using the Correct Formula
4. What is the topic of the Test-Taking Strategy page? Eliminating Answers
5. Look through the chapter and list four real-world connections that are discussed.
   Answers will vary.
6. Complete the graphic organizer below as you work through the chapter.
   - In the center, write the title of the chapter.
   - When you begin a lesson, write the lesson name in a rectangle.
   - When you complete a lesson, write a skill or key concept in a circle linked to that lesson block.
   - When you complete the chapter, use this graphic organizer to help you review.

   Check students' diagrams.

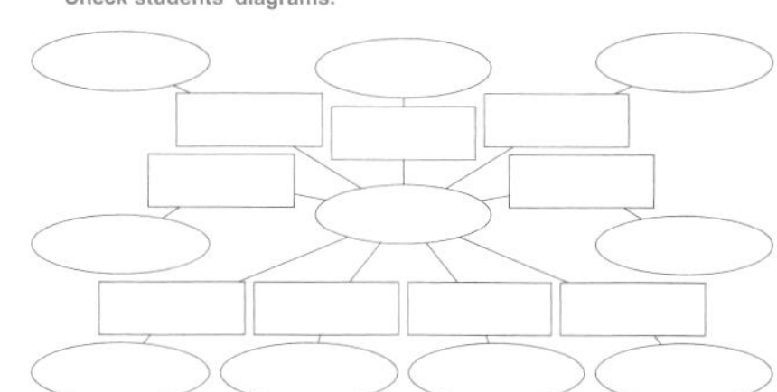

Available in Spanish

Chapter 9: Geometry and Measurement

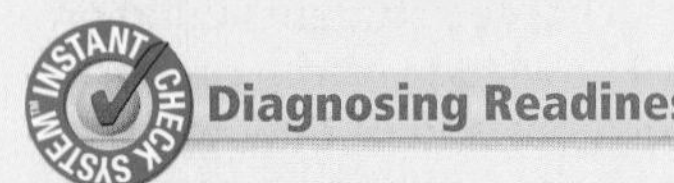

Students will find answers to these exercises in the back of their textbooks.

Prescribing Intervention
For intervention, direct students to:

Finding Areas
Lesson 8-7: Examples 1–3. Lesson 8-8: Example 2. Extra Practice, p. 709.

Solving Proportions
Lesson 5-4: Example 2. Extra Practice, p. 706.

Rounding
Skills Handbook: Rounding, p. 716.

Chapter 9 Preview

Where You've Been

- In Chapter 8, you learned to classify polygons and to find the area of parallelograms, triangles, trapezoids, and circles.

Where You're Going

- In Chapter 9, you will identify different solids and draw views and nets of them.
- You will find the surface area and volume of prisms, cylinders, pyramids, and cones.
- Applying what you learn, you will find the lateral area of the Great Pyramid of Khufu.

The pyramid at the entrance to the Louvre in Paris is a modern version of an ancient design.

Instant self-check online and on CD-ROM

Diagnosing Readiness

For help, go to the lesson in green.

Finding Area (Lessons 8-7 and 8-8)

Find the area of each figure. Round to the nearest whole number.

1. 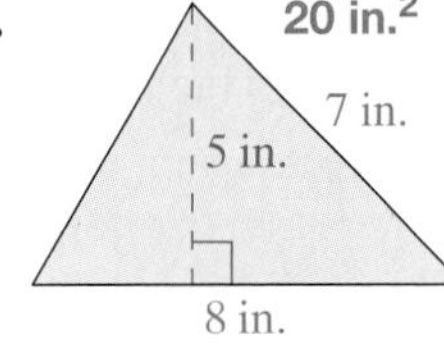

20 in.^{2}

2. 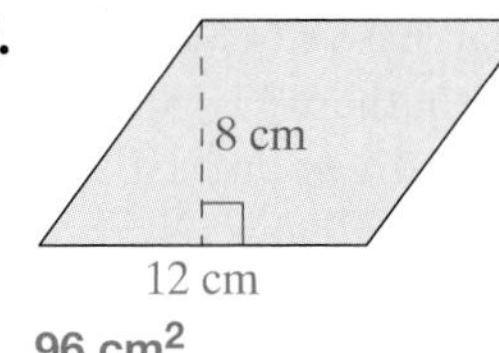

96 cm^2

3. 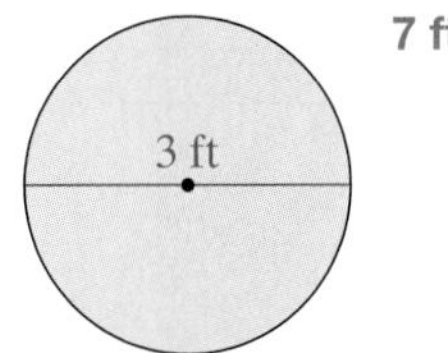

7 ft^2

4. 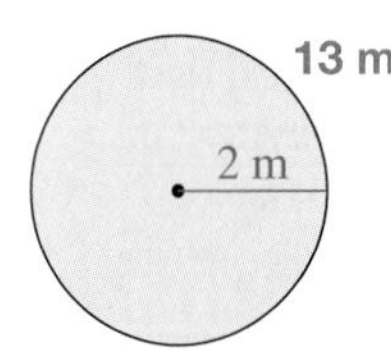

13 m^2

5. 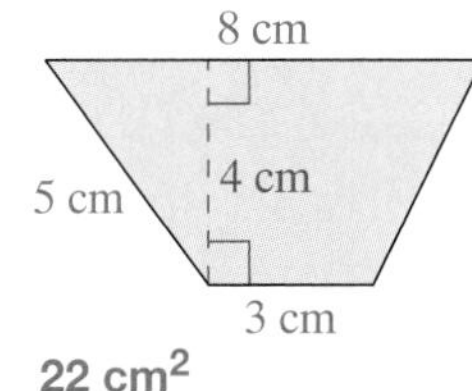

22 cm^2

6. 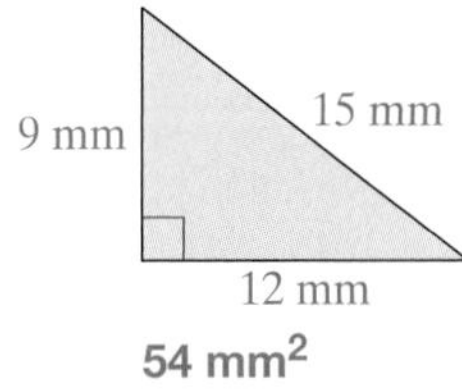

54 mm^2

Solving Proportions (Lesson 5-4)

Solve each proportion.

7. $\frac{x}{4} = \frac{15}{20}$ 3 **8.** $\frac{a}{9} = \frac{21}{27}$ 7 **9.** $\frac{26}{5} = \frac{13}{b}$ 2.5 **10.** $\frac{10}{h} = \frac{15}{18}$ 12

Rounding (Skills Handbook page 716)

Round to the place of the underlined digit.

11. 12.5<u>9</u>3 12.59 **12.** 192.<u>6</u>225 192.6 **13.** 0.00<u>4</u>62 0.005 **14.** 0.0<u>1</u>079 0.01

15. 5<u>5</u>5.555 560 **16.** <u>1</u>,293.99 1,000 **17.** 45<u>9</u> 459 **18.** 6<u>3</u>,752 64,000

9-1 Solids

What You'll Learn

 To name solids

 To recognize skew lines

. . . And Why

To design composite solids, as in Example 2

Check Skills You'll Need

For help, go to Lesson 8-5.

Determine the best name for each figure.

1. scalene triangle
2. parallelogram
3. trapezoid
4. pentagon

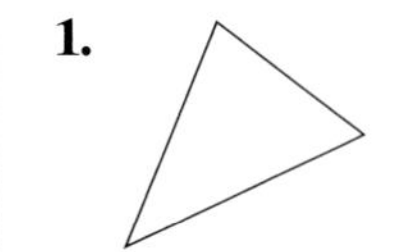

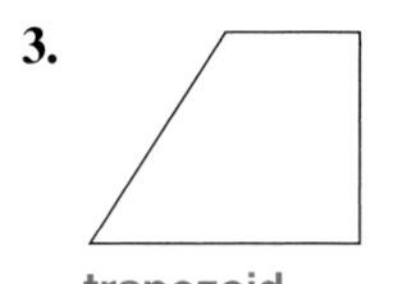

New Vocabulary

• solids • prism • pyramid • cylinder • cone • polyhedron • skew lines

Interactive lesson includes instant self-check, tutorials, and activities.

OBJECTIVE 1 Naming Solids

Solids, or three-dimensional figures, are objects that do not lie in a plane. They have length, width, and height. Below are some common solids.

A **prism** has two parallel bases that are congruent polygons. The lateral faces are parallelograms.

A **pyramid** has exactly one base, which is a polygon. The lateral faces are triangles.

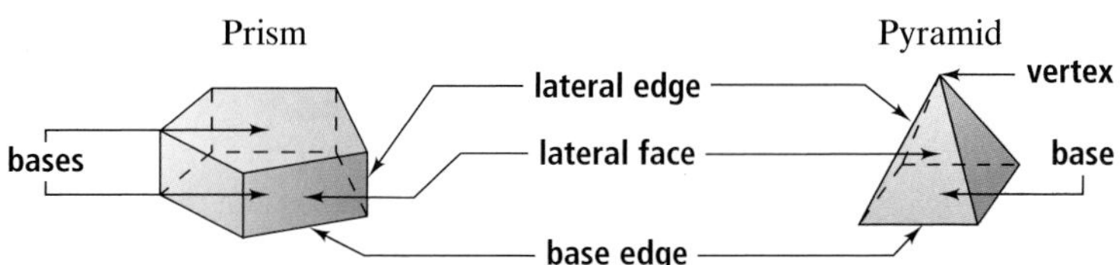

A prism is named for the shape of its bases. The prism above is a pentagonal prism.

A pyramid is named for the shape of its base. The pyramid above is a square pyramid.

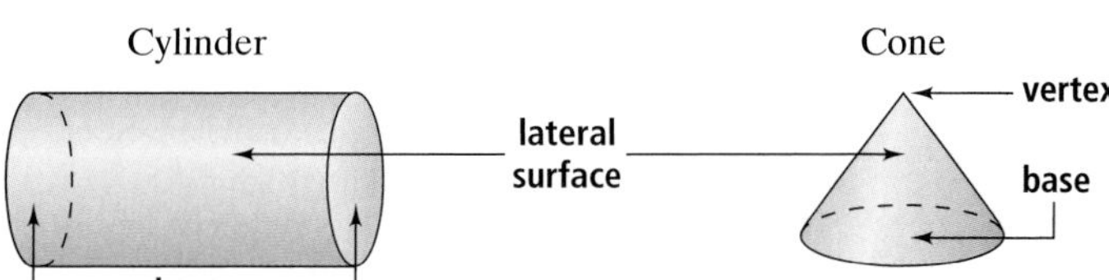

A **cylinder** has two bases that are parallel, congruent circles.

A **cone** has exactly one circular base and one vertex.

A **polyhedron** is a solid with a polygon for each face. Of the solids above, only prisms and pyramids are polyhedrons.

Reading Math

Polyhedron means "many surfaces."

9-1

1. Plan

Lesson Preview

PowerPoint

Check Skills You'll Need

Classifying Triangles and Quadrilaterals

Lesson 8-5: Examples 1–2. Extra Practice, p. 709.

Lesson Resources

Teaching Resources

Practice, Reteaching, Enrichment

Reaching All Students

Practice Workbook 9-1
Spanish Practice Workbook 9-1
Guided Problem Solving 9-1
Hands-On Activities 33

Presentation Assistant Plus!

Transparencies
- Check Skills You'll Need 9-1
- Problem of the Day 9-1
- Additional Examples 9-1
- Student Edition Answers 9-1
- Lesson Quiz 9-1

PH Presentation Pro CD-ROM 9-1

PRENTICE HALL ASSESSMENT SYSTEM

Computer Test Generator CD

Technology

Resource Pro® CD-ROM
Computer Test Generator CD
PH Presentation Pro CD-ROM

www.PHSchool.com

Student Site
- Teacher Web Code: ack-5500
- Self-grading Lesson Quiz

PH SuccessNet Teacher Center
- Lesson Planner
- Resources

Plus iTEXT

Ongoing Assessment and Intervention

Before the Lesson
Diagnose prerequisite skills using:
- Check Skills You'll Need

During the Lesson
Monitor progress using:
- Check Understanding
- Additional Examples
- Test Prep

After the Lesson
Assess knowledge using:
- Lesson Quiz
- Computer Test Generator CD

2. Teach

Math Background

Solids are three-dimensional objects that do not lie in a plane. A polyhedron is a solid with a polygon for each face. Prisms and pyramids are polyhedrons. Cylinders and cones are not polyhedrons because they have at least one circular base. In this lesson, a cylinder is assumed to be a right circular cylinder; a prism is assumed to be a right prism. In general, the height is perpendicular to the base. Skew lines are lines that do not intersect and are not parallel.

Teaching Notes

Tactile Learners
Give students a chance to handle and examine a variety of three-dimensional figures.

Teaching Tip
To help students connect the word *lateral* with "side", have a volunteer explain a lateral pass in football.

English Learners
Ask students to explain why a cylinder and a cone are not polyhedrons. **The face of the base is a circle and not a polygon.**

1 EXAMPLE Auditory Learners
Ask:
- *How can you tell which faces are lateral faces? Explain.* **Sample: First find the base or bases. Any face that is not a base is a lateral face or surface.**
- *Does the solid have to be resting or sitting on its base? Explain.* **No; see Example 1c.**

2 EXAMPLE Visual Learners
Have students copy the figure and shade in color the pair of bases.

3 EXAMPLE Inclusion
Have students work with a partner to hold two pencils in space to model two parallel line segments, and then move the pencils to model two skew line segments. Have them explain the difference to each other.

1 EXAMPLE Naming Solids and Their Parts

For each figure, describe the base(s), name the figure, and name the part labeled $\overline{RL}$.

a.

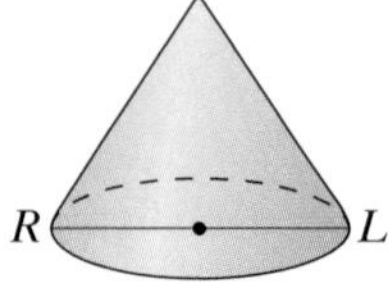

The only base is a circle. The figure is a cone. $\overline{RL}$ is a diameter.

b.

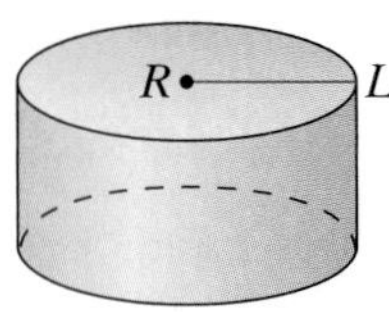

The two bases are congruent circles. The figure is a cylinder. $\overline{RL}$ is a radius.

c.

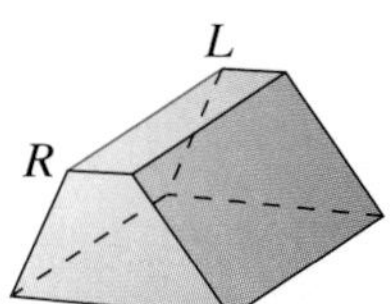

The two bases are trapezoids. This is a trapezoidal prism. $\overline{RL}$ is a lateral edge.

Check Understanding 1 For each figure, describe the base(s), name the figure, and name the part labeled $\overline{JK}$. **See left.**

a.

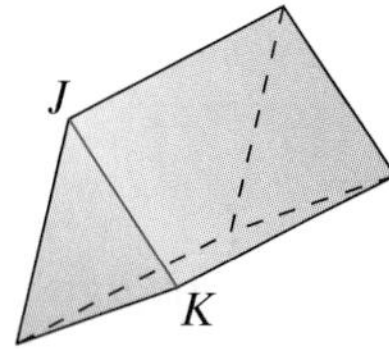

b.

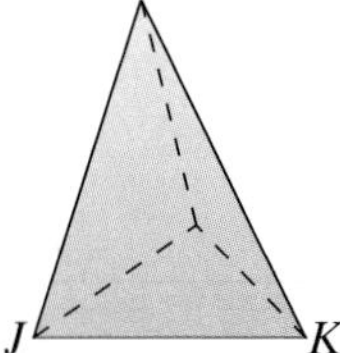

c. J K

1a. **The two bases are triangles. The figure is a triangular prism. $\overline{JK}$ is a base edge.**
b. **The only base is a triangle. The figure is a triangular pyramid. $\overline{JK}$ is a base edge.**
c. **The two bases are pentagons. The figure is a pentagonal prism. $\overline{JK}$ is a lateral edge.**

Common solids are everywhere, from toy building blocks to skyscrapers. Often, you see solids grouped together to form complex structures.

2 EXAMPLE Recognizing Solids

Set Design The stage crew for the school play is building a ramp in three sections so that it will be easy to move on and off stage. Name the three solids used to construct the ramp pictured below.

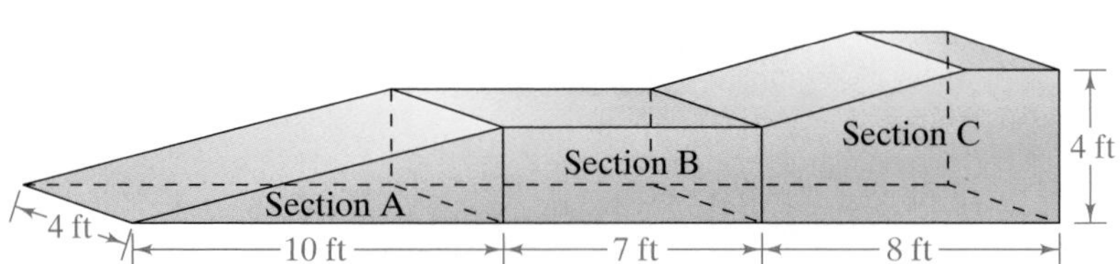

Section A is a triangular prism. Section B is a rectangular prism. Section C is a pentagonal prism.

Check Understanding 2 **a.** What common solids will the stage crew use to build the stage prop at the right? **See back of book.**
b. Reasoning How else could the stage crew divide this structure into different common solids?

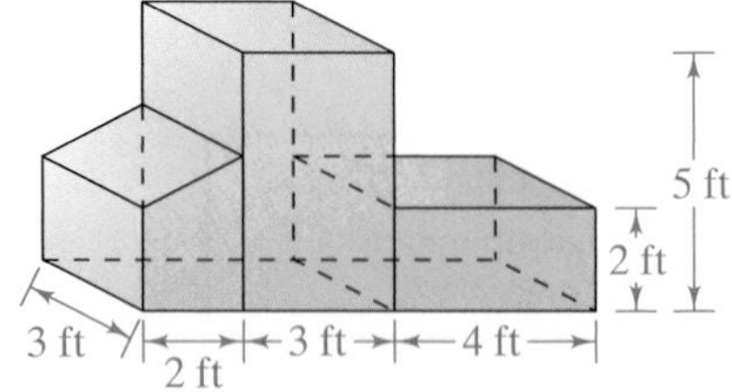

Reaching All Students

Below Level Have students identify and describe as geometric solids a soup can, a cereal or tissue box, a cone-shaped paper cup, and other examples in the classroom.	**Advanced Learners** Have students draw a plane intersecting a cone and discuss what plane figures the intersection might form. **circle, ellipse, point, intersecting lines**	**English Learners** See note on page 472. **Inclusion** See note on page 472.

OBJECTIVE

2 Recognizing Skew Lines

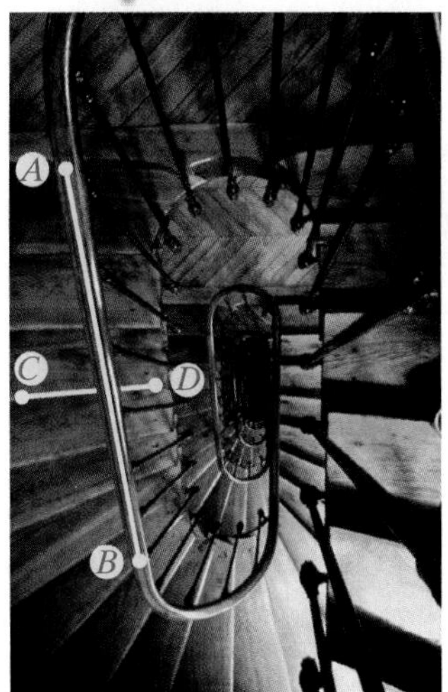

$\overline{AB}$ and $\overline{CD}$ are skew line segments.

Skew lines are lines that do not intersect and are not parallel. Unlike a pair of parallel lines or a pair of intersecting lines, skew lines do not lie in the same plane.

3 EXAMPLE Identifying Skew Line Segments

For each figure, name a pair of skew line segments, a pair of parallel line segments, and a pair of intersecting line segments.

a.

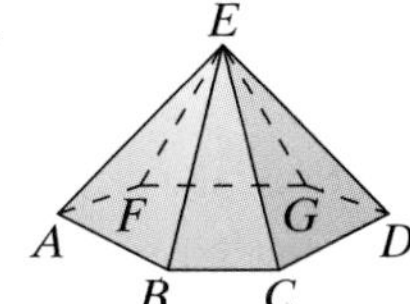

$\overline{AF}$ and $\overline{ED}$ are skew.
$\overline{BC}$ and $\overline{FG}$ are parallel.
$\overline{EA}$ and $\overline{EC}$ intersect.

b.

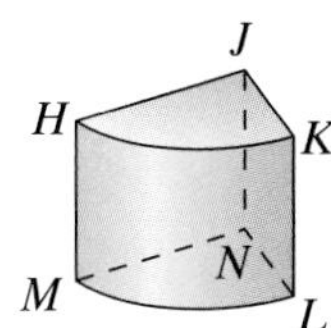

$\overline{HM}$ and $\overline{NL}$ are skew.
$\overline{NL}$ and $\overline{JK}$ are parallel.
$\overline{MN}$ and $\overline{NL}$ intersect.

Check Understanding 3 For each figure, name a pair of skew line segments, a pair of parallel line segments, and a pair of intersecting line segments. See margin.

a.

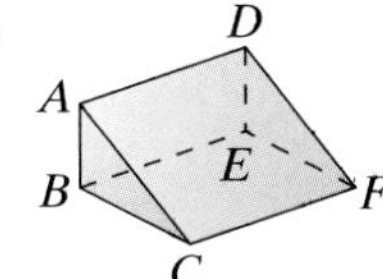

b.

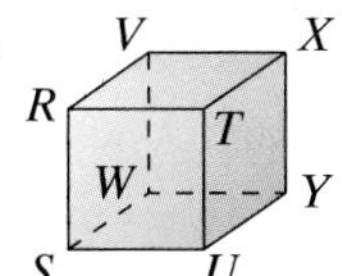

c.

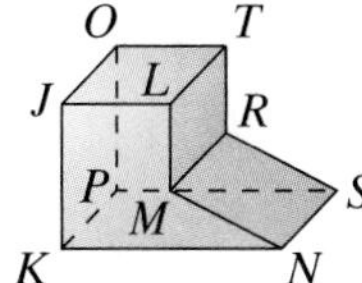

EXERCISES

For more practice, see *Extra Practice*.

A Practice by Example

Example 1 (page 472)

For each figure, describe the base(s), name the figure, and name the part labeled $\overline{PQ}$. 1–3. See margin.

1.

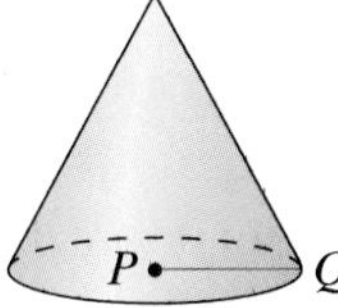

2.

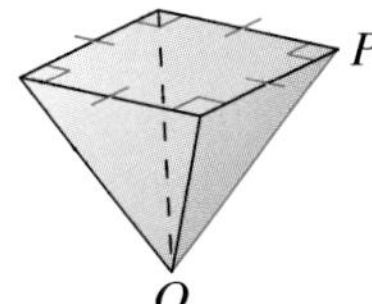

3.

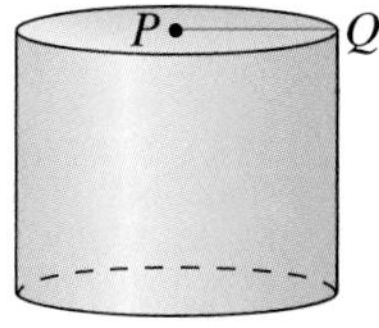

Example 2 (page 472)

List the common solids that make up each figure. 4–6. See back of book.

4.

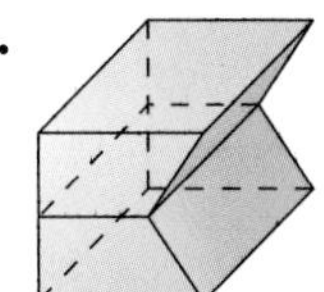

5.

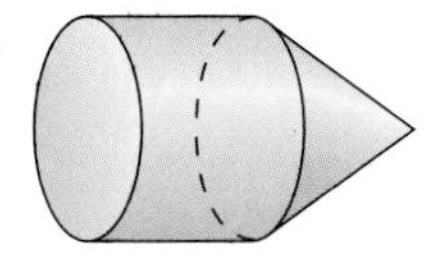

6.

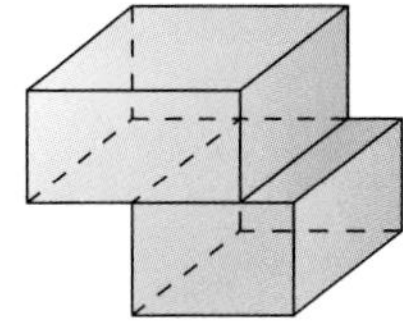

1 In the figure below, describe the base, name the figure, and name the part labeled $\overline{CD}$. square, rectangular pyramid; base edge

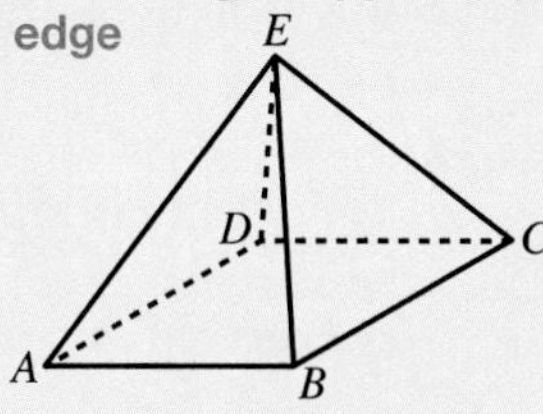

2 Which common solids make up this toy? rectangular prism, spheres, cone

3 For each figure, name a pair of skew line segments, a pair of parallel line segments, and a pair of intersecting line segments.

a.

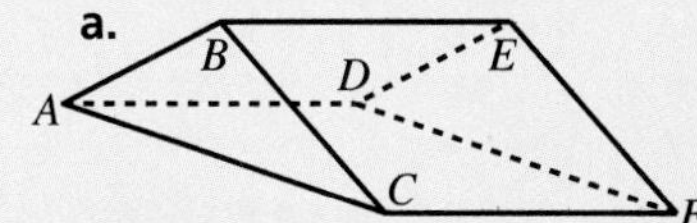

Sample: $\overline{BC}$ and $\overline{DE}$, $\overline{EF}$ and $\overline{AC}$, $\overline{BE}$ and $\overline{AC}$ are skew; $\overline{AB}$ and $\overline{DE}$, $\overline{AC}$ and $\overline{DF}$, $\overline{BC}$ and $\overline{EF}$ are parallel; $\overline{AB}$ and $\overline{BE}$, $\overline{EF}$ and $\overline{DF}$ intersect.

b.

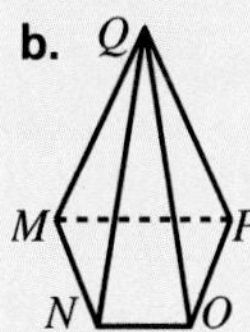

Sample: $\overline{MP}$ and $\overline{QO}$ are skew; $\overline{MP}$ and $\overline{NO}$ are parallel; $\overline{QP}$ and $\overline{PO}$, $\overline{PO}$ and $\overline{ON}$ intersect.

Closure

- Consider prisms, pyramids, cones, and cylinders. Which are polyhedrons and which are not? Explain. Sample: Prisms and pyramids are polyhedrons because each face is a polygon. Cones and cylinders are not, because they have at least one circular face.
- Explain how you can tell when two lines are skew. Sample: They do not lie in the same plane, they do not intersect, and they are not parallel.

2–3. See back of book.

Check Understanding

3a–c. Answers may vary. Samples are given.

a. $\overline{DE}$ and $\overline{AC}$ are skew lines. $\overline{AC}$ and $\overline{DF}$ are parallel lines. $\overline{AB}$ and $\overline{BC}$ are intersecting lines.

b. $\overline{VX}$ and $\overline{TU}$ are skew lines. $\overline{RT}$ and $\overline{SU}$ are parallel lines. $\overline{VW}$ and $\overline{WY}$ are intersecting lines.

c. $\overline{LM}$ and $\overline{RS}$ are skew lines. $\overline{KN}$ and $\overline{PS}$ are parallel lines. $\overline{JO}$ and $\overline{OP}$ are intersecting lines.

Exercises

1. The base is circular. The figure is a cone. $\overline{PQ}$ is a radius of the base.

3. Practice

Assignment Guide

1 Objective 1

A B Core 1–7, 11–19

C Extension 23

2 Objective 2

A B Core 8–10, 20–22

C Extension 24

Test Prep 25–28

Mixed Review 29–35

Error Prevention!

Exercises 11–14 Have students make a rough sketch of each solid.

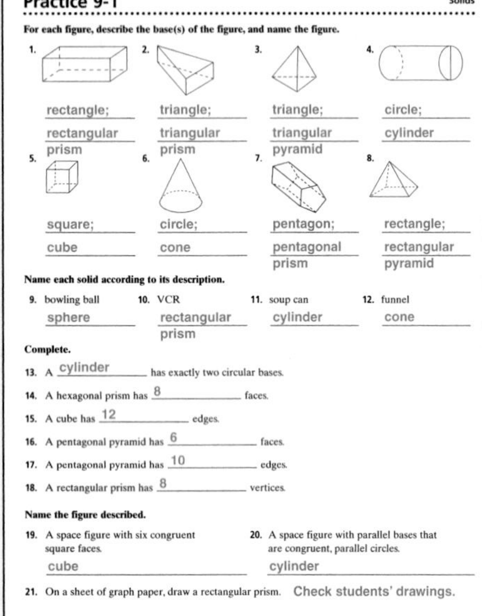

Practice 9-1 — Solids

For each figure, describe the base(s) of the figure, and name the figure.

1. rectangle; rectangular prism
2. triangle; triangular prism
3. triangle; triangular pyramid
4. circle; cylinder
5. square; cube
6. circle; cone
7. pentagon; pentagonal prism
8. rectangle; rectangular pyramid

Name each solid according to its description.

9. bowling ball sphere
10. VCR rectangular prism
11. soup can cylinder
12. funnel cone

Complete.

13. A cylinder has exactly two circular bases.
14. A hexagonal prism has 8 faces.
15. A cube has 12 edges.
16. A pentagonal pyramid has 6 faces.
17. A pentagonal pyramid has 10 edges.
18. A rectangular prism has 8 vertices.

Name the figure described.

19. A space figure with six congruent square faces. cube
20. A space figure with parallel bases that are congruent, parallel circles. cylinder
21. On a sheet of graph paper, draw a rectangular prism. Check students' drawings.

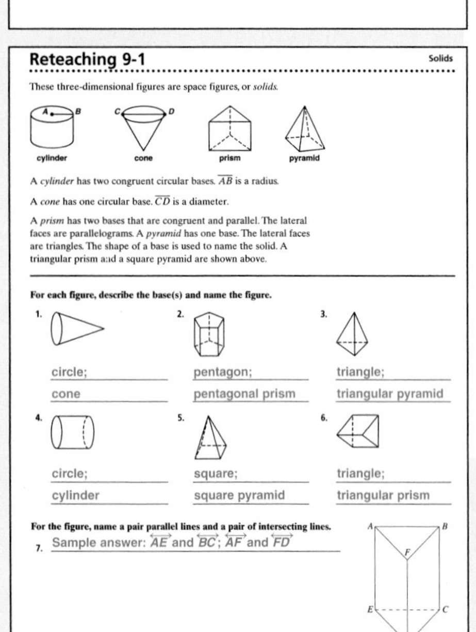

Reteaching 9-1 — Solids

These three-dimensional figures are space figures, or *solids*.

cylinder cone prism pyramid

A *cylinder* has two congruent circular bases. $\overline{AB}$ is a radius.

A *cone* has one circular base. $\overline{CD}$ is a diameter.

A *prism* has two bases that are congruent and parallel. The lateral faces are parallelograms. A *pyramid* has one base. The lateral faces are triangles. The shape of a base is used to name the solid. A triangular prism and a square pyramid are shown above.

For each figure, describe the base(s) and name the figure.

1. circle; cone
2. pentagon; pentagonal prism
3. triangle; triangular pyramid
4. circle; cylinder
5. square; square pyramid
6. triangle; triangular prism

For the figure, name a pair parallel lines and a pair of intersecting lines.

7. Sample answer: $\overleftrightarrow{AE}$ and $\overleftrightarrow{BC}$; $\overleftrightarrow{AF}$ and $\overleftrightarrow{FD}$

7. **Architecture** For a social studies project, you are building the arch at the right out of balsa wood. What solids will you use to construct this model?
3 rectangular prisms, 2 cylinders, and a triangular prism

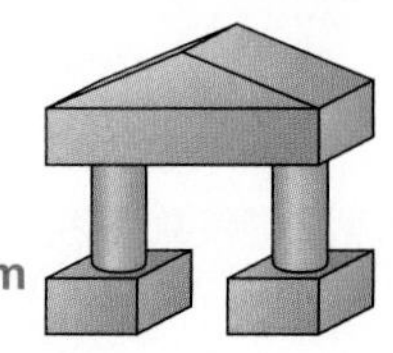

Example 3 (page 473)

For each figure, name a pair of skew line segments, a pair of parallel line segments, and a pair of intersecting line segments. 8–10. See margin.

8. 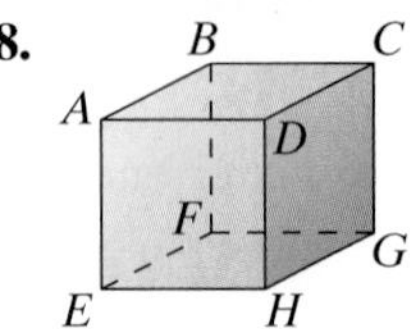

9. 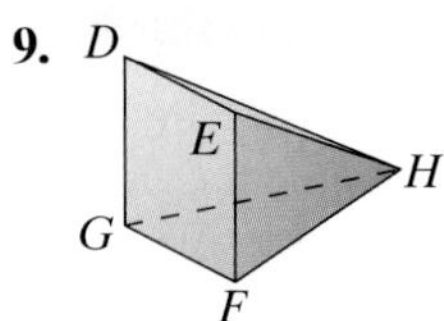

10. 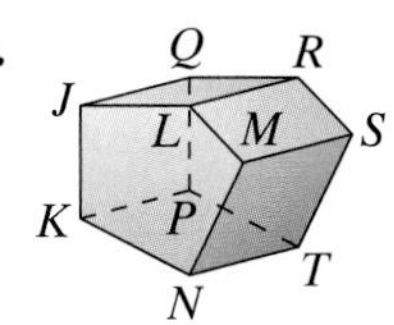

B Apply Your Skills

Name each solid according to its description.

11. The figure has four lateral faces that are triangles. rectangular pyramid
12. The figure has three lateral faces that are rectangles. triangular prism
13. The figure has one lateral surface and two bases. cylinder
14. The figure has one lateral surface and one base. cone

15. **Design** You have been asked to serve on a committee that is designing the skating terrain for a local skate park. Explain which common three-dimensional figures you would choose to make the terrain challenging and fun for all skaters. Check students' work.

Real-World Connection
Polyhedrons and other solids make a skate park interesting and challenging.

Name the common solids that make up each structure.

16. 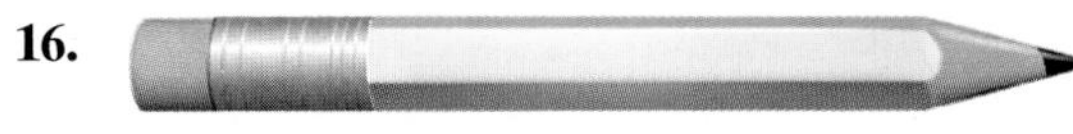
cylinder, hexagonal prism, cone

17. 

See left.

18. 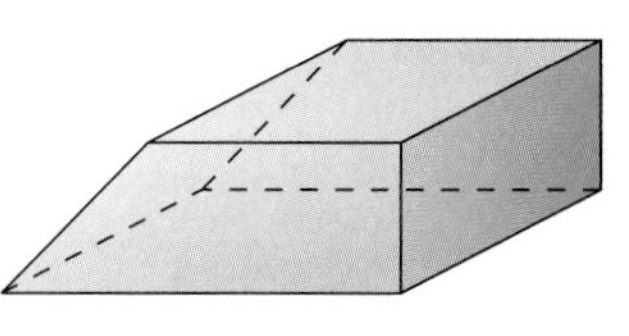
five rectangular prisms

17. Answers may vary. Sample: cylinder, cone, rectangular prism, triangular prism

19. **Writing in Math** Kenji says that the figure at the right is a trapezoidal prism. Ester says that it is a triangular prism and a rectangular prism combined. Is each person correct? Explain.
See margin.

Use the rectangular pyramid at the right. State whether each pair of line segments is *intersecting, parallel,* or *skew.*

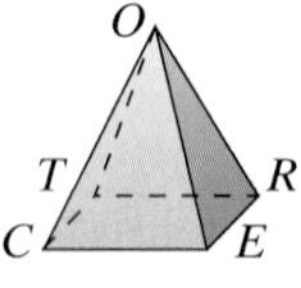

20. $\overline{CO}, \overline{CE}$ intersecting
21. $\overline{OR}, \overline{CE}$ skew
22. $\overline{CT}, \overline{ER}$ parallel

Use the Guided Problem Solving worksheet with Exercises 20–22.

8–10. Answers may vary. Samples are given.

8. $\overline{AD}$ and $\overline{CG}$, $\overline{DC}$ and $\overline{HG}$, $\overline{AE}$ and $\overline{EH}$

9. $\overline{DE}$ and $\overline{FH}$, $\overline{GD}$ and $\overline{EF}$, $\overline{EF}$ and $\overline{FH}$

10. $\overline{JL}$ and $\overline{ST}$, $\overline{LR}$ and $\overline{KP}$, $\overline{JK}$ and $\overline{KN}$

19. Kenji is right in that there are 2 parallel, congruent trapezoidal bases and the lateral faces are parallelograms. Ester is also right; a vertical cut could separate the figure into a rectangular prism and a triangular prism.

C Challenge

23. **Open Ended** Name one way the solid at the right could be made from three different types of prisms. See margin.

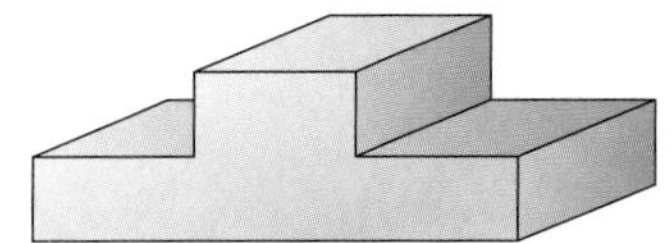

24. a. Which of the refrigerator magnets at the right are polyhedrons? 1, 4, 7
b. **Stretch Your Thinking** Using two polyhedron digits and two non-polyhedron digits, what is the greatest number you can make if you only use each digit once? 9,874

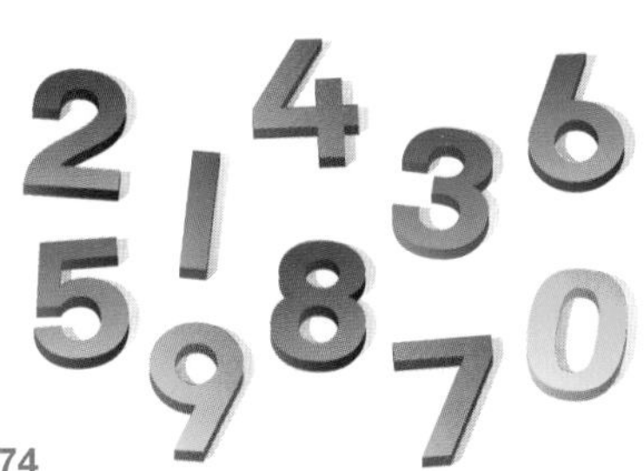

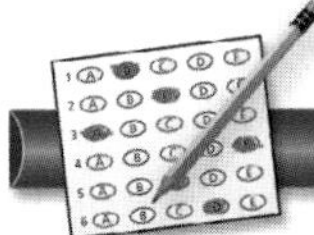

Test Prep

Multiple Choice

Use the figure at the right for Exercises 25–27.

W X S T V Y R U

25. What is the best name for the solid? A
   A. prism   B. rhombus
   C. pyramid   D. polygon

26. Which are skew lines? H
   F. $\overline{RS}$, $\overline{XY}$ G. $\overline{VW}$, $\overline{UT}$ H. $\overline{SW}$, $\overline{XY}$ I. $\overline{RU}$, $\overline{TU}$

Take It to the NET
Online lesson quiz at **www.PHSchool.com**
Web Code: aca-0901

27. Which set of common three-dimensional figures CANNOT be combined to create the common solid above? C
   A. two rectangular prisms
   B. two trapezoidal prisms
   C. one rectangular prism and one triangular prism
   D. one rectangular prism and two triangular prisms

Short Response

28. Describe the shape and number of bases and lateral faces of a triangular prism. See margin.

Mixed Review

Lesson 7-5 **Solve the problem by writing an equation. Check your answer.**

29. There are 5.256×10^5 minutes in one year. The heart of a teenager beats about 80 times per minute. How many times does it beat per year?
4.2048×10^7 times

Lesson 6-2 **Estimate each product.** 30–35. Answers may vary. Samples are given.

30. 15% of 506 75   31. 60% of 38 24   32. 94% of 440 420
33. 125% of 79 100   34. 18% of 250 50   35. 9% of 1,034 100

23. Answers may vary. Sample: The solid could be broken down into one triangular prism, one rectangular prism, and one trapezoidal prism.

28. [2] A triangular prism has two parallel, congruent triangular bases and three lateral faces that are parallelograms.

28. [1] correct but incomplete description

4. Assess

Lesson Quiz 9-1

Use this figure to answer each question below.

1. Describe the base(s), name the figure, and name the part labeled $\overline{BJ}$.
octagons; octagonal prism; lateral edge

State whether each pair of lines is intersecting, parallel, or skew.

2. $\overleftrightarrow{NM}$, $\overleftrightarrow{JK}$ intersecting
3. $\overleftrightarrow{IJ}$, $\overleftrightarrow{ME}$ skew
4. $\overleftrightarrow{OG}$, $\overleftrightarrow{IA}$ parallel

Test Prep

Resources
For additional practice with a variety of test item formats:
- Test Prep, p. 527
- Test-Taking Strategies, p. 523
- Test-Taking Strategies with Transparencies

Alternative Assessment

Students sketch a bird house and name all the solids contained in it. They then identify a pair of edges that are skew.

Enrichment 9-1 Solids
Patterns in Geometry

Study the prisms and pyramids shown below.

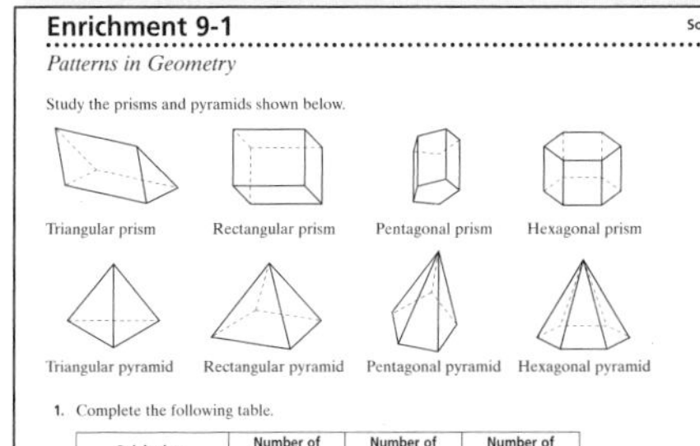

1. Complete the following table.

Polyhedron	Number of faces (F)	Number of vertices (V)	Number of edges (E)
Triangular prism	5	6	9
Triangular pyramid	4	4	6
Rectangular prism	6	8	12
Rectangular pyramid	5	5	8
Pentagonal prism	7	10	15
Pentagonal pyramid	6	6	10
Hexagonal prism	8	12	18
Hexagonal pyramid	7	7	12

2. Do the prisms have more or fewer faces than vertices?
fewer faces

3. Look at the pyramids. What is the relationship between the faces and the vertices?
They are equal.

4. Write a formula to show how the number of vertices, faces, and edges are related for prisms and pyramids.
$V + F = E + 2$

9-2

1. Plan

Lesson Preview

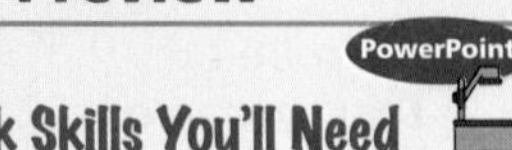

Check Skills You'll Need

Translating a Figure
Lesson 3-8: Example 2. Extra Practice, p. 704.

Lesson Resources

Optional Materials
- isometric dot paper
- ruler

Teaching Resources
Practice, Reteaching, Enrichment

Reaching All Students
Practice Workbook 9-2
Spanish Practice Workbook 9-2
Guided Problem Solving 9-2
Hands-On Activities 33, 35

Presentation Assistant Plus!
Transparencies
- Check Skills You'll Need 9-2
- Problem of the Day 9-2
- Additional Examples 9-2
- Student Edition Answers 9-2
- Lesson Quiz 9-2
- Classroom Aid 2, 6

PH Presentation Pro CD-ROM 9-2

PRENTICE HALL ASSESSMENT SYSTEM
Computer Test Generator CD

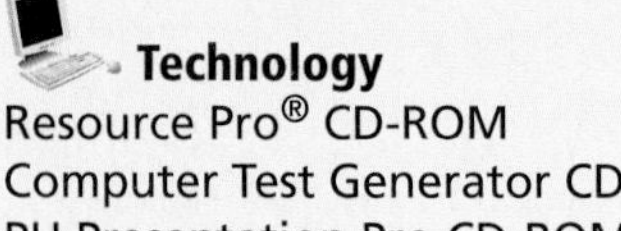

Technology
Resource Pro® CD-ROM
Computer Test Generator CD
PH Presentation Pro CD-ROM

www.PHSchool.com
Student Site
- Teacher Web Code: ack-5500
- Self-grading Lesson Quiz

PH SuccessNet Teacher Center
- Lesson Planner
- Resources

Plus iTEXT

9-2 Drawing Views of Solids

What You'll Learn

Objective 1: To draw a base plan

Objective 2: To draw top, front, and right views

. . . And Why

To create an architectural drawing, as in Example 2

Check Skills You'll Need

For help, go to Lesson 3-8.

Use graph paper to graph the image of *JKLMN* after each translation. 1–4. See back of book.

1. right three units; up one unit
2. right three units; down two units
3. left five units; down six units
4. Write a rule to describe each of the three translations above.

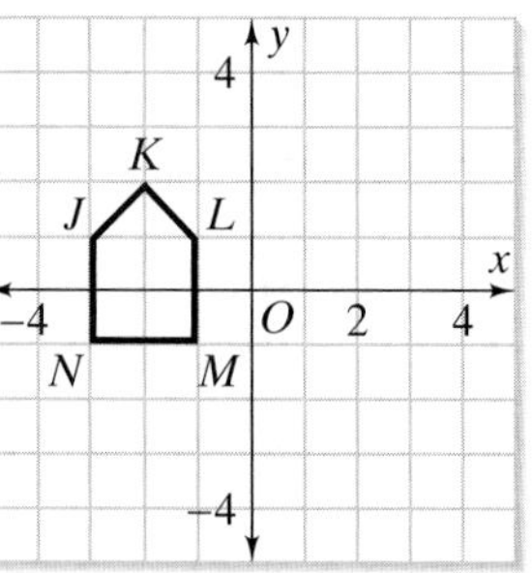

New Vocabulary
- base plan
- isometric view

iTEXT Interactive lesson includes instant self-check, tutorials, and activities.

OBJECTIVE 1

Drawing a Base Plan

Investigation: Sketching Solids

Follow the instructions to make each solid. 1–2. Check students' work.

1. Begin with a rectangle. Translate it and connect the four corresponding corners. Make the hidden lines dashed lines.

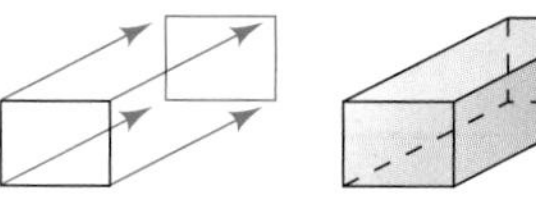

2. Begin with a circle. Translate it and connect the circles at corresponding points. Make the hidden lines dashed lines.

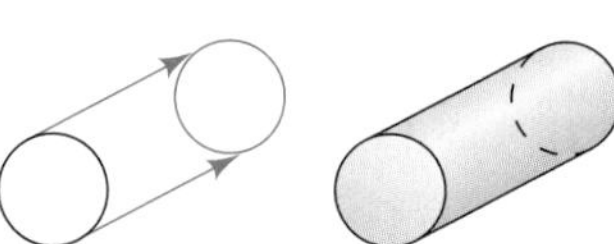

3. Copy the diagram at the right. Use it to draw a three-dimensional view of porch steps.

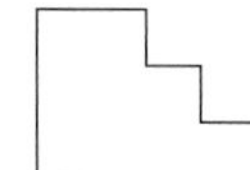

3.

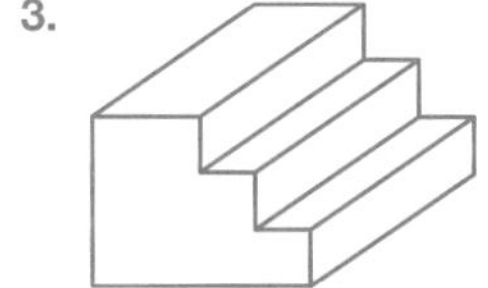

Engineers and architects design solids like bridges, cars, and furniture. They use drawings from different perspectives to communicate their ideas to the people who will build their designs.

Ongoing Assessment and Intervention

Before the Lesson
Diagnose prerequisite skills using:
- Check Skills You'll Need

During the Lesson
Monitor progress using:
- Check Understanding
- Additional Examples
- Test Prep

After the Lesson
Assess knowledge using:
- Lesson Quiz
- Computer Test Generator CD

A **base plan** shows the shape of the base and indicates the height of each part of a solid. Base plans are particularly useful for representing structures with rectangular faces.

1 EXAMPLE **Drawing a Base Plan**

Draw the base plan for the stacked cubes in the photo at the left.

3	2
3	

Front; Right

Draw a square for each stack as seen from above.

Write the number of cubes in the stack inside each square.

Label the front and right sides.

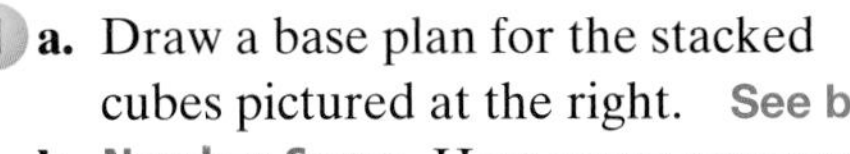

Check Understanding **1** **a.** Draw a base plan for the stacked cubes pictured at the right. See below left.

b. Number Sense How many squares will this base plan require? 5

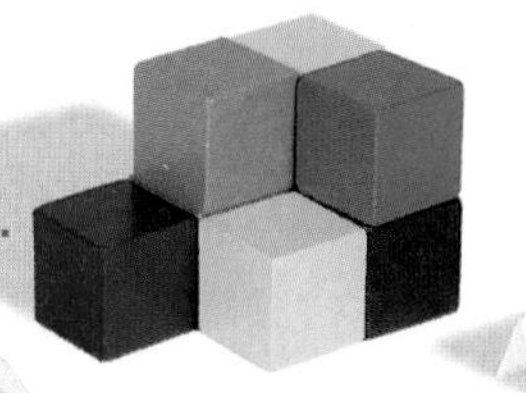

1a.

2	2
2	1
1	

Front; Right

2 EXAMPLE **Real-World Problem Solving**

Gardening A landscaper can use a base plan to describe the shape of a multilevel garden. Draw a base plan for the garden at the right, where each square is equal to one square foot.

2	2	2	1
2	2	1	1
2	1	1	1
1	1	1	1

Front; Right

Draw one square for each square foot of planting surface as seen from above.

Then write the height of each square foot in the corresponding square.

2a.

3	2	2	1
2	2	1	1
2	1	1	1
1	1	1	1

Front; Right

Check Understanding **2** **a.** The landscaper wants to build a third level of the garden above. Draw a new base plan by continuing the pattern of moving in before stepping up. 2a. See left.

b. Number Sense How many square feet of planting surface will be available in this new base plan? 16 square feet

OBJECTIVE 2

Drawing Top, Front, and Right Views

An **isometric view** is a corner view of a solid. It is usually drawn on isometric dot paper. An isometric view allows you to see the top, front, and right side of an object in the same drawing.

Reaching All Students

Below Level On an overhead projector, place various objects without letting students see them. Have them name the objects.

Advanced Learners Have students use isometric dot paper to draw a view of the school or an object in the classroom.

Inclusion
See note on page 477.
Tactile Learners
See note on page 477.

2. Teach

Math Background

You can sketch a solid geometric figure by drawing the bases and connecting them with straight lines. Make sure to indicate hidden lines with dashed lines. When a solid is drawn as connected rectangular prisms at different heights, a base plan shows the "footprint" of the base and indicates the height of each part. Isometric dot paper is useful for drawing isometric, or corner, views in order to see the top, front, and right sides of an object.

Teaching Notes

Investigation (Optional)
Suggest that students use these same techniques to draw each solid in a different position, such as placed upright on a table.

1 EXAMPLE Tactile Learners

Give students plastic or wooden cubes and have them model the solid shown in the figure.

2 EXAMPLE Inclusion

Have students who need reinforcement in naming and drawing solid figures work together with index cards and tape to build models and manipulate them.

PowerPoint

Additional Examples

1. Draw the base plan for the stacked cubes.

2	1	2
1	1	1

front; right

2. The Rhythm Singers perform in three rows on steps 7 ft long and 12 in. deep. The first step is 12 in. high, and each row is 12 in. higher than the step in front of it. Draw a base plan for the steps where each square on graph paper is equal to one square foot.

3	3	3	3	3	3	3
2	2	2	2	2	2	2
1	1	1	1	1	1	1

front; right

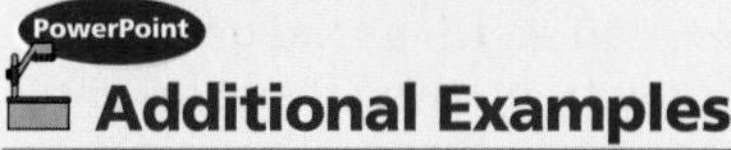

3 EXAMPLE Art Connection

Have students who have studied perspective in art class share what they know about perspective in drawing and painting.

PowerPoint
Additional Examples

3 Draw the top, front, and right view of the figure. Assume no blocks are hidden from view.

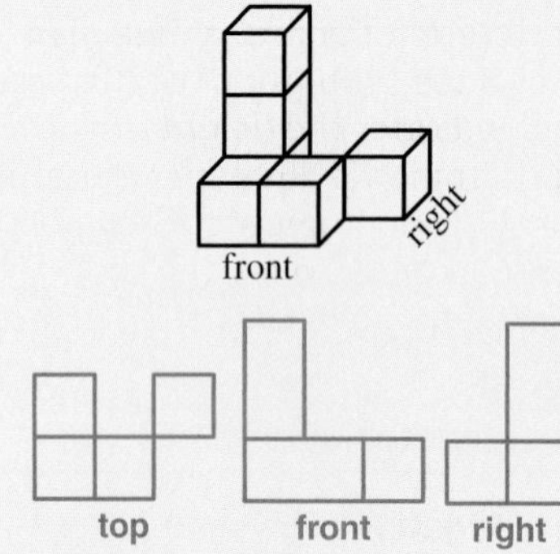

Closure

- *What is shown in a base plan for a solid figure?* Sample: The plan shows the shape of the base and indicates the height. The front and right side are labeled.
- *What is shown in an isometric view of a solid?* Sample: This view shows the top, front, and right sides of a solid in the same drawing. A dashed line shows a hidden edge.

An architect might draw a separate top view, front view, and right view to help builders visualize and understand a three-dimensional structure.

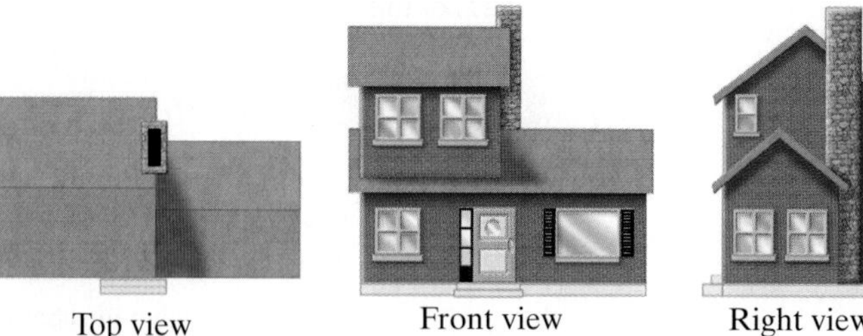

3 EXAMPLE Drawing Top, Front, and Right Views

Draw the top, front, and right views of each figure. Assume no blocks are hidden from view.

a.

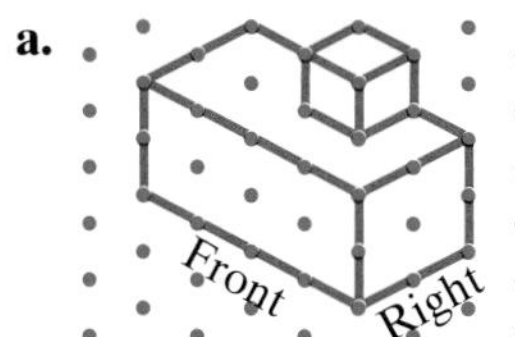

b.

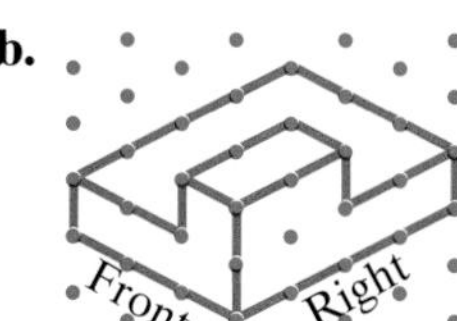

Treat each face like a two-dimensional figure.

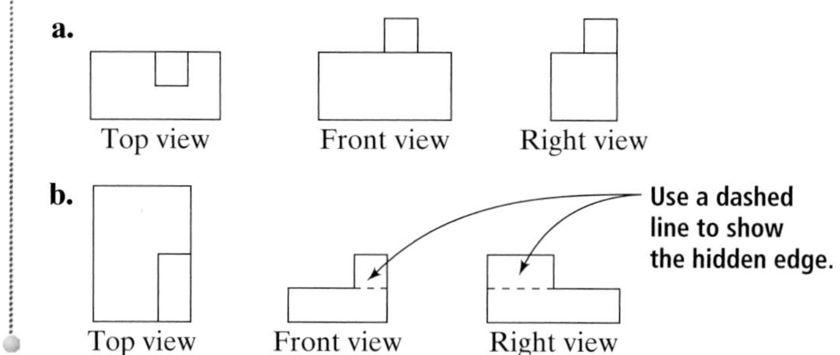

Check Understanding 3 Draw the top, front, and right views of the figure at the right. Assume no blocks are hidden from view. See margin.

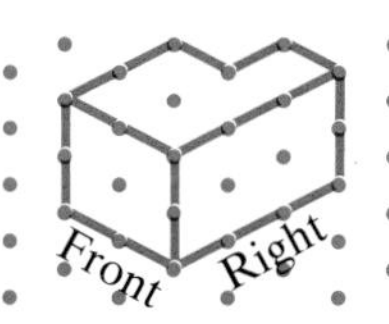

EXERCISES

For more practice, see *Extra Practice.*

A Practice by Example

Example 1 (page 477)

Draw a base plan for each set of stacked cubes. 1–3. See margin.

1.

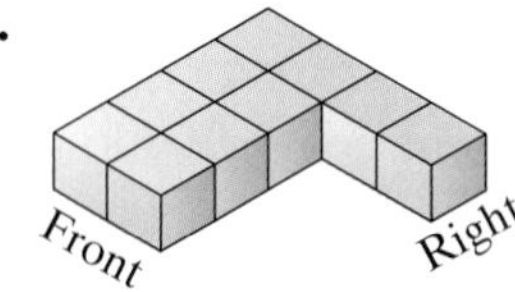

2.

3.

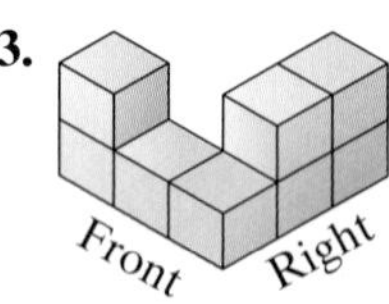

Check Understanding

3.

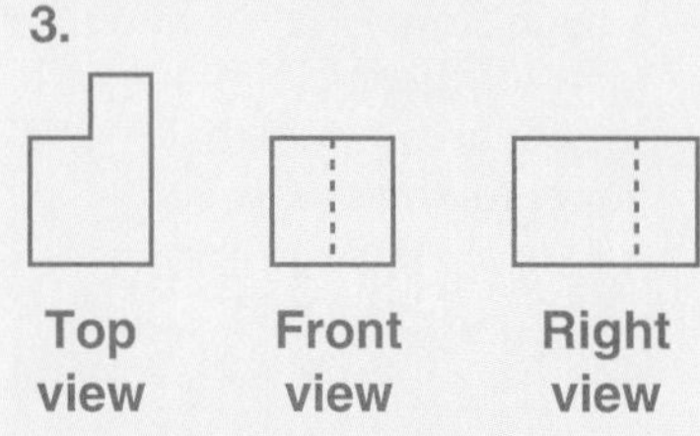

Exercises

1.

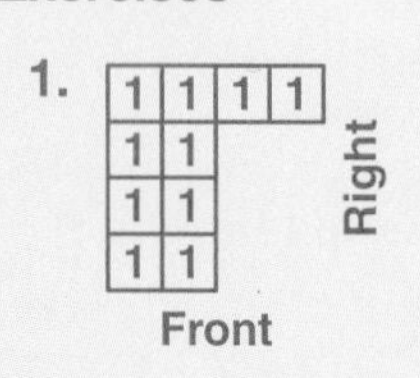

2.

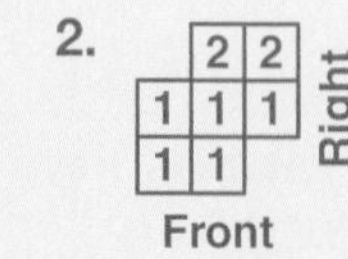

3.

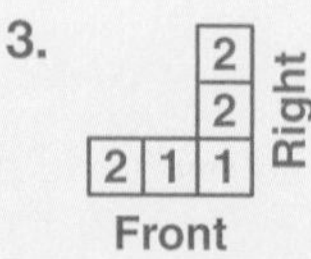

Example 2 (page 477)

4. **Sculpture** The city council has voted to build a fountain in a nearby park. Use the isometric view at the right to draw a base plan for the fountain. See margin.

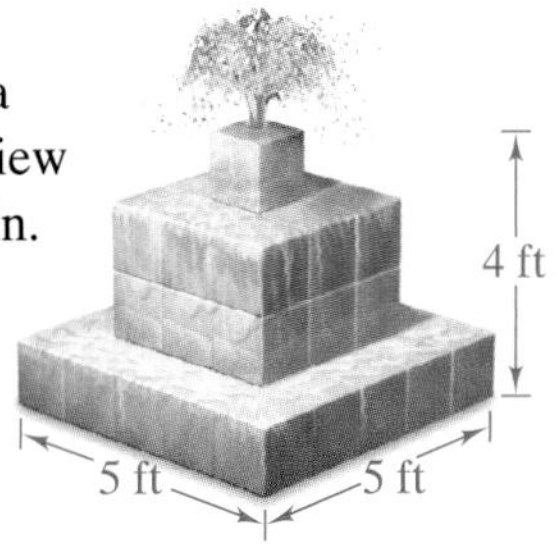

Example 3 (page 478)

Draw the top, front, and right views of each figure. 5–6. See back of book.

5. 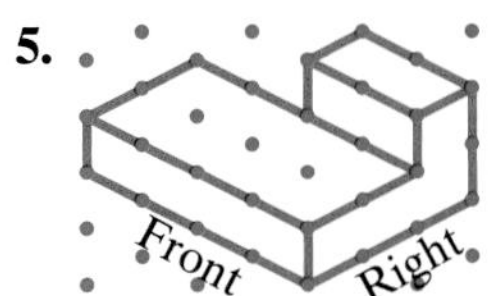

6. 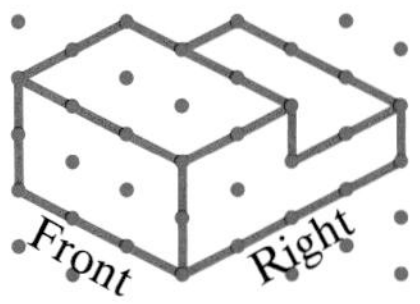 Front Right

B Apply Your Skills

Draw a base plan for each set of stacked cubes. 7–9. See left.

7. 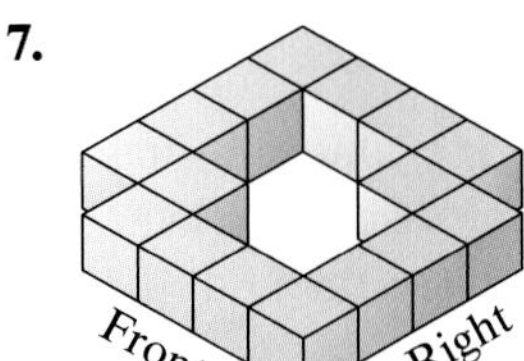

8. GPS 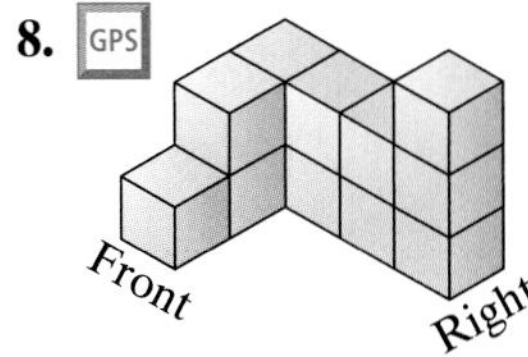

9. 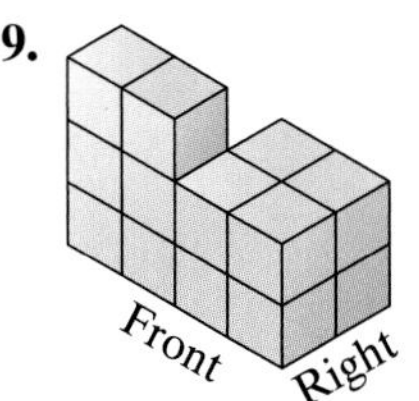

Draw the top, front, and right views of each figure. 10–11. See back of book.

10. 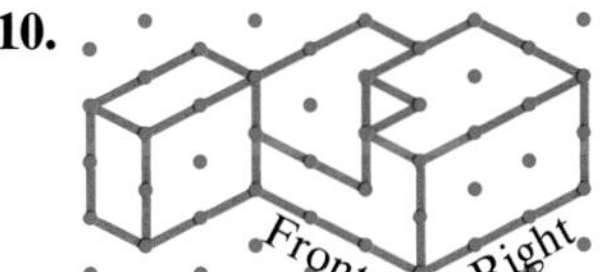

11. 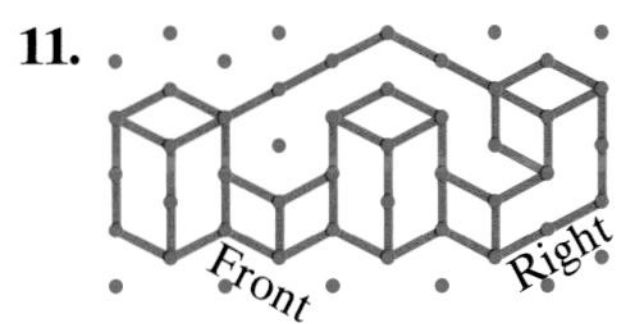

12. In each figure below, the red area shows a cross section of a square pyramid formed by a plane passing through the pyramid. What is the shape of each cross section?

a. 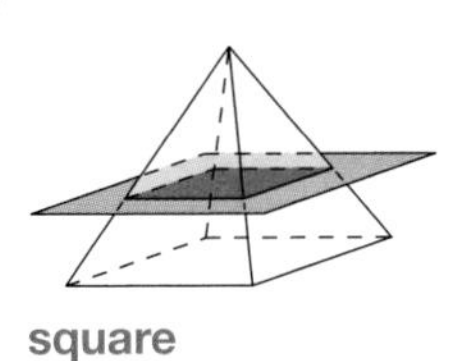
square

b. 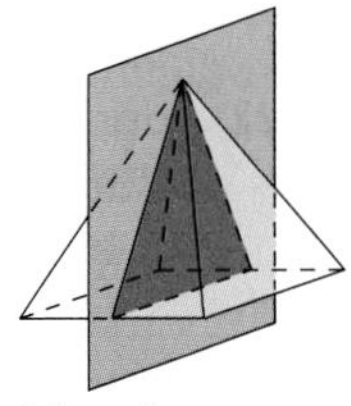
triangle

c. 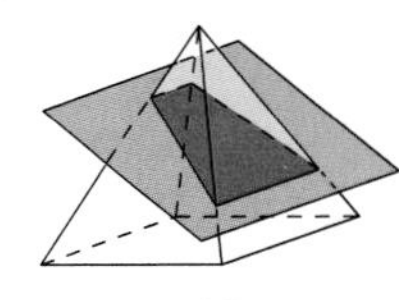
trapezoid

13. **Reasoning** Can a plane passing through the cylinder at the right create a cross section in each shape below? Explain.

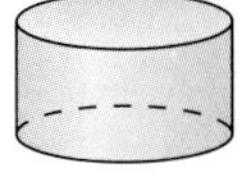

a. circle b. rectangle c. triangle

13a–c. See margin.

14. **Archaeology** A ziggurat is a terraced square pyramid. Draw a base plan for Chichen Itza, the Mayan ziggurat at the left. Check students' work.

15. **Writing in Math** Describe a situation in which each type of drawing would be useful. See back of book.

a. base plan b. top, front, and right views

7. 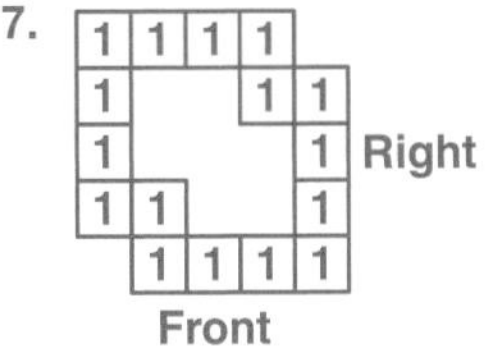

1	1	1	1		
1			1	1	
1				1	Right
1	1			1	
	1	1	1	1	

Front

8. 

2	2	2	3	
2				Right
1				

Front

9. 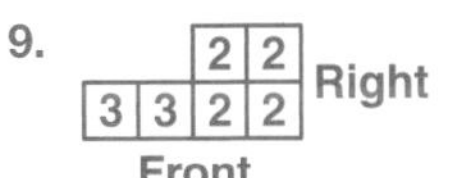

		2	2	
3	3	2	2	Right

Front

4.

1	1	1	1	1	
1	3	3	3	1	
1	3	4	3	1	Right
1	3	3	3	1	
1	1	1	1	1	

Front

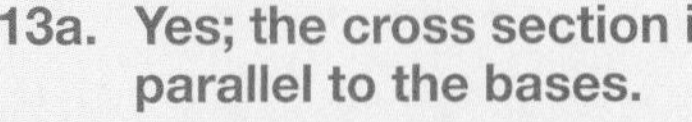
13a. Yes; the cross section is parallel to the bases.

b. Yes; the cross section is perpendicular to the bases.

c. No; the curved lateral surface makes a triangular cross section impossible.

Use the Guided Problem Solving worksheet with Exercise 8.

3. Practice

Assignment Guide

1 Objective 1

A B Core 1–4, 7–9, 14

2 Objective 2

A B Core 5–6, 10–13, 15

C Extension 16–19

Test Prep 20–23

Mixed Review 24–30

Error Prevention!

Exercises 7–9 Point out that a base plan is the view from above.

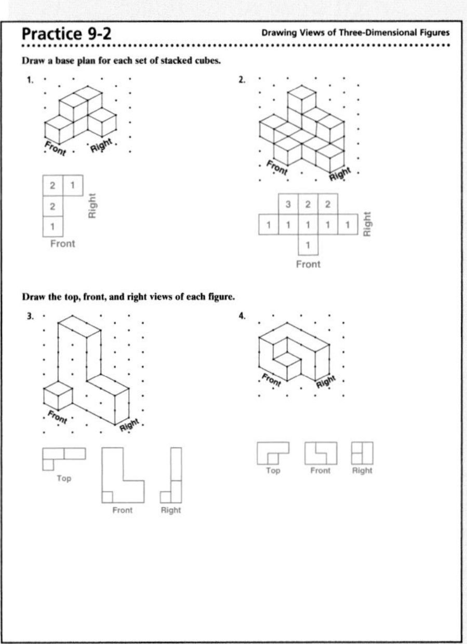

Practice 9-2 Drawing Views of Three-Dimensional Figures

Draw a base plan for each set of stacked cubes.

1. 2.

Draw the top, front, and right views of each figure.

3. 4.

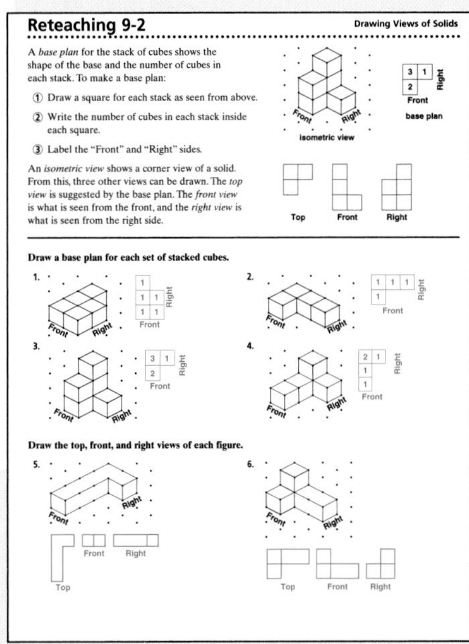

Reteaching 9-2 Drawing Views of Solids

A *base plan* for the stack of cubes shows the shape of the base and the number of cubes in each stack. To make a base plan:

① Draw a square for each stack as seen from above.

② Write the number of cubes in each stack inside each square.

③ Label the "Front" and "Right" sides.

An *isometric view* shows a corner view of a solid. From this, three other views can be drawn. The *top view* is suggested by the base plan. The *front view* is what is seen from the front, and the *right view* is what is seen from the right side.

Draw a base plan for each set of stacked cubes.

1. 2. 3. 4.

Draw the top, front, and right views of each figure.

5. 6.

4. Assess

Lesson Quiz 9-2

Use this figure of stacked cubes to answer the questions.

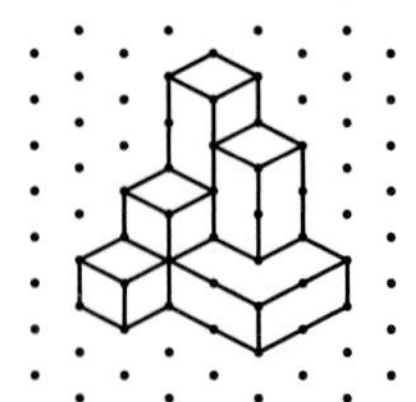

1. Draw a base plan for the stacked cubes.

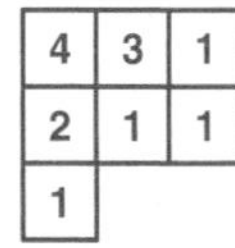

4	3	1
2	1	1
1		

2. Draw the top, front, and right views of the figure.

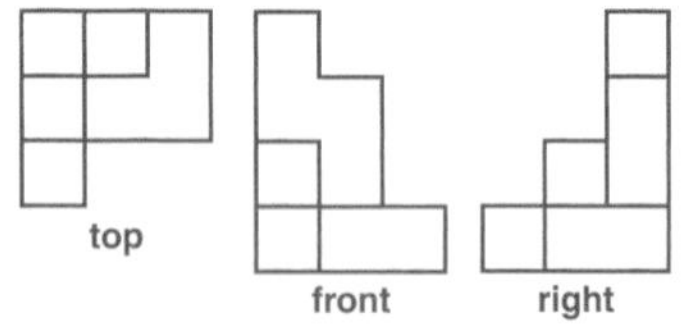

Alternative Assessment

Students draw the top, front, and right views of the figure having this base plan.

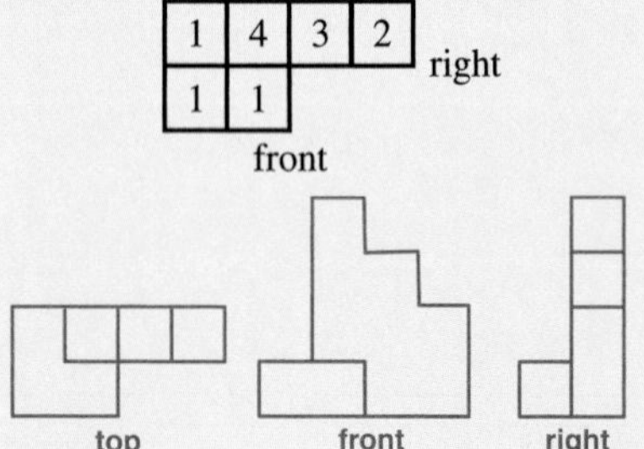

1	4	3	2
1	1		

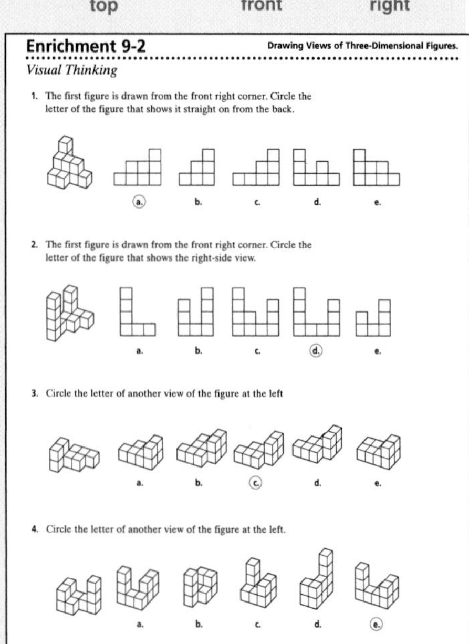

Enrichment 9-2 Drawing Views of Three-Dimensional Figures

Visual Thinking

1. The first figure is drawn from the front right corner. Circle the letter of the figure that shows it straight on from the back.

a. b. c. d. e.

2. The first figure is drawn from the front right corner. Circle the letter of the figure that shows the right-side view.

a. b. c. d. e.

3. Circle the letter of another view of the figure at the left.

a. b. c. d. e.

4. Circle the letter of another view of the figure at the left.

a. b. c. d. e.

C Challenge

Reasoning **Draw the top, front, and right views for each base plan.**

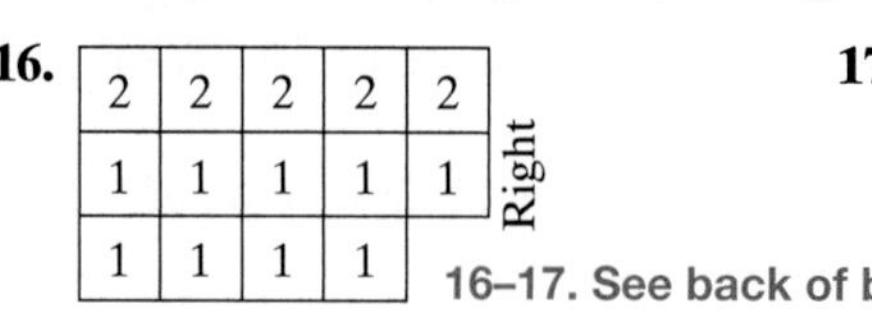

16.

2	2	2	2	2
1	1	1	1	1
1	1	1	1	

Right; Front

17.

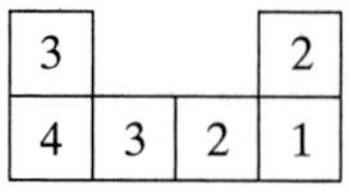

3			2
4	3	2	1

Right; Front

16–17. See back of book.

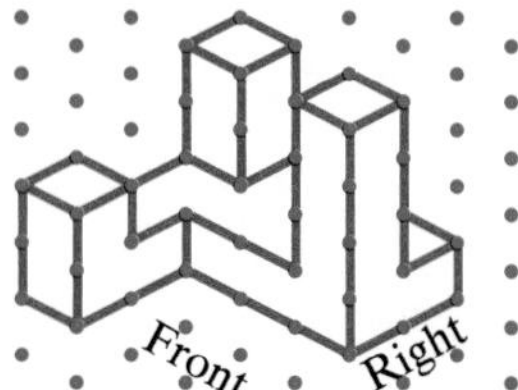

18. Error Analysis Ayla used the isometric view at the left to draw the top, front, and side views below. What errors did she make? See margin.

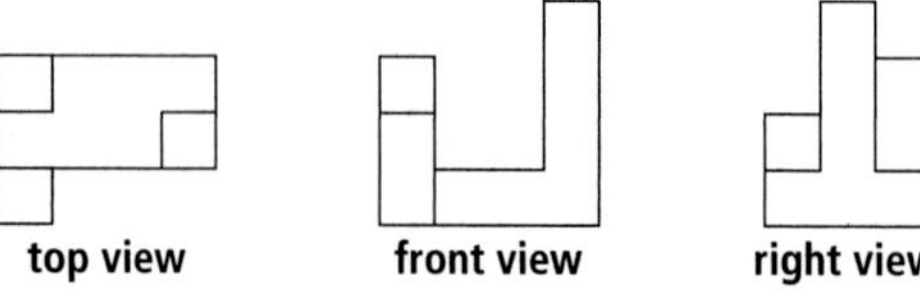

19. Stretch Your Thinking One cube has six faces. A stack of two cubes together still has only six faces. What are the different number of faces possible with an arrangement of three cubes? With four cubes? 6, 8; 6, 8, 10

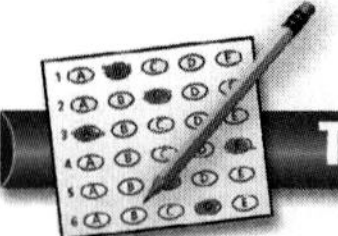

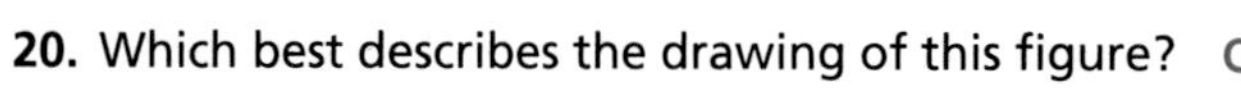

Test Prep

Multiple Choice

Use the diagram at the right for Exercises 20–23.

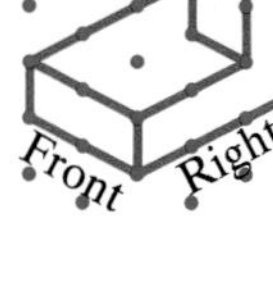

20. Which best describes the drawing of this figure? C
    A. base plan
    B. top view
    C. isometric view
    D. polygon

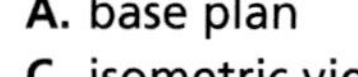

Take It to the NET
Online lesson quiz at **www.PHSchool.com**
Web Code: aca-0902

21. Which of the following is a base plan of the figure? I

F.

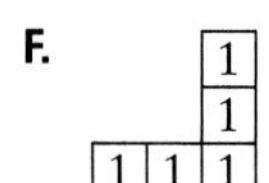

		1
		1
1	1	1

G.

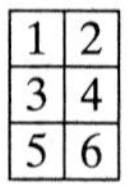

1	2
3	4
5	6

H.

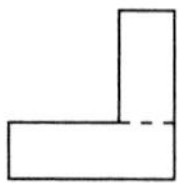

I.

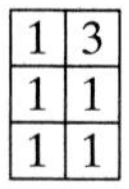

1	3
1	1
1	1

22. Suppose each face of each cube in the figure above were equal to 9 square feet. How tall would the highest part of the structure be? D
    A. 36 ft
    B. 18 ft
    C. 12 ft
    D. 9 ft

Extended Response

23. Draw the top, front, and right views of the figure. See back of book.

Mixed Review

Lesson 8-8 **Find the area of each circle. Round to the nearest tenth.**

24. $r = 6.4$ m 128.7 m^2 **25.** $d = 3.9$ in. 11.9 in.^{2} **26.** $d = 167$ cm 21,904 cm^2

Lesson 7-6 **Find the decimal value of each binary number.**

27. 100_2 4 **28.** 1111_2 15 **29.** 10_2 2 **30.** 10001_2 17

Test Prep

Resources
For additional practice with a variety of test item formats:
- Test Prep, p. 527
- Test-Taking Strategies, p. 523
- Test-Taking Strategies with Transparencies

18. The top view and right view are incorrect because the back-to-front distance should be 4 units, not 3.

9-3 Nets and Solids

What You'll Learn

 To identify nets of solids

. . . And Why

To design product packaging, as in Example 1

Check Skills You'll Need

For help, go to Lesson 9-1.

For each figure, describe its base(s) and then name the figure.

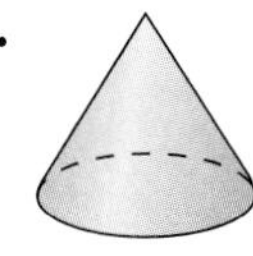

1. one circular base; cone
2. two hexagonal bases; hexagonal prism
3. two circular bases; cylinder

New Vocabulary

- net

 Interactive lesson includes instant self-check, tutorials, and activities.

OBJECTIVE 1

Identifying Nets of Solids

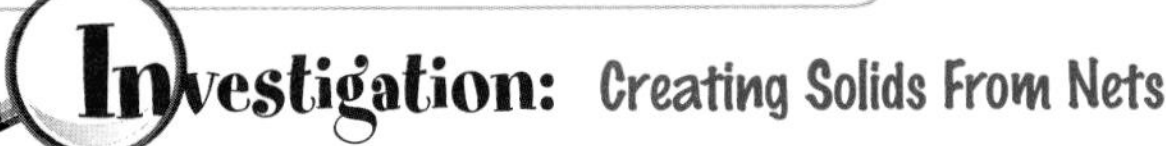

Investigation: Creating Solids From Nets

Copy the pattern below onto graph paper. Use scissors to cut out the pattern. Fold the pattern along each black segment. Then tape the edges together to form a solid.

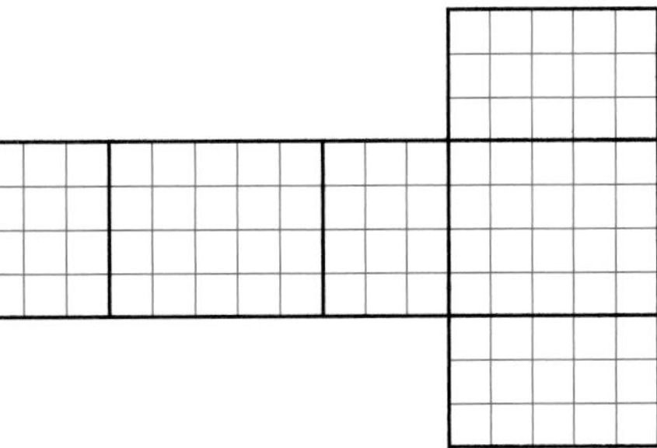

1. What solid does this pattern form? What shapes make up its faces? a rectangular prism; rectangles
2. Look at the solid at the right. Describe the shapes that make up its faces. a square and 4 isosceles triangles
3. Use scissors and paper to cut out a pattern that can be folded without any overlaps to form this solid. Check students' work.

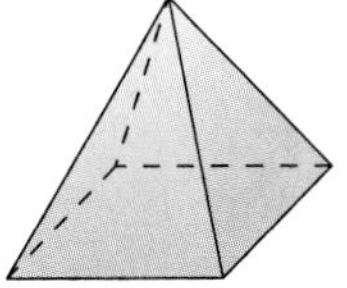

A **net** is a pattern that can be folded to form a solid. A net of a figure shows all the surfaces of that figure in one view.

Ongoing Assessment and Intervention

Before the Lesson
Diagnose prerequisite skills using:
- Check Skills You'll Need

During the Lesson
Monitor progress using:
- Check Understanding
- Additional Examples
- Test Prep

After the Lesson
Assess knowledge using:
- Lesson Quiz
- Computer Test Generator CD
- Chapter Checkpoint 1 (p. 485)

9-3

1. Plan

Lesson Preview

Check Skills You'll Need

Naming Solids and Their Parts
Lesson 9-1: Example 1. Extra Practice, p. 710.

Lesson Resources

Optional Materials
- graph paper
- scissors
- tape

Teaching Resources
Practice, Reteaching, Enrichment
Checkpoint Quiz 1

Reaching All Students
Practice Workbook 9-3
Spanish Practice Workbook 9-3
Reading and Math Literacy 9B
Spanish Reading and Math Literacy 9B
Spanish Checkpoint Quiz 1
Guided Problem Solving 9-3
Technology Activities 46

Presentation Assistant Plus!
Transparencies
- Check Skills You'll Need 9-3
- Problem of the Day 9-3
- Additional Examples 9-3
- Student Edition Answers 9-3
- Lesson Quiz 9-3
- Classroom Aid 2

PH Presentation Pro CD-ROM 9-3

PRENTICE HALL ASSESSMENT SYSTEM

Checkpoint Quiz 1
Computer Test Generator CD

Technology
Resource Pro® CD-ROM
Computer Test Generator CD
PH Presentation Pro CD-ROM

www.PHSchool.com
Student Site
- Teacher Web Code: ack-5500
- Algebra Readiness Puzzles 33
- Self-grading Lesson Quiz

PH SuccessNet Teacher Center
- Lesson Planner
- Resources

Plus 

2. Teach

Math Background

A *net* is a pattern, showing all the faces of a solid in one view. You can fold the pattern to form a solid. A given solid, such as a tissue box, for example, may have several different associated nets. Each net will have the same faces, but the various faces may be connected in different ways.

Teaching Notes

Investigation (Optional)
Make sure students understand that the black segments on the nets represent fold lines.

1 EXAMPLE English Learners
Suggest that students think of the flat net "catching" or enclosing space to make a solid figure.

2 EXAMPLE Inclusion
Some students may have difficulty envisioning the solid from its net. Encourage students to make the nets and fold them into solids.

PowerPoint

Additional Examples

1. Match each shape with its net.

a. 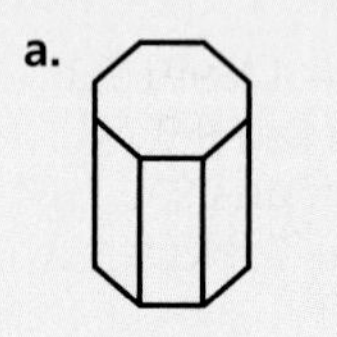

b. 

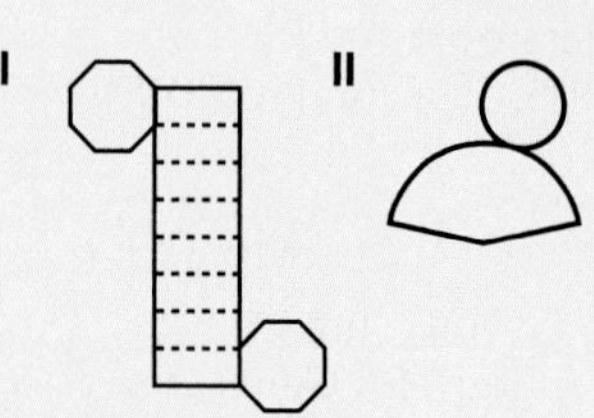

a with I; b with II

2. Identify the solid that this net forms. hexagonal pyramid

Closure

How can you identify a solid figure from a net? Sample: Look at the shape of the base(s) and the sides.

Real-World Connection
Not all food is packaged in closed, airtight containers.

1 EXAMPLE Recognizing Nets of Solids

Packaging Match each package with its net.

a. 

b. 

I. 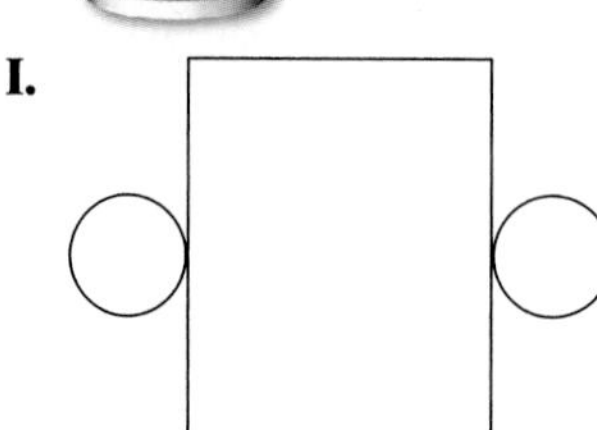

II. 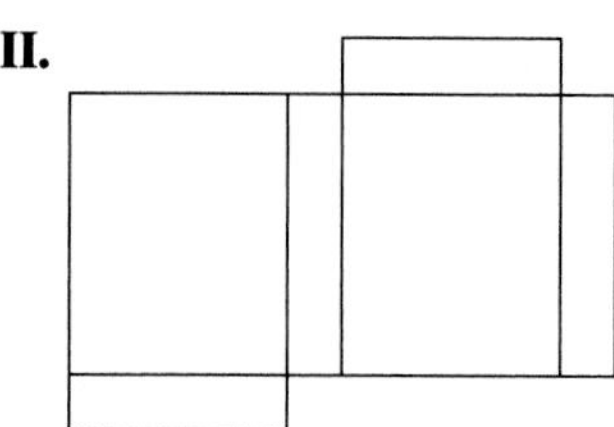

The oatmeal container is a cylinder, which has two circular bases. Figure I shows a net with two circles.

The rice box is a rectangular prism, which has six rectangular faces. Figure II shows a net with six rectangles.

Check Understanding 1 a. What would you expect the net of a standard number cube to look like? 1a. six congruent squares

b. **Reasoning** No surface of a cylinder is a polygon. Explain why the net of a cylinder will always include a rectangle. Answers may vary. Sample: You create a rectangle when you split the lateral surface of a cylinder and spread it out flat.

Examining the different shapes in a net can help you determine which solid the net will form.

2 EXAMPLE Identifying Solids From Nets

Identify the solid that each net forms.

a. 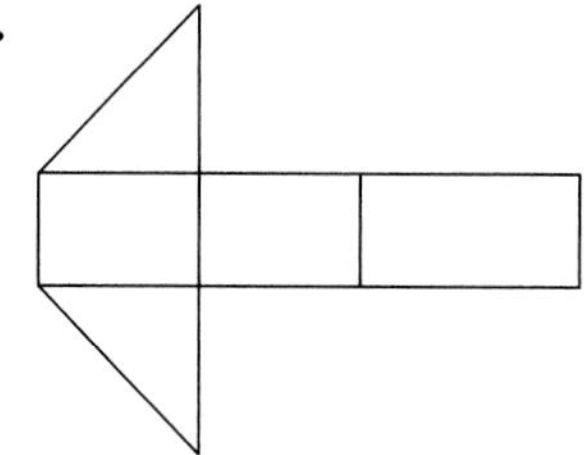

b.

The net shows two congruent triangles and three rectangles. The two triangles form the bases of a triangular prism.

The net shows one square and four congruent triangles. The one square forms the base of a square pyramid.

Check Understanding 2 A net consists of one regular pentagon and five congruent triangles. What solid will it form? pentagonal pyramid

Reaching All Students

Below Level Have students draw and label a square, a circle, a pyramid, a prism, and a cone.	**Advanced Learners** Have students work with a partner to draw as many different nets for a cube as they can.	**English Learners** See note on page 482. **Inclusion** See note on page 482.

EXERCISES

For more practice, see *Extra Practice*.

A Practice by Example

Example 1 (page 482)

Match each solid with its net.

1. 

B

2. 

C

3. 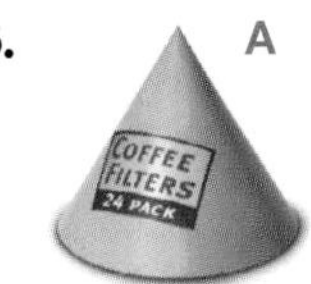

A

A. 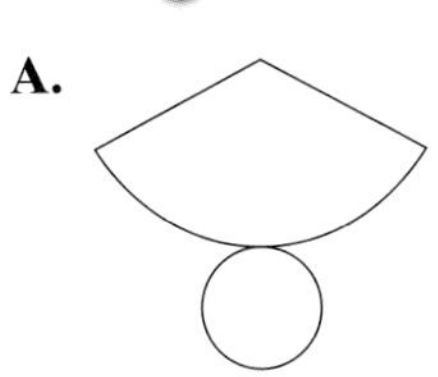

B. 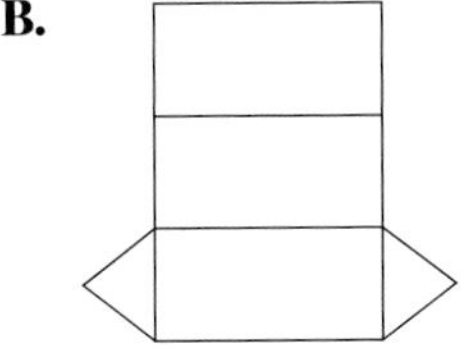

C. 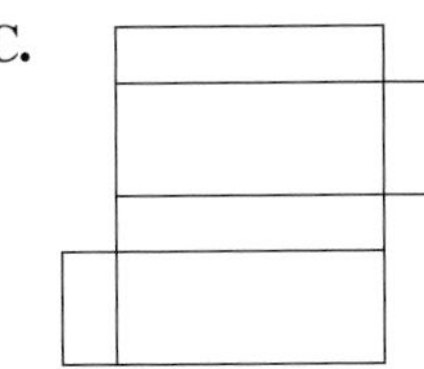

Example 2 (page 482)

Identify the solid that each net forms.

4. 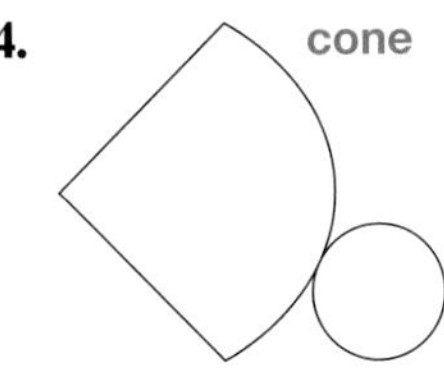 cone

5. 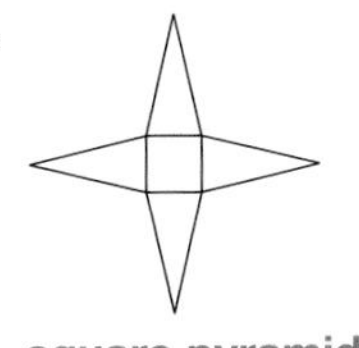 square pyramid

6. 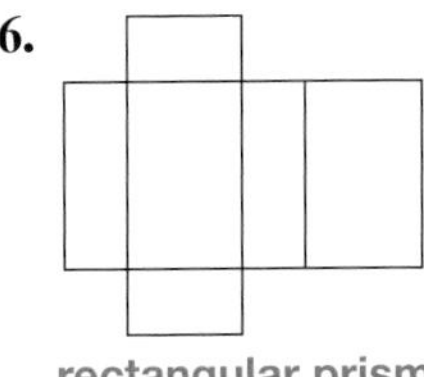 rectangular prism

7. 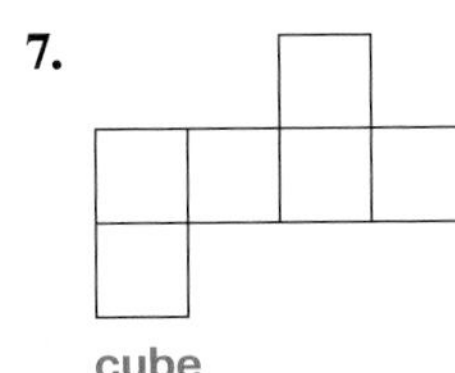 cube

8. 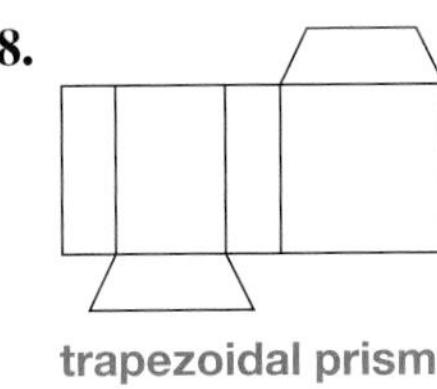 trapezoidal prism

9. 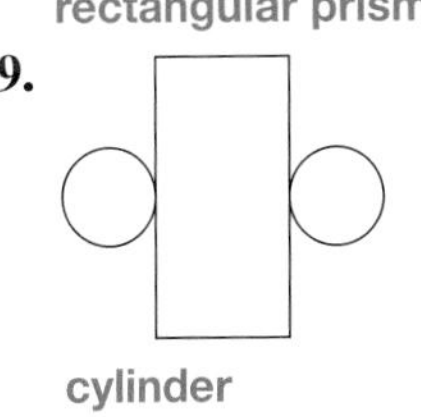 cylinder

B Apply Your Skills

List the shapes that make up the net for each figure, and write the number of times each shape is used.

10. 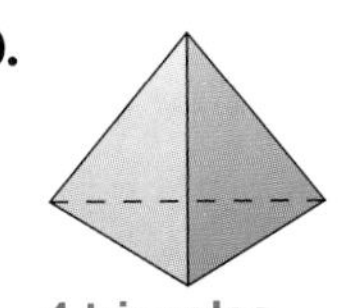 4 triangles

11. 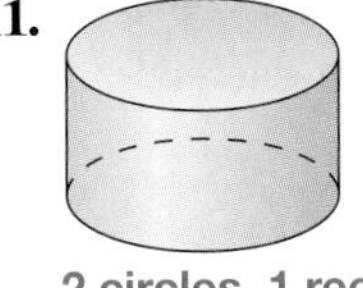 2 circles, 1 rectangle

12. 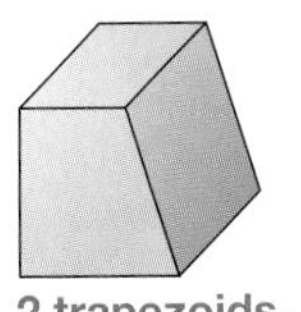 2 trapezoids, 4 rectangles

Draw a net to represent each solid.

13. 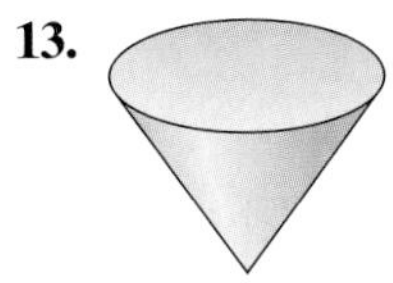

14. 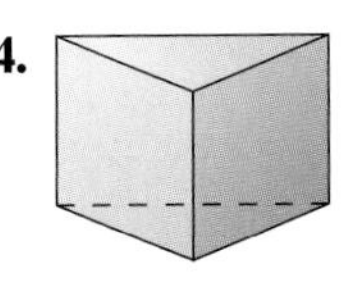

15. 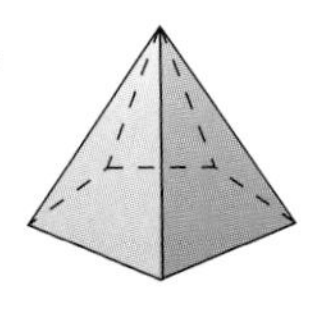

16. 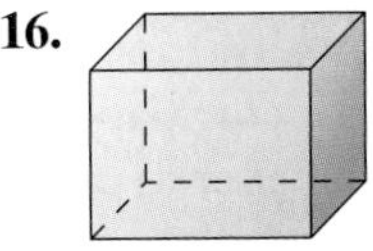

17. 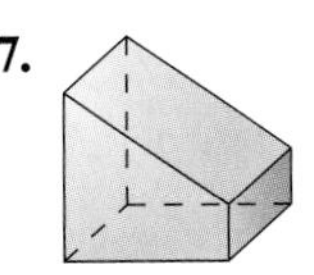

18. 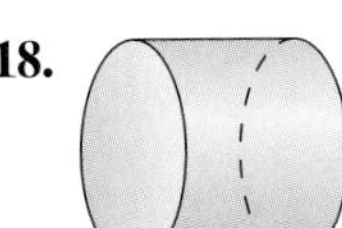

13–18. Answers may vary. See margin for samples.

13. 

14. 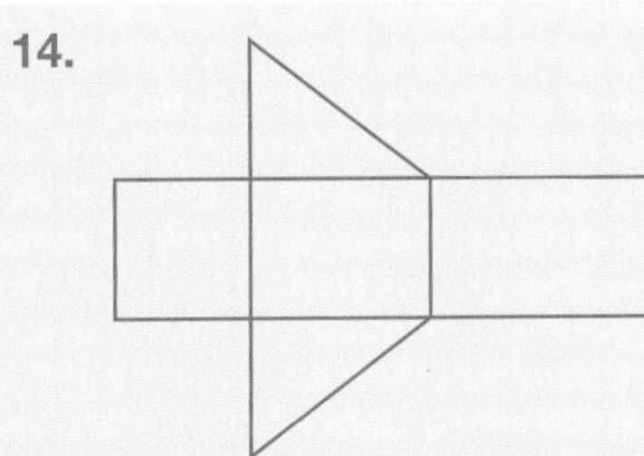

15–18. See back of book.

3. Practice

Assignment Guide

Objective 1

A B Core 1–27

C Extension 28–32

Test Prep 33–36

Mixed Review 37–44

Error Prevention!

Exercises 1–9 Suggest that students count how many faces there are for each net to match them to the correct solid.

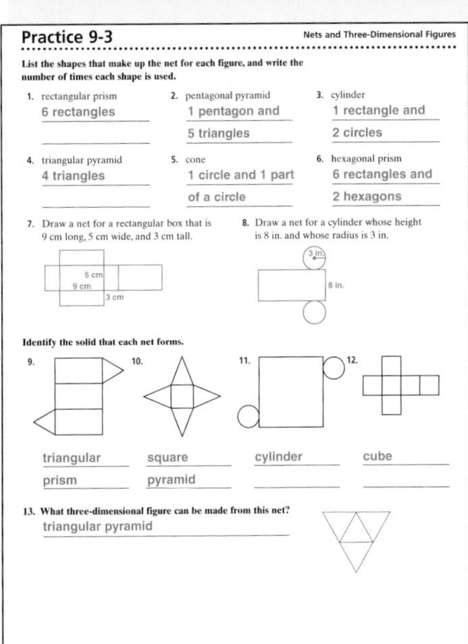

Practice 9-3 Nets and Three-Dimensional Figures

List the shapes that make up the net for each figure, and write the number of times each shape is used.

1. rectangular prism — 6 rectangles
2. pentagonal pyramid — 1 pentagon and 5 triangles
3. cylinder — 1 rectangle and 2 circles
4. triangular pyramid — 4 triangles
5. cone — 1 circle and 1 part of a circle
6. hexagonal prism — 6 rectangles and 2 hexagons
7. Draw a net for a rectangular box that is 9 cm long, 5 cm wide, and 3 cm tall.
8. Draw a net for a cylinder whose height is 8 in. and whose radius is 3 in.

Identify the solid that each net forms.

9. triangular prism
10. square pyramid
11. cylinder
12. cube

13. What three-dimensional figure can be made from this net? triangular pyramid

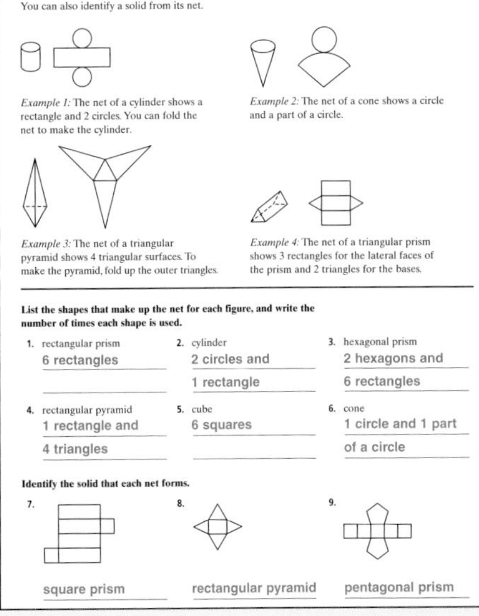

Reteaching 9-3 Nets and Solids

You can make *nets*, or flat patterns, of solids. You can also identify a solid from its net.

Example 1: The net of a cylinder shows a rectangle and 2 circles. You can fold the net to make the cylinder.

Example 2: The net of a cone shows a circle and a part of a circle.

Example 3: The net of a triangular pyramid shows 4 triangular surfaces. To make the pyramid, fold up the outer triangles.

Example 4: The net of a triangular prism shows 3 rectangles for the lateral faces of the prism and 2 triangles for the bases.

List the shapes that make up the net for each figure, and write the number of times each shape is used.

1. rectangular prism — 6 rectangles
2. cylinder — 2 circles and 1 rectangle
3. hexagonal prism — 2 hexagons and 6 rectangles
4. rectangular pyramid — 1 rectangle and 4 triangles
5. cube — 6 squares
6. cone — 1 circle and 1 part of a circle

Identify the solid that each net forms.

7. square prism
8. rectangular pyramid
9. pentagonal prism

Real-World Connection

Careers Professional movers keep customers' moving costs low by loading and unloading trucks quickly and efficiently.

19. Moving The net at the right shows the dimensions of a storage box. How many of these boxes can be stacked on top of each other to fit inside a moving van with a cargo space that is 7 feet high? 5

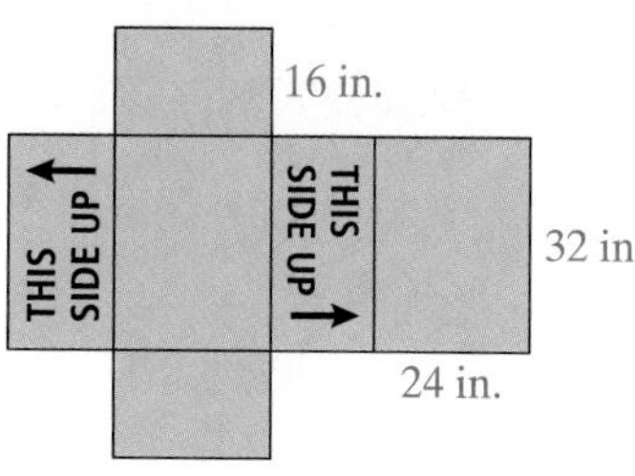

20. Draw a net for a cylinder with a height of 8 cm and a radius of 4 cm. See margin.

21. Reasoning Is it possible to have different nets that fold to form the same solid? Explain. Yes; one solid can have several different nets depending on which edges you cut along to unfold and flatten the solid.

List the shapes that make up the net for each figure, and write the number of times each shape is used. See left.

22. triangular prism **23.** trapezoidal pyramid **24.** hexagonal prism

22. 2 triangles, 3 rectangles
23. 1 trapezoid, 4 triangles
24. 2 hexagons, 6 rectangles

25. Packaging Ship-Tight Manufacturing Co. has signed a contract to produce boxes for DVD players. Draw a net to represent the package at the right. See margin.

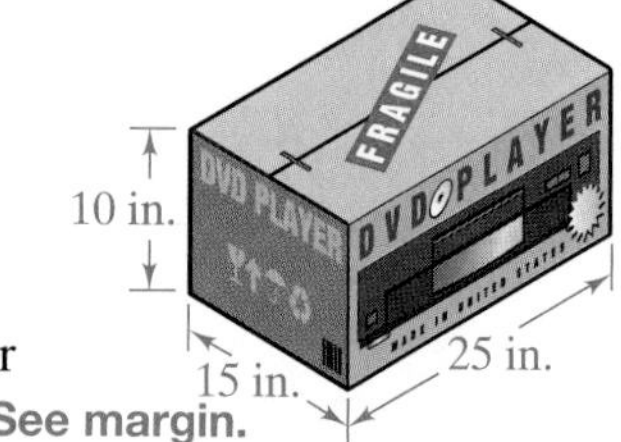

26. Writing in Math Explain how you can tell the difference between a net for a triangular pyramid and a net for a triangular prism. See margin.

27. a. Draw the solid shown in the top, front, and right views below.
b. Draw a net of this solid. See margin.

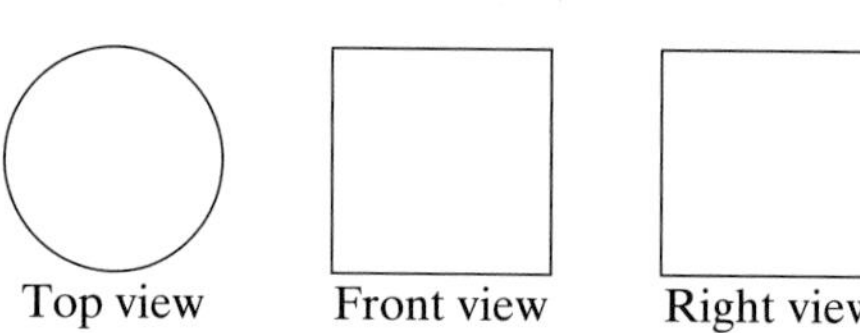

Challenge

For each net, draw a second net that will form the same solid.

28. **29.** **30.**

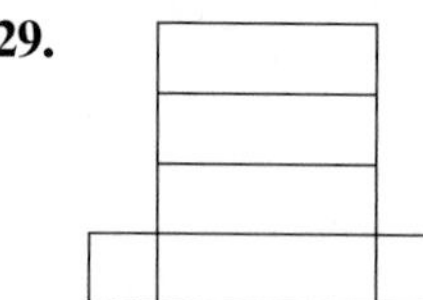

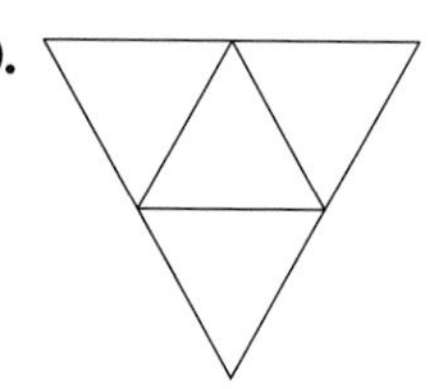

28–30. Answers may vary. See margin for samples.

31. Stretch Your Thinking Draw six different nets for the cube at the left. Check students' work.

32. Number Sense You are wrapping a birthday gift for your friend. You have placed the gift in a box that measures 9 in. by 7 in. by 12 in. You have a square sheet of wrapping paper that measures one yard on each side. Do you have enough paper to cover the box? Explain. Yes; the box can be represented by a net that fits in a 26-in. by 32-in. rectangle, so the 36-in. by 36-in. wrapping paper will cover it.

20.

4 cm
8 cm
4 cm

25.

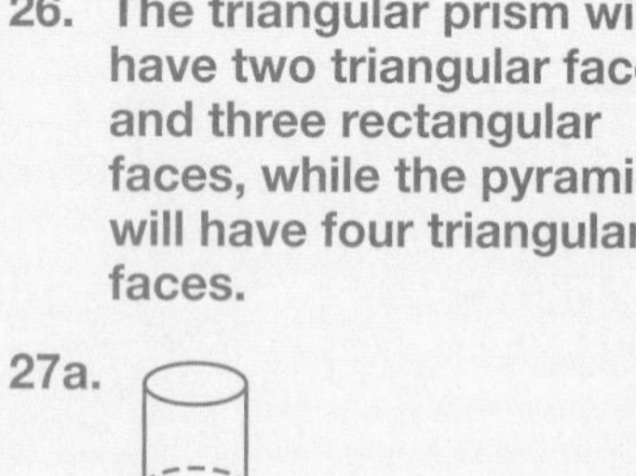

26. The triangular prism will have two triangular faces and three rectangular faces, while the pyramid will have four triangular faces.

27a.

b.

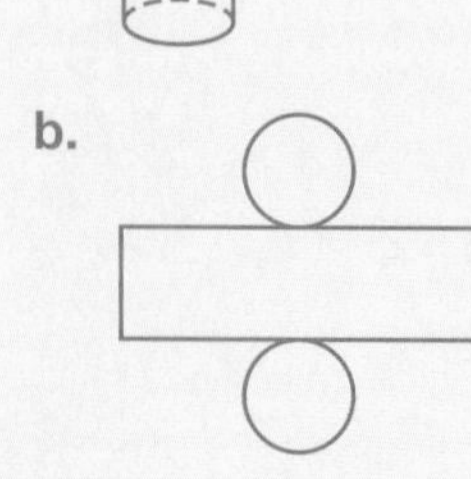

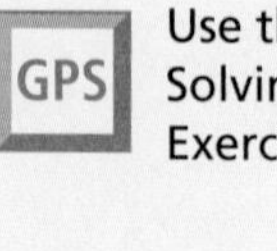

Use the Guided Problem Solving worksheet with Exercise 19.

28.

29.

30.

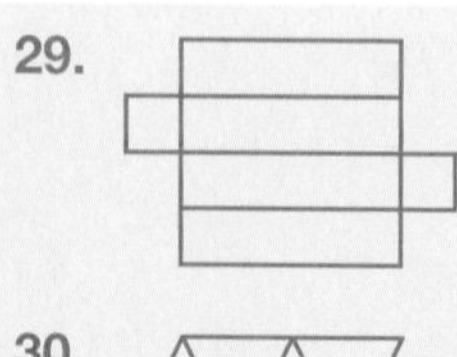

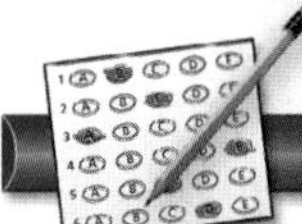

Test Prep

Multiple Choice

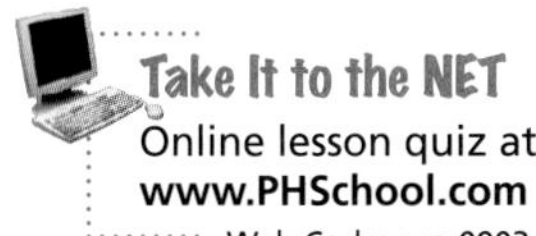

Take It to the NET
Online lesson quiz at **www.PHSchool.com**
Web Code: aca-0903

Use the diagram at the right for Exercises 33–35.

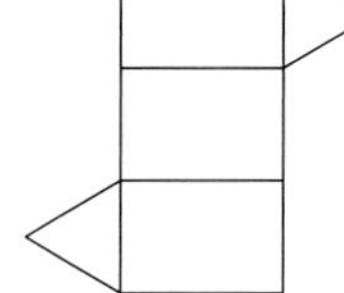

33. How many bases will the solid formed by this net have? C
    A. 5 B. 4
    C. 2 D. 1

34. How many lateral faces will the solid formed by this net have? G
    F. 2 G. 3 H. 4 I. 5

35. What common three-dimensional figure will this net form? B
    A. cone B. prism C. pyramid D. cylinder

Short Response

36. A cylinder has a radius of 6 cm and a height of 9 cm. All sides of a cube are 10 cm. Would either figure fit inside the other? Explain.
See margin.

Mixed Review

Lesson 8-6 **Find the measure of each angle of a regular polygon with the given number of sides.**

37. 3 sides 60° 38. 5 sides 108° 39. 8 sides 135° 40. 14 sides 154.3°

Lesson 7-4 **Write each expression using one base and one exponent.**

41. $(3^4)^5$ 3^{20} 42. $(h^{-5})^{-8}$ h^{40} 43. $(10^0)^{10}$ 10^0 44. $(-7^2)^{-3}$ -7^{-6}

Checkpoint Quiz 1 — Lessons 9-1 through 9-3

Instant self-check quiz online and on CD-ROM

Use the figure at the right for Exercises 1 and 2.

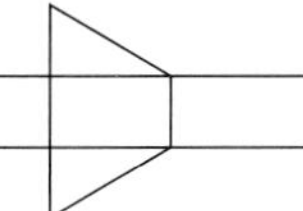

1. What three-dimensional figure will this net form? triangular prism
2. Name the shapes that make up the lateral faces of this figure. rectangles

Use the figure at the right for Exercises 3 and 4.

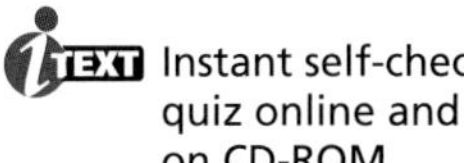

3. Draw a base plan for this figure.

3.
		2
2	1	1

4. Draw top, front, and right views for this figure.
See back of book.

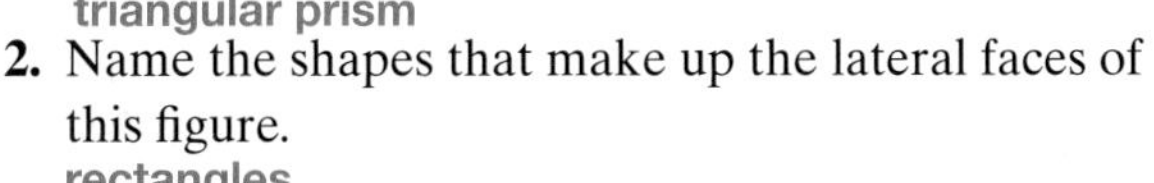

5. Name a pair of skew lines in the figure at the right. Answers may vary. Sample: $\overline{AH}$, $\overline{DE}$

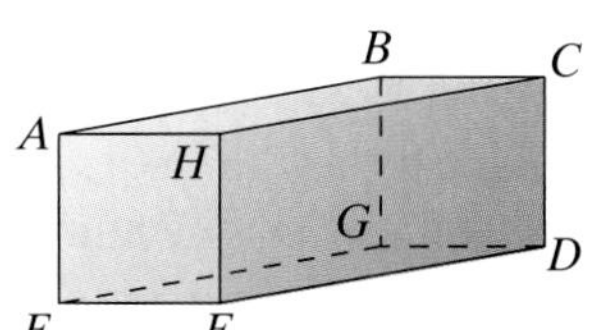

36. [2] The cylinder would not fit inside the cube because its diameter is 12 cm, and the cube would not fit inside the cylinder because its height is 10 cm.
    [1] incorrect explanation

Alternative Assessment

Students in pairs take turns drawing a net and having the partner identify the solid.

4. Assess

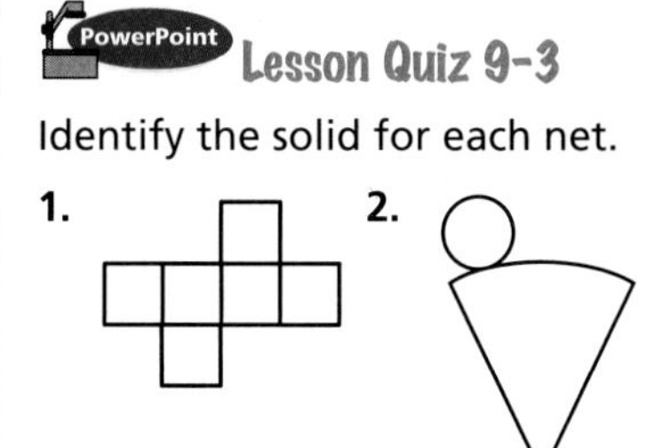

PowerPoint
Lesson Quiz 9-3
Identify the solid for each net.
1.
2.
cube
cone

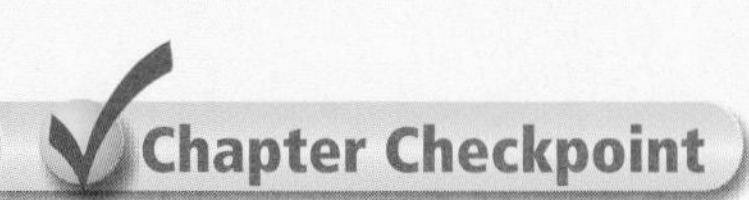

Chapter Checkpoint

To check understanding of Lessons 9-1 to 9-3:

Checkpoint Quiz 1 (p. 485)

Teaching Resources
Checkpoint Quiz 1 (also in Prentice Hall Assessment System)

Reaching All Students
Reading and Math Literacy 9B

Spanish versions available

Test Prep

Resources
For additional practice with a variety of test item formats:
- Test Prep, p. 527
- Test-Taking Strategies, p. 523
- Test-Taking Strategies with Transparencies

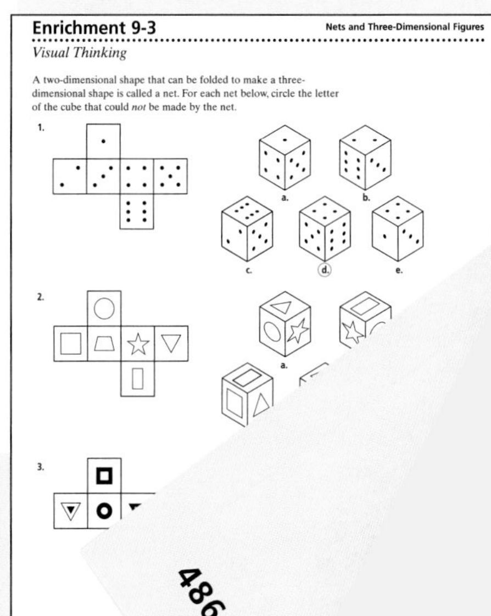

Investigation

Precision and Greatest Possible Error

This investigation introduces the key concept that no measurement is exact. The precision of any measurement is related to the unit of measure used. A measurement can be no more precise than the accuracy of the instrument making the measurement.

Teaching Notes

Refer students to the Table of Measures on p. 729.

Teaching Tip
To prepare students to work with and compare measurements, provide opportunities to practice converting one unit of metric measurement to another with exercises such as these:

440 mm = ■ cm 44
4.7 m = ■ cm 470

Inclusion
Work through the first two examples with students. Then ask: *If you had several different kinds of rulers with which to measure the length of your pencil, which one would give the most precise measurement? Explain.* Sample: the one with the smallest units of measure

Investigation Precision and Greatest Possible Error

For Use With Lesson 9-4

No measurement is exact. The precision of a measurement is the degree to which a measurement is accurate. A measurement can be no more precise than the accuracy of the instrument used to make the measurement.

When comparing measurements, the measurement that uses the smaller units is more precise. To show precision, you do not express fractional measurements in simplest form.

1 EXAMPLE Comparing Precision in Measurements

Choose the more precise measurement.

a. $2\frac{2}{8}$ in., $2\frac{1}{4}$ in.

Since eighth inches are smaller than quarter inches, $2\frac{2}{8}$ in. is the more precise measurement.

b. 26 L, 260 mL

Since milliliters are smaller than liters, 260 mL is the more precise measurement.

Tape measures are typically precise to sixteenth inches.

Any calculations with measurements will only be as accurate as the least precise measurement. Round your answer to match the precision of the least precise measurement.

2 EXAMPLE Adding or Subtracting With Precision

Compute. Round your answer to match the less precise measurement.

a. 20.08 km + 5.2 km

$20.08 + 5.2 = 25.28$ ← **Add.**

≈ 25.3 km ← **Since 5.2 is less precise than 20.08, round to the nearest tenth.**

b. 36 g − 12.3 g

$36 - 12.3 = 23.7$ ← **Subtract.**

≈ 24 g ← **Since 36 is less precise than 12.3, round to the nearest whole unit.**

To the nearest half inch, the line segment at the right measures $1\frac{1}{2}$ inches. When a measurement is rounded to the nearest half inch, it can vary from the actual length by as much as one fourth inch. We say that one fourth inch is the greatest possible error of measurement.

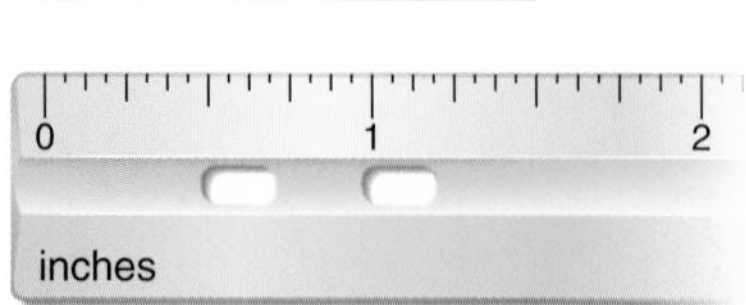

The greatest possible error of a measurement is half the unit of measure to which the measurement has been rounded.

3 EXAMPLE Finding Greatest Possible Error

Find the greatest possible error for each measurement.

a. 28.3 L — The measurement is rounded to the nearest tenth of a liter. Since $\frac{1}{2} \cdot 0.1 = 0.05$, the greatest possible error is 0.05 L.

b. $2\frac{1}{4}$ ft — The measurement is rounded to the nearest quarter foot. Since $\frac{1}{2} \cdot \frac{1}{4} = \frac{1}{8}$, the greatest possible error is $\frac{1}{8}$ ft.

c. 800 kg — The measurement is rounded to the nearest hundred kilogram. Since $\frac{1}{2} \cdot 100 = 50$, the greatest possible error is 50 kg.

EXERCISES

Choose the more precise measurement.

1. 3 mi, 2.8 mi 2.8 mi **2.** 16 tons, $17\frac{1}{2}$ tons $17\frac{1}{2}$ tons **3.** $4\frac{3}{4}$ in., $4\frac{12}{16}$ in. $4\frac{12}{16}$ in.

4. 3.2 g, 3.02 g 3.02 g **5.** ounce, pound ounce **6.** meter, centimeter centimeter

Compute. Round your answer to match the less precise measurement.

7. 34 ft + 16.9 ft 51 ft **8.** 60 s − 22.80 s 37 s **9.** 1.1 cm + 1.01 cm 2.1 cm

10. $33\frac{5}{8}$ in. + $4\frac{1}{4}$ in. 38 in. **11.** 42.00 m^2 − 21.0 m^2 21.0 m^2 **12.** 13.9 g − 4.0 g 9.9 g

Find the greatest possible error for each measurement.

13. 12 qt $\frac{1}{2}$ qt **14.** 15.5 mL 0.05 mL **15.** 4.27 km 0.005 km **16.** 255 ft 0.5 ft **17.** 2.1 mm 0.05 mm

18. $1\frac{1}{4}$ c $\frac{1}{8}$ c **19.** 15.38 gal 0.005 gal **20.** $18\frac{1}{2}$ oz $\frac{1}{4}$ oz **21.** 35.375 mg 0.0005 mg **22.** $6\frac{7}{8}$ in. $\frac{1}{16}$ in.

Determine the precision possible with each scale shown.

23.

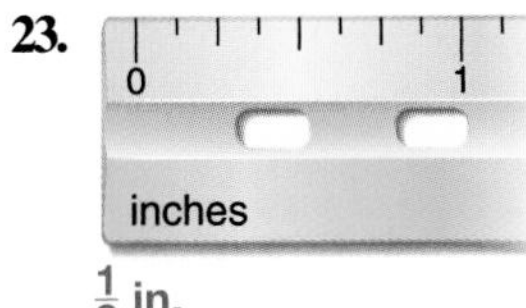

$\frac{1}{8}$ in.

24.

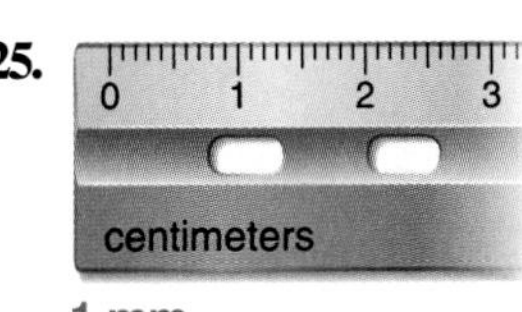

0.2 g

25. 0 1 2 3 centimeters

1 mm

26. **Writing in Math** How does the precision of a measurement relate to the greatest possible error of a measurement? Give examples. See margin.

3 EXAMPLE

Discuss the meaning of greatest possible error (GPE). After working through the example, ask:

- *If a distance measures 14.6 m, what is the GPE for the measurement?* GPE is $\frac{1}{2}$ or 0.5 of 0.1 m, or 0.05 m.
- *What is the range of measurement?* The lengths will range from 14.55 m to 14.65 m.

Error Prevention!

Students may give the GPE by finding half the number in the rightmost decimal place. For instance, for 15.5 mL in Exercise 14, they might incorrectly answer 0.25 mL instead of 0.05 mL. Provide these students with practice finding the GPE for only whole numbers first. Then move on to tenths, hundredths, and so on.

Exercises

Have students work with partners to complete the exercises.

26. The greatest possible error is one half of the precision of a measurement. If the precision of a ruler is $\frac{1}{8}$ in., the greatest possible error is $\frac{1}{16}$ in.

9-4

1. Plan

Lesson Preview

PowerPoint

Check Skills You'll Need

Finding the Area of Polygons
Lesson 8-7: Examples 1–2. Extra Practice, p. 709.

Lesson Resources

Teaching Resources
Practice, Reteaching, Enrichment

Reaching All Students
Practice Workbook 9-4
Spanish Practice Workbook 9-4
Guided Problem Solving 9-4
Hands-On Activities 34

Presentation Assistant Plus!
Transparencies
- Check Skills You'll Need 9-4
- Problem of the Day 9-4
- Additional Examples 9-4
- Student Edition Answers 9-4
- Lesson Quiz 9-4
- Classroom Aid 11

PH Presentation Pro CD-ROM 9-4

Computer Test Generator CD

Technology
Resource Pro® CD-ROM
Computer Test Generator CD
PH Presentation Pro CD-ROM

www.PHSchool.com
Student Site
- Teacher Web Code: ack-5500
- Self-grading Lesson Quiz

PH SuccessNet Teacher Center
- Lesson Planner
- Resources

Plus iTEXT

9-4 Surface Areas of Prisms and Cylinders

What You'll Learn

To find the surface areas of prisms

To find the surface areas of cylinders

. . . And Why

To find how much area you will need to paint, as in Example 3

Check Skills You'll Need

For help, go to Lesson 8-7.

Find the area of each polygon.

1. 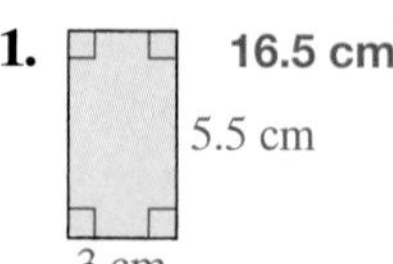

16.5 cm²

2. 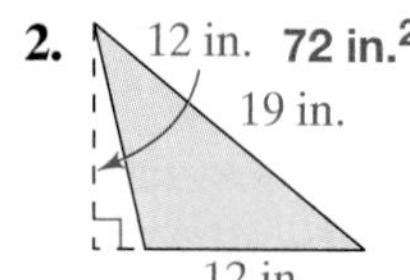

72 in.²

3. 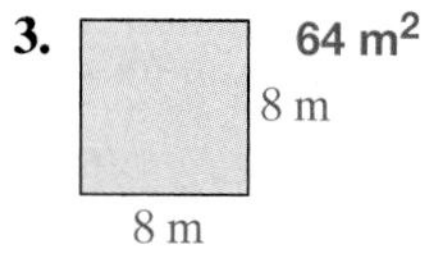

64 m²

New Vocabulary • surface area • lateral area

OBJECTIVE 1

iTEXT Interactive lesson includes instant self-check, tutorials, and activities.

Finding Surface Areas of Prisms

When you wrap a box with wrapping paper, you wrap all of the surfaces that make up the box. The **surface area** of a solid is the sum of the areas of its surfaces. The surface area of a solid is the area of its net.

1 EXAMPLE Using a Net to Find the Surface Area

Use a net to find the surface area of the prism.

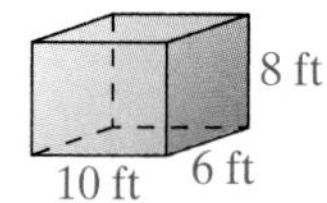

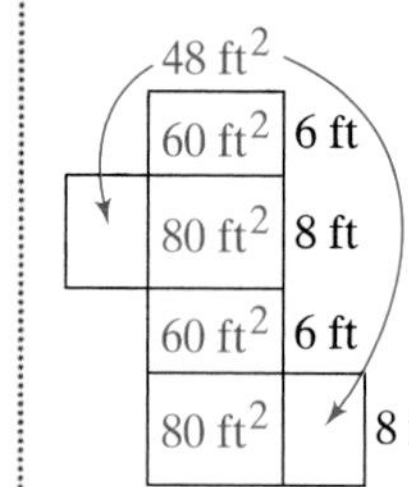

Draw a net of the prism, and find the area of each rectangle in the net.

Let S.A. stand for surface area.

S.A. = 60 + 80 + 60 + 80 + 48 + 48 ← **Add the areas.**

S.A. = 376 ← **Simplify.**

The surface area of the prism is 376 ft².

Check Understanding 1 **a.** Find the surface area of the prism at the right. **936 cm²**

b. Number Sense How will the surface area change if the height of the prism is doubled? **It becomes 1,332 cm².**

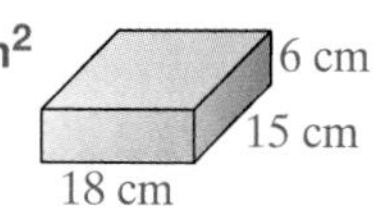

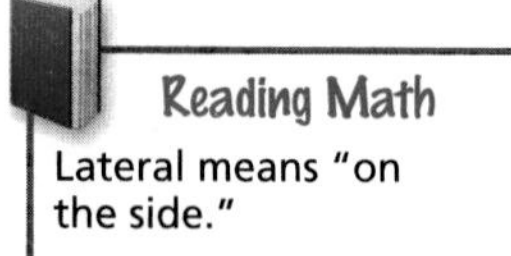

Reading Math
Lateral means "on the side."

You can also use a formula to find the surface area of a figure. First you must know how to find lateral area.

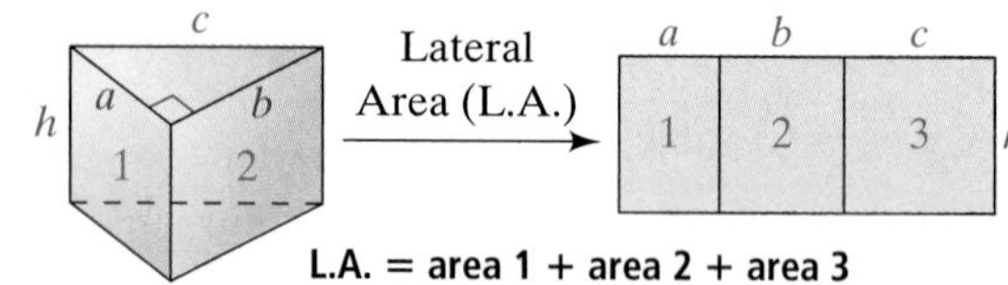

Ongoing Assessment and Intervention

Before the Lesson
Diagnose prerequisite skills using:
- Check Skills You'll Need

During the Lesson
Monitor progress using:
- Check Understanding
- Additional Examples
- Test Prep

After the Lesson
Assess knowledge using:
- Lesson Quiz
- Computer Test Generator CD

Lateral area is the sum of the areas of the lateral surfaces of a solid.

Key Concepts — Lateral Area and Surface Area of a Prism

The lateral area L.A. of a prism is the product of the perimeter of the base and the height.

$$\text{L.A.} = ph$$

The surface area S.A. of a prism is the sum of the lateral area and the area of its two bases.

$$\text{S.A.} = \text{L.A.} + 2B$$

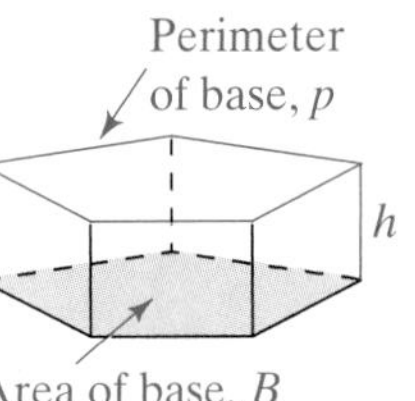

2 EXAMPLE — Using the Prism Surface Area Formula

Use a formula to find the surface area of the prism.

$\text{S.A.} = \text{L.A.} + 2B$ ← **surface area formula**

$= ph + 2\left(\frac{1}{2}bh\right)$ ← **Use *ph* for L.A. and $\frac{1}{2}bh$ for *B*.**

$= (3 \cdot 5)8 + 2\left(\frac{1}{2} \cdot 5 \cdot 4.3\right)$ ← **Substitute.**

$= 120 + 21.5$ ← **Use the order of operations.**

$= 141.5$ ← **Add.**

The surface area of the prism is 141.5 cm^2.

Check Understanding 2 The base of a rectangular prism measures 8 in. by 5 in. Its height is 12 in. Find the surface area of the prism. 392 in.^2

Real-World Connection
The size of the area to be painted determines how much paint to buy.

In some real-world situations, you only need to find a figure's lateral area.

3 EXAMPLE — Real-World Problem Solving

Painting A baseball team plans to paint the outside walls of the equipment shed at a Little League field. Find the lateral area of the shed.

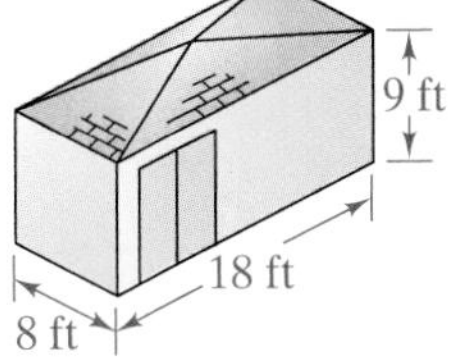

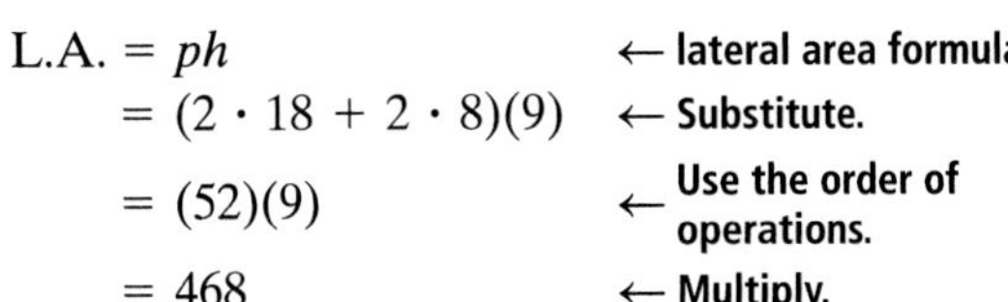

$\text{L.A.} = ph$ ← **lateral area formula**

$= (2 \cdot 18 + 2 \cdot 8)(9)$ ← **Substitute.**

$= (52)(9)$ ← **Use the order of operations.**

$= 468$ ← **Multiply.**

The lateral area of the shed is 468 ft^2.

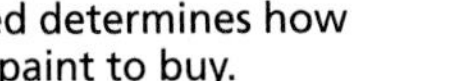

Check Understanding 3 **a.** The team will also paint the refreshment stand. See left. Find the lateral area of the refreshment stand.

3a. 440 ft^2

b. Number Sense The door measures 3 ft by 8 ft. The window measures 6 ft by 3 ft. How does the surface area change if you consider the door and the window in your calculation? It decreases by 42 ft^2 to 398 ft^2.

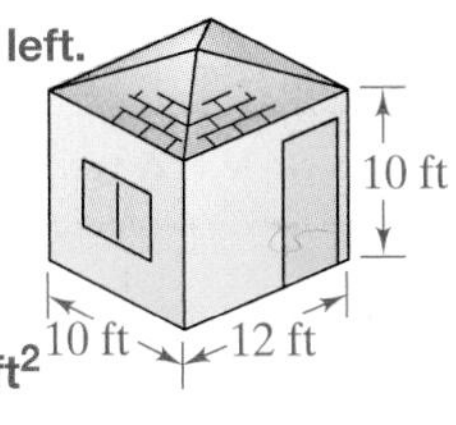

Reaching All Students

Below Level	Advanced Learners	
Below Level Give the number of lateral faces and the total number of faces for each solid: cube 4; 6 octagonal prism 8; 10	**Advanced Learners** Students work in pairs to draw prisms of 5, 6, 8, and 9 sides. They mark dimensions on their drawings. Then they find the lateral area of each prism.	**Inclusion** See note on page 489. **Diversity** See note on page 489.

2. Teach

Math Background

The sum of the areas of the surfaces of a solid is called the *surface area* (S.A.). The sum of the area of the lateral surfaces, excluding the bases, is called the *lateral area* (L.A.). For example, the lateral area of a cylindrical soup can is usually covered by a label.

Prism: L.A. = ph
(perimeter of base times height)
S.A. = L.A. + 2B
(B = area of one base)

Cylinder: L.A. = $2\pi rh$
(2π times radius times height)
S.A. = L.A. + 2B
(B = area of one base)

Teaching Notes

1 EXAMPLE Diversity
Discuss various ways of wrapping and presenting gifts in different cultures. For example, gifts in Japan are often wrapped in cloth.

Inclusion
Have students touch and name the lateral surfaces and the bases for various solid objects in the classroom.

2 EXAMPLE Error Prevention!
Make sure students understand that the surface area includes *all* the faces, including both bases and sides.

PowerPoint

Additional Examples

1. Use a net to find the surface area of this prism. 124 in.^2

2. Use a formula to find the surface area of a prism with bases made of squares that are 2 in. on a side and with a height of 3 in. 32 in.^2

3. Suppose you are going to paint the walls of a room with a floor measure of 11 ft by 12 ft and a 10 ft high ceiling. Find the lateral area of the room. 460 ft^2

4 EXAMPLE Visual Learners

Ask if the dimension shown in the picture is the diameter or the radius of the base. radius

5 EXAMPLE Alternative Method

Some students may realize that they can apply the Distributive Property to first add rh and r^2 and then multiply the sum by 2π.

PowerPoint

Additional Examples

4. Use a net to find the surface area of a cylinder that is 18.2 cm high with bases that have a radius of 5 cm. about 729 cm^2

5. Find the surface area needed to make a cylindrical can with a height of 7.2 cm. and a diameter of 3.96 cm. Give the answer to the nearest whole unit. 114 cm^2

Closure

- *How do you find the surface area of a prism?* Sample: Find the Lateral Area by multiplying the perimeter of the base by the height. Add the L.A. to the area of the two bases to find the S.A.
- *How do you find the surface area of a cylinder?* Sample: Find the Lateral Area by multiplying the circumference of the base ($2\pi r$) by the height. Add the L.A. to the area of the two bases to find the S.A.

OBJECTIVE

2 Finding Surface Areas of Cylinders

The rectangular label on the can is the lateral area of the can.

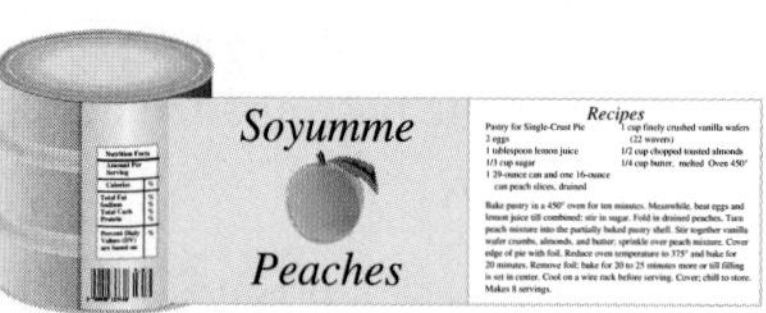

The height of the rectangle is the height of the can.

The base length of the rectangle is the circumference of the can.

4 EXAMPLE Using a Net to Find Surface Area of a Cylinder

Use a net to find the surface area of the cylinder.

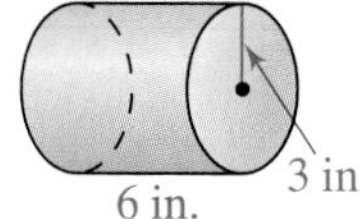

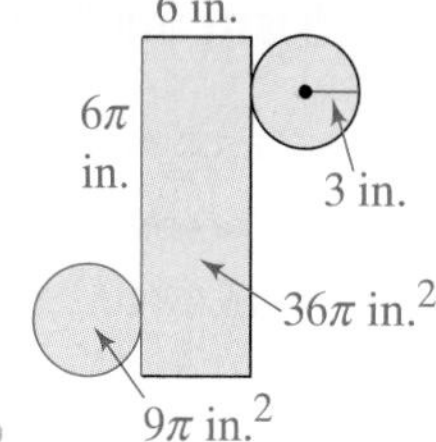

Draw a net of the cylinder, and find the area of each shape in the net.

S.A. $= 36\pi + 9\pi + 9\pi$ ← **Add the areas.**

$= 54\pi \approx 169.64$ ← **Simplify.**

The surface area of the cylinder is about 170 in.^{2}.

Check Understanding 4. Find the surface area of the cylinder if the height and radius are doubled. about 679 in.^{2}

Key Concepts **Lateral Area and Surface Area of a Cylinder**

The lateral area L.A. of a cylinder is the product of the circumference of the base and the height of the cylinder.

$$\text{L.A.} = 2\pi rh$$

The surface area S.A. of a cylinder is the sum of the lateral area and the area of the bases.

$$\text{S.A.} = \text{L.A.} + 2B$$

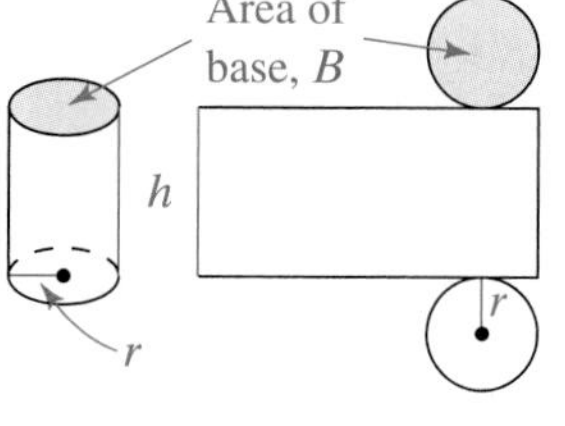

5 EXAMPLE Using the Cylinder Surface Area Formula

Need Help?

The formula for the circumference of a circle is $C = 2\pi r$.

The formula for the area of a circle is $A = \pi r^2$.

Find the surface area of the can below to the nearest square centimeter.

S.A. $=$ L.A. $+ 2B$ ← **cylinder surface area formula**

$= 2\pi rh + 2\pi r^2$ ← **L.A. $= 2\pi rh$; $B = \pi r^2$**

$= 2\pi(3.5)(11.5) + 2\pi(3.5^2)$ ← **Substitute.**

$= 105\pi \approx 329.87$ ← **Simplify.**

7 cm

BAKING POWDER

11.5 cm

The surface area of the can is approximately 330 cm^2.

✓ Check Understanding 5

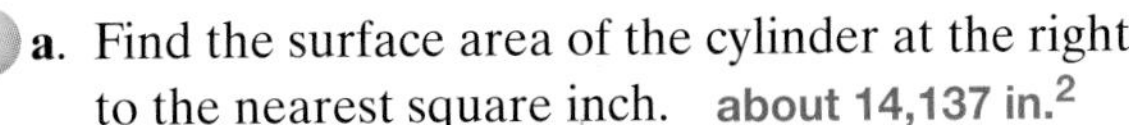
a. Find the surface area of the cylinder at the right to the nearest square inch. **about 14,137 in.²**

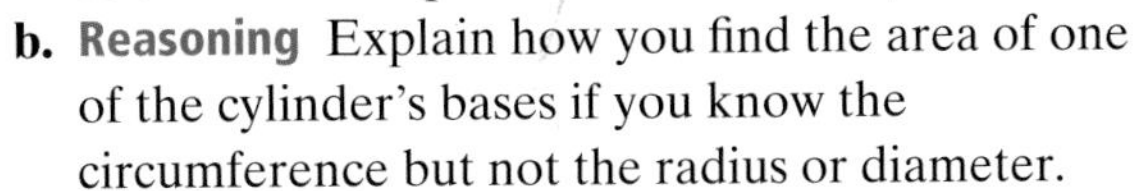
b. **Reasoning** Explain how you find the area of one of the cylinder's bases if you know the circumference but not the radius or diameter.

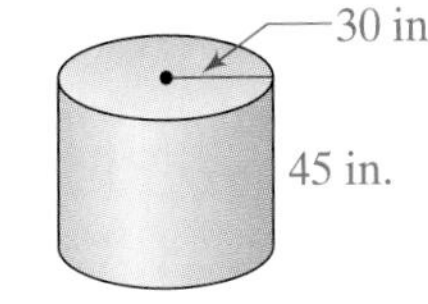

5b. Circumference divided by π is the diameter. Half of that is the radius. Square the radius and multiply by π.

EXERCISES

For more practice, see *Extra Practice*.

A Practice by Example

Example 1 (page 488)

Use each net to find the surface area of each prism.

1.

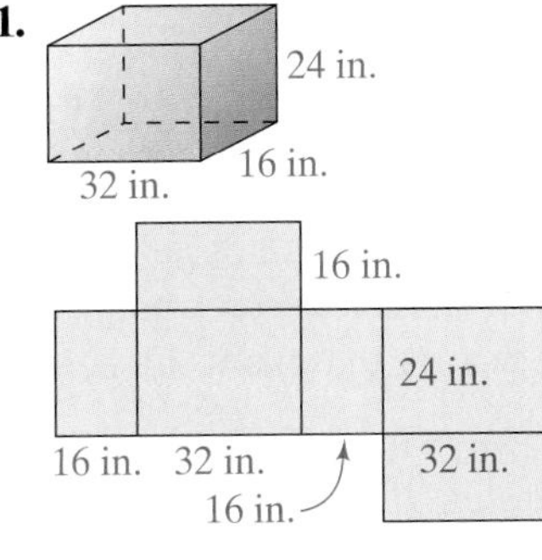

3,328 in.²

2.

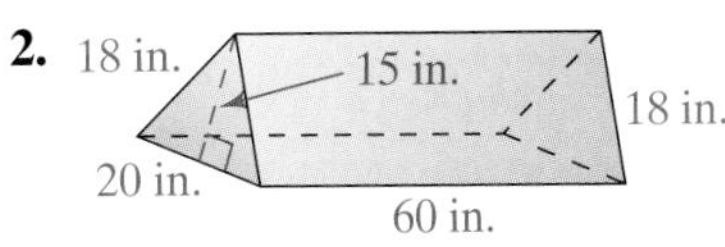

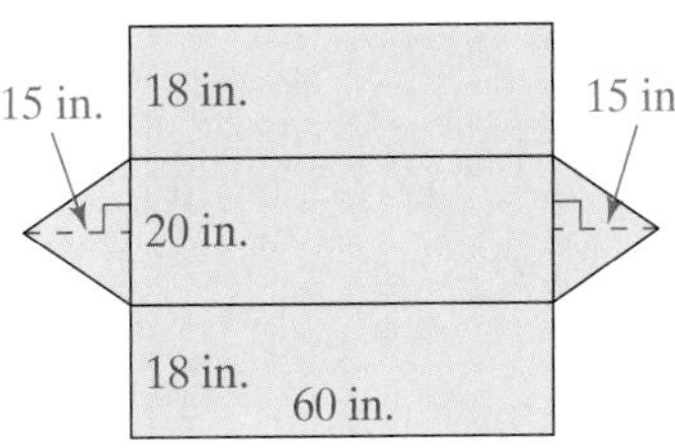

3,660 in.²

Example 2 (page 489)

Use a formula to find the surface area of each figure.

3.

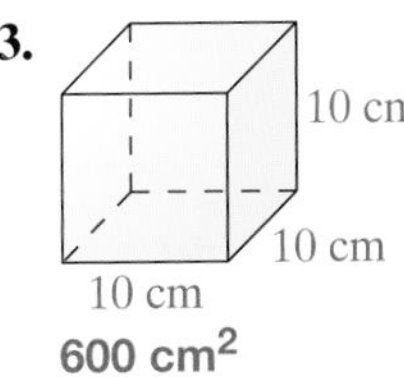

600 cm²

4.

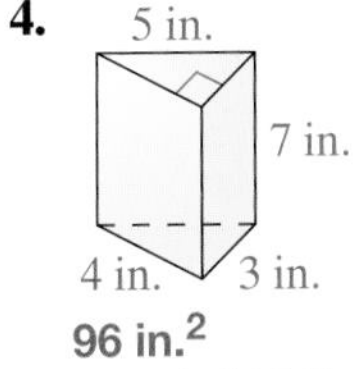

96 in.²

5.

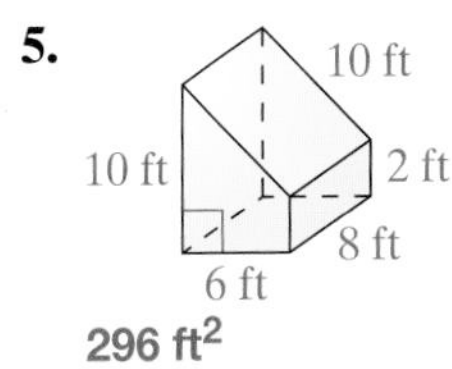

296 ft²

Example 3 (page 489)

6. **Cleaning** A cleaning company is bidding on a contract to clean the windows of the office building at the right. Find the lateral area of the outside of the building to estimate the area that will need to be cleaned. **20,790 ft²**

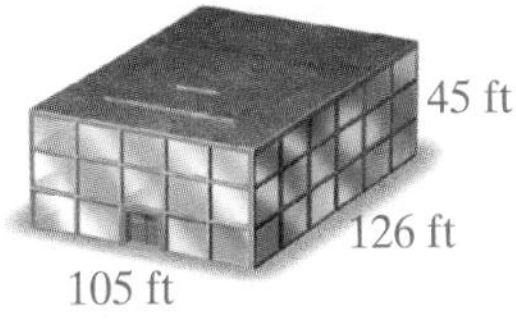

Example 4 (page 490)

Use each net to find the surface area to the nearest whole unit.

7.

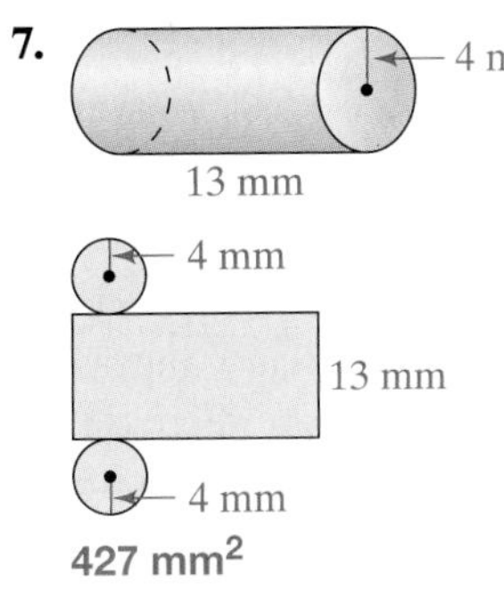

427 mm²

8.

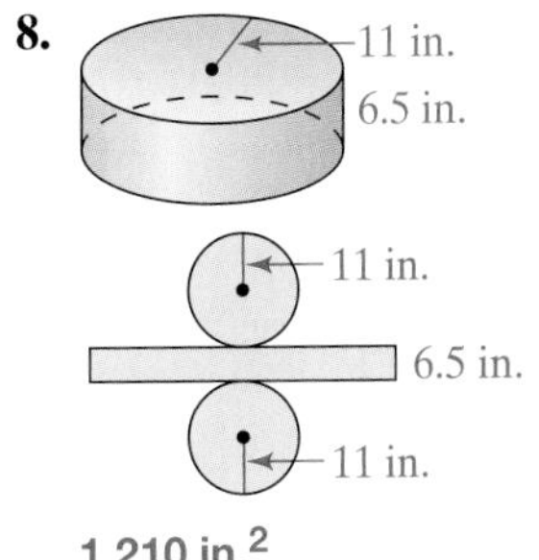

1,210 in.²

3. Practice

Assignment Guide

Objective 1

A B Core 1–6, 13–14, 17–19

C Extension 21

Objective 2

A B Core 7–12, 15–16

C Extension 20

Test Prep 22–25

Mixed Review 26–32

Business Connection

Exercise 6 Discuss the relationship between an estimate and the actual cost of a project.

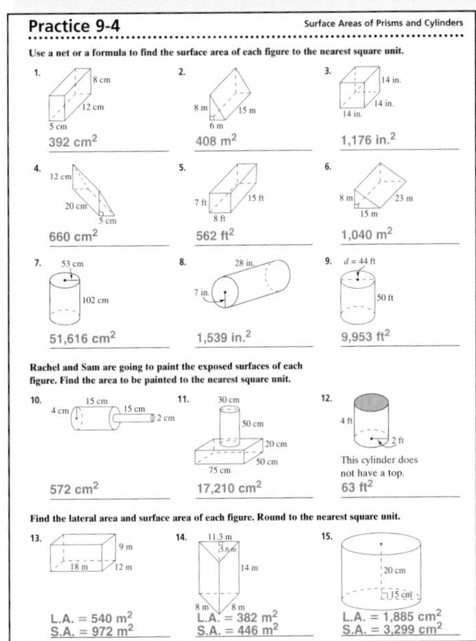

Practice 9-4 Surface Areas of Prisms and Cylinders

Use a net or a formula to find the surface area of each figure to the nearest square unit.

1. 392 cm²
2. 408 m²
3. 1,176 in.²
4. 660 cm²
5. 562 ft²
6. 1,040 m²
7. 51,616 cm²
8. 1,539 in.²
9. 9,953 ft²

Rachel and Sam are going to paint the exposed surfaces of each figure. Find the area to be painted to the nearest square unit.

10. 572 cm²
11. 17,210 cm²
12. This cylinder does not have a top. 63 ft²

Find the lateral area and surface area of each figure. Round to the nearest square unit.

13. L.A. = 540 m² S.A. = 972 m²
14. L.A. = 382 m² S.A. = 446 m²
15. L.A. = 1,885 cm² S.A. = 3,299 cm²

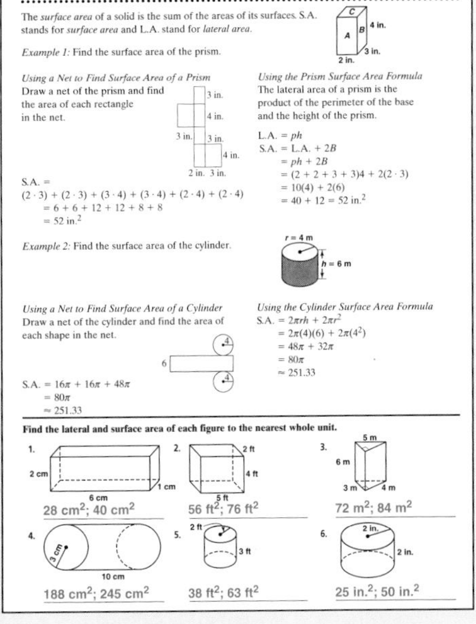

Reteaching 9-4 Surface Areas of Prisms and Cylinders

The *surface area* of a solid is the sum of the areas of its surfaces. S.A. stands for *surface area* and L.A. stand for *lateral area*.

Example 1: Find the surface area of the prism.

Using a Net to Find Surface Area of a Prism
Draw a net of the prism and find the area of each rectangle in the net.

S.A. =
$(2 \cdot 3) + (2 \cdot 3) + (3 \cdot 4) + (3 \cdot 4) + (2 \cdot 4) + (2 \cdot 4)$
$= 6 + 6 + 12 + 12 + 8 + 8$
$= 52$ in.²

Using the Prism Surface Area Formula
The lateral area of a prism is the product of the perimeter of the base and the height of the prism.

L.A. $= ph$
S.A. $=$ L.A. $+ 2B$
$= ph + 2B$
$= (2 + 2 + 3 + 3)4 + 2(2 \cdot 3)$
$= 10(4) + 2(6)$
$= 40 + 12 = 52$ in.²

Example 2: Find the surface area of the cylinder.

Using a Net to Find Surface Area of a Cylinder
Draw a net of the cylinder and find the area of each shape in the net.

S.A. $= 16\pi + 16\pi + 48\pi$
$= 80\pi$
≈ 251.33

Using the Cylinder Surface Area Formula
S.A. $= 2\pi rh + 2\pi r^2$
$= 2\pi(4)(6) + 2\pi(4^2)$
$= 48\pi + 32\pi$
$= 80\pi$
≈ 251.33

Find the lateral and surface area of each figure to the nearest whole unit.

1. 28 cm²; 40 cm²
2. 56 ft²; 76 ft²
3. 72 m²; 84 m²
4. 188 cm²; 245 cm²
5. 38 ft²; 63 ft²
6. 25 in.²; 50 in.²

Example 5 (page 490)

Use a formula to find each surface area to the nearest whole unit.

9. **10.** **11.**

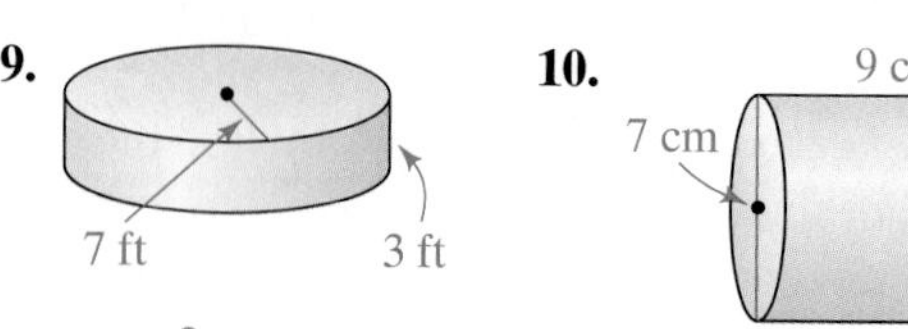

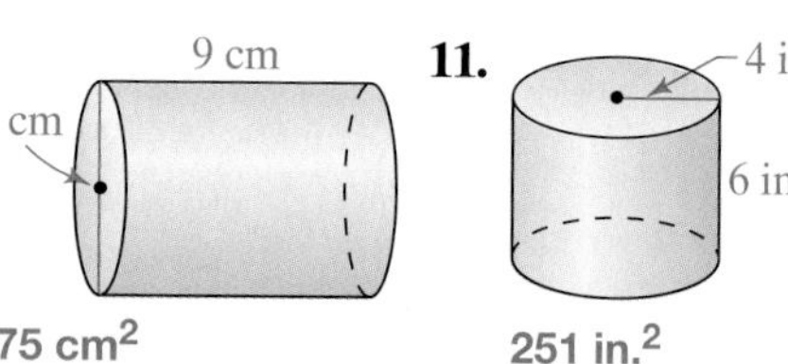

9. 440 ft^2 10. 275 cm^2 11. 251 in.^{2}

B Apply Your Skills

Find the lateral area and surface area of each figure to the nearest whole unit.

12. **13.** **14.**

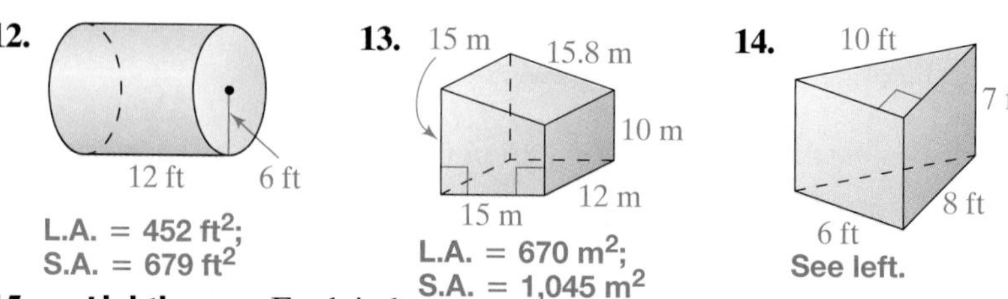

12. L.A. = 452 ft^2; S.A. = 679 ft^2
13. L.A. = 670 m^2; S.A. = 1,045 m^2
14. See left.

14. L.A. = 168 ft^2; S.A. = 216 ft^2

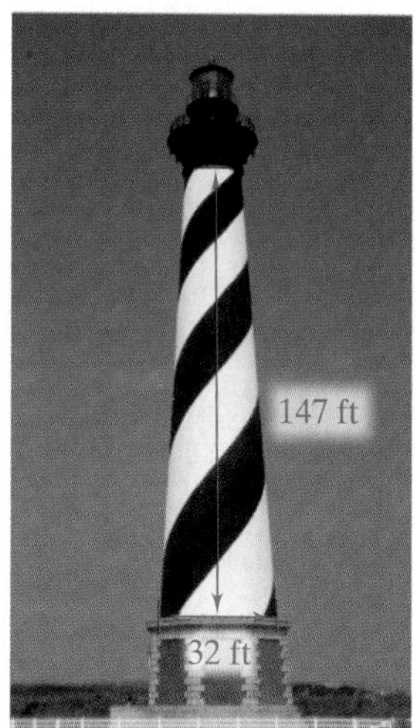

Real-World Connection

Painters need as much white paint as black paint to cover the Cape Hatteras Lighthouse.

15. a. Lighthouses Explain how you can estimate the lateral area of Cape Hatteras Lighthouse in North Carolina. See margin.

b. Estimation One gallon of paint covers 350 square feet. Estimate the number of gallons of black paint and the number of gallons of white paint necessary to repaint the lighthouse.

16. Writing in Math To find the surface area of a solid, you can draw a net and find the sum of the areas, or you can use a formula. Which method do you prefer? Why? See margin.

17. Packaging Which will require more cardboard to make: a box 9 cm by 5.5 cm by 11.75 cm, or a box 8 cm by 6.25 cm by 10.5cm? Explain. GPS See margin.

18. a. Copy and complete the table. See back of book.

Cube A		Cube B		Ratio	
Length of side	Surface area	Length of side	Surface area	Sides	Surface areas
1	6	2	24	$\frac{1}{2}$	$\frac{6}{24} = \frac{1}{4}$
2	■	5	■	■	■
3	■	6	■	■	■
3	■	8	■	■	■

b. Patterns What pattern do you see in the ratio of sides and ratio of surface areas for a cube? The ratio of the surface areas is the square of the ratio of sides.

19. Algebra Write an expression for the surface area of a rectangular prism that measures x ft by y ft by z ft. $2(xy + yz + xz)$

C Challenge

20. a. Would you expect the surface area of a rectangular prism with a cylindrical hole bored through it to increase or decrease? Explain. See margin.

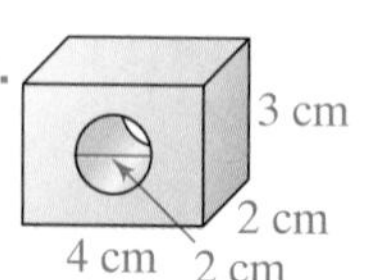

b. Find the surface area of the figure at the right. about 58.3 cm^2

15a. Treat the lighthouse as a cylinder. Multiply 3 × 30 × 150 to estimate the lateral area. L.A. ≈ 13,500 ft^2

b. about 20 gallons of black paint and 20 gallons of white paint

16. Answers may vary. Sample: Using a formula is preferable to using a net because using a formula is quicker.

17. The 9 cm by 5.5 cm by 11.75 cm box will require more cardboard because it has a greater surface area.

20a. It would most likely increase, because the reduction in surface area caused by the two openings in the surface would be more than offset by the increase caused by the walls of the hole. The exception would be if the radius were greater than the depth of the hole.

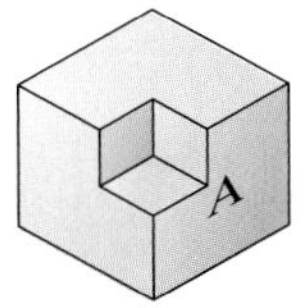

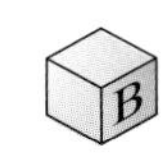

21. Stretch Your Thinking The drawing at the left shows cube A just after cube B was removed from one of cube A's corners. Before cube B was removed, the surface area of cube A was 150 cm^2. The surface area of cube B is 24 cm^2. What effect did removing cube B have on the surface area of cube A? Explain. None; the area of the three new surfaces in cube A is exactly the same as the area of the three old surfaces of cube B.

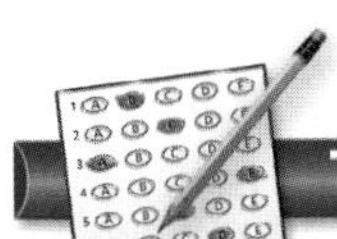

Test Prep

Gridded Response

Use the figure at the right for Exercises 22 and 23.

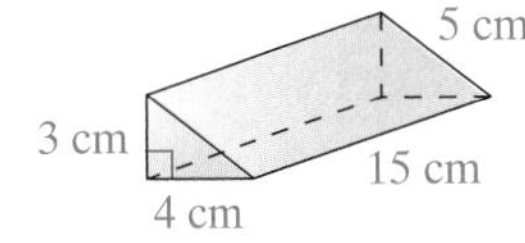

22. What is the lateral area in square centimeters of the triangular prism? 180

23. What is the surface area in square centimeters of the triangular prism? 192

Take It to the NET
Online lesson quiz at **www.PHSchool.com**
Web Code: aca-0904

24. A cube has a surface area of 337.5 ft^2. What is the length in feet of any one of its sides? 7.5

25. What is the surface area to the nearest square centimeter of a cylinder whose height is 19 cm and whose diameter is 10 cm? 754

Mixed Review

Lesson 8-1 **Find the measure of each angle.**

26. supplement of 62° 118°
27. complement of 78° 12°
28. complement of 15° 75°

Lesson 6-5 **Find each percent of decrease. Round to the nearest tenth of a percent.**

29. 34 to 22 35.3%
30. 456 to 92 79.8%
31. 100 to 85 15%
32. 675 to 634 6.1%

Math at Work

Landscape Architect

Landscape architects design residential areas, parks, shopping centers, golf courses, and college campuses. Their knowledge of geometry helps them prepare sketches and models of a proposed site. They also use their mathematical skills to estimate the costs of their projects.

Take It to the NET For more information about landscape architecture, go to **www.PHSchool.com.**
Web Code: acb-2031

GPS Use the Guided Problem Solving worksheet with Exercise 17.

4. Assess

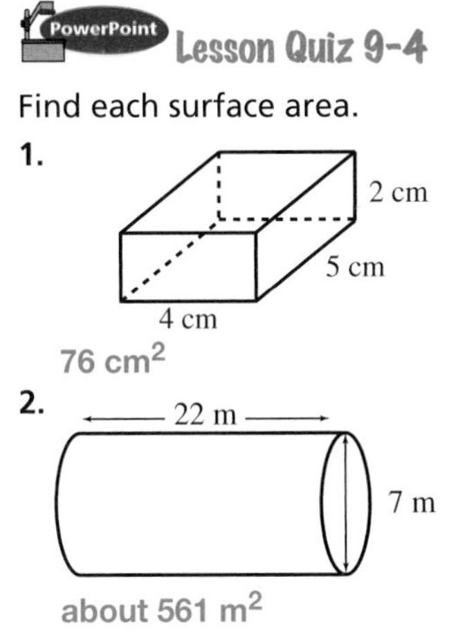

PowerPoint **Lesson Quiz 9-4**

Find each surface area.

1.

76 cm^2

2.

about 561 m^2

Alternative Assessment

Students compare surface areas of a cylinder whose radius and height are 10 cm, with that of a cube whose sides are 10 cm.
1,257 cm^2 > 600 cm^2

Test Prep

Resources
A sheet of blank grids is available in the *Test-Taking Strategies with Transparencies* booklet. Give copies of this sheet to students so they can practice filling in grids.

For additional practice with a variety of test item formats:
- Test Prep, p. 527
- Test-Taking Strategies, p. 523
- Test-Taking Strategies with Transparencies

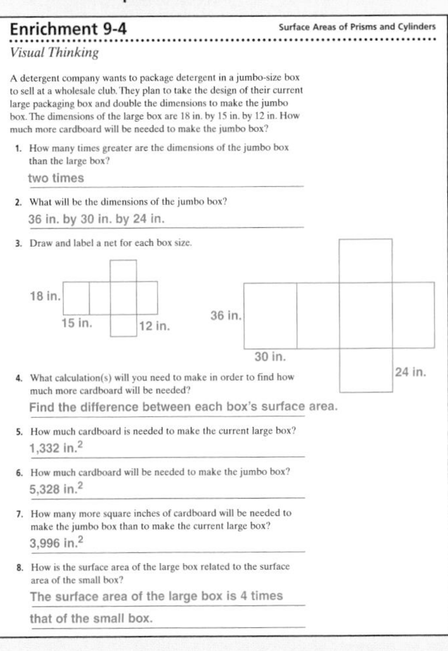

Enrichment 9-4 Surface Areas of Prisms and Cylinders

Visual Thinking

A detergent company wants to package detergent in a jumbo-size box to sell at a wholesale club. They plan to take the design of their current large packaging box and double the dimensions to make the jumbo box. The dimensions of the large box are 18 in. by 15 in. by 12 in. How much more cardboard will be needed to make the jumbo box?

1. How many times greater are the dimensions of the jumbo box than the large box?
two times
2. What will be the dimensions of the jumbo box?
36 in. by 30 in. by 24 in.
3. Draw and label a net for each box size.
18 in. 15 in. 12 in. 36 in. 30 in. 24 in.
4. What calculation(s) will you need to make in order to find how much more cardboard will be needed?
Find the difference between each box's surface area.
5. How much cardboard is needed to make the current large box?
1,332 $in.^2$
6. How much cardboard will be needed to make the jumbo box?
5,328 $in.^2$
7. How many more square inches of cardboard will be needed to make the jumbo box than to make the current large box?
3,996 $in.^2$
8. How is the surface area of the large box related to the surface area of the small box?
The surface area of the large box is 4 times that of the small box.

9-5

1. Plan

Lesson Preview

Check Skills You'll Need

Finding the Area of Polygons
Lesson 8-7: Examples 1–2. Extra Practice, p. 709.

Lesson Resources

Teaching Resources
Practice, Reteaching, Enrichment

Reaching All Students
Practice Workbook 9-5
Spanish Practice Workbook 9-5
Guided Problem Solving 9-5
Technology Activities 47

Presentation Assistant Plus!
Transparencies
- Check Skills You'll Need 9-5
- Problem of the Day 9-5
- Additional Examples 9-5
- Student Edition Answers 9-5
- Lesson Quiz 9-5
- Classroom Aid 11

PH Presentation Pro CD-ROM 9-5

Computer Test Generator CD

Technology
Resource Pro® CD-ROM
Computer Test Generator CD
PH Presentation Pro CD-ROM

www.PHSchool.com
Student Site
- Teacher Web Code: ack-5500
- Self-grading Lesson Quiz

PH SuccessNet Teacher Center
- Lesson Planner
- Resources

Plus

Surface Areas of Pyramids and Cones

What You'll Learn

To find the surface areas of pyramids

To find the surface areas of cones

. . . And Why

To find the amount of material needed to cover a pyramid, as in Example 3

Check Skills You'll Need

For help, go to Lesson 8-7.

Find the area of each figure to the nearest whole unit.

1. 

10 ft²

2. 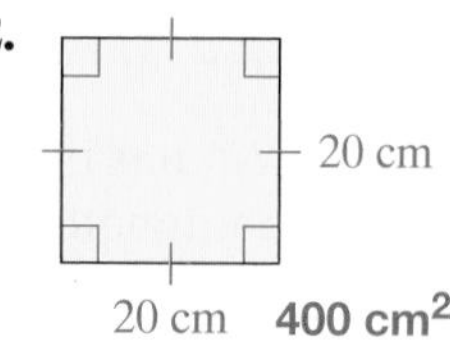

400 cm²

3. 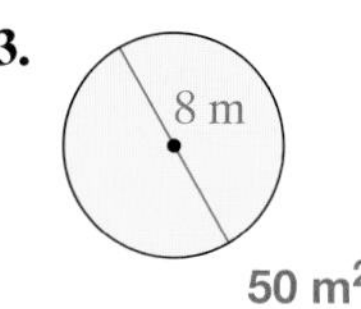

50 m²

New Vocabulary • slant height

OBJECTIVE 1

Interactive lesson includes instant self-check, tutorials, and activities.

Finding Surface Areas of Pyramids

The height of a pyramid is different from the height of its lateral faces. For this reason, the height of a pyramid's lateral faces is called the **slant height** and is indicated by the symbol ℓ.

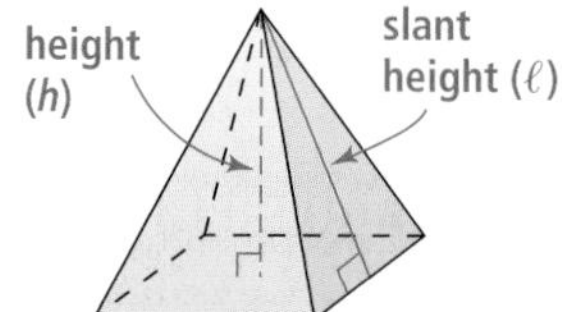

You can draw a net to find the surface area of a square pyramid. The four triangular faces are congruent isosceles triangles.

1 EXAMPLE Using a Net to Find the Surface Area

Find the surface area of the square pyramid at the right.

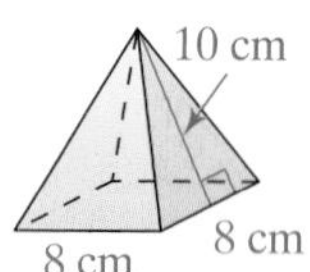

First draw a net of the pyramid.

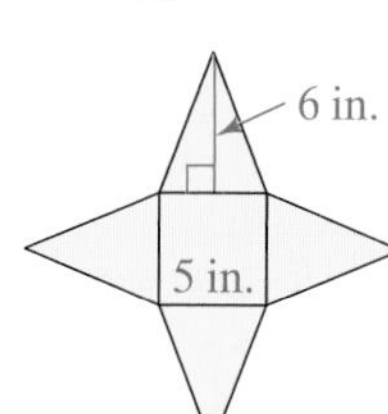

Then find the area of the faces and the base.

$$
\begin{aligned}
\text{S.A.} &= 4 \cdot \text{area of triangle} + \text{area of square} \\
&= 4 \cdot \tfrac{1}{2}bh + s^2 \\
&= 4 \cdot \tfrac{1}{2}(5 \cdot 6) + 5^2 \quad \leftarrow \textbf{Substitute.} \\
&= 60 + 25 \quad \leftarrow \textbf{Simplify.} \\
\text{S.A.} &= 85 \quad \leftarrow \textbf{Add.}
\end{aligned}
$$

The surface area is 85 in.².

1 Draw a net of the square pyramid at the right. Then find its surface area.

1. 10 cm, 8 cm

224 cm²

Ongoing Assessment and Intervention

Before the Lesson
Diagnose prerequisite skills using:
- Check Skills You'll Need

During the Lesson
Monitor progress using:
- Check Understanding
- Additional Examples
- Test Prep

After the Lesson
Assess knowledge using:
- Lesson Quiz
- Computer Test Generator CD

You can also use a formula to find the surface area of a square pyramid.

Key Concepts **Lateral Area and Surface Area of a Square Pyramid**

The lateral area L.A. of a square pyramid is four times the area of one of the lateral faces.

$$\text{L.A.} = 4 \cdot \left(\tfrac{1}{2}b\ell\right) = 2b\ell$$

The surface area S.A. of a square pyramid is the sum of the lateral area and the area of the base.

$$\text{S.A.} = \text{L.A.} + B$$

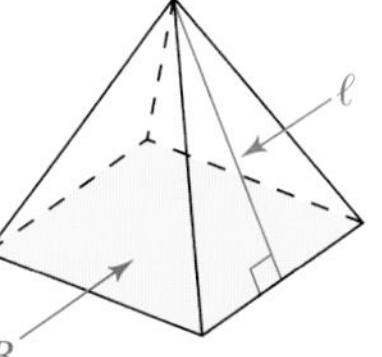

2 EXAMPLE Using the Pyramid Surface Area Formula

Use the formula for surface area of a square pyramid to find the surface area of the square pyramid at the right.

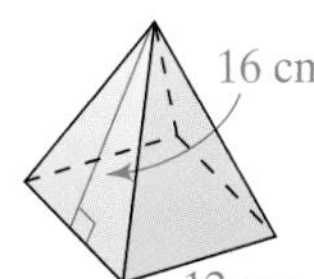

S.A. =	L.A.	+ B	← **surface area formula**
=	$2b\ell$	+ b^2	← **Substitute $2b\ell$ for L.A. Substitute b^2 for B.**
=	2(12)(16)	+ 12^2	← **Substitute.**
=	384	+ 144	← **Simplify.**
=	528		← **Add.**

The surface area is 528 cm^2.

Check Understanding 2 **a.** Use the formula for surface area of a square pyramid to find the surface area of the square pyramid at the right. 6,552 m^2

b. Reasoning Can you use this surface area formula to find the surface area of a triangular pyramid? Explain. See left.

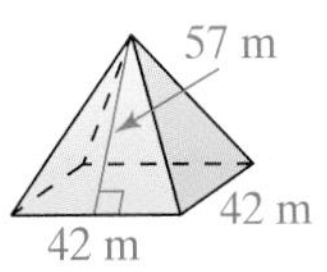

2b. Yes; the same formula will work, but you must use $\frac{1}{2}bh$ instead of b^2 to find B because the base of the pyramid is a triangle.

Sometimes, you only need to find the lateral area of a pyramid.

3 EXAMPLE Real-World Problem Solving

Architecture Find the lateral area of the Pyramid Arena in Memphis, Tennessee, shown at the right, to determine how much siding material the facility requires.

L.A. =	$2b\ell$	← **lateral area formula**
=	2(450)(367)	← **Substitute.**
=	330,300	← **Multiply.**

The lateral area of the Pyramid Arena is approximately 330,300 ft^2.

Real-World Connection

The Great Pyramid of Khufu in Egypt was the model for the Pyramid Arena.

Check Understanding 3 Find the lateral area of the Great Pyramid of Khufu, shown at the left. 922,610 ft^2

Reaching All Students

Below Level Have students sketch a square pyramid and a cone and identify the bases, the lateral faces, the slant height, and the perimeter (or circumference) of the bases.

Advanced Learners Have students make cones of various dimensions. For each cone, compare the height (perpendicular from vertex to base), slant height, and radius to verify that $\ell > h$, $\ell > r$, and $\ell^2 = h^2 + r^2$.

Inclusion See note on page 495.

Diversity See note on page 497.

2. Teach

Professional Development

Math Background

The height of one of a pyramid's lateral faces is called the *slant height*, or ℓ. For a square pyramid, each of the four faces is an isosceles triangle and the L.A. $= 4(\frac{1}{2}b\ell)$ or $2b\ell$ and the S.A. = L.A. + B, where B is the area of the base. For a cone, the L.A. $= \frac{1}{2}(2\pi r)\ell$ or $\pi r\ell$ and the S.A. = L.A. + B.

Teaching Notes

1 EXAMPLE Inclusion

For students who have difficulty visualizing solids from a drawing, provide models or have students build models. Have them write the measurements on pieces of tape to mark dimensions on the model.

2 EXAMPLE Auditory Learners

Many students will benefit from hearing the formulas repeated. Say formulas using the full terms, such as "lateral area" instead of "L.A."

3 EXAMPLE Error Prevention

Ask: *What do the* b *and the* ℓ *represent in this formula?* For each triangular face, the b is the base and ℓ is the slant height, or altitude.

PowerPoint

Additional Examples

1 Find the surface area of this square pyramid. 161 cm^2

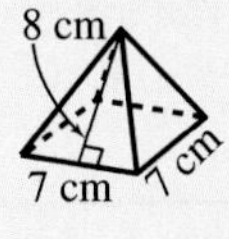

2 In order to buy paint to cover the inside of the roof and the floor of this playhouse, use the formula for S.A. of a square pyramid to find the area. 78 ft^2

3 Find the lateral area of the roof of the playhouse in Exercise 2 to determine the amount of roofing material needed. 42 ft^2

Technology Tip

On many calculators, π is a second function, so you will press the key marked 2nd before pressing the key marked π.

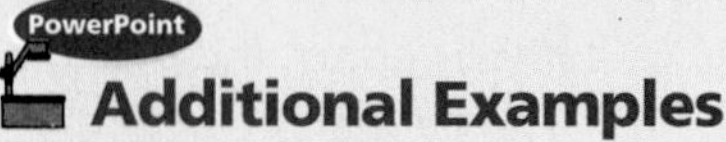

4 EXAMPLE Teaching Tip

Have students cut a cone-shaped paper drinking cup along a slant height. Then have them flatten it out to see the shape of the part of the net for the lateral area of a cone.

PowerPoint

Additional Examples

4 Find the surface area of a cone with a radius of 9 ft and a slant height of 15 ft to the nearest whole unit. 679 ft^2

Closure

- *How do you find the surface area of a square pyramid?* Sample: Find the Lateral Area by multiplying four times the area of one of the lateral faces. Add the L.A. to the area of the base (s^2) to find the Surface Area.
- *How do you find the surface area of a cone?* Sample: Find the Lateral Area by multiplying one-half times the circumference of the base ($2\pi r$) times the slant height. Add the L.A. to the area of the base (πr^2) to find the Surface Area.

OBJECTIVE

2 Finding Surface Areas of Cones

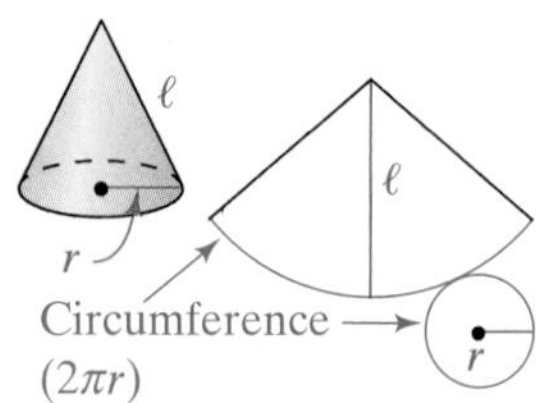

The curved surface of a cone is its lateral area. In the net at the left, the cone's lateral area may remind you of a triangle.

The height of the lateral area is the slant height ℓ. The base of the lateral area is the circumference of the circular base $2\pi r$.

You can substitute ℓ and $2\pi r$ in the formula for area of a triangle to find the lateral area of a cone.

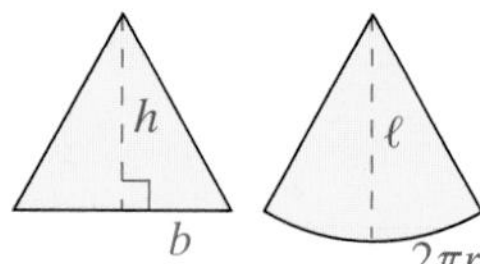

$A = \frac{1}{2}bh \quad$ L.A. $= \frac{1}{2}(2\pi r)\ell$

L.A. $= \frac{1}{2}bh$ ← **Use the triangle area formula.**

$= \frac{1}{2}(2\pi r)\ell$ ← **Substitute $2\pi r$ for b, and ℓ for h.**

$= \pi r\ell$ ← **Simplify.**

Key Concepts — Lateral Area and Surface Area of a Cone

The lateral area L.A. of a cone is one half the product of the circumference of the base and the slant height.

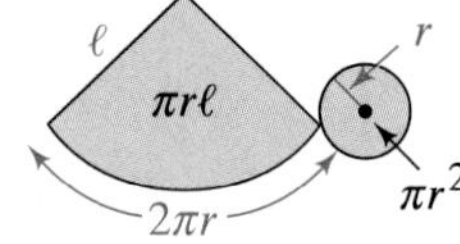

$$\text{L.A.} = \tfrac{1}{2}(2\pi r)\ell = \pi r\ell$$

The surface area S.A. of a cone is the sum of the lateral area and the area of the base.

$$\text{S.A.} = \text{L.A.} + B$$

4 EXAMPLE Using the Cone Surface Area Formula

Find the surface area of the cone to the nearest whole unit.

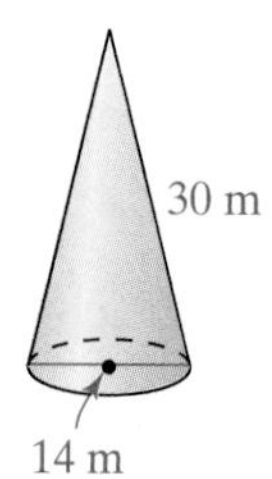

S.A. = L.A. + B ← **cone surface area formula**

$= \pi r\ell + \pi r^2$ ← **Substitute $\pi r\ell$ for L.A. Substitute πr^2 for B.**

$= \pi(7)(30) + \pi(7^2)$ ← **Substitute for r and ℓ.**

$= 210\pi + 49\pi$ ← **Use the order of operations.**

$= 259\pi$ ← **Add.**

≈ 813.67 ← **Use a calculator.**

To the nearest square meter, the surface area of the cone is 814 m^2.

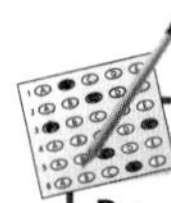

Test-Prep Tip

Be sure you use the proper formula and substitute correctly when solving geometry problems.

4b. No, because doubling the slant height doubles the lateral area but does not change the base area.

Check Understanding 4 **a.** Find the surface area of the cone at the right to the nearest whole unit. 113 yd^2

b. **Reasoning** Is the surface area doubled if the slant height of the cone is doubled? Explain.

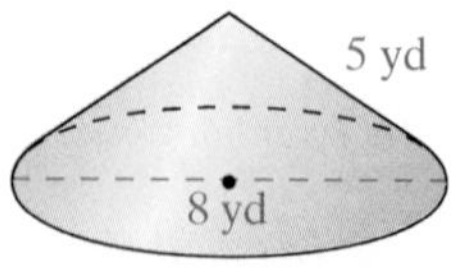

EXERCISES

For more practice, see *Extra Practice*.

A Practice by Example

Example 1 (page 494)

Use a net to find the surface area of each pyramid.

1. 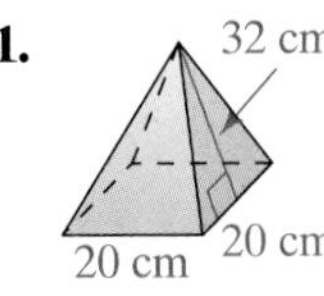

1,680 cm^2

2. 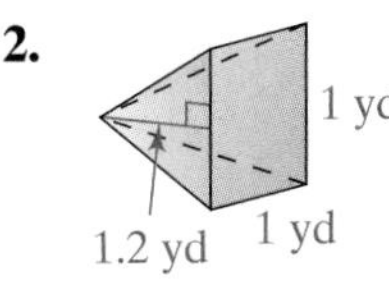

3.4 yd^2

3. 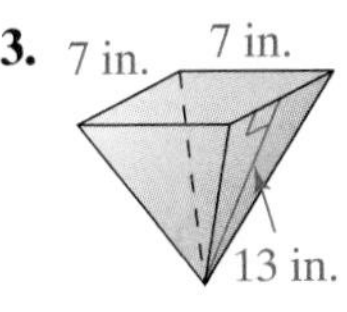

231 in.^{2}

Example 2 (page 495)

Use the formula for surface area of a square pyramid to find the surface area of each pyramid.

4. 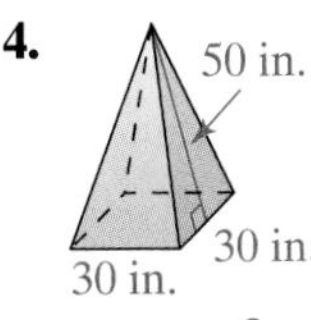

3,900 in.^{2}

5. 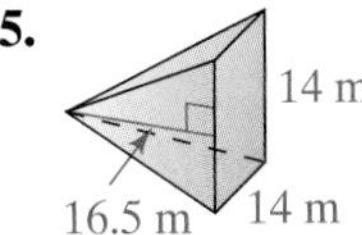

658 m^2

6. 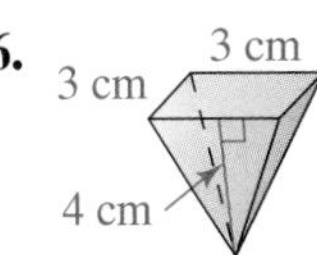

33 cm^2

Example 3 (page 495)

Find the lateral area of each pyramid to the nearest whole unit.

7. 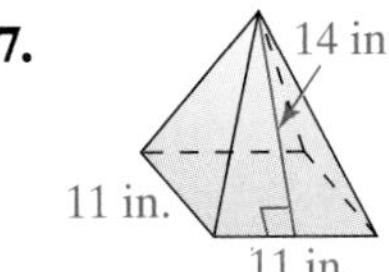

308 in.^{2}

8. 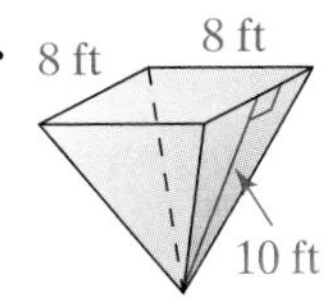

160 ft^2

9. 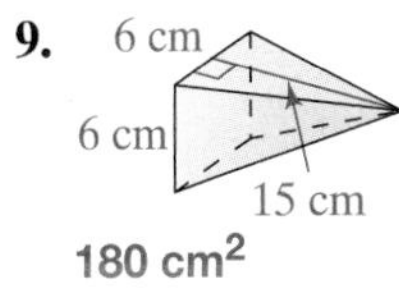

180 cm^2

10. Roofing You are helping your uncle put new shingles on the roof of the doghouse at the right. The roof is a square pyramid. Find the lateral area of the roof to determine how many square feet of shingles you need. 40 ft^2

Example 4 (page 496)

Find the surface area of each cone to the nearest whole unit.

11. 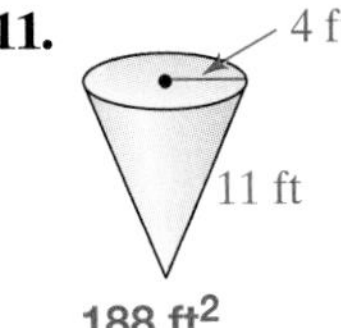

188 ft^2

12. 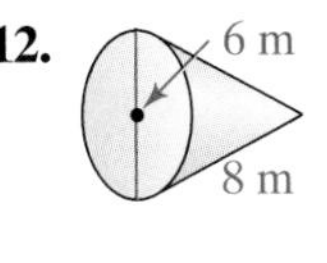

104 m^2

13. 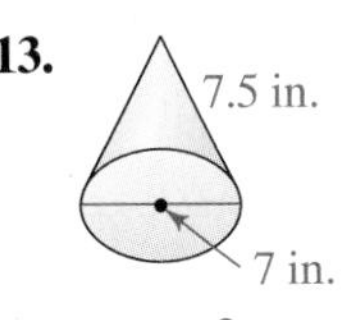

121 in.^{2}

B Apply Your Skills

Find the surface area of each figure to the nearest whole unit.

14. a square pyramid with a base-edge length of 24 in. and a slant height of 13 in. 1,200 in.^{2}

15. a cone with a radius of 4 m and a slant height of 14 m 226 m^2

16. 369 ft^2

16. a square pyramid with a base area of 81 ft^2 and a slant height of 16 ft

17. a cone with a diameter of 12 mm and a slant height of 14 mm 377 mm^2

3. Practice

Assignment Guide

Objective 1

A B Core 1–10, 14, 16,18, 25

C Extension 27, 30, 31

Objective 2

A B Core 11–13, 15, 17, 19–24, 26

C Extension 28–29, 32

Test Prep 33–38

Mixed Review 39–42

Diversity

Exercise 10 Some cultures do not treat dogs as valued pets.

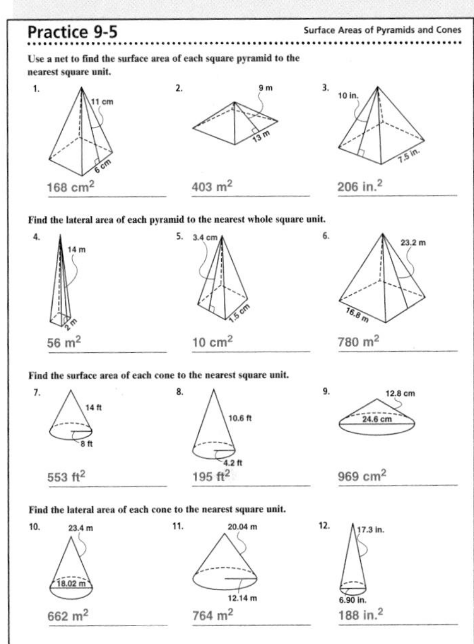

Practice 9-5 Surface Areas of Pyramids and Cones

Use a net to find the surface area of each square pyramid to the nearest square unit.

1. 11 cm, 6 cm — 168 cm^2
2. 9 m, 13 m — 403 m^2
3. 10 in., 7.5 in. — 206 in.^{2}

Find the lateral area of each pyramid to the nearest whole square unit.

4. 14 m, 2 m — 56 m^2
5. 3.4 cm, 1.5 cm — 10 cm^2
6. 23.2 m, 16.8 m — 780 m^2

Find the surface area of each cone to the nearest square unit.

7. 14 ft, 8 ft — 553 ft^2
8. 10.6 ft, 4.2 ft — 195 ft^2
9. 12.8 cm, 24.6 cm — 969 cm^2

Find the lateral area of each cone to the nearest square unit.

10. 23.4 m, 18.02 m — 662 m^2
11. 20.04 m, 12.14 m — 764 m^2
12. 17.3 in., 6.90 in. — 188 in.^{2}

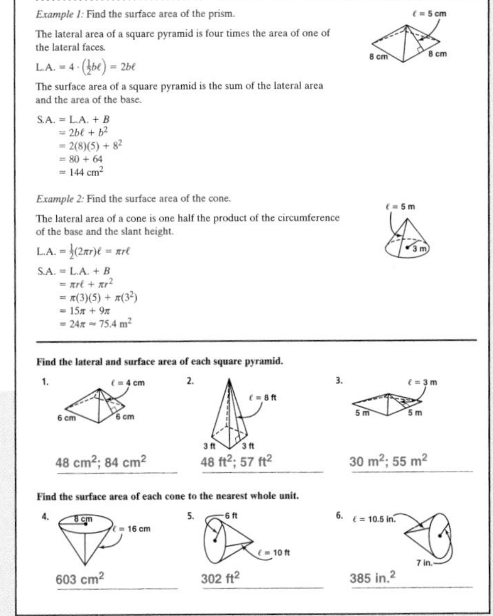

Reteaching 9-5 Surface Areas of Pyramids and Cones

Example 1: Find the surface area of the prism.

($\ell = 5$ cm, 8 cm, 8 cm)

The lateral area of a square pyramid is four times the area of one of the lateral faces.

$$\text{L.A.} = 4 \cdot \left(\tfrac{1}{2}b\ell\right) = 2b\ell$$

The surface area of a square pyramid is the sum of the lateral area and the area of the base.

$$\begin{aligned}\text{S.A.} &= \text{L.A.} + B \\ &= 2b\ell + b^2 \\ &= 2(8)(5) + 8^2 \\ &= 80 + 64 \\ &= 144\ \text{cm}^2\end{aligned}$$

Example 2: Find the surface area of the cone.

($\ell = 5$ m, 3 m)

The lateral area of a cone is one half the product of the circumference of the base and the slant height.

$$\text{L.A.} = \tfrac{1}{2}(2\pi r)\ell = \pi r\ell$$

$$\begin{aligned}\text{S.A.} &= \text{L.A.} + B \\ &= \pi r\ell + \pi r^2 \\ &= \pi(3)(5) + \pi(3^2) \\ &= 15\pi + 9\pi \\ &= 24\pi \approx 75.4\ \text{m}^2\end{aligned}$$

Find the lateral and surface area of each square pyramid.

1. $\ell = 4$ cm, 6 cm, 6 cm — 48 cm^2; 84 cm^2
2. $\ell = 8$ ft, 3 ft, 3 ft — 48 ft^2; 57 ft^2
3. $\ell = 3$ m, 5 m, 5 m — 30 m^2; 55 m^2

Find the surface area of each cone to the nearest whole unit.

4. 8 cm, $\ell = 16$ cm — 603 cm^2
5. 6 ft, $\ell = 10$ ft — 302 ft^2
6. $\ell = 10.5$ in., 7 in. — 385 in.^{2}

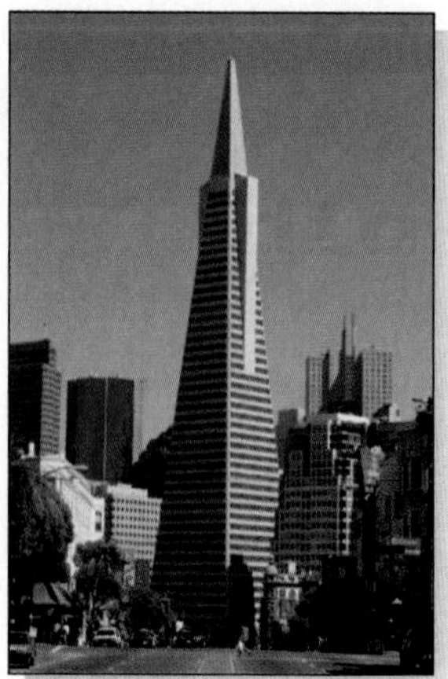

Real-World Connection

The tapered shape of the Transamerica building in San Francisco allows more sunlight to reach the street.

18. **Architecture** The Transamerica building in San Francisco is roughly a square pyramid with a height of 853 ft and a base-edge length of 145 ft.
   a. Find the slant height. 856 ft
   b. Find the lateral area. 248,240 ft^2
   c. **Reasoning** If you increase the height of a square pyramid without changing the base-edge length, what happens to the difference between its height and its slant height? Explain. See margin.

Find the lateral area of each cone to the nearest whole unit.

19. 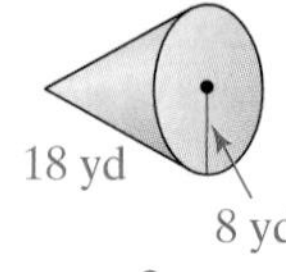

452 yd^2

20. 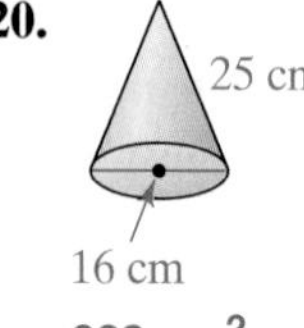

628 cm^2

21. 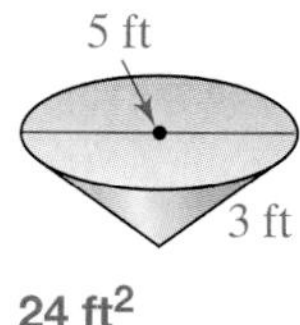

24 ft^2

22. **Writing in Math** Alicia says that if you double the radius and divide the slant height of a cone by two, the lateral area will stay the same. Do you agree? Explain. Yes, because $\pi r\ell = \pi(2r)\left(\frac{\ell}{2}\right)$.

23. The student used 8 for the radius, rather than 4; the correct solution is about 88 cm^2.

23. **Error Analysis** GPS A student tried to find the lateral area of the cone below. Explain his mistake at the right. Then find the correct solution.

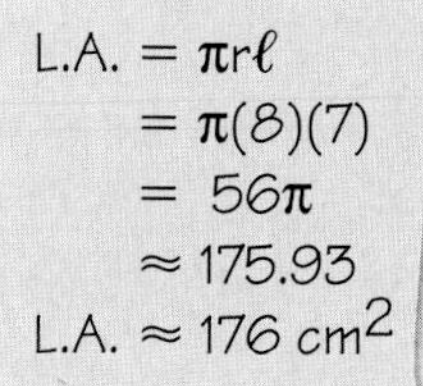

24. **Model Rockets** The nose cone on the model rocket at the right is one quarter of the rocket's overall length.
   a. Find the lateral area of the nose cone. 13 $in.^2$
   b. Find the lateral area of the body of the rocket. 75 $in.^2$

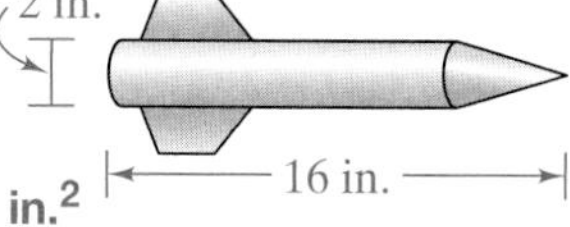

25a. Answers may vary. Sample: 270 m^2
b. 268 m^2

25. a. **Estimation** Estimate the lateral area of the square pyramid at the right.
   b. Find the actual lateral area to the nearest square meter.

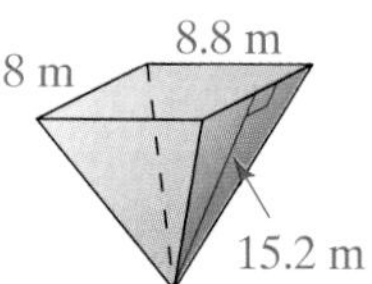

26. **Algebra** Corey uses the formula S.A. $= \pi r(r + \ell)$ to find the surface area of a cone. Will this always work? Explain. Yes, because it is equivalent to $\pi r^2 + \pi r\ell$.

Find the surface area of each solid to the nearest whole unit.

27. 

170 $in.^2$

28. 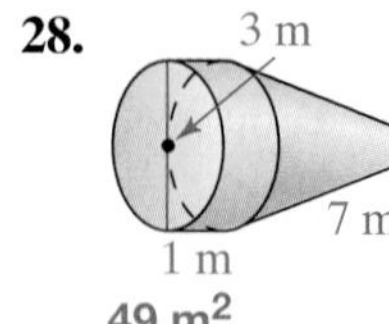

49 m^2

29. 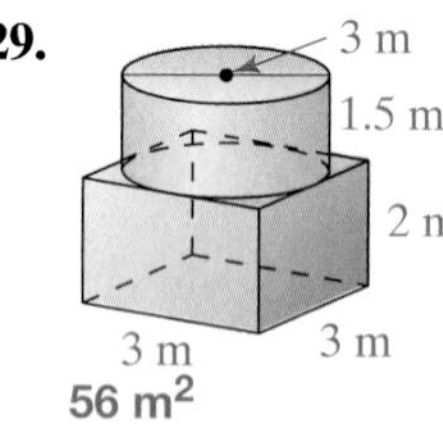

56 m^2

18c. The difference decreases. As the height of a pyramid increases, the slant height gets closer to vertical, and closer to the pyramid's overall height.

GPS Use the Guided Problem Solving worksheet with Exercise 23.

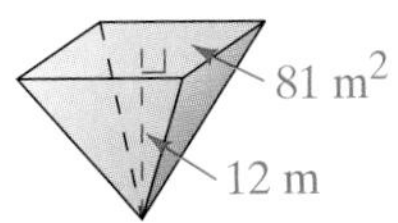

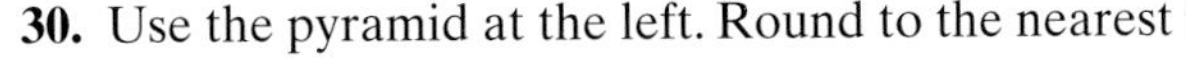

30. Use the pyramid at the left. Round to the nearest tenth.
- **a.** Find the slant height. 12.8 m
- **b.** Find the lateral area. 230.4 m^2
- **c.** Find the surface area. 311.4 m^2

31. 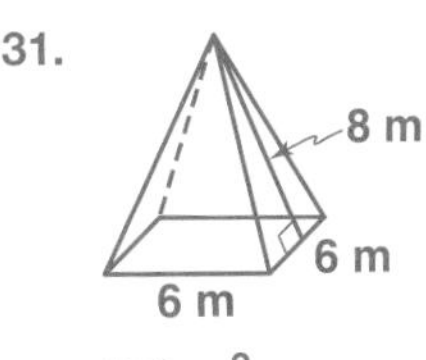

132 m^2

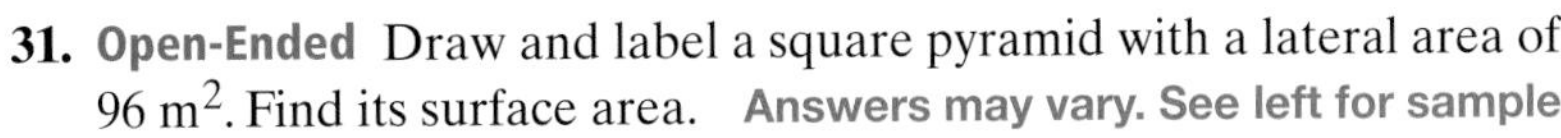

31. Open-Ended Draw and label a square pyramid with a lateral area of 96 m^2. Find its surface area. Answers may vary. See left for sample.

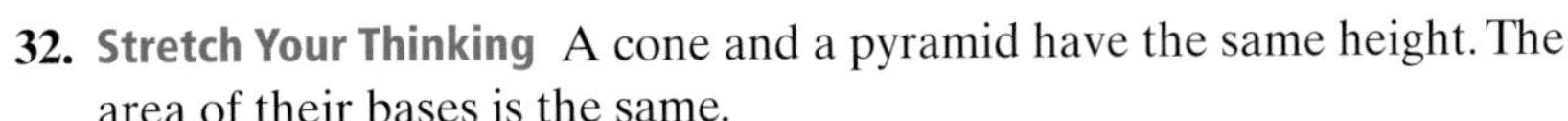

32. Stretch Your Thinking A cone and a pyramid have the same height. The area of their bases is the same.
- **a.** Which has the larger surface area? Explain. the pyramid
- **b.** Could one of them fit inside the other? Explain. No; answers may vary. Sample: The bases are different shapes with different dimensions. Neither base could be contained within the other because their areas are equal.

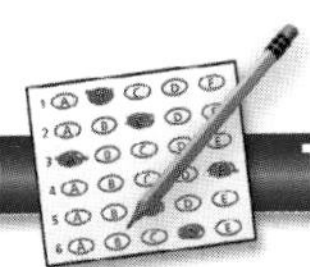

Test Prep

Multiple Choice

Refer to the figure at the right for Exercises 33–37.

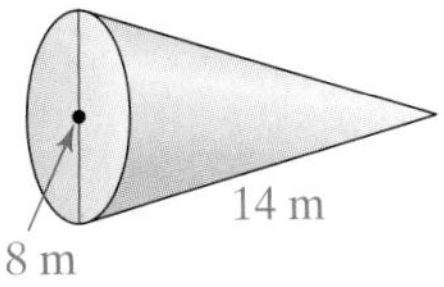

(Figure: cone labeled 8 m, 14 m)

33. What is the radius of the cone? B

A. 3.14 m	B. 4 m
C. 8 m	D. 14 m

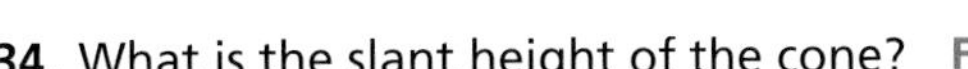

34. What is the slant height of the cone? F

F. 14 m G. 8 m H. 4 m I. 3.14 m

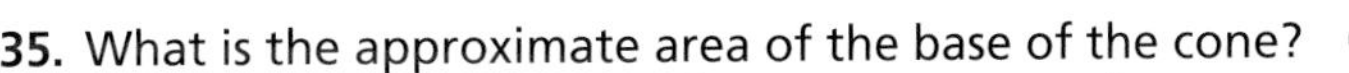

35. What is the approximate area of the base of the cone? C

A. 3 m^2 B. 25 m^2 C. 50 m^2 D. 112 m^2

36. What is the approximate lateral area of the cone? F

F. 176 m^2 G. 112 m^2 H. 56 m^2 I. 25 m^2

37. What is the approximate surface area of the cone? B

A. 176 m^2 B. 226 m^2 C. 703 m^2 D. 2,813 m^2

Take It to the NET
Online lesson quiz at **www.PHSchool.com**
Web Code: aca-0905

Short Response

38. Explain how to find the surface area of a square pyramid with a base-edge length of 19 ft and a slant height of 22 ft. See margin.

Mixed Review

39–41. See margin.

Lesson 8-9

39. Draw a segment $\overline{CD}$. Construct its perpendicular bisector.

40. Draw an acute angle. Construct its angle bisector.

41. Draw an obtuse $\angle K$. Construct $\angle L$ congruent to $\angle K$.

Lesson 8-3

42. List the congruent parts of the congruent triangles at the right. Then write a congruence statement.

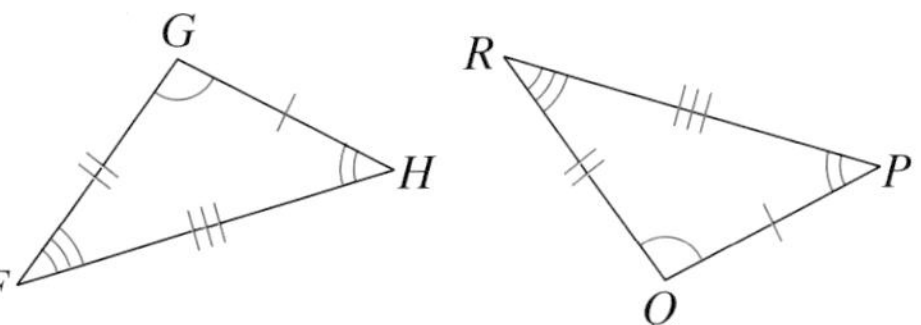

42. $\overline{FG} \cong \overline{RQ}$, $\overline{GH} \cong \overline{QP}$, $\overline{FH} \cong \overline{RP}$, $\angle F \cong \angle R$, $\angle G \cong \angle Q$, $\angle H \cong \angle P$; $\triangle FGH \cong \triangle RQP$

38. [2] Apply the formula S.A. $= 2b\ell + b^2$. Substituting, S.A. $= 2(19)(22) + 19^2$. Then S.A. $= 1{,}197$ ft^2.
[1] minor error, OR correct answer without work shown

39. 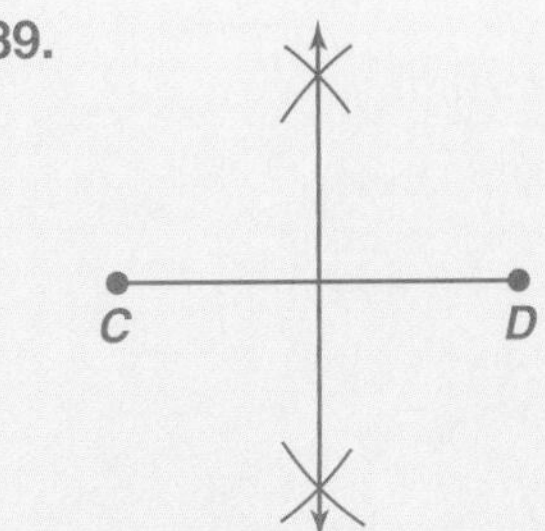

40. 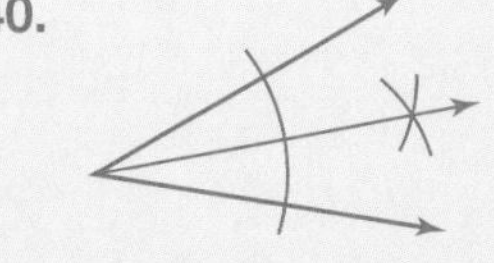

41. See back of book.

4. Assess

Lesson Quiz 9-5

Find each surface area to the nearest whole unit.

1. 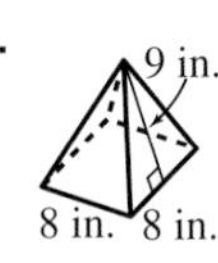

208 in.^{2}

2. 

176 ft^2

Alternative Assessment

Each student in a pair draws and labels measures for a cone and a square pyramid. Partners trade papers and find the surface area for each of their partner's figures.

Test Prep

Resources

For additional practice with a variety of test item formats:
- Test Prep, p. 527
- Test-Taking Strategies, p. 523
- Test-Taking Strategies with Transparencies

Exercise 35 Suggest that students round π to 3. The area, then, is a little greater than the product of 3 and 4^2.

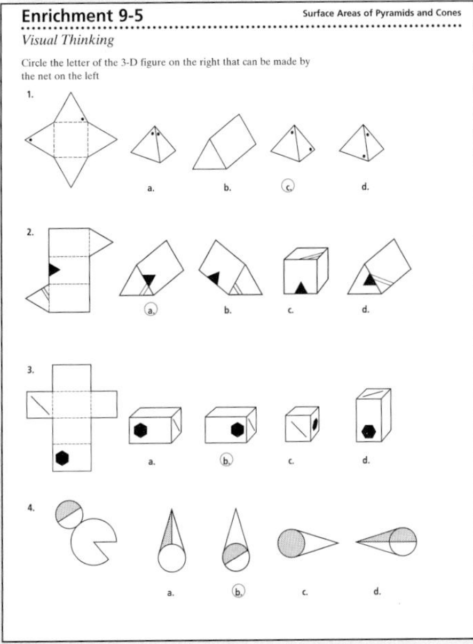

Enrichment 9-5 Surface Areas of Pyramids and Cones

Visual Thinking

Circle the letter of the 3-D figure on the right that can be made by the net on the left.

1. a. b. (c.) d.

2. (a.) b. c. d.

3. a. (b.) c. d.

4. a. (b.) c. d.

9-6

1. Plan

Lesson Preview

Check Skills You'll Need

Finding Surface Area of Prisms and Cylinders
Lesson 9-4: Examples 1–2, 4–5.
Extra Practice, p. 710.

Lesson Resources

Optional Materials
- unit cubes

Teaching Resources
Practice, Reteaching, Enrichment

Reaching All Students
Practice Workbook 9-6
Spanish Practice Workbook 9-6
Guided Problem Solving 9-6
Hands-On Activities 34, 38

Presentation Assistant Plus!
Transparencies
- Check Skills You'll Need 9-6
- Problem of the Day 9-6
- Additional Examples 9-6
- Student Edition Answers 9-6
- Lesson Quiz 9-6

PH Presentation Pro CD-ROM 9-6

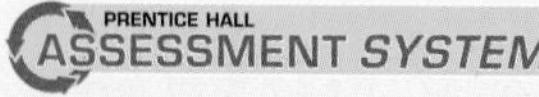

Computer Test Generator CD

Technology
Resource Pro® CD-ROM
Computer Test Generator CD
PH Presentation Pro CD-ROM

www.PHSchool.com
Student Site
- Teacher Web Code: ack-5500
- Self-grading Lesson Quiz

PH SuccessNet Teacher Center
- Lesson Planner
- Resources

Plus 

9-6 Volumes of Prisms and Cylinders

What You'll Learn

To find the volumes of prisms

To find the volumes of cylinders

. . . And Why

To find out how much room exists inside a tent, as in Example 1

Check Skills You'll Need

For help, go to Lesson 9-4.

Find the surface area of each figure to the nearest whole unit.

1. 4 cm, 4 cm, 4 cm — 96 cm²

2. 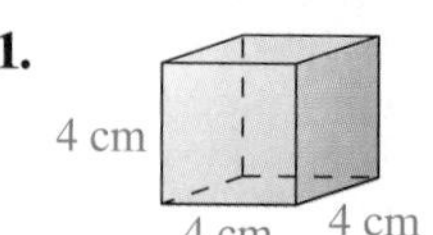

105 ft²

3. 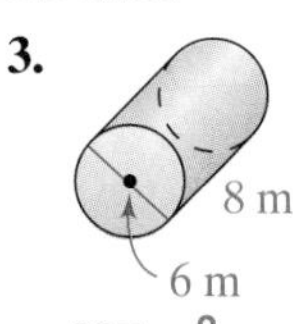

207 m²

New Vocabulary
- volume

Interactive lesson includes instant self-check, tutorials, and activities.

OBJECTIVE 1

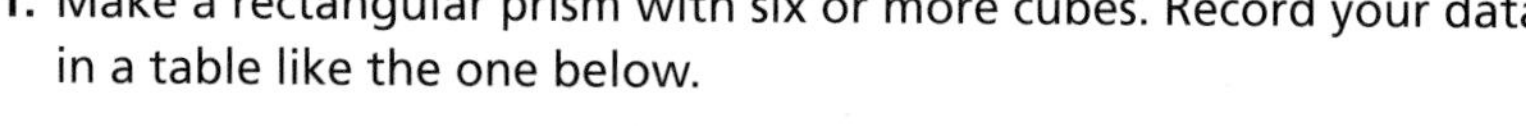

Finding Volumes of Prisms

Investigation: Looking at Rectangular Prisms

1–3a. Check students' work.

Use unit cubes to make rectangular prisms of different dimensions.

1. Make a rectangular prism with six or more cubes. Record your data in a table like the one below.

Base Dimensions	Base Area (square units)	Height	Number of Cubes in Prism
■ × ■	■	■	■

2. a. Make another prism with different dimensions.
   b. Record your data in the table.

3. a. Continue making prisms with different dimensions and recording data until you notice a pattern in the table.
   b. How do the base area and the height relate to the total number of cubes in a prism? Summarize your findings in one sentence. See left.

3b. The total number of cubes in a prism is equal to the product of the base area and the height.

Volume is the number of unit cubes, or cubic units, needed to fill a solid. A rectangular prism with a volume of 24 unit cubes appears above.

Key Concepts — Volume of a Prism

The volume V of a prism is the product of the base area B and the height h.

$$V = Bh$$

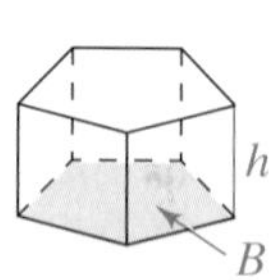

Ongoing Assessment and Intervention

Before the Lesson
Diagnose prerequisite skills using:
- Check Skills You'll Need

During the Lesson
Monitor progress using:
- Check Understanding
- Additional Examples
- Test Prep

After the Lesson
Assess knowledge using:
- Lesson Quiz
- Computer Test Generator CD

You can abbreviate a unit of volume such as cubic feet as ft^3.

1 EXAMPLE Finding Volume of a Triangular Prism

Camping How comfortable you are in a tent depends, in part, on how much room there is inside the tent. Find the volume of the tent at the left.

Real-World Connection

Tent manufacturers try to minimize surface area while maximizing volume.

Step 1 Find the area of the base.

$B = \frac{1}{2}bh$ ← **Use the triangle area formula.**

$= \frac{1}{2} \cdot 5 \cdot 4$ ← **Substitute 5 for *b*. For *h*, substitute 4, the height of the triangle.**

$= 10$ ← **Multiply.**

The area of the base is 10 ft^2.

Step 2 Use the base area to find the volume.

$V = Bh$ ← **Use the prism volume formula.**

$= 10 \cdot 7.5$ ← **Substitute 10 for *B*. For *h*, substitute 7.5, the height of the prism.**

$= 75$ ← **Multiply.**

The volume of the tent is 75 ft^3.

Check Understanding 1 Find the volume of each prism below.

a.

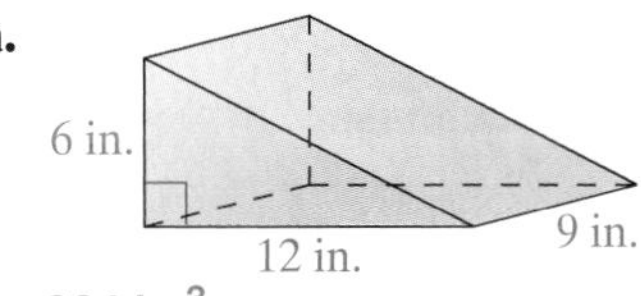

324 $in.^3$

b.

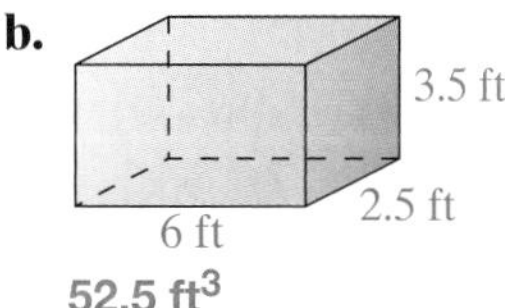

52.5 ft^3

c. **Reasoning** A rectangular prism has a base area of 50 m^2 and a height of 4.2 m. A triangular prism has the same base area and height. How do their volumes compare? Explain. They are the same, since the product of their base areas and their heights are the same.

OBJECTIVE

2 Finding Volumes of Cylinders

Finding the volume of a cylinder is similar to finding the volume of a prism. You multiply the base area of the cylinder by the cylinder's height.

Since the bases of cylinders are circles, you can use the formula for the area of a circle to find a cylinder's base area.

Key Concepts **Volume of a Cylinder**

The volume V of a cylinder is the product of the base area B and the height h.

$$V = Bh$$

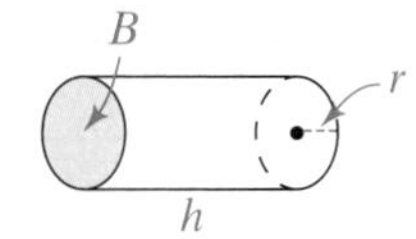

2. Teach

Math Background

The volume V of a prism is the product of the base area B and the height h, $V = Bh$. For a rectangular prism, this formula can also be written as $V = lwh$.

The volume of a cylinder is also the product of the base area B and the height h, $V = Bh$. The area of the circular base is given by $B = \pi r^2$ so the formula for the volume of a cylinder can also be written as $V = \pi r^2 h$.

Teaching Notes

Investigation (Optional)

Ask:

- *How many cubes are in the bottom layer of each rectangular prism?* lw
- *How many layers are in each rectangular prism?* h
- *How many cubes are in all the layers of each rectangular prism?* lwh

Discuss with the class whether it is possible to make a rectangular prism that contains an odd number of cubes. Yes, for example, a prism that is 3 × 5 × 7.

Error Prevention!

Some students may think that the base of a prism must be the face that is resting on a plane surface. Remind them that a prism has two bases that are in parallel planes, regardless of how the solid itself is turned or placed. This means that for the tent in Example 1, the face with the entrance is one of the bases.

1 EXAMPLE Diversity

Have students who have used tents tell how the height and the area of the base affect the users.

PowerPoint

Additional Examples

1 Find the volume of this prism. 14 cm^3

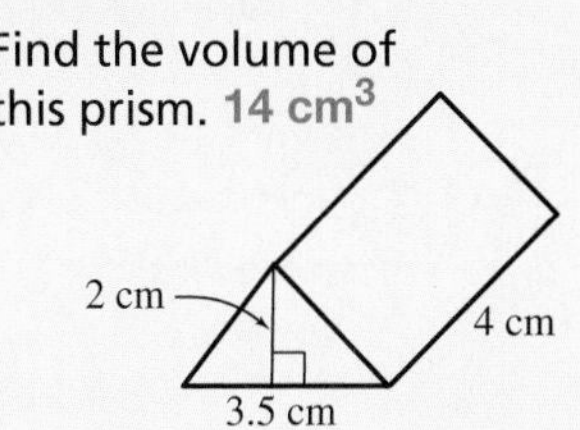

Reaching All Students

Below Level Have students explain volume in their own words. Have them point out examples in the classroom, such as the volume of a waste basket, a book, or a backpack.	**Advanced Learners** Ask students to decide whether they can make more different rectangular prisms with 12 or 15 unit cubes, and why. You can make more with 12, because 12 has more factors.	**Diversity** See note on page 501. **Tactile Learners** See note on page 502.

Auditory Learners
Ask students to recite any rhymes or memory devices they may know for remembering the formula for the area of a circle. For instance: "Pie are square" = πr^2; or "Pie are square. No, pie are round."

2 EXAMPLE Tactile Learners
Have students use circular chips to build cylinders. Discuss the fact that the total volume is the volume of one chip multiplied by how many chips high the cylinder is.

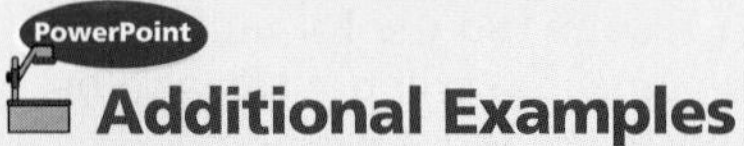

Additional Examples

2 Find the volume of a cylindrical cake that is 5 in. tall with a diameter of 15 in. Give your answer to the nearest whole unit. 884 in.^3

Closure

- *What is similar about finding the volume of prisms and the volume of cylinders?* Sample: For both, the volume is the product of the area of the base and the height, $V = Bh$.
- *What is different in the formulas for finding the volume of prisms and the volume of cylinders?* Sample: The area of the base of a cylinder is always πr^2 while the area of the base of a prism may use the formula for the area of a triangle, a rectangle, or other polygon.

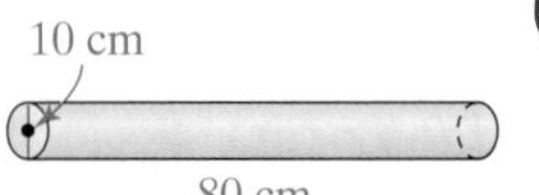

2 EXAMPLE Finding Volume of a Cylinder

Find the volume of the cylinder at the left to the nearest whole unit.

Step 1 Find the area of the base.

$B = \pi r^2$ ← circle area formula

$= \pi(5^2)$ ← Substitute.

≈ 78.53 ← Simplify.

The base area is about 78.53 cm^2.

Step 2 Use the base area to find the volume.

$V = Bh$ ← cylinder volume formula

$= 78.53 \cdot 80$ ← Substitute.

$= 6{,}282.4$ ← Multiply.

The volume of the cylinder is approximately 6,282 cm^3.

Reading Math
The abbreviation for cubic centimeters can be written as cc.

Check Understanding 2 Find the volume of a cylinder with a radius of 10 cm and a height of 75 cm. about 23,562 cm^3

More Than One Way

Find the volume of a cylinder with a height of 3 m and a radius of 8 m.

Nicole's Method

I can find the volume by finding the base area first and then multiplying the base area and the height.

$B = \pi r^2$ ← circle area formula

$= \pi(3^2)$ ← Substitute.

≈ 28.27 ← Simplify.

$V = Bh$ ← prism volume formula

$\approx 28.27 \cdot 8$ ← Substitute.

≈ 226.16 ← Multiply.

The volume is approximately 226 m^3.

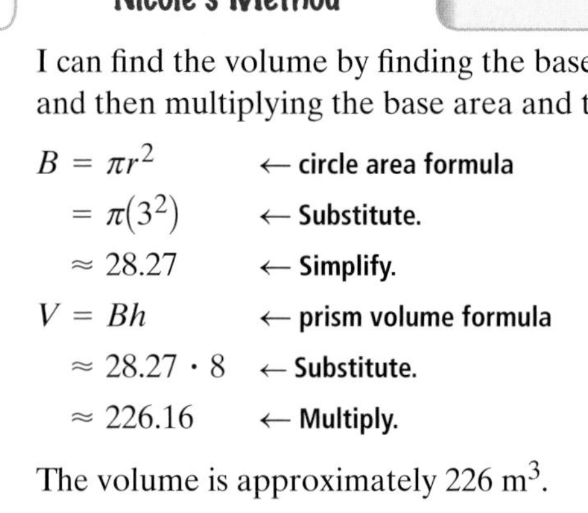

Daryl's Method

I can find the volume by combining formulas before substituting values.

$V = Bh$ ← cylinder volume formula

$= \pi r^2 h$ ← Substitute πr^2 for B.

$= \pi(3^2)(8)$ ← Substitute.

$= 72\pi$ ← Simplify.

≈ 226.19 ← Use a calculator.

The volume is approximately 226 m^3.

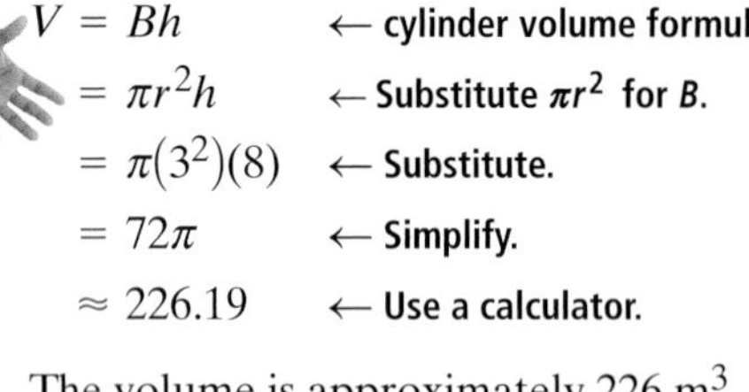

Choose a Method

Find the volume of a cylinder with a radius of 12 ft and a height of 4.5 ft. Explain why you chose the method you did.

Approximately 2,036 ft^3; check students' methods.

EXERCISES

For more practice, see *Extra Practice.*

A Practice by Example

Example 1 (page 501)

Find the volume of each prism.

1. 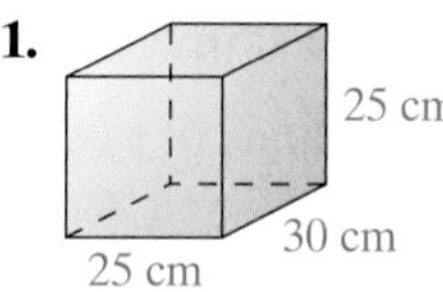

18,750 cm^3

2. 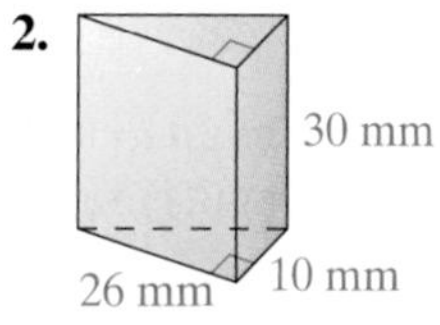

3,900 mm^3

3. 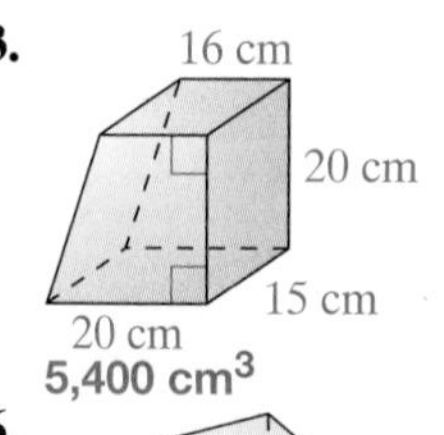

5,400 cm^3

4. 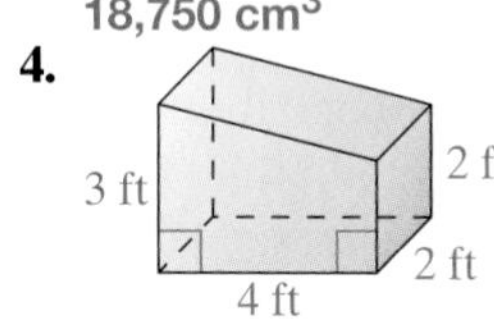

20 ft^3

5. 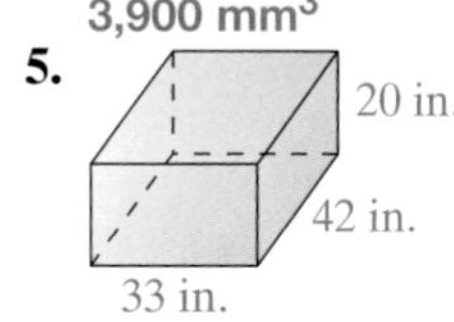

27,720 in.^{3}

6. 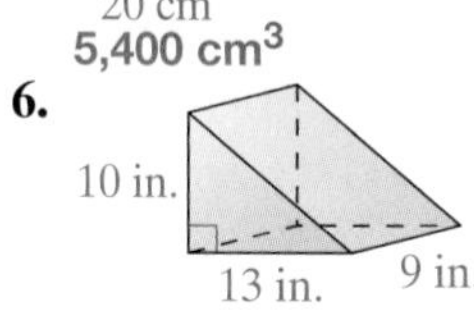

585 in.^{3}

7. **Goldfish Ponds** A goldfish pond in the shape of a triangular prism sits in the center of the local mall. Use the sketch at the right to find the volume of the pond. 784 ft^3

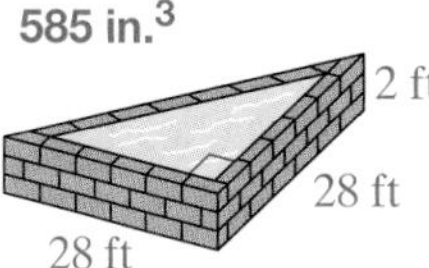

Example 2 (page 502)

Find the volume of each cylinder to the nearest whole unit.

8. 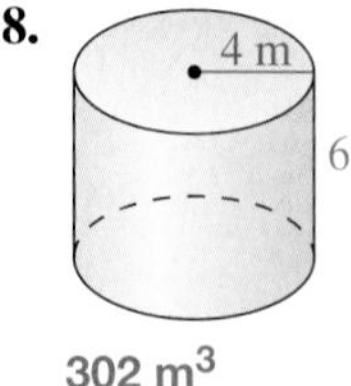

302 m^3

9. 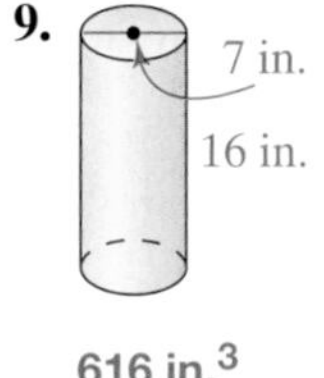

616 in.^{3}

10. 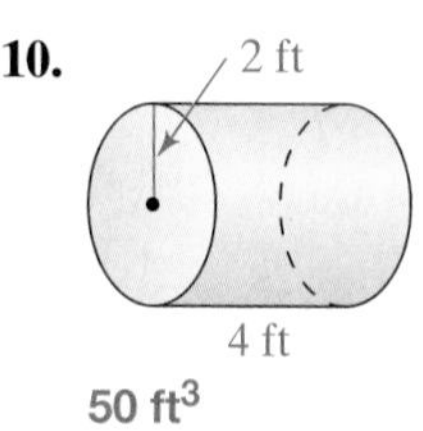

50 ft^3

B Apply Your Skills

Find the volume of each solid to the nearest whole unit.

11. a cylinder with a diameter of 11 ft and a height of 6.2 ft 589 ft^3

12. a rectangular prism measuring 6 mm by 8 mm by 7.2 mm 346 mm^3

Find the volume of each solid to the nearest whole unit.

13. 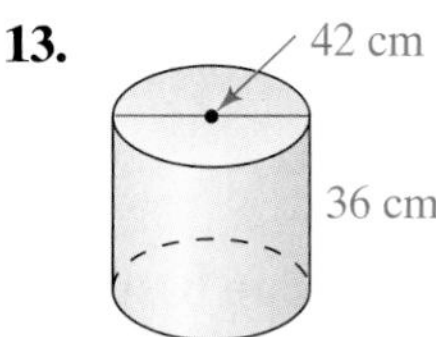

49,876 cm^3

14. 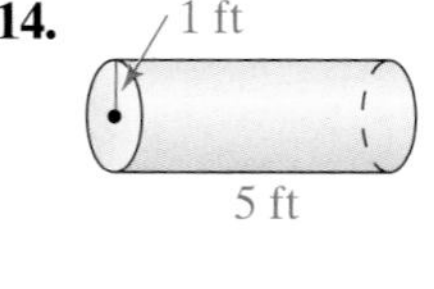

16 ft^3

15. 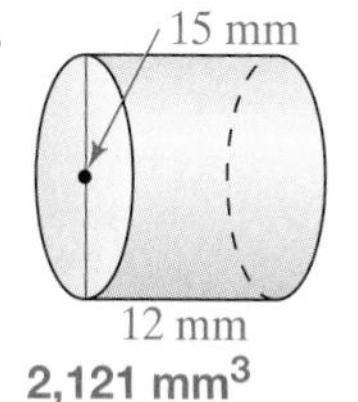

2,121 mm^3

16. **Estimation** Estimate the volume of a rectangular prism with the dimensions 7.92 cm by 6.14 cm by 3.1 cm. 144 cm^3

17. **Open-Ended** Draw and label the dimensions of two different rectangular prisms with a volume of 32 cubic units. Check students' work.

3. Practice

Assignment Guide

Objective 1

A B Core 1–7, 12, 16–19, 23, 24

C Extension 25–27

Objective 2

A B Core 8–11, 13–15, 20–22

C Extension 28

Test Prep 29–32

Mixed Review 33–41

Error Prevention!

Exercise 11 Remind students to use the radius, not the diameter.

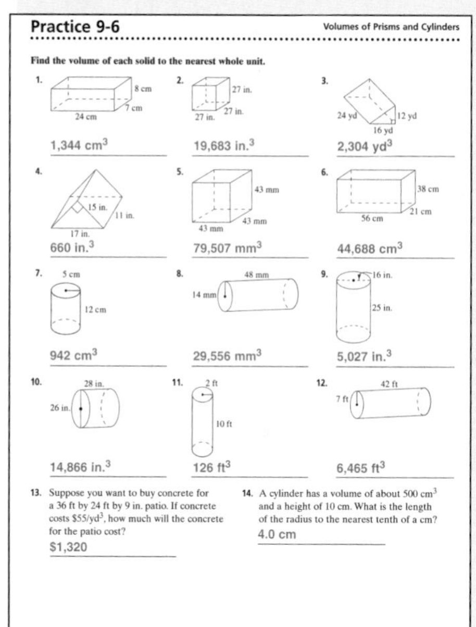

Practice 9-6 Volumes of Prisms and Cylinders

Find the volume of each solid to the nearest whole unit.

1. 24 cm, 7 cm, 8 cm — 1,344 cm^3
2. 27 in., 27 in., 27 in. — 19,683 in.^{3}
3. 24 yd, 16 yd, 12 yd — 2,304 yd^3
4. 15 in., 17 in., 11 in. — 660 in.^{3}
5. 43 mm, 43 mm, 43 mm — 79,507 mm^3
6. 56 cm, 21 cm, 38 cm — 44,688 cm^3
7. 5 cm, 12 cm — 942 cm^3
8. 48 mm, 14 mm — 29,556 mm^3
9. 16 in., 25 in. — 5,027 in.^{3}
10. 28 in., 26 in. — 14,866 in.^{3}
11. 2 ft, 10 ft — 126 ft^3
12. 42 ft, 7 ft — 6,465 ft^3

13. Suppose you want to buy concrete for a 36 ft by 24 ft by 9 in. patio. If concrete costs \$55/yd^3, how much will the concrete for the patio cost? $1,320

14. A cylinder has a volume of about 500 cm^3 and a height of 10 cm. What is the length of the radius to the nearest tenth of a cm? 4.0 cm

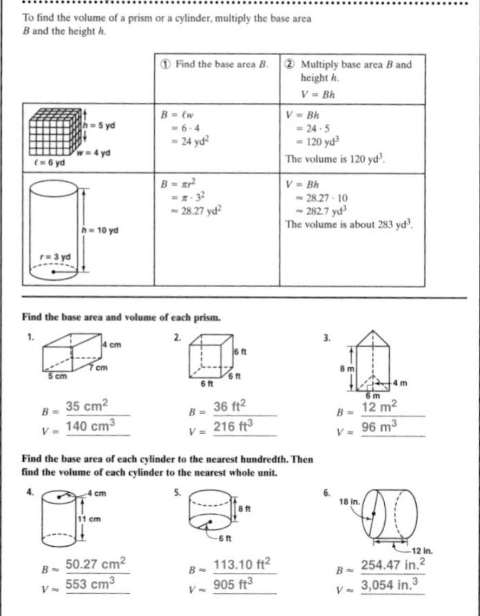

Reteaching 9-6 Volumes of Prisms and Cylinders

To find the volume of a prism or a cylinder, multiply the base area B and the height h.

	① Find the base area B.	② Multiply base area B and height h. $V = Bh$
h = 5 yd, w = 4 yd, ℓ = 6 yd	$B = \ell w$ $= 6 \cdot 4$ $= 24$ yd^2	$V = Bh$ $= 24 \cdot 5$ $= 120$ yd^3 The volume is 120 yd^3.
h = 10 yd, r = 3 yd	$B = \pi r^2$ $= \pi \cdot 3^2$ ≈ 28.27 yd^2	$V = Bh$ $\approx 28.27 \cdot 10$ ≈ 282.7 yd^3 The volume is about 283 yd^3.

Find the base area and volume of each prism.

1. 5 cm, 7 cm, 4 cm — B = 35 cm^2, V = 140 cm^3
2. 6 ft, 6 ft, 6 ft — B = 36 ft^2, V = 216 ft^3
3. 8 m, 6 m, 4 m — B = 12 m^2, V = 96 m^3

Find the base area of each cylinder to the nearest hundredth. Then find the volume of each cylinder to the nearest whole unit.

4. 4 cm, 11 cm — $B \approx$ 50.27 cm^2, $V \approx$ 553 cm^3
5. 8 ft, 6 ft — $B \approx$ 113.10 ft^2, $V \approx$ 905 ft^3
6. 18 in., 12 in. — $B \approx$ 254.47 in.^{2}, $V \approx$ 3,054 in.^{3}

Real-World Connection

Store managers use sales predictions to decide how much inventory to keep in stock.

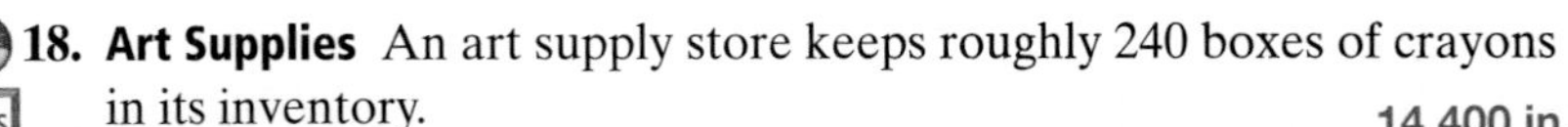

18. Art Supplies An art supply store keeps roughly 240 boxes of crayons in its inventory.

a. If each box measures 6 in. by 2.5 in. by 4 in., how many cubic inches of storage space does the store need for the boxes of crayons? **14,400 in.^{3}**

b. One cubic foot is equal to $(12 \text{ in.})^3$, or 1,728 in.^{3}. Find the number of cubic feet necessary for storing 240 boxes of crayons. **8.3 ft^3**

19. Mental Math Find the volume of a rectangular prism whose edge lengths are 2.5 m by 6 m by 5 m. **75 m^3**

20. Number Sense Which has a greater effect on the volume of a cylinder, doubling the radius or doubling the height? Explain. **See margin.**

21. Number Sense Ron estimated that the volume of the cylinder at the right is approximately 120 cm^3. Does his estimate make sense? Explain. **See margin.**

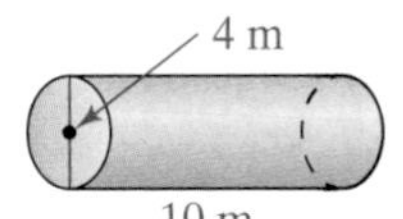

22. Writing in Math Explain how you would find the radius of a cylinder with a height of 20 in. and a volume of 565.5 in.^{3}.

22. **Answers may vary. Sample: Start with the equation $\pi r^2(20) = 565.5$. Divide each side by 20π, which results in $r^2 = 9.0002$. Take the square root of each side to find the radius. $r \approx 3$ in.**

23. Swimming Below are the top, front, and right views of the pool at the local Boys and Girls Club. Find the volume of the pool. **3,808 ft^3**

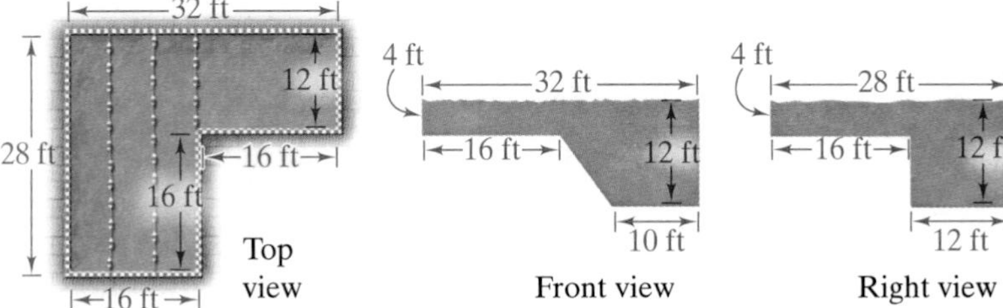

24. Algebra A rectangular prism with a volume of 48 cubic units has edge lengths that are in whole units. If one edge of the prism is 4 units, what are the possible combinations of lengths of the other two edges? **1 and 12, 2 and 6, 3 and 4**

C Challenge

Find the volume of each prism.

25. **26.**

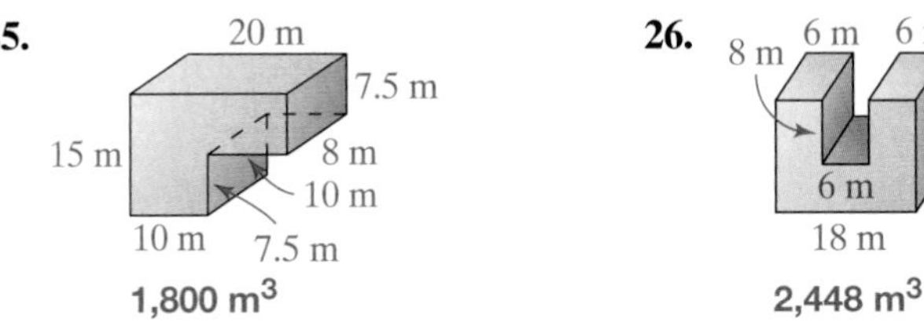

25. **1,800 m^3** 26. **2,448 m^3**

27. A rectangular prism has square bases and a height of 11 ft. Its lateral area is 308 ft^2. Find its volume. **539 ft^3**

28. Stretch Your Thinking A wedding cake consists of four layers. Each layer is in the shape of a cylinder and is 5 inches tall. The top layer has a 12-inch diameter. Each of the other layers has a diameter 2 inches greater than the layer above it. Find the volume of the wedding cake to the nearest in.^{3}. **3,613 in.^{3}**

Use the Guided Problem Solving worksheet with Exercise 18.

20. **doubling the radius, since the radius is squared in calculating the volume**

21. **yes; $\pi(2)^2 \cdot 10 \approx 3 \cdot 4 \cdot 10 = 120$**

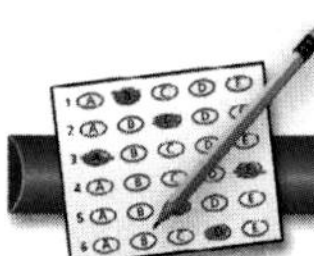

Test Prep

Reading Comprehension **Read the passage and answer the questions below.**

Salt of the Earth

Cylindrical cartons for salt were introduced in the early 1900s. They had the advantage of being stronger than boxes. A cylinder of salt can support a person standing on it. Years after cylinders became the standard for salt containers, the Leslie Salt Company decided to put its salt into boxes measuring 9 cm by 15 cm by 15 cm. They touted the fact that their container was a more efficient use of shelf space. Old habits die hard, though. The cylinders of salt sold out, while the boxes sat on the shelves.

29. What was the volume of the salt boxes manufactured by the Leslie Salt Company? C

A. 135 cm^3 **B.** 225 cm^3 **C.** 2,025 cm^3 **D.** 18,225 cm^3

Take It to the NET
Online lesson quiz at
www.PHSchool.com
Web Code: aca-0906

30. How tall would a cylindrical container with the same volume as a Leslie Salt Company box have to be if its base area were 162 cm^2? G

F. 9 cm **G.** 12.5 cm **H.** 15 cm **I.** 25 cm

31. Which of the following measurements CANNOT make a box with one half the volume of a Leslie Salt Company box? D

A. 4.5 cm by 15 cm by 15 cm **B.** 9 cm by 15 cm by 7.5 cm
C. 9 cm by 10 cm by 11.25 cm **D.** 4.5 cm by 7.5 cm by 7.5 cm

Short Response

32. Which gives a cylinder greater volume: a radius of 16 in. and a height of 20 in., or a radius of 20 in. and a height of 16 in.? Explain.
See margin.

Mixed Review

Lesson 8-5 **Classify each triangle by its sides and its angles.**

33. 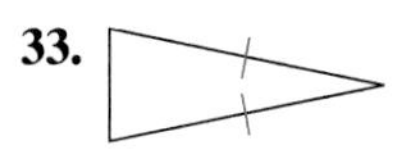
isosceles triangle

34. 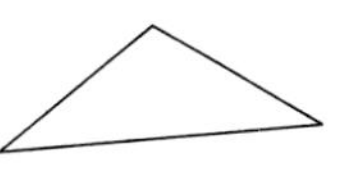
scalene triangle

35. 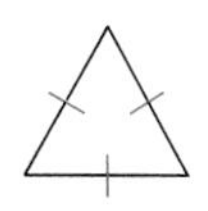
equilateral triangle

Lesson 8-2 **In the diagram below, $\ell \parallel m$. If $m\angle 3 = 34°$, find each angle measure.**

36. $m\angle 1$ 34° **37.** $m\angle 6$ 146°

38. $m\angle 2$ 146° **39.** $m\angle 7$ 34°

40. $m\angle 4$ 146° **41.** $m\angle 8$ 146°

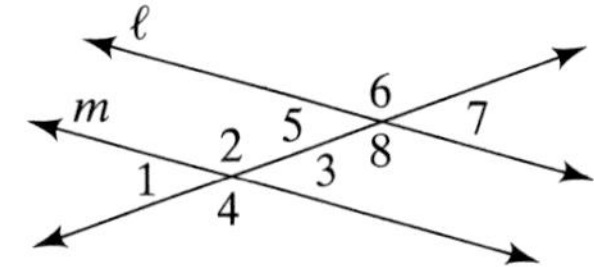

32. [2] A cylinder with a radius of 20 in. and a height of 16 in. has greater volume.
$(20)^2 \cdot \pi \cdot 16 > (16)^2 \cdot \pi \cdot 20$
[1] correct answer with incorrect or no explanation.

Alternative Assessment

Students find the volume of a square prism whose base is 3 in. on each side and whose height is 4 in. 36 in.^{3} They then find the height of a cylinder with the same volume and a radius of 2 in. $\frac{9}{\pi}$ in. or about 2.9 in.

4. Assess

Lesson Quiz 9-6

Find the volume.

1.

12 m
9 m
5 m

270 m^3

2.

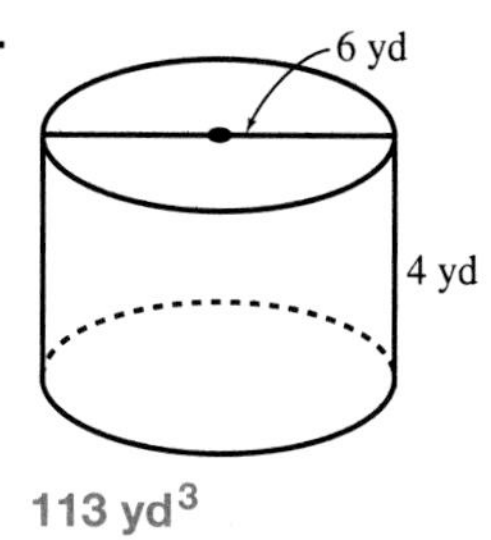

113 yd^3

Test Prep

Resources
For additional practice with a variety of test item formats:

- Test Prep, p. 527
- Test-Taking Strategies, p. 523
- Test-Taking Strategies with Transparencies

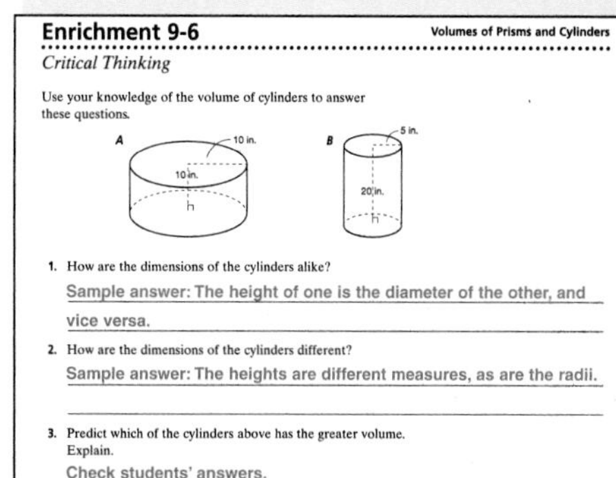

Enrichment 9-6 Volumes of Prisms and Cylinders
Critical Thinking

Use your knowledge of the volume of cylinders to answer these questions.

A 10 in. 10 in. h B 5 in. 20 in. h

1. How are the dimensions of the cylinders alike?
Sample answer: The height of one is the diameter of the other, and vice versa.

2. How are the dimensions of the cylinders different?
Sample answer: The heights are different measures, as are the radii.

3. Predict which of the cylinders above has the greater volume. Explain.
Check students' answers.

4. Calculate the volume of Cylinder *A*.
3,140 in.^{3}

5. Calculate the volume of Cylinder *B*.
1,570 in.^{3}

6. Which cylinder has the greater volume? Why do you think this is true?
Cylinder *A*; even though its height is only half the height of Cylinder *B*, the area of its base is four times greater, so the volume is greater.

7. Which cylinder has the greater surface area?
Cylinder *A*; its surface area is 1,256 in.^{2} Cylinder B's surface area is 785 in.^{2}.

9-7

1. Plan

Lesson Preview

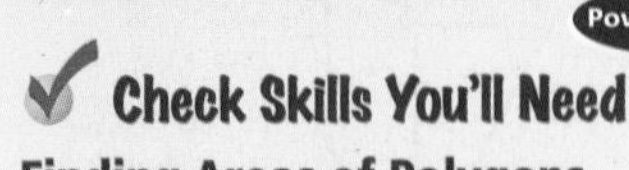

Finding Areas of Polygons
Lesson 8-7: Examples 1–2. Extra Practice, p. 709.

Lesson Resources

Teaching Resources
Practice, Reteaching, Enrichment

Reaching All Students
Practice Workbook 9-7
Spanish Practice Workbook 9-7
Guided Problem Solving 9-7
Technology Activities 48

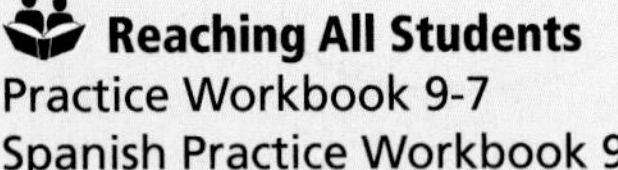

Transparencies
- Check Skills You'll Need 9-7
- Problem of the Day 9-7
- Additional Examples 9-7
- Student Edition Answers 9-7
- Lesson Quiz 9-7
- Classroom Aid 11

PH Presentation Pro CD-ROM 9-7

PRENTICE HALL ASSESSMENT SYSTEM

Computer Test Generator CD

Resource Pro® CD-ROM
Computer Test Generator CD
PH Presentation Pro CD-ROM

www.PHSchool.com
Student Site
- Teacher Web Code: ack-5500
- Self-grading Lesson Quiz

PH SuccessNet Teacher Center
- Lesson Planner
- Resources

Plus 

Volumes of Pyramids and Cones

What You'll Learn

To find the volumes of pyramids

To find the volumes of cones

. . . And Why

To create a design for a solid, as in Example 3

Check Skills You'll Need

For help, go to Lesson 8-7.

Find the area of each figure to the nearest whole unit.

1. 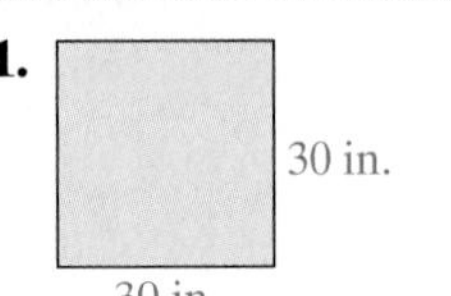

900 in.^{2}

2. 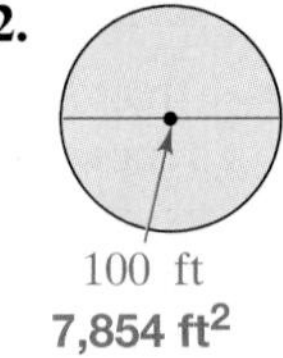

7,854 ft^2

3. 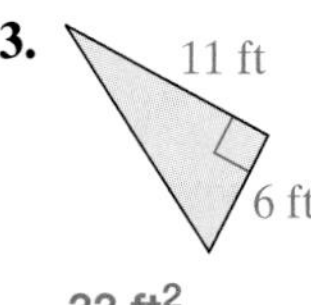

33 ft^2

Interactive lesson includes instant self-check, tutorials, and activities.

1 Finding Volumes of Pyramids

The amount of sand needed to fill a prism with base area B and height h will exactly fill three pyramids with the same base area and height.

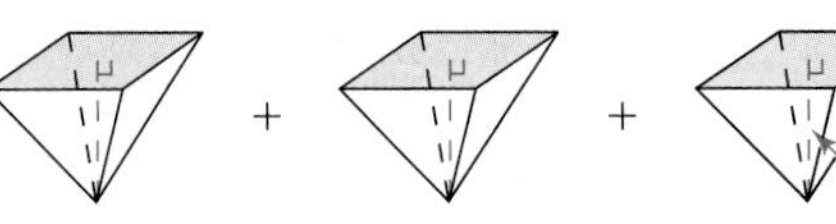

This relationship suggests the formula for the volume of a pyramid.

Key Concepts — Volume of a Pyramid

The volume V of a pyramid is one third the product of the base area B and the height h.

$$V = \frac{1}{3}Bh$$

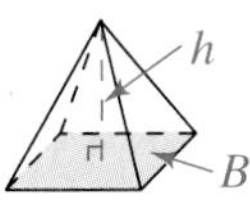

1 EXAMPLE Finding Volume of a Square Pyramid

Find the volume of the square pyramid at the left to the nearest whole unit.

5 m, 11 m, 5 m

Step 1 Find the area of the base.

$B = s^2$ ← area of a square formula
$= 5^2$ ← Substitute.
$= 25$ ← Simplify.

Step 2 Use the base area to find the volume.

$V = \frac{1}{3}Bh$ ← volume of a pyramid formula
$= \frac{1}{3}(25)11$ ← Substitute.
$= 91.66667$ ← Multiply.

The volume of the pyramid is approximately 92 in.^{3}.

Ongoing Assessment and Intervention

Before the Lesson	During the Lesson	After the Lesson
Diagnose prerequisite skills using:	Monitor progress using:	Assess knowledge using:
• Check Skills You'll Need	• Check Understanding	• Lesson Quiz
	• Additional Examples	• Computer Test Generator CD
	• Test Prep	

Check Understanding 1 a. Find the volume of the square pyramid at the right.
b. **Estimation** Estimate the volume of a square pyramid with a base-edge length of 6.1 m and a height of 3.8 m. 48 m^3

1a. 19,200 $in.^3$

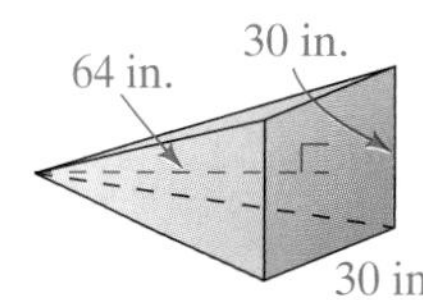

OBJECTIVE

2 Finding Volumes of Cones

As with pyramids and prisms, the contents of three cones with base area B and height h fill a cylinder with the same base area and height.

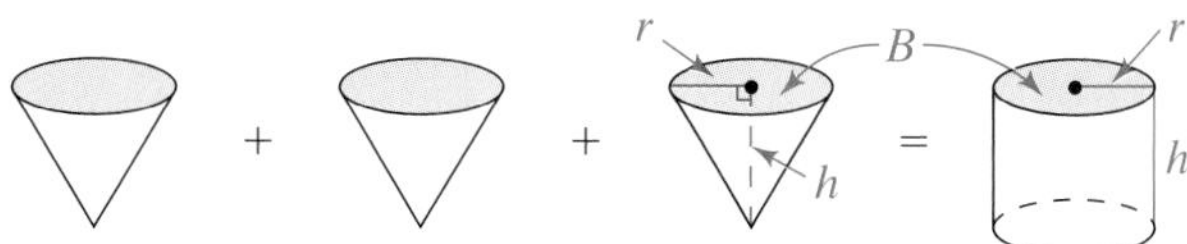

This relationship suggests the formula for the volume of a cone.

Key Concepts **Volume of a Cone**

The volume V of a cone is one third the product of the base area B and the height h.

$$V = \frac{1}{3}Bh$$

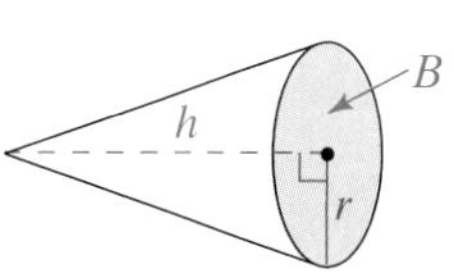

2 EXAMPLE Finding Volume of a Cone

Find the volume of the cone at the left to the nearest cubic meter.

18 m
4 m

Step 1 Find the area of the base.

$B = \pi r^2$ ← area of a square formula

$= \pi(4^2)$ ← Substitute.

$= 16\pi$ ← Simplify.

Step 2 Use the base area to find the volume.

$V = \frac{1}{3}Bh$ ← cone volume formula

$= \frac{1}{3}(16\pi)18$ ← Substitute.

$= 96\pi$ ← Simplify.

To the nearest cubic meter, the volume of the cone is 302 m^3.

Check Understanding 2 a. Find the volume of the cone at the right to the nearest cubic meter. 113 m^3
b. **Number Sense** How would the volume change if the height of the cone were 50% of the height shown at the right? Explain. See left.

2b. The volume would be 50% of the original volume. $\frac{1}{3}B\left(\frac{1}{2}h\right) = \frac{1}{2}\left(\frac{1}{3}Bh\right)$

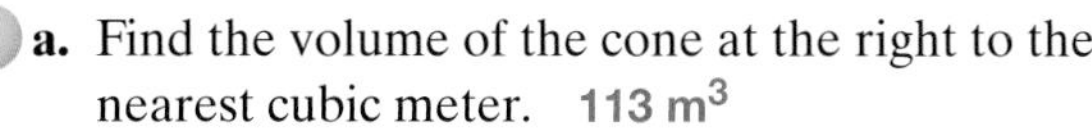

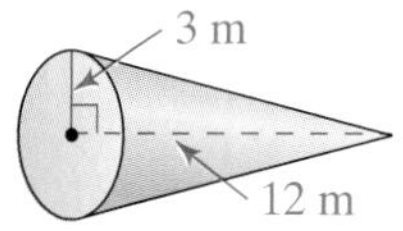

If you know the volume of a cone and either its height or its radius, you can use the volume formula to find the missing dimension.

Reaching All Students

Below Level Which of these figures have two bases: pyramid, prism, cone, cylinder? prism and cylinder Which have a circle as a base? cone and cylinder	**Advanced Learners** What effect does doubling the height have on the volume of a cone? doubling the radius? increases the volume by 2; increases the volume by 4	**English Learners** See note on page 507. **Tactile Learners** See note on page 507.

2. Teach

Math Background

When a prism and a pyramid have congruent bases and the same height, the volume of the prism will be three times the volume of the matching pyramid. Similarly, when a cylinder and a cone have congruent bases and the same height, the volume of the cylinder will be three times the volume of the matching cone. For a pyramid, $V = \frac{1}{3}Bh$. If the base of the pyramid is square, this becomes $V = \frac{1}{3}s^2h$. For a cone, $V = \frac{1}{3}Bh$. Since the base of a cone is a circle, this becomes $V = \frac{1}{3}\pi r^2h$.

Teaching Notes

1 EXAMPLE English Learners

To verify that students understand the meaning of the formula, use models to review the meanings of *volume*, *pyramid*, *base*, and *height*.

2 EXAMPLE Tactile Learners

Have students work in groups and use heavy paper to make a cylinder and a cone with congruent bases and heights. (This works best if they make the models as large as possible.) Have them use the cone to fill the cylinder with sand to find how many cone volumes equal one cylinder volume. 3

Technology Tip

To calculate $\frac{1}{3}\pi r^2h$, students may wish to begin by entering the value for r, squaring it, multiplying by h, and then by π to find a partial result, and finally dividing by 3 as the last step.

PowerPoint

Additional Examples

1 Find the volume of this square pyramid to the nearest whole unit. 213 ft^3

10 ft
8 ft
8 ft

2 Find the volume of this cone to the nearest cubic centimeter. 105 cm^3

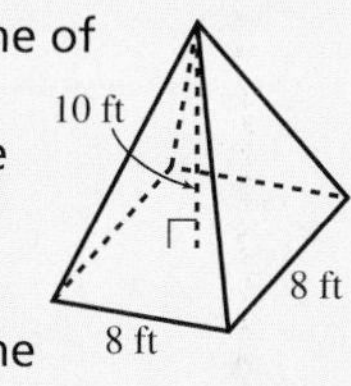

3 EXAMPLE Error Prevention

As a first step, have students write the formula before they begin to substitute values or calculate.

Algebra Connection

The double cone will be an important figure when students study algebra, geometry, conic sections, and the various ways a plane can intersect a double cone such as this.

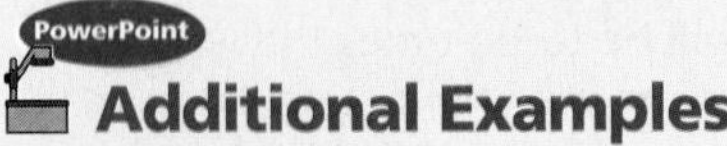

Additional Examples

3 A glass ornament has the shape of a double cone with a radius of 2 in. The double cone has a volume of 240 in.^{3}. What is the height of each of the two cones? about 28.6 in.

Closure

- *How are the volume of a prism and the volume of a pyramid related?* Sample: Both use the product of the area of the base times the height to find the volume, but, for the pyramid, this product is also multiplied by one third.
- *How are the volume of a cylinder and the volume of a cone related?* Sample: Both use the product of the area of the circular base times the height to find the volume, but, for the cone, this product is also multiplied by one third.

Real-World Connection

Careers Glassblowers heat glass to extremely high temperatures.

3 EXAMPLE Real-World Problem Solving

Glassblowing A glassblower decides to make an hourglass that will hold approximately 47 in.^{3} in each one of its cones. What will the height of the cones have to be if she makes the radius 3 in.?

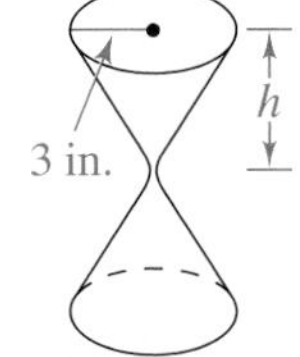

$V = \frac{1}{3}\pi r^2 h$ ← volume of a cone formula

$47 = \frac{1}{3}\pi(3^2)h$ ← Substitute.

$47 = 3\pi h$ ← Simplify.

$\frac{47}{3\pi} = \frac{3\pi h}{3\pi}$ ← Divide each side by 3π.

$4.986 \approx h$ ← Simplify. Use a calculator.

The height will be approximately 5 in.

Check Understanding 3 **a.** What should the radius of the cones be if she makes the height 7 in.? 3a. about 2.5 in.

b. **Reasoning** Will the volume stay the same if she decides to add an inch to the radius and subtract an inch from the height? Explain. no; $\frac{1}{3}\pi(r + 1)^2(h - 1) \neq \frac{1}{3}\pi r^2 h$

EXERCISES

For more practice, see *Extra Practice*.

A Practice by Example

Example 1 (page 506)

Find the volume of each pyramid to the nearest whole unit.

1. 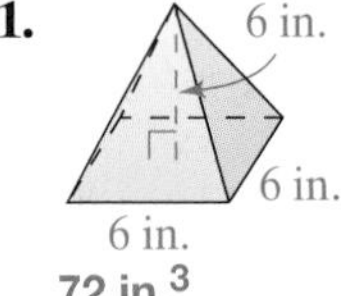

72 in.^{3}

2. 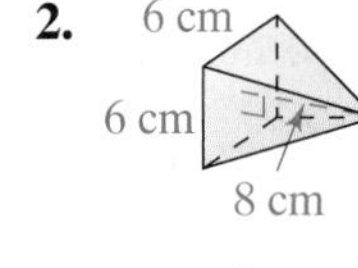

96 cm^3

3. 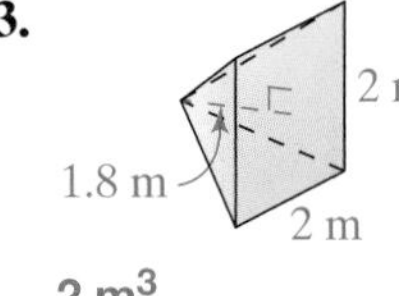

2 m^3

Example 2 (page 507)

Find the volume of each cone to the nearest whole unit.

4. 12 cm, 30 cm — 4,524 cm^3

5. 3 ft, 4 ft — 13 ft^3

6. 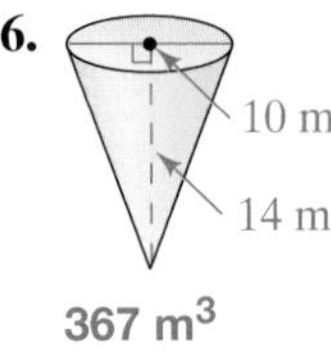

367 m^3

Example 3 (page 508)

Algebra **Find the missing radius or height of each cone with the given characteristics. Round to the nearest whole unit.**

7. an approximate volume of 22 ft^3 and a height of 21 ft radius 1 ft

8. an approximate volume of 85 in.^{3} and a radius of 3 in. height 9 in.

9. **Waffle Cones** Your uncle is designing a new frozen yogurt cone for the upcoming state fair. He will keep the volume of the cone at approximately 240 cm^3. If he makes the cone 14 cm tall, what will the diameter of the cone be? 8 cm

B Apply Your Skills

Find the volume of each figure to the nearest whole unit.

10. 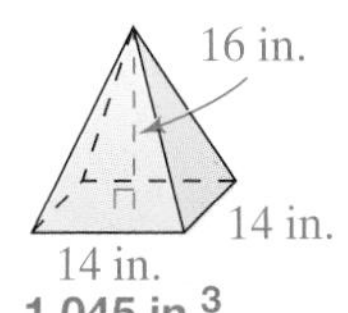

1,045 in.^{3}

11. 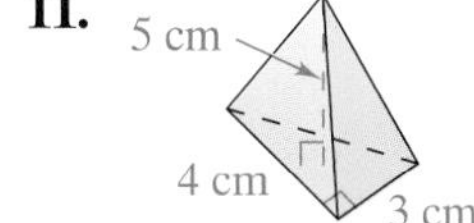

10 cm^3

12. 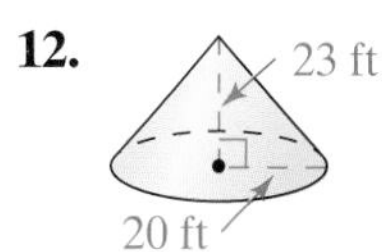

9,634 ft^3

13. 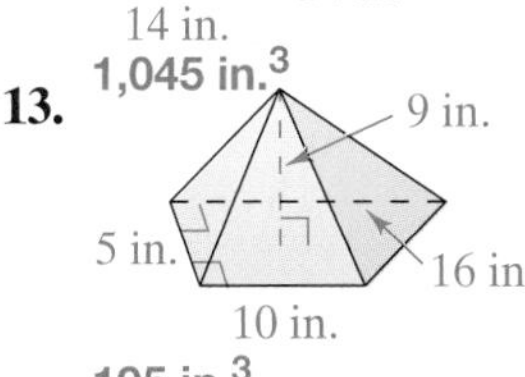

195 in.^{3}

14. 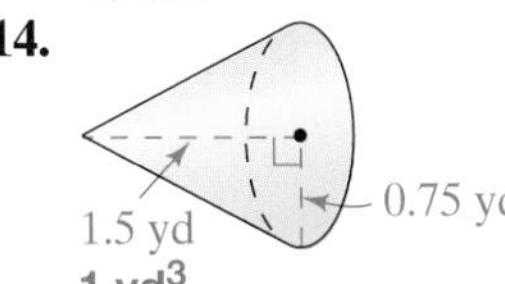

1 yd^3

15. 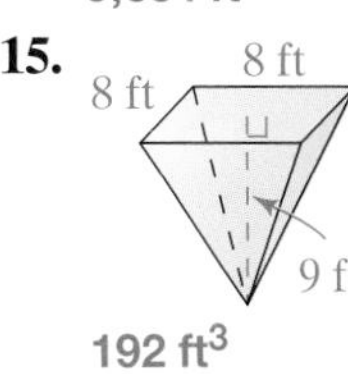

192 ft^3

16. It has six times the volume.

16. **Number Sense** How much greater is the volume of a rectangular prism that is twice as tall as a square pyramid with the same base area?

GPS **17.** **Algebra** The volume of a square pyramid is 15 ft^3. Its base area is 9 ft^2. What is its height? 5 ft

18. Each volume formula involves the product of the height h and the base area B. You can substitute the appropriate area formula for B when finding the volume. For cones and pyramids, you must also multiply the product by $\frac{1}{3}$.

18. **Writing in Math** Explain how you might use the area formulas for rectangles and triangles to help you remember the volume formulas for pyramids, cones, prisms, and cylinders. See left.

Find the volume of each solid to the nearest whole unit.

19. 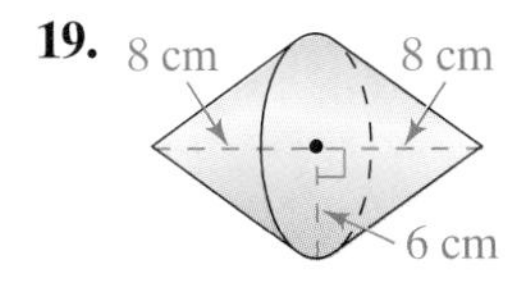

603 cm^3

20. 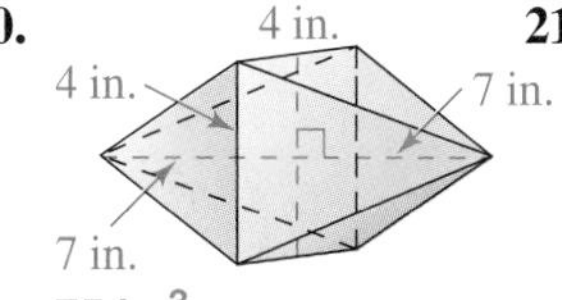

75 in.^{3}

21. 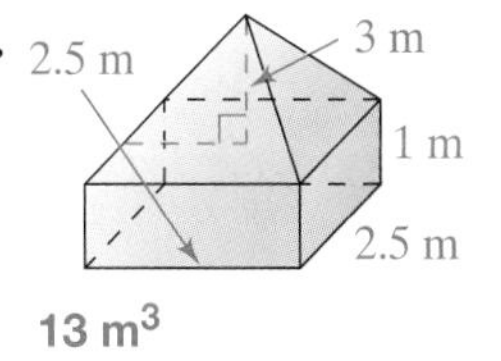

13 m^3

22. **Data File, p. 469** Birds' nests often are shaped like half a ball, or half a sphere. The formula for the volume of a full sphere is $V = \frac{4}{3}\pi r^3$. Find the volume of the typical eagle's nest. 56,549 in.^{3}

Real-World Connection
An eagle's nest, known as an eyrie, can weigh as much as two tons.

23. **Error Analysis** Lian says that if you double the dimensions of a square pyramid, you double its volume. What is her error? See margin.

24. **Estimation** Estimate the volume of a cone with a radius of 10 cm and a height of 10 cm. 1,000 cm^3

25. **Cars** When adding antifreeze to the radiator of his car, Will uses the funnel at the right, designed to hold approximately 500 cm^3 (half a liter). What must the diameter be if the height of the cone (without the stem) is 12 cm? about 13 cm

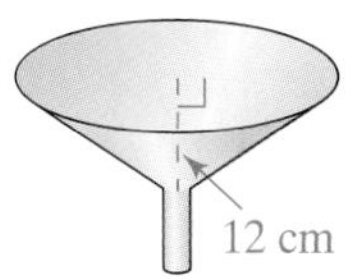

26. **a.** **Ice Sculpture** Jacques is creating ice sculptures for an upcoming party. What is the volume of the largest pyramid he can sculpt if he starts with a cube of ice that measures 5 feet on an edge? about 42 ft^3

b. How much ice from that cube gets discarded? about 83 ft^3

27. **Algebra** Write an equation to find the volume of a square pyramid whose height is three times its base-edge length. $V = b^3$

23. Suppose the original volume is $\frac{1}{3}b^2h$. If the dimensions are doubled, the new volume is $\frac{1}{3}(2b)^2(2h)$, which simplifies to $\frac{8}{3}b^2h$. The new volume is 8 times the original.

Use the Guided Problem Solving worksheet with Exercise 17.

3. Practice

Assignment Guide

Objective 1

A B Core 1–3, 10–11, 13, 15–17, 20–21, 23, 26, 27

C Extension 28, 30

Objective 2

A B Core 4–9, 12, 14, 18–19, 22, 24, 25

C Extension 29, 31, 32

Test Prep 33–37
Mixed Review 38–41

Exercise 9 Have a volunteer explain a "waffle" cone.

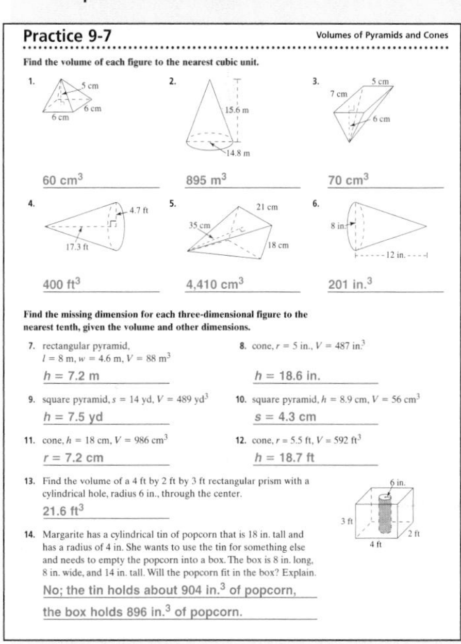

Practice 9-7 Volumes of Pyramids and Cones

Find the volume of each figure to the nearest cubic unit.

1. 60 cm^3
2. 895 m^3
3. 70 cm^3
4. 400 ft^3
5. 4,410 cm^3
6. 201 in.^{3}

Find the missing dimension for each three-dimensional figure to the nearest tenth, given the volume and other dimensions.

7. rectangular pyramid, $l = 8$ m, $w = 4.6$ m, $V = 88$ m^3 — $h = 7.2$ m
8. cone, $r = 5$ in., $V = 487$ in.^{3} — $h = 18.6$ in.
9. square pyramid, $s = 14$ yd, $V = 489$ yd^3 — $h = 7.5$ yd
10. square pyramid, $h = 8.9$ cm, $V = 56$ cm^3 — $s = 4.3$ cm
11. cone, $h = 18$ cm, $V = 986$ cm^3 — $r = 7.2$ cm
12. cone, $r = 5.5$ ft, $V = 592$ ft^3 — $h = 18.7$ ft
13. Find the volume of a 4 ft by 2 ft by 3 ft rectangular prism with a cylindrical hole, radius 6 in., through the center. 21.6 ft^3
14. Margarite has a cylindrical tin of popcorn that is 18 in. tall and has a radius of 4 in. She wants to use the tin for something else and needs to empty the popcorn into a box. The box is 8 in. long, 8 in. wide, and 14 in. tall. Will the popcorn fit in the box? Explain. No; the tin holds about 904 in.^{3} of popcorn, the box holds 896 in.^{3} of popcorn.

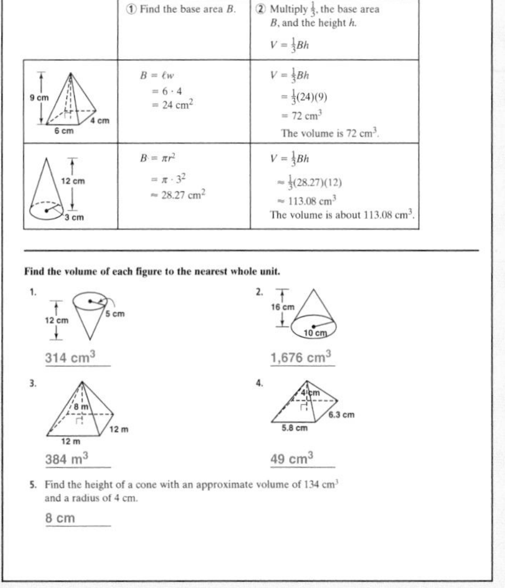

Reteaching 9-7 Volumes of Pyramids and Cones

To find the volume of a pyramid or cone, multiply $\frac{1}{3}$, the base area B, and the height h.

	① Find the base area B.	② Multiply $\frac{1}{3}$, the base area B, and the height h. $V = \frac{1}{3}Bh$
9 cm, 6 cm, 4 cm	$B = \ell w = 6 \cdot 4 = 24$ cm^2	$V = \frac{1}{3}Bh = \frac{1}{3}(24)(9) = 72$ cm^3 The volume is 72 cm^3.
12 cm, 3 cm	$B = \pi r^2 = \pi \cdot 3^2 \approx 28.27$ cm^2	$V = \frac{1}{3}Bh \approx \frac{1}{3}(28.27)(12) \approx 113.08$ cm^3 The volume is about 113.08 cm^3.

Find the volume of each figure to the nearest whole unit.

1. 314 cm^3
2. 1,676 cm^3
3. 384 m^3
4. 49 cm^3

5. Find the height of a cone with an approximate volume of 134 cm^3 and a radius of 4 cm. 8 cm

4. Assess

Lesson Quiz 9-7

1. Find the volume of a pyramid with a base of 7 m by 7 m and height of 12 m. **196 m^3**
2. Find the volume of a cone with radius 4 cm and height 8 cm. Round your answer to the nearest cubic centimeter. **134 cm^3**
3. Find the height of a cone with a volume of 150.8 cm^3 and a radius of 6 cm. **4 cm**

Alternative Assessment

A cone has a volume equal to that of a square pyramid having 15-m sides and height. The diameter of the cone is 15 m. What is the height of the cone to the nearest tenth? **19.1 m**

Test Prep

Resources

For additional practice with a variety of test item formats:

- Test Prep, p. 527
- Test-Taking Strategies, p. 523
- Test-Taking Strategies with Transparencies

Exercise 35 Review the difference between finding surface area and finding volume.

Enrichment 9-7 — Volumes of Pyramids and Cones

Critical Thinking

Look at the solids to the right. Both have bases with 5 cm measurements, and heights of 12 cm. Can you predict which solid has the greater volume, the pyramid or cone?

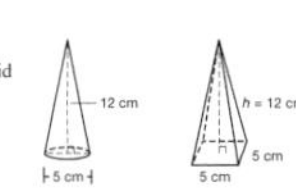

1. Compare the formulas for calculating the volume of a pyramid and of a cone. How are they alike? How are they different?
   You use the same formula to calculate the volume of both figures, $V = \frac{1}{3}(B \cdot h)$. The way you calculate the bases of the two figures is different.
2. How could you find the greater volume without actually calculating the volume of each figure? Explain.
   Sample answer: Compare the areas of the bases. Since both volumes are calculated as $\frac{1}{3}(B \cdot h)$, and figures have same height, the area of the base will determine the greater volume.
3. Which solid figure do you think has the greater volume? Explain your reasoning.
   Pyramid; the base area of the pyramid is 25 cm^2 and the base area of the cone is 19.6 cm^2. Sample answer: Since the heights are the same, the pyramid has the greater volume.
4. Calculate the volume of each solid. Is your prediction accurate?
   $V_{pyramid} = 100$ cm^3 and $V_{cone} = 78.5$ cm^3; yes.
5. Write a rule that can be used to quickly determine which has a larger volume, a pyramid or a cone, given that the heights of each solid are equal.
   If the heights of a pyramid and a cone are the same, compare the areas of the base. Whichever solid has the greater base area also has the greater volume.

C Challenge

Find the volume of the following figures to the nearest whole unit.

28. 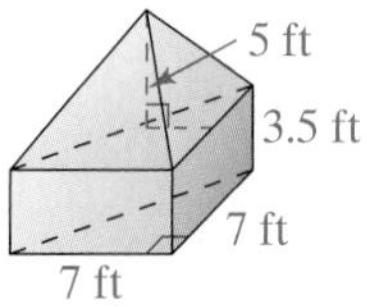 5 ft, 3.5 ft, 7 ft, 7 ft — **127 ft^3**

29.

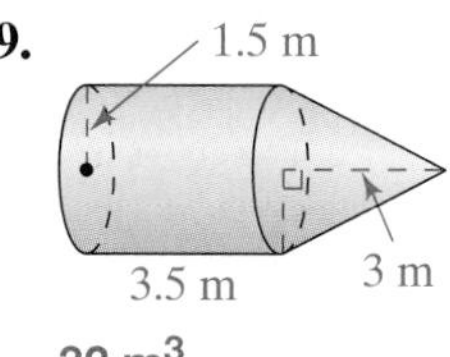

32 m^3

30.

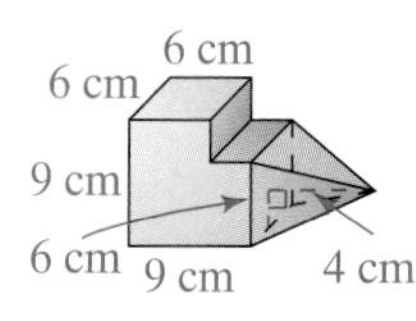

480 cm^3

31. Reasoning A cone and a square pyramid have the same height. The perimeter of the base of the pyramid is equal to the circumference of the base of the cone. Which figure has a greater volume? Explain. **See margin.**

32. Stretch Your Thinking Find the volume of a cone with a slant height of 7.5 in. and a lateral area of approximately 106 in.^{2}. **about 127 in.^{3}**

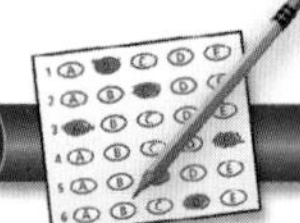

Test Prep

Multiple Choice

Use the figure at the right for Exercises 33–36. (8 m, 9.7 m, 11 m, 11 m)

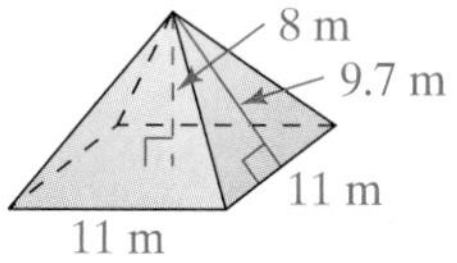

33. What is the base area? **C**
A. 11 m^2 B. 88 m^2
C. 121 m^2 D. 986 m^2

34. What is the slant height? **G**
F. 8 m G. 9.7 m H. 11 m I. 22 m

35. What is the surface area? **B**
A. 986 m^2 B. 334.4 m^2 C. 106.7 m^2 D. 88 m^2

36. What is the volume? **F**
F. 322.7 m^3 G. 121.0 m^3 H. 88.0 m^3 I. 16.0 m^3

Take It to the NET
Online lesson quiz at **www.PHSchool.com**
Web Code: aca-0907

Short Response

37. Find the volume to the nearest cubic meter of a cone with a diameter of 16 m and a height of 24 m. Justify your answer. **See margin.**

Mixed Review

Lesson 9-4 **Find the surface area of each figure.**

38. 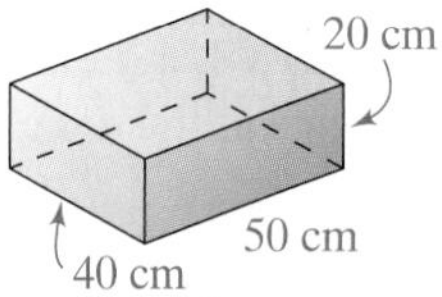 20 cm, 50 cm, 40 cm — **7,600 cm^2**

39.

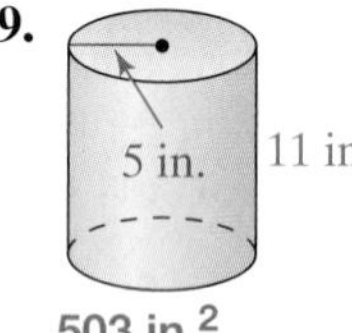

503 in.^{2}

40.

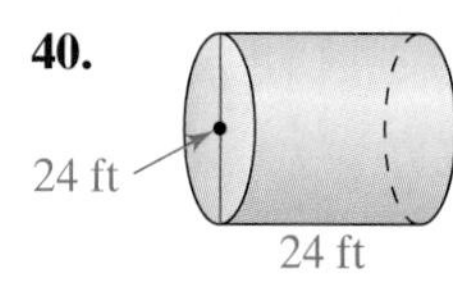

2,714 ft^2

Lesson 8-4

41. A number of toothpicks is arranged in triangles as shown at the right. How many toothpicks are needed to form an equilateral triangle with 15 toothpicks on each edge? **360 toothpicks**

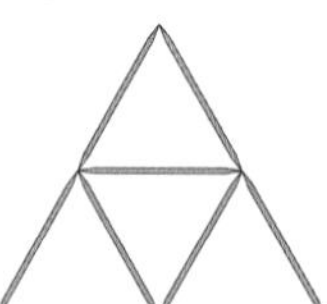

31. Cone; if the perimeter of the base of the pyramid and the circumference of the base of the cone are equal, the base area and volume of the pyramid will be $\frac{\pi}{4}$, or about $\frac{3}{4}$, of the base area and volume of the cone.

37. [2] Start with the formula $V = \frac{1}{3}\pi r^2 h$. Substitute 8 for the variable r and 24 for the variable h. Then evaluate using the order of operations. The volume is 1,608 m^3.
    [1] incorrect formula OR incomplete explanation

Formulas for Spheres

For Use With Lesson 9-7

The surface area of a sphere is given by the formula S.A. $= 4\pi r^2$, where r is the radius of the sphere.

1 EXAMPLE Finding the Surface Area of a Sphere

Find the surface area of the sphere at the right to the nearest whole unit.

9 cm

S.A. $= 4\pi r^2$ ← **Use the formula for the surface area of a sphere.**

$= 4\pi(9)^2$ ← **Substitute 9 for *r*.**

$\approx 1{,}017.87 \approx 1{,}018 \text{ cm}^2$ ← **Simplify. Use a calculator.**

The volume V of a sphere is given by the formula $V = \frac{4}{3}\pi r^3$, where r is the radius of the sphere.

2 EXAMPLE Finding the Volume of a Sphere

Find the volume of the sphere at the right to the nearest whole unit.

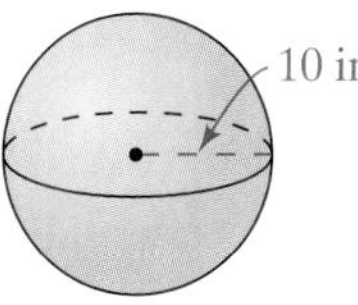

$V = \frac{4}{3}\pi r^3$ ← **Use the formula for the volume of a sphere.**

$= \frac{4}{3}\pi(10)^3$ ← **Substitute 10 for *r*.**

$\approx 4{,}188.79 \approx 4{,}189 \text{ in.}^3$ ← **Simplify. Use a calculator.**

EXERCISES

Find each sphere's surface area and volume to the nearest whole unit.

1.
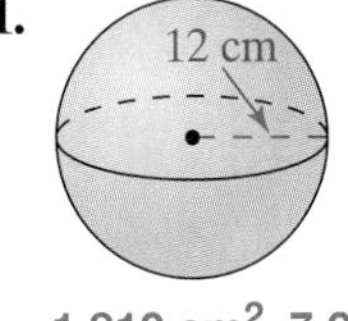

$1{,}810 \text{ cm}^2, 7{,}238 \text{ cm}^3$

2.
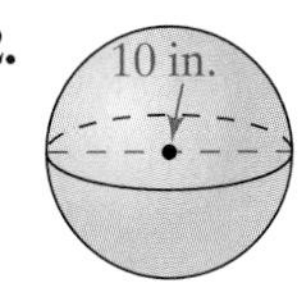

$314 \text{ in.}^2, 524 \text{ in.}^3$

3.
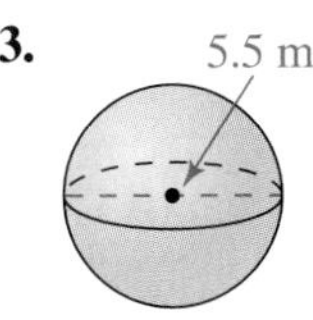

$95 \text{ m}^2, 87 \text{ m}^3$

4. **Tennis** Tennis balls with a diameter of 2.5 in. are sold in cans of three. The cans are cylinders. Find each volume to the nearest whole unit.
   a. the total volume of the balls 24.5 in.^3
   b. the volume of a can (Assume the balls touch the can on the sides, top, and bottom.) 36.8 in.^3

5. **Geography** Approximately 70% of the earth's surface is covered with water. If the diameter of the earth is about 13,000 km, find the approximate area covered by water. $3.7165 \times 10^8 \text{ km}^2$

Formulas for Spheres

In previous lessons, students found the surface area and volume of prisms, pyramids, cylinders, and cones. This extension of Lesson 9-7 focuses on using formulas to find the surface area and volume of spheres.

Resources

- calculators
- Classroom Aid 11

Teaching Notes

Point out that if you cut through the center of a sphere with a plane, the intersection of the plane and the sphere would be a circle (called a *great circle*). Elicit from students that the radius of that circle is the same as the radius of the sphere.

Work through both examples with students. Review rounding decimals, as needed.

Inclusion
Tell students that a sphere is a ball. Then provide several spherical objects for them to examine.

Exercises
Assign the exercises for independent work. Encourage students to work with calculators.

Error Prevention!

Remind students that surface area is measured in square units and that volume is measured in cubic units.

9-8

1. Plan

Lesson Preview

PowerPoint

Check Skills You'll Need

Finding Volume of Prisms and Cylinders
Lesson 9-6: Examples 1–2. Extra Practice, p. 710.

Lesson Resources

Teaching Resources
Practice, Reteaching, Enrichment
Checkpoint Quiz 2

Reaching All Students
Practice Workbook 9-8
Spanish Practice Workbook 9-8
Reading and Math Literacy 9C
Spanish Reading and Math Literacy 9C
Spanish Checkpoint Quiz 2
Guided Problem Solving 9-8
Hands-On Activities 34

Presentation Assistant Plus!
Transparencies
- Check Skills You'll Need 9-8
- Problem of the Day 9-8
- Additional Examples 9-8
- Student Edition Answers 9-8
- Lesson Quiz 9-8

PH Presentation Pro CD-ROM 9-8

PRENTICE HALL ASSESSMENT SYSTEM

Checkpoint Quiz 2
Computer Test Generator CD

Technology
Resource Pro® CD-ROM
Computer Test Generator CD
PH Presentation Pro CD-ROM

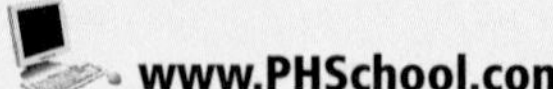

www.PHSchool.com
Student Site
- Teacher Web Code: ack-5500
- Self-grading Lesson Quiz

PH SuccessNet Teacher Center
- Lesson Planner
- Resources

Plus 

Problem Solving

9-8 Draw a Diagram and Make a Table

What You'll Learn

To solve a problem by combining strategies

. . . And Why

To combine strategies to solve problems, as in Example 1

Check Skills You'll Need

For help, go to Lesson 9-6.

Find the volume of each figure to the nearest whole unit.

1.

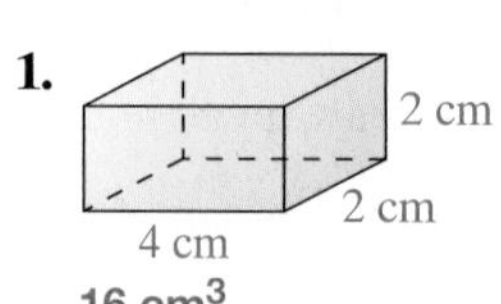

16 cm^3

2.

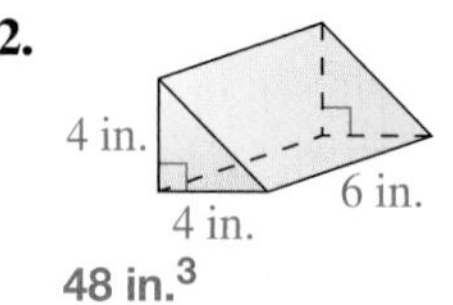

48 in.^{3}

3.

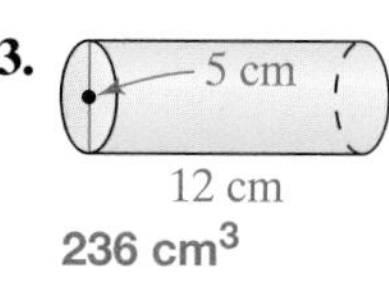

236 cm^3

OBJECTIVE 1

Solving a Problem by Combining Strategies

Interactive lesson includes instant self-check, tutorials, and activities.

When to Use These Strategies You can ***draw a diagram*** to help you understand what a problem is asking. Once you understand the problem you can apply another strategy to find the solution.

You can ***make a table*** to help you keep track of possible solutions to a problem. A table can help you organize your data and compare solutions.

Real-World Connection
Businesses can reduce expenses by minimizing packaging materials.

1 EXAMPLE Real-World Problem Solving

Manufacturing A company makes boxes without tops by cutting the square corners out of rectangular sheets of cardboard. Each rectangular sheet is 7 in. by 10 in. Using whole-inch lengths only, find the dimensions of a box that result in the greatest volume.

Read and Understand The goal is to find the dimensions of a box that will result in the greatest volume, knowing that the piece of cardboard used to make the box is 7 in. by 10 in.

Plan and Solve Draw a diagram to help you understand the problem. Let x represent the size of the cut, since it is unknown.

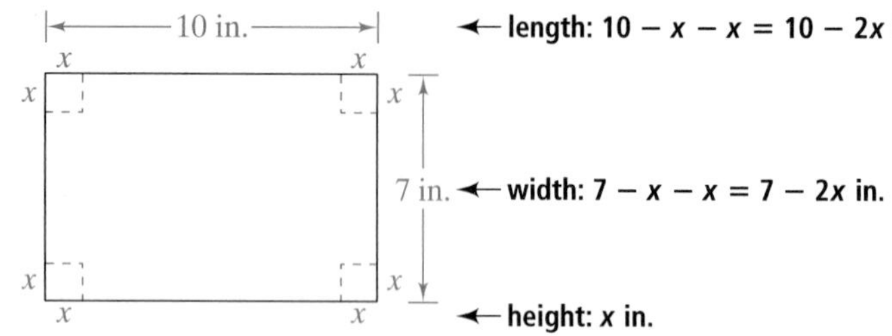

Ongoing Assessment and Intervention

Before the Lesson
Diagnose prerequisite skills using:
- Check Skills You'll Need

During the Lesson
Monitor progress using:
- Check Understanding
- Additional Examples
- Test Prep

After the Lesson
Assess knowledge using:
- Lesson Quiz
- Computer Test Generator CD
- Chapter Checkpoint 2 (p. 515)

Make a table. Start with a cut of 1 in. Then increase the cut by 1-inch increments.

Height (Size of Cut) x	Length $10 - 2x$	Width $7 - 2x$	Volume $x(10 - 2x)(7 - 2x)$
1 in.	8 in.	5 in.	40 in.^{3}
2 in.	6 in.	3 in.	36 in.^{3}
3 in.	4 in.	1 in.	12 in.^{3}

Notice that as the size of the cut increases, the volume decreases. The dimensions of a box in whole-inch lengths that result in the maximum volume, 40 in.^{3}, is 8 in. by 5 in. by 1 in.

Look Back and Check Can you find a greater volume using $\frac{1}{2}$-in. cuts? Since the greatest volume in the table above results from a 1-in. cut, try cuts of $\frac{1}{2}$ in. and $1\frac{1}{2}$ in.

Height (Size of Cut) x	Length $10 - 2x$	Width $7 - 2x$	Volume $x(10 - 2x)(7 - 2x)$
$\frac{1}{2}$ in.	9 in.	6 in.	27 in.^{3}
$1\frac{1}{2}$ in.	7 in.	4 in.	42 in.^{3}

Making a $1\frac{1}{2}$-in. cut results in a greater volume.

Check Understanding 1 Suppose you cut square corners off a piece of cardboard with dimensions 16 in. by 20 in. to make a pattern for a box without a top. To the nearest half inch, what dimensions result in the greatest volume? **14 in. by 10 in. by 3 in.**

EXERCISES

For more practice, see *Extra Practice*.

A Practice by Example

Example 1 (page 512)

Solve each problem by first drawing a diagram and then making a table.

1. **Fencing** A dog owner has 200 ft of fencing and wants to enclose the greatest possible area for her dog. She wants the fenced area to be rectangular. What dimensions should she use? **50 ft by 50 ft**

2. **Packaging** A company plans to package snack mix in cylindrical tubes. Each tube will be made from a rectangular piece of cardboard. The bases of the cylinder will be plastic. The cardboard comes in $8\frac{1}{2}$-in. by 11-in. sheets. To hold the greatest amount of mix, which edge of the cardboard should be the height of the cylindrical tube? **The shorter side should be the height.**

2. Teach

Math Background

Draw a diagram is a visual problem-solving strategy that helps students clarify what information is known and what information remains unknown. Often multiple diagrams are used to clarify relationships. You can organize the results from multiple diagrams into a table by using the problem-solving strategy *Make a Table*.

Teaching Notes

1 EXAMPLE Tactile Learners

Have students make several different boxes, each starting with a piece of paper that is 9 in. by 12 in. Have them measure the dimensions and compare the volumes.

Inclusion

Encourage students who have difficulty translating flat diagrams into three-dimensional models to use the problem-solving strategy of *make a model* in addition to *draw a diagram*.

PowerPoint

Additional Examples

1 You can cut square corners from a piece of cardboard that is 15 in. by 20 in. to make a pattern for a box without a top. What size squares should you cut from each corner to get the greatest volume? Give the dimensions of the square to the nearest half inch. **3 in.**

Closure

How might you use draw a diagram *and* make a table *to help you solve a problem?* **Sample: Begin by making a drawing to help you understand the problem, and then try various numbers, making a table to record the results. You might also need to write an equation or look for a pattern.**

Reaching All Students

Below Level Find the area of a square that is 5 cm on each side. **25 cm^2** Find the volume of a box that is 5 cm by 6 cm by 7 cm. **210 cm^3**	**Advanced Learners** You want to use 100 feet of fencing to enclose the greatest possible area. What shape should you fence in? **a circle**	**Inclusion** See note on page 513. **Tactile Learners** See note on page 513.

3. Practice

Assignment Guide

Objective 1

A B Core 1–8

C Extension 9–11

Test Prep 12–15

Mixed Review 16–24

Error Prevention!

Exercise 3 Point out that students are to find the dimensions of the box and not the cut-off square.

3. Suppose you cut square corners off a piece of sheet metal with dimensions 10 cm by 12 cm and fold up the sides to make a box without a top. To the nearest centimeter, what dimensions give the greatest volume? **8 cm by 6 cm by 2 cm**

B Apply Your Skills

Need Help?
- Reread the problem.
- Identify the key facts and details.
- Tell the problem in your own words.
- Try a different strategy.
- Check your work.

Choose a strategy or a combination of strategies to solve each problem.

4. You are standing in the park at point A. The exit to the park is at point E. How many different routes can you take from point A to point E if you only go to the left and up, never retracing your route?

9 paths

Strategies
- Draw a Diagram
- Look for a Pattern
- Make a Graph
- Make an Organized List
- Make a Table
- Simulate a Problem
- Solve a Simpler Problem
- Try, Check, and Revise
- Use Logical Reasoning
- Work Backward
- Write an Equation

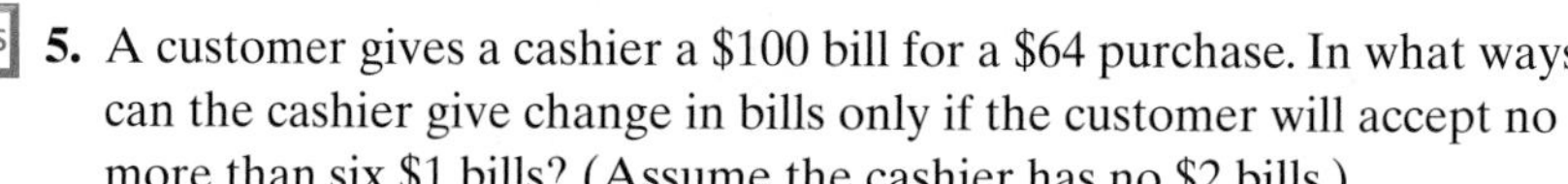

GPS 5. A customer gives a cashier a \$100 bill for a \$64 purchase. In what ways can the cashier give change in bills only if the customer will accept no more than six \$1 bills? (Assume the cashier has no \$2 bills.) **See back of book.**

6. a. **Writing in Math** A circle and a square each have an area of 144 cm^2. Explain how you would determine if the circumference of the circle is less than, greater than, or equal to the perimeter of the square. **6a. See margin.**

   b. **Number Sense** If you change the radius of the circle so that its circumference is equal to the perimeter of the square, then what would the area of the circle be? **about 183 cm^2**

7. **Restaurant** A local restaurant offers special group rates. The price list for the breakfast buffet at the right was found torn. Based on the pattern in the price list, what is the group rate for 6 people? **\$39**

Buffet Prices
\$9 for 1
\$17 for 2
\$24 for 3
\$30 for 4
...for 5

8. In how many ways can 47 be written as the sum of two prime numbers? **none**

C Challenge

9. What are the dimensions to the nearest inch of the rectangular prism with the greatest volume that can be completely covered in 100 $in.^2$ of wrapping paper? **4 in. × 4 in. × 4 in.**

10. **Fish Tank** A rectangular fish tank with base edges of 20 in. and 12 in. and a height of 10 in. should only be filled to one inch from the top. How many solid glass decorative square pyramids with a base-edge length of 4 in. and a height of 3 in. can you place in the bottom of the tank if the water level is currently at 8.75 in.? **3**

11. **Stretch Your Thinking** The consecutive even integers from 2 to n are $2, 4, 6, \ldots, n$. The square of the sum of the integers is 5,184. What is the value of n? **16**

Use the Guided Problem Solving worksheet with Exercise 5.

6a. The area of the square is 144, so $s^2 = 144$, and $s = 12$. The perimeter is 4(12), or 48. The area of the circle is also 144, so $\pi r^2 = 144$, and $r = \sqrt{\frac{144}{\pi}}$, or about 6.8. The circumference is $2\pi(6.8)$, or about 42.7. The perimeter of the square is greater.

Practice 9-8 Problem Solving: Draw a Diagram and Make a Table

Choose a strategy or a combination of strategies to solve each problem.

1. You can cut square corners off an 11 in. by 14 in. piece of cardboard to get a pattern that you could fold into a box without a top.
   a. What dimensions for the corners, to the nearest quarter-inch, will give the greatest volume? **1.25 in. by 1.25 in.**
   b. What is the greatest volume of the box to the nearest tenth? **122.2 $in.^3$**
2. Corinda has 400 ft of fencing to make a play area. She wants the fenced area to be rectangular. What dimensions should she use in order to enclose the maximum possible area? **100 ft by 100 ft**
3. A restaurant dining room measures 100 ft by 150 ft. The height of the room is 9 ft. If the occupancy guidelines recommend at least 150 ft^3 per person, what is the maximum number of people that can be in the room? **900 people**
4. Maurice lives at point A. The library is at point B. How many different routes can Maurice take from home to the library if he only goes to the right and down, never retracing his route? **20 routes**
5. The consecutive even integers from 2 to n are $2, 4, 6, \ldots, n$. The square of the sum of the integers is 5,184. What is the value of n? **16**
6. A bicyclist has 120 mi to cover on a trip. One day she bicycles 40% of the distance. The next day she cycles 60% of the remaining distance. How much further does she have to cycle? **28.8 mi**

Use the dartboard shown at the right.

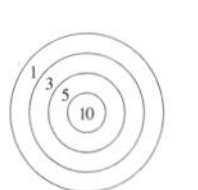

7. Three darts are thrown at the target. If each dart lands on the target, how many *different* point totals are possible? **16 point totals**
8. If 3 darts are thrown at the target and each dart lands on a different zone, find the maximum number of points scored. **18 points**

Reteaching 9-8 Problem Solving: Draw a Diagram and Make a Table

A farmer has 100 ft of fencing. He wants to enclose the greatest possible area for his garden. He wants the fenced area to be rectangular. What dimensions should he use?

Read and Understand The goal is to find the dimension of the fence that will give the largest area. The area has to be rectangular.

Plan and Solve Draw a diagram to help you solve the problem and make a table to show possible dimensions of the fence and area.

100 ft of fence

Length (ft)	Width (ft)	Area (ft^2)
10	40	400
15	35	525
20	30	600

Length(ft)	Width (ft)	Area (ft^2)
25	25	625
30	20	600
35	15	525

Look Back and Check Can you find a greater area using 2-ft increments?

Length (ft)	Width (ft)	Area (ft^2)
10	40	400
12	38	456
14	36	504
16	34	544

Length(ft)	Width (ft)	Area (ft^2)
18	32	576
20	30	600
22	28	616
24	26	624

Making the fence 25 ft by 25 ft will result in the largest area.

Make a drawing to help you solve each problem.

1. Fred wants to protect his rectangular workbench by covering it with paper. The workbench is 24 in. by 36 in. He wants the paper to hang over the edges by 4 in. How big should the paper be? What would be its area? **32 in. by 44 in.; 1,408 $in.^2$**
2. The convention center uses cloths cover display tables. The cloths must hang over the edges of the tables by 24 in. The tables are 30 in. by 72 in. How big are the cloths? What is the area of one cloth? **78 in. by 120 in.; 9,360 $in.^2$**
3. Meera is covering a bulletin board with fabric. The bulletin board is 36 in. by 48 in. She needs 6 in. overhang on each side to staple the fabric to the back of the board. How big should the piece of fabric be? What is the area of the fabric? **48 in. by 60 in.; 2,880 $in.^2$**
4. Ethan wants to put a plastic liner in the bed of his truck. The truck bed measures 42 in. by 64 in. He wants 8 in. extra on each side to go against the truck bed walls. How big should the liner be? What would be its area? **58 in. by 80 in.; 4,640 $in.^2$**

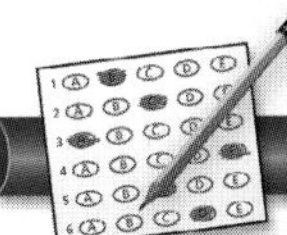

Test Prep

Multiple Choice

12. A box measures 2 in. by 7 in. by 10 in. What is its volume? C
A. 104 in.^{3} **B.** 108 in.^{3} **C.** 140 in.^{3} **D.** 208 in.^{3}

Take It to the NET
Online lesson quiz at **www.PHSchool.com**
Web Code: aca-0908

13. Ignoring overlap, how much cardboard is used to make a box that measures 10 in. by 7 in. by 2 in.? I
F. 104 in.^{2} **G.** 108 in.^{2} **H.** 140 in.^{2} **I.** 208 in.^{2}

14. A box measuring 2 in. by 3 in. by 3 in. is packed inside a gift box that is a 4-in. cube. How much space is left inside for packing materials? B
A. 20 in.^{3} **B.** 46 in.^{3} **C.** 58 in.^{3} **D.** 82 in.^{3}

Short Response

15. A tablecloth covers a rectangular table measuring 36 in. by 88 in. and has 9 in. of overhang on all four sides. **(a)** Draw a diagram to represent this situation. **(b)** Find the area of the tablecloth.
See margin.

Mixed Review

Lesson 8-7 **Find the area of each polygon.**

16.
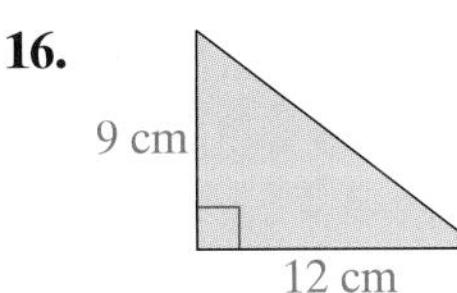

54 cm^2

17.
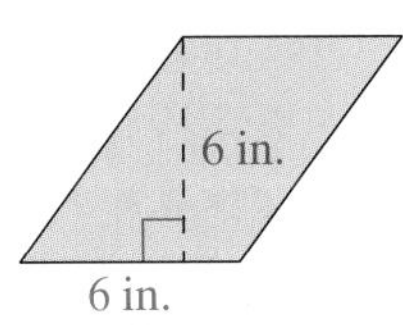

36 in.^{2}

18.
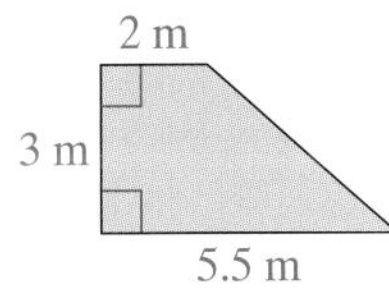

11.25 m^2

Lesson 7-1 **Write each number in scientific notation.**

19. 128,000,000 — 1.28×10^8
20. 709,000 — 7.09×10^5
21. 2,300,000,000,000 — 2.3×10^{12}
22. 0.000670 — 6.7×10^{-4}
23. 0.081 — 8.1×10^{-2}
24. 0.0000402 — 4.02×10^{-5}

Checkpoint Quiz 2 — Lessons 9-4 through 9-8

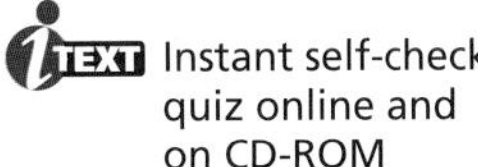

Instant self-check quiz online and on CD-ROM

Find the surface area and volume of each figure to the nearest whole unit.

1.
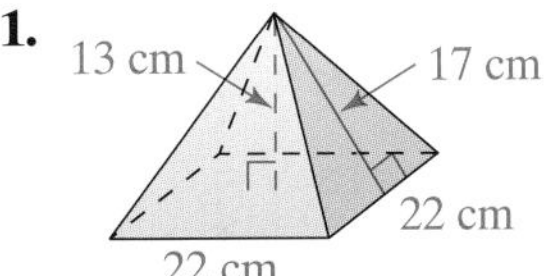

1,232 cm^2; 2,097 cm^3

2. 14 in.; 22 in.; 26 in.
1,759 in.^{2}; 4,516 in.^{3}

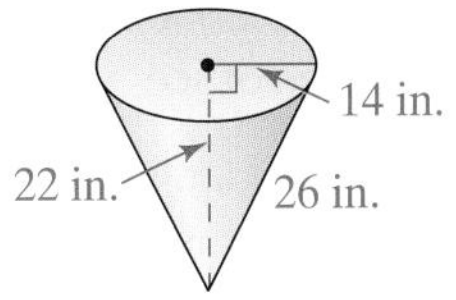

3.
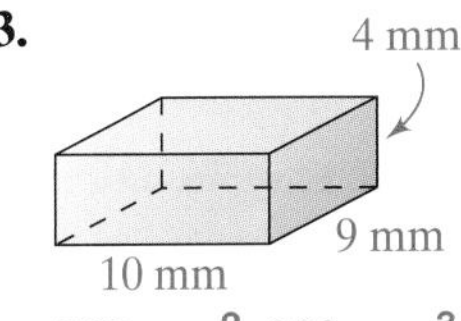

332 mm^2; 360 mm^3

4. To the nearest whole unit, find the height of a cone with an approximate volume of 1,005 mm^3 and a diameter of 8 mm. 60 mm

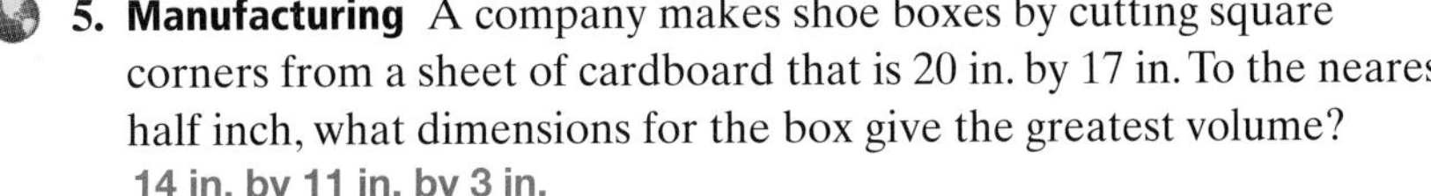

5. Manufacturing A company makes shoe boxes by cutting square corners from a sheet of cardboard that is 20 in. by 17 in. To the nearest half inch, what dimensions for the box give the greatest volume?
14 in. by 11 in. by 3 in.

4. Assess

Lesson Quiz 9-8

1. To form an open box, squares are cut from the corners of a rectangular piece of cardboard that measures 24 in. by 36 in. Using only whole numbers, find the dimensions of the box that give the greatest volume. 5 in. by 14 in. by 26 in.

Chapter Checkpoint

To check understanding of Lessons 9-4 to 9-8:

Checkpoint Quiz 2 (p. 515)

Teaching Resources
Checkpoint Quiz 2 (also in Prentice Hall Assessment System)

Reaching All Students
Reading and Math Literacy 9C

Spanish versions available

Alternative Assessment

Students write a word problem that can be solved using *draw a diagram* and *make a table*. They challenge classmates to solve the problem.

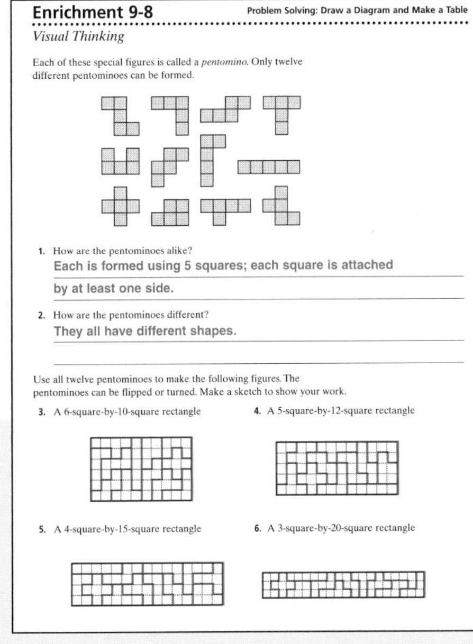

Enrichment 9-8 Problem Solving: Draw a Diagram and Make a Table
Visual Thinking

Each of these special figures is called a *pentomino*. Only twelve different pentominoes can be formed.

1. How are the pentominoes alike?
Each is formed using 5 squares; each square is attached by at least one side.
2. How are the pentominoes different?
They all have different shapes.

Use all twelve pentominoes to make the following figures. The pentominoes can be flipped or turned. Make a sketch to show your work.

3. A 6-square-by-10-square rectangle
4. A 5-square-by-12-square rectangle
5. A 4-square-by-15-square rectangle
6. A 3-square-by-20-square rectangle

15. [2] a.

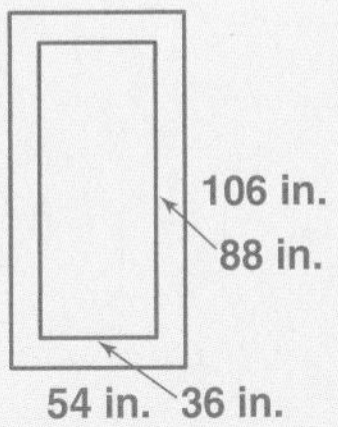

b. 5,724 in.^{2}
[1] one part correct

Test Prep

Resources
For additional practice with a variety of test item formats:
- Test Prep, p. 527
- Test-Taking Strategies, p. 523
- Test-Taking Strategies with Transparencies

Reading Math

Using the Correct Formula

To correctly read formulas and apply them in problem-solving situations is an important problem-solving skill. This feature provides students with strategies for using formulas to solve problems.

Resources

- calculators
- Classroom Aid 11

Teaching Notes

Review the formulas presented in Lessons 9-4 through 9-7 for finding surface area and volume of prisms, pyramids, cylinders, and cones. Discuss what the variables stand for in each formula. Elicit from students the distinction between surface area and lateral area of cones or cylinders.

EXAMPLE Teaching Tip

Work through each step in the process of solving the problem presented in the Example. Ask: *How do you know that the problem calls for finding the lateral area and not the surface area?* No material is needed for the floor of the teepee.

Number Sense Connection

Guide students to understand that 15π is an exact answer and that 47.12 is an approximation that is, in this case, more useful for answering the question the problem asks.

Exercises

Exercise 1–2 Have students work independently and use calculators. Guide them to make sketches first if it helps them to understand what the problems call for. Then they can write the formula they will use to find each solution.

Error Prevention!

Remind students that surface area is measured in square units and that volume is measured in cubic units.

Reading Math: Using the Correct Formula

For Use With Lesson 9-8

Many formulas used in mathematics look alike. To be successful, you need to learn to read formulas carefully in order to use them correctly.

Here are some strategies for working on problems involving formulas.

EXAMPLE

A student's design for a model Native American teepee appears at the right. How much material will he need for the walls of the teepee?

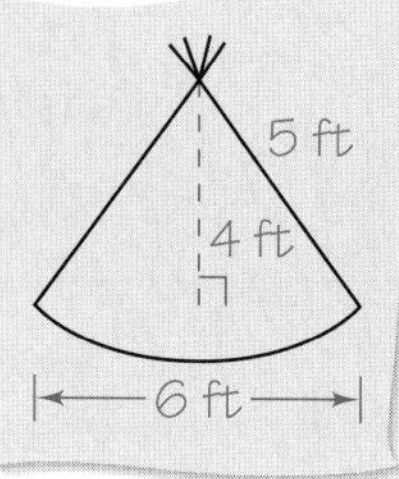

- **Identify the measure the problem calls for.**

  The amount of material covering a solid requires lateral area or surface area. A teepee is cone-shaped. The problem calls for the lateral area, but not the base area. You need the lateral area formula: L.A. = $\pi r\ell$.

- **Know what the variables in a formula represent.**

  r = radius; ℓ = slant height

- **Determine which values to use.**

  The diameter d is 6 ft, so the radius r is 3 ft. The slant height ℓ is 5 ft. You don't need to use the height h.

  $\text{L.A.} = \pi r\ell$ ← lateral area of a cone formula

  $= \pi(3)(5)$ ← Substitute 3 for r. Substitute 5 for ℓ.

  $= 15\pi$ ← Multiply.

  ≈ 47.12 ← Use a calculator.

The lateral area of the teepee is a little more than 47 ft^2. The student will need at least 48 ft^2 of material.

EXERCISES

1. **Ice** A block of ice in the shape of a rectangular prism measures 6 in. by 8 in. by 9 in. After some of the ice has melted, each dimension is half its original length.
   a. Find the surface area of the smaller block of ice. 87 in.^2
   b. How many cubic inches of ice have turned to water? 378 in.^3

2. **Clay Modeling** Karl molded a clay pyramid with a base-edge length of 4 cm and a height of 6 cm. How much clay did he use? 32 cm^3

Open-Ended **For each formula, describe a problem where you would use the formula to find the solution.** 3–5. Check students' work.

3. $V = \frac{1}{3}Bh$

4. L.A. $= ph$

5. S.A. $=$ L.A. $+ 2B$

9-9 Exploring Similar Solids

What You'll Learn

To find dimensions of similar solids using proportions

To find surface areas and volumes of similar solids

. . . And Why

To use the relationships of similar solids, as in Example 3

For help, go to Lesson 5-4.

Solve each proportion.

1. $\frac{x}{4} = \frac{7}{16}$ 1.75
2. $\frac{9}{5} = \frac{m}{24}$ 43.2
3. $\frac{3}{k} = \frac{9}{27}$ 9
4. $\frac{20}{8} = \frac{5}{c}$ 2
5. $\frac{y}{13} = \frac{5}{8}$ 8.125
6. $\frac{1}{1.2} = \frac{18}{w}$ 21.6

New Vocabulary • similar solids

OBJECTIVE

Interactive lesson includes instant self-check, tutorials, and activities.

1 Finding Dimensions Using Proportions

Two solids are **similar solids** if they have the same shape and if all of their corresponding lengths are proportional. In the photo at the left, the dolls are similar. Their heights and diameters are proportional.

You can use a proportion to find the missing dimensions of similar solids.

1 EXAMPLE Finding Dimensions of a Similar Solid

The two pyramids below are similar. Find the value of x.

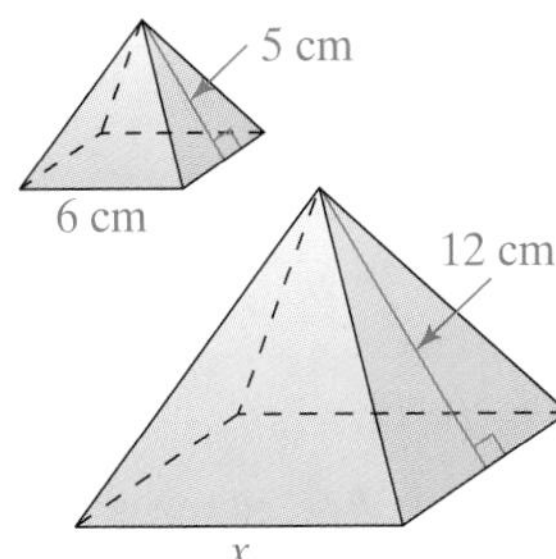

Use corresponding parts to write a proportion.

$\frac{x}{6} = \frac{12}{5}$ ← dimensions of large pyramid / ← dimensions of small pyramid

$6 \cdot \frac{x}{6} = \frac{12}{5} \cdot 6$ ← Multiply each side by 6.

$x = \frac{72}{5}$ ← Simplify.

$= 14.4$

The base-edge length x is 14.4 cm.

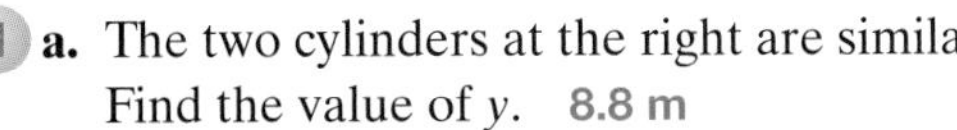

Check Understanding 1 **a.** The two cylinders at the right are similar. Find the value of y. 8.8 m

b. Reasoning You can solve the proportion in Example 1 by using cross products or by multiplying each side by 6. Which method requires fewer steps? Explain. See margin.

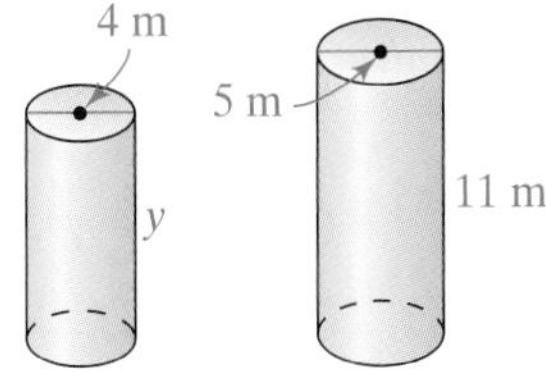

Ongoing Assessment and Intervention

Before the Lesson
Diagnose prerequisite skills using:
- Check Skills You'll Need

During the Lesson
Monitor progress using:
- Check Understanding
- Additional Examples
- Test Prep

After the Lesson
Assess knowledge using:
- Lesson Quiz
- Computer Test Generator CD

9-9

1. Plan

Lesson Preview

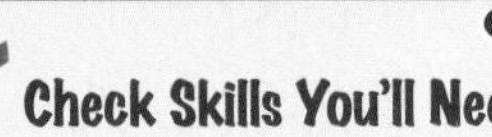

Solving Proportions
Lesson 5-4: Example 2. Extra Practice, p. 706.

Lesson Resources

Teaching Resources
Practice, Reteaching, Enrichment

Reaching All Students
Practice Workbook 9-9
Spanish Practice Workbook 9-9
Guided Problem Solving 9-9

Presentation Assistant Plus!
Transparencies
- Check Skills You'll Need 9-9
- Problem of the Day 9-9
- Additional Examples 9-9
- Student Edition Answers 9-9
- Lesson Quiz 9-9

PH Presentation Pro CD-ROM 9-9

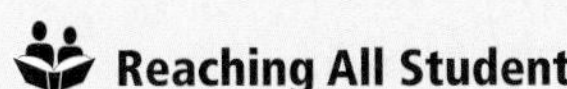

Computer Test Generator CD

Technology
Resource Pro® CD-ROM
Computer Test Generator CD
PH Presentation Pro CD-ROM

www.PHSchool.com
Student Site
- Teacher Web Code: ack-5500
- Self-grading Lesson Quiz

PH SuccessNet Teacher Center
- Lesson Planner
- Resources

1b. Multiplying each side by six requires just two steps. Using cross products requires the extra steps of multiplying each side by 5 and then dividing each side by 5.

2. Teach

Math Background

Similar solids have the same shape and proportional corresponding measurements. As with scale drawings and maps, you use proportions to find missing lengths for similar solids.

The idea that doubling linear dimensions does not simply double the area and the volume is counter-intuitive for most people. Experiments with models and actual measurements help make the effects of changing dimensions seem more reasonable.

Teaching Notes

1 EXAMPLE Inclusion

Review similarity and congruence for plane figures. Have students find two similar solids in the classroom.

Investigation (Optional)

Ask:

- *For a square with a side of 3, what are the factors of the area?* 3 × 3
- *For a cube with a side of 3, what are the factors of the volume?* 3 × 3 × 3
- *How many times is the side used as a factor for the area?* twice
- *How many times is the side used as a factor for the volume?* three times

2 EXAMPLE Sports Connection

NCAA stands for The National Collegiate Athletic Association.

3 EXAMPLE English Learners

Explain that a *creamer* is a small pitcher designed to hold cream.

Visual Learners

Caution students that it is almost impossible to compare accurately the area or volume for similar solids just by looking at their appearance.

Error Prevention!

Some students may multiply by 2 or 3 rather than squaring or cubing.

OBJECTIVE 2

Surface Areas and Volumes of Similar Solids

Investigation: Exploring Changing Dimensions

Cube A

Cube B

Cube C

1. Copy and complete the table at the right.

Cube	Dimensions	Surface Area	Volume
A	$1 \times 1 \times 1$	■ 6	■ 1
B	$2 \times 2 \times 2$	■ 24	■ 8
C	$3 \times 3 \times 3$	■ 54	■ 27

2. Based on the data in your table above, copy and complete the table at the right.

Cubes	Ratio of Side Lengths	Ratio of Surface Areas	Ratio of Volumes
A : B	1 ■ : ■ 2	1 ■ : ■ 4	1 ■ : ■ 8
B : C	2 ■ : ■ 3	4 ■ : ■ 9	8 ■ : ■ 27
C : A	3 ■ : ■ 1	9 ■ : ■ 1	27 ■ : ■ 1

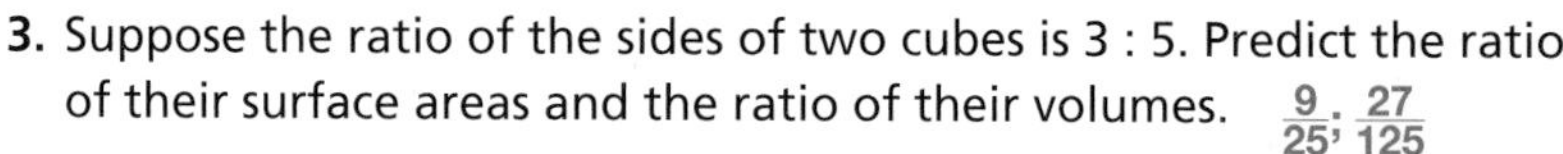

3. Suppose the ratio of the sides of two cubes is 3 : 5. Predict the ratio of their surface areas and the ratio of their volumes. $\frac{9}{25}, \frac{27}{125}$

A special relationship exists among the measures of similar solids.

Key Concepts — Surface Area and Volume of Similar Solids

If the ratios of the corresponding dimensions of similar solids is $\frac{a}{b}$, then,

- the ratio of their surface areas is $\frac{a^2}{b^2}$
- the ratio of their volumes is $\frac{a^3}{b^3}$

2 EXAMPLE Finding Surface Area of a Similar Solid

Real World

Sports Equipment A regulation NCAA men's basketball will just fit inside a cubic box with a surface area of 3,530 cm^2. A regulation NCAA women's basketball will fit inside a box with edges that are $\frac{29}{30}$ the size of the box for the men's ball. Find the surface area of the box for the women's basketball.

The ratio of corresponding dimensions is $\frac{29}{30}$, so the ratio of the surface areas is $\frac{29^2}{30^2}$, or $\frac{841}{900}$.

$$\frac{\text{surface area of women's box}}{\text{surface area of men's box}} = \frac{841}{900} \quad \leftarrow \text{Write a proportion.}$$

$$\frac{\text{S.A.}}{3{,}530} = \frac{841}{900} \quad \leftarrow \text{Substitute the known surface area.}$$

$$\text{S.A.} = \frac{841}{900} \cdot 3{,}530 \quad \leftarrow \text{Multiply each side by 3,530.}$$

$$\text{S.A.} \approx 3{,}298.59 \quad \leftarrow \text{Simplify.}$$

The surface area of the box for the women's basketball is about 3,300 cm^2.

Reaching All Students

Below Level Review the meaning of double (two times as much), triple (three times as much) and quadruple (four times as much).

Advanced Learners Design a triangular prism and a square prism that will have the same volume; draw and mark the dimensions on each. Get a partner to check the volumes.

English Learners
See note on page 518.
Inclusion
See note on page 518.

Check Understanding 2 A box fitting a regulation Major League baseball has base-edge lengths $\frac{1}{10}$ the edge lengths of the box for the men's basketball. Find the surface area of the box for the baseball. about 35 cm^2

You can use the ratio of corresponding dimensions to find the volume of a similar solid.

3 EXAMPLE Finding Volume of a Similar Solid

Real World

Pottery In art class, Jerry made the cylindrical pitcher below with a volume of 157 in.^{3} and a diameter of 6 in. He also made a creamer with a similar shape. Its diameter is 3 in. Find the volume of the creamer.

Pitcher

Creamer

The ratio of the diameters is $\frac{3}{6}$, or $\frac{1}{2}$. This means the ratio of the volumes will be $\frac{1^3}{2^3}$, or $\frac{1}{8}$.

$$\frac{\text{volume of creamer}}{\text{volume of pitcher}} = \frac{1}{8} \quad \leftarrow \text{Write a proportion.}$$

$$\frac{V}{157} = \frac{1}{8} \quad \leftarrow \text{Substitute the volume of the pitcher.}$$

$$8 \cdot V = 1 \cdot 157 \quad \leftarrow \text{Write the cross products.}$$

$$V = 19.625 \quad \leftarrow \text{Simplify.}$$

The volume of the creamer is about 20 cubic inches.

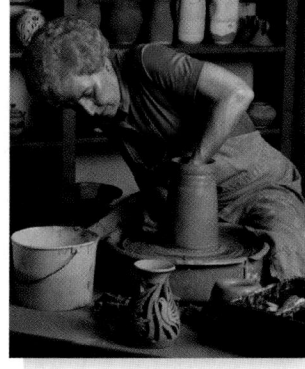

Real-World Connection

Careers Potters create ceramic pieces by shaping wet clay as it spins on a potter's wheel.

Check Understanding 3 **a.** Suppose Jerry had decided to make the creamer with a diameter of 2 inches. Find its volume. about 6 in.^{3}

b. Reasoning Using this new proportion, how would you expect the height of the creamer to compare to the height of the pitcher? Explain. The creamer would be one third the height of the pitcher. Since the objects are similar, all their dimensions would be in the same proportion.

EXERCISES

For more practice, see *Extra Practice*.

Practice by Example

Example 1 (page 517)

For each pair of similar solids, find the value of the variable.

1.

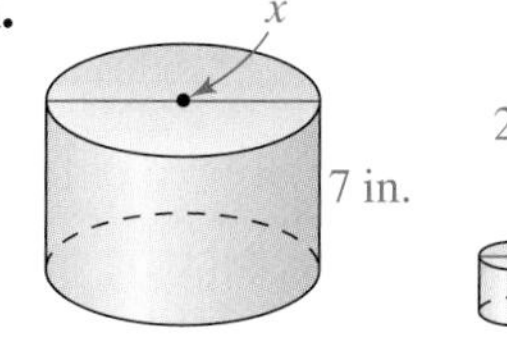

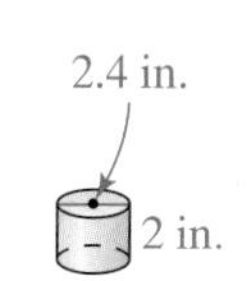

8.4 in.

2.

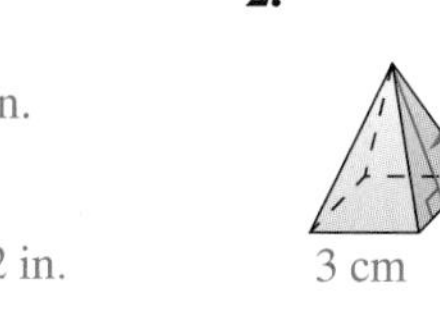

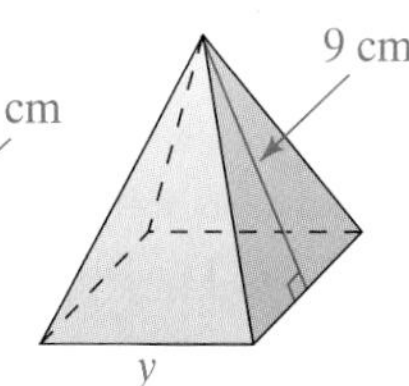

6.75 cm

Additional Examples

1 Two triangular pyramids are similar. In the triangles that form their bases, the height of the smaller is 12 in. and the height of the larger is 18 in. The slant height of the larger is 30 in. Find the slant height of the smaller. 20 in.

2 Two prisms are similar, but in the second the dimensions of the first are quadrupled. The first has a surface area of 26 ft^2. Find the surface area of the second. 416 ft^2

3 A cylindrical pitcher with a diameter of 6 in. has a similar-shaped cylindrical sugar bowl that holds $\frac{1}{27}$ of what the pitcher holds. Find the diameter of the sugar bowl. 2 in.

Closure

- *How do you find the dimensions of similar solids using proportions?* Sample: Set up a proportion between the corresponding dimensions and use cross products to solve for the missing measurement.
- *How do you find surface areas and volumes of similar solids?* Sample: Set up a proportion using the fact that the ratio of the surface areas equals the ratio of the squares of the linear measurements and the ratio of the volumes equals the ratio of the cubes of the linear dimensions.

3. Practice

Assignment Guide

Objective 1

A B Core 1–2, 13, 15

Objective 2

A B Core 3–12, 14, 16

C Extension 17–21

Test Prep 22–25

Mixed Review 26–29

Carpentry Connection
Exercises 12 Show the edge of plywood to see each ply, or layer.

Practice 9-9 — Exploring Similar Solids

Complete the table for each prism.

	Original Size		Doubled Dimensions		
	Dimensions (m)	S.A. (m^2)	Dimensions (m)	S.A. (m^2)	New S.A. ÷ Old S.A.
1.	2 × 3 × 4	52	4 × 6 × 8	208	4
2.	5 × 5 × 9	230	10 × 10 × 18	920	4
3.	7 × 7 × 7	294	14 × 14 × 14	1,176	4
4.	8 × 12 × 15	792	16 × 24 × 30	3,168	4
5.	15 × 15 × 20	1,650	30 × 30 × 40	6,600	4
6.	32 × 32 × 32	6,144	64 × 64 × 64	24,576	4

7. What conclusion can you draw?
Sample answer: If the three dimensions of a prism are doubled, the new surface area is four times the old surface area.

8. A rectangular prism is 8 cm by 10 cm by 15 cm. What are the volume and surface area of the prism?
1,200 cm^3; 700 cm^2

9. In Exercise 8, if each dimension of the prism is halved, what are the new volume and surface area?
150 cm^3; 175 cm^2

Use the triangular prism shown at the right for Exercises 10 and 11.

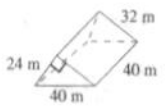

10. Find the volume and surface area.
15,360 m^3; 4,608 m^2

11. If each dimension of the prism is doubled, what are the new volume and surface areas?
122,880 m^3; 18,432 m^2

12. A rectangular prism is 9 in. long, 15 in. wide, and 21 in. high. The length is halved. What happens to the volume?
It is one-half the volume; 1,417.5 $in.^3$

13. A rectangular prism is 8 cm long, 24 cm wide, and 43 cm high. The length is doubled, and the width is tripled. What happens to the volume?
It is multiplied by 6.

Reteaching 9-9 — Explaning Similar Solids

Two solids are *similar solids* if they have the same shape and all of their corresponding lengths are proportional. A special relationship exists among the measures of similar solids:

- The ratios of the corresponding dimensions of similar solids is $\frac{a}{b}$.
- The ratio of their surface areas is $\frac{a^2}{b^2}$.
- The ratio of their volumes is $\frac{a^3}{b^3}$.

Example: Two similar cylindrical watering cans have diameters of 14 in. and 18 in. Find the volume of the larger watering can if the volume of the smaller watering can is 882 $in.^3$.

① Write the ratio of corresponding dimensions.
$\frac{14}{18} = \frac{7}{9}$, so the ratio of the volumes is $\frac{a^3}{b^3} = \frac{7^3}{9^3}$, or $\frac{343}{729}$.

② Write a proportion: $\frac{\text{volume of small watering can}}{\text{volume of large watering can}} = \frac{343}{729}$

$\frac{882}{x} = \frac{343}{729}$ ← Substitute the known volume.
$343x = (882)(729)$ ← Cross multiply.
$343x = 642{,}978$ ← Divide both sides by 343.
$x = 1{,}874.57$ ← Simplify.

The volume of the larger watering can is about 1,875 $in.^3$.

For each pair of similar solids find the value of the variable.

1.
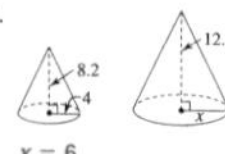

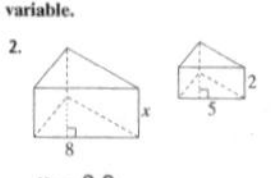

$x = 6$

2.

$x = 3.2$

3. A triangular prism has a height of 18 cm, surface area of 463 cm^2, and volume of 279 cm^3. Find the surface area and volume of a similar prism with a height of 12 cm. Round your answers to the nearest whole number.
S.A. = 206 cm^2; V = 83 cm^3

4. A rectangular prism has a height of 24 inches, a surface area of 1,088 $in.^2$ and a volume of 2,112 $in.^3$. Find the surface area and volume of a similar prism with a height of 36 in.
S.A. = 2,448 $in.^2$; V = 7,128 $in.^3$

Example 2 (page 518)

Find the surface area of each similar figure to the nearest whole unit.

3. A triangular prism has a height of 9 cm and a surface area of 160 cm^2. Find the surface area of a similar prism with a height of 7 cm. 97 cm^2

4. A cone has a radius of 2 ft and a surface area of 75 ft^2. Find the surface area of a similar cone with a radius of 3.5 ft. 230 ft^2

5. **Picnics** Shauna brought two similar blocks of ice to the family picnic. The larger block has a surface area of 6,000 cm^2. The smaller block has dimensions that are $\frac{3}{4}$ as long. What is the surface area of the smaller block of ice? 3,375 cm^2

Example 3 (page 519)

Find the volume of each similar solid.

6.
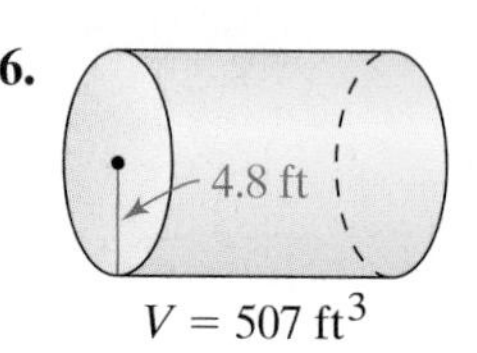

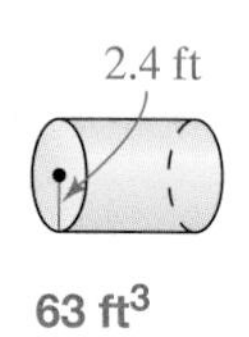

63 ft^3

7.
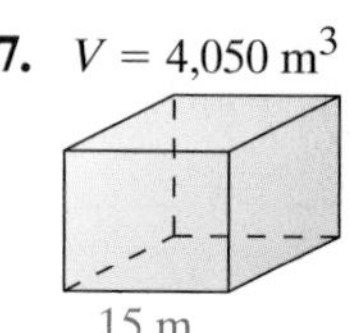

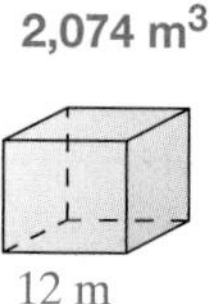

2,074 m^3

8. **Vases** Two similar cylindrical flower vases have diameters of 6 inches and 8 inches. Find the volume of the larger vase if the volume of the smaller vase is 339 $in.^3$. 804 $in.^3$

B Apply Your Skills

In each exercise, the surface area and volume of a solid are given. Use the ratio of the corresponding dimensions of this solid to a similar solid to find the surface area and volume of the similar solid.

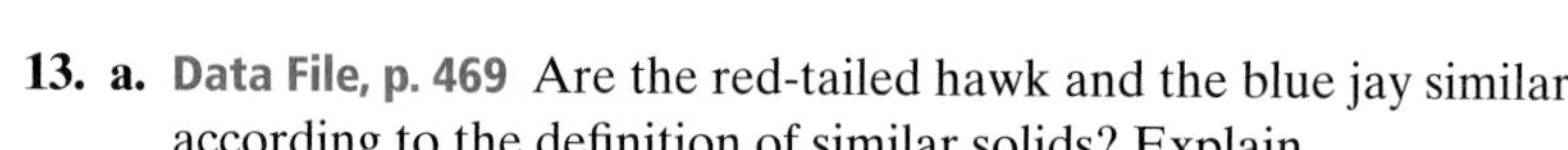

9. S.A. = 23 ft^2, V = 12 ft^3, ratio = $\frac{1}{2}$ — 92 ft^2; 96 ft^3

10. S.A. = 39 $in.^2$, V = 16.5 $in.^3$, ratio = $\frac{4}{3}$ — 22 $in.^2$; 7 $in.^3$

11. S.A. = 103 yd^2, V = 51 yd^3, ratio = $\frac{8}{1}$ — 2 yd^2; 0.1 yd^3

12. **Carpentry** Gina used 78 square feet of plywood to build a storage bin to hold her gardening supplies. How much plywood will she need to build a similar box for her hand tools if the dimensions of the box are half the dimensions of the bin? 20 ft^2

GPS

13. a. **Data File, p. 469** Are the red-tailed hawk and the blue jay similar according to the definition of similar solids? Explain.
b. In general, the larger the bird, the larger the ratio of its wingspan to its body length. Why do you suppose this might be true?
13a–b. See margin.

14. **Number Sense** Amelia sees two cubes in a sculpture garden and estimates that the edge length of the larger cube is between 2.5 and 3 times the edge length of the smaller cube. How much greater should she estimate the volume of the larger cube to be? Explain. See margin.

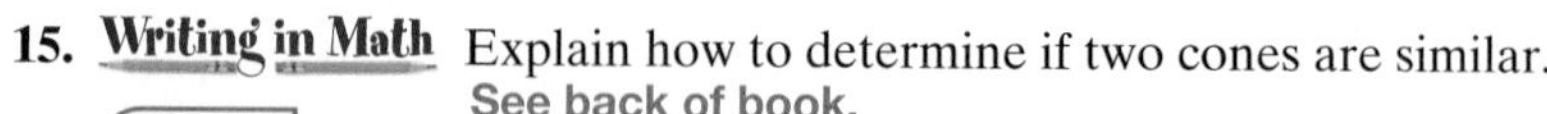

15. **Writing in Math** Explain how to determine if two cones are similar. See back of book.

16. **Algebra** Two prisms are similar. The surface area of one is four times the surface area of the other. What is the ratio of corresponding dimensions? $\frac{2}{1}$

Real-World Connection
Carpenters use algebra and geometry to plan and build their woodworking projects.

GPS Use the Guided Problem Solving worksheet with Exercise 12.

13a. No; their typical wingspans and lengths are not proportional.

b. Answers may vary. Sample: Larger birds weigh more and require far greater wingspans to provide enough lift to keep the birds flying.

14. Answers may vary. Sample: about 20 times as great
$\frac{2.5^3}{1^3} = \frac{V}{1}, V \approx 16$
$\frac{3^3}{1^3} = \frac{V}{1}, V \approx 27$
So the volume would be between 16 and 27 times as great.

Challenge

For each figure, one dimension of a similar figure is given below. Use the ratio of corresponding dimensions to find the surface area and volume for the second figure to the nearest whole unit.

17. 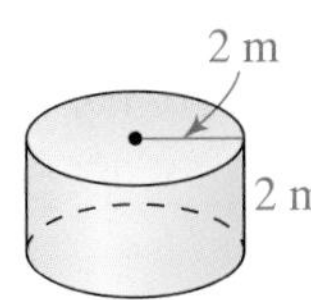

radius = 4 m
201 m^2; 201 m^3

18. 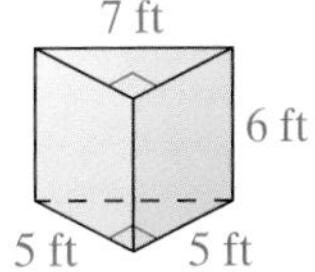

height = 19 ft
1,274 ft^2; 2,382 ft^3

19. 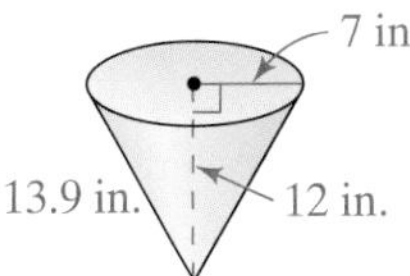

radius = 16 in.
2,403 $in.^2$; 7,353 $in.^3$

20. 10.1 cm

20. To the nearest tenth, find the edge length of a cube that has a volume twice that of the cube shown at the right.

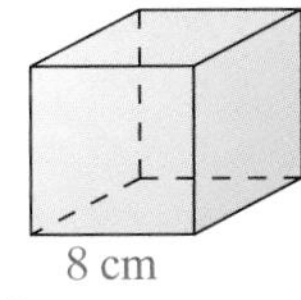

21. **Stretch Your Thinking** A square pyramid has a base-edge length of 5 in. and a volume of 75 $in.^3$. A similar pyramid has a height of 12 in. What is its volume? 178 $in.^3$

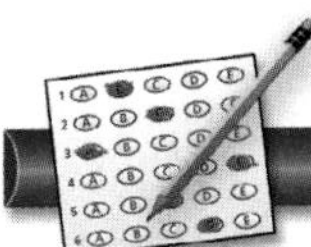

Test Prep

Multiple Choice

Use the figures at the right for Exercises 22–24.

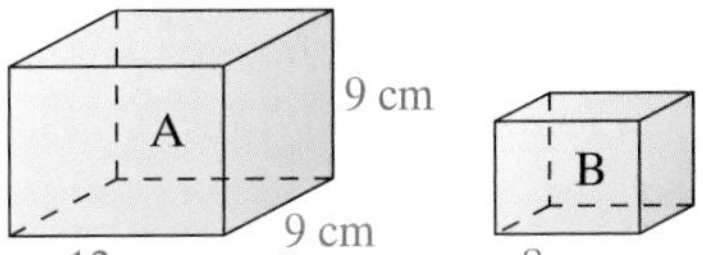

A: 12 cm, 9 cm, 9 cm
B: 8 cm

22. What is the ratio of corresponding dimensions of the larger prism to the similar smaller prism? C

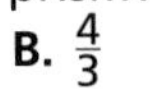

A. $\frac{1}{2}$ B. $\frac{4}{3}$ C. $\frac{3}{2}$ D. $\frac{12}{1}$

Take It to the NET
Online lesson quiz at
www.PHSchool.com
Web Code: aca-0909

23. What is the volume of Prism A? F

F. 972 cm^3 G. 594 cm^2 H. 108 cm^2 I. 30 cm^3

24. What is the surface area of Prism B? B

A. 594 cm^3 B. 264 cm^2 C. 111 cm^2 D. 30 cm^2

Short Response

25. A cone has a height of 5 cm and a volume of 62.8 cm^3. What is the volume of a similar cone whose height is 8 cm? Show your work. See margin.

Mixed Review

Lesson 7-2

Find each product. Write the answer in scientific notation.

26. $(5 \times 10^6)(15 \times 10^7)$
7.5×10^{14}

27. $(4 \times 10^4)(6 \times 10^7)(8.1 \times 10^8)$
1.944×10^{21}

Lesson 6-8

Find the final balance in each account. Round to the nearest cent.

28. \$492 at $3\frac{1}{4}$% simple interest for 16 years \$747.84

29. \$12,098 at 5% simple interest for 4 years \$14,517.60

25. [2] $\frac{8^3}{5^3} = \frac{V}{62.8}$
$V = 257.2288$
[1] minor error OR correct answer without work shown

Alternative Assessment

Students make a rectangular solid from a graph-paper net. They then count squares to find its surface area. Students then double and halve the dimensions to create two other rectangular solids. Then they compare their surface areas.

4. Assess

Lesson Quiz 9-9

Use these similar square pyramids to answer the questions.

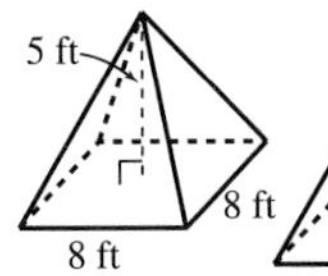

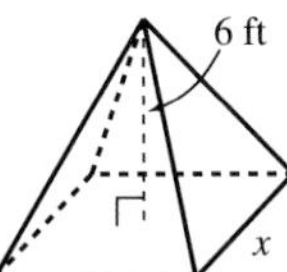

1. Find the similarity ratio of the smaller pyramid to the larger pyramid. 5 : 6
2. The surface area of the larger pyramid is 239.7 ft^2. Find the surface area of the smaller pyramid. about 166.5 ft^2
3. Find the volume of the larger pyramid to the nearest whole unit. 184 ft^3
4. Find the value of x. 9.6 ft

Test Prep

Resources
For additional practice with a variety of test item formats:
- Test Prep, p. 527
- Test-Taking Strategies, p. 523
- Test-Taking Strategies with Transparencies

Enrichment 9-9 Exploring Similar Solids

Patterns in Geometry

Use your knowledge of volume and surface area to find the relationship between the rectangular prisms below.

1. Find the volume and the surface area for each set of dimensions of the prisms below.

Base		Height	Volume ($units^3$)	Surface area ($units^2$)
length	width			
1	36	6	216	516
2	18	6	216	312
3	12	6	216	252
4	9	6	216	228
6	6	6	216	216

2. What pattern do you notice in the dimensions of the prisms?
Sample answer: Dimensions of the base change, but have an area of 36 $units^2$ while the height stays the same.

3. What is the relationship of the volume and surface area?
Sample answer: As the dimensions approach the cube, the surface area become less for the same volume. The cube has the same surface area as volume.

4. Repeat the analysis for four sets of dimensions with a volume of 384 $units^3$. Was your outcome the same?

Base		Height	Volume ($units^3$)	Surface area ($units^2$)
length	width			
1	64	6	384	908
2	32	6	384	536
4	16	6	384	368
8	8	6	384	320

Extension

Significant Digits

Earlier in this chapter, students investigated the concept of precision. In this extension to Lesson 9-9, they explore the concept of significant digits.

Teaching Notes

Discuss with students that using significant digits in a calculation is a way of keeping track of the precision in a measurement that they might make in a science class experiment.

Discuss the introductory sentences about significant digits. As an example, point out that 22 has two significant digits, whereas 22.4 has three. Then go over the information in the chart. Have students provide additional examples for each of the cases presented.

Inclusion
Finding significant digits when zeros are involved can be challenging for some students. There are three significant digits in 7.90 (including the zero after the decimal point). But, it is impossible to tell whether the zeros in 7,900 are significant. A way around this problem is to use scientific notation: $7900 = 7.9 \times 10^3$, which shows two significant digits.

Error Prevention!

Tell students that zeros placed *between* other digits are *always* significant: 0.046 has two significant digits, whereas 4009 has four. This explains why the zero preceding the 4 in 0.006040 for the first case in the chart is significant.

Teaching Tip
When you work through the Example with students, point out that the same rule applies to dividing. But when adding or subtracting, the number of decimal places, *not* significant digits, in the answer should be the same as the least number of decimal places in any of the numbers being added or subtracted.

Extension Significant Digits

For Use With Lesson 9-9

Significant digits are the digits that represent an actual measurement. Nonzero digits (1–9) are always significant. Zero digits are only significant in certain places.

Type of Number	Which Zeros Are Significant	Example
Decimal numbers between 0 and 1	Zeros to the left of *all* the nonzero digits are not significant. All other zeros are significant.	Significant digits: 6040; 0.006040; Not significant digits: 0.00
Positive integers	Zeros to the right of *all* the nonzero digits are not significant. Zeros between nonzero digits are significant.	Significant digits: 2034; 203,400; Not significant digits: 00
Noninteger decimal numbers greater than 1	All zeros are significant.	Significant digits: 350,070.50

When you calculate with measurements, round your answer to match the measurement with the least number of significant digits in the problem.

EXAMPLE Multiplying With Significant Digits

Surveying A surveyor found a rectangular land lot to be 115.6 ft by 81.2 ft. Find its area to the appropriate number of significant digits.

$115.6 \cdot 81.2 = 9{,}386.72$ ← **Multiply.**

115.6 ↑ **4 significant digits**; 81.2 ↑ **3 significant digits**

Since the least number of significant digits in the measurement is 3, round the answer to 3 significant digits. The area is 9,390 ft^2.

EXERCISES

Determine the number of significant digits in each number.

1. 187.90 5 **2.** 0.00569 3 **3.** 124.706 6 **4.** 1.0101 5

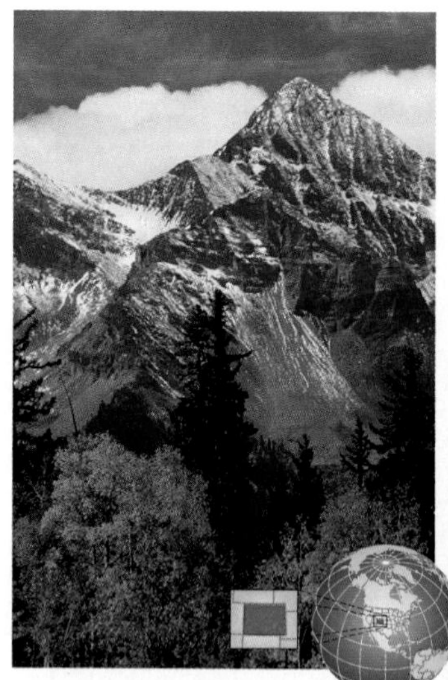

5. Land Area Colorado has a rectangular shape. It is about 372 mi wide and about 278 mi long. Find the approximate area of the entire state of Colorado to the appropriate number of significant digits. 103,000 mi^2

6. Reasoning A student says that when comparing two measurements, the measurement with the greater number of significant digits will always be the measurement with the greater precision. Do you agree? Explain. See margin.

Extension

6. No; for example, 1,230 mi has three significant digits, but it is less precise than 12 mi, with only two significant digits.

Eliminating Answers

Before solving a multiple-choice problem, you can usually eliminate some answer choices. This can save you time and help you to make an "educated" guess if you do not actually know how to find the answer.

1 EXAMPLE

Find the volume of the square pyramid at the right.

7.2 cm
7.2 cm
22.3 cm

A. 36.528 cm^3 **B.** 320.724 cm^3
C. 385.344 cm^2 **D.** 3,187.367 cm^3

Underestimate and overestimate the answer using compatible numbers.

$V = \frac{1}{3}Bh = \frac{1}{3}(7.2^2)(22.3)$

Underestimate

$V \approx \frac{1}{3}(48)(20) = \frac{1}{3}(960) = 320$

Overestimate

$V \approx \frac{1}{3}(50)(24) = \frac{1}{3}(1{,}200) = 400$

The answer is going to be between 320 and 400. Since answers A and D do not fall between 320 and 400, you can eliminate them. Answer B is very close to the underestimate, so you can make an educated guess that C is the most likely answer.

2 EXAMPLE

Determine the number of significant digits in 160.003.

A. 1 **B.** 3 **C.** 6 **D.** 8

The number of significant digits is at least 3 since there are 3 nonzero digits. It is also no more than 6 since there are only 6 digits in all. Since answer choice A is smaller than 3 and answer choice D is larger than 6, you can eliminate both choices. The correct answer must be choice B or C. Using the rules for significant digits, C is the answer.

EXERCISES

Use the following multiple-choice problem for Exercises 1 and 2.

To the nearest square meter, what is the surface area of a cone with a radius of 3 m and a slant height of 4 m?

A. 21 m^2 **B.** 66 m^2 **C.** 83 m^2 **D.** 120 m^2

1. Explain why you can eliminate answer choices A and D. A is too large; D is too small.
2. Find the correct answer to the problem. B

Test-Taking Strategies

Eliminating Answers

When students take multiple-choice tests, they can improve their chances of success, by the laws of probability, every time they are able to eliminate an answer choice. This feature focuses on the strategy of eliminating answer choices.

Resources

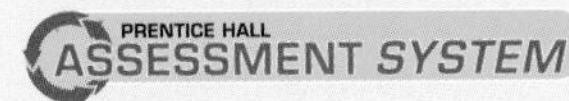

Test-Taking Strategies with Transparencies
- Transparency 6
- Practice master, p. 33

Teaching Notes

Present the following situation to students.

- *You face a test question with five answer choices. You have no idea which answer is correct. You guess at the answer. What is the probability that you are right?* $\frac{1}{5}$
- *Suppose that you know one answer choice is wrong and you eliminate it. Now what is the probability that you guess the right answer?* $\frac{1}{4}$

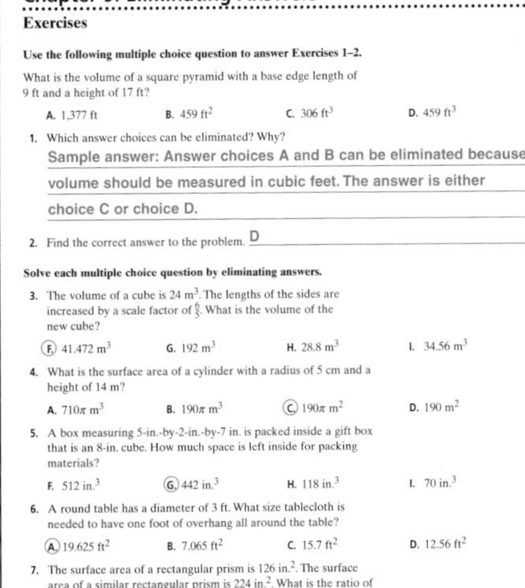

Test-Taking Strategies With Transparencies

Chapter 9: Eliminating Answers

Exercises

Use the following multiple choice question to answer Exercises 1–2.

What is the volume of a square pyramid with a base edge length of 9 ft and a height of 17 ft?

A. 1,377 ft B. 459 ft^2 C. 306 ft^3 D. 459 ft^3

1. Which answer choices can be eliminated? Why? Sample answer: Answer choices A and B can be eliminated because volume should be measured in cubic feet. The answer is either choice C or choice D.
2. Find the correct answer to the problem. D

Solve each multiple choice question by eliminating answers.

3. The volume of a cube is 24 m^3. The lengths of the sides are increased by a scale factor of $\frac{6}{5}$. What is the volume of the new cube?

   (F.) 41.472 m^3 G. 192 m^3 H. 28.8 m^3 I. 34.56 m^3

4. What is the surface area of a cylinder with a radius of 5 cm and a height of 14 m?

   A. 710π m^3 B. 190π m^3 (C.) 190π m^2 D. 190 m^2

5. A box measuring 5-in.-by-2-in.-by-7 in. is packed inside a gift box that is an 8-in. cube. How much space is left inside for packing materials?

   F. 512 $in.^3$ (G.) 442 $in.^3$ H. 118 $in.^3$ I. 70 $in.^3$

6. A round table has a diameter of 3 ft. What size tablecloth is needed to have one foot of overhang all around the table?

   (A.) 19.625 ft^2 B. 7.065 ft^2 C. 15.7 ft^2 D. 12.56 ft^2

7. The surface area of a rectangular prism is 126 $in.^2$. The surface area of a similar rectangular prism is 224 $in.^2$. What is the ratio of corresponding dimensions of the small prism to the large prism?

   F. $\frac{16}{9}$ G. $\frac{4}{3}$ H. $\frac{9}{16}$ (I.) $\frac{3}{4}$

Resources

Student Edition
Extra Practice, Ch. 9, p. 710
English/Spanish Glossary, p. 735
Table of Symbols, p. 730

 **Reaching All Students**
Reading and Math Literacy 9D
Spanish Reading and Math Literacy 9D

Test Preparation
- Chapter 9 practice in test formats

www.PHSchool.com
Student Site
- Self-grading vocabulary test

PH SuccessNet Teacher Center
- Resources

Plus

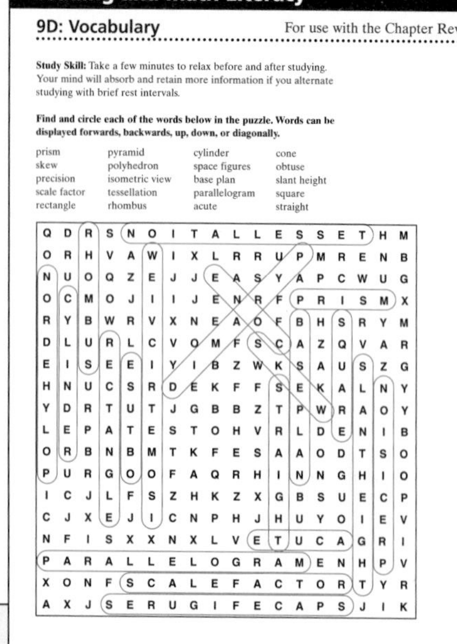

Chapter 9 Chapter Review

Vocabulary

base plan (p. 477)
cone (p. 471)
cylinder (p. 471)
isometric view (p. 477)
lateral area (p. 489)
net (p. 481)
polyhedron (p. 471)
prism (p. 471)
pyramid (p. 471)
similar solids (p. 517)
skew lines (p. 473)
slant height (p. 494)
solids (p. 471)
surface area (p. 488)
volume (p. 500)

Reading Math: Understanding Vocabulary

Choose the correct vocabulary term to complete each sentence.

1. The _?_ of an object is the number of cubic units in an object. volume
2. A(n) _?_ has one base and one vertex, but it is not a polyhedron. cone
3. Both _?_ and _?_ are measured in square units. lateral area, surface area
4. Both a(n) _?_ and a(n) _?_ have two parallel, congruent bases. cylinder, prism
5. A(n) _?_ shows all the surfaces of a solid in one view. isometric view

Take It to the NET
Online vocabulary quiz at www.PHSchool.com
Web Code: acj-0951

Skills and Concepts

9-1 Objectives
- To name solids
- To recognize skew lines

Solids are any objects that have a length, a width, and a height. If all the faces of a solid are polygons, the figure is a **polyhedron. Prisms** and **pyramids** are polyhedrons. **Cylinders** and **cones** are not polyhedrons.

For each solid, describe the shape of the base(s) and the lateral surface(s).

6. rectangular prism rectangle, parallelograms
7. square pyramid square, triangles
8. cylinder circle, curved surface

9-2 and 9-3 Objectives
- To draw a base plan
- To draw top, front, and right views
- To identify nets of solids

A **base plan** shows the shape of the base and the height of each part of a solid. Top, front, and right views show a solid from three different perspectives. A **net** is a pattern that can be folded to form a solid.

9–11. See margin.

Draw a base plan and top, front, and right views of each figure.

9. 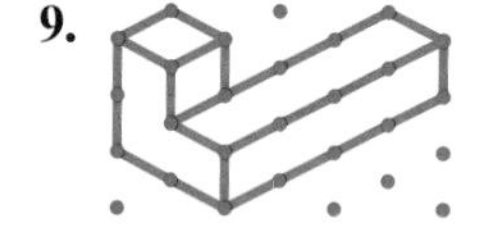
10. 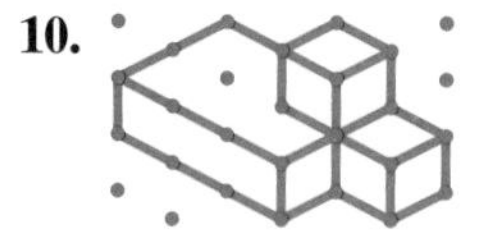
11. 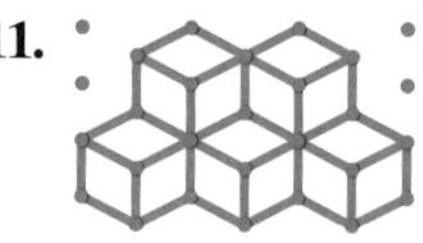

Identify the solid formed by each net.

12. cone
13. 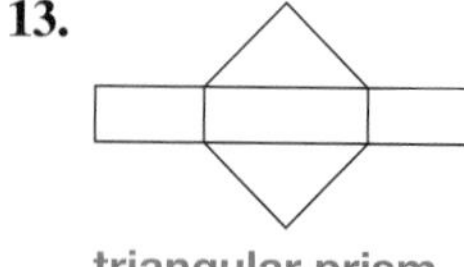 triangular prism
14. 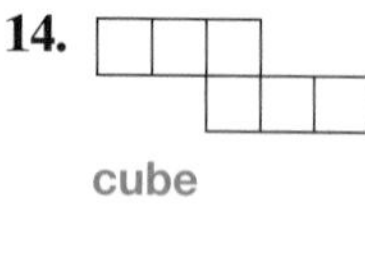 cube

Chapter Review

9. Base plan Top view Front view Side view

10. 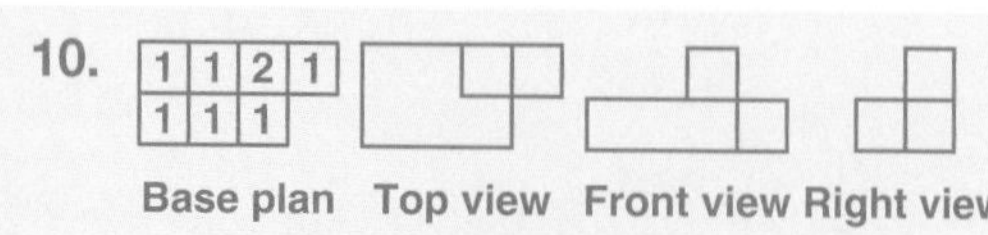

11. 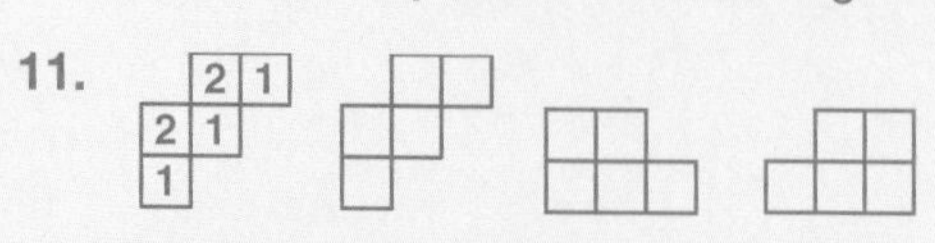

9-4 and 9-6 Objectives

- To find the surface areas of prisms
- To find the surface areas of cylinders
- To find the volumes of prisms
- To find the volumes of cylinders

Lateral area L.A. is the sum of the areas of all of a solid's surfaces except the base(s). **Surface area S.A.** is the sum of the areas of all of the surfaces of a solid. **Volume** V is the number of cubic units in a solid.

Formulas for prisms	Formulas for cylinders
$\text{L.A.} = ph$	$\text{L.A.} = 2\pi rh$
$\text{S.A.} = \text{L.A.} + 2B$	$\text{S.A.} = \text{L.A.} + 2B$
$V = Bh$	$V = Bh$

Find the lateral area, surface area, and volume to the nearest whole unit.

15. 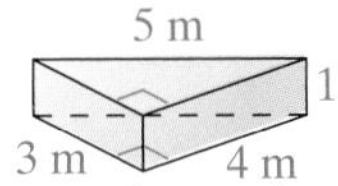 5 m, 1 m, 3 m, 4 m

12 m^2; 24 m^2; 6 m^3

16. 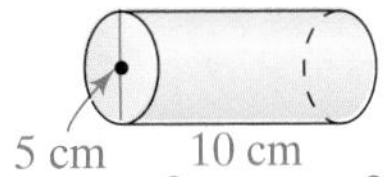 5 cm, 10 cm

157 cm^2; 196 cm^2; 196 cm^3

17.

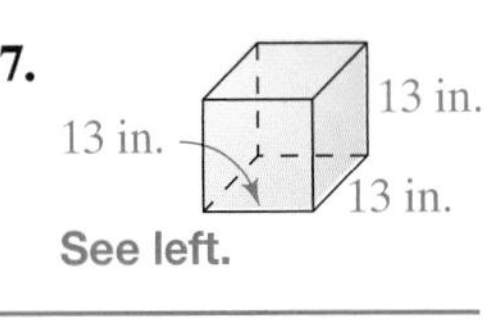

See left.

17. 676 in.^{2}; 1,014 in.^{2}; 2,197 in.^{3}

9-5 and 9-7 Objectives

- To find the surface areas of pyramids
- To find the surface areas of cones
- To find the volumes of pyramids
- To find the volumes of cones

The **slant height** ℓ of a pyramid or a cone is the distance from the figure's vertex to its base edge b. It is used to find the lateral area or surface area.

Formulas for pyramids	Formulas for cones
$\text{L.A.} = 2b\ell$	$\text{L.A.} = \pi r\ell$
$\text{S.A.} = \text{L.A.} + B$	$\text{S.A.} = \text{L.A.} + B$
$V = \frac{1}{3}Bh$	$V = \frac{1}{3}Bh$

Find the lateral area, surface area, and volume to the nearest whole unit.

18.

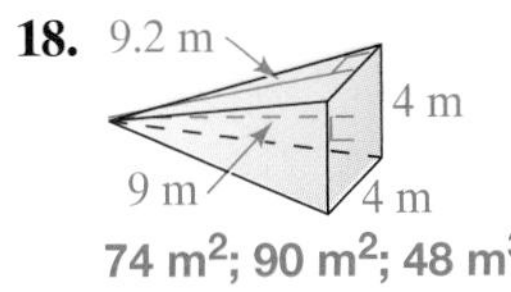

74 m^2; 90 m^2; 48 m^3

19.

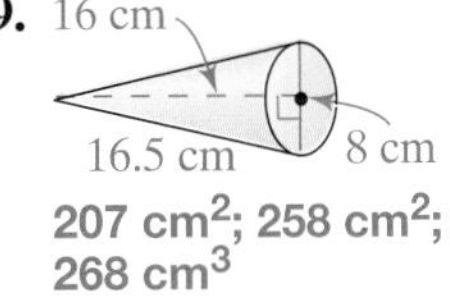

207 cm^2; 258 cm^2; 268 cm^3

20.

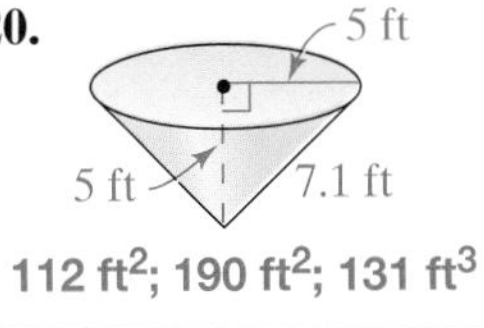

112 ft^2; 190 ft^2; 131 ft^3

9-8 Objective

- To solve a problem by combining strategies

Sometimes you need to use more than one strategy to solve a problem.

21. How many different rectangular prisms can you make using exactly 12 unit cubes? What are the dimensions of the rectangular prism with the smallest surface area? With the largest surface area?
3; 2 × 2 × 3; 1 × 1 × 12

9-9 Objectives

- To find dimensions of similar solids using proportions
- To find surface areas and volumes of similar solids

Similar solids have the same shape and corresponding lengths that are proportional. If the ratio of their corresponding lengths is $\frac{a}{b}$, the ratio of their surface areas is $\frac{a^2}{b^2}$, and the ratio of their volumes is $\frac{a^3}{b^3}$.

For each solid, find the surface area and volume of a similar solid whose height is $\frac{4}{5}$ of the height given. Round to the nearest whole unit.

22.

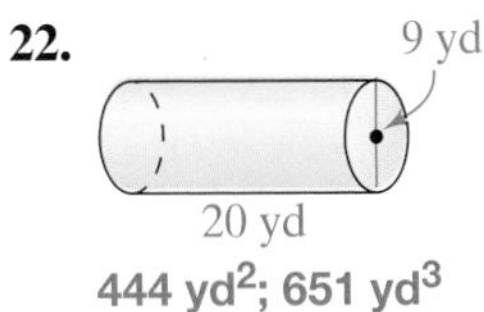

444 yd^2; 651 yd^3

23.

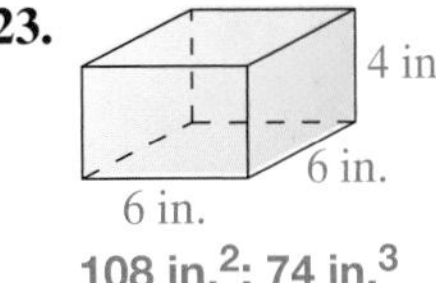

108 in.^{2}; 74 in.^{3}

24.

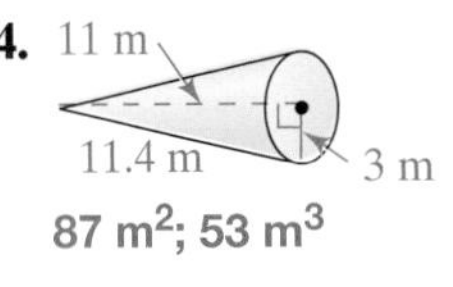

87 m^2; 53 m^3

Quarter 3 Test – Form B

Quarter 3 Test – Form A

Quarter 3 Test — Form A

Chapters 7–9

1. Saturn is about 1,430,000,000 km from the sun. Write this distance in scientific notation.
2. Write 5.45×10^5 in standard notation.
3. Simplify. $y^3 \cdot y^6$
4. Simplify. 5^{-2}
5. Write using a single exponent. $\frac{8^9}{8^4}$
6. Simplify. $(2t^3)^4$
7. Write $(8^2)^{-3}$ using one base and one exponent.
8. Light travels at 3.00×10^8 m/s. How many seconds does a light ray take to travel 12×10^9 m?
9. Write the binary number 11101_2 as a decimal number.
10. Write the decimal number 43 as a binary number.
11. Name an angle adjacent to $\angle DFC$.

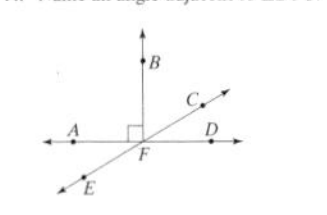

12. Use the diagram below to find the measures of $\angle 1$, $\angle 2$, $\angle 3$.

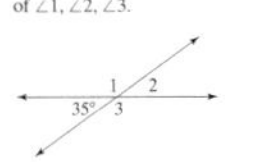

13. Find the measure of the complement of an angle with measure 47°.
14. Find the measure of the supplement of an angle with measure 128°.
15. Name the two pairs of alternate interior angles in the figure.

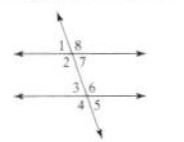

16. In the figure below, line p is parallel to line m. If $m\angle 7 = 63°$, find $m\angle 4$.

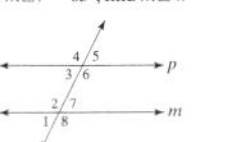

17. Determine whether the pair of triangles is congruent. Explain.

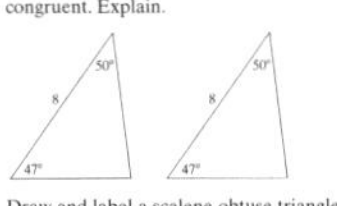

18. Draw and label a scalene obtuse triangle.
19. Determine the best name for the quadrilateral.

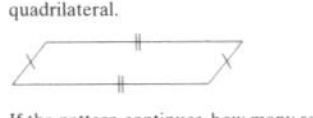

20. If the pattern continues, how many squares are in the 7th diagram?

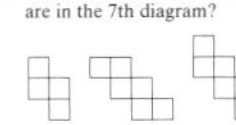

21. Find the measure of each angle of a regular hexagon.

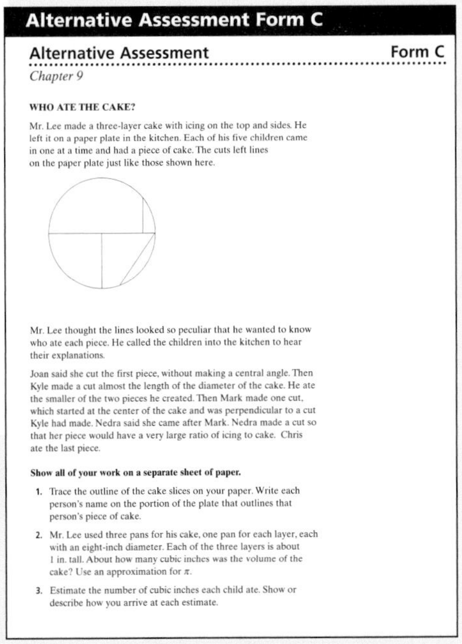

Alternative Assessment Form C

Alternative Assessment — Form C

Chapter 9

WHO ATE THE CAKE?

Mr. Lee made a three-layer cake with icing on the top and sides. He left it on a paper plate in the kitchen. Each of his five children came in one at a time and had a piece of cake. The cuts left lines on the paper plate just like those shown here.

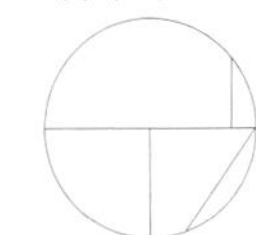

Mr. Lee thought the lines looked so peculiar that he wanted to know who ate each piece. He called the children into the kitchen to hear their explanations.

Joan said she cut the first piece, without making a central angle. Then Kyle made a cut almost the length of the diameter of the cake. He ate the smaller of the two pieces he created. Then Mark made one cut, which started at the center of the cake and was perpendicular to a cut Kyle had made. Nedra said she came after Mark. Nedra made a cut so that her piece would have a very large ratio of icing to cake. Chris ate the last piece.

Show all of your work on a separate sheet of paper.

1. Trace the outline of the cake slices on your paper. Write each person's name on the portion of the plate that outlines that person's piece of cake.
2. Mr. Lee used three pans for his cake, one pan for each layer, each with an eight-inch diameter. Each of the three layers is about 1 in. tall. About how many cubic inches was the volume of the cake? Use an approximation for π.
3. Estimate the number of cubic inches each child ate. Show or describe how you arrive at each estimate.

Chapter Test

Resources

Teaching Resources
Ch. 9 Test, Forms A & B
Ch. 9 Alternative Assessment, Form C

Reaching All Students
Spanish Ch. 9 Test, Forms A & B
Spanish Ch. 9 Alternative Assessment, Form C

Assessment Resources
- Ch. 9 Test, Forms A & B
- Ch. 9 Alternative Assessment, Form C

Computer Test Generator CD
- Ch. 9 Instant Chapter Test™
- Make your own Ch. 9 test

www.PHSchool.com
Student Site
- Self-grading Ch. 9 test

PH SuccessNet Teacher Center
- Resources

Plus iTEXT

23. Since $\pi r^2 h$ multiplies three linear measures together, the result will be in cubic units, which is appropriate for volume.

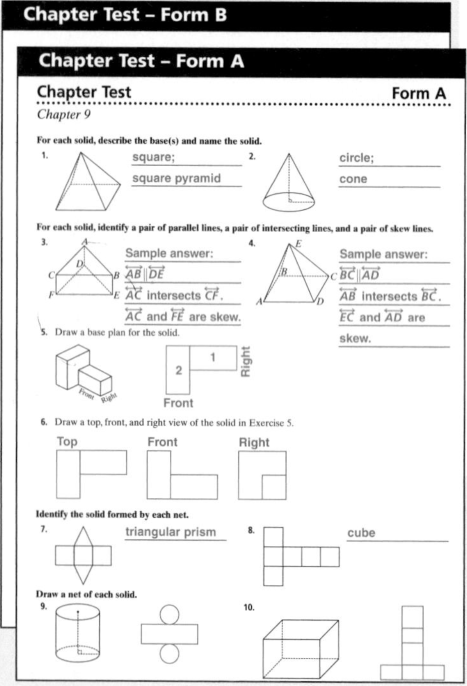

Chapter Test – Form B

Chapter Test – Form A

Chapter Test Form A
Chapter 9

For each solid, describe the base(s) and name the solid.

1. square; square pyramid
2. circle; cone

For each solid, identify a pair of parallel lines, a pair of intersecting lines, and a pair of skew lines.

3. Sample answer: $\overleftrightarrow{AB} \parallel \overleftrightarrow{DE}$; $\overleftrightarrow{AC}$ intersects $\overleftrightarrow{CF}$. $\overleftrightarrow{AC}$ and $\overleftrightarrow{FE}$ are skew.
4. Sample answer: $\overleftrightarrow{BC} \parallel \overleftrightarrow{AD}$; $\overleftrightarrow{AB}$ intersects $\overleftrightarrow{BC}$. $\overleftrightarrow{EC}$ and $\overleftrightarrow{AD}$ are skew.

5. Draw a base plan for the solid.

6. Draw a top, front, and right view of the solid in Exercise 5.
Top Front Right

Identify the solid formed by each net.

7. triangular prism
8. cube

Draw a net of each solid.

9.
10.

Chapter 9 Chapter Test

Name each solid and describe its base(s).

1. 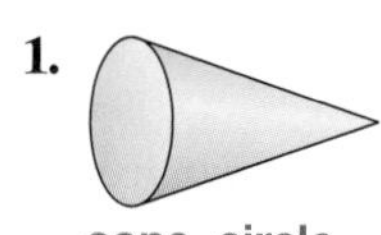 cone, circle
2. 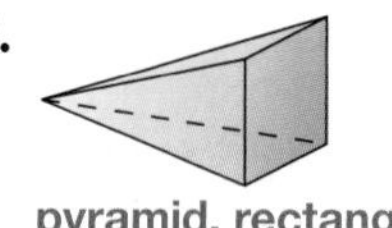 pyramid, rectangle
3. 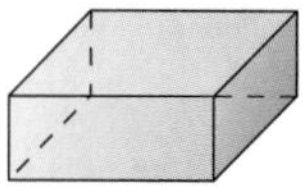 prism, rectangles
4. 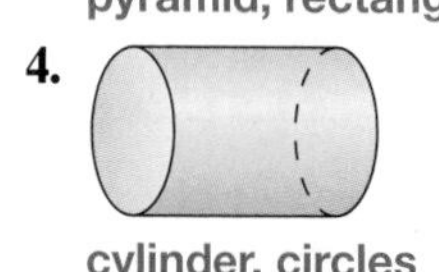 cylinder, circles

For each solid, identify a pair of parallel lines, a pair of intersecting lines, and a pair of skew lines.
5–6. Answers may vary. Samples are given.

5. 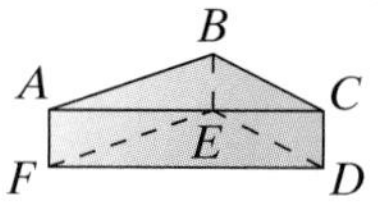 $\overline{BC}, \overline{ED}$; $\overline{FD}, \overline{CD}$; $\overline{AB}, \overline{CD}$
6. 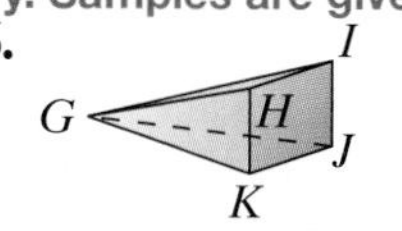

$\overline{HI}, \overline{JK}$; $\overline{GK}, \overline{HK}$; $\overline{GH}, \overline{IJ}$

Draw a base plan for each solid.
7–8. See margin.

7. 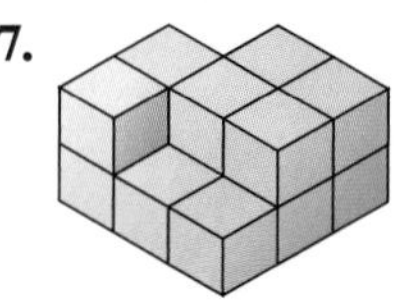
8. 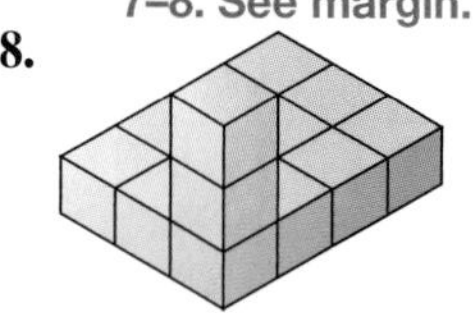

Draw a top, front, and side view of each solid.

9. 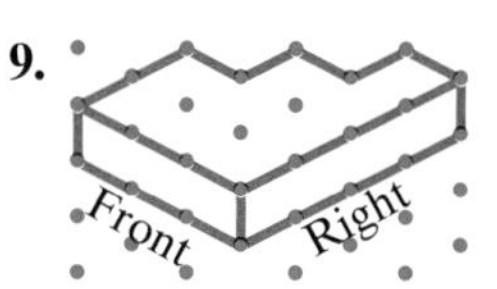

10. 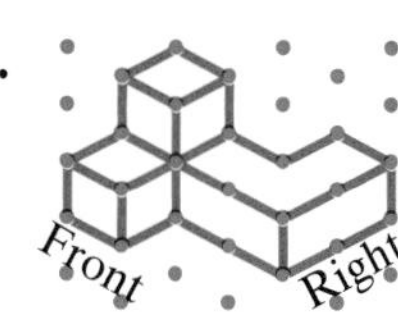

9–10. See margin.

Identify the solid formed by each net.

11. 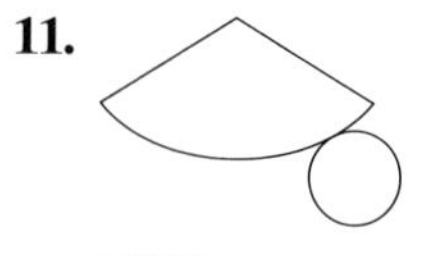 cone
12. 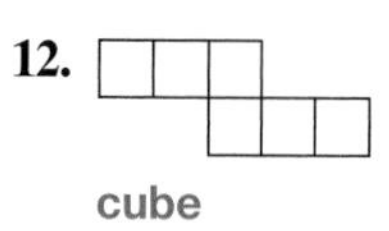 cube

Draw a net of each solid. 13–14. See margin.

13. 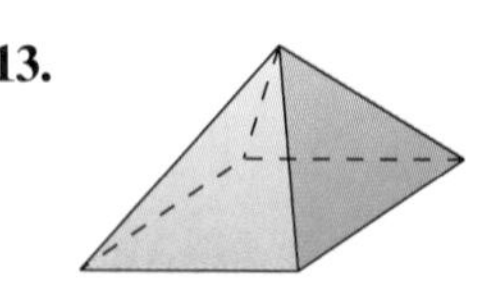
14. 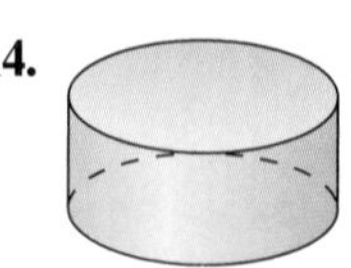

Find the lateral area and surface area of each solid to the nearest whole unit.

15. 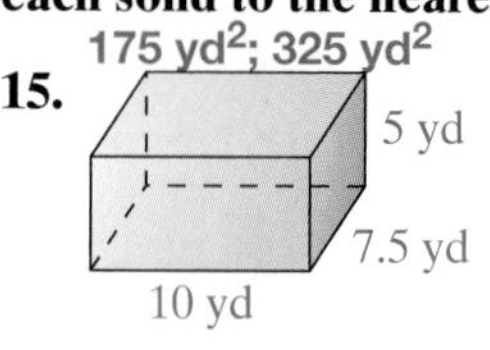

175 yd^2; 325 yd^2
16. 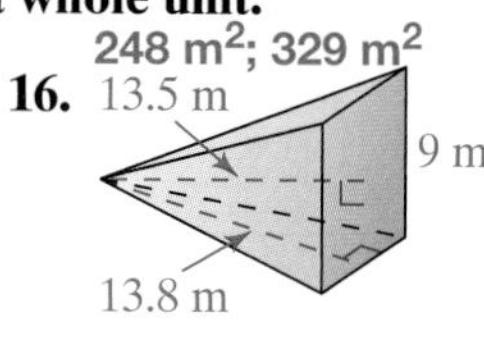

248 m^2; 329 m^2
17. 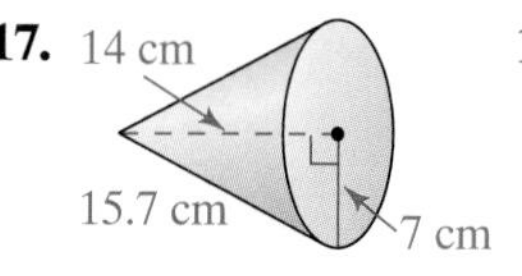

345 cm^2; 499 cm^2
18. 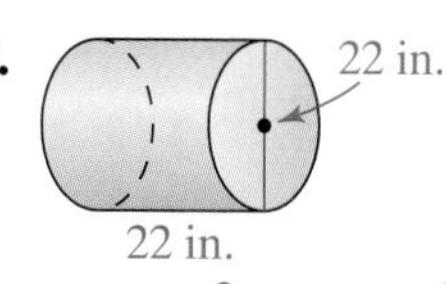

1,521 $in.^2$; 2,281 $in.^2$

Find the volume of each solid. When using π, round to the nearest whole unit.

19. 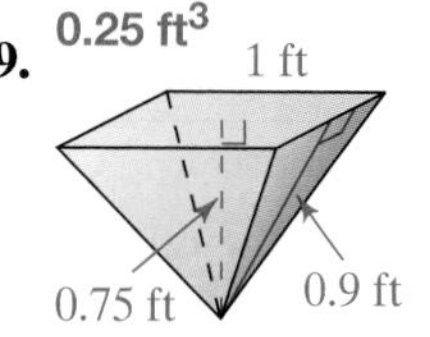

0.25 ft^3
20. 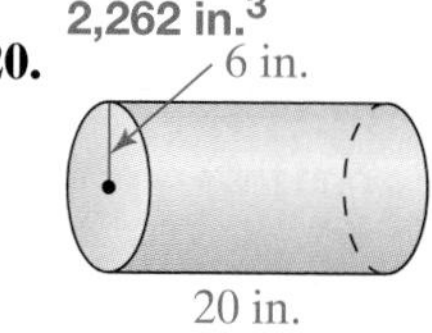

2,262 $in.^3$
21. 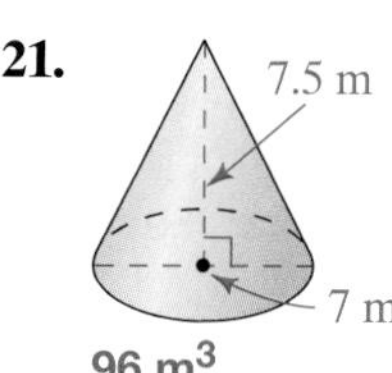

96 m^3
22. 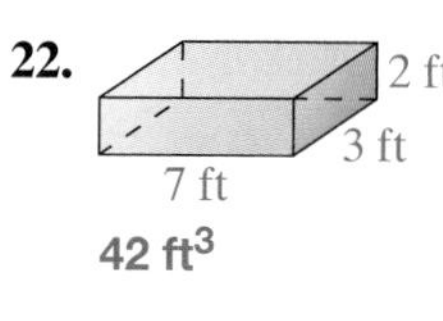

42 ft^3

23. **Writing in Math** The formulas for surface area and volume of a cylinder involve $\pi r^2 h$ and $2\pi rh + 2\pi r^2$. Explain how to tell which expression goes with which formula. See margin.

24. The figures below are similar solids. Find the measures of all missing lengths. See margin.

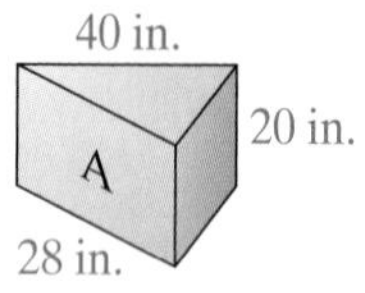

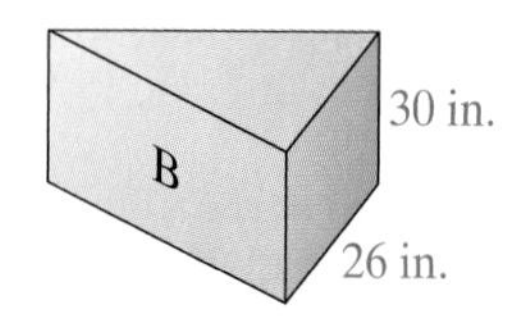

25. **Water Bottle** A cylindrical water bottle has a height of 6 in., a surface area of 44 $in.^2$, and a volume of 19 $in.^3$. To the nearest whole unit, find the surface area and volume of a similar water bottle whose height is 9 in. 99 $in.^2$; 64 $in.^3$

7. 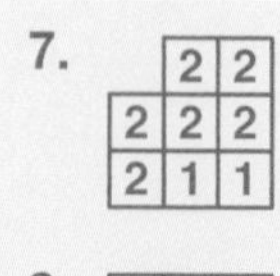

8. 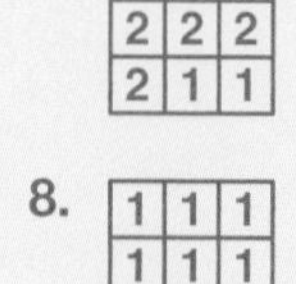

9. 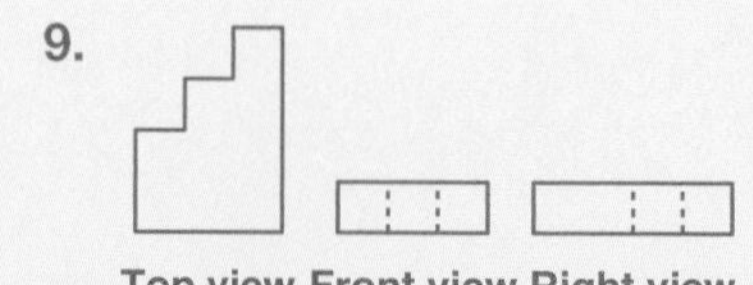
Top view Front view Right view

10. 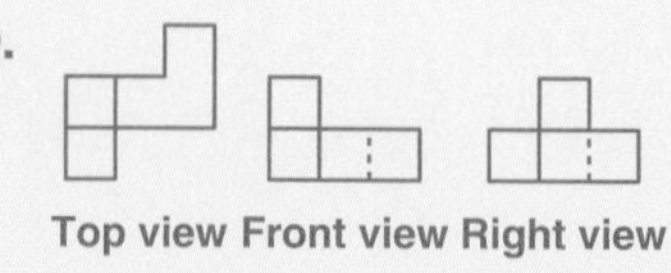
Top view Front view Right view

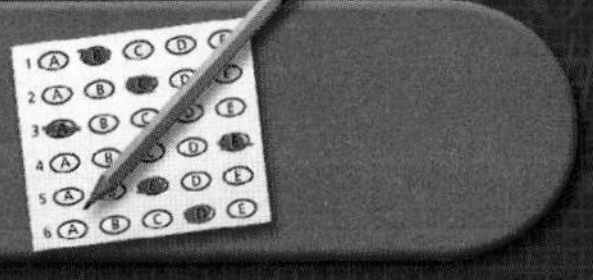

Test Prep

Reading Comprehension **Read each passage and answer the questions that follow.**

CD Players Compact disc players read the data on CDs as the discs spin, moving from the center to the outer edge of the disc. Some CD players spin at a steady rate. They read a different amount of data because the data circle gets larger with each revolution. Other CD players read data at a constant rate. Their discs spin at a variable rate, changing the speed as the circumference of the data circle changes.

1. How does the amount of data read per second change for a CD player that spins at a steady rate? C
   - **A.** less data per second as the circles grow
   - **B.** less data per second as the circles shrink
   - **C.** more data per second as the circles grow
   - **D.** more data per second as the circles shrink

2. For a disc of radius r, which expression gives the length of a data circle located halfway from the center to the disc's outer edge? H
   - **F.** $\frac{1}{2}\pi r^2$ **G.** $\frac{1}{2}\pi r$
   - **H.** πr **I.** $2\pi r$

3. How does the rate of spin change for a CD player that reads a constant amount of data per second? C
   - **A.** spins faster as the data circles grow
   - **B.** spins faster as the data circles shrink
   - **C.** spins slower as the data circles grow
   - **D.** spins slower as the data circles shrink

4. For a variable-speed CD player, the speed halfway to the outer edge is what percent of the speed at the outer edge? I
   - **F.** 25% **G.** 50%
   - **H.** 100% **I.** 200%

Airplanes Why do wings work? The top of a typical wing is curved. The underside is relatively flat. As a plane flies, air molecules sliding over a wing have as much as 15% farther to travel to reach the wing's trailing edge than molecules passing under the wing. Even so, molecules passing over the wing reach the trailing edge first. The wing shape speeds up air flowing over the wing and forces it downward. In turn, the air reacts by pushing upward on the wing, resulting in the lift needed to keep the plane aloft.

5. Which inequality is reasonable for the speed of molecule a passing above the wing and the speed of molecule u passing under it? D
   - **A.** $a < u + 0.15a$ **B.** $a < 0.15u$
   - **C.** $0.15a > u$ **D.** $a > 1.15u$

6. If the surface area of the top of a wing is 16 m^2, what might the surface area of the bottom of the wing be? G
   - **F.** 8 m^2 **G.** 14 m^2
   - **H.** 16 m^2 **I.** 19 m^2

Test Prep

Students must be able to extract information from reading passages, answer multiple-choice questions, and construct responses in order to be successful in current state and national assessments.

Resources

Teaching Resources
Cumulative Review
Quarter 3 Test, Forms A & B

Reaching All Students
Spanish Cumulative Review
Spanish Quarter 3 Test

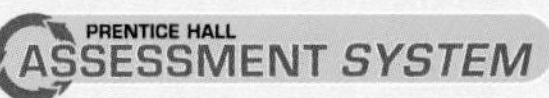

Test Preparation
- Ch. 9 standardized test prep

Assessment Resources
- Cumulative Review
- Quarter 3 Test, Forms A & B

Computer Test Generator CD
- Standardized test prep

www.PHSchool.com
- Standardized test prep
- Resources

Plus 

Cumulative Review

Cumulative Review

Chapters 1–9

Multiple Choice. Choose the letter of the best answer.

1. The points below lie in a line. What is the slope of the line?

x	y
1	2
3	8
5	14
9	26

   A. $\frac{1}{3}$ (B.) 3 C. $\frac{1}{2}$ D. 2

2. What is the y-intercept of a line with equation $y = 2x + 3$?
   F. $\frac{2}{3}$ G. 2 (H.) 3 I. 5

3. Translate point $B(-2, 5)$ up 4 units and right 3 units. What are the coordinates of its image, B'?
   A. (4, 3) B. (2, 8) C. (−5, 1) (D.) (1, 9)

4. Expenses for a school play total $175. Tickets are $4 each. Which equation shows the profit y for x tickets sold?
   (F.) $y = 4x - 175$ G. $y = 4x + 100$ H. $y = 175 - 4x$ I. $y = 100x + 4$

5. Which equation is graphed below?
   A. $y = 2x$ B. $y = -2x$ C. $y = -x - 2$ (D.) $y = -x + 2$

6. In which quadrant would you find the point (3, −5)?
   F. I G. II H. III (I.) IV

7. Cynthia used $2\frac{1}{2}$ lb of potting soil for her cactus and $3\frac{3}{4}$ lb of potting soil for her violets. If the bag of potting soil held 10 lb, how many pounds are left?
   (A.) $3\frac{3}{4}$ lb B. $6\frac{1}{4}$ lb C. $7\frac{1}{2}$ lb D. $16\frac{1}{4}$ lb

8. Solve. $n - 1\frac{1}{2} = 2\frac{3}{5}$
   F. $1\frac{1}{10}$ G. $1\frac{2}{3}$ (H.) $4\frac{1}{10}$ I. $4\frac{5}{10}$

9. The prime factorization of a number is $2^3 \times 3 \times 5^2$. What is the number?
   A. 120 B. 180 (C.) 600 D. 1,200

10. A right triangle has legs of 6 cm and 8 cm. How long is the hypotenuse of the triangle?
   F. 2 cm G. $\sqrt{28}$ cm (H.) 10 cm I. 14 cm

11. A bucket full of water has sprung a leak. After each hour, the water is $\frac{2}{3}$ as high as the previous hour. After 2 hours, the water level is 12 in. How high was the water level before the leak?
   A. 18 in. (B.) 27 in. C. 36 in D. 44 in.

12. What is the LCM of 12 and 40?
   F. 4 G. 30 (H.) 120 I. 480

Chapter Test

13.

14.

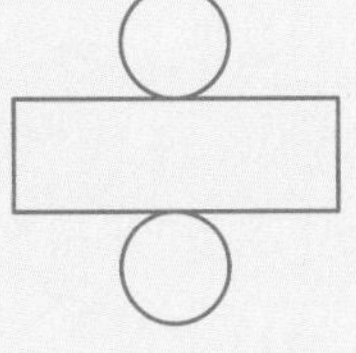

24. $a = 18$ in.
$b = 60$ in.
$c = 42$ in.

For the Birds

Students will use data from these two pages to answer the questions posed and make the models in Put It All Together.

Activating Prior Knowledge
Some animals can fly while others cannot. Certain airplane designs are better suited than others for different kinds of flight. Have students share their understanding of what it takes for an animal or a machine to lift off the ground and then stay up in the air.

Teaching Notes

Have a volunteer read the opening paragraph about flightless birds. Discuss with students that in the Put It All Together activity they will make models to investigate the relationship between a bird's weight and wingspan and its ability to fly.

History Connection
Refer students to the picture and information about dodos on page 529. Point out that dodos are not the only animals that have become extinct. Invite students to learn about (a) other animals that have suffered the fate of the dodos, or (b) why the dodo is no longer with us.

Careers
Invite interested students to find out about opportunities in the field of aeronautics. Alternatively, students can look into the requirements for becoming a commercial pilot.

Real-World Snapshots

For the Birds

Applying Measurement Did you know that not all birds can fly? Although people usually think of birds as airborne, there are more than 40 species of flightless birds. The Australian emu, New Zealand kiwi, African ostrich, and South American rhea are all birds that cannot fly. Although some birds are simply too large or heavy to get off the ground, they have learned other skills—ostriches can run up to 40 mi/h, and penguins spend most of their lives in the ocean and use their wings as flippers.

Ostriches
At 5.7 to 9 ft tall, the ostrich is the largest living bird. Its normal walking pace is 2.5 mi/h, but it can run at speeds of up to 45 mi/h.

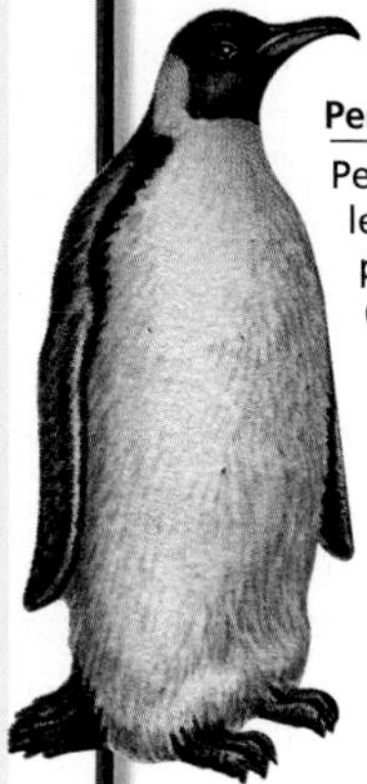

Penguins
Penguins range in size from less than 18 in. tall (the little penguin) to nearly 4 ft tall (the emperor penguin).

Kiwis
The kiwi, the national bird of New Zealand, is about the size of a chicken and weighs between 2.6 and 8.6 lb. Kiwi eggs are large and can weigh up to a pound!

Take It to the NET For more information about birds, go to **www.PHSchool.com**.
Web Code: ace-0953

1. Check students' work.
2.

Size of Bird	Volume	Wing Area	Ratio $\frac{\text{volume}}{\text{wing area}}$
Small	96 cm^3	96 cm^2	$\frac{96}{96} = \frac{1}{1}$
Large	768 cm^3	384 cm^2	$\frac{768}{384} = \frac{2}{1}$

3. 8 times
4. 4 times

Put It All Together

Data File **Use the information on these two pages and on page 469 to answer these questions.**

Materials construction paper, ruler or straightedge, tape

Copy and cut out the patterns in Figures 1 and 2 for a bird body and two bird wings. Assemble your bird.

1. Examine your bird. Think about what would happen to your bird's body and wings if it grew. Sketch a larger bird by doubling all the dimensions of the original pattern.
2. Copy and complete the table.

Size of Bird	Volume	Wing Area	Ratio $\frac{\text{volume}}{\text{wing area}}$
Small	■	■	■
Large	■	■	■

3. The upward force that keeps birds (and planes) in the air is called lift. The amount of lift needed to get off the ground is proportional to the weight of the bird. Using volume as an estimate for weight, how many times more lift will the larger bird require than the smaller bird?
4. The amount of lift from a bird's wings is proportional to the area of the wings. How many times more lift will the larger bird's wings provide than the smaller bird's?
5. **Writing in Math** Use your answers to Questions 3 and 4 to explain why the larger bird will have a harder time getting off the ground than the smaller bird.
6. **Open-Ended** Choose a bird from the table on page 469. Compare it to the two birds in the activity. How does it compare in terms of weight (volume)? How does it compare in terms of lift?

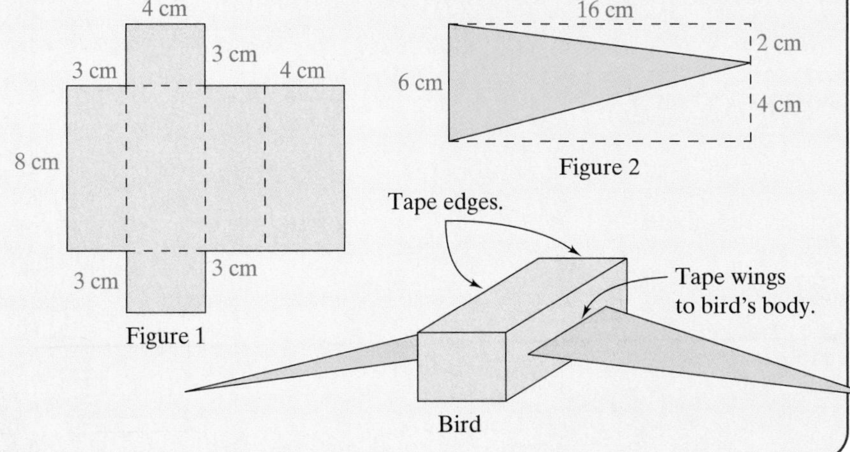

Rheas

Male rheas sit on their nests and incubate the eggs laid by females. The average clutch, or group of eggs, is about 25.

Dodos

About the size of turkeys, dodos have been extinct since the 1700s, so there are no photographs of them, only illustrations.

Put It All Together

Have students work in pairs to answer the questions and make the models. Guide them to record data as they measure and accumulate it. Then distribute the materials students need to make their model birds.

Tactile Learners
Guide students to measure and cut carefully. Remind them of the carpenter's maxim: measure twice, cut once. You may wish to have students sketch and cut out their models using centimeter graph paper.

Exercise 6 The connection between volume and weight is left for students to make. They can realize that doubling the volume also doubles the weight (in the context of this problem).

To extend the activity, have students sketch a smaller bird by halving the original dimensions. They can then expand the table to include the new data.

5. Answers may vary. Sample: The larger bird requires eight times as much lift, but its wings provide only four times as much lift. For the larger bird to fly, its wings would have to be able to carry twice as much bird volume per square centimeter of wing.
6. Check students' work.

CHAPTER 10

Using Graphs to Analyze Data

Chapter at a Glance

10-1 Displaying Frequency
pp. 533–538

Objectives

1. Making Frequency Tables and Line Plots
2. Displaying Data Using Intervals

New Vocabulary
frequency, frequency table, line plot, histogram

Optional Materials
graph paper, ruler

NCTM Standards
1, 5, 6, 7, 8, 9, 10

Local Standards

10-2 Reading Graphs Critically
pp. 540–544

Objectives

1. Recognizing and Selecting an Appropriate Scale

Optional Materials
graph paper, ruler

NCTM Standards
1, 2, 5, 6, 7, 8, 9, 10

Local Standards

10-3 Stem-and-Leaf Plots
pp. 546–551

Objectives

1. Making Stem-and-Leaf Plots
2. Using Stem-and-Leaf Plots

New Vocabulary
stem-and-leaf plot

NCTM Standards
1, 2, 3, 6, 7, 8, 9, 10

Local Standards

✓ Checkpoint Quiz 1

10-4 Box-and-Whisker Plots
pp. 552–556

Objectives

1. Making and Using Box-and-Whisker Plots

New Vocabulary
box-and-whisker plot, quartiles

NCTM Standards
1, 5, 6, 7, 8, 9, 10

Local Standards

10-5 Making Predictions From Scatter Plots
pp. 557–562

Objectives

1. Making Scatter Plots
2. Using Scatter Plots to Find Trends

New Vocabulary
scatter plot, positive trend, negative trend, no trend, trend line

Optional Materials
graph paper, ruler

NCTM Standards
1, 2, 5, 6, 7, 8, 9, 10

Local Standards

10-6 Circle Graphs
pp. 563–568

Objectives

1. Reading Circle Graphs
2. Making Circle Graphs

New Vocabulary
circle graph, central angle

Optional Materials
compass, protractor

NCTM Standards
1, 2, 3, 4, 5, 6, 7, 8, 9, 10

Local Standards

✓ Checkpoint Quiz 2

10-7 Choosing an Appropriate Graph
pp. 569–574

Objectives

1. Choosing an Appropriate Graph

NCTM Standards
1, 5, 6, 7, 8, 9, 10

Local Standards

10-8 Problem Solving
Draw a Diagram and Use Logical Reasoning
pp. 576–579

Objectives

1. Solving a Problem by Combining Strategies

NCTM Standards
1, 3, 6, 7, 8, 9, 10

Local Standards

Reaching All Students

Additional Instructional Options in Chapter 10

Reading and Math Literacy

Reading Math

Reading Graphical Displays, p. 539

Reading Math hints, pp. 535, 548, 558, 566

Reading Comprehension, p. 574

Understanding Vocabulary, p. 582

Writing in Math

Writing to Persuade, p. 580

Daily Writing Practice, pp. 536, 543, 545, 550, 555, 561, 566, 573, 578, 584

Above Level

Challenge exercises

pp. 538, 543, 550, 556, 562, 567, 573, 579

Extension

Stacked and Sliding Bar Graphs, p. 545

Hands-On and Technology

Investigations

Creating Graphs to Tell a Story, p. 541

Height vs. Arm Span, p. 557

Summarizing Types of Graphs, p. 569

Technology

Graphing Data Using Spreadsheets, p. 575

Activities and Projects

Real-World Snapshots

Using Graphs, pp. 586-587

Chapter Project

News Flash, p. 700

Test Prep

Daily Test Prep

pp. 538, 544, 550, 556, 562, 567, 574, 579

Test-Taking Strategies

Finding a Multiple Correct Answers, p. 581

Test Prep

Cumulative Review (Chapters 1–10), p. 585

Chapter Assessment

Checkpoint Quiz

pp. 551, 568

Chapter Review

pp. 582–583

Chapter Test

p. 584

Pacing Options

This chart suggests pacing only for the core lessons and their parts. It is provided as a possible guide. It will help you determine how much time you have in your schedule to cover the additional features and assessment, as described at the left.

Day	Traditional 45-minute class periods	Block 90-minute class periods
1	10-1 ▼1	10-1 ▼1 ▼2 10-2 ▼1
2	10-1 ▼2	10-3 ▼1 ▼2 10-4 ▼1
3	10-2 ▼1	10-5 ▼1 ▼2
4	10-3 ▼1 ▼2	10-6 ▼1 ▼2
5	10-4 ▼1	10-7 ▼1 10-8 ▼1
6	10-5 ▼1	
7	10-5 ▼2	
8	10-6 ▼1	
9	10-6 ▼2	
10	10-7 ▼1	
11	10-8 ▼1	
12		
13		
14		
15		

NCTM STANDARDS 2000

1 Number and Operations
2 Algebra
3 Geometry
4 Measurement
5 Data Analysis and Probability
6 Problem Solving
7 Reasoning and Proof
8 Communication
9 Connections
10 Representation

Math Background

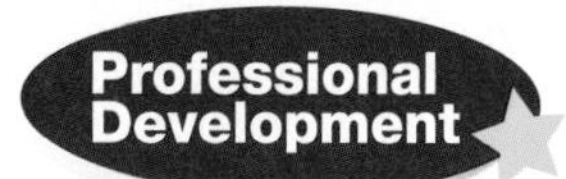

Skills Trace

BEFORE Chapter 10

Course 2 introduced making and interpreting various types of graphical displays.

DURING Chapter 10

Course 3 extends the critical reading and making of various graphs to include selecting an appropriate graph for a given set of data.

AFTER Chapter 10

Throughout this course students make and interpret a wide variety of graphs.

10-1 10-2 Displaying Frequency and Reading Graphs Critically

Math Understandings

- A frequency table shows how often each data value occurs.
- You can use a frequency table or line plot to show the distribution or shape of a set of data.
- Line plots are useful for fairly small data sets when the data points are tightly grouped.
- Bar graphs and line graphs can give a misleading visual impression by changing an axis scale.

The number of times a data item occurs is the **frequency** of the item. A **frequency table** lists the frequency of each item in a set of data. A **line plot** displays data values with an **✗** mark above each data value on a number line.

Temp. (°F)	100	101	102	103	104
Tally	|	~~||||~~	||||	|	|
Frequency	1	5	4	1	1

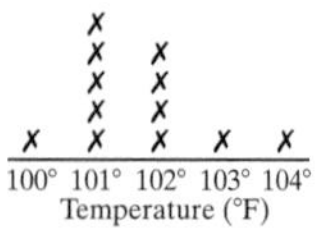

When there are too many values to display separately, you can use a grouped-frequency table to organize data into intervals of equal size that do not overlap. A **histogram** is a special type of bar graph with no spaces between the bars. The height of each bar shows the frequency of data within that interval.

Stem-and-Leaf Plots

Math Understandings

- A stem-and-leaf plot can quickly show the distribution of a data set and retains each data value.
- Each stem-and-leaf plot must include a key that shows what the stems and leaves represent for a particular plot.

A **stem-and-leaf plot** shows numeric data arranged in order. Each data item is broken into a stem and a leaf.

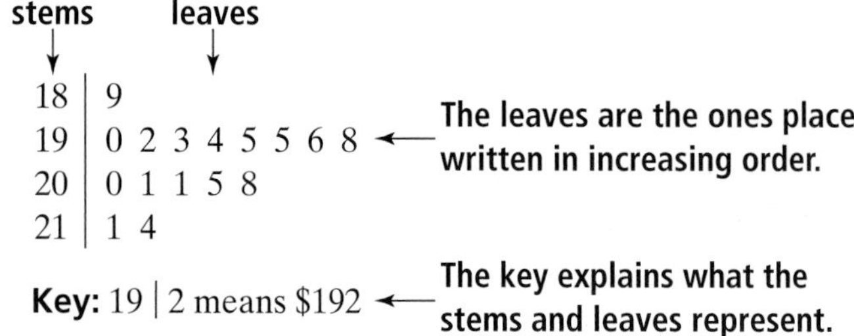

Box-and-Whisker Plots

Math Understandings

- Box-and-whisker plots do not include every data value.
- By comparing the lengths of the four quartiles, you can easily see where data values are more spread out.
- Box-and-whisker plots are useful with very large data sets, or for making comparisons between data sets.

A **box-and-whisker plot** uses five summary values to show the distribution of a data set along a number line. **Quartiles** are numbers that divide the data set into four equal parts.

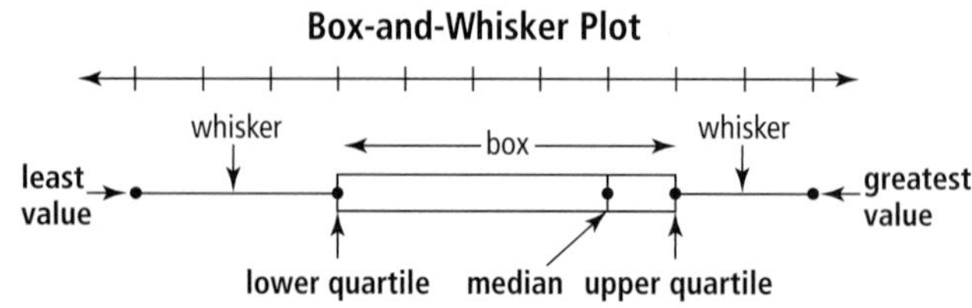

Transparencies

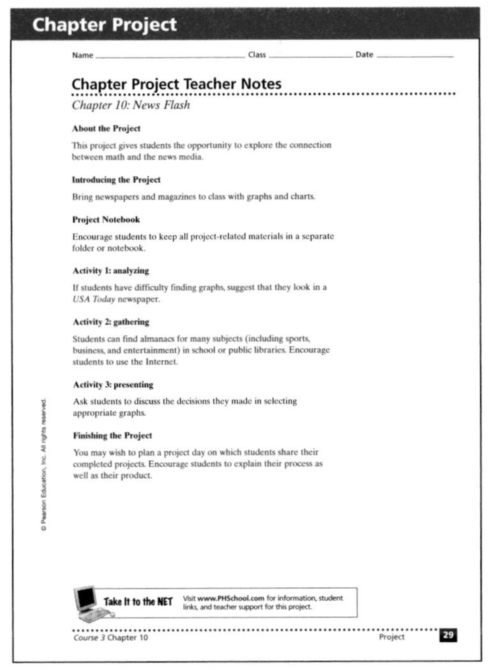

Chapter Project

Name ______ Class ______ Date ______

Chapter Project Teacher Notes

Chapter 10: News Flash

About the Project

This project gives students the opportunity to explore the connection between math and the news media.

Introducing the Project

Bring newspapers and magazines to class with graphs and charts.

Project Notebook

Encourage students to keep all project-related materials in a separate folder or notebook.

Activity 1: analyzing

If students have difficulty finding graphs, suggest that they look in a *USA Today* newspaper.

Activity 2: gathering

Students can find almanacs for many subjects (including sports, business, and entertainment) in school or public libraries. Encourage students to use the Internet.

Activity 3: presenting

Ask students to discuss the decisions they made in selecting appropriate graphs.

Finishing the Project

You may wish to plan a project day on which students share their completed projects. Encourage students to explain their process as well as their product.

Take It to the NET Visit www.PHSchool.com for information, student links, and teacher support for this project.

Course 3 Chapter 10 Project 29

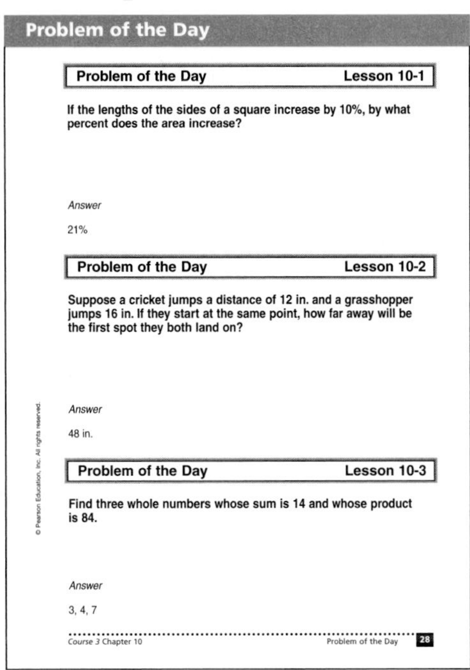

Problem of the Day

Problem of the Day — Lesson 10-1

If the lengths of the sides of a square increase by 10%, by what percent does the area increase?

Answer

21%

Problem of the Day — Lesson 10-2

Suppose a cricket jumps a distance of 12 in. and a grasshopper jumps 16 in. If they start at the same point, how far away will be the first spot they both land on?

Answer

48 in.

Problem of the Day — Lesson 10-3

Find three whole numbers whose sum is 14 and whose product is 84.

Answer

3, 4, 7

Course 3 Chapter 10 Problem of the Day 28

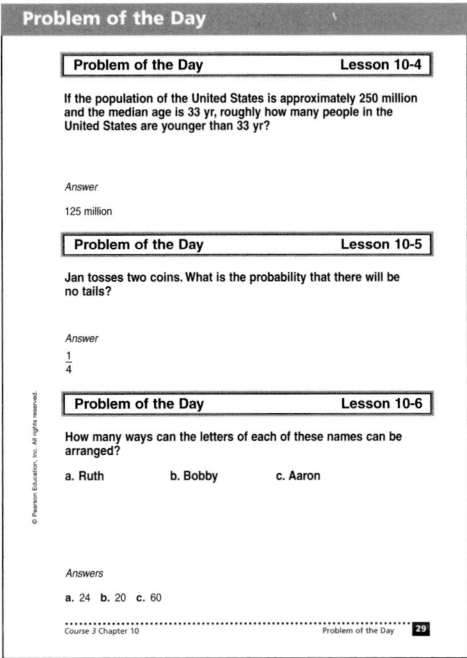

Problem of the Day

Problem of the Day — Lesson 10-4

If the population of the United States is approximately 250 million and the median age is 33 yr, roughly how many people in the United States are younger than 33 yr?

Answer

125 million

Problem of the Day — Lesson 10-5

Jan tosses two coins. What is the probability that there will be no tails?

Answer

$\frac{1}{4}$

Problem of the Day — Lesson 10-6

How many ways can the letters of each of these names can be arranged?

a. Ruth b. Bobby c. Aaron

Answers

a. 24 **b.** 20 **c.** 60

Course 3 Chapter 10 Problem of the Day 29

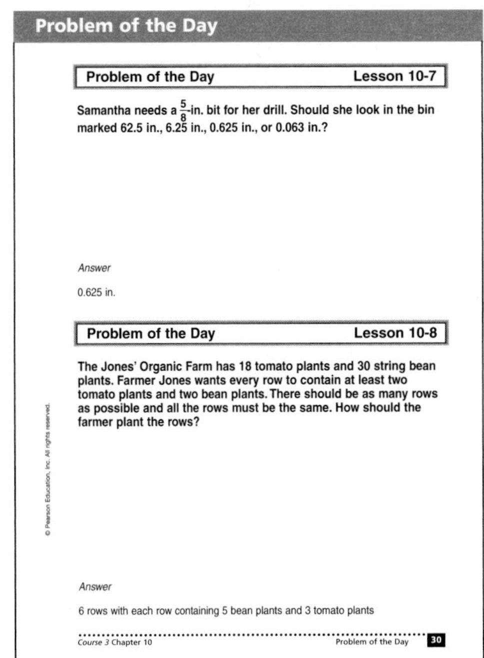

Problem of the Day

Problem of the Day — Lesson 10-7

Samantha needs a $\frac{5}{8}$-in. bit for her drill. Should she look in the bin marked 62.5 in., 6.25 in., 0.625 in., or 0.063 in.?

Answer

0.625 in.

Problem of the Day — Lesson 10-8

The Jones' Organic Farm has 18 tomato plants and 30 string bean plants. Farmer Jones wants every row to contain at least two tomato plants and two bean plants. There should be as many rows as possible and all the rows must be the same. How should the farmer plant the rows?

Answer

6 rows with each row containing 5 bean plants and 3 tomato plants

Course 3 Chapter 10 Problem of the Day 30

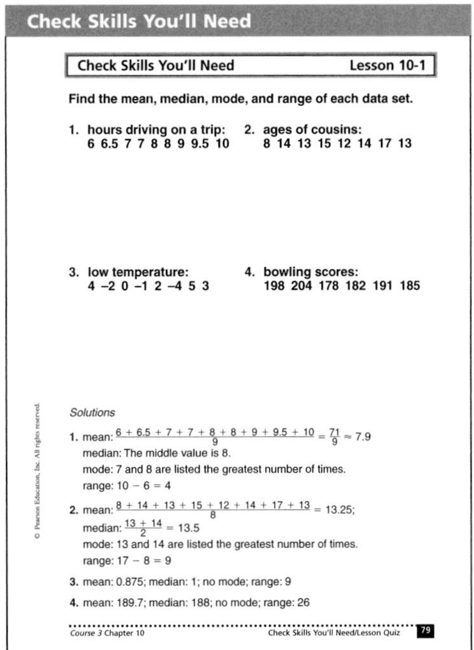

Check Skills You'll Need

Check Skills You'll Need — Lesson 10-1

Find the mean, median, mode, and range of each data set.

1. hours driving on a trip: 6 6.5 7 7 8 8 9 9.5 10
2. ages of cousins: 8 14 13 15 12 14 17 13
3. low temperature: 4 −2 0 −1 2 −4 5 3
4. bowling scores: 198 204 178 182 191 185

Solutions

1. mean: $\frac{6 + 6.5 + 7 + 7 + 8 + 8 + 9 + 9.5 + 10}{9} = \frac{71}{9} \approx 7.9$
median: The middle value is 8.
mode: 7 and 8 are listed the greatest number of times.
range: $10 - 6 = 4$

2. mean: $\frac{8 + 14 + 13 + 15 + 12 + 14 + 17 + 13}{8} = 13.25$;
median: $\frac{13 + 14}{2} = 13.5$
mode: 13 and 14 are listed the greatest number of times.
range: $17 - 8 = 9$

3. mean: 0.875; median: 1; no mode; range: 9

4. mean: 189.7; median: 188; no mode; range: 26

Course 3 Chapter 10 Check Skills You'll Need/Lesson Quiz 79

Sample page; see p. H for complete list.

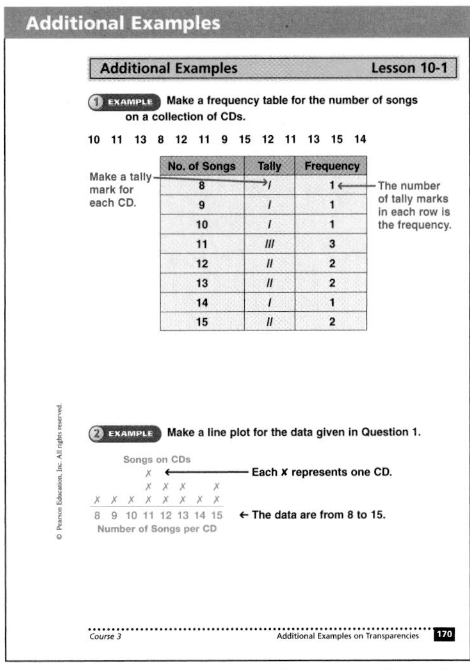

Additional Examples

Additional Examples — Lesson 10-1

1 EXAMPLE Make a frequency table for the number of songs on a collection of CDs.

10 11 13 8 12 11 9 15 12 11 13 15 14

No. of Songs	Tally	Frequency
8	/	1
9	/	1
10	/	1
11	///	3
12	//	2
13	//	2
14	/	1
15	//	2

Make a tally mark for each CD.

The number of tally marks in each row is the frequency.

2 EXAMPLE Make a line plot for the data given in Question 1.

Course 3 Additional Examples on Transparencies 170

Sample page; see p. H for complete list.

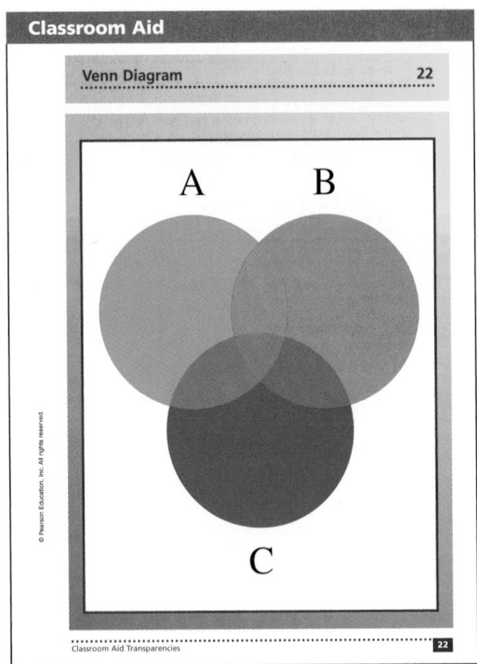

Classroom Aid

Venn Diagram 22

A B

C

© Pearson Education, Inc. All rights reserved.

Classroom Aid Transparencies 22

Sample page.

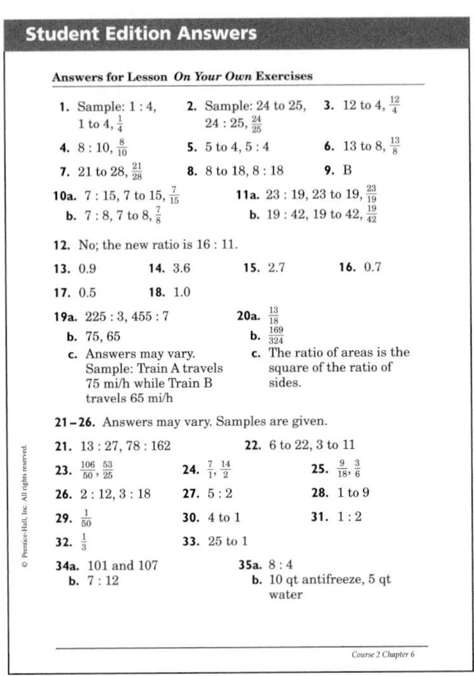

Student Edition Answers

Answers for Lesson *On Your Own* Exercises

1. Sample: 1 : 4, 1 to 4, $\frac{1}{4}$
2. Sample: 24 to 25, 24 : 25, $\frac{24}{25}$
3. 12 to 4, $\frac{12}{4}$
4. 8 : 10, $\frac{8}{10}$
5. 5 to 4, 5 : 4
6. 13 to 8, $\frac{13}{8}$
7. 21 to 28, $\frac{21}{28}$
8. 8 to 18, 8 : 18
9. B

10a. 7 : 15, 7 to 15, $\frac{7}{15}$
b. 7 : 8, 7 to 8, $\frac{7}{8}$

11a. 23 : 19, 23 to 19, $\frac{23}{19}$
b. 19 : 42, 19 to 42, $\frac{19}{42}$

12. No; the new ratio is 16 : 11.
13. 0.9
14. 3.6
15. 2.7
16. 0.7
17. 0.5
18. 1.0

19a. 225 : 3, 455 : 7
b. 75, 65
c. Answers may vary. Sample: Train A travels 75 mi/h while Train B travels 65 mi/h

20a. $\frac{13}{18}$
b. $\frac{169}{324}$
c. The ratio of areas is the square of the ratio of sides.

21–26. Answers may vary. Samples are given.

21. 13 : 27, 78 : 162
22. 6 to 22, 3 to 11
23. $\frac{106}{50}$, $\frac{53}{25}$
24. $\frac{7}{1}$, $\frac{14}{2}$
25. $\frac{9}{18}$, $\frac{3}{6}$
26. 2 : 12, 3 : 18
27. 5 : 2
28. 1 to 9
29. $\frac{1}{50}$
30. 4 to 1
31. 1 : 2
32. $\frac{1}{3}$
33. 25 to 1

34a. 101 and 107
b. 7 : 12

35a. 8 : 4
b. 10 qt antifreeze, 5 qt water

© Prentice-Hall, Inc. All rights reserved.

Course 2 Chapter 6

Sample page; see p. H for complete list.

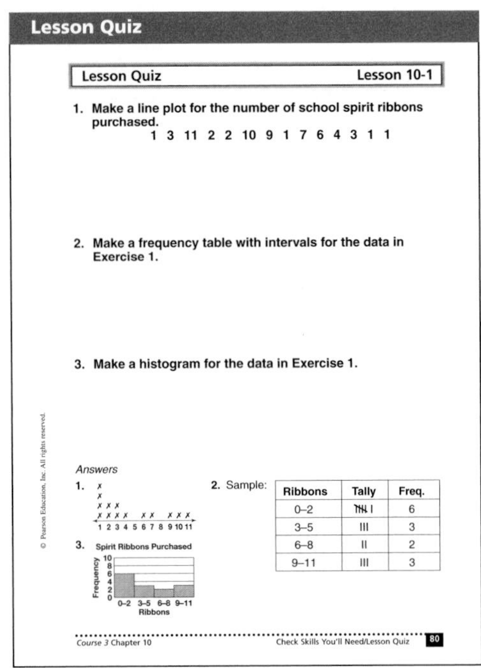

Lesson Quiz

Lesson Quiz — Lesson 10-1

1. Make a line plot for the number of school spirit ribbons purchased.
   1 3 11 2 2 10 9 1 7 6 4 3 1 1
2. Make a frequency table with intervals for the data in Exercise 1.
3. Make a histogram for the data in Exercise 1.

Answers

1. (line plot, 1 2 3 4 5 6 7 8 9 10 11)
2. Sample:

Ribbons	Tally	Freq.
0–2	𝍸 I	6
3–5	III	3
6–8	II	2
9–11	III	3

3. Spirit Ribbons Purchased (Frequency; 0–2, 3–5, 6–8, 9–11; Ribbons)

© Pearson Education, Inc. All rights reserved.

Course 3 Chapter 10 — Check Skills You'll Need/Lesson Quiz 80

Sample page; see p. H for complete list.

Assessment

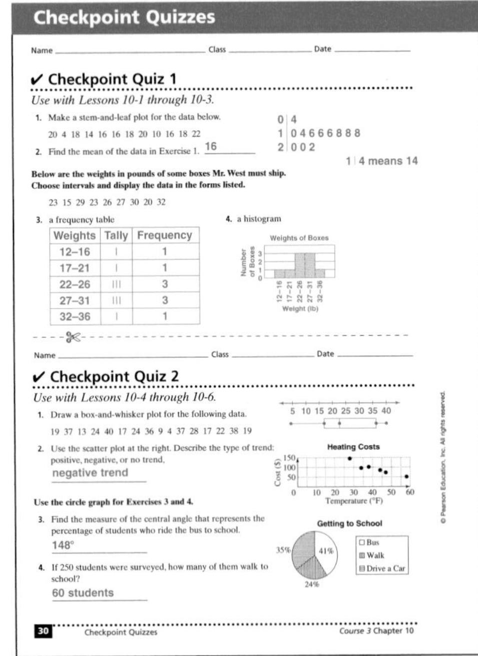

Checkpoint Quizzes

Name ____ Class ____ Date ____

✓ Checkpoint Quiz 1

Use with Lessons 10-1 through 10-3.

1. Make a stem-and-leaf plot for the data below.
   20 4 18 14 16 16 18 20 10 16 18 22
   0 | 4
   1 | 0 4 6 6 6 8 8 8
   2 | 0 0 2
   1 | 4 means 14
2. Find the mean of the data in Exercise 1. 16

Below are the weights in pounds of some boxes Mr. West must ship. Choose intervals and display the data in the forms listed.
23 15 29 23 26 27 30 20 32

3. a frequency table

Weights	Tally	Frequency
12–16	I	1
17–21	I	1
22–26	III	3
27–31	III	3
32–36	I	1

4. a histogram (Weights of Boxes; Number of Boxes; Weight (lb))

Name ____ Class ____ Date ____

✓ Checkpoint Quiz 2

Use with Lessons 10-4 through 10-6.

1. Draw a box-and-whisker plot for the following data.
   19 37 13 24 40 17 24 36 9 4 37 28 17 22 38 19
2. Use the scatter plot at the right. Describe the type of trend: positive, negative, or no trend.
   negative trend
   (Heating Costs; Cost ($); Temperature (°F))

Use the circle graph for Exercises 3 and 4.

3. Find the measure of the central angle that represents the percentage of students who ride the bus to school.
   148°
4. If 250 students were surveyed, how many of them walk to school?
   60 students

(Getting to School: Bus, Walk, Drive a Car; 35%, 41%, 24%)

© Pearson Education, Inc. All rights reserved.

30 Checkpoint Quizzes — Course 3 Chapter 10

Available in Spanish

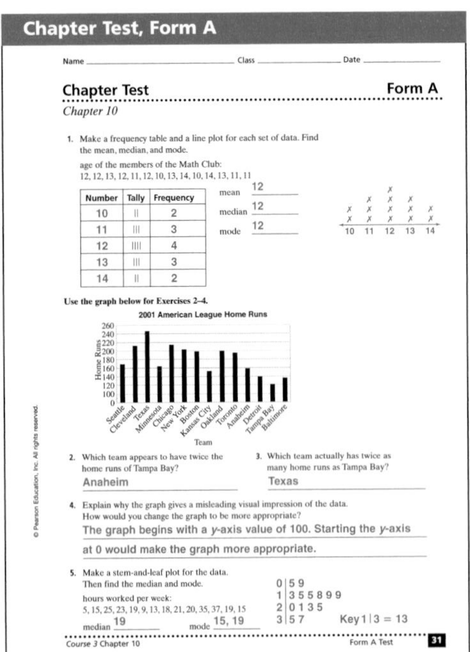

Chapter Test, Form A

Name ____ Class ____ Date ____

Chapter Test — **Form A**

Chapter 10

1. Make a frequency table and a line plot for each set of data. Find the mean, median, and mode.
   age of the members of the Math Club:
   12, 12, 13, 12, 11, 12, 10, 13, 14, 10, 14, 13, 11, 11

Number	Tally	Frequency
10	II	2
11	III	3
12	IIII	4
13	III	3
14	II	2

mean 12
median 12
mode 12

Use the graph below for Exercises 2–4.

2001 American League Home Runs (Home Runs; Team: Seattle, Cleveland, Texas, Minnesota, Chicago, New York, Boston, Kansas City, Oakland, Toronto, Anaheim, Detroit, Tampa Bay, Baltimore)

2. Which team appears to have twice the home runs of Tampa Bay?
   Anaheim
3. Which team actually has twice as many home runs as Tampa Bay?
   Texas
4. Explain why the graph gives a misleading visual impression of the data. How would you change the graph to be more appropriate?
   The graph begins with a y-axis value of 100. Starting the y-axis at 0 would make the graph more appropriate.
5. Make a stem-and-leaf plot for the data. Then find the median and mode.
   hours worked per week:
   5, 15, 25, 23, 19, 9, 13, 18, 21, 20, 35, 37, 19, 15
   0 | 5 9
   1 | 3 5 5 8 9 9
   2 | 0 1 3 5
   3 | 5 7
   Key 1 | 3 = 13
   median 19 mode 15, 19

© Pearson Education, Inc. All rights reserved.

Course 3 Chapter 10 — Form A Test 31

Available in Spanish

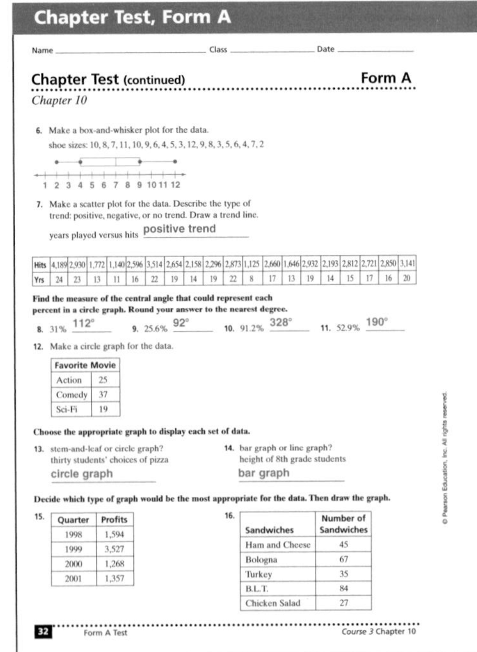

Chapter Test, Form A

Name ____ Class ____ Date ____

Chapter Test (continued) — **Form A**

Chapter 10

6. Make a box-and-whisker plot for the data.
   shoe sizes: 10, 8, 7, 11, 10, 9, 6, 4, 5, 3, 12, 9, 8, 3, 5, 6, 4, 7, 2
7. Make a scatter plot for the data. Describe the type of trend: positive, negative, or no trend. Draw a trend line.
   years played versus hits positive trend

Hits	4,189	2,930	1,772	1,340	2,596	3,514	2,654	2,158	2,296	2,873	1,325	2,660	1,646	2,932	2,193	2,812	2,721	2,850	3,141
Yrs	24	23	13	11	16	22	19	14	19	22	8	17	13	19	14	15	17	16	20

Find the measure of the central angle that could represent each percent in a circle graph. Round your answer to the nearest degree.

8. 31% 112°
9. 25.6% 92°
10. 91.2% 328°
11. 52.9% 190°

12. Make a circle graph for the data.

Favorite Movie	
Action	25
Comedy	37
Sci-Fi	19

Choose the appropriate graph to display each set of data.

13. stem-and-leaf or circle graph? thirty students' choices of pizza
    circle graph
14. bar graph or line graph? height of 8th grade students
    bar graph

Decide which type of graph would be the most appropriate for the data. Then draw the graph.

15.

Quarter	Profits
1998	1,594
1999	3,527
2000	1,268
2001	1,357

16.

Sandwiches	Number of Sandwiches
Ham and Cheese	45
Bologna	67
Turkey	35
B.L.T.	84
Chicken Salad	27

© Pearson Education, Inc. All rights reserved.

32 Form A Test — Course 3 Chapter 10

Available in Spanish

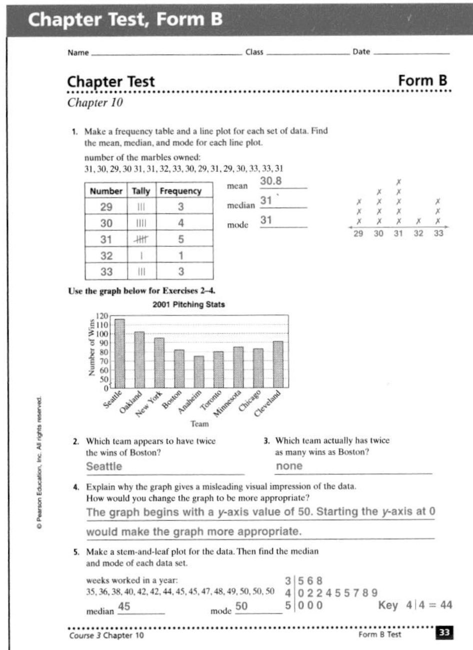

Chapter Test, Form B

Name ______ Class ______ Date ______

Chapter Test — Form B

Chapter 10

1. Make a frequency table and a line plot for each set of data. Find the mean, median, and mode for each line plot.

   number of the marbles owned:
   31, 30, 29, 30 31, 31, 32, 33, 30, 29, 31, 29, 30, 33, 33, 31

Number	Tally	Frequency
29	III	3
30	IIII	4
31	~~IIII~~	5
32	I	1
33	III	3

mean 30.8
median 31
mode 31

Use the graph below for Exercises 2–4.

2. Which team appears to have twice the wins of Boston? Seattle
3. Which team actually has twice as many wins as Boston? none
4. Explain why the graph gives a misleading visual impression of the data. How would you change the graph to be more appropriate?
   The graph begins with a y-axis value of 50. Starting the y-axis at 0 would make the graph more appropriate.
5. Make a stem-and-leaf plot for the data. Then find the median and mode of each data set.

   weeks worked in a year:
   35, 36, 38, 40, 42, 42, 44, 45, 45, 47, 48, 49, 50, 50, 50

   median 45 mode 50

   3 | 5 6 8
   4 | 0 2 2 4 5 5 7 8 9
   5 | 0 0 0
   Key 4 | 4 = 44

Course 3 Chapter 10 Form B Test 33

Available in Spanish

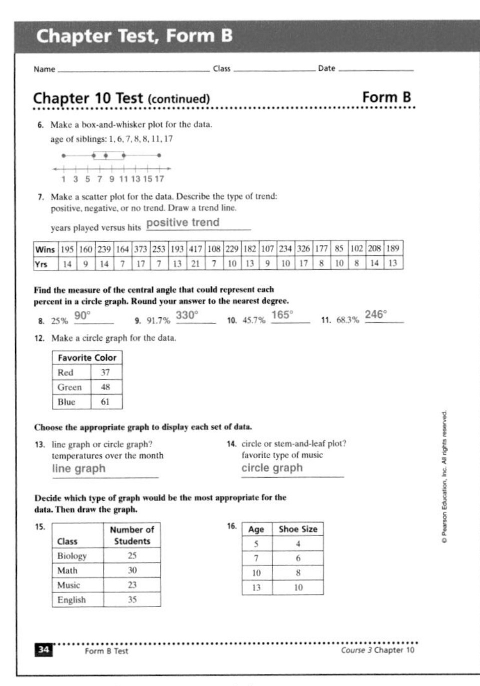

Chapter Test, Form B

Name ______ Class ______ Date ______

Chapter 10 Test (continued) — Form B

6. Make a box-and-whisker plot for the data.
   age of siblings: 1, 6, 7, 8, 8, 11, 17

7. Make a scatter plot for the data. Describe the type of trend: positive, negative, or no trend. Draw a trend line.
   years played versus hits positive trend

Wins	195	160	239	164	373	253	193	417	108	229	182	107	234	326	177	85	102	208	189
Yrs	14	9	14	7	17	7	13	21	7	10	13	9	10	17	8	10	8	14	13

Find the measure of the central angle that could represent each percent in a circle graph. Round your answer to the nearest degree.

8. 25% 90°
9. 91.7% 330°
10. 45.7% 165°
11. 68.3% 246°
12. Make a circle graph for the data.

Favorite Color	
Red	37
Green	48
Blue	61

Choose the appropriate graph to display each set of data.

13. line graph or circle graph? temperatures over the month
    line graph
14. circle or stem-and-leaf plot? favorite type of music
    circle graph

Decide which type of graph would be the most appropriate for the data. Then draw the graph.

15.

Class	Number of Students
Biology	25
Math	30
Music	23
English	35

16.

Age	Shoe Size
5	4
7	6
10	8
13	10

34 Form B Test Course 3 Chapter 10

Available in Spanish

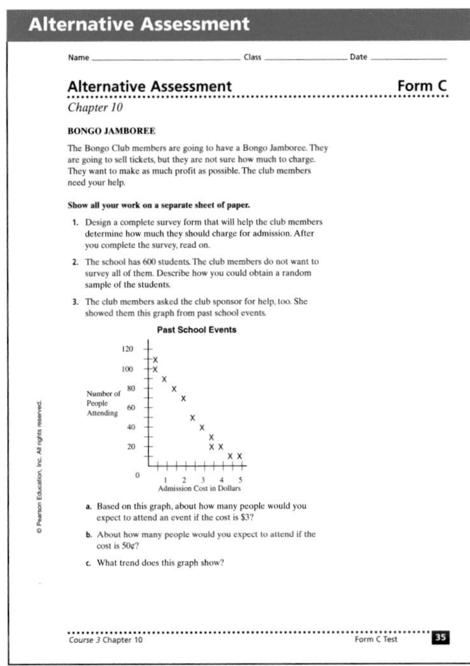

Alternative Assessment

Name ______ Class ______ Date ______

Alternative Assessment — Form C

Chapter 10

BONGO JAMBOREE

The Bongo Club members are going to have a Bongo Jamboree. They are going to sell tickets, but they are not sure how much to charge. They want to make as much profit as possible. The club members need your help.

Show all your work on a separate sheet of paper.

1. Design a complete survey form that will help the club members determine how much they should charge for admission. After you complete the survey, read on.
2. The school has 600 students. The club members do not want to survey all of them. Describe how you could obtain a random sample of the students.
3. The club members asked the club sponsor for help, too. She showed them this graph from past school events.

   a. Based on this graph, about how many people would you expect to attend an event if the cost is $3?
   b. About how many people would you expect to attend if the cost is 50¢?
   c. What trend does this graph show?

Course 3 Chapter 10 Form C Test 35

Available in Spanish

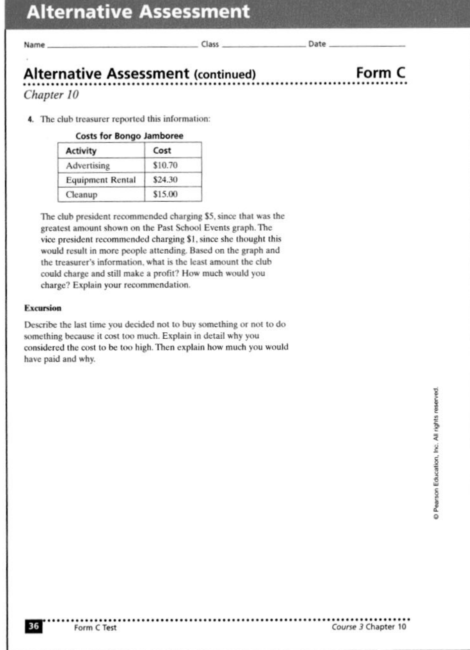

Alternative Assessment

Name ______ Class ______ Date ______

Alternative Assessment (continued) — Form C

Chapter 10

4. The club treasurer reported this information:

Costs for Bongo Jamboree

Activity	Cost
Advertising	$10.70
Equipment Rental	$24.30
Cleanup	$15.00

The club president recommended charging $5, since that was the greatest amount shown on the Past School Events graph. The vice president recommended charging $1, since she thought this would result in more people attending. Based on the graph and the treasurer's information, what is the least amount the club could charge and still make a profit? How much would you charge? Explain your recommendation.

Excursion

Describe the last time you decided not to buy something or not to do something because it cost too much. Explain in detail why you considered the cost to be too high. Then explain how much you would have paid and why.

36 Form C Test Course 3 Chapter 10

Available in Spanish

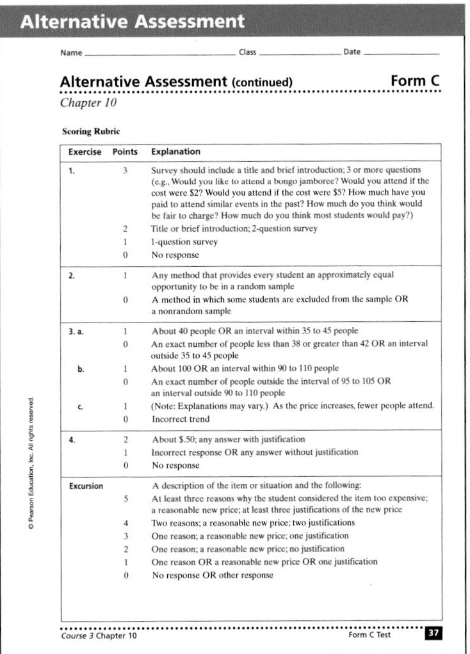

Alternative Assessment

Name ______ Class ______ Date ______

Alternative Assessment (continued) — Form C

Chapter 10

Scoring Rubric

Exercise	Points	Explanation
1.	3	Survey should include a title and brief introduction; 3 or more questions (e.g., Would you like to attend a bongo jamboree? Would you attend if the cost were $2? Would you attend if the cost were $5? How much have you paid to attend similar events in the past? How much do you think would be fair to charge? How much do you think most students would pay?)
	2	Title or brief introduction; 2-question survey
	1	1-question survey
	0	No response
2.	1	Any method that provides every student an approximately equal opportunity to be in a random sample
	0	A method in which some students are excluded from the sample OR a nonrandom sample
3. a.	1	About 40 people OR an interval within 35 to 45 people
	0	An exact number of people less than 38 or greater than 42 OR an interval outside 35 to 45 people
b.	1	About 100 OR an interval within 90 to 110 people
	0	An exact number of people outside the interval of 95 to 105 OR an interval outside 90 to 110 people
c.	1	(Note: Explanations may vary.) As the price increases, fewer people attend.
	0	Incorrect trend
4.	2	About $.50; any answer with justification
	1	Incorrect response OR any answer without justification
	0	No response
Excursion		A description of the item or situation and the following:
	5	At least three reasons why the student considered the item too expensive; a reasonable new price; at least three justifications of the new price
	4	Two reasons; a reasonable new price; two justifications
	3	One reason; a reasonable new price; one justification
	2	One reason; a reasonable new price; no justification
	1	One reason OR a reasonable new price OR one justification
	0	No response OR other response

Course 3 Chapter 10 Form C Test 37

Available in Spanish

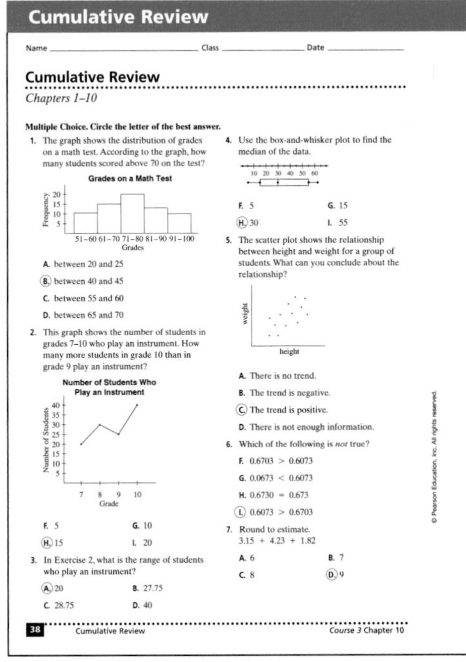

Cumulative Review

Name ______ Class ______ Date ______

Cumulative Review

Chapters 1–10

Multiple Choice. Circle the letter of the best answer.

1. The graph shows the distribution of grades on a math test. According to the graph, how many students scored above 70 on the test?

   A. between 20 and 25
   (B.) between 40 and 45
   C. between 55 and 60
   D. between 65 and 70

2. This graph shows the number of students in grades 7–10 who play an instrument. How many more students in grade 10 than in grade 9 play an instrument?

   F. 5 G. 10
   (H.) 15 I. 20

3. In Exercise 2, what is the range of students who play an instrument?
   (A.) 20 B. 27.75
   C. 28.75 D. 40

4. Use the box-and-whisker plot to find the median of the data.

   F. 5 G. 15
   (H.) 30 I. 55

5. The scatter plot shows the relationship between height and weight for a group of students. What can you conclude about the relationship?

   A. There is no trend.
   B. The trend is negative.
   (C.) The trend is positive.
   D. There is not enough information.

6. Which of the following is *not* true?
   F. $0.6703 > 0.6073$
   G. $0.0673 < 0.6073$
   H. $0.6730 = 0.673$
   (I.) $0.6073 > 0.6703$

7. Round to estimate.
   $3.15 + 4.23 + 1.82$
   A. 6 B. 7
   C. 8 (D.) 9

38 Cumulative Review Course 3 Chapter 10

Available in Spanish

Cumulative Review

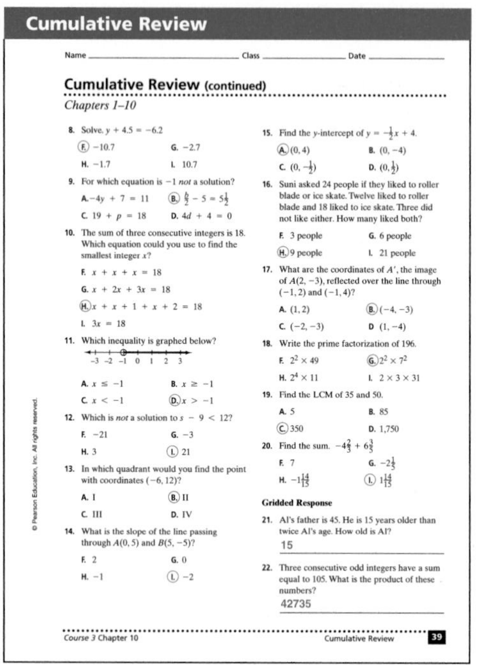

Name ______ Class ______ Date ______

Cumulative Review (continued)
Chapters 1–10

8. Solve. $y + 4.5 = -6.2$
 F. −10.7 G. −2.7 H. −1.7 I. 10.7
9. For which equation is −1 *not* a solution?
 A. $-4y + 7 = 11$ B. $\frac{6}{2} - 5 = 5\frac{1}{2}$ C. $19 + p = 18$ D. $4d + 4 = 0$
10. The sum of three consecutive integers is 18. Which equation could you use to find the smallest integer *x*?
 F. $x + x + x = 18$ G. $x + 2x + 3x = 18$ H. $x + x + 1 + x + 2 = 18$ I. $3x = 18$
11. Which inequality is graphed below?
 A. $x \le -1$ B. $x \ge -1$ C. $x < -1$ D. $x > -1$
12. Which is *not* a solution to $s - 9 < 12$?
 F. −21 G. −3 H. 3 I. 21
13. In which quadrant would you find the point with coordinates (−6, 12)?
 A. I B. II C. III D. IV
14. What is the slope of the line passing through $A(0, 5)$ and $B(5, -5)$?
 F. 2 G. 0 H. −1 I. −2
15. Find the *y*-intercept of $y = -\frac{1}{4}x + 4$.
 A. (0, 4) B. (0, −4) C. $(0, -\frac{1}{4})$ D. $(0, \frac{1}{4})$
16. Suni asked 24 people if they liked to roller blade or ice skate. Twelve liked to roller blade and 18 liked to ice skate. Three did not like either. How many liked both?
 F. 3 people G. 6 people H. 9 people I. 21 people
17. What are the coordinates of *A'*, the image of *A*(2, −3), reflected over the line through (−1, 2) and (−1, 4)?
 A. (1, 2) B. (−4, −3) C. (−2, −3) D. (1, −4)
18. Write the prime factorization of 196.
 F. $2^2 \times 49$ G. $2^2 \times 7^2$ H. $2^4 \times 11$ I. $2 \times 3 \times 31$
19. Find the LCM of 35 and 50.
 A. 5 B. 85 C. 350 D. 1,750
20. Find the sum. $-4\frac{2}{3} + 6\frac{1}{3}$
 F. 7 G. $-2\frac{1}{3}$ H. $-1\frac{11}{12}$ I. $1\frac{11}{12}$

Gridded Response

21. Al's father is 45. He is 15 years older than twice Al's age. How old is Al?
 15
22. Three consecutive odd integers have a sum equal to 105. What is the product of these numbers?
 42735

Available in Spanish

Benchmark Test

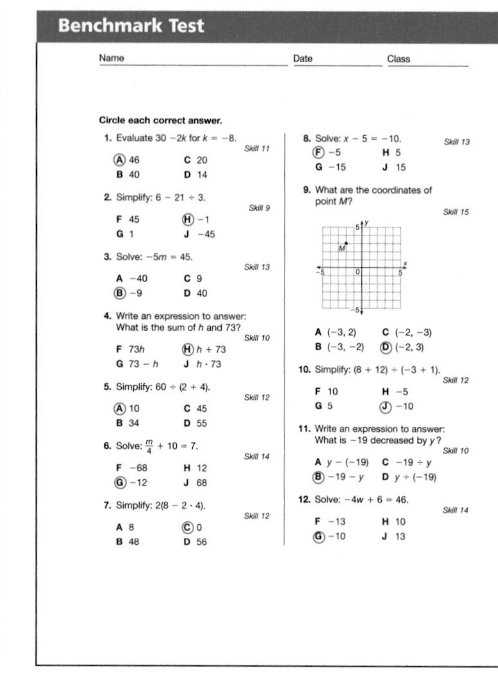

Name ______ Date ______ Class ______

Circle each correct answer.

1. Evaluate $30 - 2k$ for $k = -8$. *Skill 11*
 A 46 C 20 B 40 D 14
2. Simplify: $6 - 21 \div 3$. *Skill 9*
 F 45 H −1 G 1 J −45
3. Solve: $-5m = 45$. *Skill 13*
 A −40 C 9 B −9 D 40
4. Write an expression to answer: What is the sum of *h* and 73? *Skill 10*
 F $73h$ H $h + 73$ G $73 - h$ J $h \cdot 73$
5. Simplify: $60 \div (2 + 4)$. *Skill 12*
 A 10 C 45 B 34 D 55
6. Solve: $\frac{m}{4} + 10 = 7$. *Skill 14*
 F −68 H 12 G −12 J 68
7. Simplify: $2(8 - 2 \cdot 4)$. *Skill 12*
 A 8 C 0 B 48 D 56
8. Solve: $x - 5 = -10$. *Skill 13*
 F −5 H 5 G −15 J 15
9. What are the coordinates of point *M*? *Skill 15*
 A (−3, 2) C (−2, −3) B (−3, −2) D (−2, 3)
10. Simplify: $(8 + 12) \div (-3 + 1)$. *Skill 12*
 F 10 H −5 G 5 J −10
11. Write an expression to answer: What is −19 decreased by *y*? *Skill 10*
 A $y - (-19)$ C $-19 \div y$ B $-19 - y$ D $y \div (-19)$
12. Solve: $-4w + 6 = 46$. *Skill 14*
 F −13 H 10 G 5 J 13

Test-Taking Strategies transparency

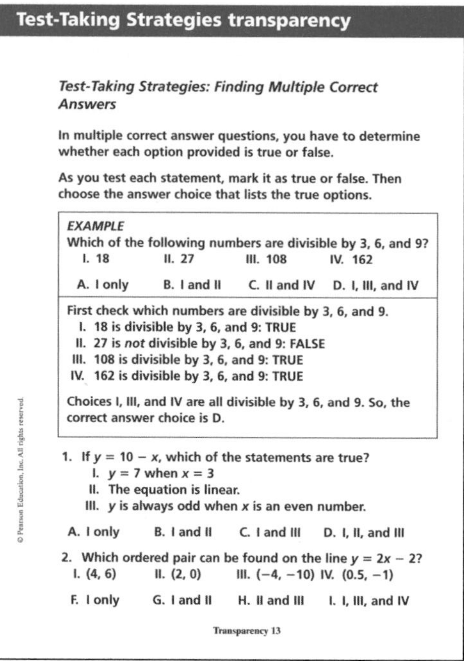

Test-Taking Strategies: Finding Multiple Correct Answers

In multiple correct answer questions, you have to determine whether each option provided is true or false.

As you test each statement, mark it as true or false. Then choose the answer choice that lists the true options.

EXAMPLE
Which of the following numbers are divisible by 3, 6, and 9?
I. 18 II. 27 III. 108 IV. 162
A. I only B. I and II C. II and IV D. I, III, and IV

First check which numbers are divisible by 3, 6, and 9.
I. 18 is divisible by 3, 6, and 9: TRUE
II. 27 is *not* divisible by 3, 6, and 9: FALSE
III. 108 is divisible by 3, 6, and 9: TRUE
IV. 162 is divisible by 3, 6, and 9: TRUE

Choices I, III, and IV are all divisible by 3, 6, and 9. So, the correct answer choice is D.

1. If $y = 10 - x$, which of the statements are true?
 I. $y = 7$ when $x = 3$
 II. The equation is linear.
 III. *y* is always odd when *x* is an even number.
 A. I only B. I and II C. I and III D. I, II, and III
2. Which ordered pair can be found on the line $y = 2x - 2$?
 I. (4, 6) II. (2, 0) III. (−4, −10) IV. (0.5, −1)
 F. I only G. I and II H. II and III I. I, III, and IV

Transparency 13

On PH Website

Test-Taking Strategies worksheet

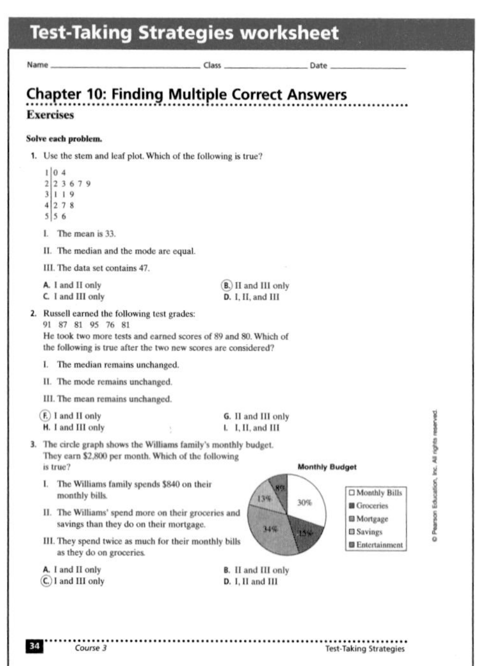

Name ______ Class ______ Date ______

Chapter 10: Finding Multiple Correct Answers
Exercises

Solve each problem.

1. Use the stem and leaf plot. Which of the following is true?
 1 | 0 4
 2 | 2 3 6 7 9
 3 | 1 1 9
 4 | 2 7 8
 5 | 5 6
 I. The mean is 33.
 II. The median and the mode are equal.
 III. The data set contains 47.
 A. I and II only B. II and III only C. I and III only D. I, II, and III
2. Russell earned the following test grades: 91 87 81 95 76 81
 He took two more tests and earned scores of 89 and 80. Which of the following is true after the two new scores are considered?
 I. The median remains unchanged.
 II. The mode remains unchanged.
 III. The mean remains unchanged.
 F. I and II only G. II and III only H. I and III only I. I, II, and III
3. The circle graph shows the Williams family's monthly budget. They earn \$2,800 per month. Which of the following is true?
 I. The Williams family spends \$840 on their monthly bills.
 II. The Williams' spend more on their groceries and savings than they do on their mortgage.
 III. They spend twice as much for their monthly bills as they do on groceries.
 A. I and II only B. II and III only C. I and III only D. I, II, and III

Home Activities

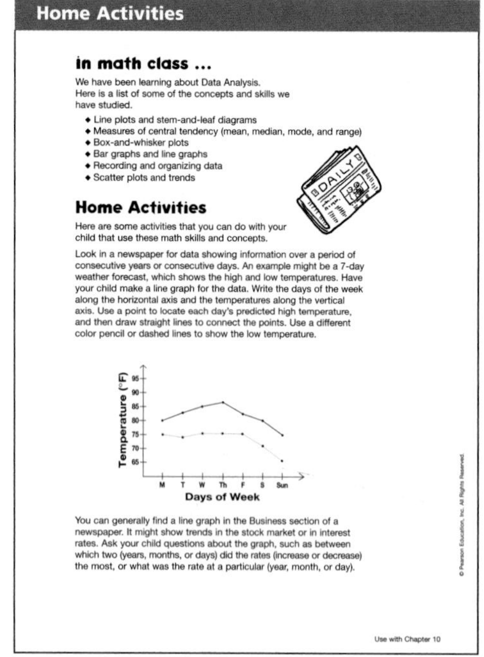

in math class ...

We have been learning about Data Analysis. Here is a list of some of the concepts and skills we have studied.

- Line plots and stem-and-leaf diagrams
- Measures of central tendency (mean, median, mode, and range)
- Box-and-whisker plots
- Bar graphs and line graphs
- Recording and organizing data
- Scatter plots and trends

Home Activities

Here are some activities that you can do with your child that use these math skills and concepts.

Look in a newspaper for data showing information over a period of consecutive years or consecutive days. An example might be a 7-day weather forecast, which shows the high and low temperatures. Have your child make a line graph for the data. Write the days of the week along the horizontal axis and the temperatures along the vertical axis. Use a point to locate each day's predicted high temperature, and then draw straight lines to connect the points. Use a different color pencil or dashed lines to show the low temperature.

You can generally find a line graph in the Business section of a newspaper. It might show trends in the stock market or in interest rates. Ask your child questions about the graph, such as between which two (years, months, or days) did the rates (increase or decrease) the most, or what was the rate at a particular (year, month, or day).

Use with Chapter 10

Available in Spanish;
Web Code: ack-5500

Interdisciplinary Activities

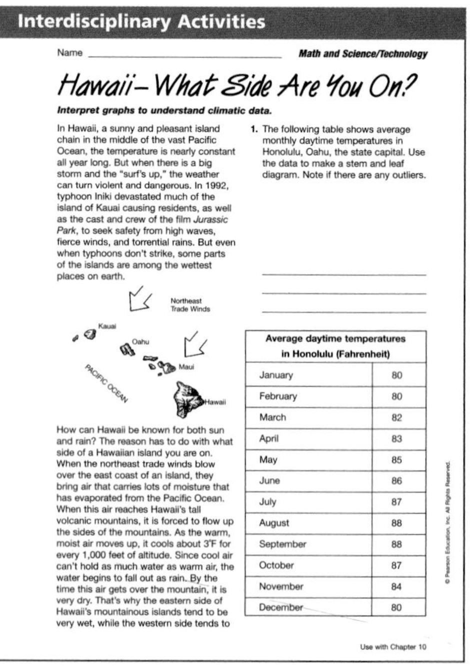

Name ______ **Math and Science/Technology**

Hawaii–What Side Are You On?

Interpret graphs to understand climatic data.

In Hawaii, a sunny and pleasant island chain in the middle of the vast Pacific Ocean, the temperature is nearly constant all year long. But when there is a big storm and the "surf's up," the weather can turn violent and dangerous. In 1992, typhoon Iniki devastated much of the island of Kauai causing residents, as well as the cast and crew of the film *Jurassic Park*, to seek safety from high waves, fierce winds, and torrential rains. But even when typhoons don't strike, some parts of the islands are among the wettest places on earth.

How can Hawaii be known for both sun and rain? The reason has to do with what side of a Hawaiian island you are on. When the northeast trade winds blow over the east coast of an island, they bring air that carries lots of moisture that has evaporated from the Pacific Ocean. When this air reaches Hawaii's tall volcanic mountains, it is forced to flow up the sides of the mountains. As the warm, moist air moves up, it cools about 3°F for every 1,000 feet of altitude. Since cool air can't hold as much water as warm air, the water begins to fall out as rain. By the time this air gets over the mountain, it is very dry. That's why the eastern side of Hawaii's mountainous islands tend to be very wet, while the western side tends to

1. The following table shows average monthly daytime temperatures in Honolulu, Oahu, the state capital. Use the data to make a stem and leaf diagram. Note if there are any outliers.

Average daytime temperatures in Honolulu (Fahrenheit)	
January	80
February	80
March	82
April	83
May	85
June	86
July	87
August	88
September	88
October	87
November	84
December	80

Use with Chapter 10

Web Code: ack-5500

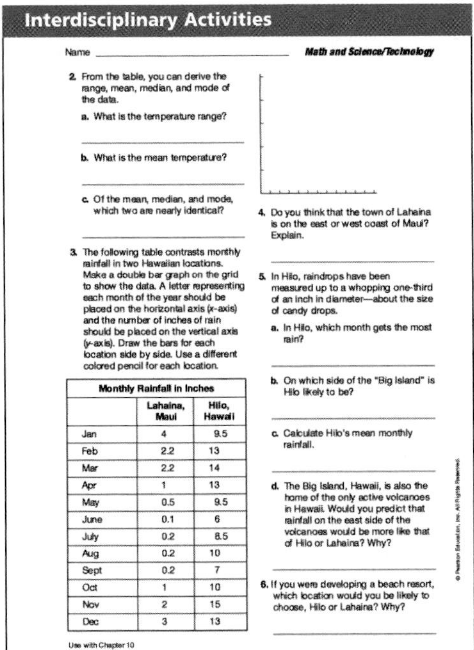

Interdisciplinary Activities

Name ______________________ ***Math and Science/Technology***

2. From the table, you can derive the range, mean, median, and mode of the data.
   a. What is the temperature range?

   ____

   b. What is the mean temperature?

   ____

   c. Of the mean, median, and mode, which two are nearly identical?

   ____

3. The following table contrasts monthly rainfall in two Hawaiian locations. Make a double bar graph on the grid to show the data. A letter representing each month of the year should be placed on the horizontal axis (*x*-axis) and the number of inches of rain should be placed on the vertical axis (*y*-axis). Draw the bars for each location side by side. Use a different colored pencil for each location.

Monthly Rainfall in Inches		
	Lahaina, Maui	Hilo, Hawaii
Jan	4	9.5
Feb	2.2	13
Mar	2.2	14
Apr	1	13
May	0.5	9.5
June	0.1	6
July	0.2	8.5
Aug	0.2	10
Sept	0.2	7
Oct	1	10
Nov	2	15
Dec	3	13

4. Do you think that the town of Lahaina is on the east or west coast of Maui? Explain.

   ____

5. In Hilo, raindrops have been measured up to a whopping one-third of an inch in diameter—about the size of candy drops.
   a. In Hilo, which month gets the most rain?

   ____

   b. On which side of the "Big Island" is Hilo likely to be?

   ____

   c. Calculate Hilo's mean monthly rainfall.

   ____

   d. The Big Island, Hawaii, is also the home of the only active volcanoes in Hawaii. Would you predict that rainfall on the east side of the volcanoes would be more like that of Hilo or Lahaina? Why?

   ____

6. If you were developing a beach resort, which location would you be likely to choose, Hilo or Lahaina? Why?

   ____

Use with Chapter 10

Web Code: ack-5500

Algebra Readiness Puzzles

Name ______________ Class ______________ Date ______________

Circle Time — Puzzle 34

Using Graphs to Analyze Data

Jane surveyed all 300 of her eighth grade classmates to find out their preferences about the class trip, how they spend their time after school, and what they plan to do after graduating from high school. Jane wants to organize the data into three circle graphs. Use the clues below to draw each of the graphs. Then answer the questions. Be sure to include a legend for each graph.

Eighth Grade Class Trip Preferences
15, 5%
45, 15%
Water Park
Museum

After-School Activities
70, 26%
Band

Future Plans
15, 5%
Trade School

Clues

- Half of the students would like to go to a theme park for the eighth grade trip.
- Ten percent of the students are involved in the after-school tutoring program.
- Forty-five students are planning to work in the emergency care field after high school.
- Thirty percent of the students play in a sport after school.
- Ninety students want to go to Washington, D.C.
- Sixty percent of the students plan to attend a college after graduation.
- There are 100 students participating in an arts and craft activity after school.
- Sixty students are undecided about their plans for after high school.

1. What percent of students are in the school band? ______________
2. How many students would like to go to a water park? ______________
3. What percent of the students plan to attend a trade school after graduating? ______________

34 Algebra Readiness Puzzles

Web Code: ack-5500

Algebra Readiness Puzzles

Name ______________ Class ______________ Date ______________

The Glogs of Nog — Puzzle 110

On the imaginary island of Nog, money is measured in units called glogs. Here are the weights of the coins.

1-glog coin = 4 grams

5-glog coins = 10 grams

10-glog coins = 12 grams

25-glog coins = 20 grams

Use the weights of the coins to determine how much money each person has. Some may have more than one amount.

1. Alberto has 14 grams in coins.

   ____

2. Matthew has 10 coins weighing a total of 200 grams.

   ____

3. Jessika has 40 grams in coins. Use at least one 1-glog coin.

   ____

4. Misha has 3 coins, weighing a total of 24 grams.

   ____

5. Natalie has 2 coins weighing a total of 24 grams.

   ____

6. Tyrell has 42 grams in coins.

   ____

7. What is the greatest possible weight of 100 glogs?

   ____

8. What is the smallest possible weight of 100 glogs?

   ____

110 Algebra Readiness Puzzles

Web Code: ack-5500

CHAPTER 10

Using Graphs to Analyze Data

Chapter 10 Overview

In this chapter, students learn to read graphs critically and to make various kinds of graphs. They work with stem-and-leaf plots, box-and-whisker plots, scatter plots, and circle graphs. They draw upon their understanding of graphs to choose the appropriate graph for a given set of data.

Reading Math
- Reading Graphical Displays, p. 539
- **Vocabulary:** A complete list, plus exercises, in the Chapter Review, p. 582
- **Illustrated Glossary:** Examples for each vocabulary term, plus definitions in English and Spanish, on p. 735

Writing in Math
Writing to Persuade, p. 580

Test-Taking Strategies
Finding Multiple Correct Answers, p. 581

Real-World Problem Solving
- **Strategies:** Draw a Diagram and Use Logical Reasoning, p. 576–579
- **Real-World Snapshots:** Conic Cuisine, pp. 586–587
- **Chapter Project:** News Flash, p. 700

www.PHSchool.com
Internet support includes:
- Self-grading Vocabulary and Chapter 10 Tests
- Activity Masters
- Chapter Project support
- Chapter Planner
- Ch. 10 Resources

Plus iTEXT

CHAPTER 10

Using Graphs to Analyze Data

Lessons

Key Vocabulary
- box-and-whisker plot (p. 552)
- central angle (p. 564)
- circle graph (p. 563)
- frequency (p. 533)
- frequency table (p. 533)
- histogram (p. 535)
- line plot (p. 534)
- negative trend (p. 558)
- no trend (p. 558)
- positive trend (p. 558)
- quartiles (p. 552)
- scatter plot (p. 557)
- stem-and-leaf plot (p. 546)
- trend line (p. 558)

Real-World Snapshots

Wheat is the number one food grain grown in the world. The United States ranks fourth in the world in wheat production. It exports more than 50% of the wheat it produces each year to other countries.

Data File

Production of Crops in the United States (billions of bushels)

	Wheat		Soybeans	
Year	Acres Harvested (millions)	Bushels (billions)	Acres Harvested (millions)	Bushels (billions)
1995	61	2.2	62	2.2
1996	63	2.3	63	2.4
1997	63	2.5	69	2.7
1998	59	2.5	70	2.7
1999	54	2.3	72	2.7
2000	53	2.2	72	2.8
2001	49	2.0	73	2.9

SOURCE: National Agricultural Statistics Service

You will use the data above throughout this chapter:

- p. 537 Lesson 10-1
- p. 543 Lesson 10-2
- p. 561 Lesson 10-5

 **Real-World Snapshots** On pages 586 and 587, you will solve problems involving food production.

Teaching Notes

Activating Prior Knowledge
In this chapter, students build on their knowledge of bar graphs, pictographs, and line graphs. They use graphs of equations to solve problems. They also draw upon their understanding of how to solve proportions. Ask questions such as:

- *A bar graph shows the following numbers of cars sold in each of four years: 2,500, 3,200, 3,800, 4,000. What is the mean of this data?* 3,375
- *Solve:* $\frac{3}{8} = \frac{n}{40}$. $n = 15$

Real-World Snapshots
The data here about crops will be used throughout the chapter. Have a volunteer read the opening sentences about wheat production in the United States and the title of the chart. Focus students on the data in the chart and ask:

- *In what year was the number of harvest acres the same for wheat and soybeans?* 1996
- *For which crop was the number of bushels produced the same for three consecutive years?* soybeans
- *What can you say about the trend in the numbers of acres harvested for the two crops?* number of acres rising slowing for soybeans, decreasing steadily for wheat

Reading and Math Literacy

10A: Graphic Organizer For use before Lesson 10-1

Study Skill: Pay attention in class and concentrate when reading assignments so information does not slip out of your "short-term" memory.

Write your answers.

1. What is the chapter title? Using Graphs to Analyze Data
2. How many lessons are there in this chapter? 8
3. What is the topic of the Reading Math page? Reading Graphical Displays
4. What is the topic of the Test-Taking Strategy page? Finding Multiple Correct Answers
5. Look through the chapter and list four real-world connections that are discussed. Answers will vary.
6. Complete the graphic organizer below as you work through the chapter.
   - In the center, write the title of the chapter.
   - When you begin a lesson, write the lesson name in a rectangle.
   - When you complete a lesson, write a skill or key concept in a circle linked to that lesson block.
   - When you complete the chapter, use this graphic organizer to help you review.

   Check students' diagrams.

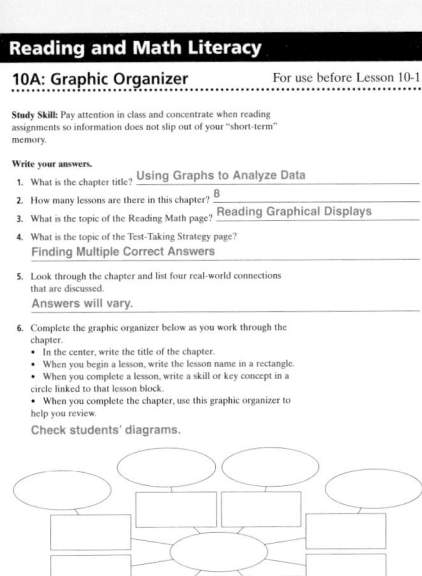

Available in Spanish

Chapter 10: Using Graphs to Analyze Data

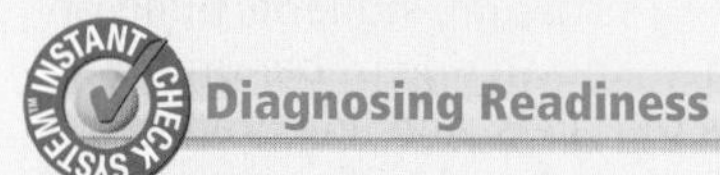

Students will find answers to these exercises in the back of their textbooks.

Prescribing Intervention
For intervention, direct students to:

Using Integers With Mean, Median, and Mode
Lesson 1-6: Examples 1–2.
Extra Practice, p. 702.

Graphing Points
Lesson 3-1: Example 3.
Extra Practice, p. 704.

Solving Proportions
Lesson 5-4: Example 2.
Extra Practice, p. 706.

Fractions, Decimals, and Percents
Lesson 6-1: Example 4.
Extra Practice, p. 707.

Chapter 10 Preview

Where You've Been

- In Chapter 3, you learned to graph equations and to use graphs of equations to solve problems.
- In Chapter 5, you learned how to solve proportions.

Where You're Going

- In Chapter 10, you will learn to use various types of graphs. You will also learn to read graphs critically and to choose the appropriate graph for a set of data.
- Applying what you learn, you will use graphs to compare the mileage of cars. You will also examine the amount of money visitors to the United States spend.

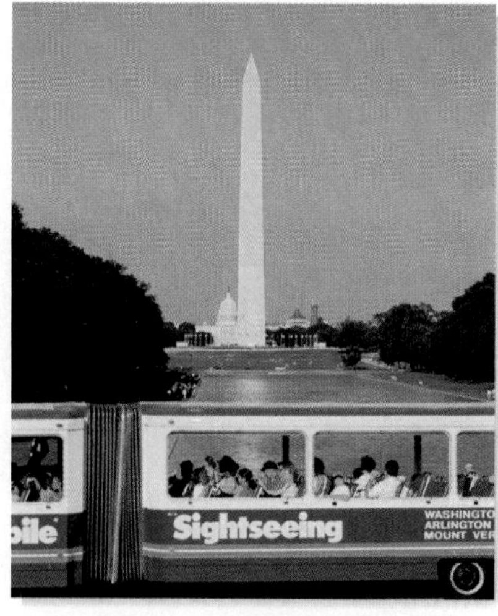

The tourism industry uses graphs to analyze the amount of money visitors to the United States spend.

Instant self-check online and on CD-ROM

Diagnosing Readiness

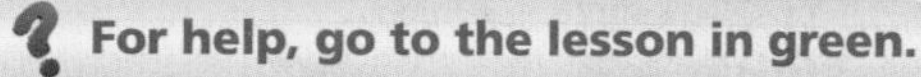

Using Integers With Mean, Median, and Mode (Lesson 1-6)

Find the mean, median, mode, and range of each data set.

1. cell phone minutes used per week:
23 45 36 41 45 28 36 35 40 52 37
38; 37; 36 and 45; 29

2. time to run 5 kilometers (min):
22 23 28 20 24 25 26 30 18 24 22 25
23.9; 24; 22, 24, and 25; 12

Graphing Points (Lesson 3-1)

Graph each point on the same coordinate plane. 3–10. See margin.

3. $(2, 5)$ **4.** $(8, 0)$ **5.** $(-5, 4)$ **6.** $(3, -1)$

7. $(-6, -8)$ **8.** $(-4, 0)$ **9.** $(3, 7)$ **10.** $(-3, -6)$

Solving Proportions (Lesson 5-4)

Solve each proportion.

11. $\frac{8}{9} = \frac{16}{x}$ 18 **12.** $\frac{a}{24} = \frac{14}{12}$ 28 **13.** $\frac{6}{3} = \frac{s}{12}$ 24 **14.** $\frac{3}{m} = \frac{75}{125}$ 5

Fractions, Decimals, and Percents (Lesson 6-1)

Write each percent as a fraction in simplest form.

15. 26% $\frac{13}{50}$ **16.** 48% $\frac{12}{25}$ **17.** 13% $\frac{13}{100}$ **18.** 72% $\frac{18}{25}$

19. 20% $\frac{1}{5}$ **20.** 47% $\frac{47}{100}$ **21.** 50% $\frac{1}{2}$ **22.** 10% $\frac{1}{10}$

3–10.

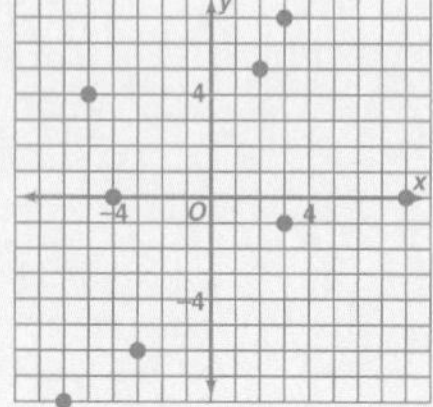

10-1 Displaying Frequency

What You'll Learn

 To make frequency tables and line plots

 To display data using intervals

. . . And Why

To compare the battery life of batteries using a histogram, as in Example 5

Check Skills You'll Need

For help, go to Lesson 1-6.

1–4. See back of book.

Find the mean, median, mode, and range of each data set.

1. hours driving on a trip:
   6 6.5 7 7 8 8 9 9.5 10
2. ages of cousins:
   8 14 13 15 12 14 17 13
3. low temperature:
   4 −2 0 −1 2 −4 5 3
4. bowling scores:
   198 204 178 182 191 185

New Vocabulary

- frequency
- frequency table
- line plot
- histogram

Interactive lesson includes instant self-check, tutorials, and activities.

OBJECTIVE 1 Making Frequency Tables and Line Plots

The number of times a data item occurs is the **frequency** of the item. A **frequency table** lists the frequency of each item in a set of data.

1 EXAMPLE Making a Frequency Table

Language Vowels are speech sounds you make when breath moves through your open vocal tract. In English, the letters *a*, *e*, *i*, *o*, *u* represent these sounds. Make a frequency table for the number of vowels in the quotation below.

"The great glory of American democracy is the right to protest for right."

—Reverend Martin Luther King, Jr. (1929–1968)

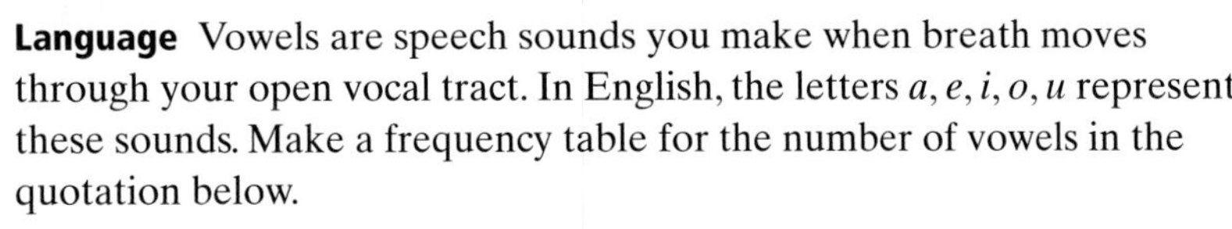

Reverend Martin Luther King, Jr.

Make a tally mark each time a vowel occurs.

Letter	Tally	Frequency
a	////	4
e	~~////~~ /	6
i	////	4
o	~~////~~ /	6
u		0

The number of tally marks in each row is the frequency.

Check Understanding 1

1a–b. See back of book.

a. Make a frequency table for the number of consonants in the above quotation. Use it to find the letter(s) that occurs most often.

b. Make a frequency table for the set of data.
   length of time (minutes): 25 25 20 25 20 24 30 25 31 26 28 30 27 28

Ongoing Assessment and Intervention

Before the Lesson
Diagnose prerequisite skills using:
- Check Skills You'll Need

During the Lesson
Monitor progress using:
- Check Understanding
- Additional Examples
- Test Prep

After the Lesson
Assess knowledge using:
- Lesson Quiz
- Computer Test Generator CD

10-1

1. Plan

Lesson Preview

PowerPoint

Check Skills You'll Need

Finding the Mean, Median, Mode, and Range
Lesson 1-6: Examples 1–2. Extra Practice, p. 702.

Lesson Resources

Optional Materials
- graph paper
- ruler

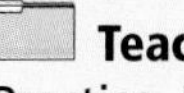

Teaching Resources
Practice, Reteaching, Enrichment

Reaching All Students
Practice Workbook 10-1
Spanish Practice Workbook 10-1
Guided Problem Solving 10-1
Hands-On Activities 26

Presentation Assistant Plus!
Transparencies
- Check Skills You'll Need 10-1
- Problem of the Day 10-1
- Additional Examples 10-1
- Student Edition Answers 10-1
- Lesson Quiz 10-1
- Classroom Aid 2

PH Presentation Pro CD-ROM 10-1

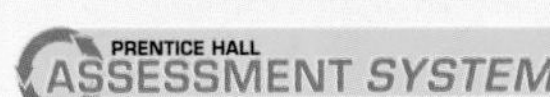

Computer Test Generator CD

Technology
Resource Pro® CD-ROM
Computer Test Generator CD
PH Presentation Pro CD-ROM

www.PHSchool.com
Student Site
- Teacher Web Code: ack-5500
- Self-grading Lesson Quiz

PH SuccessNet Teacher Center
- Lesson Planner
- Resources

Plus iText

2. Teach

Math Background

Data items in a list are often difficult to interpret or to use as information. One way of organizing data so that their meaning is easier to see is by making a *frequency table* that shows how often repeated data items occur. A *line plot* stacks X marks for repeated data items on a number line. Data can be grouped into intervals and displayed on a frequency table or a histogram. A *histogram* is a type of bar graph that shows data grouped in intervals and represented by bars that have no spaces between them.

Teaching Notes

1 EXAMPLE English Learners

Make sure students understand that a *consonant* is a letter that is NOT a vowel. The letter Y is here considered a consonant, although it sometimes fills the role of a vowel, as in *why*.

2 EXAMPLE Teaching Tip

Ask:

- *How is a line plot similar to a frequency table?* Sample: Both show the number of times a data value occurs.
- *How does a line plot differ from a frequency table?* Sample: A line plot stacks Xs above repeated data values on a number line while the table uses tally marks.

3 EXAMPLE Inclusion

Remind students that the median is the middle value when the data items are ordered. There may be no mode or more than one mode.

4 EXAMPLE Error Prevention

Point out that the intervals must not overlap so that a value will always be in only one interval.

5 EXAMPLE Visual Learners

Have volunteers sketch regular bar graphs where there are spaces between the bars because bars do not represent intervals.

Another way to display frequency is to use a line plot. A **line plot** is a graph that displays data with ✗ marks above each data value on a number line.

Body Temperatures of Cats (°F)
101, 102, 101, 100, 102, 103
102, 101, 101
104, 101, 102

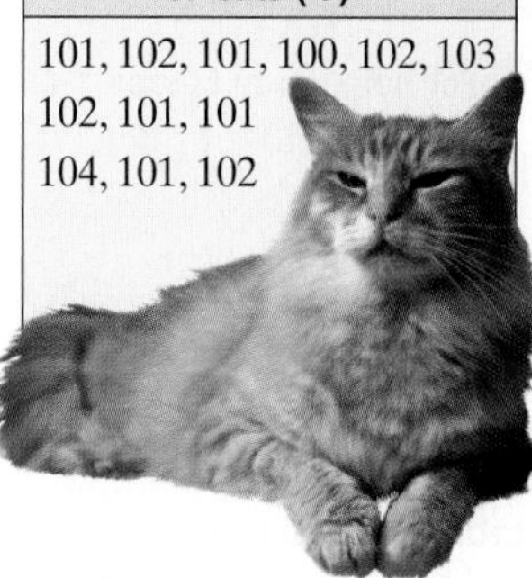

2 EXAMPLE Making a Line Plot

Anatomy Make a line plot for these body temperatures of cats.

Body Temperatures of Cats

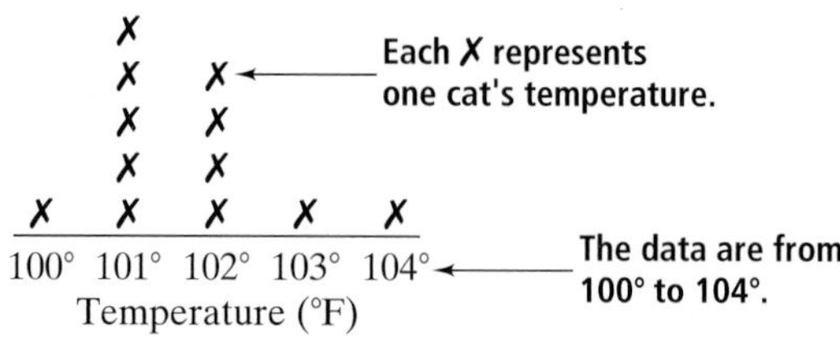

Check Understanding 2 **a.** Make a line plot for these human body temperatures (°F).
98 98 99 97 98 96 99 98 97 100 99 98 99 **2a. See back of book.**

b. Reasoning Why does the number line for the line plot in Example 2 start at 100 instead of 0?
100°F is the lowest body temperature given in the data.

You can find the mean, median, and mode of a set of data using a line plot. Use the frequency of each data item to find the sum of the items and the total number of items.

> **Need Help?**
> The mean is the sum of the data items divided by the number of items.

3 EXAMPLE Finding Mean, Median, and Mode

Find the mean, median, and mode of the data in the line plot in Example 2.

Mean $\frac{(1 \cdot 100) + (5 \cdot 101) + (4 \cdot 102) + (1 \cdot 103) + (1 \cdot 104)}{1 + 5 + 4 + 1 + 1}$ ← **Multiply each data value by its frequency.**

↑ **Add the frequency of each item to find the total number of items.**

$= \frac{1220}{12}$ ← **Simplify.**

≈ 101.7 ← **Round to the nearest tenth.**

Median There are 12 data items. Since the data are ordered, the median is the mean of the sixth and seventh items. The median is $\frac{101 + 102}{2} = 101.5$.

Mode The mode is the item that occurs most often, which is 101.

Check Understanding 3 Find the mean, median, and mode of the data in the line plot. Round to the nearest tenth.

✗				✗		✗
✗		✗	✗	✗	✗	✗
✗		✗	✗	✗	✗	✗
✗	✗	✗	✗	✗	✗	✗
50	51	52	53	54	55	56

53.2; 53.5; 50, 54, and 56

Reaching All Students

Below Level Discuss tally marks and have students make a tally chart for items such as the number of chairs, desks, and tables in the room.	**Advanced Learners** Have students make a histogram for Example 5 with unequal intervals. Have them explain how these intervals could be misleading.	**English Learners** See note on page 534. **Inclusion** See note on page 534.

OBJECTIVE

2 Displaying Data Using Intervals

In some sets of data, there are too many values to display separately. A grouped-frequency table organizes data into intervals of equal size that do not overlap.

4 EXAMPLE Using Intervals

Energy A survey measured the battery life of different brands of batteries used in portable stereos and CD players. Make a frequency table with intervals for the data below.

hours of battery life: 12 9 10 14 10 11 10 18 21 10 14 22

The data range from 9 to 22. Use equal-size intervals that begin with multiples of 5. →

Battery Life

Hours	Tally	Frequency
0–4		0
5–9	/	1
10–14	𝍸 ///	8
15–19	/	1
20–24	//	2

Reading Math
An interval of 8–12 includes the numbers 8, 9, 10, 11, and 12.

Check Understanding 4 Make a frequency table using intervals of equal size to group the data.
cost of a movie: \$5.00, \$6.00, \$8.50, \$9.00, \$5.50, \$7.00, \$7.00, \$7.50, \$6.00, \$7.50, \$4.00, \$9.00, \$8.00, \$5.50 See left.

4. Answers may vary. Sample:

Cost (Dollars)	Frequency
4–5.99	4
6–7.99	6
8–9.99	4

A **histogram** is a special type of bar graph with no spaces between the bars. The height of each bar shows the frequency of data within that interval.

5 EXAMPLE Making a Histogram

Make a histogram for the data from Example 4.

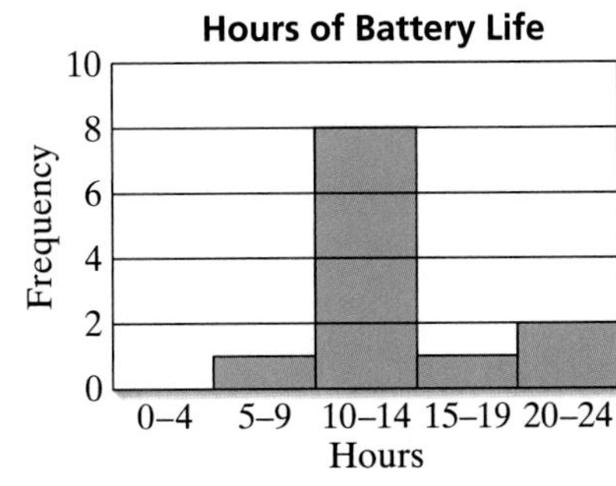

5a.

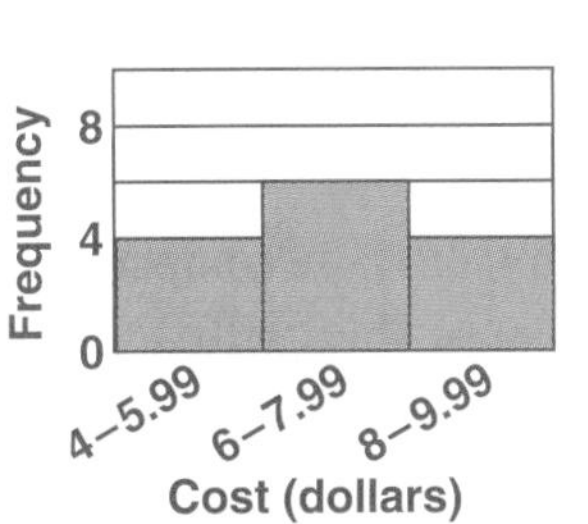

5a. See above left.

Check Understanding 5 **a.** Make a histogram for the cost of a movie in Check Understanding 4.
b. **Number Sense** How would making the interval larger make the graph more difficult to read? You wouldn't see as much detail.

PowerPoint

Additional Examples

1 Make a frequency table for the number of songs on a collection of CDs. 10 11 13 8 12 11 9 15 12 11 13 15 14

No. of Songs	Tally	Freq.
8	I	1
9	I	1
10	I	1
11	III	3
12	II	2
13	II	2
14	I	1
15	II	2

2 Make a line plot for the data given in Question 1.

Songs on CDs

			X				
			X	X	X		X
X	X	X	X	X	X	X	X
8	9	10	11	12	13	14	15

Number of Songs per CD

3 Find the mean, median, and mode of the data in the line plot in Question 2. mean: 11.8; median: 12; mode: 11

4 The number of goals a soccer team scored in each game of the season is shown. Make a frequency table with intervals for the data. 0 3 0 0 7 2 1 0 4 1 0 3 6 0 1

Goals	Tally	Freq.
0–1	𝍸 IIII	9
2–3	III	3
4–5	I	1
6–7	II	2

5 Make a histogram for the data from Question 4.

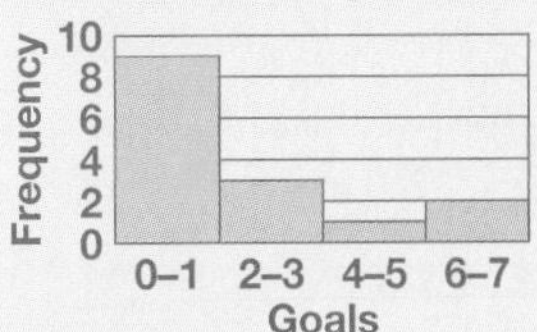

Closure

- *Why are frequency tables and line plots useful?* Sample: They quickly organize and display raw data by the number of times each item occurs.
- *When is a frequency table with intervals or a histogram useful?* Sample: when there are a large number of data values

3. Practice

Assignment Guide

1 Objective 1

A B Core 1–6, 14–16, 20–23

2 Objective 2

A B Core 7–13, 17–19

C Extension 24–25

Test Prep 26–29
Mixed Review 30–38

Diversity
Exercises 21–23 Have students describe their family reunions.

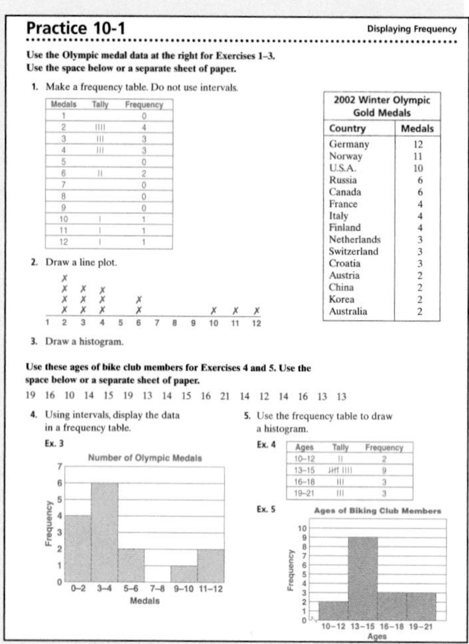
Practice 10-1 Displaying Frequency

Use the Olympic medal data at the right for Exercises 1–3. Use the space below or a separate sheet of paper.

1. Make a frequency table. Do not use intervals.

Medals	Tally	Frequency
1		0
2	IIII	4
3	III	3
4	III	3
5		0
6	II	2
7		0
8		0
9		0
10	I	1
11	I	1
12	I	1

2002 Winter Olympic Gold Medals

Country	Medals
Germany	12
Norway	11
U.S.A.	10
Russia	6
Canada	6
France	4
Italy	4
Finland	4
Netherlands	3
Switzerland	3
Croatia	3
Austria	2
China	2
Korea	2
Australia	2

2. Draw a line plot.

1 2 3 4 5 6 7 8 9 10 11 12

3. Draw a histogram.

Use these ages of bike club members for Exercises 4 and 5. Use the space below or a separate sheet of paper.

19 16 10 14 15 19 13 14 15 16 21 14 12 14 16 13 13

4. Using intervals, display the data in a frequency table.

5. Use the frequency table to draw a histogram.

Ex. 3

Number of Olympic Medals

Frequency: 0 1 2 3 4 5 6 7
Medals: 0–2 3–4 5–6 7–8 9–10 11–12

Ex. 4

Ages	Tally	Frequency
10–12	II	2
13–15	HHT IIII	9
16–18	III	3
19–21	III	3

Ex. 5

Ages of Biking Club Members

Frequency: 0 1 2 3 4 5 6 7 8 9 10
Ages: 10–12 13–15 16–18 19–21

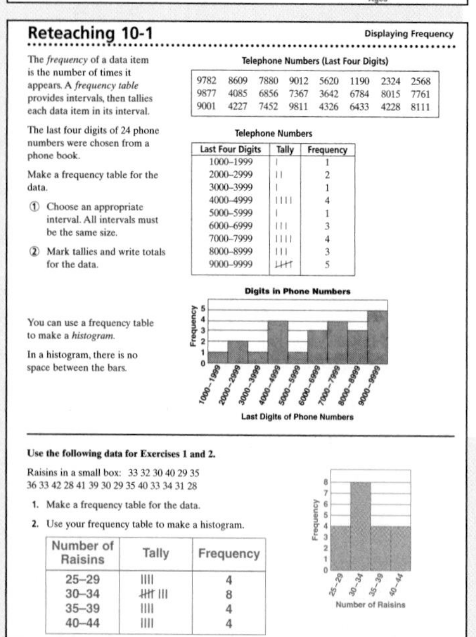
Reteaching 10-1 Displaying Frequency

The *frequency* of a data item is the number of times it appears. A *frequency table* provides intervals, then tallies each data item in its interval.

Telephone Numbers (Last Four Digits)

9782	8609	7880	9012	5620	1190	2324	2568
9877	4085	6856	7367	3642	6784	8015	7761
9001	4227	7452	9811	4326	6433	4228	8111

The last four digits of 24 phone numbers were chosen from a phone book.

Make a frequency table for the data.

① Choose an appropriate interval. All intervals must be the same size.

② Mark tallies and write totals for the data.

Telephone Numbers

Last Four Digits	Tally	Frequency
1000–1999	I	1
2000–2999	II	2
3000–3999	I	1
4000–4999	IIII	4
5000–5999	I	1
6000–6999	III	3
7000–7999	IIII	4
8000–8999	III	3
9000–9999	HHT	5

You can use a frequency table to make a *histogram*.

In a histogram, there is no space between the bars.

Digits in Phone Numbers

Frequency: 0 1 2 3 4 5
Last Digits of Phone Numbers: 1000–1999 2000–2999 3000–3999 4000–4999 5000–5999 6000–6999 7000–7999 8000–8999 9000–9999

Use the following data for Exercises 1 and 2.

Raisins in a small box: 33 32 30 40 29 35 36 33 42 28 41 39 30 29 35 40 33 34 31 28

1. Make a frequency table for the data.

2. Use your frequency table to make a histogram.

Number of Raisins	Tally	Frequency
25–29	IIII	4
30–34	HHT III	8
35–39	IIII	4
40–44	IIII	4

Frequency: 0 1 2 3 4 5 6 7 8
Number of Raisins: 25–29 30–34 35–39 40–44

EXERCISES

For more practice, see *Extra Practice*.

A Practice by Example

Examples 1, 2 (pages 533, 534)

Make a frequency table and a line plot for each set of data. 1–4. See margin.

1. cookies in a pound: 19 20 20 19 21 20 19 23 20 19 21 22 21 21 19 20 22 21 21

2. hours spent on homework each night: 2 2 3 1 1 2 0 3 2 0 4 2 1 3 1 3 1 4 2 2

3. hard-drive sizes (gigabytes): 8 10 8 12 16 20 18 16 12 14 18 24 12 8

4. low temperatures of a city in February (°F): −2 −1 0 −2 −1 −4 2 3 0 −1 2 −3 −1 0 1 2 3 2 −2 3 4 2 1 5 6 4 3 1

Example 3 (page 534)

Find the mean, median, and mode. Round to the nearest tenth.

5. 6.

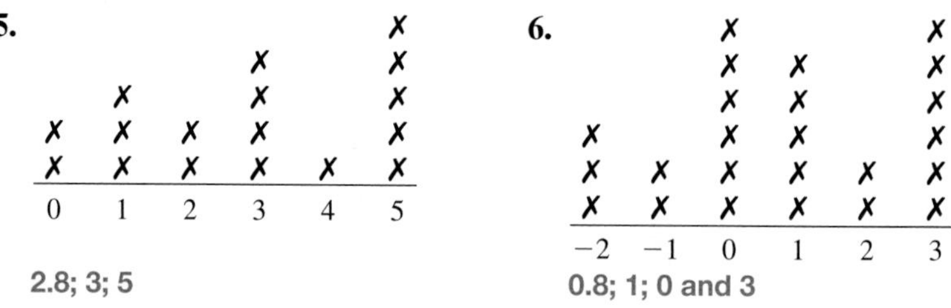

5. 2.8; 3; 5 6. 0.8; 1; 0 and 3

Examples 4, 5 (page 535)

Make a frequency table and histogram for each data set. Use intervals of equal sizes to group the data.
7–11. See back of book.

7. ages of members of the Seniors Hiking Club: 58 73 80 66 67 59 60 73 76 82 78 78 60 57 75 62

8. televisions sold at a store each day: 7 8 9 13 14 18 5 9 11 16 5 6 14 12 10 9 7 9 2 21

9. monthly car payments: 205 190 305 346 452 325 140 376 289 368 512 337 254 398

10. cars sold per month: 24 25 23 26 28 29 21 27 31 28 26 24

11. golf scores: 0 −2 −1 0 3 −1 0 2 1 −2 3 0 1 −5 4 3 4 5 −2 0 −1 4 0 −2 3 2 3 1 4 0 −2 1

B Apply Your Skills

12. Answers may vary. Sample: The bars will not be as high and the graph will be wider when using smaller intervals.

12. **Writing in Math** How will the appearance of a histogram change if you use many small intervals instead of a few large intervals? See above left.

Cost of Binders

$2.25	$2.29
$3.89	$3.69
$7.49	$3.50
$4.29	$7.79

13. **Price Comparison** While shopping for school supplies, José compared the prices of binders. The prices he found are shown at the left.
    a. Make a frequency table. Use intervals such as $2.00–$2.99.
    b. Use part (a) to make a histogram. 13a–b. See back of book.
    c. José does not want to spend over $5.00 for a binder. He does not like the quality of the least expensive binders. In what price range(s) should he look? Explain. $3.00–3.99 and $4.00–4.99; these intervals are less than $5 but not the least expensive.

Use the Guided Problem Solving worksheet with Exercise 16.

2–4. See back of book.

1.

Cookies in a Pound	Frequency
19	5
20	5
21	6
22	2
23	1

14. **Data File, p. 531** Make a frequency table and a line plot for the number of bushels of wheat produced in the United States. See margin.

Distribution of Gold Medals at the 2002 Winter Olympics

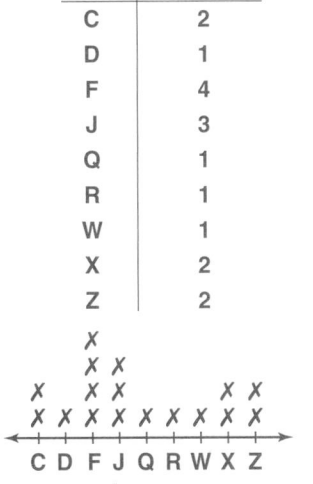

Country	Medals
Germany	12
Norway	11
United States	10
Canada	6
Russian Federation	6
Finland	4
France	4
Italy	4

SOURCE: *The World Almanac*

Use the table at the left.

15. **Error Analysis** Your friend says that the table of data is not a frequency table. Is your friend correct? Explain. See below left.

GPS 16. Use a line plot to display the frequency of the number of medals won. See margin.

Write the intervals described in each statement. 17–19. Answers may vary. See margin for samples.

17. intervals with multiples of 5 for data that range from 17 to 43

18. intervals with multiples of 10 for data that range from 58 to 100

19. intervals with multiples of 20 for data that range from 305 to 458

20. **Cryptography** The message below is in code. It is a message spoken by astronaut Neil Armstrong from the moon on July 20, 1969.

QCF FJDXF CJR XJWZFZ.

- The letter that occurs most often represents *e*.
- The letter that occurs next most often represents *a*.
- The letters that represent *d*, *h*, and *l* all occur twice.
- The letters that represent *g*, *n*, *s*, and *t* all occur once.

a. Make a frequency table and line plot for the letters in the message. See below left.

b. Use the hints to decide what the message says. The Eagle has landed.

15. No; the table of data shows the frequency of the number of medals.

20a.

Letter	Frequency
C	2
D	1
F	4
J	3
Q	1
R	1
W	1
X	2
Z	2

C D F J Q R W X Z

Letters

Families Use the line plots to answer Exercises 21–23. The Bakers and the Smiths are having a family reunion. The number of children attending from each family is recorded in the line plots below.

Smith Reunion

0 1 2 3 4 5

Number of Children Attending per Family

Baker Reunion

0 1 2 3 4 5

Number of Children Attending per Family

21. Do the Bakers or the Smiths have more families without children? the Smiths

22. Which family, the Bakers or the Smiths, has more large families attending? the Bakers

23. Find the mean, median, and mode for each line plot. Round to the nearest tenth. Smith: 1.6; 1; 0 Baker: 2.4; 3; 3

14.

Bushels of Wheat (in billions)	Frequency
2.0	1
2.1	0
2.2	2
2.3	2
2.4	0
2.5	2

Bushels of Wheat Produced in the United States

2.0 2.1 2.2 2.3 2.4 2.5

Bushels

16.

1 2 3 4 5 6 7 8 9 10 11 12

Number of Medals

17. 15–19, 20–24, 25–29, 30–34, 35–39, 40–44

18. 50–59, 60–69, 70–79, 80–89, 90–99, 100–109

19. 300–319, 320–339, 340–359, 360–379, 380–399, 400–419, 420–439, 440–459

4. Assess

Lesson Quiz 10-1

1. Make a line plot for the number of school spirit ribbons purchased. 1 3 11 2 2 10 9 1 7 6 4 3 1 1

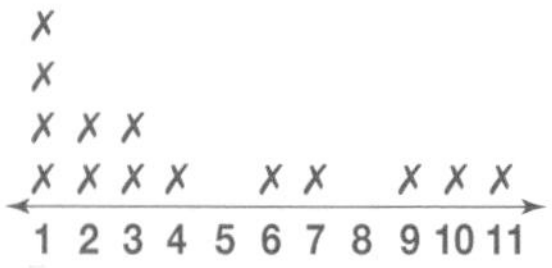

   ✗ ✗ ✗ ✗ (1); ✗ ✗ (2); ✗ ✗ (3); ✗ (4); ✗ (6); ✗ (7); ✗ (9); ✗ (10); ✗ (11)

   1 2 3 4 5 6 7 8 9 10 11

2. Make a frequency table with intervals for data in Exercise 1. Sample:

Ribbons	Tally	Freq.
0–2	𝍸 I	6
3–5	III	3
6–8	II	2
9–11	III	3

3. Make a histogram for the data in Exercise 1?

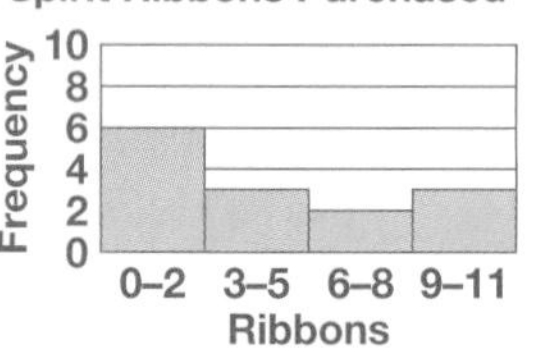

Alternative Assessment

Students toss two number cubes. They record the sums in a frequency table and make a histogram.

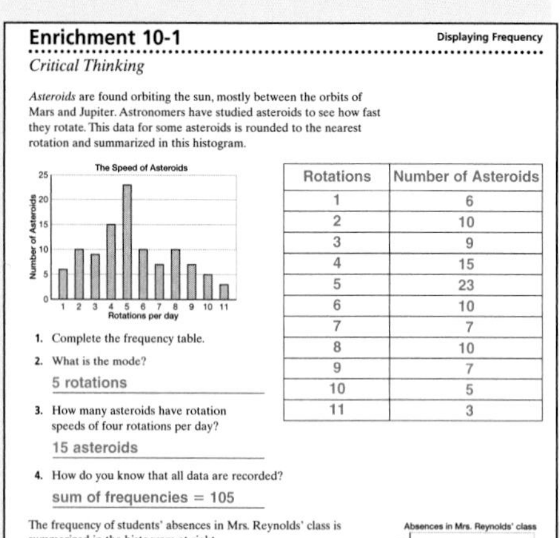

Enrichment 10-1 — Displaying Frequency

Critical Thinking

Asteroids are found orbiting the sun, mostly between the orbits of Mars and Jupiter. Astronomers have studied asteroids to see how fast they rotate. This data for some asteroids is rounded to the nearest rotation and summarized in this histogram.

The Speed of Asteroids

Rotations	Number of Asteroids
1	6
2	10
3	9
4	15
5	23
6	10
7	7
8	10
9	7
10	5
11	3

1. Complete the frequency table.
2. What is the mode? 5 rotations
3. How many asteroids have rotation speeds of four rotations per day? 15 asteroids
4. How do you know that all data are recorded? sum of frequencies = 105

The frequency of students' absences in Mrs. Reynolds' class is summarized in the histogram at right.

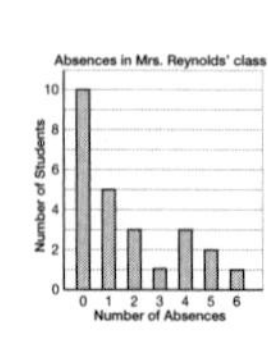

5. How many students have 5 absences? 2 students
6. Make a frequency table of this data on another sheet of paper. Check students' answers.
7. What is the mode? 0 absences
8. How many students are in Mrs. Reynolds' class? 25 students

C Challenge

24. Answers may vary. Sample:

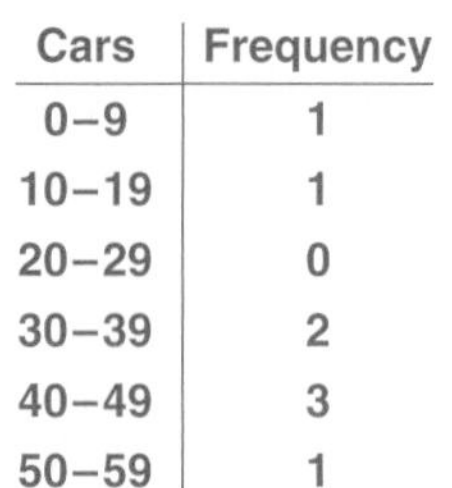

Cars	Frequency
0–9	1
10–19	1
20–29	0
30–39	2
40–49	3
50–59	1

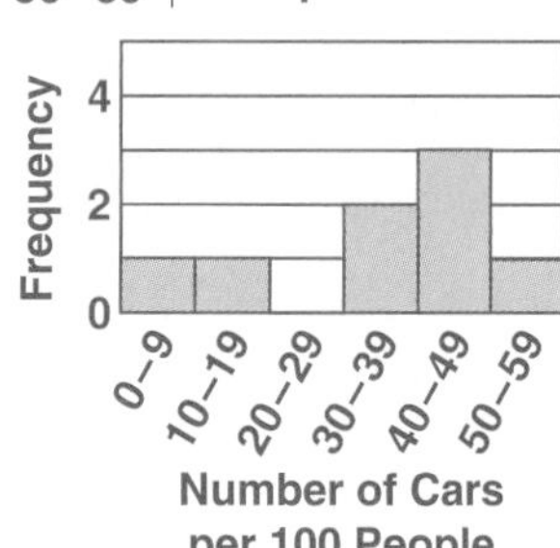

24. Transportation Use equal intervals to make a frequency table and histogram of the number of cars per 100 people. See left.

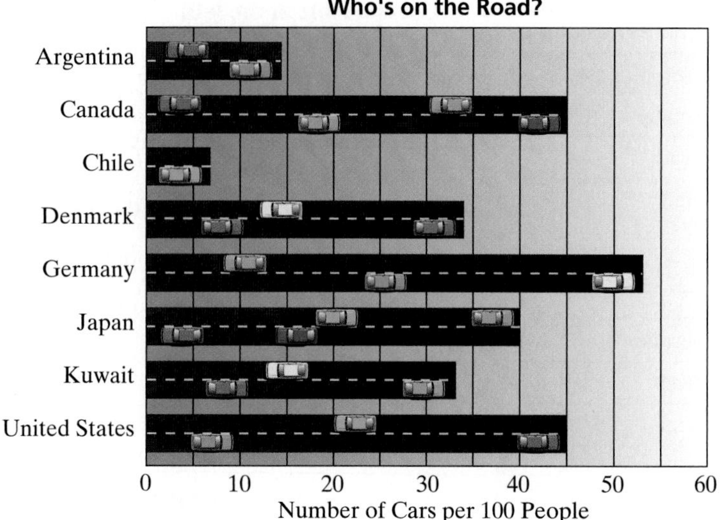

SOURCE: *Ward's Motor Vehicle Facts & Figures*

25. Stretch Your Thinking What whole number increased by the sum of its digits equals 94? 83

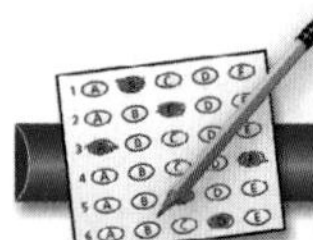

Test Prep

Gridded Response

Take It to the NET
Online lesson quiz at **www.PHSchool.com**
Web Code: aca-1001

26. How many students read 6–8 books? 5
27. How many students were in the Read-A-Thon? 17
28. How many students read fewer than 9 books? 8
29. How many more students read 9–11 books than 12–14 books? 3

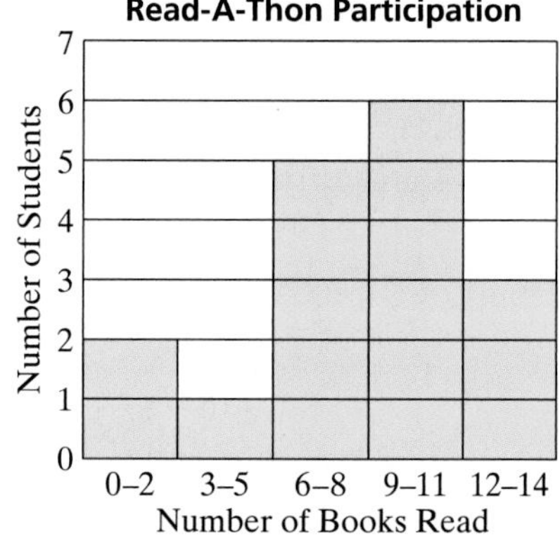

Mixed Review

31. $9x^8y^6$
32. $r^4s^4t^4$
33. $4r^6s^2$
34. $125x^{12}$

Lesson 8-4

30. When you find the value of 3^{98}, what digit is in the ones place? 9

Lesson 7-4

Simplify each expression. 31–34. See left.

31. $(3x^4y^3)^2$
32. $(rst)^4$
33. $(-2r^3s)^2$
34. $(5x^4)^3$
35. $(-6n^2p)^2$ $36n^4p^2$
36. $-(2r^2s)^3$ $-8r^6s^3$
37. $(3 \cdot k^4)^3$ $27k^{12}$
38. $(g^6h^2)^5$ $g^{30}h^{10}$

Test Prep

Resources

A sheet of blank grids is available in the *Test-Taking Strategies with Transparencies* booklet. Give copies of this sheet to students so they can practice filling in grids.

For additional practice with a variety of test item formats:
- Test Prep, p. 585
- Test-Taking Strategies, p. 581
- Test-Taking Strategies with Transparencies

Reading Graphical Displays

For Use With Lesson 10-2

Graphical displays, such as a picture or a graph, are often easier to read than a group of data values. There are several characteristics you need to consider, however, to be able to read a graph correctly.

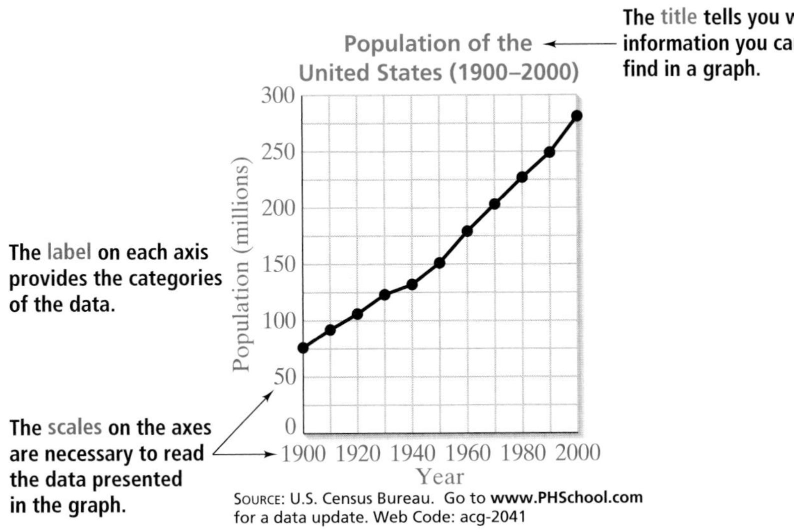

SOURCE: U.S. Census Bureau. Go to **www.PHSchool.com** for a data update. Web Code: acg-2041

Before you begin to read the data in a graph, look for such items as a title, a key, or labels that can help you interpret the data being displayed.

EXERCISES

Use the graph for Exercises 1–4.

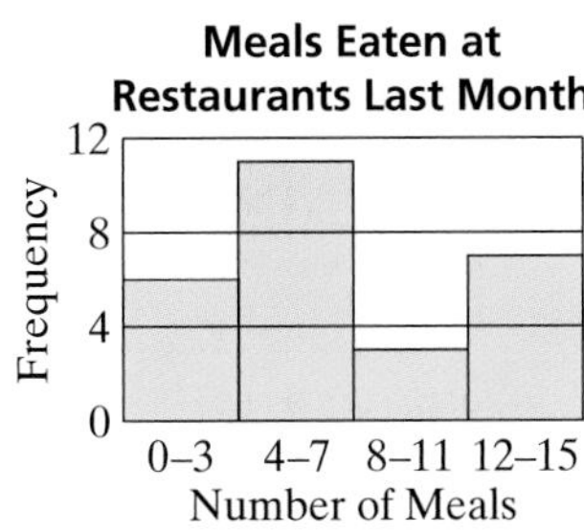

1. What type of graph is it? What kind of data might be displayed using this type of graph? **Histogram; it gives the frequency of data using intervals.**
2. What does the title tell you? **It tells you the data deals with the number of meals eaten at restaurants in a month.**
3. What do you know from reading the horizontal scale and label? **the intervals for the number of meals eaten at restaurants**
4. What does the vertical scale tell you? **the frequency of the number of meals eaten out**

Use the circle graph for Exercises 5 and 6.

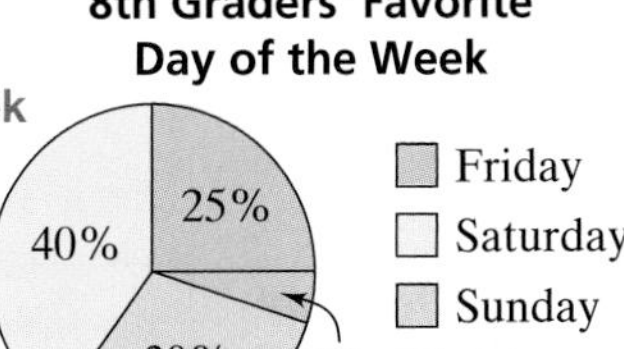

5. What is the title of the graph? **8th Graders' Favorite Day of the Week**
6. A legend, or key, identifies the data compared in a graph. What do you know from the key in the graph? **The key identifies the students' favorite days.**

Reading Math

Reading Graphical Displays

Because students can read a written passage does not ensure that they can read a graph. Therefore, students need instruction and practice in reading information that appears in tables, charts, and graphs. This feature introduces students to key characteristics of graphical displays to help them read and interpret the graphs correctly.

Resources

www.PHSchool.com
- Updated Data

Teaching Notes

Elicit from students that graphs provide valuable information. Being able to read graphs as effortlessly as they read text is a skill students need not only in math but in all other subjects and the real-world.

Review the meaning and characteristics of the following key terms: *axes*, *title*, *label*, *scale*, and *key* or *legend*. Have students use the descriptions provided on this page to add these terms to their personal math dictionaries. Elicit from students where each of these items is to be found in a graph.

English Learners
Make sure that students distinguish the specific "math" meanings of the terms associated with graphic displays from their meanings in ordinary English.

Exercises
Exercises 1–4 Elicit from students that a histogram works best for showing frequencies of intervals of data, such as ages, scores, times, or numbers.

10-2

1. Plan

Lesson Preview

PowerPoint

Check Skills You'll Need
Making and Interpreting Line Graphs
Skills Handbook: Line Graphs, p. 728.

Lesson Resources

Optional Materials
- graph paper
- ruler

Teaching Resources
Practice, Reteaching, Enrichment

Reaching All Students
Practice Workbook 10-2
Spanish Practice Workbook 10-2
Guided Problem Solving 10-2

Presentation Assistant Plus!
Transparencies
- Check Skills You'll Need 10-2
- Problem of the Day 10-2
- Additional Examples 10-2
- Student Edition Answers 10-2
- Lesson Quiz 10-2
- Classroom Aid 23–26

PH Presentation Pro CD-ROM 10-2

PRENTICE HALL ASSESSMENT SYSTEM
Computer Test Generator CD

Technology
Resource Pro® CD-ROM
Computer Test Generator CD
PH Presentation Pro CD-ROM

www.PHSchool.com
Student Site
- Updated Data
- Teacher Web Code: ack-5500
- Self-grading Lesson Quiz

PH SuccessNet Teacher Center
- Lesson Planner
- Resources

Plus iTEXT

10-2 Reading Graphs Critically

What You'll Learn

To recognize and select an appropriate scale

. . . And Why

To draw accurate graphs for real-world data, as in Example 2

Check Skills You'll Need

For help, go to Skills Handbook page 732.

The average price of a DVD player from 1997 to 2002 is shown.

Year	1997	1998	1999	2000	2001	2002
Price	$490	$390	$270	$201	$193	$146

SOURCE: Consumer Electronics Association

1. Display the data in a line graph. See back of book.
2. How has the price of DVD players changed over time? It has decreased.

Interactive lesson includes instant self-check, tutorials, and activities.

OBJECTIVE 1

Recognizing and Selecting an Appropriate Scale

The same set of data may be graphed in different ways. Sometimes, however, a graph can give a misleading visual impression.

1 EXAMPLE Recognizing Misleading Graphs

Travel Which graph gives the impression that Atlanta Hartsfield International Airport is twice as busy as Chicago O'Hare Airport? Explain.

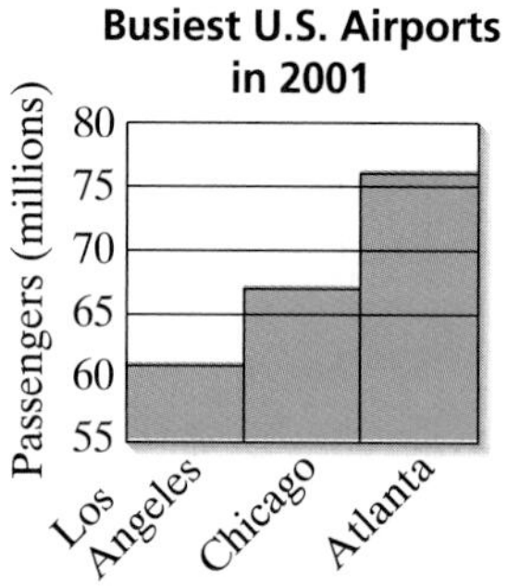

Busiest U.S. Airports in 2001

Passengers (millions): 55, 60, 65, 70, 75, 80
Los Angeles, Chicago, Atlanta

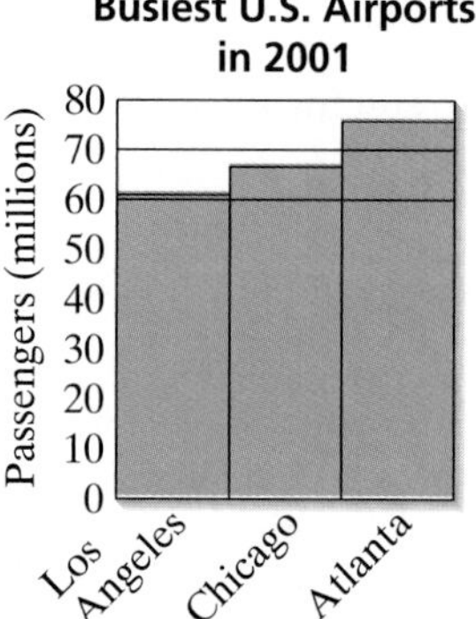

In 2001, Atlanta Hartsfield International Airport had about 75 million passengers, while Chicago O'Hare Airport had about 65 million passengers. The graph at the left, however, gives the impression that Atlanta had twice as many passengers as Chicago.

Real-World Connection
Large airports, such as Los Angeles International Airport, can average over 160,000 passengers each day.

Check Understanding 1 1a–b. See back of book.

a. Explain what makes the graph on the left misleading.
b. **Reasoning** Why might someone working at Atlanta Hartsfield International Airport use the graph at the left in a presentation?

Ongoing Assessment and Intervention

Before the Lesson
Diagnose prerequisite skills using:
- Check Skills You'll Need

During the Lesson
Monitor progress using:
- Check Understanding
- Additional Examples
- Test Prep

After the Lesson
Assess knowledge using:
- Lesson Quiz
- Computer Test Generator CD

When some of the values on an axis of a graph have been left out, the graph should have a break symbol, ⋞, to alert the reader.

2 EXAMPLE Selecting an Appropriate Scale

Real World

Projected U.S. College Enrollment

Year	Students (millions)
2003	15.8
2004	16.1
2005	16.3
2006	16.5
2007	16.8
2008	17.0
2009	17.2
2010	17.5
2011	17.7

SOURCE: U.S. National Center for Educational Statistics

Education Using different scales, make two line graphs for the data at the left. Use a break symbol in only one of the graphs.

The highest projected college enrollment is 17.7 million. Label the vertical axis with multiples of 5 from 0 to 20.

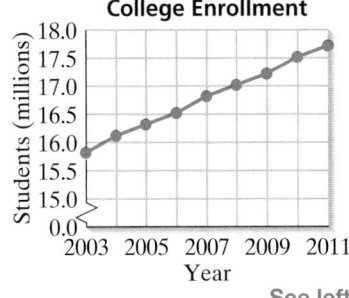

Projected U.S. College Enrollment

Students (millions): 0, 5, 10, 15, 20

Year: 2003 2005 2007 2009 2011

The data start at 15 million. Label the vertical axis with multiples of 0.50, beginning with 15. Use a break symbol.

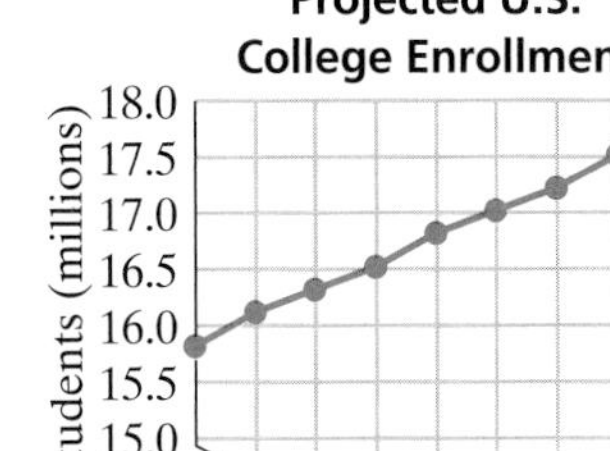

Check Understanding

2 a. **Reasoning** Which graph above shows the data more clearly? Explain. See left.

b. Suppose you used multiples of 10 for the scale of the vertical axis. Would the projected enrollment appear to increase slowly or rapidly? Explain. See left.

2a. The graph with the break symbol shows the data more clearly because the scale is more spread out.

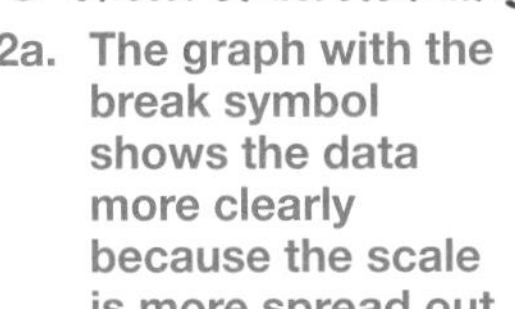

2b. Slowly; the line would appear almost flat.

Investigation: Creating Graphs to Tell a Story

Visitors to National Parks

Year	1995	1996	1997	1998	1999	2000	2001
Visitors (millions)	387.8	399.8	418.2	435.7	436.3	429.9	424.3

SOURCE: National Park Service. Go to **www.PHSchool.com** for a data update. Web Code: acg-2041

1. Create a graph that gives the visual impression of a large annual change in the number of visitors. See back of book.
2. Create a second graph that gives the visual impression of a modest annual change in the number of visitors. See back of book.
3. Compare your graphs. Which graph do you think more fairly represents the data in the table? Explain. See left.

3. Answers may vary. Sample: The second graph; the first graph visually exaggerates the increase in visitors.

2. Teach

Math Background

An appropriate scale for a graph must include the least and the greatest values, with the interval between these divided into equal increments. A break symbol can be used on either axis to show that some increments have been omitted. A scale that does not begin at zero may be misleading.

Teaching Notes

Investigation (Optional)
Help students find vertical axis intervals that exaggerates the change in visitors.

Additional Examples

1 Use the graph below.

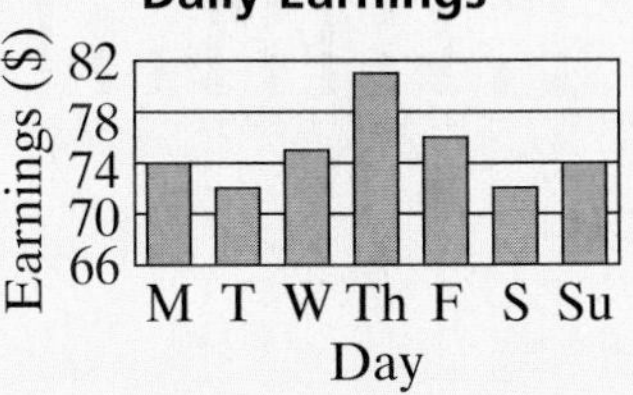

a. Which day appears to have almost twice the earnings of Monday? Thursday

b. Why might the graph appear misleading? Sample: The vertical scale begins at 66, making the differences between daily earnings appear greater.

2 Using different scales, make two bar graphs for the data. Use a break symbol in only one of the graphs. See back of book for graphs.

Quarter Mile Records

Car	Time (s)
Indy car	8
Sprint car	9
NASCAR stock car	10
Stock Pontiac Bonneville	17

Closure

Explain what you would look for in a graph to see if the scale is an appropriate one. Sample: See where each scale starts and if breaks in the data are indicated.

Reaching All Students

Below Level Review key terms with students: axes, title, label, scale, key, and legend.

Advanced Learners Have students find misleading graphs in advertisements, share them, and explain why they are misleading.

English Learners
See note on page 543.
Inclusion
See note on page 543.

3. Practice

Assignment Guide

1 Objective 1

- A B Core 1–15
- C Extension 16–17

Test Prep 18–20

Mixed Review 21–29

Error Prevention!

Exercises 1–2 Call students' attention to the difference between comparing the areas of the bars and the values where the bars stop.

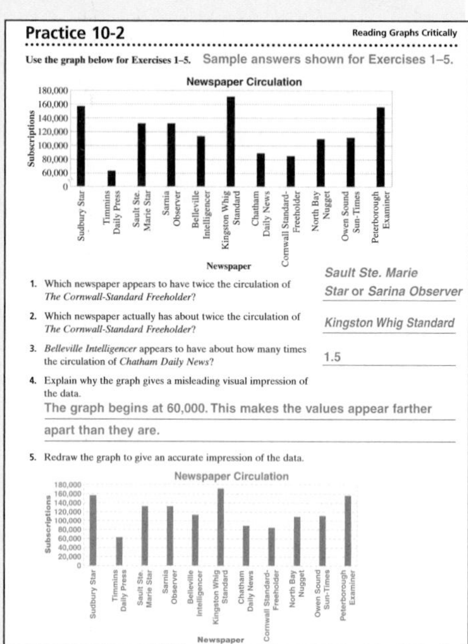

Practice 10-2 — Reading Graphs Critically

Use the graph below for Exercises 1–5. Sample answers shown for Exercises 1–5.

1. Which newspaper appears to have twice the circulation of *The Cornwall-Standard Freeholder*? Sault Ste. Marie Star or Sarina Observer
2. Which newspaper actually has about twice the circulation of *The Cornwall-Standard Freeholder*? Kingston Whig Standard
3. *Belleville Intelligencer* appears to have about how many times the circulation of *Chatham Daily News*? 1.5
4. Explain why the graph gives a misleading visual impression of the data.
   The graph begins at 60,000. This makes the values appear farther apart than they are.
5. Redraw the graph to give an accurate impression of the data.

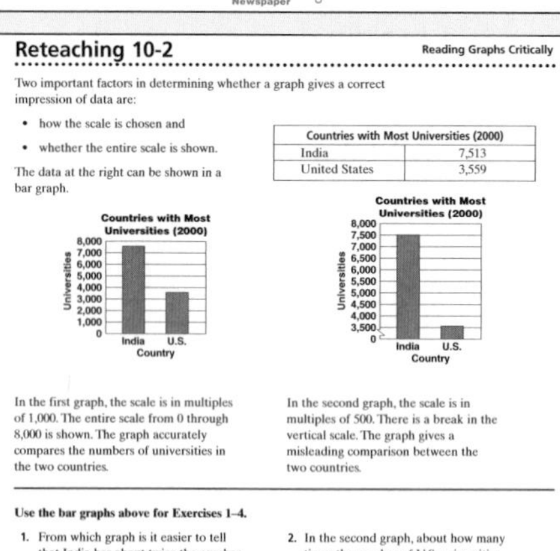

Reteaching 10-2 — Reading Graphs Critically

Two important factors in determining whether a graph gives a correct impression of data are:

- how the scale is chosen and
- whether the entire scale is shown.

The data at the right can be shown in a bar graph.

Countries with Most Universities (2000)	
India	7,513
United States	3,559

In the first graph, the scale is in multiples of 1,000. The entire scale from 0 through 8,000 is shown. The graph accurately compares the numbers of universities in the two countries.

In the second graph, the scale is in multiples of 500. There is a break in the vertical scale. The graph gives a misleading comparison between the two countries.

Use the bar graphs above for Exercises 1–4.

1. From which graph is it easier to tell that India has about twice the number of universities as the United States? the first graph
2. In the second graph, about how many times the number of U.S. universities does India *appear* to have? about 9 times
3. Which graph makes it easier to estimate the number of universities in each country? Why? The second graph; since the scale is smaller, the bars can be read more accurately.
4. Why does the second graph give a misleading impression of the data? By using the break, most of the bar for the United States has been left out.

EXERCISES

For more practice, see *Extra Practice*.

A Practice by Example

Example 1 (page 540)

Publishing **Use the graph below for Exercises 1–5.**

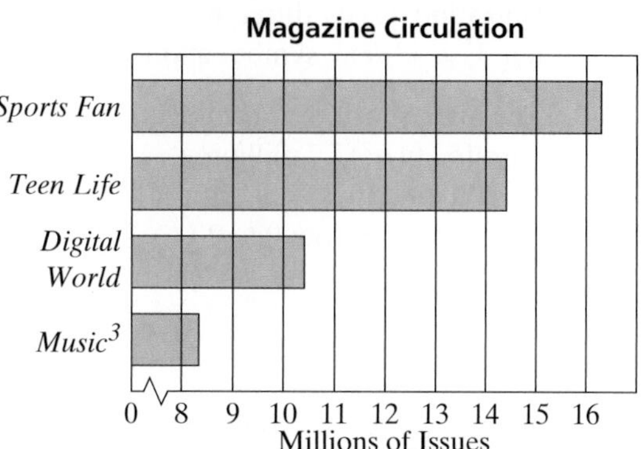

Real-World Connection

The top magazines for teenage girls have circulations over 2 million issues each.

1. Looking at the length of the bars, which magazine appears to have about twice the circulation of *Music*³? **Digital World**
2. Which magazine actually has about twice the circulation of *Music*³? **Sports Fan**
3. *Teen Life* appears to have about how many times the circulation of *Digital World*? 2
4. Explain why the graph gives a misleading visual impression of the data.
   4. The horizontal scale does not start at 0, so the differences are exaggerated.
5. Redraw the graph to give an accurate impression of the data. See back of book.

Example 2 (page 541)

Using different scales, make either two line graphs or two bar graphs for each set of data. Use a break symbol in only one of the graphs. Explain which graph shows the data more clearly. 6–8. See margin.

6. **Fish Tournament's Winning Fish Weights**

Year	1996	1997	1998	1999	2000	2001
Weight (lb-oz)	31-14	34-13	46-3	55-10	27-13	32-5

Source: Infoplease.com

7. **Top Films**

Film	Total (millions)
Titanic	$601
Star Wars	$461
E.T., The Extra-Terrestrial	$435
Spider-Man	$402

Source: *Variety*

8. **Population Density**

Year	Population/mi^2
1960	50.6
1970	57.4
1980	64.0
1990	70.3
2000	79.6

Source: U.S. Census Bureau. Go to **www.PHSchool.com** for a data update. Web Code: acg-2041

Use the Guided Problem Solving worksheet with Exercise 12.

B Apply Your Skills

Real-World Connection

Jean Driscoll has won the women's wheelchair division of the Boston Marathon a record eight times.

Marathon **The graph below shows the winning times for men and women runners in the Boston Marathon.**

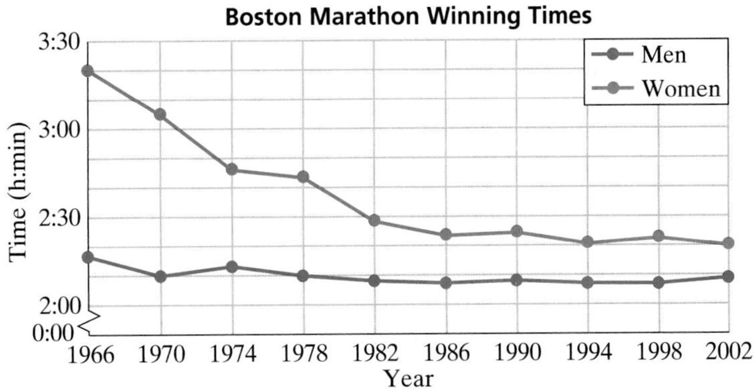

Boston Marathon Winning Times

Time (h:min): 0:00, 2:00, 2:30, 3:00, 3:30

Year: 1966, 1970, 1974, 1978, 1982, 1986, 1990, 1994, 1998, 2002

Men

Women

9. The graph gives the visual impression that the winning times for women have decreased to less than one third of what they were in 1966. Why is this impression incorrect? The vertical scale does not start at 0.

The vertical scale does not start at 0.

10. **Error Analysis** Your friend says that based on the graph, the men's winning time in 2002 was two thirds the women's winning time that same year. Is your friend correct? Explain. See left.

10. No; each grid represents 10 minutes, but the "bottom" of the graph is missing. It does not mean $\frac{20}{30}$ or $\frac{2}{3}$, but rather $\frac{2:10}{2:20}$ or $\frac{130 \text{ min}}{140 \text{ min}}$ or $\frac{13}{14}$.

11. Redraw the graph to give a more accurate impression of the data. See back of book.

Recycling **Use the table for Exercises 12–14.**

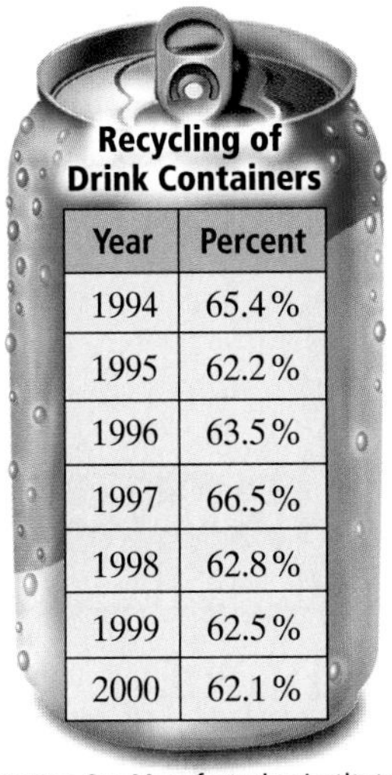

GPS **12.** Make a line graph to show that the recycling rate of drink containers has stayed about the same. See back of book.

13. Make a line graph to show that the recycling rate has varied. See margin.

14. **Writing in Math** Explain how the scale you chose for each graph gives the visual impression you want to create.

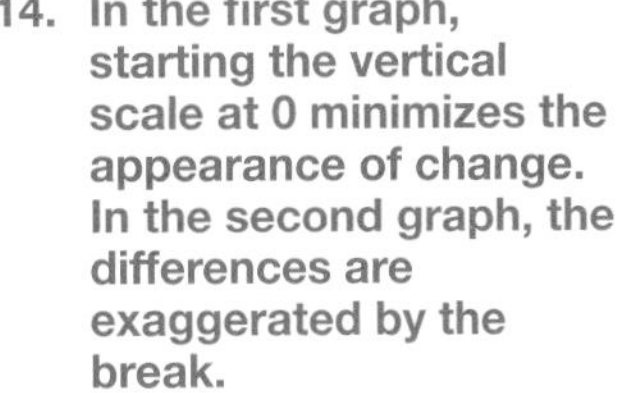

14. In the first graph, starting the vertical scale at 0 minimizes the appearance of change. In the second graph, the differences are exaggerated by the break.

Recycling of Drink Containers

Year	Percent
1994	65.4%
1995	62.2%
1996	63.5%
1997	66.5%
1998	62.8%
1999	62.5%
2000	62.1%

SOURCE: Can Manufacturing Institute

15. **Data File, p. 531** Make a line graph that gives the impression that the number of bushels of soybeans has increased greatly. See back of book.

C Challenge

16. **Algebra** A graph uses the following labels at equal intervals on an axis: 1940, 1945, 1955, 1975, 2015. See left.

a. What are the intervals being used?

b. Is this an appropriate scale? Explain.

c. **Patterns** Is there a pattern in the scale? Explain.

16a. 5; 10; 20; 40

b. No; the differences are not the same.

c. Yes; each difference is twice the number before it.

17. **Stretch Your Thinking** Using the drawing at the right, remove eight sides of the small squares to leave two squares. See left.

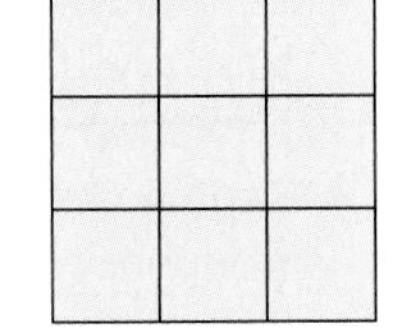

17.

English Learners

Exercises 6–8 Some students may confuse a line *plot* with a line *graph*. Have them review Example 2 in Lesson 10-1 and compare it to Example 2 in Lesson 10-2.

Inclusion

Exercises 6–8 Help students identify the least value and the greatest value for each axis scale.

6–7. See back of book.

8.

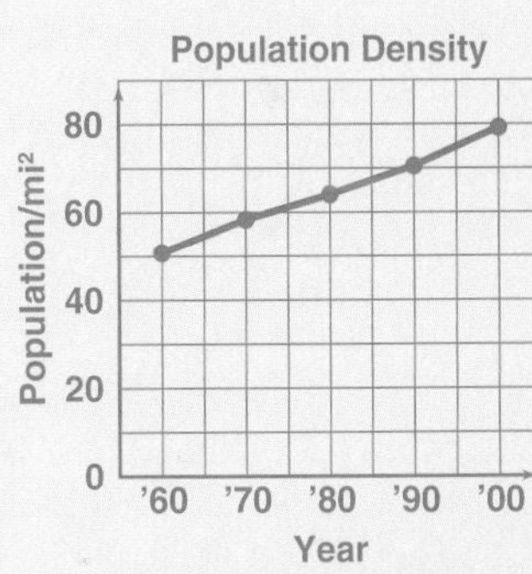

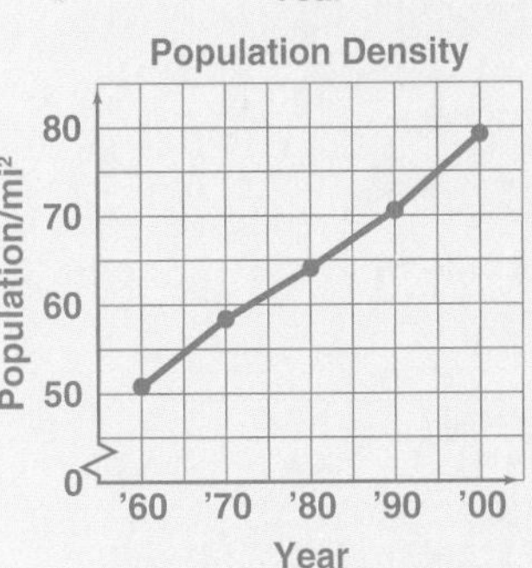

The graph with the break allows you to approximate the population more closely, but the changes are exaggerated.

13.

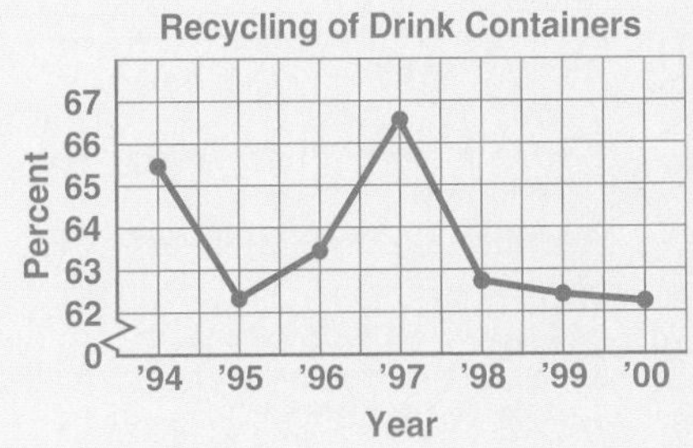

4. Assess

Lesson Quiz 10-2

1. What can be used to give a graph a misleading visual impression? **Sample: a break in an axis scale**
2. The average daily temperature of a town varies from 55°F to 98°F. Describe an appropriate scale you could use to create a bar graph for the data. **Sample: Break between 0 and 50. Show 50°, 55°, 60°, 65°, 70°, 75°, 80°, 85°, 90°, 95°, and 100° on the axis.**

Alternative Assessment

Have students find in newspapers and magazines examples of bar or line graphs with a broken axis. Have students explain whether the published graph is misleading and redraw the graph if it is.

Test Prep

Resources
For additional practice with a variety of test item formats:
- Test Prep, p. 585
- Test-Taking Strategies, p. 581
- Test-Taking Strategies with Transparencies

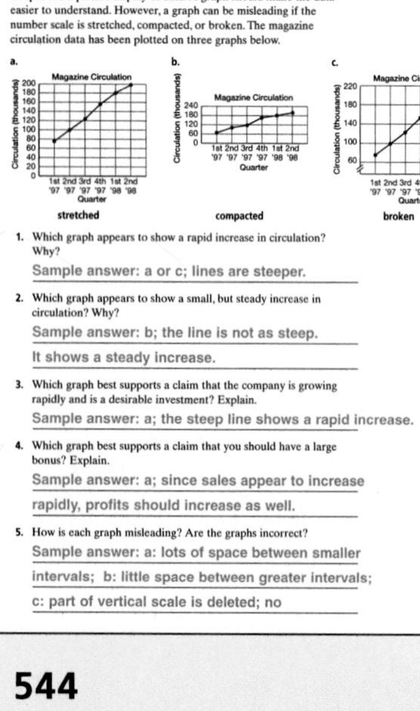

Enrichment 10-2 — Reading Graphs Critically

Decision Making

Graphs are a picture display of data. A graph should make the data easier to understand. However, a graph can be misleading if the number scale is stretched, compacted, or broken. The magazine circulation data has been plotted on three graphs below.

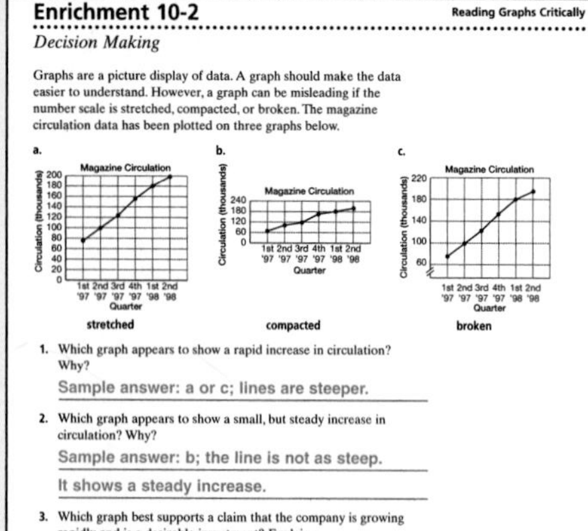

1. Which graph appears to show a rapid increase in circulation? Why?
   Sample answer: a or c; lines are steeper.
2. Which graph appears to show a small, but steady increase in circulation? Why?
   Sample answer: b; the line is not as steep. It shows a steady increase.
3. Which graph best supports a claim that the company is growing rapidly and is a desirable investment? Explain.
   Sample answer: a; the steep line shows a rapid increase.
4. Which graph best supports a claim that you should have a large bonus? Explain.
   Sample answer: a; since sales appear to increase rapidly, profits should increase as well.
5. How is each graph misleading? Are the graphs incorrect?
   Sample answer: a: lots of space between smaller intervals; b: little space between greater intervals; c: part of vertical scale is deleted; no

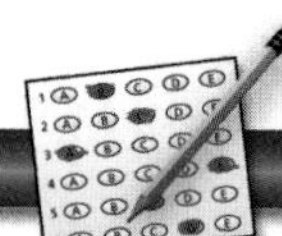

Test Prep

Multiple Choice

The following data are the responses shoppers gave when asked, "How many kinds of cereal do you usually have to choose from in the morning?"

2 1 5 4 1 3 7 8 2 2 3 4 1 6 8 9 1 1 2 4 5 4 3 5 4 3 2 1

Take It to the NET
Online lesson quiz at **www.PHSchool.com**
Web Code: aca-1002

18. What is the range of the data? **D**
    A. 4 B. 5 C. 7 D. 8
19. Which type of graph would be most appropriate to show the response that occurred most often? **H**
    F. circle graph G. scatter plot
    H. line plot I. double bar graph

Short Response

20. You want to show that the difference in the number of kinds of cereal is very small. Which type of graph would be most appropriate? Explain your reasoning and draw the graph. **See margin.**

Mixed Review

Lesson 9-9

21. **Geometry** A cone has a radius of 4 in. and a surface area of 176 in.^{2}. Find the surface area of a similar cone with a radius of 6.5 in. **464.75 in.^{2}**

Lesson 8-8

Calculator **Find the area of a circle with the given radius or diameter. Round to the nearest tenth.**

22. $r = 8$ cm **201.1 cm^2**
23. $d = 14$ in. **153.9 in.^{2}**
24. $r = 9.6$ m **289.5 m^2**
25. $d = 1.2$ m **1.1 m^2**
26. $d = 5$ yd **19.6 yd^2**
27. $r = 7$ ft **153.9 ft^2**
28. $d = 1$ in. **0.8 in.^{2}**
29. $r = 6.5$ cm **132.7 cm^2**

Practice Game

Frequent Spinner

What You'll Need
- 2 spinners, each with three equal sections numbered 1, 2, and 3
- a copy of the number line shown at the right

How to Play
- Player A and Player B choose different numbers between −2 and 2.
- Each player spins a spinner. The result from Player B's spinner is subtracted from Player A's spinner, and recorded on the line plot with an ✗ mark.
- Repeat until the ✗ marks for a player's chosen number reach a frequency of 6. That player is the winner.
- Repeat the game with Player B choosing a number first.

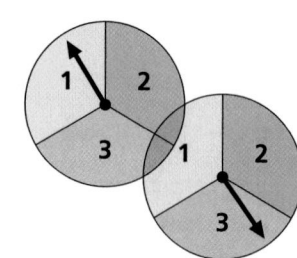

20. [2] A line plot shows the frequencies of different data types.

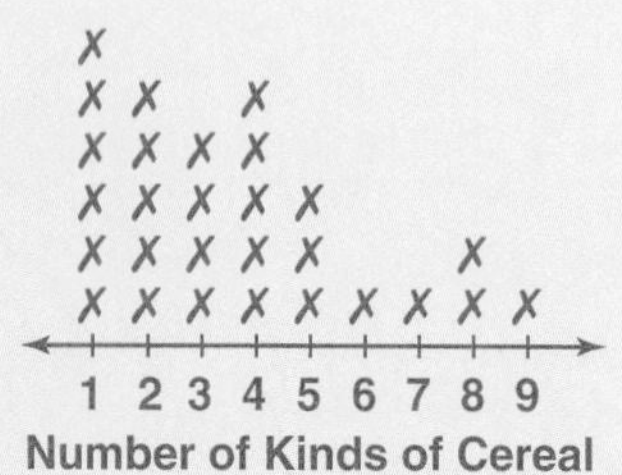

[1] appropriate graph with no explanation

Stacked and Sliding Bar Graphs

For Use With Lesson 10-2

You can use a bar graph when comparing amounts. A *stacked bar graph* has bars that are divided into categories. Each bar represents a total. Use a key, or legend, to identify each category within a bar.

A *sliding bar graph* shows two categories in each bar. The bars extend on either side of the center, which is zero. Each side represents one category.

EXAMPLE Using Bar Graphs

Clubs The table at the right shows the number of girls and boys in the Environmental Club. Display the data using two types of bar graphs.

a. stacked bar graph
b. sliding bar graph

Environmental Club Members

Grade	Girls	Boys
6	23	16
7	17	14
8	21	26

a. stacked bar graph

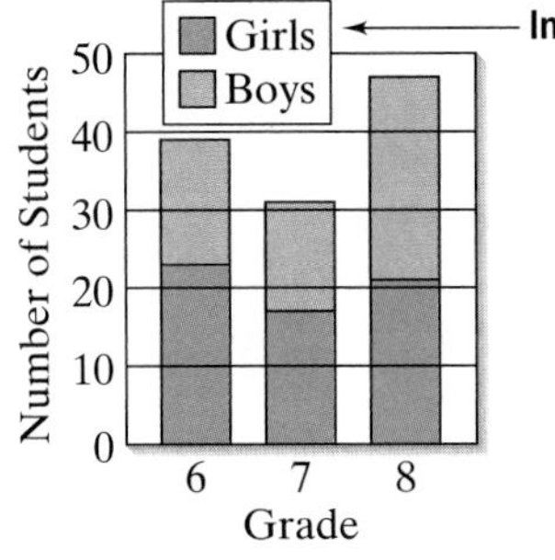

b. sliding bar graph

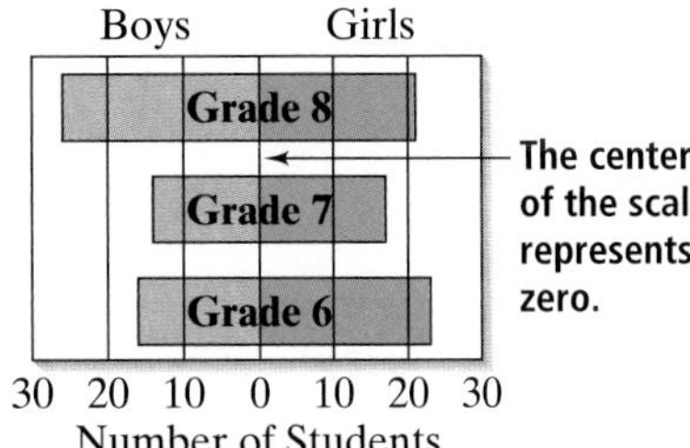

EXERCISES

1. Display the data below in a stacked bar graph and in a sliding bar graph. See back of book.

Beef and Chicken Eaten by Americans Each Year (pounds per person)

Year	1995	1996	1997	1998	1999	2000
Beef	63.6	64.1	62.7	63.6	64.4	64.4
Chicken	48.2	48.8	49.5	49.8	52.9	52.9

SOURCE: U.S. Dept. of Agriculture. Go to **www.PHSchool.com** for a data update. Web Code: acg-2041

2. **Writing in Math** What are the advantages and disadvantages of each type of graph you made in Exercise 1? See above right.

2. Answers may vary. Sample: The stacked graph emphasizes the total amount, but does not compare amounts of the two groups. The sliding bar compares amounts of the two groups, but does not provide total amounts.

Stacked and Sliding Bar Graphs

Your students know that bar graphs and double bar graphs visually compare discrete data. This activity introduces them to two kinds of bar graphs: stacked bar graphs and sliding bar graphs. Both kinds of graphs show how a total is divided into parts.

Optional Materials

- graph paper
- ruler
- Classroom Aid 2

Resources

www.PHSchool.com
- Updated Data

Teaching Notes

Discuss what a bar graph looks like, what it shows, and how it differs from a histogram. Elicit that both graphs show magnitude or frequency. Emphasize that the main way in which bar graphs differ from histograms is that bar graphs display categories representing discrete, rather than continuous, values.

Visual Learners
Ask:
- *In what ways are these graphs like circle graphs?* They show a total divided into categories.
- *How is each of these graphs an improvement over the table for presenting the data? Explain.* Sample: Each provides a clear visual way to compare the boy/girl breakdowns of the clubs.

Exercise 2 Ask:
- *Which kind of bar graph makes it easier to see which grade has the most members? Explain.* Stacked bar graph; the three bars start from the same horizontal line, making it easy to see which bar is tallest.
- *Which graph makes it easier to see which grade has the most girl members? Explain.* Sliding bar graph; the three bars start from the same vertical line, making it easy to see which bar is longest.

10-3

1. Plan

Lesson Preview

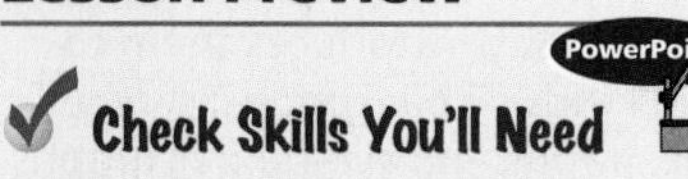

PowerPoint

Check Skills You'll Need

Finding the Mean, Median, and Mode From a Line Plot
Lesson 10-1: Example 3. Extra Practice, p. 711.

Lesson Resources

Teaching Resources
Practice, Reteaching, Enrichment
Checkpoint Quiz 1

Reaching All Students
Practice Workbook 10-3
Spanish Practice Workbook 10-3
Reading and Math Literacy 10B
Spanish Reading and Math Literacy 10B
Spanish Checkpoint Quiz 1
Guided Problem Solving 10-3
Hands-On Activities 26

Presentation Assistant Plus!
Transparencies
- Check Skills You'll Need 10-3
- Problem of the Day 10-3
- Additional Examples 10-3
- Student Edition Answers 10-3
- Lesson Quiz 10-3
- Classroom Aid 29–30

PH Presentation Pro CD-ROM 10-3

PRENTICE HALL ASSESSMENT SYSTEM

Checkpoint Quiz 1
Computer Test Generator CD

Technology
Resource Pro® CD-ROM
Computer Test Generator CD
PH Presentation Pro CD-ROM

www.PHSchool.com
Student Site
- Teacher Web Code: ack-5500
- Self-grading Lesson Quiz

PH SuccessNet Teacher Center
- Lesson Planner
- Resources

Plus iText

10-3 Stem-and-Leaf Plots

What You'll Learn

OBJECTIVE 1 To make stem-and-leaf plots

OBJECTIVE 2 To use stem-and-leaf plots

. . . And Why

To analyze earthquakes, as in Example 2

Check Skills You'll Need

For help, go to Lesson 10-1.

Use the line plot for Exercises 1–3.

1. Find the mean. 29.2

2. Find the median. 30

3. Find the mode. 40

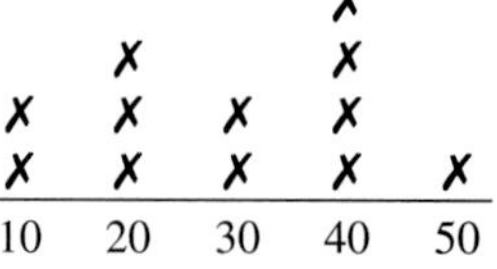

New Vocabulary

- stem-and-leaf plot

OBJECTIVE

iText Interactive lesson includes instant self-check, tutorials, and activities.

1 Making Stem-and-Leaf Plots

A **stem-and-leaf plot** is a graph that shows numeric data arranged in order. Each data item is broken into a stem and a leaf.

The leaf is the last digit and the stem is the preceding digit or digits.

10 ← leaf, ↑ stem   3.8 ← leaf, ↑ stem   5.52 ← leaf, ↑ stem

1 EXAMPLE Making Stem-and-Leaf Plots (Real World)

Prices of Portable MP3 Players (dollars)
189, 214, 200, 195, 190, 192, 193, 211, 201, 196, 195, 194, 205, 198, 208, 201

Prices Make a stem-and-leaf plot for the data in the table at the left.

Step 1 Choose the stems. The least value is 189; the greatest value is 214. Leaves are single digits, so use the first two digits as the stems. The stems in this case are 18, 19, 20, and 21.

Step 2 Draw the stem-and-leaf plot. Include a key.

stems	leaves
18	9
19	0 2 3 4 5 5 6 8
20	0 1 1 5 8
21	1 4

Key: 19 | 2 means $192

← The leaves are the ones place written in increasing order.

← The key explains what the stems and leaves represent.

Check Understanding 1 Below are the monthly high temperatures for Death Valley, California. Make a stem-and-leaf plot for the data. See back of book.
87 91 101 111 120 125 134 126 120 113 97 86

Ongoing Assessment and Intervention

Before the Lesson
Diagnose prerequisite skills using:
- Check Skills You'll Need

During the Lesson
Monitor progress using:
- Check Understanding
- Additional Examples
- Test Prep

After the Lesson
Assess knowledge using:
- Lesson Quiz
- Computer Test Generator CD
- Chapter Checkpoint 1 (p. 551)

OBJECTIVE 2

Using Stem-and-Leaf Plots

Stem-and-leaf plots display data items in numerical order. This makes stem-and-leaf plots useful tools for finding median and mode.

Real-World Connection

An earthquake of magnitude 8 moves the ground ten times as much as one of magnitude 7.

2 EXAMPLE Using Stem-and-Leaf Plots

Earthquakes Use the stem-and-leaf plot to find the median and mode of the magnitudes of the ten largest earthquakes of the twentieth century.

The 5's represent repeated leaves. Use them for the mode.

Stem	Leaves
8	5 5 5 6 7 8
9	0 1 2 5

The ten leaves means that there are ten items.

Key: 9 | 0 means 9.0 on the Richter Scale

SOURCE: Infoplease.com

Since there are ten items, you should average the fifth and sixth items, 8.7 and 8.8, to find the median. The median is magnitude 8.75. The mode is magnitude 8.5.

Check Understanding 2 Find the mode and median of the stem-and-leaf plot at the right. magnitude 4.7; magnitude 3.8

Stem	Leaves
2	1 2 8 8
3	1 2 6 7 9
4	5 7 7 7 8 8 9

Key: 2 | 1 means 2.1

You can use back-to-back stem-and-leaf plots to compare two sets of the same type of data.

3 EXAMPLE Real-World Problem Solving

Test-Prep Tip

When comparing two quantities or sets of data, look at their differences and similarities.

Gas Mileage Shown at the right are the city and highway mileage of seven new cars. Compare the city mileage to the highway mileage using the mode of each data set.

New Car Mileage (mi/gal)

City	Stem	Highway
9 8 8	1	
7 4 2	2	4 5 7 8
0	3	3 3
	4	0

Key: means 27 ← 7 | 2 | 8 → means 28

The mode for the city mileage is 18 mi/gal, while the mode for the highway mileage is 33 mi/gal. This measure of central tendency gives the impression that the highway mileage of the new cars is higher than the city mileage.

Check Understanding 3 Compare the city mileage to the highway mileage using the mean and median of each data set. The mean and median for the city mileage is 22.6 mi/gal and 22 mi/gal, respectively. The mean and median for the highway mileage is 30 mi/gal and 28 mi/gal, respectively. Both the mean and median give the impression that the highway mileage of the new cars is higher than the city mileage.

2. Teach

Professional Development

Math Background

A stem-and-leaf plot groups data as leaves coming off the side(s) of each stem. The last digit, or leaf, is recorded alongside the preceding digit(s), written just once as the stem. The plot has a number of stems, each with many or no leaves. A key explains how to read the numbers in the plot.

PowerPoint

Additional Examples

1 Make a stem-and-leaf plot for the data: 51, 56, 67, 44, 50, 63, 65, 58, 49, 51, 66, 59, 63, 47.

Stem	Leaves
4	4 7 9
5	0 1 1 6 8 9
6	3 3 5 6 7

Key: 4 | 4 means 44

2 Find the median and mode of the data in this stem-and-leaf plot. mode: 14.3; median: 14.5

Stem	Leaves
13	8 9
14	3 3 7
15	2 5
16	0

Key: 14 | 3 means 14.3

3 Compare the number of basketball and baseball cards using the mode of each data set.

Basketball and Baseball Cards

Basketball	Stem	Baseball
9 9 8	1	
4 2 1 0	2	8 9
	3	1 2 2 3 4

Key: means 24 ← 4 | 2 | 9 → means 29

basketball: 19; baseball: 32; no. of baseball cards appears greater than the no. of basketball cards

Closure

Describe how to read a stem-and-leaf plot. Answers should include how stems and leaves are related and how to read the key.

Reaching All Students

Below Level Have volunteers review the definitions for mean, mode, and median. Have them give examples of each.

Advanced Learners Have students find suitable data, perhaps from newspapers or magazines, and make their own stem-and-leaf plot.

Visual Learners See note on page 549.

3. Practice

Assignment Guide

1 Objective 1

A B Core 1–7, 19–20, 23

2 Objective 2

A B Core 8–18, 21–22

C Extension 24–26

Test Prep 27–32

Mixed Review 33–40

Error Prevention!

Exercises 1–7 Make sure that students include a key.

Practice 10-3 — Stem-and-Leaf Plots

The stem-and-leaf plot at the right shows the bowling scores for 20 bowlers. Use the plot for Exercises 1–3.

10	0 2 2 4 4 4
11	1 3 5 5 5 9
12	4 5 9 9
13	0 6 8 8

Key 13 | 8 means 138

1. What numbers make up the stems? 10, 11, 12, 13
2. What are the leaves for the stem 12? 4, 5, 9, 9
3. Find the median and mode. 115; 104 and 115

Make a stem-and-leaf plot for each set of data. Then find the median and mode. Check students' work.

4. 8 19 27 36 35 24 6 15 16 24 38 23 20 — 23; 24
5. 8.6 9.1 7.4 6.3 8.2 9.0 7.5 7.9 6.3 8.1 7.1 8.2 7.0 9.6 9.9 — 8.1; 8.2 and 6.3
6. 436 521 470 586 692 634 417 675 526 719 817 — 586; no mode
7. 17.9 20.4 18.6 19.5 17.6 18.5 17.4 18.5 19.4 — 18.5; 18.5

The back-to-back stem-and-leaf plot at the right shows the high and low temperatures for a week in a certain city. Use this plot for Exercises 8–10.

Low		High
8 7	5	
4 3	6	5 9 9
2 1 0	7	2 5 6
	8	0

63 ← 3 | 6 | 5 → 65

8. Find the mean for the high temperatures. 72.3°
9. Find the median for the low temperatures. 64°
10. Find the mode for the high temperatures. 69°
11. Make a back-to-back stem-and-leaf plot for the following data. Then find the median and mode. Check students' work.

Set A: 75 82 79 80 75 76 83 74 75 86 80 71 75 — 76; 75

Set B: 71 73 75 80 79 80 74 80 74 79 76 80 81 — 79; 80

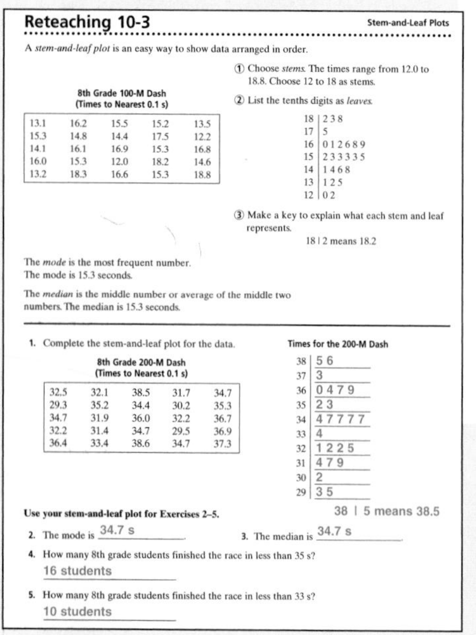

Reteaching 10-3 — Stem-and-Leaf Plots

A *stem-and-leaf plot* is an easy way to show data arranged in order.

8th Grade 100-M Dash (Times to Nearest 0.1 s)

13.1	16.2	15.5	15.2	13.5
15.3	14.8	14.4	17.5	12.2
14.1	16.1	16.9	15.3	16.8
16.0	15.3	12.0	18.2	14.6
13.2	18.3	16.6	15.3	18.8

① Choose *stems*. The times range from 12.0 to 18.8. Choose 12 to 18 as stems.

② List the tenths digits as *leaves*.

18	2 3 8
17	5
16	0 1 2 6 8 9
15	2 3 3 3 3 5
14	1 4 6 8
13	1 2 5
12	0 2

③ Make a key to explain what each stem and leaf represents.

18 | 2 means 18.2

The *mode* is the most frequent number. The mode is 15.3 seconds.

The *median* is the middle number or average of the middle two numbers. The median is 15.3 seconds.

1. Complete the stem-and-leaf plot for the data.

8th Grade 200-M Dash (Times to Nearest 0.1 s)

32.5	32.1	38.5	31.7	34.7
29.3	35.2	34.4	30.2	35.3
34.7	31.9	36.0	32.2	36.7
32.2	31.4	34.7	29.5	36.9
36.4	33.4	38.6	34.7	37.3

Times for the 200-M Dash

38	5 6
37	3
36	0 4 7 9
35	2 3
34	4 7 7 7 7
33	4
32	1 2 2 5
31	4 7 9
30	2
29	3 5

38 | 5 means 38.5

Use your stem-and-leaf plot for Exercises 2–5.

2. The mode is 34.7 s.
3. The median is 34.7 s.
4. How many 8th grade students finished the race in less than 35 s? 16 students
5. How many 8th grade students finished the race in less than 33 s? 10 students

548

EXERCISES

For more practice, see *Extra Practice*.

A Practice by Example

Example 1 (page 546)

Make a stem-and-leaf plot for each set of data. 1–7. See margin.

1. 54 48 52 53 67 61 68 49 40 50 69 73 74 76 78

2. 124 129 131 116 138 107 105 116 122 137 138 134

3. 295 308 286 312 315 302 300 284 294 296 297 298 291

4. 3.7 5.0 6.9 3.2 4.5 6.3 6.7 5.8 5.2 6.9 5.0 4.3 4.1

5. 87.5 86.4 87.9 87.2 85.3 85.0 86.9 87.5 88.1 88.3

6. 4.5 4.3 0.8 0.6 1.2 3.5 3.6 3.2 2.2 2.0 0.2 4.3 6.0 2.6 3.8

7. 786 785 774 773 792 789 784 792 767 772 779 782

Example 2 (page 547)

Find the mode and median for each stem-and-leaf plot.

8. Percent of Population Under the Age of 15 in Selected Countries

47	1 1 2 3 4 7 8 9
48	2
49	1
50	9

Key: 47 | 1 means 47.1%

8. 47.1%; 47.7%

9. Average Speed

5	8 9 9 9
6	0 0 0 2 2 5 6 7 8 8 9
7	0 0 0 1 1 1 1 2 2 3 5

Key: 5 | 8 means 58 mi/h

71 mi/h; 68 mi/h

10. Number of Customers per Hour for a 24-Hour Period

0	4 4 5 5 6 7 8
1	1 2 2 2 3 4 8 9
2	5 5 6 9
3	0 1 2 3 3

Key: 0 | 4 means 4 customers

12 customers; 13.5 customers

11. Lengths of Used Pencils

12	9 9 9 9
13	0 1 4 8 9
14	2 3 3 5 6 6 8
15	2 2 3 7 7 8 9
16	0 1 2

Key: 12 | 9 means 12.9 cm

12.9 cm; 14.55 cm

Example 3 (page 547)

12. Health A survey looked at the blood pressure of 40 men and women who are the same age. Use the mean and median of each data set to compare the men's blood pressure to the women's blood pressure. See back of book.

Blood Pressure

Men		Women
8	6	5 5 6 8
9 7 7 6	7	0 1 1 2 5 6 8 8 9
9 9 8 7 4 4 1	8	0 0 3 5 6
8 5 4 2 0 0	9	0 1
2 0	10	

Key: means 94 ← 4 | 9 | 1 → means 91

Reading Math

In a stem-and-leaf plot of two sets of data, 8 | 6 | 5 means that both 8 and 5 are leaves of the stem, which is 6.

Use the Guided Problem Solving worksheet with Exercise 19.

1.

4	0 8 9
5	0 2 3 4
6	1 7 8 9
7	3 4 6 8

Key: 4 | 8 means 48

2.

10	5 7
11	6 6
12	2 4 9
13	1 4 7 8 8

Key: 13 | 1 means 131

3.

28	4 6
29	1 4 5 6 7 8
30	0 2 8
31	2 5

Key: 28 | 4 means 284

4–7. See back of book.

13. The mean, median, and mode for the men's golf scores are around 279 strokes, while the women's scores were around 280. This indicates that the difference in scores isn't very large. However, the fact that one of the modes for the women's scores was 290 shows that women frequently do have a higher number of strokes.

13. Golf In golf, a player's score is based on the total number of strokes needed to get the ball in the hole. So, the player with the lowest score is the winner. Use the mean, median, and mode of each set to compare men's scores to women's scores in a four-round tournament.

U.S. Open 1983–2002

Men's Scores		Women's Scores
9 9 9 9 8 8 8 7 7 6 6 6 2 2	27	2 2 3 4 6 7 7 8 8
5 2 0 0 0 0	28	0 0 0 2 3 4 5 7
	29	0 0 0

Key: means 276 ← 6 | 27 | 2 → means 272

SOURCE: *Sports Illustrated Sports Almanac*

Exercises 12–13 Visual Learners
Elicit an explanation of why these plots are called back-to-back stem-and-leaf plots or double stem-and-leaf plots. Sample: The leaves extend to either side of the stems.

B Apply Your Skills

Animals **Use the stem-and-leaf plot for Exercises 14–18.**

Life Spans of Different Animals

0	1 3 4 5 6 7 7
1	0 0 0 2 2 3 5 5 5 5 5 8
2	0 0 0 0 2 5 5
3	
4	0

Key: 1 | 3 means 13 years

SOURCE: Infoplease.com

14. What numbers make up the stems?
0, 1, 2, 3, 4

15. What are the leaves for the first stem?
1, 3, 4, 5, 6, 7, 7

16. How many data items are shown in the stem-and-leaf plot?
27

17. Find the median and mode of the data.
15 years; 15 years

18. **Reasoning** Suppose the key showed that 1|3 means 1.3. How would this change the mean, median, and mode?
The answers would be divided by 10.

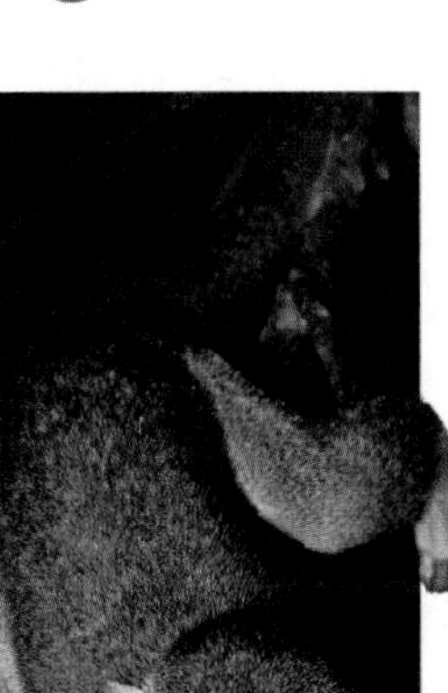

Real-World Connection

A 13-year-old person is still considered young, but a squirrel monkey of the same age is an adult.

Make a stem-and-leaf plot for each set of data. Then find the median and mode of each data set. 19–20. See margin.

GPS **19.** population of each species of fish at an aquarium: 18 19 27 8 19 20 19 6 18 27 16 13 12 7 8 18 19 11 10 19 18 18 8 17 16 12

20. miles per gallon: 23.5 22.5 23 20 19.5 21.5 22 21.6 24.8 22.6 21.2 23.6 29.8 25.7 20.4 26.2 29.3 21.7 28.6 23.7 24.6 21.8 27.9

Make a back-to-back stem-and-leaf plot for each pair of data sets. Then find the median and mode.

21. **Width of Wood Boards (in.)** See margin.

Saw A	Saw B
64 58 63 57 54 61 52 54	72 63 52 57 64 49 45 43

22. **Daily Precipitation (cm)** See back of book.

First Two Weeks of May	Second Two Weeks of July
1.08 0.94 0.88 1.07 0.45 0.45 0.65 0.67 0.55 0.87 0.63 0.81 0.55 0.63	0.28 0.48 0.02 0.63 0.81 0.00 0.10 0.40 0.07 0.61 0.00 0.50 0.48 0.00

19. **Population of Fish**

0	6 7 8 8 8
1	0 1 2 2 3 6 6 7 8 8 8 8 8 9 9 9 9 9
2	0 7 7

Key: 0 | 6 means 6

17.5; 18 and 19

21. **Width of Wood**

Saw A		Saw B
	4	3 5 9
8 7 4 4 2	5	2 7
4 3 1	6	3 4
	7	2

Key: 61 ← means 1 | 6 | 3 means → 63

Saw A: 57.5; 54
Saw B: 54.5; no mode

20. **MPG**

19	5
20	0 4
21	2 5 6 7 8
22	0 5 6
23	0 5 6 7
24	6 8
25	7
26	2
27	9
28	6
29	3 8

Key: 29 | 3 means 29.3

23; no mode

23. **Writing in Math** A set of data contains numbers in the 30's, 40's and 60's only. Is it necessary to put a 5 on the stem of a stem-and-leaf plot? Justify your answer. It is not necessary, but it would help show the range of data.

Challenge

24. **Tests** Two classes took the same math test. The results are below.

Period 1: 78 82 81 85 86 87 82 78 68 92 95 87 78 85 92 95 84 87 98 95 68 87 84 84

Period 2: 87 81 85 88 99 100 85 65 62 63 99 100 88 86 84 100 100 98 65 74 72 71 71 73 24a–c. See margin.

Need Help?
When dealing with large sets of data, cross off each data item as you use it.

a. Make a back-to-back stem-and-leaf plot for the test scores.
b. Use the stem-and-leaf plot to find the mean, median, mode, and range of each set of data.
c. Use the measures of central tendency to compare the data.

25. The back-to-back stem-and-leaf plot below is missing some data. The two sets of data have the same mean, median, mode, and range. Copy the back-to-back stem-and-leaf plot. Fill in the missing items of data. See margin.

7 6 ■	3	1 2 3
6 5 4 3 1	4	2 ■ ■ 6
■ 0	5	0 0 1

Key: means 3■ ← ■ | 3 | 1 → means 31

26. **Stretch Your Thinking** What is the least four-digit number that has 2, 3, 5, and 7 as factors? 1,050

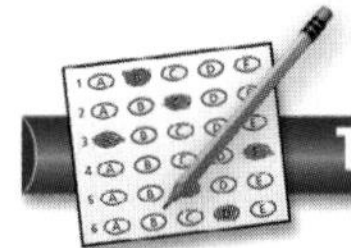

Test Prep

Multiple Choice

Use the stem-and-leaf plot at the right for Exercises 27–31.

Temperatures (°F)

7	2 3 3
8	0 1 1
9	2 2 2 5

Key: 7 | 2 means 72

27. What is the mean temperature? B
A. 92° B. 83.1°
C. 81° D. 23°

28. What do the stem 8 and the leaf 0 represent? F
F. 80° G. 18° H. 8° I. 0.8°

29. What is the median temperature? C
A. 92° B. 83.1° C. 81° D. 23°

30. What is the mode temperature? I
F. 72° G. 73° H. 81° I. 92°

31. What is the range of the temperatures? D
A. 92° B. 83.1° C. 81° D. 23°

Take It to the NET
Online lesson quiz at **www.PHSchool.com**
Web Code: aca-1003

25.

7 6 0	3	1 2 3
6 5 4 3 1	4	2 3 4 6
0 0	5	0 0 1

Key: means 30 ← 0 | 3 | 1 → means 31

24a.

Period 1		Period 2
8 8	6	2 3 5 5
8 8 8	7	1 1 2 3 4
7 7 7 7 6 5 5 4 4 4 2 2 1	8	1 4 5 5 6 7 8 8
8 5 5 5 2 2	9	8 9 9
	10	0 0 0 0

Key: 68 ← means 8 | 6 | 2 means → 62

b. Period 1: 84.9; 85; 87; 30
Period 2: 83.2; 85; 100; 38

c. Period 1 has a higher mean. They both have the same median, so in each class half the class did worse than 85, and half did better. Period 2 has a greater range. Period 2's grades are slightly more spread out than Period 1's grades.

Short Response

32. In three weeks, a restaurant served the following numbers of dinners: 79 50 83 81 75 79 74 62 65 67 83 62 74 75 66 75 79 73 61 77 63. Make a stem-and-leaf plot for the set of data. Use the stem-and-leaf plot to find the median. See back of book.

Mixed Review

33–37. See back of book.

Lesson 10-1 **Make a frequency table and a line plot for each set of data.**

33. 178 179 180 182 177 183 185 180 180 179 181 178 177 182 183

34. 10 30 20 40 30 50 10 40 30 50 40 30 40 50

35. 4 2 4 8 10 12 10 6 4 8 4 6 8 4 6 8 10

36. 15 15 15 14 12 12 16 15 12 13 14 15 14 16 14

37. 70 80 85 75 70 85 90 95 95 75 70 75 80 85 75 85 80 90

Lesson 9-6 **Find the volume of each prism.**

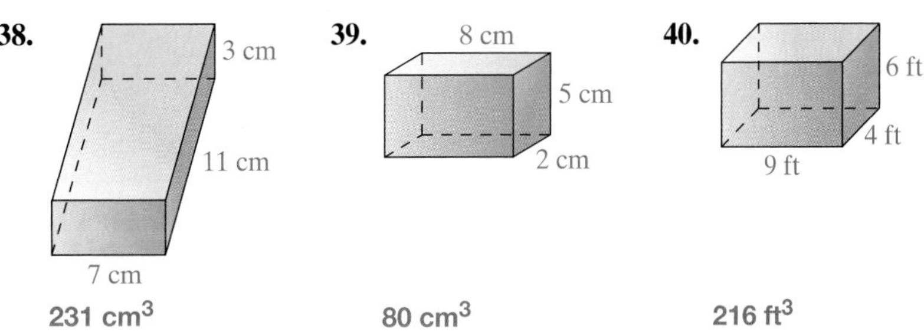

38. 231 cm^3 39. 80 cm^3 40. 216 ft^3

Checkpoint Quiz 1 Lessons 10-1 through 10-3

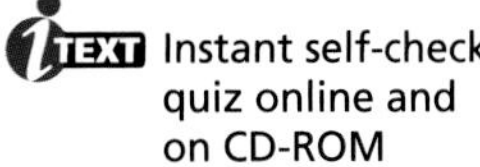
Instant self-check quiz online and on CD-ROM

Use these math test scores for Exercises 1–4. 1–5. See back of book.

93 75 87 83 99 75 80 90 72 77 95 98 82 87 100 91 68

1. Make a frequency table. Use intervals of equal size.
2. Make a line plot.
3. Use the frequency table from Exercise 1 to make a histogram.
4. Make a stem-and-leaf plot.
5. Make two bar graphs for the set of data. In one of the graphs, use a break symbol. Explain which graph shows the data more clearly.

Average Number of Students per Computer

High School	10.5
Middle School	12.75
Elementary School	13.25

4. Assess

Lesson Quiz 10-3

1. Make a stem-and-leaf plot for the data.
21 39 20 22 22 31 40 33

2	0 1 2 2
3	1 3 9
4	0

Key: 4 | 0 means 40

2. Use your stem-and-leaf plot from Question 1 to find the median and mode.
median: 26.5; mode: 22

Chapter Checkpoint

To check understanding of Lessons 10-1 to 10-3:

Checkpoint Quiz 1 (p. 551)

Teaching Resources
Checkpoint Quiz 1 (also in *Prentice Hall Assessment System*)

Reaching All Students
Reading and Math Literacy 10B

Spanish versions available

Test Prep

Resources
For additional practice with a variety of test item formats:
- Test Prep, p. 585
- Test-Taking Strategies, p. 581
- Test-Taking Strategies with Transparencies

Alternative Assessment

Students in small groups find appropriate data and make a stem-and-leaf plot. Groups exchange plots and find the median and the mode of the data.

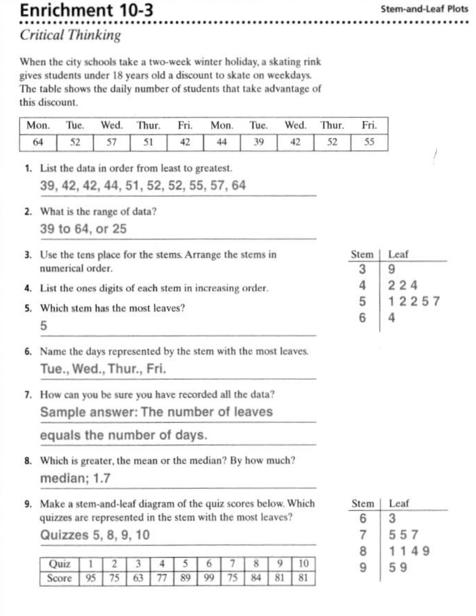

Enrichment 10-3 Stem-and-Leaf Plots

Critical Thinking

When the city schools take a two-week winter holiday, a skating rink gives students under 18 years old a discount to skate on weekdays. The table shows the daily number of students that take advantage of this discount.

Mon.	Tue.	Wed.	Thur.	Fri.	Mon.	Tue.	Wed.	Thur.	Fri.
64	52	57	51	42	44	39	42	52	55

1. List the data in order from least to greatest.
39, 42, 42, 44, 51, 52, 52, 55, 57, 64
2. What is the range of data?
39 to 64, or 25
3. Use the tens place for the stems. Arrange the stems in numerical order.
4. List the ones digits of each stem in increasing order.
5. Which stem has the most leaves?
5

Stem	Leaf
3	9
4	2 2 4
5	1 2 2 5 7
6	4

6. Name the days represented by the stem with the most leaves.
Tue., Wed., Thur., Fri.
7. How can you be sure you have recorded all the data?
Sample answer: The number of leaves equals the number of days.
8. Which is greater, the mean or the median? By how much?
median; 1.7
9. Make a stem-and-leaf diagram of the quiz scores below. Which quizzes are represented in the stem with the most leaves?
Quizzes 5, 8, 9, 10

Quiz	1	2	3	4	5	6	7	8	9	10
Score	95	75	63	77	89	99	75	84	81	81

Stem	Leaf
6	3
7	5 5 7
8	1 1 4 9
9	5 9

10-4

1. Plan

Lesson Preview

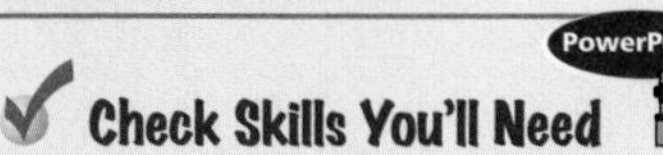

Check Skills You'll Need

Finding the Median
Lesson 1-6: Example 1. Extra Practice, p. 702.

Lesson Resources

Teaching Resources
Practice, Reteaching, Enrichment

Reaching All Students
Practice Workbook 10-4
Spanish Practice Workbook 10-4
Guided Problem Solving 10-4
Technology Activities 49
Hands-On Activities 26

Presentation Assistant Plus!
Transparencies
- Check Skills You'll Need 10-4
- Problem of the Day 10-4
- Additional Examples 10-4
- Student Edition Answers 10-4
- Lesson Quiz 10-4
- Classroom Aid 31–33

PH Presentation Pro CD-ROM 10-4

ASSESSMENT SYSTEM

Computer Test Generator CD

Technology
Resource Pro® CD-ROM
Computer Test Generator CD
PH Presentation Pro CD-ROM

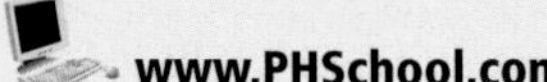

www.PHSchool.com
Student Site
- Updated Data
- Teacher Web Code: ack-5500
- Self-grading Lesson Quiz

PH SuccessNet Teacher Center
- Lesson Planner
- Resources

Plus iTEXT

10-4 Box-and-Whisker Plots

What You'll Learn

To make and use box-and-whisker plots

. . . And Why

To compare prices at two stores, as in Example 2

Check Skills You'll Need

For help, go to Lesson 1-6.

Find the median of each data set.

1. 23 32 24 22 25 24 35 24
2. 27 15 36 27 21 28 49 27
3. 6 2 9 3 5 4 2 9 4 2 3 4
4. 90 95 92 91 95 96 97 98 96 95

New Vocabulary • box-and-whisker plot • quartiles

Interactive lesson includes instant self-check, tutorials, and activities.

OBJECTIVE 1 Making and Using Box-and-Whisker Plots

A **box-and-whisker plot** is a graph that summarizes a data set along a number line. To make a box-and-whisker plot, you use values called quartiles. **Quartiles** are numbers that divide data into four equal parts.

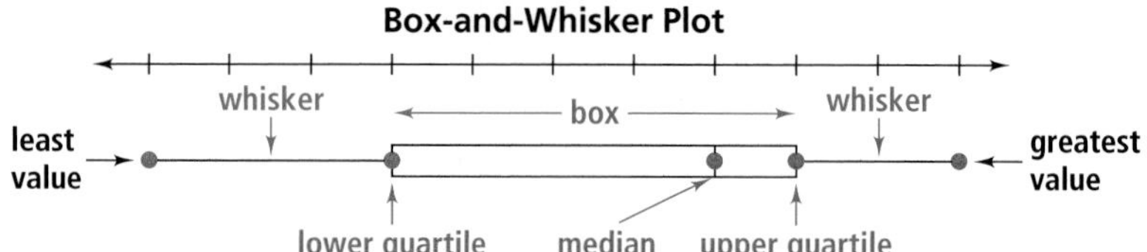

1 EXAMPLE Making Box-and-Whisker Plots

Real World

Travel Make a box-and-whisker plot for the travel data.

Average Amount Spent by Visitors to the United States (per person)

Country	Amount	Country	Amount
Canada	$440	France	$2,200
Mexico	$415	Brazil	$3,058
Japan	$2,012	Italy	$2,701
United Kingdom	$1,975	South Korea	$2,507
Germany	$2,246	Venezuela	$3,074

SOURCE: *The World Almanac*

Need Help?
When a data set has two middle values, find the average of the two.

Step 1 Arrange the data in order from least to greatest. Find the median.

415 440 1,975 2,012 2,200 2,246 2,507 2,701 3,058 3,074

The median is $\frac{2,200 + 2,246}{2}$, or 2,223.

Ongoing Assessment and Intervention

Before the Lesson
Diagnose prerequisite skills using:
- Check Skills You'll Need

During the Lesson
Monitor progress using:
- Check Understanding
- Additional Examples
- Test Prep

After the Lesson
Assess knowledge using:
- Lesson Quiz
- Computer Test Generator CD

Step 2 Find the lower quartile and the upper quartile. They are the medians of the lower and upper halves.

415 440 **1,975** 2,012 2,200 2,246 2,507 **2,701** 3,058 3,074

The lower quartile is 1,975, and the upper quartile is 2,701.

Step 3 Draw a number line that spans all of the data values. Mark points below the number line at the least and greatest values, at the median, and at the lower and upper quartiles.

Use the lower and upper quartiles to form a box. Mark the median. Then draw whiskers from the box to the least and greatest values.

1a.

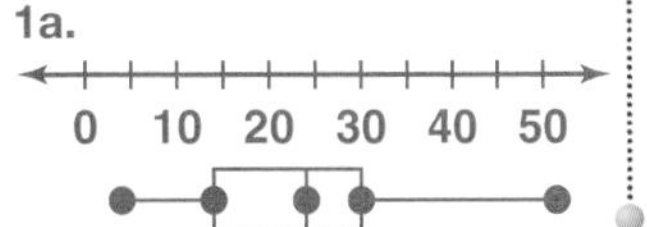

Amount Spent by Visitors to the United States (dollars per person)

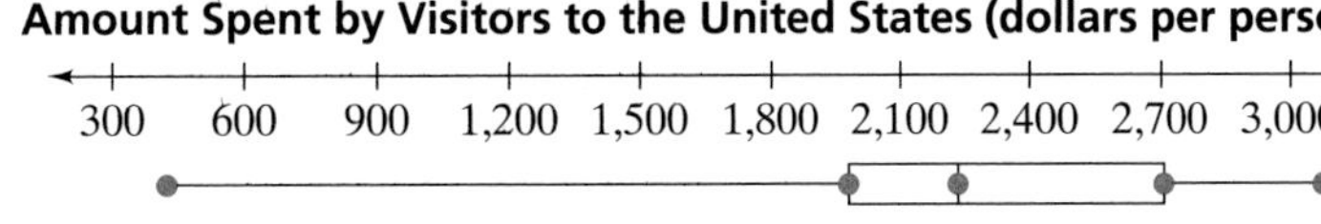

Check Understanding 1 **a.** Make a box-and-whisker plot for the set of data.
10 16 24 11 35 26 29 31 4 53 47 12 21 24 25 26 See left.

b. Number Sense By looking at a box-and-whisker plot, can you determine the mean? The median? The mode? The range? See left.

b. You cannot get the mean. The median is the value associated with the middle dot (or line). You cannot determine the mode. The range is the difference between the values represented by the first and last dots.

Box-and-whisker plots do not display every piece of data. Because they summarize data, box-and-whisker plots are useful with very large data sets, or for making comparisons between data sets.

2 EXAMPLE Comparing Two Sets of Data

Real-World Connection

On average, teens make about 15 shopping trips per month.

Shopping The box-and-whisker plots below show the prices for items at two clothing stores. Write a paragraph to compare the data.

Clothing Prices (dollars)

10 20 30 40 50

Mall Store

Discount Store

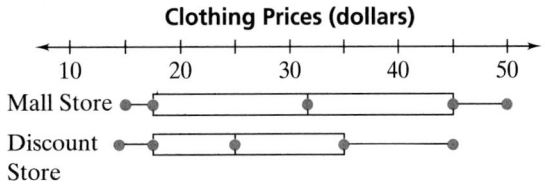

The range for the mall store's prices is greater than the discount store's. The discount store's shorter box means that its prices are more consistent.

For less expensive items, there is not much difference in price. The two stores have the same lower quartile. For more expensive items, the discount store offers lower prices.

Check Understanding 2 Write a paragraph to compare the data.

2. Answers may vary. Sample: The range for the girls' heights is greater than the boys'. Overall the boys tend to be taller than the girls. The girls' upper quartile is equal to the boys' lower quartile.

Students' Heights (in.)

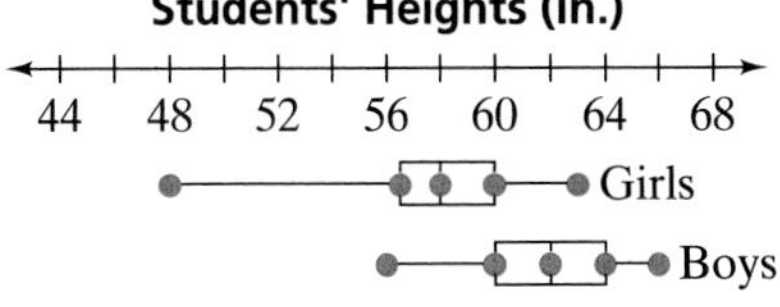

Reaching All Students

Below Level Review median by finding the median of these sets of data. 5, 10, 8, 12, 3 8; 19, 23, 15, 21, 17, 14 18	**Advanced Learners** Have students find appropriate data and make a double box-and-whisker plot.	**English Learners** See note on page 553. **Tactile Learners** See note on page 553.

2. Teach

Professional Development

Math Background

A box-and-whisker plot groups data into quartiles, separated by the median of all the data and the medians of the upper and lower halves of the data.

Teaching Notes

1 EXAMPLE Tactile Learners

Have students write each data value on a separate index card, order the cards, and group the cards by quartile.

2 EXAMPLE English Learners

Help students remember the meaning of *quartile* by asking them to name words related to *four* in several languages, such as *quarter*, *quatre* (French), and *cuatro* (Spanish).

PowerPoint

Additional Examples

1 Make a box-and-whisker plot for this data on study hours per week: 10, 13, 16, 17, 20, 22, 23, 24, 26, 30, 31.

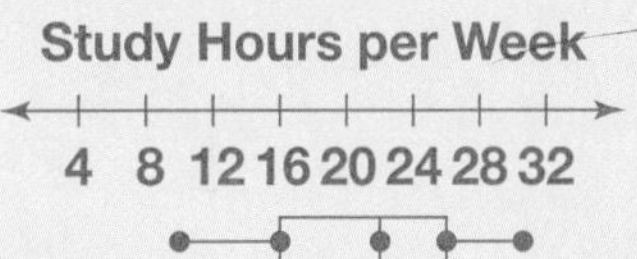

2 Write a paragraph to compare the data shown in these plots.

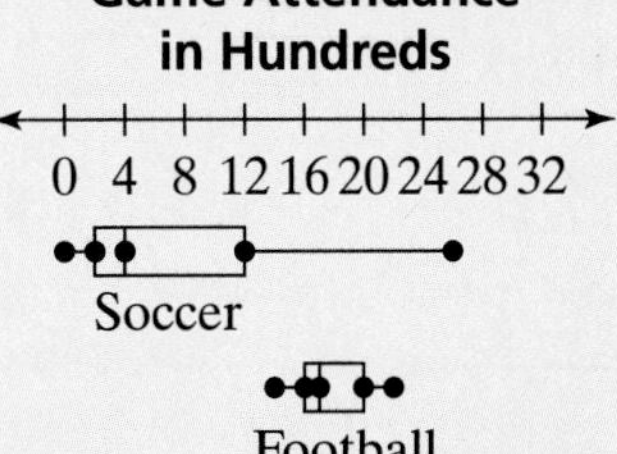

Answers will vary but should include: soccer: median 400, range 2,600, has a larger range; football: median 1,750, range 800, attendance clusters around the median

Closure

Explain how to make a box-and-whisker plot. Answers should include ordering data, finding quartiles, and drawing the box and the whiskers.

3. Practice

Assignment Guide

Objective 1

A B Core 1–19

C Extension 20–21

Test Prep 22–25

Mixed Review 26–31

Error Prevention!

Exercises 1–7 Make sure students first arrange the data in order.

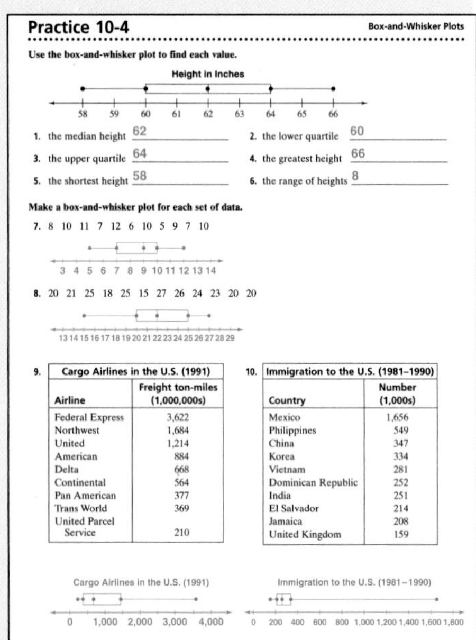

Practice 10-4 — Box-and-Whisker Plots

Use the box-and-whisker plot to find each value.

Height in Inches

1. the median height 62
2. the lower quartile 60
3. the upper quartile 64
4. the greatest height 66
5. the shortest height 58
6. the range of heights 8

Make a box-and-whisker plot for each set of data.

7. 8 10 11 7 12 6 10 5 9 7 10

8. 20 21 25 18 25 15 27 26 24 23 20 20

9.

Cargo Airlines in the U.S. (1991)	
Airline	Freight ton-miles (1,000,000s)
Federal Express	3,622
Northwest	1,684
United	1,214
American	884
Delta	668
Continental	564
Pan American	377
Trans World	369
United Parcel Service	210

10.

Immigration to the U.S. (1981–1990)	
Country	Number (1,000s)
Mexico	1,656
Philippines	549
China	347
Korea	334
Vietnam	281
Dominican Republic	252
India	251
El Salvador	214
Jamaica	208
United Kingdom	159

Reteaching 10-4 — Box-and-Whisker Plots

A *box-and-whisker plot* is a graph that summarizes a data set along a number line. Make a box-and-whisker plot for the data in the table at the right.

Letters per Word in a Newspaper Article (30-Word Sample)				
9	4	2	11	1 8
8	2	6	1	7 3
3	3	8	6	8 5
2	7	8	9	2 4
7	1	6	14	8 4

1. Order the data 1 1 1 2 2 2 2 3 3 3 4 4 4 5 6 6 6 7 7 7 8 8 8 8 8 8 9 9 11 14
2. Find the median. The median is 6.
3. Find the medians of the lower and upper halves of the data. (lower) 1 1 1 2 2 2 2 3 3 3 4 4 4 5 6 (upper) 6 6 7 7 7 8 8 8 8 8 8 9 9 11 14
4. Mark the least and greatest values below a number line. Mark the three medians.
5. Draw a box connecting the lower and upper medians. This box shows where at least half the data lies. Draw a line through the box at the median of all the data.
6. Draw whiskers from the box to the least and greatest values.

Complete the steps to make a box-and-whisker plot for the data.

1. Order the data. 1 2 2 2 2 2 3 3 3 3 3 3 3 3 4 4 5 5 6 7 7 7 8 8 8 9 9 10 11 13
2. Find the median. 4
3. Find the median of the lower and upper halves. lower median = 3; upper median = 8
4. Draw the box-and-whisker plot.

Letters per Word in a Magazine Article (30-Word Sample)				
3	7	8	3	7
4	6	4	3	7
3	1	13	3	2
8	8	2	11	5
5	3	9	9	2
3	2	10	3	2

EXERCISES

For more practice, see *Extra Practice*.

A Practice by Example

Make a box-and-whisker plot for each set of data. 1–7. See margin.

Example 1 (page 552)

1. numbers of CDs:
2 9 3 1 7 6 5 8 11 14 9 7 2 1 8 7 6 13 11 10
2. ages of players on a baseball team:
22 24 25 26 32 19 37 34 39 24 21 26 28 33
3. lengths of snakes at a zoo (ft):
2 9 5 6 8 5 4 6 13 5 8 11 6 14 10 9 13 8 5 7 6 18 9 12
4. bowling scores:
229 152 161 267 193 184 271 199 161 273 221 180
5. weekly salaries (dollars):
445 462 378 394 296 503 556 419 363 683 396 439 375
6. baleen whales' weight (tons):
16 51 57 75 130 27 30 66 76 25 30 46
7. numbers of pairs of shoes:
4 5 8 2 7 6 8 5 2 12 10 4 8 6 9 10 11 12 15 6 3 4 7

Example 2 (page 553)

For each box-and-whisker plot, write a paragraph to compare the data.

8. **On-Time Flight Arrivals and Departures in 2000 (percent per day)**

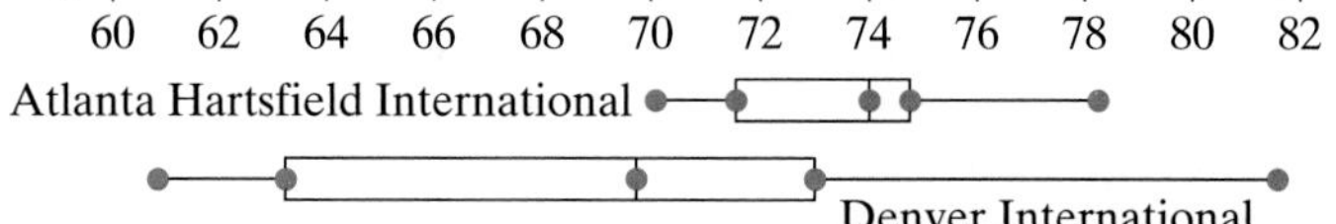

Source: U.S. Census Bureau. Go to **www.PHSchool.com** for a data update. Web Code: acg-2041

See back of book.

9. **Median Income for Men and Women 1981 to 2000 (thousands of dollars)**

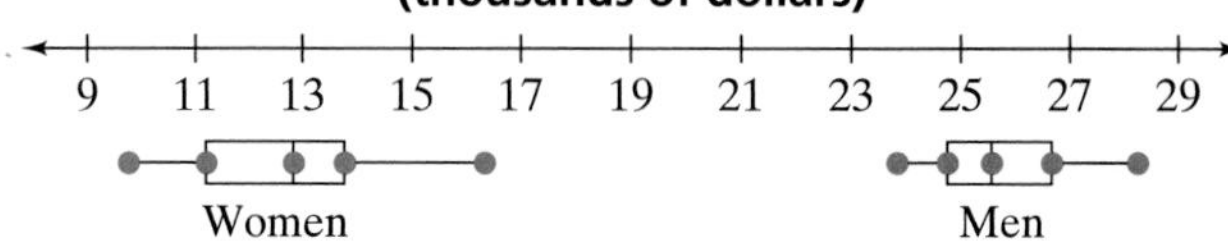

Source: U.S. Census Bureau. Go to **www.PHSchool.com** for a data update. Web Code: acg-2041

See left.

9. Answers may vary. Sample: The median income for men exceeded that of women from 1981 to 2000. The range for women's incomes was greater than men's. The men's incomes were more consistent than the women's.

B Apply Your Skills

10. Use the box-and-whisker plot below to find each value.

Test Scores

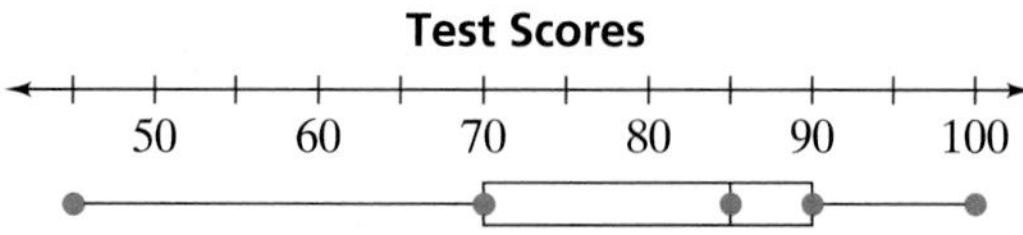

a. the median 85
b. the upper quartile 90
c. the lower quartile 70
d. the greatest value 100

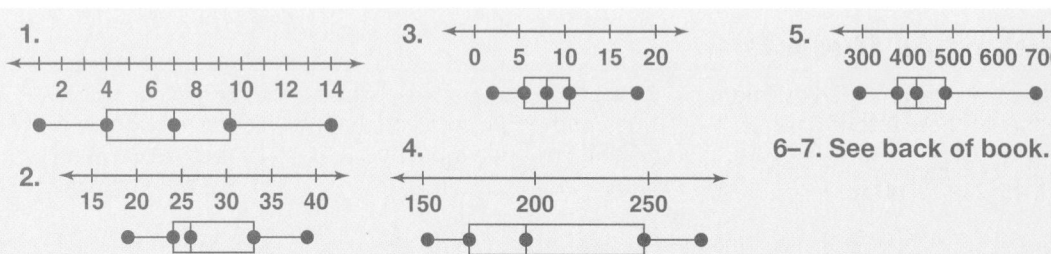

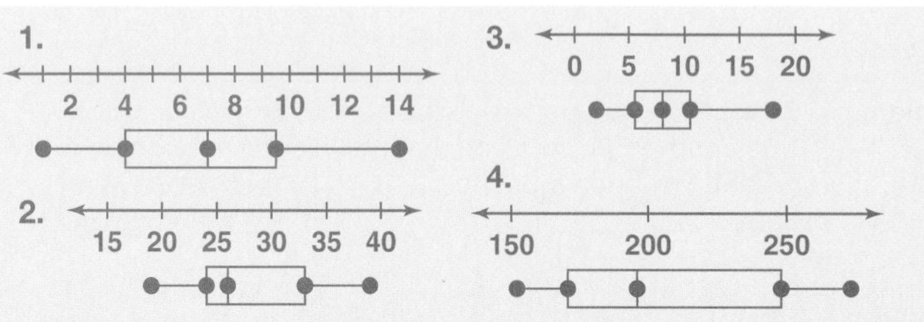

6–7. See back of book.

Make a box-and-whisker plot on a single number line for each set of data. Write a paragraph to compare the two sets of data. 11–12. See margin.

11. **Home Runs Hit by League Leaders (2001 Season)**

American League	52	49	47	41	41	39	38	37	35
National League	73	64	57	49	49	45	41	39	38

SOURCE: Major League Baseball Association

12. **Median Age at First Marriage**

Year	1920	1930	1940	1950	1960	1970	1980	1990	2000
Women	21.2	21.3	21.5	20.3	20.3	20.8	22.0	23.9	25.1
Men	24.6	24.3	24.3	22.8	22.8	23.2	24.7	25.9	26.8

SOURCE: U.S. Census Bureau. Go to **www.PHSchool.com** for a data update. Web Code: acg-2041

13. The data are not evenly distributed.

13. **Writing in Math** Describe what it means when the median is not exactly in the middle of the box.

Racing **Use the table below for Exercises 14 and 15.**

Average Speed of Daytona 500 Winners

Year	1995	1996	1997	1998	1999	2000	2001	2002
Speed (mi/h)	142	154	148	173	162	156	162	143

SOURCE: NASCAR

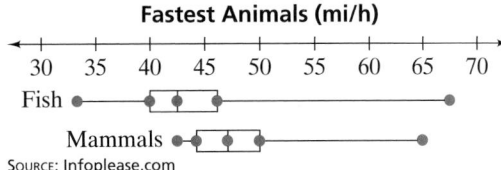

14. Make a box-and-whisker plot for the data.

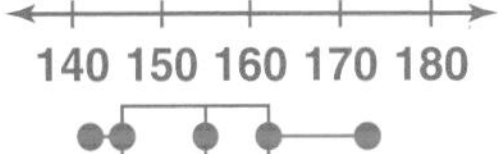

15. **Number Sense** Would the size of the box change if the average speed was 192 mi/h in 2003? Explain. Yes; the upper quartile would move from 162 to 167.5.

16. **Reasoning** When a box-and-whisker plot has a very long box, what do you know about the data? The data are spread out and not very consistent.

Real-World Connection

Stock cars, which are American-made automobiles, reach speeds of over 200 miles per hour.

Animal Speeds **Use the box-and-whisker plot for Exercises 17 and 18.**

Fastest Animals (mi/h)

30 35 40 45 50 55 60 65 70

Fish

Mammals

SOURCE: Infoplease.com

17. Write a paragraph to compare the two sets of data. See left.

17. Answers may vary. Sample: Most mammals are faster than fish, but the fastest fish is faster than the fastest mammal. The slowest mammal travels at the median speed for fish. Fish have a greater range of speed than mammals.

18. What are two facts about the fish and mammals represented in the box-and-whisker plot that you are unable to tell from the plot? See below left.

18. Answers may vary. Sample: You cannot tell the mean speed. You also do not know how many fish or mammals were in the data.

19. **Data Analysis** Gather data on a topic of your choice. Make a box-and-whisker plot to display the data. Write a paragraph interpreting the data. Check students' work.

Use the Guided Problem Solving worksheet with Exercise 14.

11.

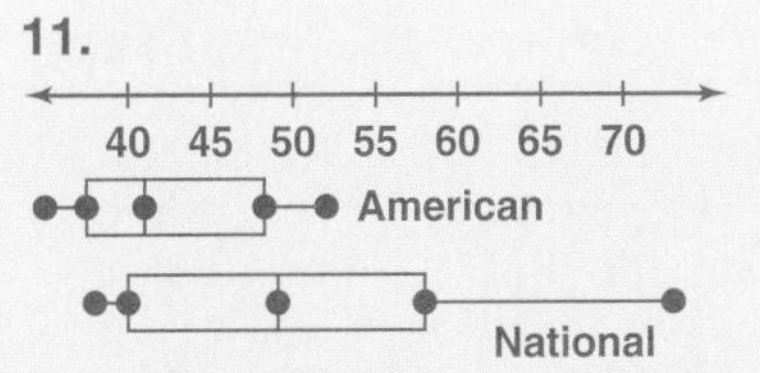

Answers may vary. Sample: The top National League players had a greater range of home runs. Overall, they hit more home runs than the top American League players. The top American League players, however, were more consistent.

12.

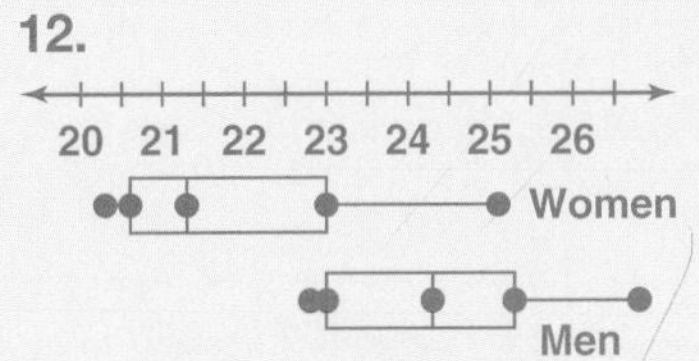

Answers may vary. Sample: Men tend to be older than women when they first get married. The lowest age for men is about the same as the upper quartile for women.

4. Assess

Lesson Quiz 10-4

1. Describe the following box-and-whisker plot.

Miles Run by Track Club Members

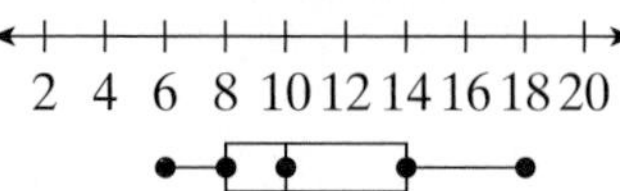

lower quartile is 8, upper quartile is 14, median is 10, whiskers extend to 6 and 18

2. Make box-and-whisker plots on a single number line to compare the individual points scored by boys and girls.

Girls: 14, 15, 18, 20, 21, 21, 24, 24, 25, 27, 29

Boys: 8, 8, 9, 10, 14, 18, 25, 25, 28, 28, 30

Individual Points Scored

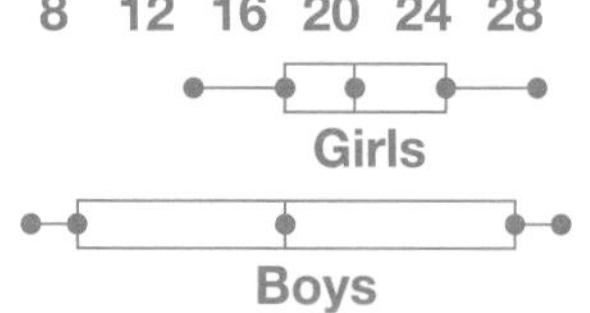

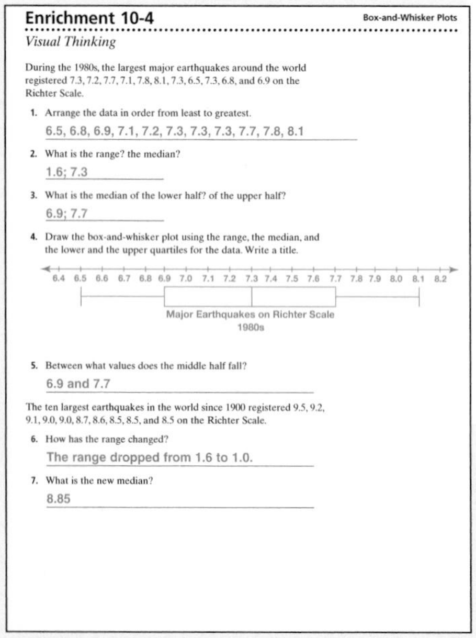

Enrichment 10-4 — Box-and-Whisker Plots

Visual Thinking

During the 1980s, the largest major earthquakes around the world registered 7.3, 7.2, 7.7, 7.1, 7.8, 8.1, 7.3, 6.5, 7.3, 6.8, and 6.9 on the Richter Scale.

1. Arrange the data in order from least to greatest.
   6.5, 6.8, 6.9, 7.1, 7.2, 7.3, 7.3, 7.3, 7.7, 7.8, 8.1
2. What is the range? the median?
   1.6; 7.3
3. What is the median of the lower half? of the upper half?
   6.9; 7.7
4. Draw the box-and-whisker plot using the range, the median, and the lower and the upper quartiles for the data. Write a title.
   6.4 6.5 6.6 6.7 6.8 6.9 7.0 7.1 7.2 7.3 7.4 7.5 7.6 7.7 7.8 7.9 8.0 8.1 8.2
   Major Earthquakes on Richter Scale 1980s
5. Between what values does the middle half fall?
   6.9 and 7.7

The ten largest earthquakes in the world since 1900 registered 9.5, 9.2, 9.1, 9.0, 9.0, 8.7, 8.6, 8.5, 8.5, and 8.5 on the Richter Scale.

6. How has the range changed?
   The range dropped from 1.6 to 1.0.
7. What is the new median?
   8.85

Challenge

20. **Algebra** A scientist has 10 pieces of data in order. The median is 60.5. The sixth piece of data is 71. What is the fifth piece of data? 50

21. **Stretch Your Thinking** If 3 cooks can make 15 pizzas in $1\frac{1}{2}$ hours, how long do 6 cooks take to make 20 pizzas? 1 hour

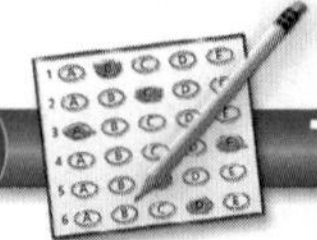

Test Prep

Multiple Choice

22. Find the median of the following data: 32 36 39 42 43 46 47. C
    A. 32 B. 36 C. 42 D. 46

Take It to the NET
Online lesson quiz at **www.PHSchool.com**
Web Code: aca-1004

23. Identify the box-and-whisker plot for the data given below. F
    70 76 80 74 78 56 86 80 80 81 40 75 98 101 103

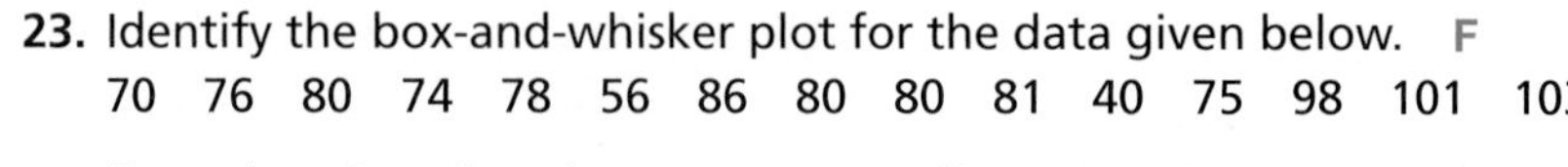

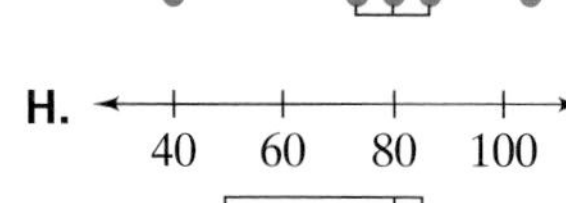

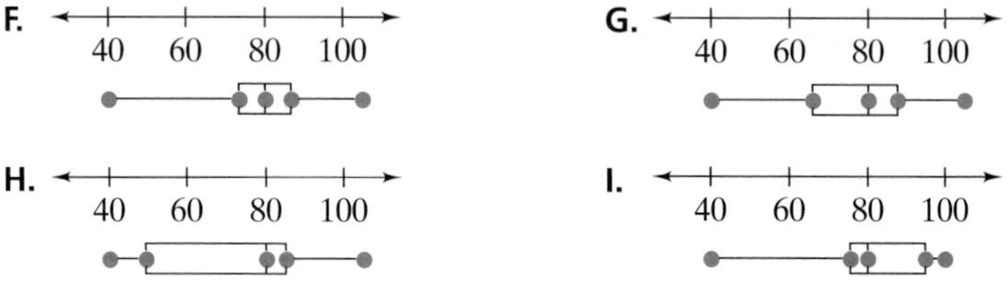

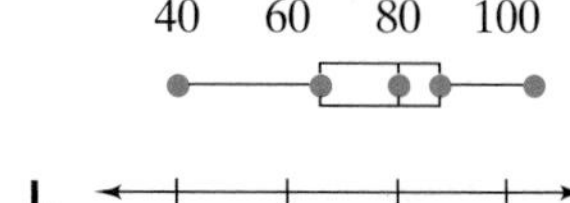

24. Which of the following is NOT a part of a box-and-whisker plot? D
    A. median B. quartile C. whisker D. mean

Extended Response

25. The data below show the average lengths, to the nearest quarter inch, of some species of beetles. Use the data to make a box-and-whisker plot. Describe each point in the graph. See back of book.
    lengths (in.): 0.5 1.5 3.25 2.5 1.25 3.0 6.0 2.75 1.25 2 0.25 1.5 1.0 0.5 1.0 1.5 0.75 0.25 1.75 1.25 0.25 0.75 0.25

Mixed Review

Lesson 10-3

Make a stem-and-leaf plot for each set of data. 26–28. See back of book.

26. 120 123 125 130 124 125 126 123 119 131 126 127 132 118

27. 4.5 4.3 0.8 3.5 2.6 1.4 0.2 0.8 4.3 6.0 0.3 3.2 4.2

28. 23 26 25 26 23 25 25 24 21 21 22 23

Lesson 9-8

Choose a strategy or a combination of strategies to solve each problem.

29. A pencil and an eraser together cost \$2.00. The eraser costs \$1.50 more than the pencil. How much does the eraser cost? \$1.75

30. How many segments can be drawn that will connect any two of nine distinct points on a circle? 36 segments

31. What are two integers that have a sum of −9 and a difference of 5? −2 and −7

Alternative Assessment

Each student draws a general diagram of a box-and-whisker plot and labels the five key points in their plot. Students then write a paragraph that explains what each whisker shows and what each part of the box represents.

Test Prep

Resources
For additional practice with a variety of test item formats:
- Test Prep, p. 585
- Test-Taking Strategies, p. 581
- Test-Taking Strategies with Transparencies

10-5 Making Predictions From Scatter Plots

What You'll Learn

OBJECTIVE 1 To make scatter plots

OBJECTIVE 2 To use scatter plots to find trends

. . . And Why

To make predictions based on a trend in a scatter plot, as in Example 3

Check Skills You'll Need

For help, go to Lesson 3-1.

Graph each point on the same coordinate plane. 1–4. See back of book.

1. $A(1, -2)$ **2.** $B(-3, 5)$ **3.** $C(1, 0)$

4. $D(0, -6)$ **5.** $E(-2, 7)$ **6.** $F(-3, -5)$

7. $G(-1, 0)$ **8.** $H(4, 4)$ **9.** $I(0, 0)$

New Vocabulary

- scatter plot
- positive trend
- negative trend
- no trend
- trend line

OBJECTIVE 1

Making Scatter Plots

Interactive lesson includes instant self-check, tutorials, and activities.

Investigation: Height and Arm Span

1–4. Check students' work.

1. Measure your height and your arm span in centimeters. Arm span is the greatest possible distance between the tips of your index fingers when your arms are stretched outward. To measure your arm span, hold one end of a tape measure in each hand and stretch your arms outward.
2. Write your data as an ordered pair (height, arm span).
3. Collect the ordered pairs your classmates recorded.
4. Make a graph of the ordered pairs. Label the horizontal axis *Height* (cm) and the vertical axis *Arm Span* (cm). Choose an appropriate scale based upon the measurements.
5. What do you notice about the graph? Can you predict a person's arm span based upon the person's height? Explain. See below left.

5. A person's arm span is about the same as his or her height. So, as height increases, arm span increases.

Does the age of a car relate to what the car is worth? You can use a scatter plot to find the answer. A **scatter plot,** such as the one at the right, is a graph that displays two sets of data as ordered pairs. It can help you decide whether one set of data is related to another.

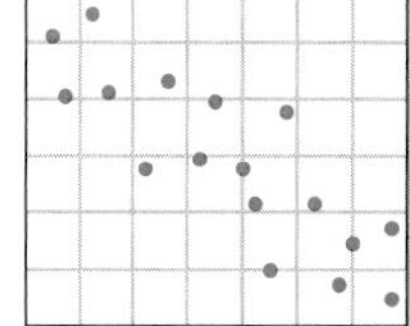

Ongoing Assessment and Intervention

Before the Lesson
Diagnose prerequisite skills using:
- Check Skills You'll Need

During the Lesson
Monitor progress using:
- Check Understanding
- Additional Examples
- Test Prep

After the Lesson
Assess knowledge using:
- Lesson Quiz
- Computer Test Generator CD

10-5

1. Plan

Lesson Preview

Check Skills You'll Need PowerPoint

Graphing Points
Lesson 3-1: Example 3. Extra Practice, p. 704.

Lesson Resources

Optional Materials
- graph paper
- ruler

Teaching Resources
Practice, Reteaching, Enrichment

Reaching All Students
Practice Workbook 10-5
Spanish Practice Workbook 10-5
Guided Problem Solving 10-5

Presentation Assistant Plus!
Transparencies
- Check Skills You'll Need 10-5
- Problem of the Day 10-5
- Additional Examples 10-5
- Student Edition Answers 10-5
- Lesson Quiz 10-5
- Classroom Aid 2, 3, 34–35

PH Presentation Pro CD-ROM 10-5

PRENTICE HALL ASSESSMENT SYSTEM
Computer Test Generator CD

Technology
Resource Pro® CD-ROM
Computer Test Generator CD
PH Presentation Pro CD-ROM

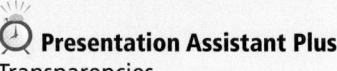

www.PHSchool.com
Student Site
- Updated Data
- Teacher Web Code: ack-5500
- Self-grading Lesson Quiz

PH SuccessNet Teacher Center
- Lesson Planner
- Resources

Plus 

2. Teach

Math Background

One way to examine a possible relationship between two measured quantities is to make a scatter plot of the values, one value plotted along the *x*-axis and the other value on the *y*-axis. When the plotted points appear to lie approximately along a line, called a *trend line*, it is reasonable to conjecture that there is some relationship between the two measurements plotted. A trend can be used to predict other values for similar data.

Teaching Notes

Investigation (Optional)
Have students make conjectures about whether arm span and height are related before they begin. Be sensitive that some students may feel uncomfortable taking these measurements.

1 EXAMPLE Auditory Learners

Have students suggest examples of data about a car that might have no relationship to the age of the car. Sample: color or number of doors

2 EXAMPLE English Learners

Ask a volunteer to explain and demonstrate the meaning of *circumference*. Discuss the meaning of *trend*, including the fact that a trend indicates a relationship that is not exact but that is generally true.

3 EXAMPLE Geography Connection

Have students look on a map or in an atlas to find cities at about 25° north latitude, such as Monterrey, CA, and Miami, Fl.

Teaching Tip
Discuss some possible situations that might result in a graph that shows no trend. For example, plotting height against length of hair or yearly hours of sunshine against letters in the name of a city would generally have no trend.

1 EXAMPLE Making Scatter Plots

Real World

Cars Make a scatter plot for the data.

What's a Car Worth?
Average Value of a Midsize Sedan (dollars)

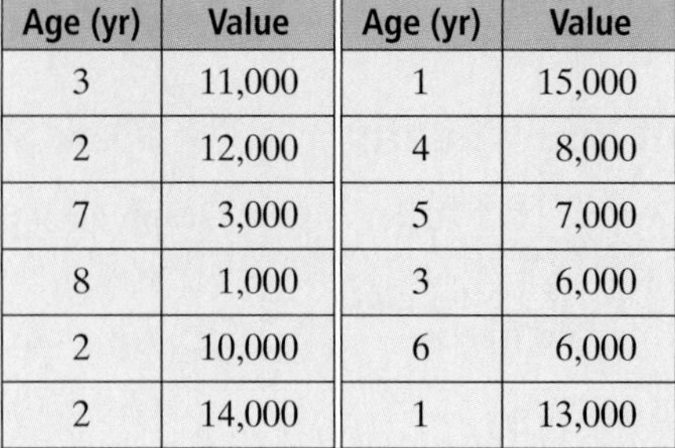

Age (yr)	Value	Age (yr)	Value
3	11,000	1	15,000
2	12,000	4	8,000
7	3,000	5	7,000
8	1,000	3	6,000
2	10,000	6	6,000
2	14,000	1	13,000

Step 1 Choose a scale along the *x*-axis to represent the age of the car. The *y*-axis scale will represent the car's value.

Step 2 (3, 11,000) represents a data pair. Plot each data pair.

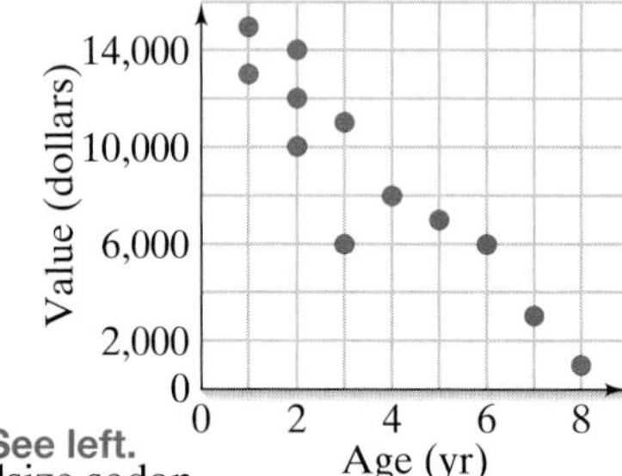

Check Understanding 1 a. **Reasoning** Describe the relationship between the age and the value of a midsize sedan. See left.

1a. As the car's age increases, its value decreases.

b. Make a scatter plot for the set of data below. See back of book.

Age and Sleep Time

Age (yr)	1	15	6	19	12	3	5	13	20	6
Sleep Time (h)	15	8.5	9.5	7	9.25	12	11	9	7	9.75

OBJECTIVE

2 Using Scatter Plots to Find Trends

Reading Math
A trend can also be a vogue, or current style, as in fashions.

The three scatter plots below show the types of relationships, or trends, two sets of data may have.

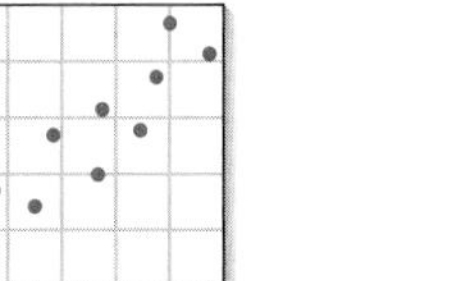

Positive trend
As one set of values increases, the other set tends to increase.

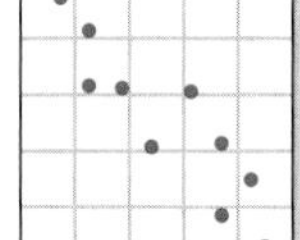

Negative trend
As one set of values increases, the other set tends to decrease.

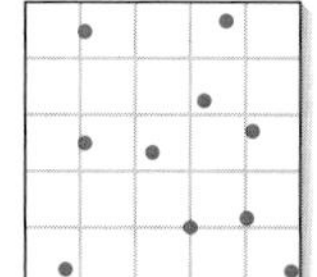

No trend
The points show no relationship.

A **trend line** is a line you draw on a graph to approximate the relationship between the two sets of data.

Reaching All Students

Below Level Review the meaning of an ordered pair, such as (−3, 2), and describe how it relates to the position of a point on the coordinate plane.

Advanced Learners Ask students to discuss examples of two events which may occur simultaneously, but one does not cause the other. Sample: Tuesday and winning a game

English Learners
See note on page 558.
Auditory Learners
See note on page 558.

Real-World Connection You can tell the age of a tree by the number of rings it has.

2 EXAMPLE Drawing Trend Lines

Trees The table below shows the circumference and height of a variety of trees. Make a scatter plot for the data. Describe the type of trend: positive, negative, or no trend. If possible, draw a trend line.

Tree Height and Circumference

Height (ft)	19	32	57	43	75	97	110
Circumference (in.)	10	63	72	111	150	185	214

Step 1 Plot each data pair.

Step 2 Determine the type of trend.

The type of trend tells you the direction and slope of the trend line. This scatter plot shows a positive trend.

Step 3 Draw a line with a positive slope. Make sure there are about as many points above the line as there are below it.

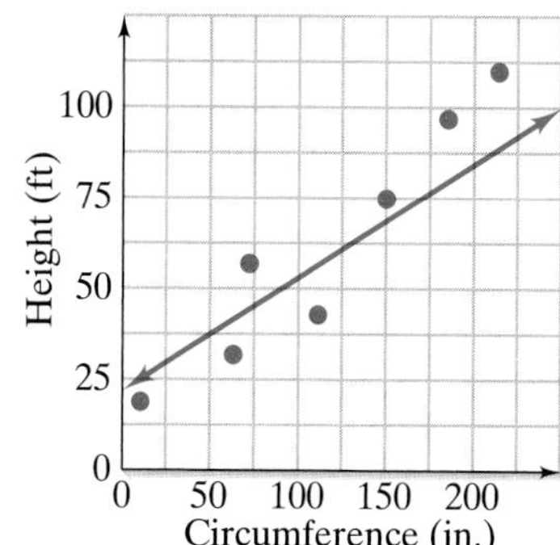

Check Understanding 2 **a.** Describe the trend in the scatter plot from Example 1. negative trend
b. Redraw the scatter plot for the data in Example 1. Draw a trend line. See margin.

You can use trend lines to make predictions about data values that do not appear on a scatter plot.

3 EXAMPLE Real-World Problem Solving

Weather Use the scatter plot and trend line. Describe the trend in the data. Predict the mean April temperature for a city at 25° north latitude.

Latitude and Temperature

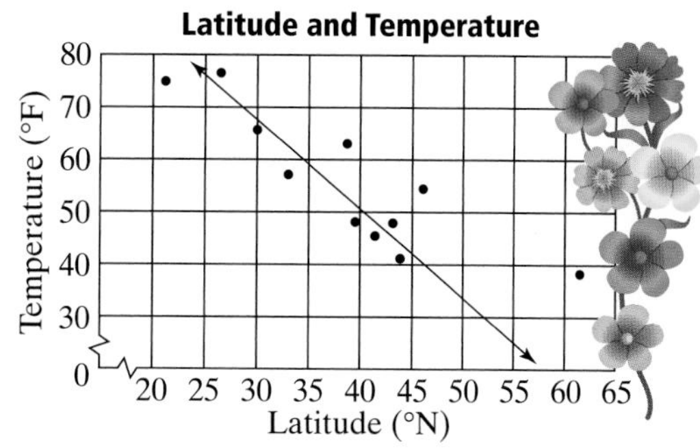

As the latitude increases, the temperature decreases. This is a negative trend.

Find 25° along the horizontal axis. At 25°, the trend line seems to go through the 75°F mark. The mean April temperature should be near 75°F.

Check Understanding 3 Predict the mean April temperature for a city at 45° north latitude. 42°F

Error Prevention!

Students may have difficulty seeing a trend in a scatter plot. Emphasize the importance of graphing data accurately, particularly choosing an appropriate scale.

Additional Examples

1 Make a scatter plot for the data.

Miles Traveled and Gas Used

Gas (gal)	Miles
5	150
4	112
7	217
3	87
8	216
5	155

Miles Traveled and Gas Used

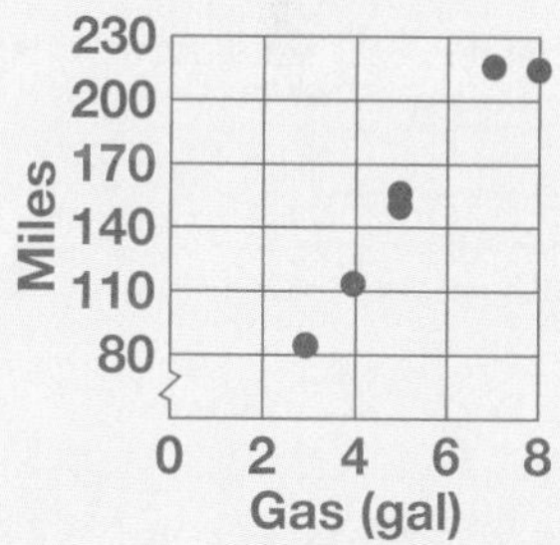

2 Does the scatter plot in Question 1 show a positive trend, a negative trend, or no trend? If possible, draw a trend line. a positive trend

3 Predict the miles for 6 gallons of gas. about 195 miles

Closure

Explain how to make a scatter plot and how to use it to find a trend. Answers should include plotting data pairs, looking for a trend line, and deciding whether the plot shows a positive trend, a negative trend, or no trend.

Check Understanding 2b.

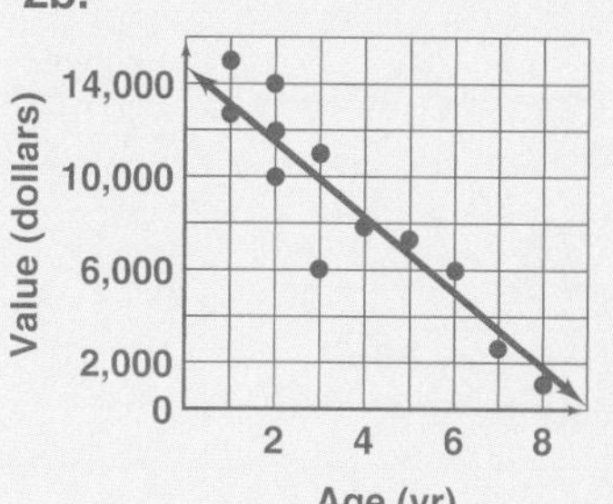

3. Practice

Assignment Guide

Objective 1
- A B Core 1–4, 13–14
- C Extension 17

Objective 2
- A B Core 5–12, 15–16
- C Extension 18–21

Test Prep 22–25
Mixed Review 26–29

Example 16 Ask students for examples to support their reasoning.

Practice 10-5 — Making Predictions from Scatter Plots

Tell whether a scatter plot made for each set of data would describe a positive trend, a negative trend, or no trend.

1. amount of education and annual salary — positive trend
2. weight and speed in a foot race — negative trend
3. test score and shoe size — no trend

4. Make a scatter plot showing the number of homeowners on one axis and vacation homeowners on the other axis. If there is a trend, draw a trend line. Students' graphs should show a negative trend. Sample shown.

Residents of Maintown		
Year	Homeowners	Vacation Homeowners
1997–98	2,050	973
1996–97	1,987	967
1995–96	1,948	1,041
1994–95	1,897	1,043
1993–94	1,862	1,125
1992–93	1,832	1,126

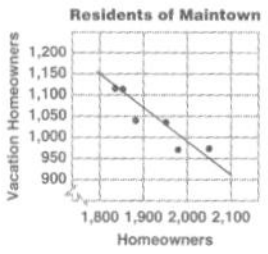

5. Make a scatter plot for the data. If there is a trend, draw a trend line. Students' graphs should show a positive trend. Sample shown.

Arm Span vs. Height		
Person #	Arm Span	Height
1	156	162
2	157	160
3	159	162
4	160	155
5	161	160
6	161	162
7	162	170
8	165	166
9	170	170
10	170	167
11	173	185
12	173	176

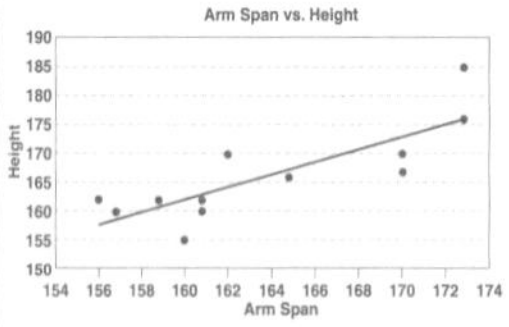

6. Wynetta found the graph shown at the right. The title of the graph was missing. What could the graph be describing?
Sample answer: time spent skating up a hill vs. speed of skater

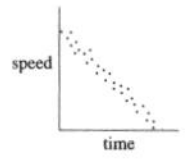

Reteaching 10-5 — Making Predictions from Scatter Plots

Example Make a scatter plot and find a trend for the data below

① Choose a scale along each axis to represent the two sets of data.

② Locate the ordered pairs on the graph for the data.

③ Is there a trend? Do both sets of values increase? Does one decrease as the other increases? If neither occurs, there is no trend.

④ If there is a trend, draw a trend line that closely fits the data.

Age and Height Survey

Age (y)	Height (in.)	Age (y)	Height (in.)	Age (y)	Height (in.)
11	55	4	39	12	55
10	55	13	62	10	54
8	49	11	52	7	47
6	45	5	41	13	63
10	52	14	62	9	60
11	59	12	56	9	52
7	45	8	52	12	58
12	60	6	44	13	60
6	48	7	48	8	50
5	45	4	39	11	56

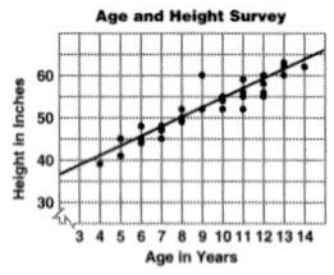

Use the data below for Exercises 1–5.

Weight (lb)	78	63	67	52	81	92	60	34	83	47	73	98	45	31	95	71	76	41
Height (in.)	56	52	55	47	58	60	50	39	58	45	54	61	45	36	60	54	56	41

1. Draw the scatter plot and a trend line.
2. Use your graph to estimate the height of a person who weighs about 90 lb.
about 61 in.
3. Use your graph to estimate the weight of a student 51 in. tall.
about 63 lb
4. Is there a relationship between height and weight?
yes
5. Write a sentence to explain your answer to Exercise 4.
Sample answer: As height increases, weight increases.

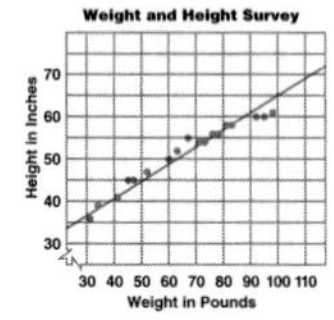

EXERCISES

For more practice, see *Extra Practice*.

A Practice by Example

Make a scatter plot for each set of data. 1–4. See margin.

Example 1 (page 558)

1. Number of Roommates and Monthly Rent

Roommates	3	2	3	2	4
Rent (per person)	$400	$900	$500	$700	$300

2. Softball Game Results

Hits	7	8	4	11	8	2	5	9	1	4
Runs	3	2	2	7	4	2	1	3	0	1

3. Minimum Wage (1965–2000)

Year	1965	1970	1975	1980	1985	1990	1995	2000
Minimum Wage	$1.25	$1.60	$2.10	$3.10	$3.35	$3.80	$4.25	$5.15

SOURCE: U.S. Dept. of Labor. Go to **www.PHSchool.com** for a data update. Web Code: acg-2041

4. Area and Population

Area (millions of km^2)	2.4	7.7	1.1	8.5	0.1	10.0	0.1	1.1	0.1
Population (millions)	31.7	19.4	8.3	174.5	7.7	31.6	11.2	65.9	3.8

Example 2 (page 559)

Is a *positive trend,* a *negative trend,* or *no trend* shown by the two sets of data in each scatter plot? Explain your choice. 5–6. See below left.

5. the scatter plot in Exercise 3
6. the scatter plot in Exercise 4

Need Help?
Remember, the slope of the trend line depends on the type of trend.

5. Positive trend; as the years increase, so does the minimum wage.
6. No trend; no relationship is shown.

Make a scatter plot for the data. If possible, draw a trend line.
7–8. See back of book.

7. Life Expectancy

Current Age (yr)	10	15	20	25	30	35	40	45
Life Expectancy (yr)	67.4	62.5	57.7	53.0	48.2	43.5	38.8	34.3

SOURCE: U.S. Census Bureau. Go to **www.PHSchool.com** for a data update. Web Code: acg-2041

8. Farm Sizes in the United States (1940–2000)

Number of Farms (millions)	6.30	6.10	5.39	3.96	2.95	2.44	2.15	2.17
Average Size (acres)	157	175	216	297	373	426	460	434

SOURCE: U.S. National Agricultural Statistics. Go to **www.PHSchool.com** for a data update. Web Code: acg-2041

GPS Use the Guided Problem Solving worksheet with Exercise 16.

1, 3–4. See back of book.

2.

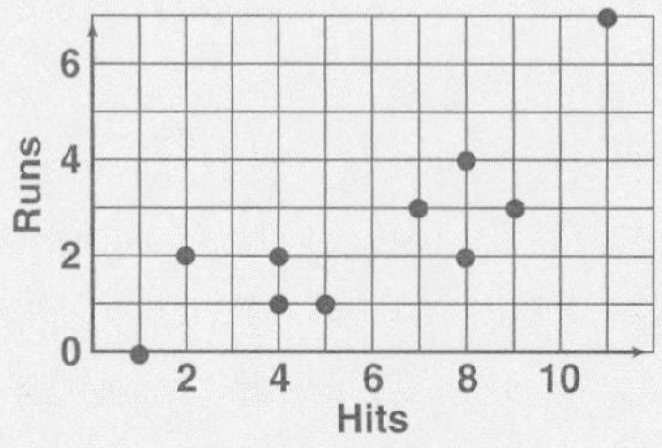

Example 3 (page 559)

Use the scatter plot and trend line for Exercises 9 and 10.

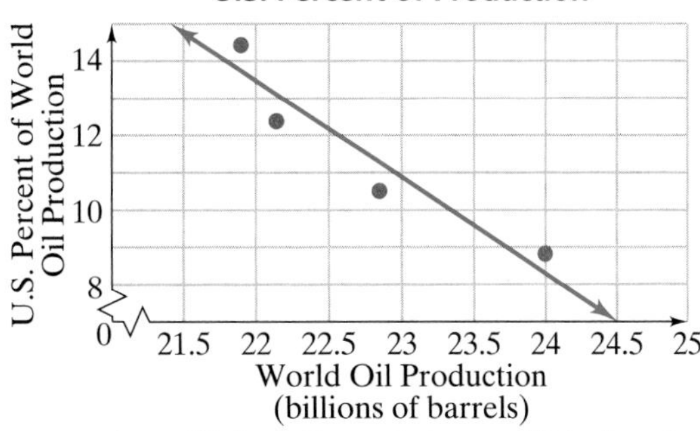

SOURCE: U.S. Census Bureau. Go to www.PHSchool.com for a data update. Web Code: acg-2041

9. Describe the trend in the data. negative trend

10. What was the world's production of oil when the United States produced 12% of the world's oil? about 22.5 billion barrels

B Apply Your Skills

For each topic, decide which type of trend a scatter plot of the data would likely show. Explain your choice.

11. age of owner and number of pets owned

12. outdoor temperature and layers of clothing

11. No trend; people of all ages own varying numbers of pets.

12. Negative trend; as the temperatures increase, you wear fewer layers of clothing.

13. Data File, p. 531 Make a scatter plot for the number of acres used for wheat and the number of bushels produced in the United States. See back of book.

14. Writing in Math Do you think predictions made from a trend line will always be accurate? Explain why or why not. See margin.

15. Reasoning As the number of women holding jobs increased, the record time in the women's 200-m run decreased. Does this negative trend mean that one set of data *caused* the other to occur? Explain. See margin.

16a–b. See margin.

16. a. **Baseball** Make a scatter plot for the data.
 b. Draw a trend line.
 c. How many hits would a player be expected to have with 500 at-bats?
 d. How many at-bats would a player have with 250 hits?

GPS

	A	B	C
1	Name	At Bats	Hits
2	T. Hunter	564	147
3	I. Rodriguez	442	136
4	C. Beltran	617	189
5	G. Anderson	672	194
6	R. Sierra	344	100
7	B. Daubach	407	107
8	J. Liefer	254	65

SOURCE: Major League Baseball Association

16c. about 140

16d. about 850

Real-World Connection

Careers A baseball bat maker needs to have an understanding of the physics of baseball and carpentry.

14. No; it depends on how close the points are to the line. Also, the further your prediction point is from the last point used to create the trend line, the less accurate your predictions may be.

15. No; there is no relationship between these two variables—one did not cause the other.

16a–b.

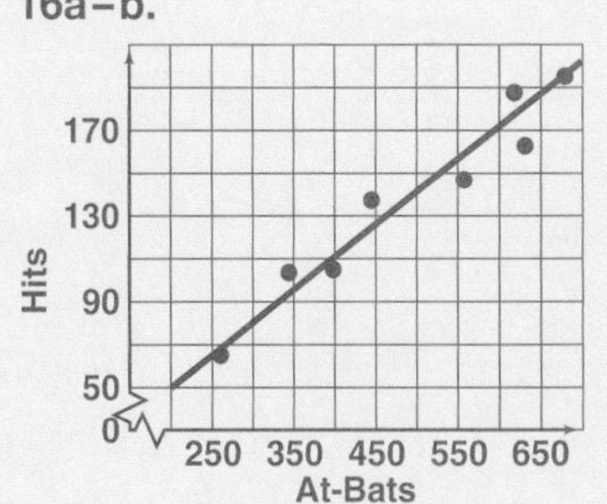

4. Assess

Lesson Quiz 10-5

The following data give the high temperatures for the first week in June. Use this data to answer the questions. (1, 68), (2, 70), (3, 65), (4, 67), (5, 71), (6, 75), (7, 74)

1. Make a scatter plot for the data.

High Temperatures in June

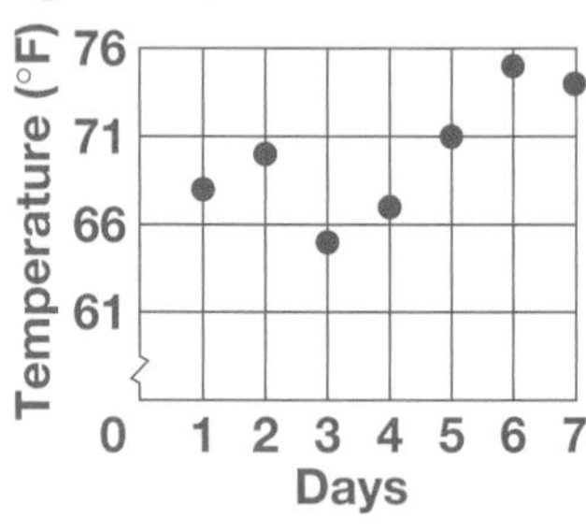

2. Describe the trend in the data. positive trend

Test Prep

Resources

For additional practice with a variety of test item formats:

- Test Prep, p. 585
- Test-Taking Strategies, p. 581
- Test-Taking Strategies with Transparencies

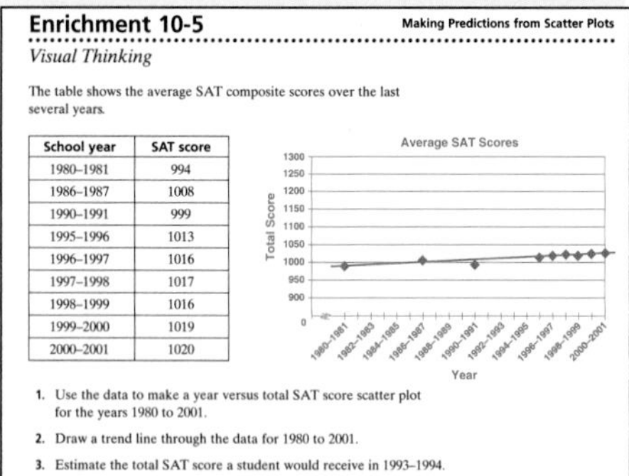

Enrichment 10-5 — Making Predictions from Scatter Plots

Visual Thinking

The table shows the average SAT composite scores over the last several years.

School year	SAT score
1980–1981	994
1986–1987	1008
1990–1991	999
1995–1996	1013
1996–1997	1016
1997–1998	1017
1998–1999	1016
1999–2000	1019
2000–2001	1020

Average SAT Scores (Total Score vs. Year)

1. Use the data to make a year versus total SAT score scatter plot for the years 1980 to 2001.
2. Draw a trend line through the data for 1980 to 2001.
3. Estimate the total SAT score a student would receive in 1993–1994. Sample answer: 1010
4. Use two points to calculate the approximate slope of your trend line. Let $x = 1$ for 1980–1981, $x = 2$ for 1981–1982 and so on. Sample answer: 1.23
5. Use your trend line to approximate a y-intercept. Sample answer: 990
6. Use your answer to Exercises 4 and 5 to write an equation for the trend line. Sample answer: $y = 1.23x + 990$
7. Use the equation from Exercise 6 to calculate the test score in the year 1993-1994. Compare your result to your prediction in Exercise 3. Sample answer: 1007; the result is lower than predicted.

Challenge

17. **Data Collection** Toss a coin 20 times. After each toss, record the total number of heads and tails up to that point. For example, after 13 tosses, you might have 6 heads and 7 tails. Draw a scatter plot for the data pairs. Check students' work.

Open-Ended **What type of trend does each scatter plot show? Describe a real-world situation that each scatter plot might represent.** 18–20. See left.

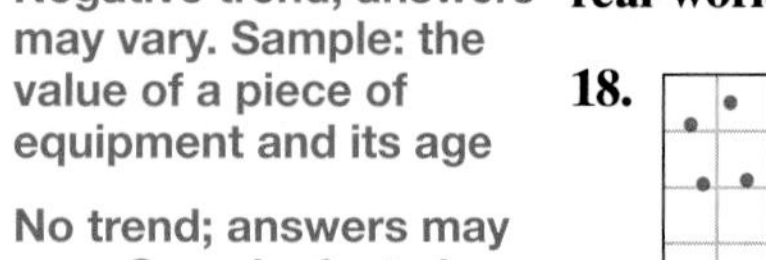

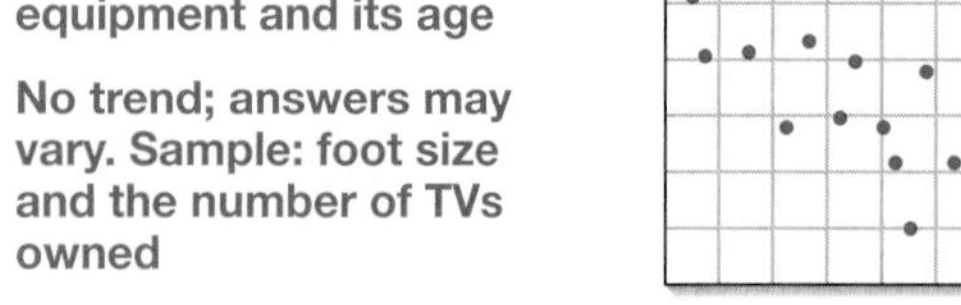

18. Negative trend; answers may vary. Sample: the value of a piece of equipment and its age
19. No trend; answers may vary. Sample: foot size and the number of TVs owned
20. Positive trend; answers may vary. Sample: weight and height

18. 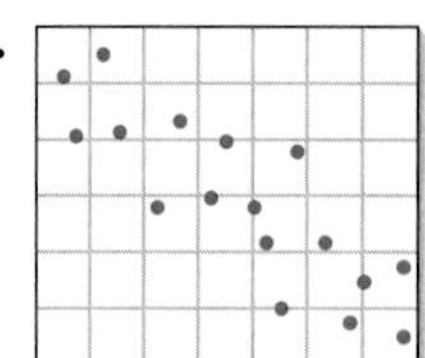 **19.** 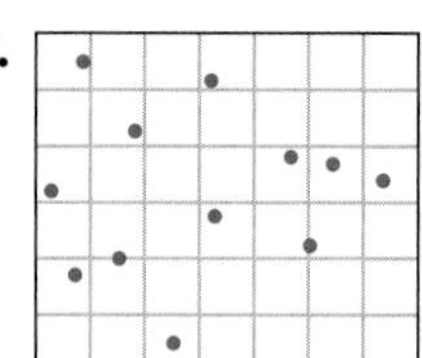 **20.** 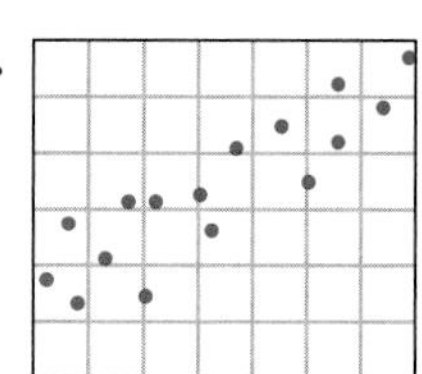

21. **Stretch Your Thinking** Rita can take off every seventh day and Roberta can take off every eighth day. Rita is off today and Roberta is off tomorrow. How many days will it be before they both can take the same day off? 49 days

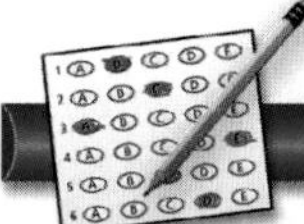

Test Prep

Multiple Choice

22. Describe the trend in the scatter plot at the right. B
    A. positive B. negative
    C. none D. opposite

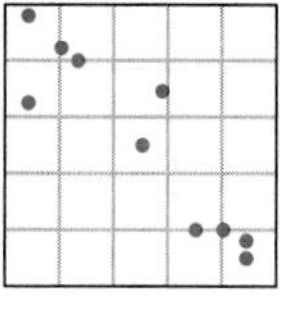

Take It to the NET
Online lesson quiz at **www.PHSchool.com**
Web Code: aca-1005

23. What type of trend would you expect to see in a scatter plot comparing mosquito population and the sale of insect repellent? F
    F. positive G. negative H. none I. opposite

24. What type of trend would you expect to see in a scatter plot comparing the temperature and the number of pets in a family? C
    A. positive B. negative C. none D. opposite

Short Response

25. What type of trend would you expect to see in a scatter plot comparing the outside temperature and the amount of heating oil used by a furnace? Explain your reasoning. See margin.

Mixed Review

Lesson 10-4 **Make a box-and-whisker plot for each set of data.** 26–29. See back of book.

26. 9 8 1 8 7 6 3 7 9 8 6 4 7 8 9 10 10

27. 42 96 84 92 191 86 80 80 87 92 86 82 83 78 90 73 70

Lesson 8-9

28. Draw a segment $\overline{AB}$. Construct $\overline{CD}$ congruent to $\overline{AB}$.

29. Draw an angle $\angle M$. Construct $\angle P$ congruent to $\angle M$.

Alternative Assessment

Have students copy the graph for Example 1. Have them sketch a trend line. Ask what happens to the trend line when (6, 6,000), (7, 7,000), (1, 12,000), and (2, 8,000) are added to the data. The slope becomes less steep.

25. [2] I would expect to see a negative trend because as the temperature decreases, the amount of oil used increases.
    [1] correct answer with no explanation

10-6 Circle Graphs

What You'll Learn

To read a circle graph

To make a circle graph

. . . And Why

To display environmental data in a circle graph, as in Example 2

Check Skills You'll Need

For help, go to Lesson 5-4.

Solve each proportion.

1. $\frac{2}{3} = \frac{16}{y}$ 24
2. $\frac{s}{12} = \frac{5}{2}$ 30
3. $\frac{7}{3} = \frac{r}{12}$ 28
4. $\frac{25}{p} = \frac{75}{125}$ $41\frac{2}{3}$
5. $\frac{k}{16} = \frac{10}{2}$ 80
6. $\frac{12}{15} = \frac{t}{5}$ 4

New Vocabulary

- circle graph
- central angle

Interactive lesson includes instant self-check, tutorials, and activities.

OBJECTIVE 1

Reading Circle Graphs

A **circle graph** is a graph of data where the entire circle represents the whole. Each wedge, or sector, in the circle represents part of the whole. The total of the data must equal 100% or 1.

1 EXAMPLE Reading Circle Graphs

Real World

Food Pantries It is estimated that 21.3 million people in the United States use food pantries each year. The circle graph below shows their ages.

Ages of People Using Food Pantries

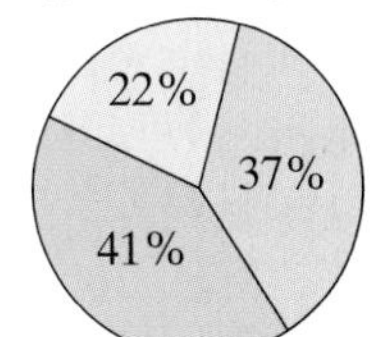

SOURCE: America's Second Harvest

Real-World Connection

Food pantries distribute unprepared food and other grocery products to people in need.

a. What percent of the people who use food pantries are 17 or younger?

Use the key. The age group for people 17 or younger is graphed in pink. So, 41% of the people who use food banks are 17 or younger.

b. How many people who use food pantries are 17 or younger?

$21{,}300{,}000 \cdot 41\% = 21{,}300{,}000$ × 0.41 ENTER 8733000

There are about 8,733,000 people 17 or younger using food banks.

Check Understanding 1

a. What percent of the people who use food pantries are ages 18–49? 37%

b. How many people who use food pantries are 50 or older?

1b. 4,686,000 people

c. Reasoning Explain why a key to a circle graph is important.

A key tells what each sector represents.

Ongoing Assessment and Intervention

Before the Lesson
Diagnose prerequisite skills using:
- Check Skills You'll Need

During the Lesson
Monitor progress using:
- Check Understanding
- Additional Examples
- Test Prep

After the Lesson
Assess knowledge using:
- Lesson Quiz
- Computer Test Generator CD
- Chapter Checkpoint 2 (p. 568)

10-6

1. Plan

Lesson Preview

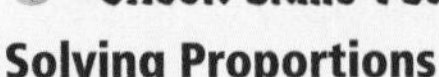
PowerPoint

Check Skills You'll Need

Solving Proportions
Lesson 5-4: Example 2.
Extra Practice, p. 706.

Lesson Resources

Optional Materials
- compass
- protractor

Teaching Resources
Practice, Reteaching, Enrichment
Checkpoint Quiz 2

Reaching All Students
Practice Workbook 10-6
Spanish Practice Workbook 10-6
Reading and Math Literacy 10C
Spanish Reading and Math Literacy 10C
Spanish Checkpoint Quiz 2
Guided Problem Solving 10-6
Hands-On Activities 24

Presentation Assistant Plus!
Transparencies
- Check Skills You'll Need 10-6
- Problem of the Day 10-6
- Additional Examples 10-6
- Student Edition Answers 10-6
- Lesson Quiz 10-6
- Classroom Aid 11, 23–35

PH Presentation Pro CD-ROM 10-6

PRENTICE HALL ASSESSMENT SYSTEM

Checkpoint Quiz 2
Computer Test Generator CD

Technology
Resource Pro® CD-ROM
Computer Test Generator CD
PH Presentation Pro CD-ROM

www.PHSchool.com
Student Site
- Updated Data
- Teacher Web Code: ack-5500
- Algebra Readiness Puzzles 34
- Self-grading Lesson Quiz

PH SuccessNet Teacher Center
- Lesson Planner
- Resources

Plus 

2. Teach

Math Background

When the data values add to a whole, or 100%, and when there are only a few categories, a circle graph is often an effective way to present the data so that the categories can be easily compared.

Teaching Notes

1 EXAMPLE Diversity

The topic of food pantries may be a sensitive issue for some students.

PowerPoint

Additional Examples

1. Use this circle graph for a school with a total enrollment of 1,308 students.

Central Middle School Enrollment (by Grade)

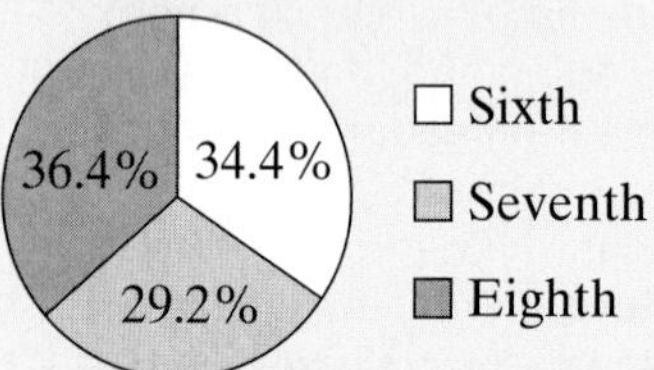

a. What percent of the students are in the eighth grade? 36.4%

b. How many students are there in the eighth grade? 476

2. Make a circle graph for the results of a survey of students' favorite seasons.

Favorite Season	Number	Central Angle
Spring	20	60°
Summer	53	159°
Fall	28	84°
Winter	19	57°

See back of book for graph.

Closure

Explain how a circle graph represents data. Circles represent a whole and each sector is a part of the whole. The central angle of each sector is proportional to its percent.

OBJECTIVE

2 Making Circle Graphs

To make a circle graph, you must find the measure of each central angle. A **central angle** is an angle whose vertex is the center of a circle. The sum of the measures of the central angles of a circle is 360°. Use this to set up proportions to find the measure of each central angle.

2 EXAMPLE Making Circle Graphs

Endangered Species

Group	Number of Species
Mammals	342
Birds	273
Fish	126
Reptiles	115
Clams	72
Insects	48
Other	94

SOURCE: U.S. Fish and Wildlife Service. Go to **www.PHSchool.com** for a data update. Web Code: acg-2041

Environment Make a circle graph for the set of data in the table.

Step 1 Add each number of species to find the total number of species.

$$342 + 273 + 126 + 115 + 72 + 48 + 94 = 1{,}070$$

Step 2 Use proportions to find the measures of the central angles.

$\frac{342}{1,070} = \frac{m}{360°}$ $m \approx 115°$ $\frac{273}{1,070} = \frac{b}{360°}$ $b \approx 92°$

$\frac{126}{1,070} = \frac{f}{360°}$ $f \approx 42°$ $\frac{115}{1,070} = \frac{r}{360°}$ $r \approx 39°$

$\frac{72}{1,070} = \frac{c}{360°}$ $c \approx 24°$ $\frac{48}{1,070} = \frac{i}{360°}$ $i \approx 16°$

$\frac{94}{1,070} = \frac{o}{360°}$ $o \approx 32°$

Step 3 Use a compass to draw a circle. Mark the center of the circle and draw a radius. Construct a central angle with a protractor.

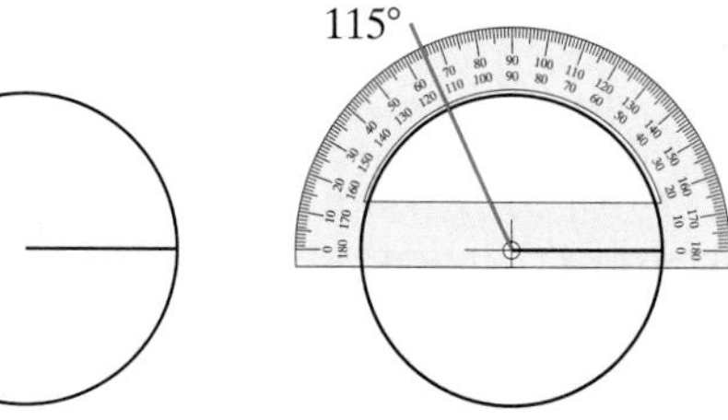

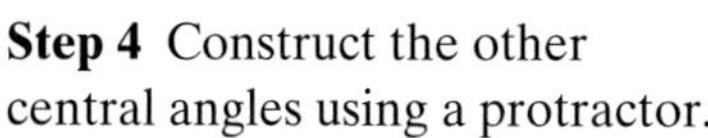

Step 4 Construct the other central angles using a protractor.

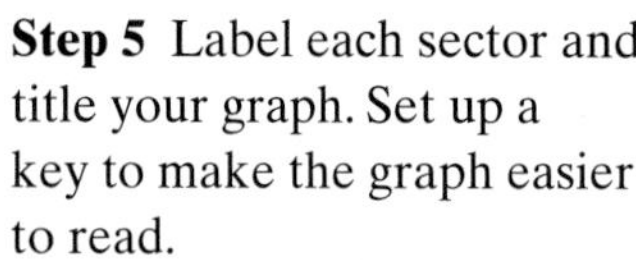

Step 5 Label each sector and title your graph. Set up a key to make the graph easier to read.

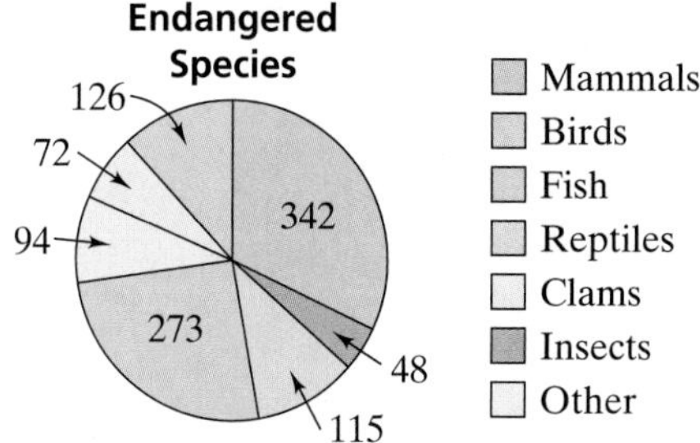

Check Understanding 2 Make a circle graph for the set of data. See back of book.

Fuel Used by Types of Vehicles (billions of gallons)

Cars	Vans, Pickups, SUVs	Trucks	Other
73	53	33	2

SOURCE: U.S. Census Bureau. Go to **www.PHSchool.com** for a data update. Web Code: acg-2041

Reaching All Students

Below Level Use drawings to review the number of degrees in a circle, 360 the degrees in a right angle, 90 and the definition of a central angle. vertex at the center of the circle

Advanced Learners Have students make a chart showing the degrees in the central angle for 10%, 25%, 30%, 50%, and 75%. 36°, 90°, 108°, 180°, 270°

Inclusion
See note on page 566.
Diversity
See note on page 564.

EXERCISES

For more practice, see *Extra Practice.*

 **Practice by Example**

Example 1 (page 563)

Survey **A group of 200 students were surveyed about their favorite sports. The results are in the circle graph below.**

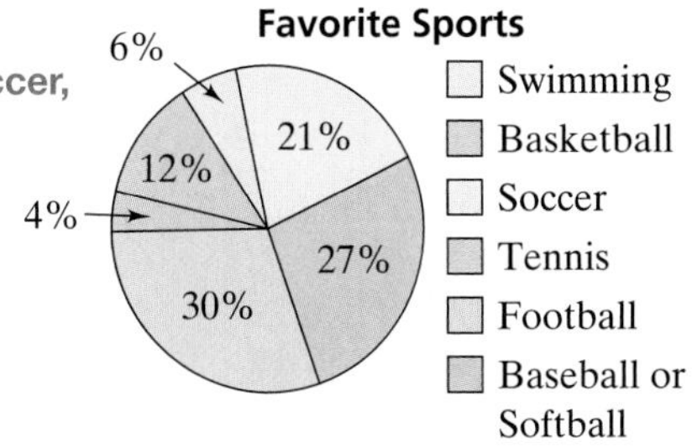

Favorite Sports

1. What two sports make up about half of the total? football and soccer, or soccer and baseball or softball
2. How many students favored each sport?
3. What is the total percent of all the categories? 100%
4. Suppose 90 of the students said their favorite sport was football. How many students in all would have been surveyed? 300 students
5. If the percents were not written on the graph, could you still find the sport that had the least percent of votes? Explain. Yes; it would be the smallest sector.

2. football: 60; baseball: 54; soccer: 42; basketball: 24; swimming: 12; tennis: 8

Example 2 (page 564)

Need Help?
When the data are in percents, set up the proportion $\frac{\text{percent}}{100} = \frac{\text{central angle}}{360^\circ}$.

Make a circle graph for each set of data. 6–10. See margin.

6. **Boxes Sold**

Size of Box (in.)	Number Sold
12 × 12 × 12	215
20 × 20 × 20	175
24 × 24 × 24	85
36 × 36 × 36	192
48 × 48 × 48	315

7. **Pet Owner Survey**

Pet	Percent
Dog	31
Cat	27
Bird	7
Fish	18
Other	17

8. **Favorite Categories**

Book Type	People
Adventure	82
Romance	86
Horror	22
Science Fiction	10

9. **Vehicles Owned**

Vehicle Type	Percent
Small	28
Midsize	48
Large	7
Luxury	17

10. **Running** A doctor surveyed 340 patients who ran a mile or more each day. The results are in the table below. Make a circle graph for the data.

Miles	More than 6	6	5	4	3	Less than 3
Number of Patients	34	29	41	73	65	98

7. Pet Ownership

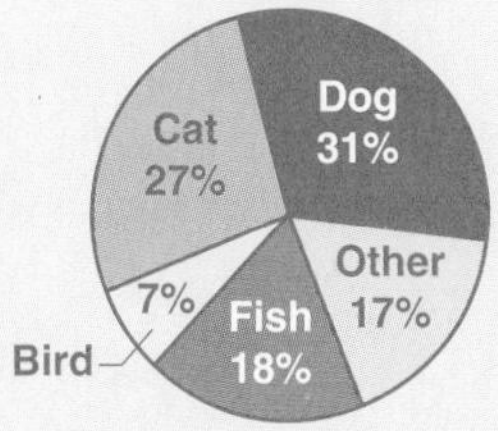

8. Book Types Read

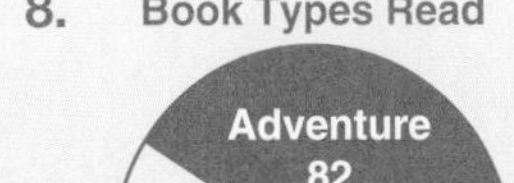

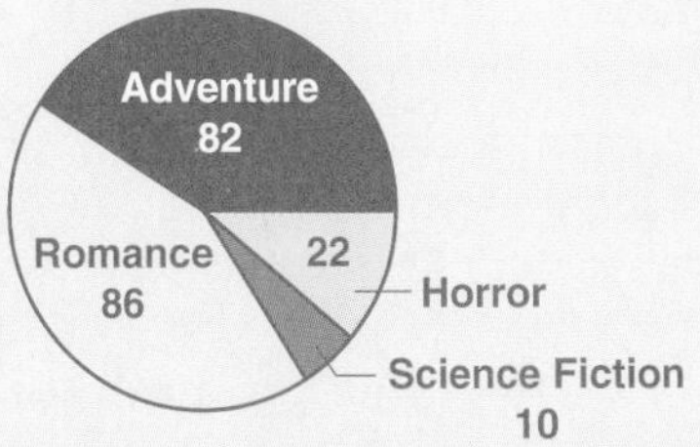

6, 9–10. See back of book.

3. Practice

Assignment Guide

 Objective 1

 Core 1–5, 17

 Objective 2

A B Core 6–14, 15–16, 18–20

C Extension 21–22

Test Prep 23–26

Mixed Review 27–35

Error Prevention!

Exercises 6–9 Students may draw an angle equal to the percent.

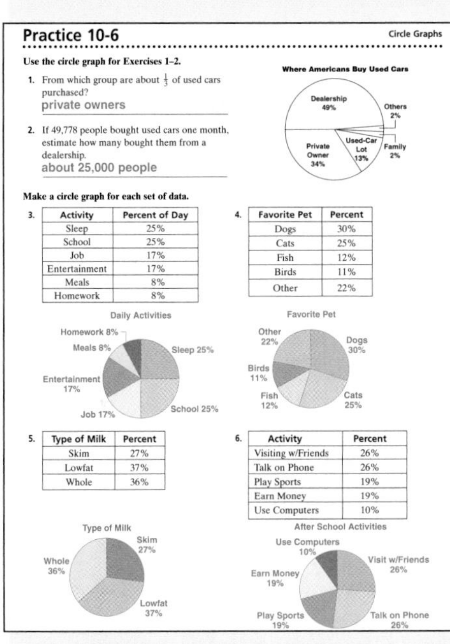

Practice 10-6 Circle Graphs

Use the circle graph for Exercises 1–2.

1. From which group are about $\frac{1}{3}$ of used cars purchased? private owners
2. If 49,778 people bought used cars one month, estimate how many bought them from a dealership. about 25,000 people

Make a circle graph for each set of data.

3.

Activity	Percent of Day
Sleep	25%
School	25%
Job	17%
Entertainment	17%
Meals	8%
Homework	8%

4.

Favorite Pet	Percent
Dogs	30%
Cats	25%
Fish	12%
Birds	11%
Other	22%

5.

Type of Milk	Percent
Skim	27%
Lowfat	37%
Whole	36%

6.

Activity	Percent
Visiting w/Friends	26%
Talk on Phone	26%
Play Sports	19%
Earn Money	19%
Use Computers	10%

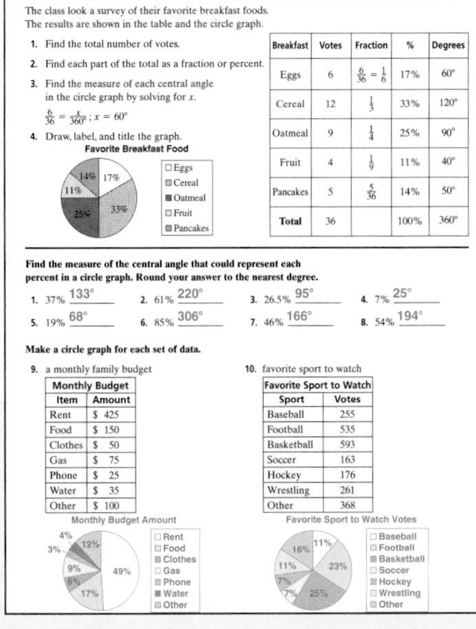

Reteaching 10-6 Circle Graphs

The class look a survey of their favorite breakfast foods. The results are shown in the table and the circle graph.

1. Find the total number of votes.
2. Find each part of the total as a fraction or percent.
3. Find the measure of each central angle in the circle graph by solving for x.
   $\frac{6}{36} = \frac{x}{360^\circ}$; $x = 60^\circ$
4. Draw, label, and title the graph.

Breakfast	Votes	Fraction	%	Degrees
Eggs	6	$\frac{6}{36} = \frac{1}{6}$	17%	60°
Cereal	12	$\frac{1}{3}$	33%	120°
Oatmeal	9	$\frac{1}{4}$	25%	90°
Fruit	4	$\frac{1}{9}$	11%	40°
Pancakes	5	$\frac{5}{36}$	14%	50°
Total	36		100%	360°

Find the measure of the central angle that could represent each percent in a circle graph. Round your answer to the nearest degree.

1. 37% 133°
2. 61% 220°
3. 26.5% 95°
4. 7% 25°
5. 19% 68°
6. 85% 306°
7. 46% 166°
8. 54% 194°

Make a circle graph for each set of data.

9. a monthly family budget

Monthly Budget	
Item	**Amount**
Rent	$ 425
Food	$ 150
Clothes	$ 50
Gas	$ 75
Phone	$ 25
Water	$ 35
Other	$ 100

10. favorite sport to watch

Favorite Sport to Watch	
Sport	**Votes**
Baseball	255
Football	535
Basketball	593
Soccer	163
Hockey	176
Wrestling	261
Other	368

Inclusion

Exercises 11–14 Ask: *How will each percent change when it is converted into a sector angle?* The numerical value gets larger.

B **Apply Your Skills**

Find the measure of the central angle that could represent each percent in a circle graph. Round your answer to the nearest degree.

11. 9% 32° **12.** 42.1% 152° **13.** 23.5% 85° **14.** 36% 130°

GPS **15. Food** Ella surveyed 81 students in the cafeteria about their favorite school lunch. Display the results from her survey in a circle graph.

pizza: 35 spaghetti: 20 hamburger: 18 grilled cheese: 8

See margin.

16. Publishing A women's magazine conducted a survey about the kinds of images women prefer to see on magazine covers. Out of 400 women surveyed, 17.7% preferred images of models, 37.4% preferred images of athletes, and 44.9% preferred images of celebrities.

a. Display the results in a circle graph. See margin.

b. About how many women surveyed preferred images of athletes? b. 150 women

c. How many women did not prefer images of celebrities? 220 women

Real-World Connection

Careers Magazine publishers use market research and surveys when designing magazines.

17. Blood Type The population of the United States is about 288 million.

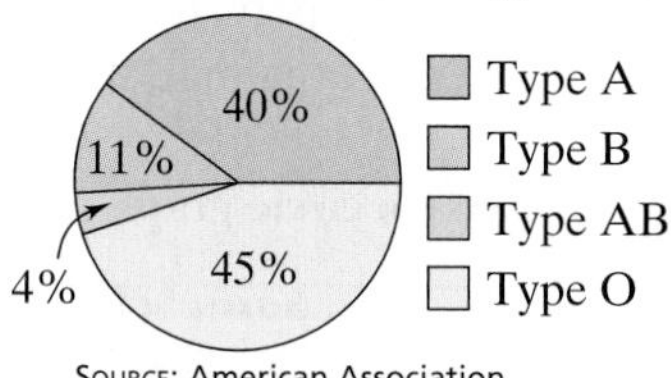

Source: American Association of Blood Banks

a. How many people in the United States have blood type B?

b. Which blood type do the least number of people in the United States have? How many people have it?

c. Which blood type do the most number of people in the United States have? How many people have it?

17a. 31,680,000 people
b. Type AB; 11,520,000 people
c. Type O; 129,600,000 people

18. Writing in Math Explain why it is easier to make a circle graph for a budget if it is in percents rather than dollars. See margin.

19. Budgets The spreadsheet below shows the budget for a museum field trip. Copy and complete the spreadsheet. Display the data in a percent circle graph. Round to the nearest percent and degree. See margin.

	A	B	C	D
1	Expense	Budgeted Amount	Percent of Total	Angle Measure
2	Bus	$350	■	■
3	Admission	$250	■	■
4	Lunch	$175	■	■

Reading Math

A sample is the people studied in a survey.

20. Open-Ended Write a survey question with four choices and use it to conduct a survey. Create a circle graph based on the results. Check students' work.

16a.

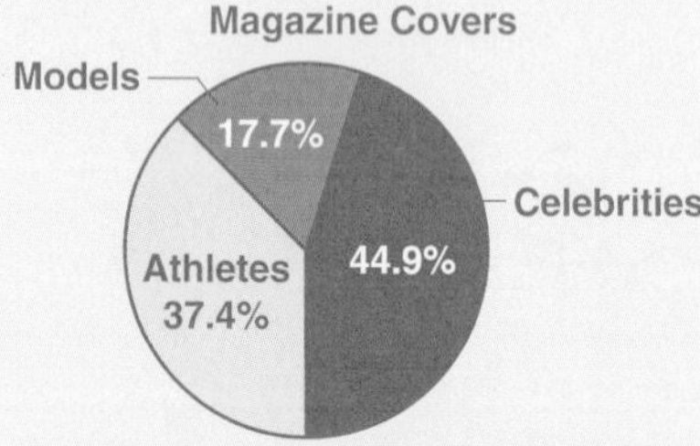

18. If it is already in percent form, you simply need to multiply the percent by 360 to get the number of degrees in the sector. You don't have to find what percent the part is of the total.

15.

Favorite Lunch

Pizza 35, Spaghetti 20, Hamburger 18, Grilled cheese 8

19.

	A	B	C	D
1	Expense	Budgeted Amount	Percent of Total	Angle Measure
2	Bus	$350	45%	163°
3	Admission	$250	32%	116°
4	Lunch	$175	23%	81°

Museum Field Trip

Bus 45%, Admission 32%, Lunch 23%

C Challenge

21. Marketing What color is your cell phone? Students at a local school responded to this question. The results of the survey are shown in the bar graph below.

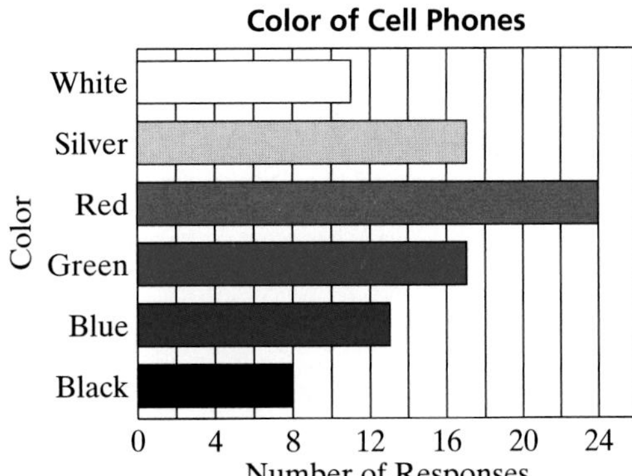

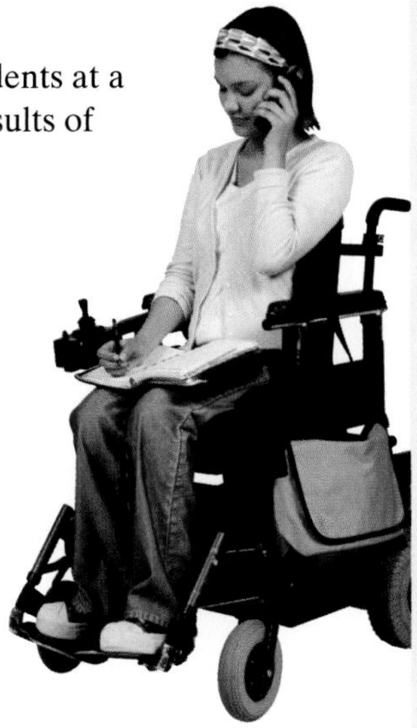

a. Display the data in a circle graph.

b. **Reasoning** Which graph do you think is a more appropriate display of the data? Explain. Check students' work.

21a.

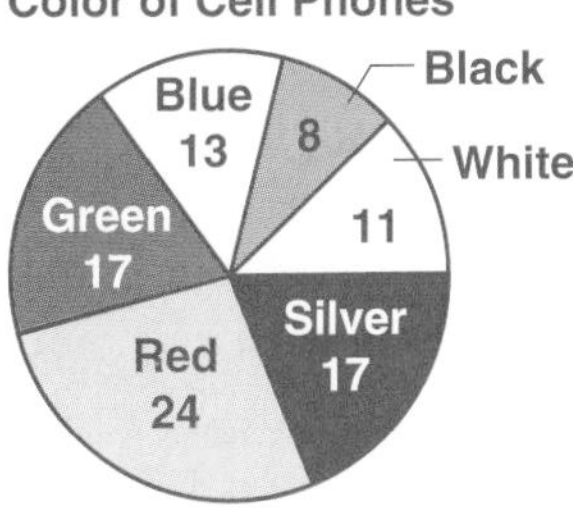

21b. The circle graph; it shows the proportions more clearly.

22. Stretch Your Thinking A total of 120 five-digit numbers can be formed using each of the digits 1, 2, 3, 4, and 5. The beginning of the list of these numbers arranged from least to greatest is shown below. If you continue this list up to 54,321, what number is the seventy-fifth number listed? 41,325

12,345 12,354 12,435 12,453

Test Prep

Multiple Choice

Your older sister's weekly budget is shown at the right. Use it for Exercises 23–26.

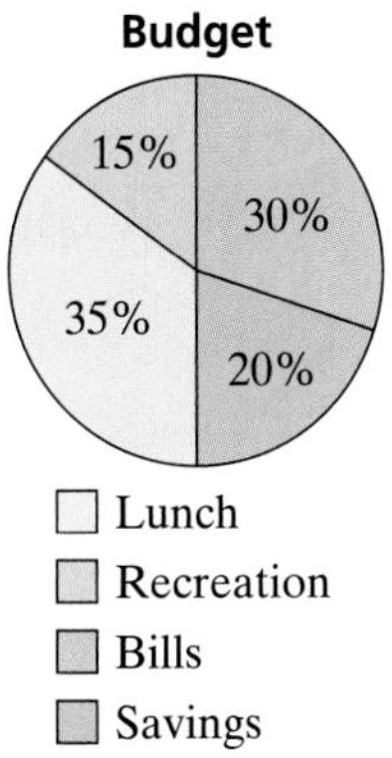

Budget

15%, 30%, 35%, 20%

☐ Lunch
☐ Recreation
☐ Bills
☐ Savings

23. For what item does your sister budget twice as much as for recreation? C

A. lunch B. recreation
C. bills D. savings

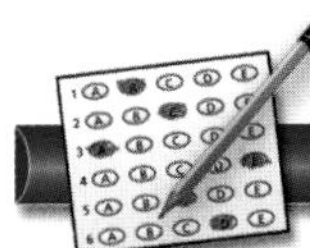

Take It to the NET
Online lesson quiz at **www.PHSchool.com**
Web Code: aca-1006

24. What is the measure of the central angle that could represent 35% in the circle graph? H

F. 220° G. 185°
H. 126° I. 87°

Short Response

25. If your sister is saving \$500 a month, how much does she spend on bills? Show your work. See margin.

26. Your sister has decided to change her budget. She will now budget 10% for recreation and 25% for savings. Redraw the circle graph. See margin.

25. [2] Let x = earnings.
$0.20x = 500$
$x = 2{,}500$
$0.30(2{,}500) = 750$
She spends \$750 on bills.
[1] correct procedure with one computational error OR correct answer, without work shown

Use the Guided Problem Solving worksheet with Exercise 15.

26. [2]

	Percent	Angle Measure
Lunch	35	126
Recreation	10	36
Bills	30	108
Savings	25	90
		✓ 360

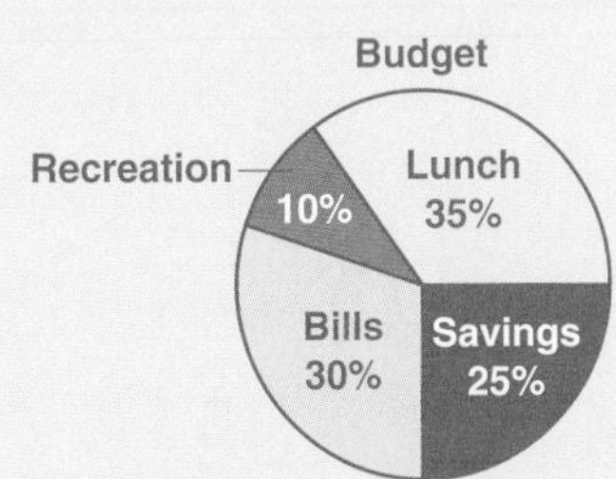

[1] minor computational error OR minor error in graph

PowerPoint **Lesson Quiz 10-6**

The circle graph shows the survey results of 400 students.

Times Students Exercise Weekly

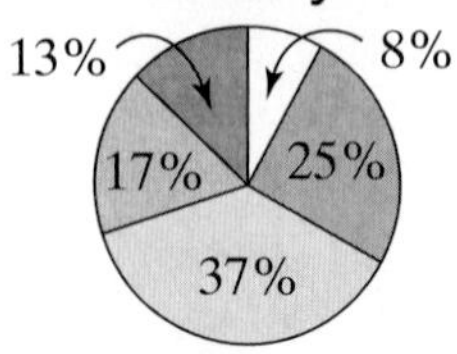

0　1–2　3–5　6–8　9 or more

1. What percent exercise 3–5 times each week? 37%
2. How many exercise 6–8 times each week? 68 students

To check understanding of Lessons 10-4 to 10-6:

Checkpoint Quiz 2 (p. 568)

Checkpoint Quiz 2 (also in *Prentice Hall Assessment System*)

Reaching All Students
Reading and Math Literacy 10C

Spanish versions available

Enrichment 10-6 Circle Graphs

Critical Thinking

You play miniature golf with a group of friends. Your scorecard is shown below. Analyze the score data, and make a circle graph to show your results.

Hole Number	1	2	3	4	5	6	7	8	9	10	11	12	13	14	15	16	17	18
Score	2	2	1	4	4	3	2	3	1	2	2	2	3	3	1	3	3	4

1. What information will the complete circle graph show? the percentage of times you made each score
2. How many holes had each score?
   a. 0 0　b. 1 3　c. 2 6
   d. 3 6　e. 4 3　f. 5 0
3. Find what percent each score was of the 18 holes. Round your answer to the nearest tenth of a percent.
   a. 0 0%　b. 1 16.7%　c. 2 33.3%
   d. 3 33.3%　e. 4 16.7%　f. 5 0%
4. Find the central angle you will need to draw for each score. Round your answer to the nearest whole degree.
   a. 0 0°　b. 1 60°　c. 2 120°
   d. 3 120°　e. 4 60°　f. 5 0°
5. Make a circle graph of the scores on your scorecard.

Scorecard
Score of 1: 60°
Score of 4: 60°
Score of 3: 120°
Score of 2: 120°

6. What scores make up the same amount on the graph Scores of 2 and 3 each make up 33.3%, and scores of 1 and 4 each make up 16.7%.
7. Use the graph to estimate your average score. Explain your reasoning. Sample answer: 2.5, because half of the scores are ≤ 2 and the other half are ≥ 3.

Mixed Review

Lesson 10-5

Algebra **Make a scatter plot for the set of data. Describe the type of trend shown by the data. If possible, draw a trend line.** See back of book.

27. height (in.): 56 52 55 47 58 60 50 39 58 45 54 61 45 36
weight (lb): 78 63 67 52 81 92 60 34 83 47 73 98 45 31

Lesson 8-6

Find the sum of the measures of the interior angles of each polygon.

28. decagon 1,440°　**29.** dodecagon 1,800°

30. octagon 1,080°　**31.** hexagon 720°

Find the measure of each angle of a regular polygon with the given number of sides.

32. 5 sides 108°　**33.** 12 sides 150°

34. 18 sides 160°　**35.** 20 sides 162°

Lessons 10-4 through 10-6

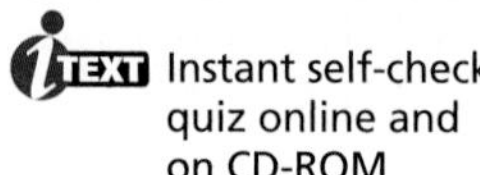

Instant self-check quiz online and on CD-ROM

Make a box-and-whisker plot for each set of data. 1–3. See back of book.

1. numbers of hours spent using the Internet:
   0.8 6 7 4 2 3 11 15 5 6 7 0.9 8 5 8 7 6 10 4 6 9
2. current ages of World War II veterans:
   80 83 88 88 72 73 70 85 86 89 92 92 76 77 70 71 84
3. hours spent practicing a musical instrument per week:
   1 2 8 5 9 12 4 7 5 8 11 13 8 9 2 7 6 12 11 10 4 8 9 10 7

How Students Get to School

Method	Percent
Walk	19
Bicycle	27
Bus	38
Car	10
Other	6

4. **Survey** A school board surveyed 200 middle school students about the ways they travel to school. The results are at the left.
   a. Make a circle graph for the data. See back of book.
   b. How many students use the bus? 76 students
   c. How many students walk? 38 students
   d. How many students either walk or ride a bike to school? 92 students

Make a scatter plot for the data. Describe the type of trend: *positive, negative,* or *no trend.* Draw a trend line.

5. positive trend

Electoral Votes (0, 20, 40, 60)
Population (millions) (10, 20, 30, 40)

5. **Electoral Vote Data**

State	Calif.	Fla.	Ariz.	Tex.	Del.	Ala.	Pa.
Population (millions)	33.9	16.0	5.1	20.9	0.8	4.4	12.3
Electoral Votes	55	27	10	34	3	9	21

SOURCE: *The World Almanac*

Alternative Assessment

Poll the class for favorite types of pets. Then have students make a circle graph of the data.

Test Prep

Resources
For additional practice with a variety of test item formats:
- Test Prep, p. 585
- Test-Taking Strategies, p. 581
- Test-Taking Strategies with Transparencies

10-7 Choosing an Appropriate Graph

What You'll Learn

OBJECTIVE 1 To choose an appropriate graph

. . . And Why

To determine the most appropriate graph for a set of data, as in Example 2

Check Skills You'll Need

For help, go to Lesson 10-1.

Make a frequency table and histogram for each data set. Use intervals of equal size to group the data. 1–2. See back of book.

1. miles walked at a walk-a-thon: 1 6 9 10 12 15 16 18 19 20 10 8 5 2 6 9 5 13 14 18 10 9 11 14 15
2. hours spent exercising: 2 0 8 3 4 1 2.5 0 3 1.5 4 8 7 2 0 3.5 6.5

OBJECTIVE

iTEXT Interactive lesson includes instant self-check, tutorials, and activities.

1 Choosing an Appropriate Graph

Investigation: Summarizing Types of Graphs

1–3. Check students' work.

1. Make a three-column table. In the first column, list the types of graphs you have studied in this chapter.
2. In the second column, sketch an example of each type of graph.
3. In the third column, list the different purposes for which you can use each graph. These may include showing frequency, comparing sets of data, showing changes over time, and showing parts of a whole.

When using a graph to analyze data, you must choose an appropriate type of graph. The type of graph you choose depends on the type of data.

1 EXAMPLE Choosing an Appropriate Graph

You are asked to graph data on the percent of city dwellers in the United States every decade since 1900. Decide whether a line graph or a circle graph would be the most appropriate display of that data. Explain your choice.

A circle graph shows percents, but it does not show change over time. A line graph would be more appropriate.

Check Understanding 1 Choose the appropriate graph to display each set of data. Explain your choice.

a. bar graph or scatter plot? life spans of selected animals See above left.

b. histogram or scatter plot? average household income and number of cars See left.

1a. Bar graph; scatter plots need to be numerical; bar graphs represent categorical data.

b. Scatter plot; you are looking to see if there is a trend or a relationship.

Ongoing Assessment and Intervention

Before the Lesson
Diagnose prerequisite skills using:
- Check Skills You'll Need

During the Lesson
Monitor progress using:
- Check Understanding
- Additional Examples
- Test Prep

After the Lesson
Assess knowledge using:
- Lesson Quiz
- Computer Test Generator CD

10-7

1. Plan

Lesson Preview

PowerPoint

Check Skills You'll Need

Making Frequency Tables and Histograms
Lesson 10-1: Examples 4–5. Extra Practice, p. 711.

Lesson Resources

Teaching Resources
Practice, Reteaching, Enrichment

Reaching All Students
Practice Workbook 10-7
Spanish Practice Workbook 10-7
Guided Problem Solving 10-7

Presentation Assistant Plus!
Transparencies
- Check Skills You'll Need 10-7
- Problem of the Day 10-7
- Additional Examples 10-7
- Student Edition Answers 10-7
- Lesson Quiz 10-7
- Classroom Aid 4

PH Presentation Pro CD-ROM 10-7

PRENTICE HALL ASSESSMENT SYSTEM

Computer Test Generator CD

Technology
Resource Pro® CD-ROM
Computer Test Generator CD
PH Presentation Pro CD-ROM

www.PHSchool.com
Student Site
- Updated Data
- Teacher Web Code: ack-5500
- Self-grading Lesson Quiz

PH SuccessNet Teacher Center
- Lesson Planner
- Resources

Plus iTEXT

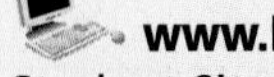

2. Teach

Math Background

Sometimes data can be shown effectively with more than one type of graph, but more often the data is suited to a particular kind of graph.

- Data showing change over time is usually shown with a *line graph*.
- Data that show parts of a whole that add to 100%, where exact values may not be needed, is usually shown with a *circle graph*.
- Data that is divided into intervals and describes frequency is usually shown by a *histogram*.
- Data in large amounts, where clustering and medians are important but exact numbers are not, can be shown with a *box-and-whisker plot*.
- Data where a number of values are fairly close together, and exact values are important, can be shown with a *stem-and-leaf plot*.

Teaching Notes

Investigation (Optional)
Have student work in groups to make their individual tables. If students have trouble completing the third column, have them examine the different types of data used in the text for each type of graph.

1 EXAMPLE Visual Learners
One way to test whether a particular type of graph is appropriate is to draw and label a rough sketch, without specific data values.

2 EXAMPLE Inclusion
Have students use the table they created in the Investigation to help them choose which type of graph to use.

Geography Connection
Ask students to share what they know about areas of the country where hurricanes are most likely to occur, such as along the East Coast or the Gulf of Mexico, including Texas, Louisiana, Mississippi, Alabama, and Florida.

Real-World Connection

Careers Meteorologists use graphs to analyze atmospheric data.

When presenting data, the idea you want to convey influences the type of graph you choose.

2 EXAMPLE Real-World Problem Solving

Weather The number of hurricanes that have struck the mainland of the United States in past decades is given in the table. Decide which type of graph would be most appropriate to illustrate the frequency of these hurricanes over time. Explain your choice and then draw the graph.

Decade	Hurricanes	Decade	Hurricanes
1900–1909	15	1950–1959	18
1910–1919	20	1960–1969	15
1920–1929	15	1970–1979	12
1930–1939	17	1980–1989	16
1940–1949	23	1990–1999	14

SOURCE: *The Weather Almanac*

The data are divided into intervals. They also describe the frequency of hurricanes. For these reasons, a histogram would be the most appropriate graph.

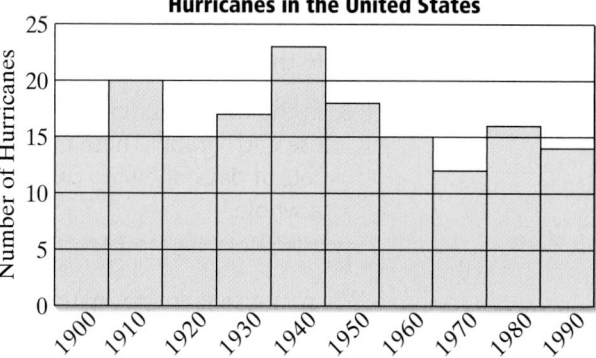

Hurricanes in the United States

Number of Hurricanes: 0, 5, 10, 15, 20, 25

1900, 1910, 1920, 1930, 1940, 1950, 1960, 1970, 1980, 1990

Check Understanding 2 **a.** Decide which type of graph would be the most appropriate for comparing the amounts budgeted for each category below. Explain your choice and then draw the graph. See back of book.

Weekly Budget

Budget Item	Lunch	Recreation	Clothes	Savings
Amount	$27.00	$13.50	$31.50	$18.00

b. Every year the amount budgeted for savings each week is increased by $2. Which type of graph would be most appropriate? Explain your choice. Line graph; you want to see a change over time.

Reaching All Students

Below Level Sketch a line graph, circle graph, histogram, box-and-whisker plot, and stem-and-leaf plot (without specific numbers or data) and ask students to name each type.

Advanced Learners Have students find graphed data in print or on the Internet. Have them graph the data in another form or explain why only the one form is appropriate.

Inclusion
See note on page 570.
Visual Learners
See note on page 570.

More Than One Way

United States Consumer Price Index

Year	Percent Change
1990	5.4
1991	4.2
1992	3.0
1993	3.0
1994	2.6
1995	2.8
1996	3.0
1997	2.3
1998	1.6
1999	2.2
2000	3.4
2001	2.8

SOURCE: Bureau of Labor Statistics. Go to **www.PHSchool.com** for a data update. Web Code: acg-2041

The table shows the annual percent change in the United States Consumer Price Index. The Consumer Price Index measures the average change in how much you pay for things. Find the median and mode.

Roberto's Method

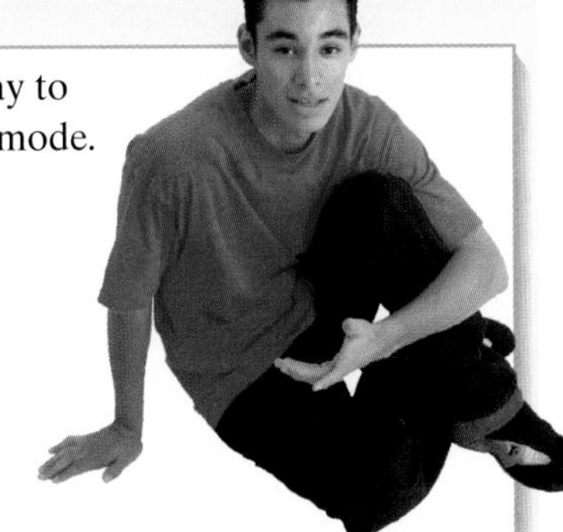

A stem-and-leaf plot is an appropriate way to organize the data to find the median and mode.

Stem	Leaves
1	6
2	2 3 6 8 8
3	0 0 0 4
4	2
5	4

Key: 3 | 0 means 3.0%

There are 12 leaves in the stem-and-leaf plot. Therefore, the average of the sixth and seventh leaf is the median.

$$\frac{2.8 + 3.0}{2} = 2.9$$

The median change in the United States Consumer Price Index is 2.9%. The mode is 3.0%.

Nicole's Method

To find the median and mode, I first need to put the data items in order.

1.6 2.2 2.3 2.6 2.8 2.8 3.0 3.0 3.0 3.4 4.2 5.4

To find the median, I average the sixth and seventh items, which is 2.9.

The median change in the United States Consumer Price Index is 2.9%. The mode is 3.0%.

Choose a Method

The table shows the average amount of time drivers in different cities spend in traffic annually. Find the median and mode of the data. Explain why you chose the method you used. **median: 41.5; mode: 34; check students' methods.**

City	Hours	City	Hours
Los Angeles	56	Denver	45
Phoenix	31	Houston	50
Seattle	53	New York	34
Las Vegas	21	Miami	42
Chicago	34	Detroit	41

SOURCE: *Time Almanac*

Teaching Tip

Remind students to look at how many data points there are and how closely the values are grouped as they decide which type of graph to use. There may be more than one type of graph that is appropriate for a given set of data.

PowerPoint

Additional Examples

1. Choose the appropriate graph—stem-and-leaf plot or circle graph—to display the data about a survey of students' favorite type of music. Explain your choice. **Sample: Limited number of categories and percents adding to 100% make the circle graph a good choice.**

2. This table shows membership in the Computer Club over several years. Decide which type of graph would be most appropriate. Explain your choice and draw the graph.

Year	Number of Members
1999	11
2000	15
2001	21
2002	22
2003	25

Sample: Since the data show a change over time, a line graph is appropriate.

Computer Club Members

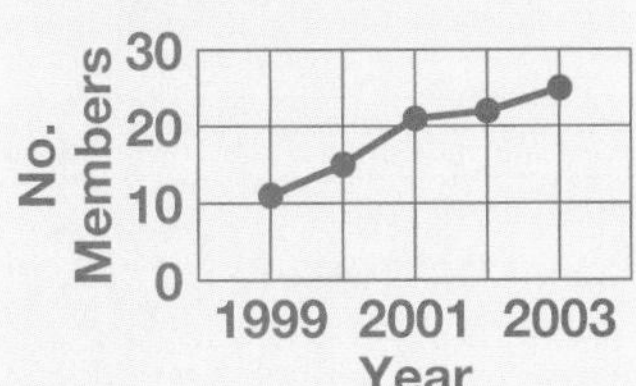

Closure

What factors go into your decision about what kind of graph is appropriate for a given set of data? **Sample: the amount of data and whether the data show a change over time or are parts of a whole or occur in intervals**

3. Practice

Assignment Guide

Objective 1

A B Core 1–15

C Extension 16–17

Test Prep 18–21

Mixed Review 22–30

Error Prevention!

Exercises 5–9 Students may not remember all the different possible types of graphs. Encourage them to use their tables from the Investigation.

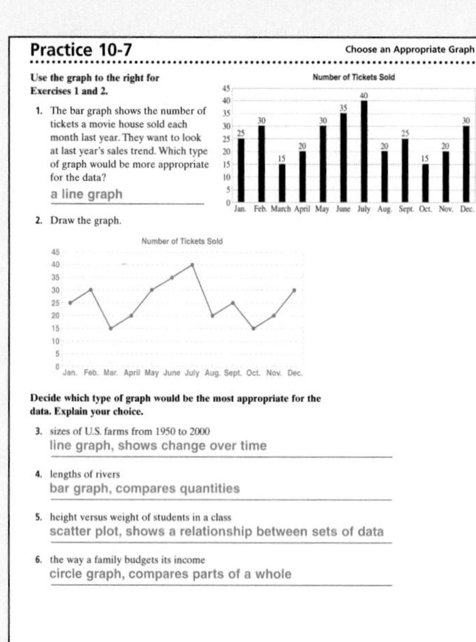

Practice 10-7 — Choose an Appropriate Graph

Use the graph to the right for Exercises 1 and 2.

1. The bar graph shows the number of tickets a movie house sold each month last year. They want to look at last year's sales trend. Which type of graph would be more appropriate for the data? a line graph

Number of Tickets Sold

Jan.	Feb.	March	April	May	June	July	Aug.	Sept.	Oct.	Nov.	Dec.
25	30	15	20	30	35	40	20	25	15	20	30

2. Draw the graph.

Number of Tickets Sold

Decide which type of graph would be the most appropriate for the data. Explain your choice.

3. sizes of U.S. farms from 1950 to 2000
   line graph, shows change over time
4. lengths of rivers
   bar graph, compares quantities
5. height versus weight of students in a class
   scatter plot, shows a relationship between sets of data
6. the way a family budgets its income
   circle graph, compares parts of a whole

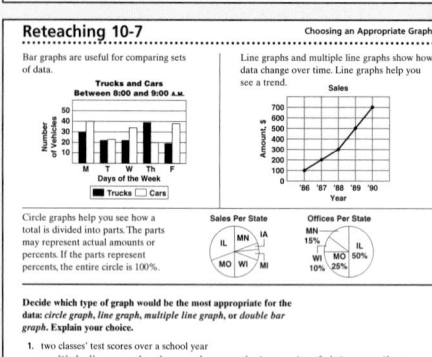

Reteaching 10-7 — Choosing an Appropriate Graph

Bar graphs are useful for comparing sets of data.

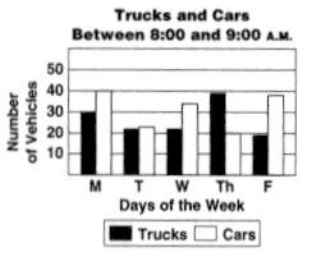

Trucks and Cars Between 8:00 and 9:00 A.M.

Line graphs and multiple line graphs show how data change over time. Line graphs help you see a trend.

Sales

Circle graphs help you see how a total is divided into parts. The parts may represent actual amounts or percents. If the parts represent percents, the entire circle is 100%.

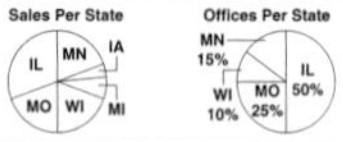

Sales Per State

Offices Per State

Decide which type of graph would be the most appropriate for the data: *circle graph*, *line graph*, *multiple line graph*, or *double bar graph*. Explain your choice.

1. two classes' test scores over a school year
   multiple line graph; shows changes in two sets of data over time
2. how a club spends its money
   circle graph; shows how the club's budget is divided into parts
3. the numbers of boys and the numbers of girls who use the playground each day for one week
   double bar graph; compares two sets of data
4. the percents of chemical elements in seawater
   circle graph; shows how 100% is divided into parts
5. a company's profit
   line graph; shows change over time

EXERCISES

For more practice, see *Extra Practice.*

A Practice by Example

Example 1 (page 569)

1. Scatter plot; if there are two sets of data, you can see if there is a relationship.
2. Line graph; this graph is better for showing data over time.
3. Double bar graph; this graph can show a comparison of the two groups.
4. Circle graph; a circle graph is a good way to compare parts of a whole.

Choose the appropriate graph to display each set of data. Explain your choice. 1–4. See left.

1. histogram or scatter plot?
   inches of rain and the temperature each day for a given city
2. line graph or scatter plot?

Percent of Total Music Sales Made Up by Country Music

Year	1994	1995	1996	1997	1998	1999	2000
Percent	16.3	16.7	14.7	14.4	14.7	10.8	10.7

SOURCE: Recording Industry Association of America

3. box-and-whisker plot or double bar graph?
   number of boys and number of girls who use a park each day
4. stem-and-leaf plot or circle graph?
   40 people's choices of five best cities to visit

Example 2 (page 570)

Decide which type of graph would be the most appropriate for the data. Explain your choice and then draw the graph. 5–9. See margin.

5. **Florida's Resident Population (thousands)**

Year	1996	1997	1998	1999	2000	2001
Population	14,427	16,683	14,908	15,111	16,054	16,397

SOURCE: U.S. Census Bureau. Go to **www.PHSchool.com** for a data update. Web Code: acg-2041

6. height (in.) of students in an 8th-grade class:
   63 60 58 56 52 53 57 57 56 55 56 57 56 67 56 58 57 61 64 55
7. ages of 20 corporate executives:
   31 62 51 44 61 47 49 50 40 52 60 51 67 47 63 54 59 43 63 52
8. **High School Graduation Rates**

State	Percent Graduating
Connecticut	91.7
Maine	94.5
Massachusetts	90.9
New Hampshire	85.1
Rhode Island	87.9
Vermont	90.8

SOURCE: National Center for Educational Statistics

9. **Cost of Owning a Car**

Category	Percent
Purchase price	52
Interest	12
Insurance	13
Gas, oil, and maintenance	20
License and registration	3

Real-World Connection

Florida attracts many retired people, partly due to its climate.

Use the Guided Problem Solving worksheet with Exercise 13.

5, 8. See back of book.

6. Answers may vary. Sample: Box-and-whisker plot; it gives a good summary of data, including high and low, median, and lower and upper quartiles.

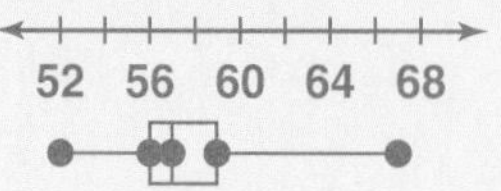

7. Answers may vary. Sample: Stem-and-leaf plot; it shows a data set arranged in order.

3	1
4	0 3 4 7 7 9
5	0 1 1 2 2 4 9
6	0 1 2 3 3 7

Key: 6 | 0 means 60

Apply Your Skills

For each graph listed, describe a set of data that would be appropriate.
10–12. See margin.

10. scatter plot **11.** circle graph **12.** line plot

Percent of Homes in the United States With Personal Computers

Year	Percent
1990	22
1992	27
1994	33
1996	40
1998	40
2000	51

SOURCE: Electronic Industries Association

GPS **13.** Use the table at the left and the circle graph at the right.

a. **Error Analysis** Explain why using a circle graph for this set of data is not appropriate. See margin.

b. Choose an appropriate graph for the data and then draw the graph. Explain your choice. See margin.

Percent of Homes in the United States With Personal Computers

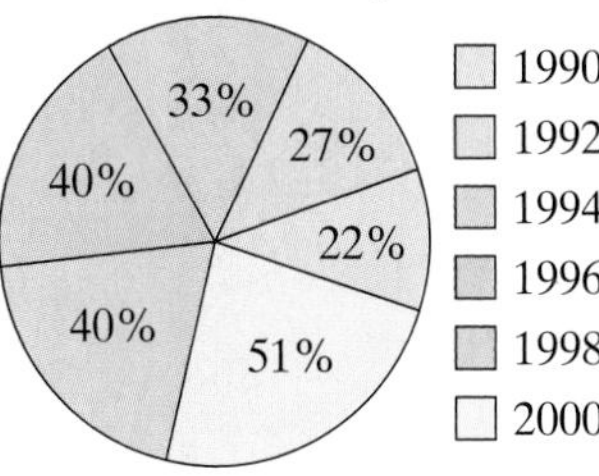

14. Wages The table below shows, by age group, the number of hourly workers in the United States who earn less than or more than $10 per hour.

Number of Workers Paid Hourly Rates in the United States (millions)

Age	Less Than $10	$10 or More
16 to 24	12.5	4.0
25 to 34	6.4	9.6
35 to 44	5.9	12.3
45 to 54	4.4	9.4
55 to 64	2.3	4.1
65 and older	1.2	0.6

SOURCE: *The World Almanac*

a. What percent of the workers ages 16 to 24 earn at least $10? Round to the nearest tenth percent. 24.2%

b. Decide which type of graph would be the most appropriate for the data. Explain your choice and then draw the graph. See left.

c. **Reasoning** Compare the number of workers in each age group who make less than or more than $10 per hour. How do earnings change as age increases? Explain why this trend might occur. See margin.

15. Writing in Math Describe data you can collect and display in both a bar graph and a circle graph. See left.

Challenge

16. Which type of graph might you choose when you have too large a set of data to graph each item? Explain. Answers may vary. Sample: You could choose a histogram with intervals.

17. Stretch Your Thinking A number that reads the same backwards as forwards is called a palindrome. The number 323 is a three-digit palindrome. There are 90 three-digit and 90 four-digit palindromes. How many five-digit palindromes are there? 900

14b. Sliding bar graph; it can show two categories in each bar.

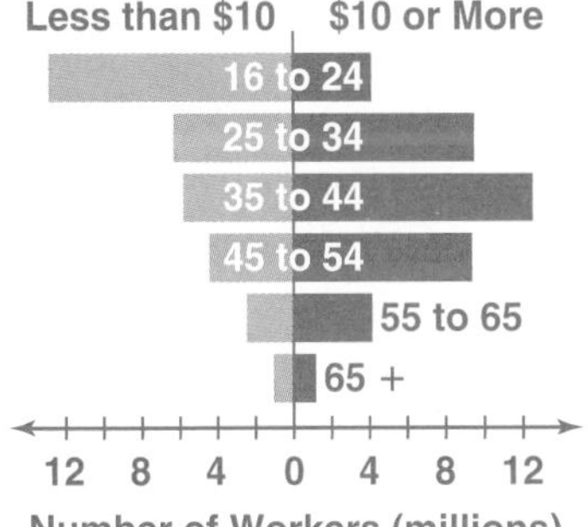

15. Any data that represent part of a whole can be represented with a circle graph or a bar graph.

10. Use a scatter plot when trying to determine whether or not two sets of data are related.

11. Use a circle graph when the data represent parts of a whole.

12. Use a line plot when the data contain frequent values.

13a. The data do not show parts of the whole.

b. A line graph shows change over time.

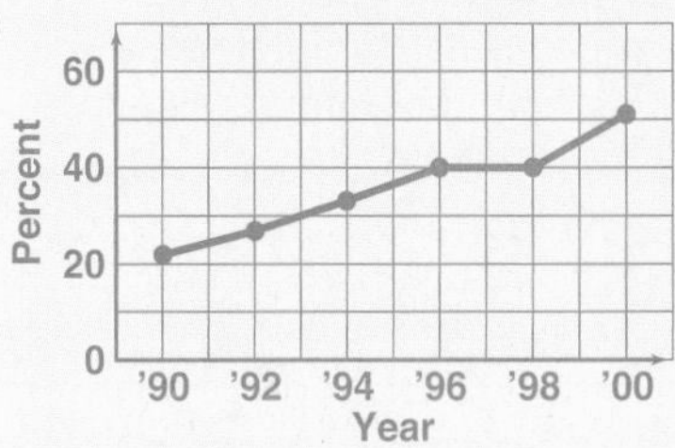

14c. Answers may vary. Sample: The number of people making less than $10/hour decreases as the people grow older. The number of people making $10 or more per hour increases until the age of 44 and then decreases. Earnings increase as age increases because people tend to make more money with job experience and education.

9. Circle graph; circle graphs show comparisons of the parts of the whole.

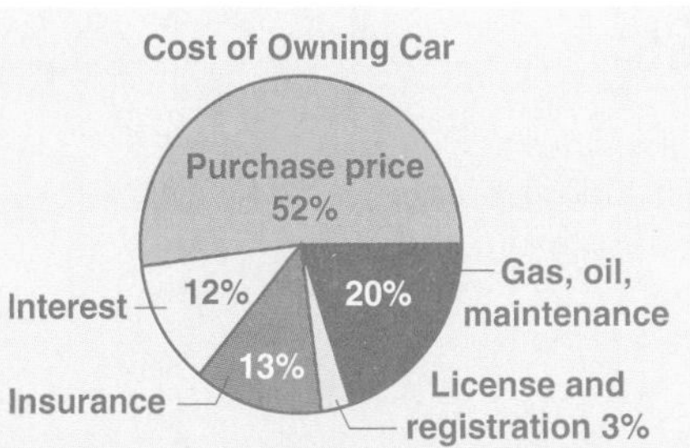

4. Assess

Lesson Quiz 10-7

Decide which type of graph would be appropriate for each set of data below and explain your choice.

1. daily high temperatures for May Sample: line graph shows changes during the month
2. heights and weights of students Sample: scatter plot shows the relationship between two variables
3. percents of boys and girls in a class Sample: circle graph that compares parts of a whole

Test Prep

Resources
For additional practice with a variety of test item formats:

- Test Prep, p. 585
- Test-Taking Strategies, p. 581
- Test-Taking Strategies with Transparencies

Exercises 18–21 Help students to see that the paragraph describes two sets of data, one for what actually exists, and the other for what people would prefer.

Enrichment 10-7

Choosing an Appropriate Graph

Visual Thinking

The 20 members of the Student Council sold t-shirts as a school fundraiser. Four teams of 5 students sold 1,000 t-shirts at $6.50 each.

Team	Number Sold
blue	250
red	375
gold	125
white	250

Construct a bar graph that shows the number of shirts sold by each team. Use unbroken axes. Check students' graphs.

1. Which team sold the greatest number of shirts? red
2. About how many times as great as the gold team was the number of shirts sold by the white team? 2 times
3. Change your graph so there is a break in one axis. Also change the scale. Make your new graph give the impression that the white team sold about three times as many shirts as the gold team. What scale did you use for the number sold? Sample answer: 62.5 to 412.5 by 50 Check students' graphs.
4. About how times as great as the gold team was the number of shirts sold by the red team? 3 times
5. About how many times as great as the gold team does the number of shirts sold by the red team seem based on your second graph? Sample answer: 5 times
6. What bar graph would members of the red team prefer? the second graph

Construct a line graph that compares the number of shirts sold and the amount of money raised. Show data for 100, 200, 300, . . . 1,000 shirts sold. Check students' graphs.

7. What scale did you use for "Money Raised"? Sample answer: 0 to 6,500 by 500s
8. What unbroken scale could you use for "shirts sold" to give the impression that the money raised would increase more rapidly with each shirt sold than your first graph? Sample answer: 0 to 1,000 by 200s
9. Which line graph would members of the gold team prefer? the first graph

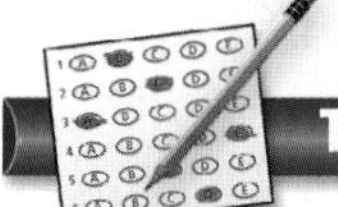

Test Prep

Reading Comprehension Read the passage and answer the questions below.

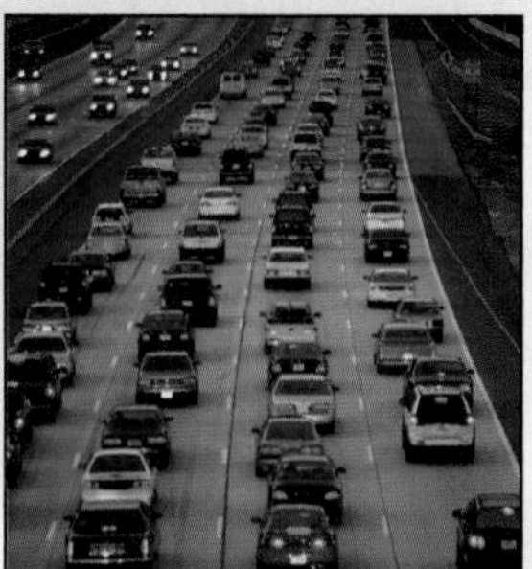

How Do Americans Get to Work?

A survey of Americans shows that 78% get to work by driving alone, 9% use a car pool, 5% use mass transportation, 5% use other methods such as walking or biking, and 3% work at home. But if they could choose the method they prefer, only 56% of Americans say they would drive to work alone. What would the rest do? The survey shows that 17% would choose to be in a car pool, 12% would like to use mass transportation, and 15% would use other methods such as walking or biking.

18. If you were making a circle graph of the data on how Americans get to work, what would the central angle for the carpool sector be? C
    A. 9° **B.** 24° **C.** 32.4° **D.** 90°

Take It to the NET
Online lesson quiz at **www.PHSchool.com**
Web Code: aca-1007

19. If you were making a circle graph of the data about how Americans would choose to get to work, what would the central angle for the other methods sector be? G
    F. 43.2° **G.** 54° **H.** 61.2° **I.** 201.6°
20. What percent of people would rather not drive alone to work? B
    A. 78% **B.** 44% **C.** 13% **D.** 8%

Extended Response

21. Choose an appropriate graph to display the data from the survey on how Americans get to work. Make the graph. See back of book.

Mixed Review

Lesson 10-6

About 56 million people ages 5 to 19 are enrolled in school. The circle graph shows the breakdown of the ages of the students.

2002 School Enrollment

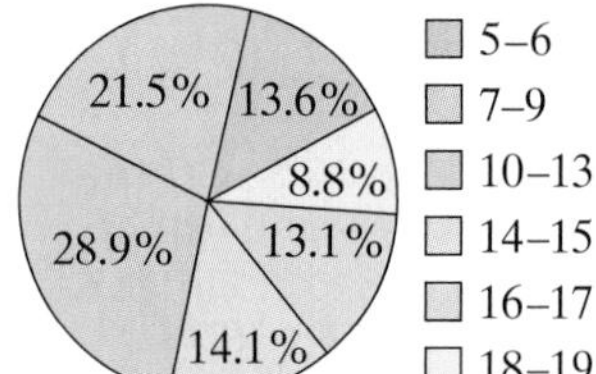

SOURCE: U.S. Census Bureau. Go to **www.PHSchool.com** for a data update.
Web Code: acg-2041

22. What percent of the students are ages 14 to 15? 14.1%
23. What percent of the students are 16 or over? 21.9%
24. How many students are 16 or older? 12,264,000 students
25. How many students are ages 10 to 13? 16,184,000 students

Lesson 8-1 **Find the measure of the supplement of each angle.**

26. 37° 143°
27. 95° 85°
28. 42° 138°
29. 170° 10°
30. 64° 116°

Alternative Assessment

Students make a table for their activities in a 24-hour school day. Have them include sleeping, attending school, eating, playing, studying, and other activities. Then have them represent the data on an appropriate graph and explain why they chose the particular graph.

Graphing Data Using Spreadsheets

For Use With Lesson 10-7

You can use a spreadsheet program to create many types of graphs. First, enter the category labels and the data in a spreadsheet.

EXAMPLE

The data at the right show the length and mass of different birds' eggs. Enter the data into the spreadsheet.

After entering the data, pick an appropriate type of graph. Choose from the graphs your spreadsheet program offers.

	A	B
1	Length (cm)	Mass (g)
2	2.5	3.6
3	3.1	9
4	3.6	14
5	3.9	20.7
6	4.0	19

A spreadsheet has no title.

Row 1 contains the type of data being compared.

Each row represents the size of one egg. Column A is the egg's length. Column B is the egg's mass.

Since you are comparing two related sets of data, a scatter plot is appropriate.

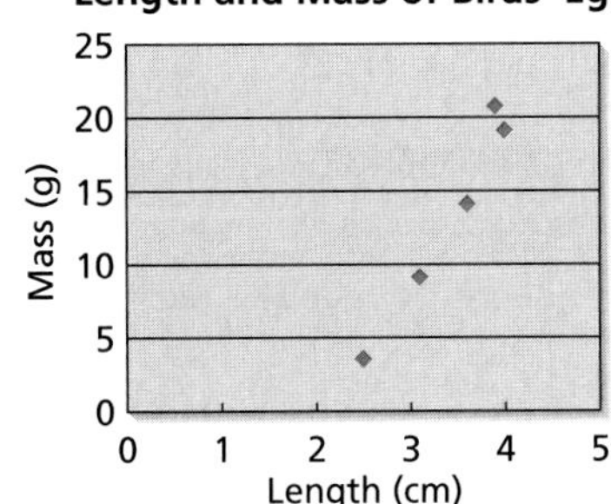

EXERCISES

Enter each data set in a spreadsheet. Choose an appropriate type of graph and use the program to make each graph. 1–2. Check students' work.

1. **Annual Spending per Child by Middle Income Families in 2001**

Age (yr)	0–2	3–5	6–8	9–11	12–14	15–17
Dollars Spent	9,030	9,260	9,260	9,190	9,940	10,140

SOURCE: U.S. Department of Agriculture. Go to **www.PHSchool.com** for a data update. Web Code: acg-2041

2. **Bedrooms in New One-Family Homes**

Bedrooms	Two or Less	Three	Four or More
Percent of Homes	12	54	34

SOURCE: U.S. Census Bureau. Go to **www.PHSchool.com** for a data update. Web Code: acg-2041

Technology

Graphing Data Using Spreadsheets

Students learn how to use spreadsheet software to create an appropriate graph for a given set of data.

Optional Materials

- any spreadsheet software
- Classroom Aid 4

Resources

www.PHSchool.com

- Updated Data

Teaching Notes

Review how formulas instruct the computer to repeat math operations using different numbers.

Error Prevention!

To help students locate information in the data, make sure they understand the distinction between columns and rows. Provide additional practice identifying cells. For example, direct students to the table of bird egg lengths and masses and ask questions like: *What would you name the cell that shows an egg with a length of 3.6 cm?* A4

Inclusion

Review, as needed, the uses and characteristics of the different graphs covered in the chapter.

Exercises

Have students work in pairs on the exercises. Then pairs combine with other pairs to form groups to share and discuss their answers. Have them justify their graph choices by asking questions like these:

- *Why would a histogram be an appropriate graph to use to display the data in Exercise 1?* Intervals of data are given in the table and histograms show the frequencies of intervals of data.
- *What must be true about the graph you choose for the data in Exercise 2?* It must be able to show how parts are related to a whole or total.

10-8

1. Plan

Lesson Preview

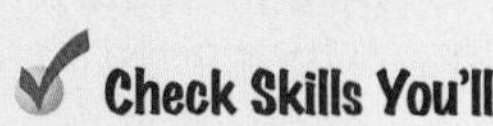

Check Skills You'll Need

Finding the Area of a Parallelogram
Lesson 8-7: Example 1. Extra Practice, p. 709.

Lesson Resources

Teaching Resources
Practice, Reteaching, Enrichment

Reaching All Students
Practice Workbook 10-8
Spanish Practice Workbook 10-8
Guided Problem Solving 10-8

Presentation Assistant Plus!
Transparencies
- Check Skills You'll Need 10-8
- Problem of the Day 10-8
- Additional Examples 10-8
- Student Edition Answers 10-8
- Lesson Quiz 10-8
- Classroom Aid 22

PH Presentation Pro CD-ROM 10-8

Computer Test Generator CD

Technology
Resource Pro® CD-ROM
Computer Test Generator CD
PH Presentation Pro CD-ROM

www.PHSchool.com
Student Site
- Teacher Web Code: ack-5500
- Algebra Readiness Puzzles 110
- Self-grading Lesson Quiz

PH SuccessNet Teacher Center
- Lesson Planner
- Resources

Plus 

Problem Solving

10-8 Draw a Diagram and Use Logical Reasoning

What You'll Learn

To solve a problem by combining strategies

. . . And Why

To combine strategies in problem solving, as in Example 1

Check Skills You'll Need

For help, go to Lesson 8-7.

Find the area of each parallelogram.

1. 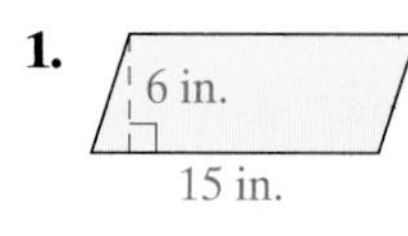

90 in.^{2}

2. 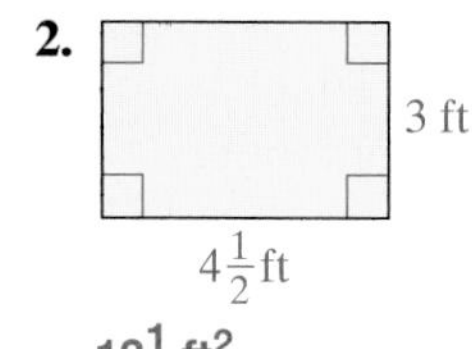

$13\frac{1}{2}$ ft^2

3. 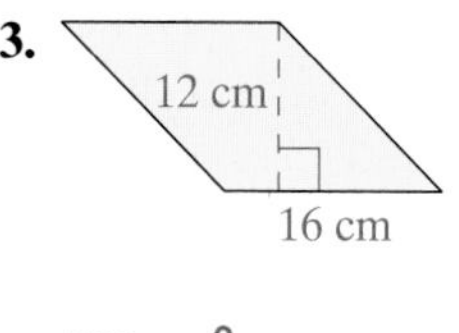

192 cm^2

Interactive lesson includes instant self-check, tutorials, and activities.

OBJECTIVE 1

Solving a Problem by Combining Strategies

When to Use These Strategies You can combine the strategies ***draw a diagram*** and ***use logical reasoning.*** In this lesson, you will draw a diagram to help you see relationships, and you will use logical reasoning to complete the diagram.

1 EXAMPLE Real-World Problem Solving

Real-World Connection
The United States consumes about 57,000 tons of wheat each day.

Food Production The chart shows countries that produced at least 10 million metric tons of rice, corn, or wheat in 2000. How many countries produced at least 10 million tons of all three grains? How many countries produced 10 million tons of only one grain?

Leading Producers of Rice, Corn, and Wheat

Rice	China, India, Bangladesh, Thailand, Burma, Brazil
Corn	United States, China, Brazil, Mexico, France, Russia, India, Italy
Wheat	China, India, United States, France, Russia, Canada, Germany, Australia, Pakistan, Turkey, United Kingdom

SOURCE: *The World Almanac*

Read and Understand You know that each country in the diagram produced at least 10 million tons of rice, corn, or wheat. Some countries produced that amount for more than one crop.

You are being asked to find out how many countries produced at least 10 million tons of all three grains and how many produced 10 million tons of only one grain.

Ongoing Assessment and Intervention

Before the Lesson
Diagnose prerequisite skills using:
- Check Skills You'll Need

During the Lesson
Monitor progress using:
- Check Understanding
- Additional Examples
- Test Prep

After the Lesson
Assess knowledge using:
- Lesson Quiz
- Computer Test Generator CD

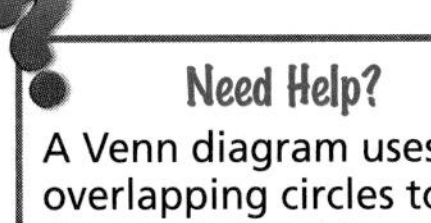

Need Help?
A Venn diagram uses overlapping circles to show relationships.

Plan and Solve You can use a Venn diagram to illustrate the relationship between sets of countries that produce rice, corn, and wheat.

To draw a Venn diagram, draw a large rectangle. Inside it, draw three loops that overlap. Label the loops *R* (for rice), *C* (for corn), and *W* (for wheat).

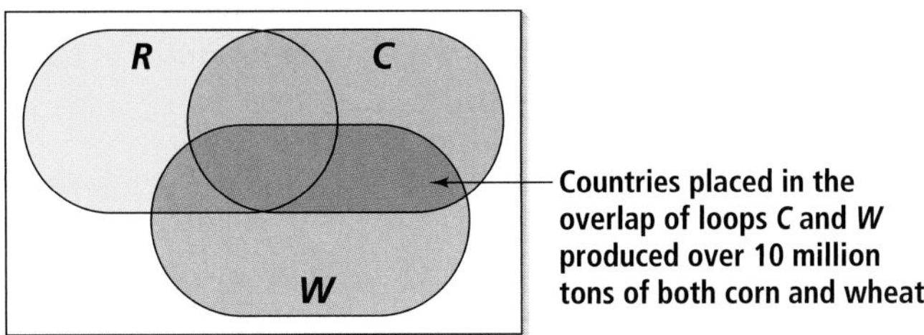
R
C
W
Countries placed in the overlap of loops C and W produced over 10 million tons of both corn and wheat.

Use information from the table and logical reasoning to place each country in the diagram.

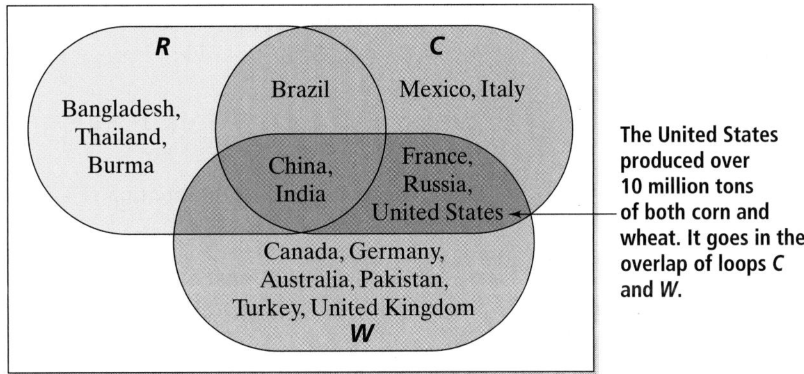
R
C
Bangladesh, Thailand, Burma
Brazil
Mexico, Italy
China, India
France, Russia, United States
Canada, Germany, Australia, Pakistan, Turkey, United Kingdom
W
The United States produced over 10 million tons of both corn and wheat. It goes in the overlap of loops C and W.

Two countries, India and China, produced at least 10 million tons of all three grains.

The 11 countries that did not appear in any overlaps were the countries that produced at least 10 million tons of only one grain.

Look Back and Check Looking at the table, only India and China appear under each of the three grains. They are the only two countries that produced at least 10 million tons of all three grains. You can check that the Venn diagram accurately reflects the data in the rest of the table.

Check Understanding 1

a. **Reasoning** Why are there no countries in the intersection of loops *R* and *W* and outside loop *C*? See left.

b. You ask a group of 30 people whether they know how to play bridge or dominoes. Use the results below to find out how many people play both games. 10 people

- 15 people play bridge.
- 5 of those people play only bridge.
- 20 people play dominoes.
- 5 people play neither.

1a. No country produced at least 10 million tons of rice and wheat but no corn.

2. Teach

Math Background

The problem-solving strategy of drawing a diagram helps students visualize and understand the situation in the problem. This strategy is particularly effective for visual and tactile learners. Most of the time, diagrams can be fairly sketchy and still enable problem solving.

The strategy of using logical reasoning underlies most of mathematics. It is applied extensively in problem solving of all types.

Teaching Notes

Visual Learners
In Check Understanding 1, have students draw vertical stripes for the play-dominoes circle, and draw horizontal stripes for the play-bridge circle. Students observe the overlapping region contains both stripes.

Additional Examples

1 Every table at the Country Café has white paper and crayons on it. The chart shows colors of crayons at three tables. Use a Venn diagram to determine how many colors are available on all three tables. 2 colors How many colors are available on just one table? 9 colors

Crayon Colors at Each Table

Table 1	blue, brown, green, red, magenta, yellow, white
Table 2	black, brown, tan, maroon, orange, peach, yellow
Table 3	aqua, brown, gray, green, magenta, yellow, white

See back of book for diagram.

Closure

How does drawing a diagram and/or using logical reasoning help you solve a problem? Sample: A diagram can help you see relationships and logical reasoning can help you complete the diagram.

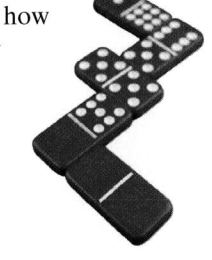

Reaching All Students

Below Level Review Venn diagrams with students.

Advanced Learners Have students write a problem that can be solved by making a Venn diagram with three overlapping regions. They can challenge classmates to solve their problems.

Visual Learners See note on page 577.
Error Prevention See note on page 578.

3. Practice

Assignment Guide

1 Objective 1

A B Core 1–8

C Extension 9–10

Test Prep 11–14

Mixed Review 15–18

Error Prevention!

Exercise 1 Ask a volunteer to explain how you can know that sports and band must overlap. The total number is 26 but 18 + 15 add to 33.

Practice 10-8 — Draw a Diagram and Use Logical Reasoning

Solve each problem using logical reasoning to organize the information in a diagram.

1. Place the factors of 32 and 24 in a Venn diagram. What are common factors of 32 and 24? What is the greatest common factor? 1, 2, 4, 8; 8

Factors
32: 1, 2, 4, 8, 16, 32
24: 1, 2, 3, 4, 6, 8, 12, 24

2. A favorite subject poll of 30 students shows that 18 like Math, 9 like History, and 10 like English. Three students like all three subjects, 3 like Math and History, 4 like Math and English, and 3 like only English. How many students did not like any class? 6 students
3. Twenty-six students were asked if they have a job or are in a club. Eighteen students have a job and 15 are in a club. Four students do neither. Place the information in a Venn Diagram. How many students have a job and are in a club? 11 students
4. A survey on favorite kinds of books shows that 9 people like mysteries, 10 like adventure stories, and 8 enjoy biographies. Three of the people read only mysteries and adventure stories, 4 read only adventure stories and biographies, 4 read only mysteries and 2 read all three kinds of books. How many people were surveyed? 16 people

Choose a strategy or a combination of strategies to solve each problem.

5. Maria plans to donate \$3 in January, \$4 in February, \$6 in March, and \$9 in April. If she continues this pattern, how much money will she donate in December? \$69
6. Elena is building a fence around her rabbit hutch. She plans to put 8 posts along each side. The diameter of each post is 6 inches. How many posts will there be? 28 posts
7. Alicia, Benito, Claudio, and Donna are musicians. One plays clarinet, one plays guitar, one is a pianist, and one is a singer. Alicia and Claudio saw the pianist perform. Benito and Claudio have heard the guitar player. The singer sang a song to Alicia and Donna. Benito plays the Clarinet. Who is the singer? Claudio
8. Laura is working on a jigsaw puzzle with 520 pieces. When she has placed four times as many pieces as she has already placed, she will have 184 pieces left. How many puzzle pieces has Laura placed? 84 pieces

Reteaching 10-8 — Draw a Diagram and Use Logical Reasoning

Example 1: Carlos has classes in English, algebra, chemistry, track, and history. Otis has classes in business, English, history, tennis, and computer science. Which classes do both students attend?

Read and Understand What do you know? *You know which classes each attends.*

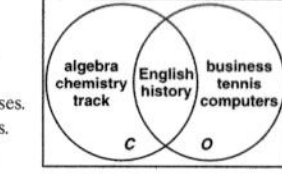

Plan and Solve You can use logical reasoning and a *Venn diagram.* Draw a rectangle. Draw circle *C* showing Carlos's classes. Draw circle *O* showing Otis's classes. The overlap shows the classes both boys attend.

Look Back and Check Which classes do both attend? *Carlos and Otis both attend English and history classes.*

Example 2: Carlos asks 25 math/science students whether they are taking math or science. Twenty-two students take science classes. Fifteen take math classes. How many students take both math and science if each student takes at least 1 class?

Read and Understand What do you know? *You know 25 students were surveyed; 22 take science and 15 take math.*

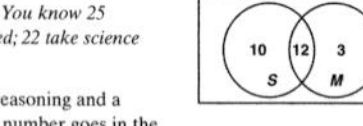

Plan and Solve You can use logical reasoning and a Venn diagram. What number goes in the overlap? *12*

Look Back and Check How can you check your answer? *There are 10 + 12 = 22 taking science, 12 + 3 = 15 taking math, and 10 + 12 + 3 = 25 students in all.*

Solve each problem using logical reasoning.

1. Phil's favorite sports are track, basketball, boxing, golf, and soccer. Jerry's favorite sports are boxing, baseball, football, bowling, and soccer. Which sports are favorites of both Phil and Jerry? boxing and soccer
2. Barbara asks 18 friends who love to read whether they read fiction or non fiction. Twelve of her friends read fiction. Eleven of her friends read nonfiction. How many read both fiction and nonfiction? 5 friends
3. Alice likes potatoes, sandwiches, fish, crackers, and steak. Rosie likes vegetables, rice, steak, chicken, and crackers. Which foods are liked by both Alice and Rosie? crackers and steak
4. Nine students like art only. Five students like music only. Twenty students were asked. How many liked both? Draw a Venn Diagram to solve. 6 students; check students' work.

EXERCISES

For more practice, see *Extra Practice*.

A Practice by Example

Example 1 (page 576)

Need Help?
- Reread the problem.
- Identify the key facts and details.
- Tell the problem in your own words.
- Try a different strategy.
- Check your work.

Solve each problem by drawing a diagram and using logical reasoning.

1. **Survey** A group of 26 students were asked if they play a sport or are in the band. Of the group, 18 students play a sport, 15 are in the band, and 11 do both activities. How many students do neither activity? 4 students
2. **Camp** At a summer camp, 20 campers try canoeing or climbing. Suppose 13 campers try canoeing and 15 try climbing. Of those 15 campers, 7 try only climbing. How many campers try only canoeing? 5 campers
3. **School** Of 15 students going to summer school, 10 take math, 8 take science, and 9 take English. Of those students taking English, 5 also take math, and 4 also take science. Two students take only math. No student takes all three classes. How many students take only science? 1 student
4. Place the information below in a Venn diagram. What are the common factors of 40 and 30? What is the greatest common factor? See back of book.

   factors of 40: 1, 2, 4, 5, 8, 10, 20, 40

   factors of 30: 1, 2, 3, 5, 6, 10, 15, 30

B Apply Your Skills

Strategies
- Draw a Diagram
- Look for a Pattern
- Make a Graph
- Make an Organized List
- Make a Table
- Simulate a Problem
- Solve a Simpler Problem
- Try, Check, and Revise
- Use Logical Reasoning
- Work Backward
- Write an Equation

Choose a strategy or a combination of strategies to solve each problem.

5. **Patterns** The bleacher seats of the school stadium are numbered as shown below. Suppose the pattern continues for all the rows in the stadium. In which row would you find seat 100? Row 14

Seat Numbers

Row 1	1				
Row 2	2	3			
Row 3	4	5	6		
Row 4	7	8	9	10	
Row 5	11	12	13	14	15

6. **Writing in Math** Jane, Gus, and Tim visited Canada, Peru, and France. Jane has never been to Europe. Tim plays ball with the person who visited Canada but Tim did not go to France. Match the people with the places they visited. Describe how you arrived at your answer. See margin.
7. Your cousin was born in the twentieth century and will be x years old in the year x^2. In what year was your cousin born? 1980

8. **Carpentry** A carpenter has exactly 36 m of fencing to make a rectangular pen for a pig. If both the length and the width must be a whole number of meters, what size rectangle will give the pig the most room? 9 m × 9 m

Use the Guided Problem Solving worksheet with Exercise 8.

6. Jane: Canada; Gus: France; Tim: Peru. Descriptions may vary. Sample: Jane has never been to Europe, so she either went to Canada or Peru. Tim plays ball with the person who went to Canada, and Tim did not go to France, so Tim went to Peru. Therefore Jane went to Canada and Gus went to France.

Challenge

9. 

9. You and two hungry friends split the tray of lasagna into thirds. Another friend wants a piece. Making only one more straight cut, how can you cut the lasagna so that you each get an equal amount?

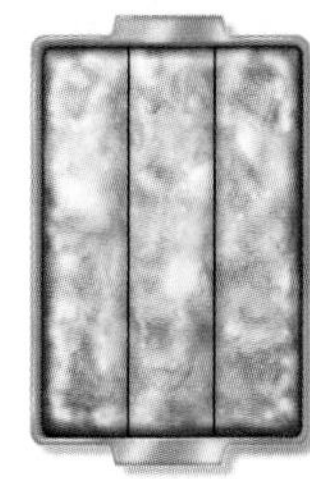

10. **Stretch Your Thinking** A dog weighs 15 pounds plus one fourth of its weight. How much does the dog weigh? 20 lb

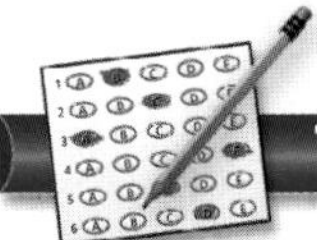

Test Prep

Multiple Choice

11. You receive $150 per month from a part-time job. This month you spent $45 on entertainment. By how much did you exceed your entertainment budget? B
    A. $20 B. $15
    C. $10 D. $5

Budget

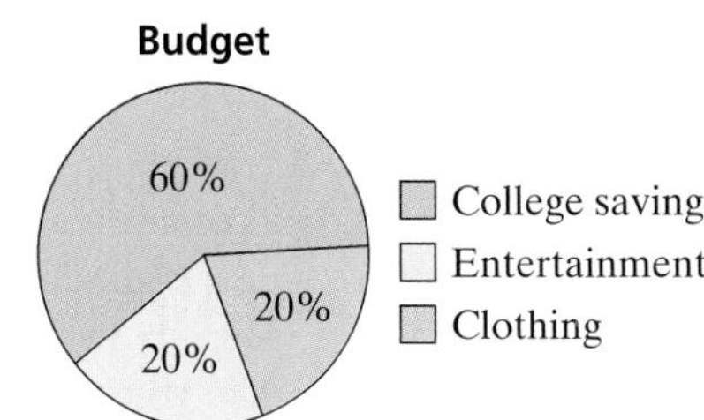

Take It to the NET
Online lesson quiz at
www.PHSchool.com
Web Code: aca-1008

12. After staying on your budget for a year, how much will you have saved for college? G
    F. $1,220 G. $1,080 H. $900 I. $720

13. A new jacket costs $60. How long will you have to save before you can buy it? B
    A. 1 month B. 2 months C. 3 months D. 4 months

Short Response

14. You received a 10% raise. If your budget does not change, how much will be put into savings monthly? Explain how you found your answer. See margin.

Mixed Review

Lesson 10-7

Choose the appropriate graph to display each set of data. Explain your choice.

15. scatter plot or stem-and-leaf plot?
    apple trees' age and the number of apples produced in a year

15. Scatter plot; it shows the relationship between 2 sets of numerical data.

16. histogram or circle graph?
    break down of an investment portfolio Circle graph; it shows parts of the whole.

Lesson 10-1

Make a frequency table and a histogram for each data set. Use intervals of equal size to group the data. 17–18. See back of book.

17. lengths of metal (cm): 23 26 25 26 23 25 25 24 21 21 22 23

18. weekly earnings (dollars): 260 270 260 300 290 300 250 270 320 260

14. [2] $99; find 110% of $150 to determine your new earnings. Then calculate 60% of your new earnings.
    [1] correct procedure with one minor computational error OR correct answer without explanation

4. Assess

Lesson Quiz 10-8

1. Of 30 students polled, 27 were taking math, 28 were taking science, and 1 was taking neither math nor science. Determine how many were taking both. 26 students

Alternative Assessment

Students write a problem similar to Example 1 and solve it by using draw a diagram and using logical reasoning. Then students challenge others to solve their problems.

Test Prep

Resources
For additional practice with a variety of test item formats:
- Test Prep, p. 585
- Test-Taking Strategies, p. 581
- Test-Taking Strategies with Transparencies

Enrichment 10-8 Draw a Diagram and Use Logical Reasoning

Critical Thinking

The Case of the Taken Tacos

Hi there, math detectives. I have an unusual case for you. This evening I was invited to join the Dill family for their Friday night of tacos and a movie. I was looking forward to an evening without incident, but before I knew it, there was a new mystery to solve.

Now there's one thing you must know about the Dill family, Bill, Phil, Gil, and Jill: They LOVE tacos, but they're very picky about their toppings. They can always agree on a movie, but figuring out taco toppings is nearly impossible!

After an hour of arguing, we finally agreed on two boxes of 6 tacos. One box had lettuce on every taco and onions on half. The second box had green peppers and onion on half of the tacos and tomatoes on the rest.

As soon as the tacos were delivered, we hurriedly crowded around the kitchen table. All this talk about tacos had made us hungry!

"I'd like two lettuce and onion tacos, please," said Bill, shoving his plate forward. "And keep away those nasty green peppers!"

"I want two tacos with just lettuce," said Phil, popping his head under Bill's arm. "I can't have anything else due to allergies."

"Onions and green pepper for me. Two of them," said Jill, her eyes wide with anticipation. "That's my idea of tacos!" As she opened the second box, she cried, "Eeewwww! I hate tomatoes!"

"No way—onions and lettuce are the worst!" said Gil, grabbing two tacos with tomatoes. "Hey, Detective, what do you like on your tacos?"

"Anything that doesn't have onions," I said, snatching up two of the remaining tacos.

When we went to the living room to watch the movie, there were two tacos left on the kitchen table.

At the first commercial, Bill asked, "Who's ready for seconds?"

"Me!" we all yelled.

After a minute, we heard Bill in the kitchen. "Hey! Who took the rest of the tacos?"

"Not I!" said Jill. "I'm not finished yet!"

"I didn't take them!" said Phil. "I'm waiting for my favorite scene."

"It wasn't me!" insisted Gil.

Solve the Mystery

Okay, sleuths—somebody snuck off during the movie and took those two tacos. Use logical reasoning to figure out who would have eaten the remaining tacos.
Who was the taco thief?

Jill

Writing in Math

Writing to Persuade

Students need to be able to write coherently and persuasively when formulating and sharing their mathematical thoughts and methods. This feature focuses on ways to use graphs as effective tools for getting across a point of view to a particular audience.

Teaching Notes

Teaching Tip

Discuss real-world examples of persuasive writing that includes graphical displays (reports, advertisements, leaflets, brochures, position papers, and so on). Invite students to share their prior knowledge of the features of persuasive writing by asking questions like these:

- *What are features and techniques common to all effective persuasive writing?* **Sample: to back up arguments with visual displays, to use meaningful examples, and so on**
- *Why is it important to know your audience when you choose your graph?* **Sample: to determine the kind of graph to use and its level of complexity, as well as the data to include**

Exercises

Have students work independently on the exercises. Direct them to include a written statement that summarizes their arguments for the graph they chose to make. In their statement, they should explain how knowing their audience and their purpose affected their choice of graph as well as the ideas they included. Then have them share their results with classmates.

Writing in Math

Writing to Persuade

For Use With Lesson 10-8

Suppose you want to display data in a way that will persuade someone to change their point of view. Here are some things you can do.

- **Identify your audience** Know where your audience stands on the topic.
- **Organize the data** You may want to group the data into categories that best support your goal.
- **Make a graph** Choose an appropriate graph to convey your message, one that best shows the data.

EXAMPLE

Grade	Current Enrollment
K	215
1	203
2	148
3	171
4	121
5	119
6	143
7	105
8	115
9	103
10	91
11	70
12	68

You are working on a committee that is trying to persuade people to approve a new high school. The current building has a capacity of 425 students. How would you use the projected enrollment data to make your case?

Identify your audience The audience will probably include people who think a new high school is unnecessary. Your goal is to persuade those people that the high school will quickly reach its capacity.

Organize the data To clarify your point, use the data to show the number of students likely to be in grades 9–12 over the next ten years.

Make a graph With a line graph, you can show your audience the projected change in enrollment over the next ten years. Indicate the current high school's capacity. This information will help your audience understand the need for a new building.

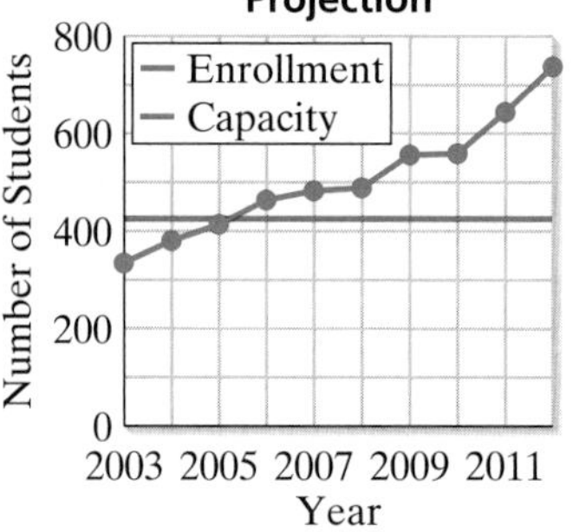

EXERCISES 1–2. Check students' work.

1. You are part of a group that opposes building a new school. Your group believes that an addition that increases the school capacity to 475 is sufficient. Make a graph using the data from the example to persuade the town that a new school is not needed.

2. In your town, the average class size is 22 students per class. The town pledged to maintain class sizes of 25 students or less. Make a graph using the data from the example to show how class size will increase and exceed the 25-student limit over the next ten years.

Finding Multiple Correct Answers

Some multiple-choice questions have more than one correct answer. Test each answer to see if it is true or false. Then choose the statement that includes only those answers that tested correctly.

EXAMPLE

In 2000, \$203.45 billion was contributed to charities. Use the circle graph at the right. Which of the following is true?

2000 Contributions by Source

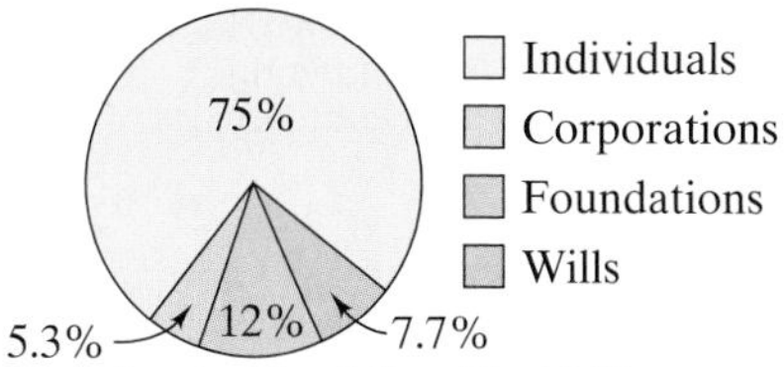

75%
12%
5.3%
7.7%
☐ Individuals
☐ Corporations
☐ Foundations
☐ Wills

SOURCE: American Association of Fund Raising

I. Corporations contributed \$10.78 billion.
II. Wills contributed twice as much as foundations.
III. Contributions from individuals totaled more than contributions made by the other three categories combined.

A. I only **B.** II and III only **C.** I and III only **D.** I, II, and III

Test each answer to see if it is true.

Corporations contributed 5.3%. Since 5.3% of \$203.45 billion is \$10.78 billion, statement I is true.

Wills contributed 7.7%, while foundations contributed 12%. So, statement II is false.

Individuals contributed 75%, while the other three categories combined contributed 25%. So, statement III is also true and the answer is C.

EXERCISES

1. Use the box-and-whisker plot. Which of the following could be true? B

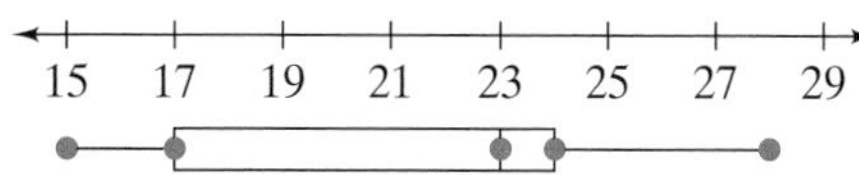

I. The data set contains 29.
II. The mode is 22.
III. The median is 23.

A. I **B.** II and III only **C.** I and III only **D.** I, II, and III

2. Use the stem-and-leaf plot. Which of the following is true? G

1	0 5 5 8
2	2 5 8
3	5 6

Key: 1 | 0 means 10

I. The mode is 5.
II. The median is 22.
III. The mean is $22.\overline{66}$.

F. I and II only **G.** II and III only **H.** I and III only **I.** I, II, and III

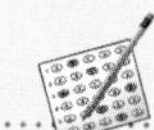

Finding Multiple Correct Answers

On some multiple-choice tests, students need to determine whether answers that have more than one part are fully correct. This feature, which focuses on test questions involving graphs, provides a strategy for distinguishing between multiple answers that are true and those that are false or only partially true.

Resources

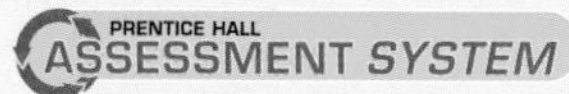

Test-Taking Strategies with Transparencies
- Transparency 13
- Practice master, p. 34

Teaching Notes

Emphasize to students that they must very carefully read all choices presented before making their decision.

Error Prevention!

You may need to review the measures of central tendency and the features and uses of box-and-whisker plots and stem-and-leaf plots.

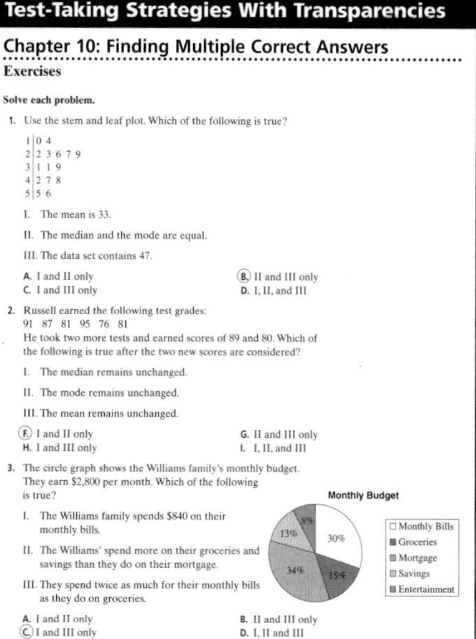
Test-Taking Strategies With Transparencies

Chapter 10: Finding Multiple Correct Answers

Exercises

Solve each problem.

1. Use the stem and leaf plot. Which of the following is true?

1	0 4
2	2 3 6 7 9
3	1 1 9
4	2 7 8
5	5 6

I. The mean is 33.
II. The median and the mode are equal.
III. The data set contains 47.

A. I and II only (B.) II and III only
C. I and III only D. I, II, and III

2. Russell earned the following test grades:
91 87 81 95 76 81
He took two more tests and earned scores of 89 and 80. Which of the following is true after the two new scores are considered?

I. The median remains unchanged.
II. The mode remains unchanged.
III. The mean remains unchanged.

(F.) I and II only G. II and III only
H. I and III only I. I, II, and III

3. The circle graph shows the Williams family's monthly budget. They earn \$2,800 per month. Which of the following is true?

I. The Williams family spends \$840 on their monthly bills.
II. The Williams' spend more on their groceries and savings than they do on their mortgage.
III. They spend twice as much for their monthly bills as they do on groceries.

A. I and II only B. II and III only
(C.) I and III only D. I, II and III

Resources

Student Edition
Extra Practice, Ch. 10, p. 711
English/Spanish Glossary, p. 735
Table of Symbols, p. 730

Reaching All Students
Reading and Math Literacy 10D
Spanish Reading and Math Literacy 10D

PRENTICE HALL ASSESSMENT SYSTEM

Test Preparation
- Chapter 10 practice in test formats

www.PHSchool.com
Student Site
- Self-grading vocabulary test

PH SuccessNet Teacher Center
- Resources

Plus 

Spanish Reading and Math Literacy

Reading and Math Literacy

10D: Vocabulary For use with the Chapter Review

Study Skill: When you have to match words and definitions from two columns, read the definitions carefully and match each with the corresponding words you know. Then do the rest, one at a time.

Match the term in Column A with its definition in Column B.

Column A		Column B
1. transformation	L	A. type of graph used to show changes over time
2. negative trend	H	B. transformation that moves points the same distance and in the same direction
3. reflection	G	C. a type of graph used to show trends
4. bar graph	C	D. two angles whose sum is 90 degrees
5. rhombus	J	E. the longest side of a right triangle
6. slope	Q	F. shows data items in order
7. trapezoid	N	G. a transformation that creates symmetry
8. complementary	D	H. as one set of values increases, the other set tends to decrease
9. positive trend	O	I. two angles whose sum is 180 degrees
10. perpendicular	M	J. a quadrilateral with four congruent sides
11. rotation	R	K. divides the data into four equal parts
12. hypotenuse	E	L. a change of position, shape, or size of a figure
13. regular polygon	P	M. lines that intersect to form right angles
14. stem-and-leaf plot	F	N. a quadrilateral with exactly one pair of parallel sides
15. translation	B	O. as one set of values increases, the other set tends to increase
16. quartiles	K	P. a figure with all sides congruent and all angles congruent
17. line graph	A	Q. a ratio that describes the steepness of a line
18. supplementary	I	R. a transformation that turns a figure about a fixed point
19. circle graph	T	S. the difference between the greatest and least values in a data set
20. range	S	T. a graph that shows parts of a whole

Chapter 10 Chapter Review

Vocabulary

box-and-whisker plot (p. 552)
central angle (p. 564)
circle graph (p. 563)
frequency (p. 533)
frequency table (p. 533)
histogram (p. 535)
line plot (p. 534)
negative trend (p. 558)
no trend (p. 558)
positive trend (p. 558)
quartiles (p. 552)
scatter plot (p. 557)
stem-and-leaf plot (p. 546)
trend line (p. 558)

Reading Math: Understanding Vocabulary

Choose the correct vocabulary term to complete each sentence.

1. _?_ divide a data set into four equal parts. quartiles
2. A _?_ displays two sets of data as ordered pairs. scatter plot
3. An angle whose vertex is the center of the circle is a _?_. central angle
4. A _?_ displays data on a number line with ✗ marks above data values. line plot
5. A display that shows numeric data in order is a _?_. stem-and-leaf plot

Take It to the NET
Online vocabulary quiz at **www.PHSchool.com**
Web Code: acj-1051

Skills and Concepts

10-1 and 10-2 Objectives
- To make frequency tables and line plots
- To display data using intervals
- To recognize and select an appropriate scale

A **frequency table** lists the frequency of each item in a set of data. A **histogram** is a special type of bar graph used to show the frequency of data.

6. Make a frequency table and a histogram for the data set. Use intervals of equal size to group the data. See margin.
53 57 78 64 68 72 77 58 60 78 80 81 55 70 52 63 65 79

7. Make two line graphs for the set of data. In one of the graphs, use a break. Explain which graph shows the data more clearly. See back of book.

School Chorus Members

Year	1998	1999	2000	2001	2002
Girls	35	32	35	34	32
Boys	41	40	43	37	39

10-3 and 10-4 Objectives
- To make stem-and-leaf and box-and-whisker plots
- To use stem-and-leaf and box-and-whisker plots

A **stem-and-leaf plot** shows numeric data arranged in order. A **box-and-whisker plot** shows the distribution of data along a number line.

8a and 9a. See margin.

The data listed shows different juice prices (in cents) at various stores.
89 79 85 79 85 67 75 99 79 63 90 72 78 65 78

8. **a.** Make a stem-and-leaf plot.
b. Find the mode and median. 79 cents; 79 cents

9. **a.** Make a box-and-whisker plot.
b. Find the quartiles. 72; 85

6. Answers may vary. Sample:

Number	Frequency
50–54	2
55–59	3
60–64	3
65–69	2
70–74	2
75–79	4
80–84	2

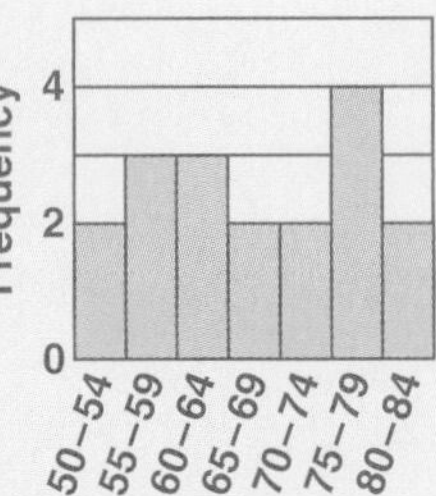

10-5 Objectives

- To make scatter plots
- To use scatter plots to find trends

A **scatter plot** is a graph that displays two sets of data as ordered pairs. It shows any relationship, or trend, that may or may not exist between the sets of data. To show a trend, draw a trend line. A **trend line** is a line you draw on a graph to approximate the data.

Length (mi) and Water Flow (1,000 ft^3/s) of Rivers

Length	Flow	Length	Flow
2,540	76	1,040	57
1,980	225	886	68
1,460	41	774	67
1,420	58	724	67
1,290	56	659	41

10. Rivers Make a scatter plot and draw a trend line for the data at the right. See back of book.

10-6 and 10-7 Objectives

- To read a circle graph
- To make a circle graph
- To choose an appropriate graph

A **circle graph** is a graph of data where the entire circle represents the whole. Each section in the circle represents part of the whole.

When using graphs to analyze data, you must choose an appropriate graph. The type of graph you choose depends on the type of data and the idea you want to convey.

Decide which type of graph would be the most appropriate for the data. Explain your choice and then draw the graph. 12–14. See margin.

11. **Weekend Sales at Media Store**

Items	DVDs	CDs	Books	Magazines
Number Sold	12	60	104	24

12. **Students Wearing Jackets**

Temperature (°F)	55	57	63	68	70	73	80
Number of Students	10	11	8	5	4	2	0

13. **Dow Jones Average**

Day	Closing Value
Monday	9,820
Tuesday	9,946
Wednesday	10,060
Thursday	10,092
Friday	10,007

14. hours a student worked each week at a summer job:
29 23 21 20 17 16 15 33 30

15. minutes it takes from the time students wake up until they leave for school:
47 28 78 47 58 93 34 35 45
53 23 43 75 27 23 87 35 33

11. Circle graph; it shows parts of the whole.

Weekend Sales at Media Store

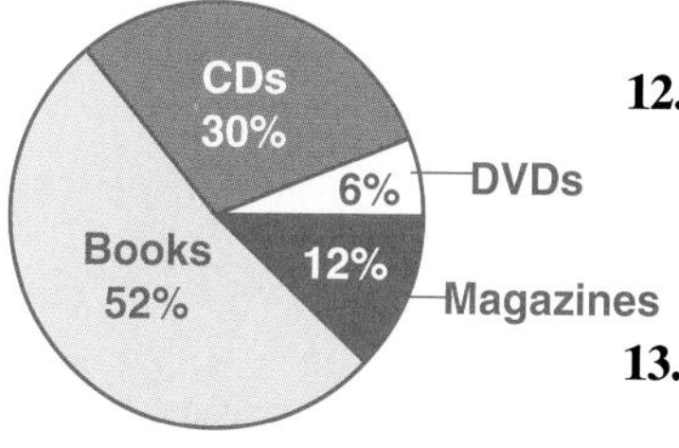

15. Answers may vary. Sample: Box-and-whisker plot; it shows the distribution of data.

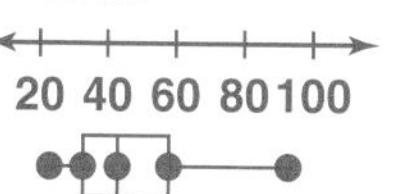

12. See back of book.

13. Line graph; it shows changes over time.

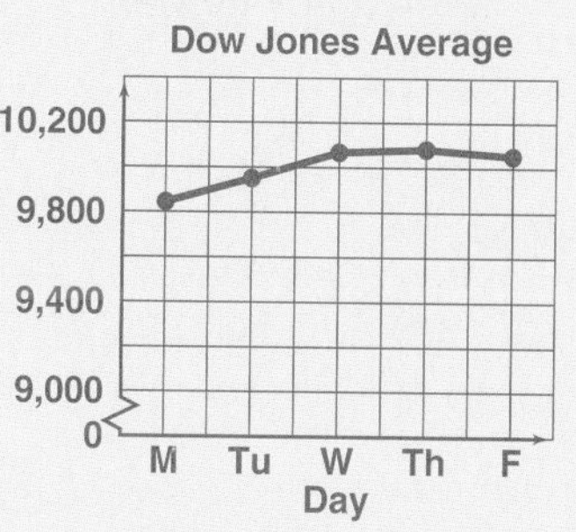

14. Answers may vary. Sample: Stem-and-leaf plot; it shows numerical data arranged in order.

1	5 6 7
2	0 1 3 9
3	0 3

Key: 3 | 0 means 30

10-8 Objective

- To solve a problem by combining strategies

16. Baseball Of the 25 people on the Houston Astros, 22 bat right-handed and 8 bat left-handed. How many members of the team are switch-hitters (can bat both left-handed and right-handed)? 5 members

8a.

6	3 5 7
7	2 5 8 8 9 9 9
8	5 5 9
9	0 9

Key: 9 | 0 means 90

9a.

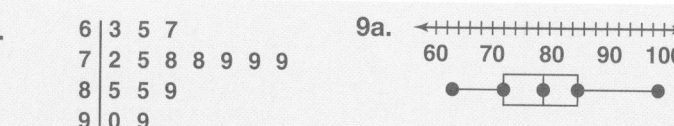

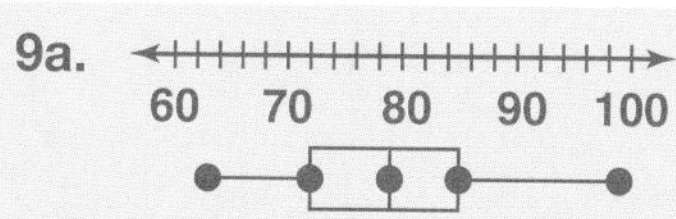

Alternative Assessment Form C

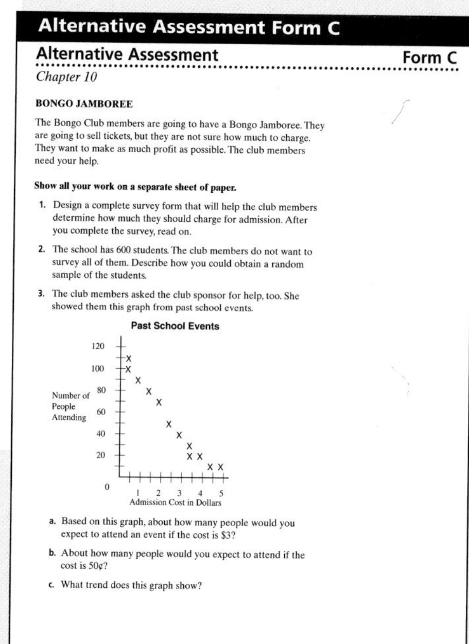

Alternative Assessment Form C

Chapter 10

BONGO JAMBOREE

The Bongo Club members are going to have a Bongo Jamboree. They are going to sell tickets, but they are not sure how much to charge. They want to make as much profit as possible. The club members need your help.

Show all your work on a separate sheet of paper.

1. Design a complete survey form that will help the club members determine how much they should charge for admission. After you complete the survey, read on.
2. The school has 600 students. The club members do not want to survey all of them. Describe how you could obtain a random sample of the students.
3. The club members asked the club sponsor for help, too. She showed them this graph from past school events.

Past School Events

Number of People Attending: 0, 20, 40, 60, 80, 100, 120
Admission Cost in Dollars: 1, 2, 3, 4, 5

a. Based on this graph, about how many people would you expect to attend an event if the cost is \$3?

b. About how many people would you expect to attend if the cost is 50¢?

c. What trend does this graph show?

Resources

Teaching Resources
Ch. 10 Test, Forms A & B
Ch. 10 Alternative Assessment, Form C

Reaching All Students
Spanish Ch. 10 Test, Forms A & B
Spanish Ch. 10 Alternative Assessment, Form C

PRENTICE HALL ASSESSMENT SYSTEM

Assessment Resources
- Ch. 10 Test, Forms A & B
- Ch. 10 Alternative Assessment, Form C

Computer Test Generator CD
- Ch. 10 Instant Chapter Test™
- Make your own Ch. 10 test

www.PHSchool.com
Student Site
- Self-grading Ch. 10 test

PH SuccessNet Teacher Center
- Resources

Plus 

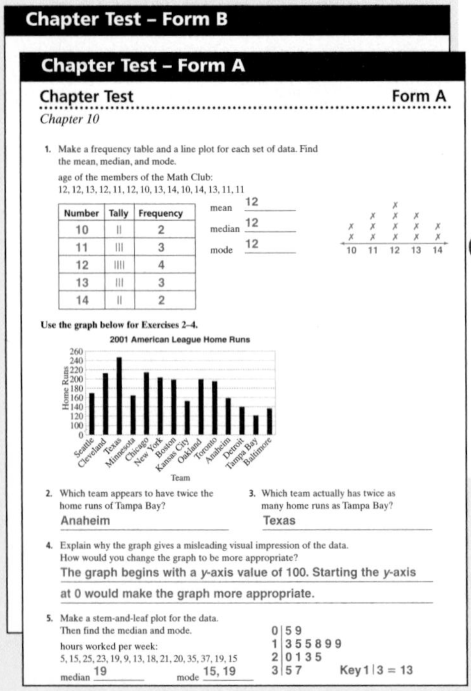

Chapter Test – Form B

Chapter Test – Form A

Chapter Test Form A
Chapter 10

1. Make a frequency table and a line plot for each set of data. Find the mean, median, and mode.
 age of the members of the Math Club:
 12, 12, 13, 12, 11, 12, 10, 13, 14, 10, 14, 13, 11, 11

Number	Tally	Frequency
10	II	2
11	III	3
12	IIII	4
13	III	3
14	II	2

mean 12
median 12
mode 12

Line plot: 10 11 12 13 14

Use the graph below for Exercises 2–4.

2001 American League Home Runs

Home Runs: 0, 100, 120, 140, 160, 180, 200, 220, 240, 260
Team: Seattle, Cleveland, Texas, Minnesota, Chicago, New York, Boston, Kansas City, Oakland, Toronto, Anaheim, Detroit, Tampa Bay, Baltimore

2. Which team appears to have twice the home runs of Tampa Bay? Anaheim
3. Which team actually has twice as many home runs as Tampa Bay? Texas
4. Explain why the graph gives a misleading visual impression of the data. How would you change the graph to be more appropriate?
 The graph begins with a y-axis value of 100. Starting the y-axis at 0 would make the graph more appropriate.
5. Make a stem-and-leaf plot for the data. Then find the median and mode.
 hours worked per week:
 5, 15, 25, 23, 19, 9, 13, 18, 21, 20, 35, 37, 19, 15
 median 19 mode 15, 19

0 | 5 9
1 | 3 5 5 8 9 9
2 | 0 1 3 5
3 | 5 7 Key 1 | 3 = 13

Chapter 10 Chapter Test

Take It to the NET
Online chapter test at
www.PHSchool.com
Web Code: aca-1053

Movies In a survey, twenty students were asked how many movies they saw in a month. The results are below.

2 3 2 2 1 0 1 2 5 7 2 1 0 3 4 4 3 0 1 2

1. Make a frequency table. **See back of book.**
2. Make a line plot. **See margin.**
3. Use the line plot to find the mean, median, and mode. **2.25 movies; 2 movies; 2 movies**

Make a frequency table and a histogram for each data set. Use intervals of equal size to group the data. **4–5. See back of book.**

4. hours of sleep per night:
 5 7 8 8 9 8 9 10 11 7 6 5 8 9 8 7 7
5. monthly salaries (in dollars) at local store:
 600 780 750 1,200 1,500 1,000 1,100
 850 900 425 832 700 900 1,000

Jobs Six hundred high school students were surveyed about the types of jobs they hold. Use the graph for Exercises 6–8.

Students' Jobs

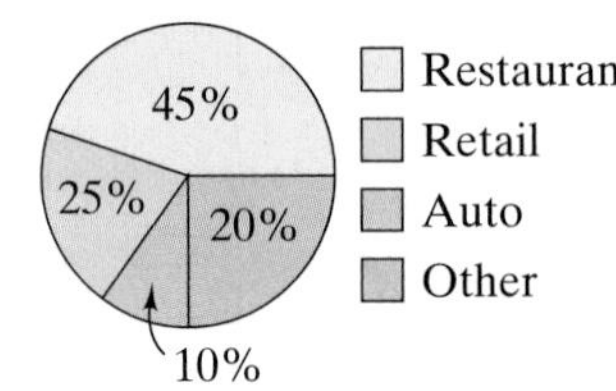

6. How many students work in a restaurant? **270 students**
7. How many students work in retail sales? **150 students**
8. What percent of the students do not work at a restaurant? How many students is that? **55%; 330 students**
9. **Cable** Make a stem-and-leaf plot for the number of subscribers (in millions) of ten cable television networks: 81.8 81.3 81.3 81.0 82.5 83.3 82.1 81.9 81.8 81.0 **See back of book.**

10. a. **Golf** The data below show the career earnings in millions of dollars of the top male and female golfers. Use a single number line to make a box-and-whisker plot for the data. **See margin.**
 Male: 21.9 18.0 17.8 15.3 14.6 14.5 14.7
 Female: 10.2 8.5 7.6 7.3 6.9 6.7 6.3
 b. **Writing in Math** Write a paragraph to compare the sets of data. **See margin.**

Decide which type of graph would be most appropriate for the set of data. Explain your choice and then draw the graph. **11–13. See back of book.**

11. **Top U.S. Apparel Businesses**

Company	Earnings (billions of dollars)
Nike	9
VF	5.7
Jones Apparel Group	4.1
Liz Claiborne	3.1
Reebok International	2.9
Kellwood	2.4
Warnaco Group	2.3

SOURCE: *The World Almanac*

12. **Percent of Music Sold on CDs**

Year	1996	1997	1998	1999	2000	2001
Percent	68	70	75	83	89	89

SOURCE: Recording Industry Association of America

13. Per capita freshwater use (gallons per day): Florida, 509; California, 1,130; Ohio, 944; Kentucky, 1,150; Oregon, 2,520; Alaska, 350
14. **Money** You have $50 in savings. Two months later, you have $80. After the third month, you have $95. You plan to continue to save the same amount each month. What will be in savings after 12 months? **$230**

2.

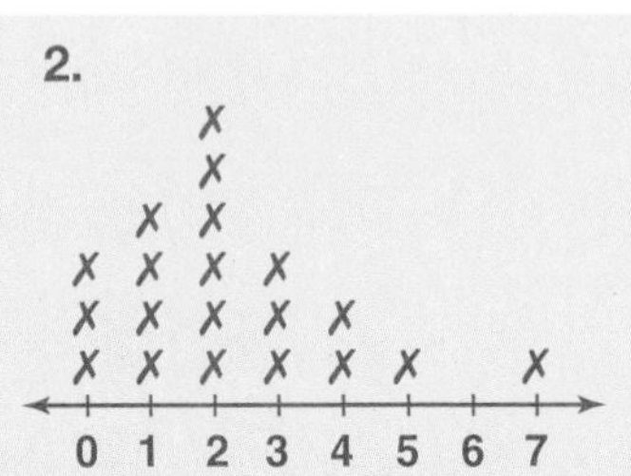

10a. Answers may vary. Sample:

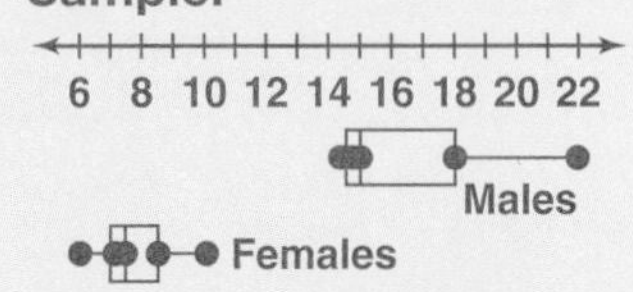

b. The earnings of top male golfers range from $14.5 million to $21.9 million, with half of them earning over $15.3 million. The top female golfers earn from $6.3 million to $10.2 million, with half earning more than $7.3 million. Each of the top male golfers makes more than the top female golfer.

Test Prep

Multiple Choice

For Exercises 1–10, choose the correct letter.

1. Find the median and the mode of the data in the line plot. B 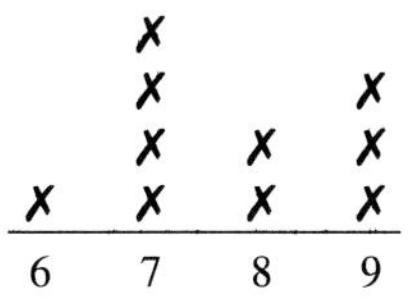
   - A. 7 and 8
   - B. 7.5 and 7
   - C. 7.5 and 8
   - D. 8 and 9

6	7	8	9
✗	✗	✗	✗
	✗	✗	✗
	✗		✗
	✗		

2. Which measure of central tendency would you use to describe the data on your classmates' favorite brand of sneakers? F
   - F. mode
   - G. median
   - H. range
   - I. mean

3. At a middle school gymnastics competition, the scores for the floor exercises were 5.1, 5.6, 5.3, 5.1, 4.8, 4.6, and 5.2. Find the mean (to the nearest tenth) and the median. B
   - A. 5.1 and 5.3
   - B. 5.1 and 5.1
   - C. 5.2 and 5.1
   - D. 5.2 and 5.2

4. Which object is not an example of a prism? I
   - F. a shoe box
   - G. a domino
   - H. a file cabinet
   - I. a soup can

5. Describe the trend in the scatter plot at the right. B 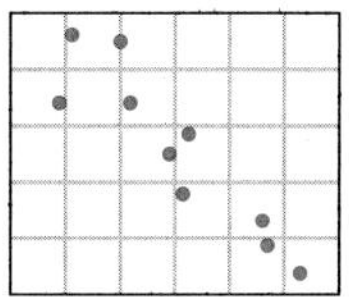
   - A. positive trend
   - B. negative trend
   - C. no trend
   - D. positive and negative trend

6. Which type of graph shows how a category changes over time? I
   - F. histogram
   - G. circle
   - H. line plot
   - I. line graph

7. At the Armstrong School, the student-to-teacher ratio is 12 : 1. There are 30 teachers in the school. How many students are there? D
   - A. 42
   - B. 250
   - C. 300
   - D. 360

8. What is the length of a rectangular garden with perimeter 32 ft and area 39 ft^2? H
   - F. 25 ft
   - G. 18 ft
   - H. 13 ft
   - I. 9 ft

9. What are the missing numbers in the pattern $-2, -3, -5, -8, -12,$ ■, $-23,$ ■, . . . ? B
   - A. -18 and -28
   - B. -17 and -30
   - C. -15 and -26
   - D. -19 and -26

10. A rectangular skateboard park has 7 curbs and 4 ramps. The width of the park is $2x$ and the length is $3x$, where x equals 48 meters. What are the dimensions of the park? G
    - F. 48 m and 72 m
    - G. 96 m and 144 m
    - H. 100 m and 4 m
    - I. 65 m and 35 m

Gridded Response

11. Round 3.0481 to the nearest hundredth. 3.05

12. A cubit was a measure used in ancient times. There are about 2 cubits in a yard. How many inches are in a cubit? 18

Short Response 13–14. See back of book.

13. Leana had $50.00 before she went shopping. She bought three books that each cost the same price, and a hat for $18.99, including tax. After her shopping trip she had $7.04 left. How much was each book? Show your work.

Extended Response

14. The ages of the players on a basketball team are below. Find the lower quartile, median, and upper quartile for their ages. Use a box-and-whisker plot to display the data. Show your work.
    23 25 34 25 19 24 25 25 26 40 33
    21 27 29 31 26 33

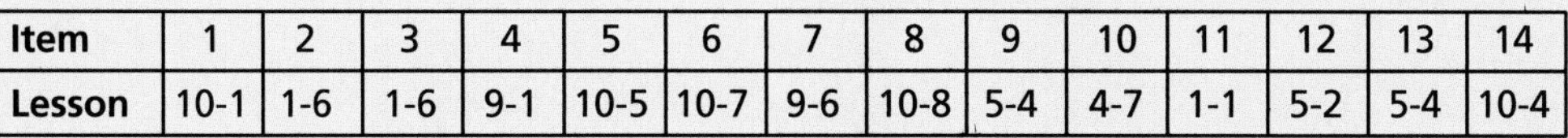

Item	1	2	3	4	5	6	7	8	9	10	11	12	13	14
Lesson	10-1	1-6	1-6	9-1	10-5	10-7	9-6	10-8	5-4	4-7	1-1	5-2	5-4	10-4

Test Prep

Resources

Teaching Resources
Cumulative Review

Reaching All Students
Spanish Cumulative Review

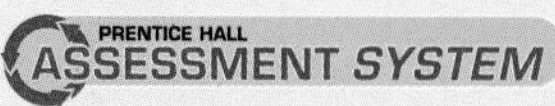

Test Preparation
- Ch. 10 standardized test prep

Assessment Resources
- Cumulative Review

Computer Test Generator CD
- Standardized test prep

www.PHSchool.com
- Standardized test prep
- Resources

Plus 

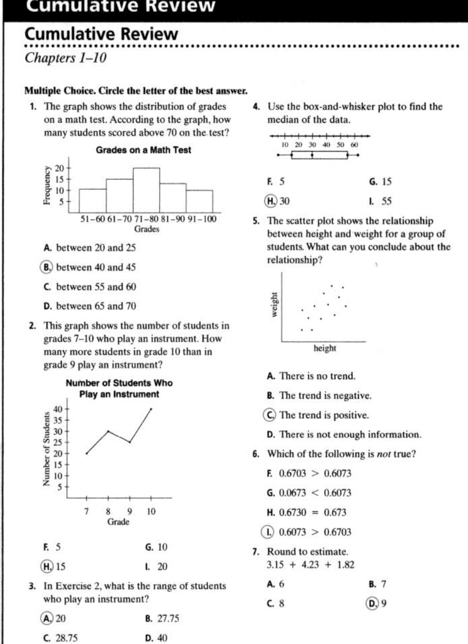

Cumulative Review

Cumulative Review

Chapters 1–10

Multiple Choice. Circle the letter of the best answer.

1. The graph shows the distribution of grades on a math test. According to the graph, how many students scored above 70 on the test?

   Grades on a Math Test (Frequency; Grades 51–60, 61–70, 71–80, 81–90, 91–100)

   - A. between 20 and 25
   - (B.) between 40 and 45
   - C. between 55 and 60
   - D. between 65 and 70

2. This graph shows the number of students in grades 7–10 who play an instrument. How many more students in grade 10 than in grade 9 play an instrument?

   Number of Students Who Play an Instrument (Number of Students; Grade 7, 8, 9, 10)

   - F. 5
   - G. 10
   - (H.) 15
   - I. 20

3. In Exercise 2, what is the range of students who play an instrument?
   - (A.) 20
   - B. 27.75
   - C. 28.75
   - D. 40

4. Use the box-and-whisker plot to find the median of the data.

   10 20 30 40 50 60

   - F. 5
   - G. 15
   - (H.) 30
   - I. 55

5. The scatter plot shows the relationship between height and weight for a group of students. What can you conclude about the relationship?

   weight / height

   - A. There is no trend.
   - B. The trend is negative.
   - (C.) The trend is positive.
   - D. There is not enough information.

6. Which of the following is *not* true?
   - F. $0.6703 > 0.6073$
   - G. $0.0673 < 0.6073$
   - H. $0.6730 = 0.673$
   - (I.) $0.6073 > 0.6703$

7. Round to estimate.
   $3.15 + 4.23 + 1.82$
   - A. 6
   - B. 7
   - C. 8
   - (D.) 9

Conic Cuisine

Students will use data from these two pages to answer the questions posed here in Put It All Together.

Activating Prior Knowledge
Tell students that people eat 35,000 tons of pineapples every day. Have them use this data as a benchmark. Then list some of the foods mentioned in this feature, but provide no consumption data about them. Ask students first to try to place the foods in order of most consumed to least consumed. Then challenge them to estimate how much of each food is eaten world-wide each day.

Teaching Notes

Have students examine the cones and information about food consumption on these pages. Discuss with students how visual images make great numbers less abstract.

History Connection
Have students research the history of some of these foods. Where were they first grown and in what conditions do they thrive? Invite students to investigate the link between the availability of certain foods in a region and the rise of civilization there. Have students look into the relationship between planting crops and the growth of towns and cities.

Careers
Invite interested students to find out more about the field of graphic design. Have them learn what jobs are available and what training, skills, and talents are required. Students can start their inquiry by talking with the art teacher.

Real-World Snapshots

Conic Cuisine

Applying Data Analysis Graphic designers often use pictures to present data. You can read that people eat 35,000 tons of pineapples every day, but seeing a pile of pineapples drawn to the size of a large hotel gives you a better sense of how many pineapples this is. The drawings on these pages show the volumes of various crops that the people of the world eat or produce each day.

Potatoes
We dig up 801,000 tons of potatoes every day.

Put It All Together

Materials scale or balance, ruler, food sample

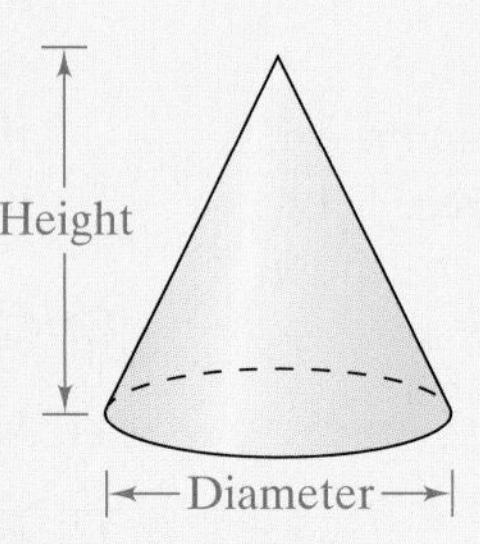

1. Weigh a serving of one of the foods shown on these pages. Remember to subtract the weight of the container if there is one. Use the conversion tables in the back of the book to convert the weight to pounds.
2. Estimate the volume of your food sample in cubic inches.
3. How many tons of your food does the world eat or produce each day? Convert this amount to pounds. Write your answer in scientific notation.
4. Suppose you piled the amount of the food eaten or produced each day into a cone. Find the volume of the cone. (*Hint:* 1,728 in.^{3} = 1 ft^3)
5. Suppose the diameter and the height of the cone are equal.
   a. Use the formula $V = \frac{2}{3}\pi r^3$ and *try, check, and revise* (see Lesson 4-7) to estimate the radius of the cone.
   b. Calculate the diameter and the height of the cone in feet.
6. **Reasoning** What would the cone of food weigh? Explain.

The world produces 58,000 tons of cucumbers every day.

The world's daily onion harvest weighs 98,000 tons, as much as the ocean liner *Queen Elizabeth.*

Take It to the NET For more information about food, go to **www.PHSchool.com**.
Web Code: ace-1053

1–6. Answers may vary.

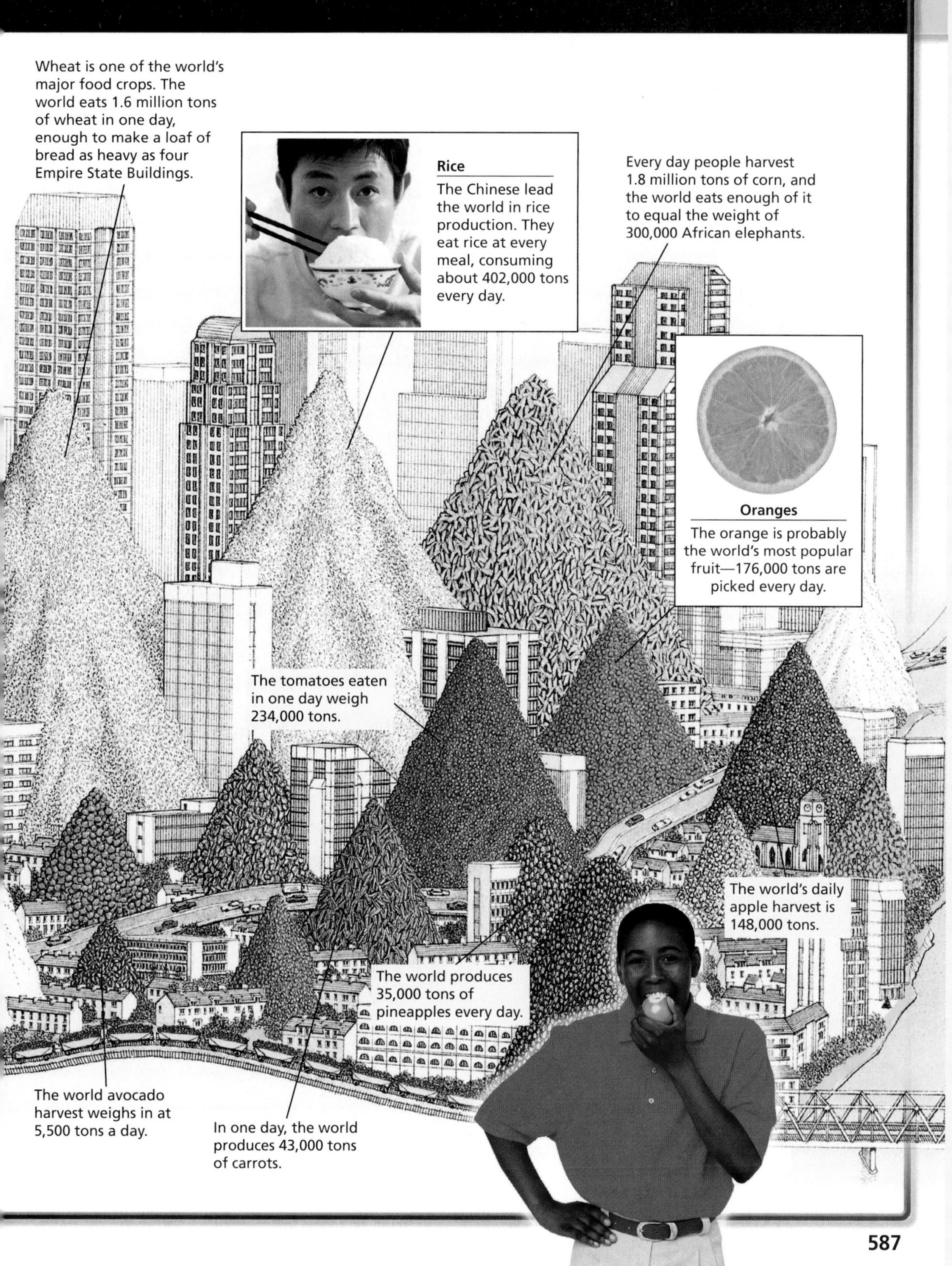

Wheat is one of the world's major food crops. The world eats 1.6 million tons of wheat in one day, enough to make a loaf of bread as heavy as four Empire State Buildings.
Rice
The Chinese lead the world in rice production. They eat rice at every meal, consuming about 402,000 tons every day.
Every day people harvest 1.8 million tons of corn, and the world eats enough of it to equal the weight of 300,000 African elephants.
Oranges
The orange is probably the world's most popular fruit—176,000 tons are picked every day.
The tomatoes eaten in one day weigh 234,000 tons.
The world's daily apple harvest is 148,000 tons.
The world produces 35,000 tons of pineapples every day.
The world avocado harvest weighs in at 5,500 tons a day.
In one day, the world produces 43,000 tons of carrots.
587

Put It All Together

Have students work in pairs to answer the questions. Guide them to record data as they measure and accumulate it.

Discuss that in this activity, students will weigh and estimate the size of food samples.

Inclusion
As needed, review what a cone is and the formula for finding its volume ($V = \frac{1}{3}Bh$). Compare finding its volume to finding the volume of a cylinder ($V = Bh$). Also review how to use scientific notation to express very large quantities.

Exercise 4 Elicit from students that when they compute volume, they measure it in cubic units—cubic feet or cubic inches in this case. Guide students to understand that $1{,}728 = 12 \times 12 \times 12$, or 12^3.

Challenge students to pick a food from the activity and estimate the height of a cone that shows how much of that food is consumed in one *year*. Ask: *Why is the height not 365 times the height of a 1-day cone?* **The cone expands in three directions, not just upwards.**

CHAPTER 11

Probability

Chapter at a Glance

11-1 Counting Outcomes
pp. 591–594

Objectives
1. Using Tree Diagrams and the Counting Principle

NCTM Standards
1, 2, 3, 5, 6, 7, 8, 9, 10

Local Standards

11-2 Permutations
pp. 595–599

Objectives
1. Finding Permutations
2. Using Permutation Notation

New Vocabulary
permutation, factorial

NCTM Standards
1, 2, 3, 5, 6, 7, 8, 9, 10

Local Standards

11-3 Combinations
pp. 600–604

Objectives
1. Finding Combinations
2. Using Combination Notation

New Vocabulary
combination

NCTM Standards
1, 2, 5, 6, 7, 8, 9, 10

Local Standards

✓ Checkpoint Quiz 1

11-4 Theoretical and Experimental Probability
pp. 606–610

Objectives
1. Finding Experimental Probability
2. Finding Complements and Odds

New Vocabulary
experimental probability, theoretical probability, complement, odds in favor, odds against

NCTM Standards
1, 2, 5, 6, 7, 8, 9, 10

Local Standards

11-5 Independent and Dependent Events
pp. 611–615

Objectives
1. Finding the Probability of Independent Events
2. Finding the Probability of Dependent Events

New Vocabulary
independent events, dependent events

NCTM Standards
1, 2, 5, 6, 7, 8, 9, 10

Local Standards

11-6 Problem Solving — Simulate a Problem and Make an Organized List
pp. 616–619

Objectives
1. Solving a Problem Using Two Different Methods

NCTM Standards
1, 3, 5, 6, 7, 8, 9, 10

Local Standards

11-7 Conducting a Survey
pp. 621–625

Objectives
1. Planning a Survey
2. Determining Biased Questions

New Vocabulary
population, sample, random sample, systematic sample, stratified sample, biased questions

NCTM Standards
1, 5, 6, 7, 8, 9, 10

Local Standards

✓ Checkpoint Quiz 2

Reaching All Students

Additional Instructional Options in Chapter 11

Reading and Math Literacy

Reading Math

Reading Math hints, pp. 597, 601, 622

Reading Comprehension, pp. 614, 631

Understanding Vocabulary, pp. 626, 628

Writing in Math

Daily Writing Practice, pp. 593, 598, 603, 609, 613, 618, 624, 630

Above Level

Challenge exercises

pp. 594, 599, 603, 610, 614, 619, 624

Extension

Pascal's Triangle, p. 605

Hands-On and Technology

Investigations

Counting Arrangements, p. 595

Experimental Probability, p. 606

Comparing Types of Events, p. 611

Technology

Simulations With Random Numbers, p. 620

Activities and Projects

Real-World Snapshots

Applying Probability pp. 632-633

Chapter Project

Start With the Stats p. 701

Test Prep

Daily Test Prep

pp. 594, 599, 604, 610, 614, 619, 624

Test-Taking Strategies

Answering the Question Asked, p. 627

Test Prep

Reading Comprehension, p. 631

Chapter Assessment

Checkpoint Quiz

pp. 604, 625

Chapter Review

pp. 628–629

Chapter Test

p. 630

Pacing Options

This chart suggests pacing only for the core lessons and their parts. It is provided as a possible guide. It will help you determine how much time you have in your schedule to cover the additional features and assessment, as described at the left.

Day	Traditional 45-minute class periods	Block 90-minute class periods
1	11-1 ▼	11-1 ▼ 11-2 ▼
2	11-2 ▼	11-2 ▼ 11-3 ▼
3	11-2 ▼	11-3 ▼ 11-4 ▼
4	11-3 ▼	11-4 ▼ 11-5 ▼
5	11-3 ▼	11-5 ▼ 11-6 ▼
6	11-4 ▼	11-7 ▼ ▼
7	11-4 ▼	
8	11-5 ▼	
9	11-5 ▼	
10	11-6 ▼	
11	11-7 ▼	
12	11-7 ▼	
13		
14		
15		

NCTM STANDARDS 2000

1 Number and Operations
2 Algebra
3 Geometry
4 Measurement
5 Data Analysis and Probability
6 Problem Solving
7 Reasoning and Proof
8 Communication
9 Connections
10 Representation

Math Background

Skills Trace

BEFORE Chapter 11

Course 2 introduced theoretical probability, experimental probability, and compound probability.

DURING Chapter 11

Course 3 reviews and extends probability with independent events, dependent events, simulations, and sampling techniques.

AFTER Chapter 11

Throughout this course students use ratios, proportions, percents, fractions, and decimals to build a foundation for probability.

11-1 Counting Outcomes

Math Understandings

- You can apply the counting principle to find the number of outcomes of two or more events.

You can use a tree diagram to find the number of possible outcomes for two or more events.

First Choice	Chicken	Tuna
Second Choice	milk juice water	milk juice water

Each banch represents a choice.

You can also use the counting principle to find the number of possible outcomes.

The Counting Principle
Suppose there are *m* ways of making one choice and *n* ways of making a second choice. Then there are $m \cdot n$ ways to make the first choice followed by the second choice

Example: You have 6 shirts and 5 jeans. You have $6 \cdot 5 = 30$ different outfits.

11-2 Permutations
11-3 Combinations

Math Understandings

- In permutations, order makes a difference.
- In combinations, order does not matter.

A **permutation** is an arrangement of a set of objects in a particular order. You can use a diagram to find the number of permutations. This diagram shows that there are six permutations, or ways that Ryan, Emily, and Justin can line up.

Ryan	Emily	Justin	①	(R, E, J)
	Justin	Emily	②	(R, J, E)
Emily	Ryan	Justin	③	(E, R, J)
	Justin	Ryan	④	(E, J, R)
Justin	Ryan	Emily	⑤	(J, R, E)
	Emily	Ryan	⑥	(J, E, R)

The product of all positive integers less than or equal to a number is a **factorial**. For example, $3! = 3 \times 2 \times 1$, or 6. The number of permutations of *n* items, using all *n* in each arrangement, is *n*!, which you read as "*n* factorial." The number of permutations of *n* items, chosen *r* at a time, is *n*! divided by $(n - r)!$.

Permutation Notation
The expression ${}_nP_r$ represents the number of permutations of *n* objects chosen *r* at a time.

Example: Simplify ${}_{25}P_2$. ${}_{25}P_2 = 25 \cdot 24 = 600$

A **combination** is a group of items in which the order of the items is *not* considered. The number of combinations of *n* items, chosen *r* at a time, is the number of permutations of *n* items taken *r* at a time divided by *r*!.

Combination Notation
The expression ${}_nC_r$ represents the number of permutations of *n* objects chosen *r* at a time. $${}_nC_r = \frac{{}_nP_r}{r!}$$

Example: Simplify ${}_{12}C_3$.

$${}_{12}C_3 = \frac{{}_{12}P_3}{3!} = \frac{12 \cdot 11 \cdot 10}{3 \cdot 2 \cdot 1} = \frac{1{,}320}{6} = 220$$

11-4 Theoretical and Experimental Probability

Math Understandings

- Probability is expressed as a number from 0 (impossible) to 1 (certain) that tells how often an event will occur.
- Experimental probability is based on the results of an actual experiment.
- Theoretical probability is based an the assumption that certain outcomes are equally likely.

Probability based on experimental data is called experimental probability. You can find the experimental and theoretical probability of an event using the following formulas.

experimental probability $= P(\text{event}) = \frac{\text{number of times an event occurs}}{\text{total number of trials}}$

theoretical probability $= P(\text{event}) = \frac{\text{number of favorable outcomes}}{\text{total number of possible outcomes}}$

The **complement of an event** is the opposite of that event.

For any event A its complement is *not A*, and $P(A) + P(\text{not } A) = 1$
To find the probability of a complement, use $P(\text{not } A) = 1 - P(A)$

Odds
odds in favor of an event = the ratio of the number of favorable outcomes to the number of unfavorable outcomes
odds against an event = the ratio of the number of unfavorable outcomes to the number of favorable outcomes

11-5 Independent and Dependent Events

Math Understandings

- Two events are independent if one event does not affect the sample space of the other event.
- Two events are dependent if one event affects the sample space of the other event.

For **independent events**, the outcome of one event does not affect the outcome of a second event. For **dependent events**, the outcome of one event affects the outcome of a second event.

Independent Events	Dependent Events
If A and B are independent events, then $P(A, \text{ then } B) = P(A) \cdot P(B)$.	If A and B are dependent events, then $P(A, \text{ then } B) = P(A) \cdot P(B \text{ after } A)$.

11-6 Simulate a Problem and Make an Organized List

You can *simulate a problem* to find experimental probabilities by conducting experiments. For instance, a coin toss can model a situation where only two outcomes are possible, such as a true-false test question. You can also *make an organized list* to find all outcomes that are possible for the situation.

11-7 Conducting a Survey

Math Understandings

- You can select a random sample to accurately represent the entire population.
- A survey question should not influence responses by making one answer appear more attractive.

Any group of objects or people in a survey is called a **population**. A **sample** is a part of the population. In a **random sample**, each object in the population has an equal chance of being selected. In a **systematic sample**, the members of a survey population are selected using a system of selection that depends on a random number. In a **stratified sample**, members of the survey population are separated into groups to ensure a balanced sample. Then a random sample is selected from each group. Unfair questions in a survey are **biased** questions.

Additional Professional Development Opportunities

Chapter 11 Math Background notes: pp. 592, 596, 601, 607, 612, 617, 622

Additional resources available from SkyLight Professional Development:

On-site courses, workshops, summer institutes. Online courses and chat rooms. Videocassettes and books. Visit www.skylightedu.com.

Ongoing Assessment and Intervention

The *Prentice Hall Mathematics* program provides many options for assessment in the Student Edition, Teacher's Edition, and teaching resources. From these options you may choose instructional materials that are appropriate for your students and that support your district's curriculum requirements.

Daily Assessment

Instant Check System™ in Chapter 11

Allows students to check their own learning before, during, and after each lesson.

Diagnosing Readiness before the chapter (p. 590)

Check Skills You'll Need exercises in each lesson (pp. 591, 595, 600, 606, 611, 616, 621)

Check Understanding questions with each Example (pp. 591, 592, 596, 597, 601, 607, 608, 612, 617, 621, 622, 623)

Checkpoint Quiz (pp. 604, 625)

Formal Assessment

Assessment in the Student Text and in Additional Resources

Assess student progress throughout the Course 2 textbook and with blackline masters and CD-ROM.

Student Edition

- Chapter 11 Review, with Vocabulary, Skills, and Concepts Review, pp. 628–629
- Chapter 11 Test, p. 630

Assessment Resources

- Checkpoint Quizzes 1 & 2
- Chapter Test, forms A & B
- Chapter Alternative Assessment

Spanish versions available.

Computer Test Generator CD-ROM

- Instant Chapter Tests™—pre-made tests with items that vary every time you print.
- Online Testing allows you to give tests online and receive progress reports.
- Prepare students by making tests based on standardized test objectives.

Algebra Readiness Tests

- Includes Basic Skills Tests and Concept-Readiness Tests.
- Assess understanding of skills and concepts needed for success in algebra.

Intervention

Skills Intervention Kit

Online Intervention

Integrated within the iText, this online intervention system includes diagnostic tests and prescribed remediation, plus reports to track student mastery.

A *complete* system for the student who is struggling with course-level work

Eight intervention units cover core skills and allow you to:

- Diagnose students' gaps in basic skills
- Prescribe an individualized course of study
- Monitor student progress

Includes print workbooks, tutorial CD-ROM, teacher editions, progress folders, and more. *Available in Spanish.*

How to Use with Chapter 11

11-1 Number Theory and Fraction Concepts, Skill 9
11-4 Ratio, Proportion, and Percent, Skill 11
11-5 Operations with Fractions, Skill 10
11-6 Operations with Fractions, Skill 10
11-7 Number Theory and Fraction Concepts, Skill 9

Standardized Test Preparation

The *Prentice Hall Mathematics* program integrates preparation for high-stakes standardized tests in every lesson of the Student Edition and continues this support in the Prentice Hall Assessment System.

Test Prep

In Student Text, Chapter 11

Teaches students strategies and gives them practice with all the test item formats they will encounter on high-stakes tests.

Test Prep exercises in each lesson (pp. 594, 599, 604, 610, 614, 619, 624)

Test-Taking Strategies (p. 627: Answering the Question Asked)

Test Prep (p. 631: Reading Comprehension)

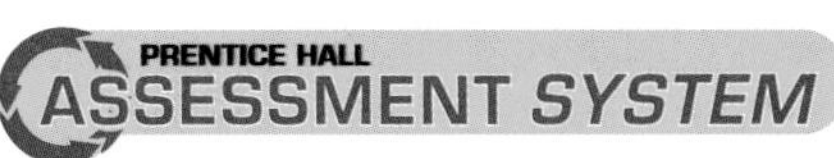
PRENTICE HALL
ASSESSMENT SYSTEM

A three-step approach to preparing students for high stakes, national, and state exams.

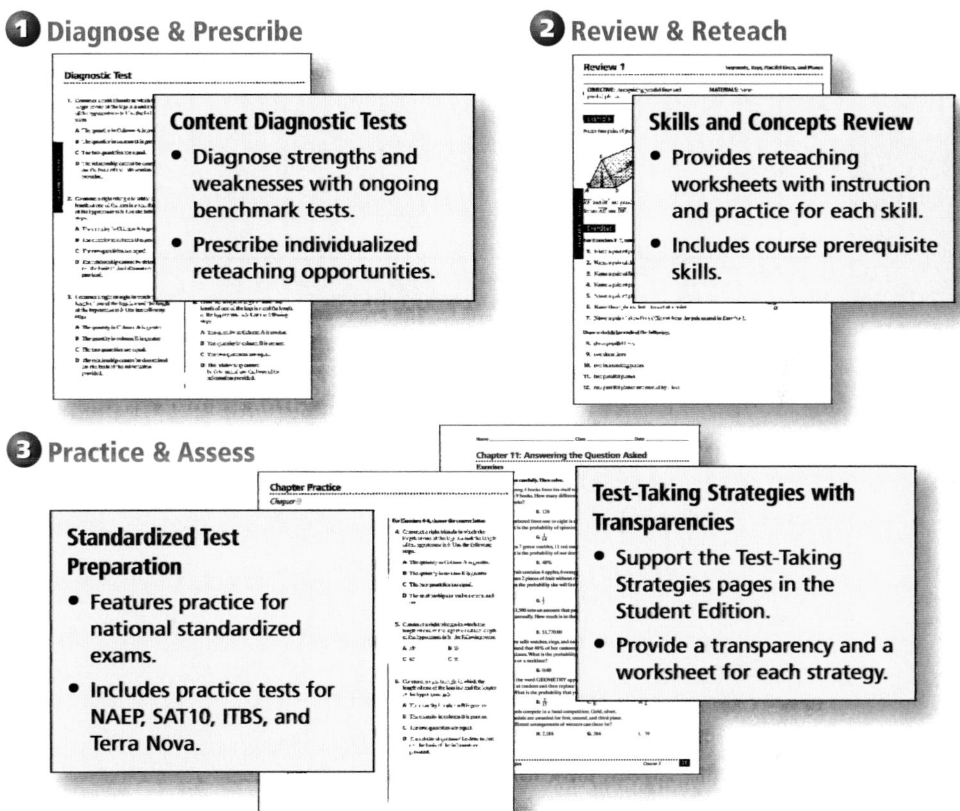
1 Diagnose & Prescribe
Content Diagnostic Tests
• Diagnose strengths and weaknesses with ongoing benchmark tests.
• Prescribe individualized reteaching opportunities.
2 Review & Reteach
Skills and Concepts Review
• Provides reteaching worksheets with instruction and practice for each skill.
• Includes course prerequisite skills.
3 Practice & Assess
Standardized Test Preparation
• Features practice for national standardized exams.
• Includes practice tests for NAEP, SAT10, ITBS, and Terra Nova.
Test-Taking Strategies with Transparencies
• Support the Test-Taking Strategies pages in the Student Edition.
• Provide a transparency and a worksheet for each strategy.

Correlation to Standardized Tests

Lesson		NAEP	Terra Nova CAT6	Terra Nova CTBS	ITBS	SAT10	Local Test
11-1	Counting Outcomes	D4e			■	■	
11-2	Permutations	D4e				■	
11-3	Combinations	D4e				■	
11-4	Theoretical and Experimental Probability	D4d	■		■	■	
11-5	Independent and Dependent Events	D4h					
11-6	Simulate a Problem and Make an Organized List	D4c					
11-7	Conducting a Survey	D3b, D3d					

NAEP National Assessment of Educational Progress
CAT6/Terra Nova California Achievement Test, 6th Ed.
CTBS/Terra Nova Comprehensive Test of Basic Skills
ITBS Iowa Test of Basic Skills, Form M.
SAT10 Stanford Achievement Test, 10th Ed.

Program Resources

	Resources in Grab & Go™ Files				Resources for Reaching All Students				Spanish Resources			Presentation Assistant Plus! Transparencies					Presentation Assistant Plus!
	Practice	Reteach	Enrich	Checkpt Quiz	Reading & Math Literacy	Technology Activities	Hands-On Activities	Guided Problem Solving	Practice	Reading & Math Literacy	Checkpt Quiz	Skills Check	Problem of the Day	Additional Examples	Answers to Exercises	Lesson Quiz	Prentice Hall Presentation Pro CD-ROM
11-1	■	■	■		■			■	■	■		■	■	■	■	■	■
11-2	■	■	■				■	■	■			■	■	■	■	■	■
11-3	■	■	■	■	■	■		■	■	■	■	■	■	■	■	■	■
11-4	■	■	■				■	■	■			■	■	■	■	■	■
11-5	■	■	■					■	■			■	■	■	■	■	■
11-6	■	■	■					■	■			■	■	■	■	■	■
11-7	■	■	■	■	■		■	■	■	■	■	■	■	■	■	■	■
For the Chapter	Chapter Projects, Chapter Tests, Alternative Assessment, Cumulative Review, Cumulative Assessment				**On web site only:** Home Activities, Interdisciplinary Activities, Algebra Readiness Puzzles				Spanish Chapter Tests, Alternative Assessment, Cumulative Review, Cumulative Assessment			Classroom Aid Transparencies					

Also available for use with the chapter:

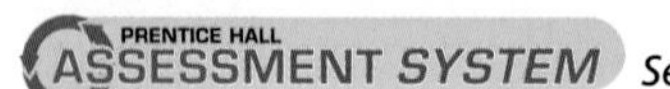

See page 588F.

- Practice Workbook
- Solution Key
- MathNotes folder

- For teacher support and access to student Web materials, use the Web Code abk-5500.
- For additional online and technology resources, *see below.*

Technology

Online and on CD-ROM

Complete Interactive Student Text online and on CD-ROM—with instant feedback assessment, tutorial help, dynamic activities, instructional and real-world videos, audio, and additional practice.

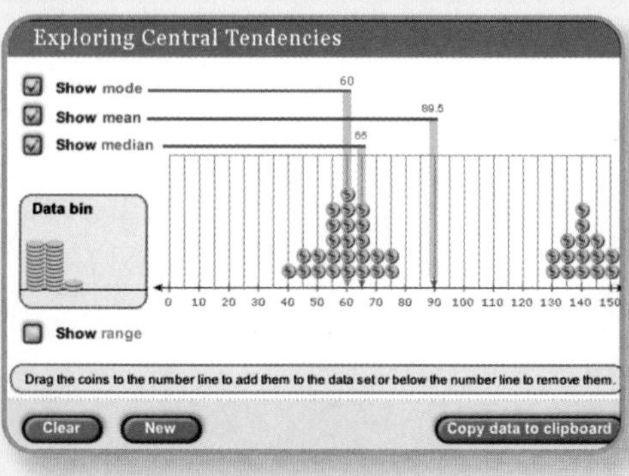

www.PHSchool.com For Students

Use Web codes for easy access to online activities, chapter projects, self-grading lesson quizzes, chapter tests, vocabulary quizzes, updated data sources, graphing calculator procedures, and more.

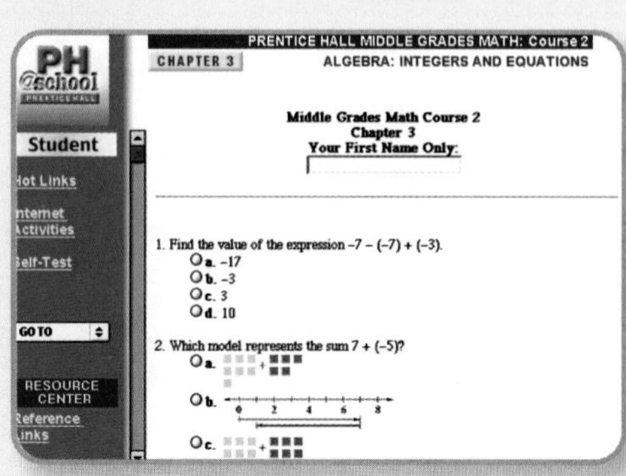

PH SuccessNet For Teachers

Online lesson planning with built-in state correlations, all the teaching resources, complete reference library, your own calendar and Teacher Web page, professional development, and more.

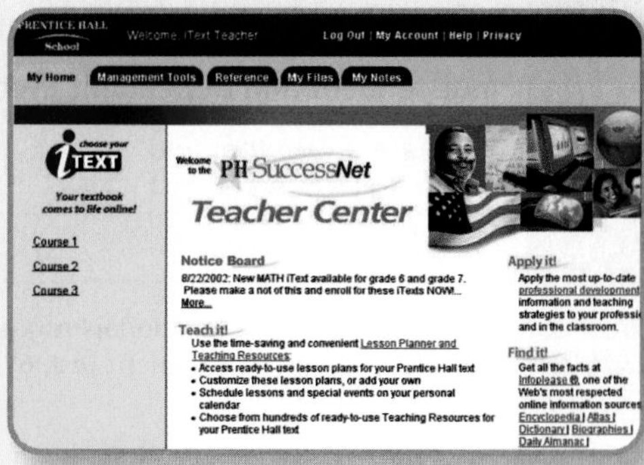

Presentation Assistant Plus!

The *Prentice Hall Presentation Assistant Plus!* provides you with the material you need to teach a lesson from beginning to end. Two easy-to-use formats—Transparencies and PowerPoint®—allow you to present a lesson the way you are most comfortable.

Transparencies

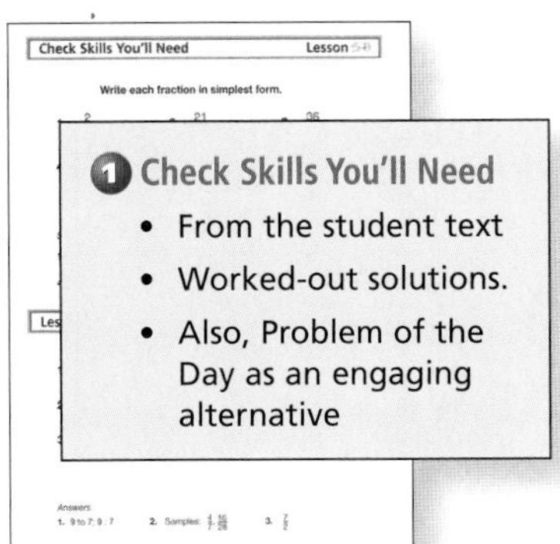

1 Check Skills You'll Need
- From the student text
- Worked-out solutions.
- Also, Problem of the Day as an engaging alternative

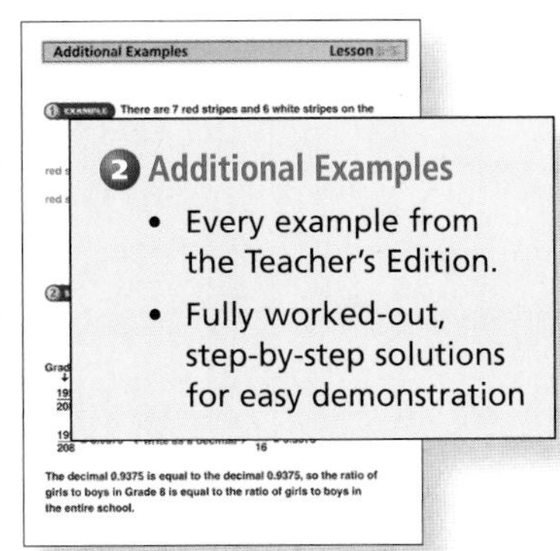

2 Additional Examples
- Every example from the Teacher's Edition.
- Fully worked-out, step-by-step solutions for easy demonstration

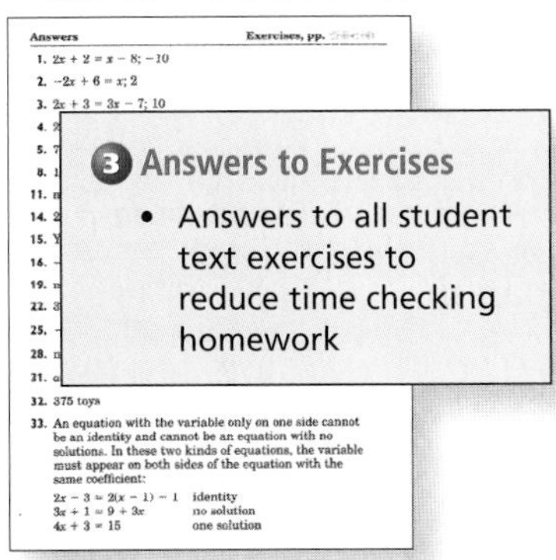

3 Answers to Exercises
- Answers to all student text exercises to reduce time checking homework

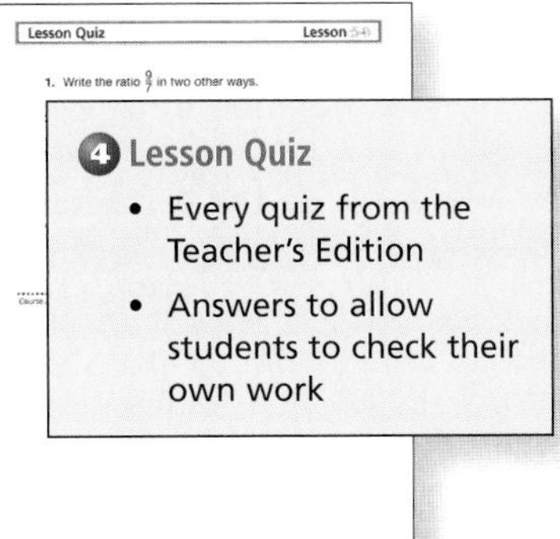

4 Lesson Quiz
- Every quiz from the Teacher's Edition
- Answers to allow students to check their own work

Throughout the Teacher's Edition, this symbol indicates material that is available in the Presentation Assistant Plus!

Prentice Hall Presentation Pro CD-ROM

- Includes all Transparencies.
- Conveniently organized by lesson so you can easily 1 Introduce, 2 Teach, 3 Check Homework, and 4 Assess each lesson.
- Animated examples allow step-by-step instruction at your own pace.
- Easy to edit so you can create custom presentations.

Teaching Chapter 11 Using Presentation Assistant Plus!

	1 Introduce	2 Teach	3 Check Homework	4 Assess
	Check Skills You'll Need	Additional Examples	Student Edition Answers	Lesson Quiz
11-1	p. 89	pp. 185–187	✔	p. 89
11-2	p. 90	pp. 188–189	✔	p. 90
11-3	p. 91	pp. 190–191	✔	p. 91
11-4	p. 92	pp. 192–193	✔	p. 92
11-5	p. 93	p. 194	✔	p. 93
11-6	p. 94	pp. 195–196	✔	p. 94
11-7	p. 95	p. 197	✔	p. 95

Prentice Hall Presentation Pro

CD-ROM with dynamic PowerPoint® presentations for every lesson. Helps you introduce and develop concepts, check homework, and assess progress. Part of Presentation Assistant Plus! *(See above.)*

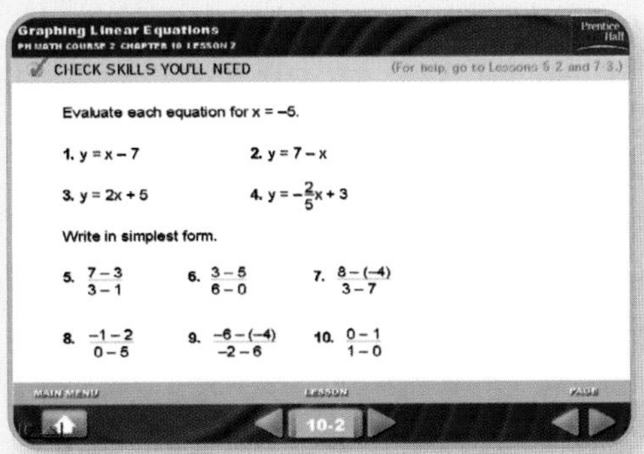

Computer Test Generator

CD-ROM to create practice sheets and tests for course objectives and standardized tests. Includes Instant Chapter Tests™, online testing, and student reports. Part of the PH Assessment System. *(See page 588F.)*

Resource Pro® with Planning Express®

CD-ROM with a lesson planning tool that allows you to import state and local objectives. Includes electronic versions of all the teaching resources.

Chapter Resources

Reading and Math Support

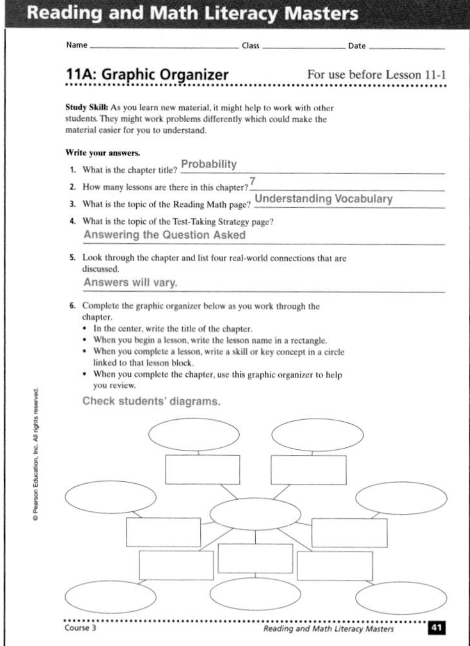

Reading and Math Literacy Masters

Name ________ Class ________ Date ________

11A: Graphic Organizer For use before Lesson 11-1

Study Skill: As you learn new material, it might help to work with other students. They might work problems differently which could make the material easier for you to understand.

Write your answers.

1. What is the chapter title? Probability
2. How many lessons are there in this chapter? 7
3. What is the topic of the Reading Math page? Understanding Vocabulary
4. What is the topic of the Test-Taking Strategy page? Answering the Question Asked
5. Look through the chapter and list four real-world connections that are discussed. Answers will vary.
6. Complete the graphic organizer below as you work through the chapter.
   - In the center, write the title of the chapter.
   - When you begin a lesson, write the lesson name in a rectangle.
   - When you complete a lesson, write a skill or key concept in a circle linked to that lesson block.
   - When you complete the chapter, use this graphic organizer to help you review.

   Check students' diagrams.

Course 3 Reading and Math Literacy Masters 41

Available in Spanish

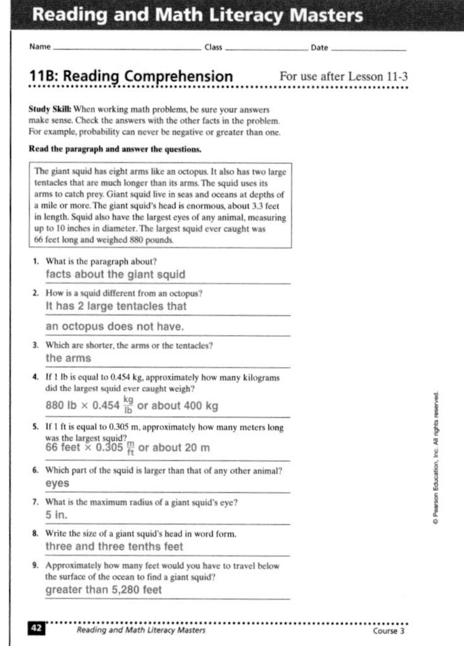

Reading and Math Literacy Masters

Name ________ Class ________ Date ________

11B: Reading Comprehension For use after Lesson 11-3

Study Skill: When working math problems, be sure your answers make sense. Check the answers with the other facts in the problem. For example, probability can never be negative or greater than one.

Read the paragraph and answer the questions.

The giant squid has eight arms like an octopus. It also has two large tentacles that are much longer than its arms. The squid uses its arms to catch prey. Giant squid live in seas and oceans at depths of a mile or more. The giant squid's head is enormous, about 3.3 feet in length. Squid also have the largest eyes of any animal, measuring up to 10 inches in diameter. The largest squid ever caught was 66 feet long and weighed 880 pounds.

1. What is the paragraph about? facts about the giant squid
2. How is a squid different from an octopus? It has 2 large tentacles that an octopus does not have.
3. Which are shorter, the arms or the tentacles? the arms
4. If 1 lb is equal to 0.454 kg, approximately how many kilograms did the largest squid ever caught weigh? $880 \text{ lb} \times 0.454 \frac{\text{kg}}{\text{lb}}$ or about 400 kg
5. If 1 ft is equal to 0.305 m, approximately how many meters long was the largest squid? $66 \text{ feet} \times 0.305 \frac{\text{m}}{\text{ft}}$ or about 20 m
6. Which part of the squid is larger than that of any other animal? eyes
7. What is the maximum radius of a giant squid's eye? 5 in.
8. Write the size of a giant squid's head in word form. three and three tenths feet
9. Approximately how many feet would you have to travel below the surface of the ocean to find a giant squid? greater than 5,280 feet

42 Reading and Math Literacy Masters Course 3

Available in Spanish

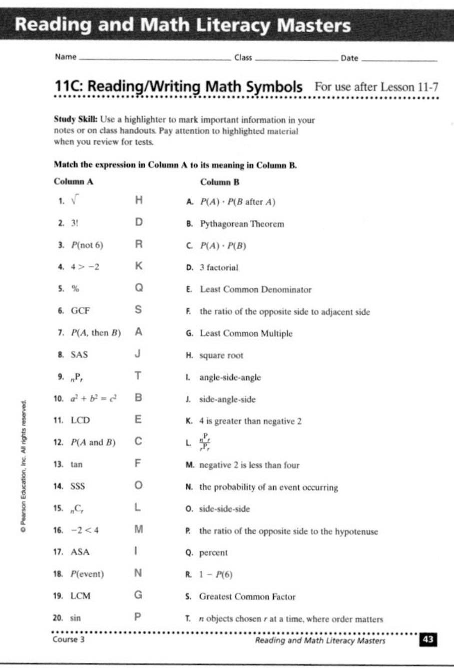

Reading and Math Literacy Masters

Name ________ Class ________ Date ________

11C: Reading/Writing Math Symbols For use after Lesson 11-7

Study Skill: Use a highlighter to mark important information in your notes or on class handouts. Pay attention to highlighted material when you review for tests.

Match the expression in Column A to its meaning in Column B.

Column A		Column B
1. $\sqrt{\ }$	H	A. $P(A) \cdot P(B \text{ after } A)$
2. 3!	D	B. Pythagorean Theorem
3. $P(\text{not } 6)$	R	C. $P(A) \cdot P(B)$
4. $4 > -2$	K	D. 3 factorial
5. %	Q	E. Least Common Denominator
6. GCF	S	F. the ratio of the opposite side to adjacent side
7. $P(A, \text{then } B)$	A	G. Least Common Multiple
8. SAS	J	H. square root
9. $_nP_r$	T	I. angle-side-angle
10. $a^2 + b^2 = c^2$	B	J. side-angle-side
11. LCD	E	K. 4 is greater than negative 2
12. $P(A \text{ and } B)$	C	L. $\frac{_nP_r}{_rP_r}$
13. tan	F	M. negative 2 is less than four
14. SSS	O	N. the probability of an event occurring
15. $_nC_r$	L	O. side-side-side
16. $-2 < 4$	M	P. the ratio of the opposite side to the hypotenuse
17. ASA	I	Q. percent
18. $P(\text{event})$	N	R. $1 - P(6)$
19. LCM	G	S. Greatest Common Factor
20. sin	P	T. n objects chosen r at a time, where order matters

Course 3 Reading and Math Literacy Masters 43

Available in Spanish

Reading and Math Literacy Masters

Name ________ Class ________ Date ________

11D: Vocabulary For use with the Chapter Review

Study Skill: Take short breaks between assignments. You will be able to concentrate on a new assignment more easily if you take a brief "time out" before starting.

Choose the term that best completes each sentence.

1. A(n) (**event**, *sample*) is one or more possible outcomes.
2. With a (**positive**, *negative*) trend, as one set of values increases, the other set tends to increase.
3. A (**combination**, *permutation*) is an arrangement of items in which the order does not matter.
4. The (*combination*, **complement**) of an event is the opposite of the event.
5. The (**absolute**, *opposite*) value of a number is its distance from 0 on a number line.
6. You can use a (**sample**, *population*) to gather information and make predictions.
7. The (*mean*, **median**) is the middle number in a set of data that has been ordered from least to greatest.
8. The x and y axes divide the coordinate plane into four regions called (**quadrants**, *planes*).
9. You can represent many probability situations using a (*permutation*, **simulation**).
10. Two angles whose sum is 90 degrees are (**complementary**, *supplementary*) angles.
11. Spinning a spinner and then tossing a coin is an example of two (**independent**, *dependent*) events.
12. (*Perpendicular*, **Parallel**) lines are in the same plane and do not intersect.
13. (**Circumference**, *Area*) is the distance around a circle.
14. A (*combination*, **permutation**) is an arrangement of a set of objects in a particular order.

44 Reading and Math Literacy Masters Course 3

Available in Spanish

Problem Solving

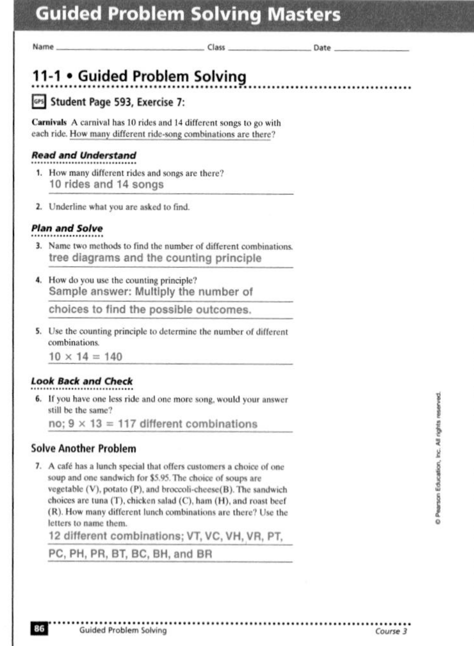

Guided Problem Solving Masters

Name ________ Class ________ Date ________

11-1 • Guided Problem Solving

GPS **Student Page 593, Exercise 7:**

Carnivals A carnival has 10 rides and 14 different songs to go with each ride. How many different ride-song combinations are there?

Read and Understand

1. How many different rides and songs are there? 10 rides and 14 songs
2. Underline what you are asked to find.

Plan and Solve

3. Name two methods to find the number of different combinations. tree diagrams and the counting principle
4. How do you use the counting principle? Sample answer: Multiply the number of choices to find the possible outcomes.
5. Use the counting principle to determine the number of different combinations. $10 \times 14 = 140$

Look Back and Check

6. If you have one less ride and one more song, would your answer still be the same? no; $9 \times 13 = 117$ different combinations

Solve Another Problem

7. A café has a lunch special that offers customers a choice of one soup and one sandwich for $5.95. The choice of soups are vegetable (V), potato (P), and broccoli-cheese(B). The sandwich choices are tuna (T), chicken salad (C), ham (H), and roast beef (R). How many different lunch combinations are there? Use the letters to name them. 12 different combinations; VT, VC, VH, VR, PT, PC, PH, PR, BT, BC, BH, and BR

86 Guided Problem Solving Course 3

Guided Problem Solving Masters

Name ________ Class ________ Date ________

11-2 • Guided Problem Solving

GPS **Student Page 598, Exercise 22:**

Dog Shows Twenty-five dogs enter a dog show. The show awards prizes for the first, second, and third place. How many different arrangements of three winners are possible?

Read and Understand

1. How many dogs enter the show? 25
2. How many prizes are given out? three
3. What are you being asked to find? the number of possible arrangements of the three winners

Plan and Solve

4. How many different dogs could win first place? 25 dogs
5. After first place is awarded, how many dogs have the possibility of winning second place? 24 dogs
6. After first and second place are awarded, how many dogs are left that could win third place? 23 dogs
7. Use the counting principle to find the number of possible arrangements. $25 \cdot 24 \cdot 23$ or 13,800 arrangements

Look Back and Check

8. Write the problem using permutation notation. Then, solve the problem. $_{25}P_3 = 25 \cdot 24 \cdot 23 = 13{,}800$ arrangements

Solve Another Problem

9. A storage company asks you to choose five different numbers from 0 to 9 as your personal identification number (PIN) to enter the property after hours. Find the number of possible five-digit numbers that you can choose from. $10 \cdot 9 \cdot 8 \cdot 7 \cdot 6 = 30{,}240$ numbers

Course 3 Guided Problem Solving 87

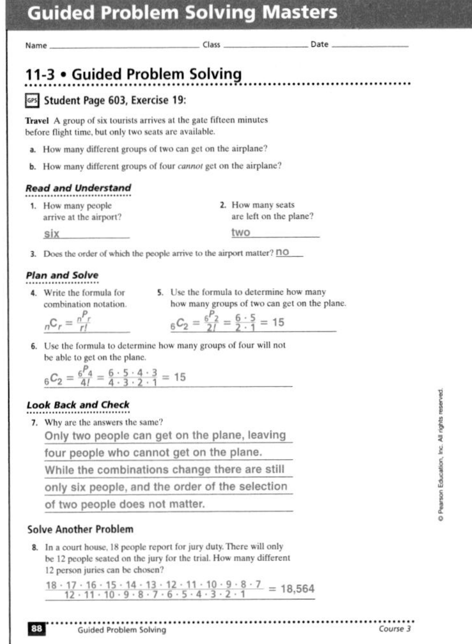
Guided Problem Solving Masters

Name ______ Class ______ Date ______

11-3 • Guided Problem Solving

Student Page 603, Exercise 19:

Travel A group of six tourists arrives at the gate fifteen minutes before flight time, but only two seats are available.

a. How many different groups of two can get on the airplane?

b. How many different groups of four *cannot* get on the airplane?

Read and Understand

1. How many people arrive at the airport? six
2. How many seats are left on the plane? two
3. Does the order of which the people arrive to the airport matter? no

Plan and Solve

4. Write the formula for combination notation. $_nC_r = \frac{_nP_r}{r!}$
5. Use the formula to determine how many groups of two can get on the plane. $_6C_2 = \frac{_6P_2}{2!} = \frac{6 \cdot 5}{2 \cdot 1} = 15$
6. Use the formula to determine how many groups of four will not be able to get on the plane. $_6C_2 = \frac{_6P_4}{4!} = \frac{6 \cdot 5 \cdot 4 \cdot 3}{4 \cdot 3 \cdot 2 \cdot 1} = 15$

Look Back and Check

7. Why are the answers the same? Only two people can get on the plane, leaving four people who cannot get on the plane. While the combinations change there are still only six people, and the order of the selection of two people does not matter.

Solve Another Problem

8. In a court house, 18 people report for jury duty. There will only be 12 people seated on the jury for the trial. How many different 12 person juries can be chosen? $\frac{18 \cdot 17 \cdot 16 \cdot 15 \cdot 14 \cdot 13 \cdot 12 \cdot 11 \cdot 10 \cdot 9 \cdot 8 \cdot 7}{12 \cdot 11 \cdot 10 \cdot 9 \cdot 8 \cdot 7 \cdot 6 \cdot 5 \cdot 4 \cdot 3 \cdot 2 \cdot 1} = 18{,}564$

Guided Problem Solving Masters

Name ______ Class ______ Date ______

11-4 • Guided Problem Solving

Student Page 609, Exercise 19:

The probability of an event is $\frac{1}{4}$. What are the odds in favor of the event occurring?

Read and Understand

1. What does the probability of an event being $\frac{1}{4}$ mean? Sample answer: There is one favorable event out of four possible outcomes.
2. What are you being asked to determine? the odds in favor of the event occurring

Plan and Solve

3. How many outcomes are there? four
4. What does the first number of a ratio mean when finding the odds in favor of an event? the number of favorable outcomes
5. What does the second number of a ratio mean when finding the odds in favor of an event? the number of unfavorable outcomes
6. Write the odds in favor of the event occurring. 1 : 3

Look Back and Check

7. How can you determine the probability when given the odds? Write the first number in the odds over the sum of both numbers $\frac{1}{1+3}$ or $\frac{1}{4}$.

Solve Another Problem

8. The probability of an event is $\frac{3}{8}$. What are the odds in favor of the event occurring? $\frac{3}{8} = \frac{3}{5+3}$, so the odds in favor are 3 : 5

Guided Problem Solving Masters

Name ______ Class ______ Date ______

11-5 • Guided Problem Solving

Student Page 613, Exercise 18:

a. **School Carnival** For a carnival game, a number cube is rolled. Each of its six faces has a different color. To win, you must select the color rolled. Find the probability of playing the carnival game twice and winning both times.

b. *Disjoint events* are events with no outcomes in common. To find the probability of two disjoint events, add the probabilities of the individual events. Suppose for the game, you choose red and your friend picks blue. What is the probability that either you or your friend wins?

Read and Understand

1. How many faces are on a game cube? six
2. How many different colors are on the game cube? six
3. Are the events dependent or independent of each other? independent

Plan and Solve

4. What is the probability of winning the first time? $\frac{1}{6}$
5. How many times is the game played in part *a*? twice
6. Multiply the probability of winning each time to find the probability of winning both times. $\frac{1}{6} \cdot \frac{1}{6} = \frac{1}{36}$
7. Add the probabilities of the individual events to find the probability of the disjoint events. $\frac{1}{6} + \frac{1}{6} = \frac{2}{6} = \frac{1}{3}$

Look Back and Check

8. Does the probability of the first roll affect the probability of the second roll? no

Solve Another Problem

9. In your pocket you have five half dollars and three quarters. You take out one coin and then put it back into your pocket. Then you take out a second coin. What is the probability of picking a quarter and a half dollar? $\frac{3}{8} \cdot \frac{5}{8} = \frac{15}{64}$

Guided Problem Solving Masters

Name ______ Class ______ Date ______

11-6 • Guided Problem Solving

Student Page 618, Exercise 11:

Day Care A day-care teacher looks out the window and sees 15 children riding either tricycles or bicycles. There are 42 wheels in motion. How many children are riding tricycles?

Read and Understand

1. Circle what you know.
2. Underline what you are asked to find.

Plan and Solve

3. How many wheels are on each type of toy? bicycle, 2; tricycle, 3
4. Write an equation that represents the problem. Let *t* represent the wheels on a tricycle and *b* represent the wheels on a bicycle. $3t + 2b = 42$
5. What must *t* plus *b* equal? 15
6. Continue the chart until you find a combination that equals 42 wheels.

3(0) + 2(15) = 30	3(5) + 2(10) = 35	3(10) + 2(5) = 40
3(1) + 2(14) = 31	3(6) + 2(9) = 36	3(11) + 2(4) = 41
3(2) + 2(13) = 32	3(7) + 2(8) = 37	3(12) + 2(3) = 42
3(3) + 2(12) = 33	3(8) + 2(7) = 38	
3(4) + 2(11) = 34	3(9) + 2(6) = 39	

7. How many children are on tricycles? How many are on bicycles? 12 on tricycles and 3 on bicycles

Look Back and Check

8. Does your number of children total 15? yes; 12 + 3 = 15

Solve Another Problem

9. Gwen's closet contains three pair of black shoes and two pair of navy shoes. What is the probability that she will pick out two matching black shoes? $\frac{6}{10} \cdot \frac{1}{9} = \frac{6}{90} = \frac{2}{30} = \frac{1}{15}$

Guided Problem Solving Masters

Name ______ Class ______ Date ______

11-7 • Guided Problem Solving

Student Page 624, Exercise 13:

Market Research A market research company interviews every hundredth person who registers a car during the year to recommend a fair purchase price for cars at a local dealership. The results are shown below.

Price Range	Frequency
\$10,000–\$14,999	15
\$15,000–\$19,999	8
\$20,000–\$24,999	12
\$25,000–\$29,999	6

a. What type of sampling is used?

b. **Probability** Find the experimental probability of a customer choosing the \$20,000-\$24,999 range.

Read and Understand

1. Who is interviewed? every hundredth person
2. What are you asked to find in part *b*? the experimental probability of a customer choosing the \$20,000–\$24,000 range

Plan and Solve

3. What are the three sampling methods you have learned so far? random, systematic, and stratified
4. Which type of sampling is used if every hundredth person is interviewed? systematic
5. What is the ratio for experimental probability? $P(\text{event}) = \frac{\text{number of times event occurs}}{\text{total number of trials}}$
6. Use the frequencies from the chart to find the experimental probability. $P(\text{event}) = \frac{12}{41}$

Look Back and Check

7. For a sample to be random, each item has an equal opportunity to be picked. Did this market research use a random sample? Explain. No; every hundredth person was chosen.

Solve Another Problem

8. A local library conducts a children's summer reading program. A complete list of all the participants is compiled by age. Then two children from each list are chosen for a prize. Determine the method of sampling. stratified

Activities and Projects

Hands-On Activities

Name ______ Class ______ Date ______

Activity 42: Exploring Order

Materials needed: four index cards per student

1. Write each of the first four letters of your first name on the index cards, one letter per card. If you have a letter in your name that repeats, use the next letter in your name. For example, if your name is Matthew, don't use M-A-T-T, use M-A-T-H. If your first name does not have enough letters, use letters from your last name. For example, Sara Smith would use S-A-R-M.
2. Copy the table below.

Number of Letters	Number of Ways to Arrange the Letters
1	1
2	
3	
4	
5	
6	

3. a. Choose two of the cards and put the other two aside. On a sheet of paper, write all of the different orders in which you can arrange the letters.
   b. Count the number of different ways you can arrange the letters and record your answer in the table.
4. Next, choose three of the cards and list the different ways you can arrange the letters. Use your cards to help you find all of the arrangements by scrambling the letters. Compare each new arrangement to the arrangements already on your list. When you have found all of the arrangements, record the number in your table.
5. a. Make a list of arrangements for four cards. Record the number of arrangements in your table.
   b. Look at your results. Use multiplication to find a pattern relating the number of letters to the number of arrangements. Write an expression for your pattern using *n* letters.
6. Use the pattern you found in Step 7 to calculate how many ways you can arrange five letters and six letters. Write your answers in the table.

Sample pages; *see p. G for complete list.*

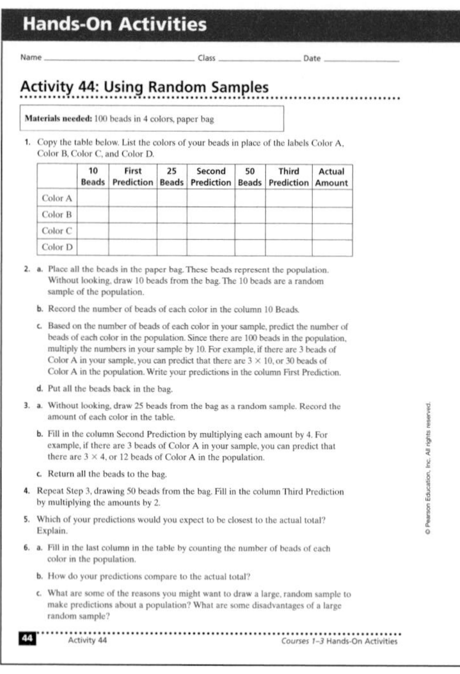

Hands-On Activities

Name ______________ Class ______________ Date ______________

Activity 44: Using Random Samples

Materials needed: 100 beads in 4 colors, paper bag

1. Copy the table below. List the colors of your beads in place of the labels Color A, Color B, Color C, and Color D.

	10 Beads	First Prediction	25 Beads	Second Prediction	50 Beads	Third Prediction	Actual Amount
Color A							
Color B							
Color C							
Color D							

2. a. Place all the beads in the paper bag. These beads represent the population. Without looking, draw 10 beads from the bag. The 10 beads are a random sample of the population.
   b. Record the number of beads of each color in the column 10 Beads.
   c. Based on the number of beads of each color in your sample, predict the number of beads of each color in the population. Since there are 100 beads in the population, multiply the numbers in your sample by 10. For example, if there are 3 beads of Color A in your sample, you can predict that there are 3×10, or 30 beads of Color A in the population. Write your predictions in the column First Prediction.
   d. Put all the beads back in the bag.
3. a. Without looking, draw 25 beads from the bag as a random sample. Record the amount of each color in the table.
   b. Fill in the column Second Prediction by multiplying each amount by 4. For example, if there are 3 beads of Color A in your sample, you can predict that there are 3×4, or 12 beads of Color A in the population.
   c. Return all the beads to the bag.
4. Repeat Step 3, drawing 50 beads from the bag. Fill in the column Third Prediction by multiplying the amounts by 2.
5. Which of your predictions would you expect to be closest to the actual total? Explain.
6. a. Fill in the last column in the table by counting the number of beads of each color in the population.
   b. How do your predictions compare to the actual total?
   c. What are some of the reasons you might want to draw a large, random sample to make predictions about a population? What are some disadvantages of a large random sample?

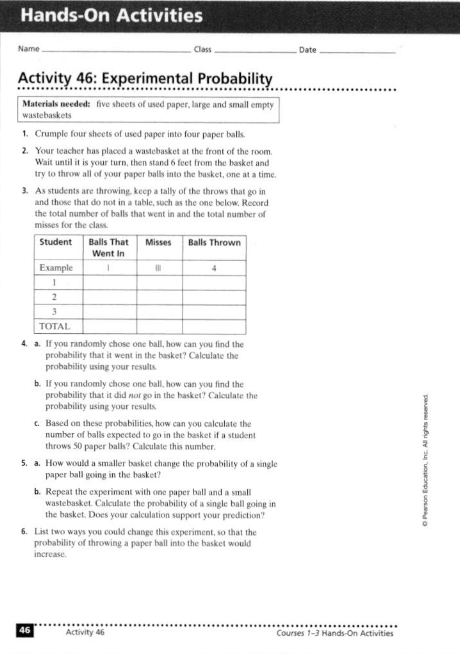

Hands-On Activities

Name ______________ Class ______________ Date ______________

Activity 46: Experimental Probability

Materials needed: five sheets of used paper, large and small empty wastebaskets

1. Crumple four sheets of used paper into four paper balls.
2. Your teacher has placed a wastebasket at the front of the room. Wait until it is your turn, then stand 6 feet from the basket and try to throw all of your paper balls into the basket, one at a time.
3. As students are throwing, keep a tally of the throws that go in and those that do not in a table, such as the one below. Record the total number of balls that went in and the total number of misses for the class.

Student	Balls That Went In	Misses	Balls Thrown
Example	I	III	4
1			
2			
3			
TOTAL			

4. a. If you randomly chose one ball, how can you find the probability that it went in the basket? Calculate the probability using your results.
   b. If you randomly chose one ball, how can you find the probability that it did *not* go in the basket? Calculate the probability using your results.
   c. Based on these probabilities, how can you calculate the number of balls expected to go in the basket if a student throws 50 paper balls? Calculate this number.
5. a. How would a smaller basket change the probability of a single paper ball going in the basket?
   b. Repeat the experiment with one paper ball and a small wastebasket. Calculate the probability of a single ball going in the basket. Does your calculation support your prediction?
6. List two ways you could change this experiment, so that the probability of throwing a paper ball into the basket would increase.

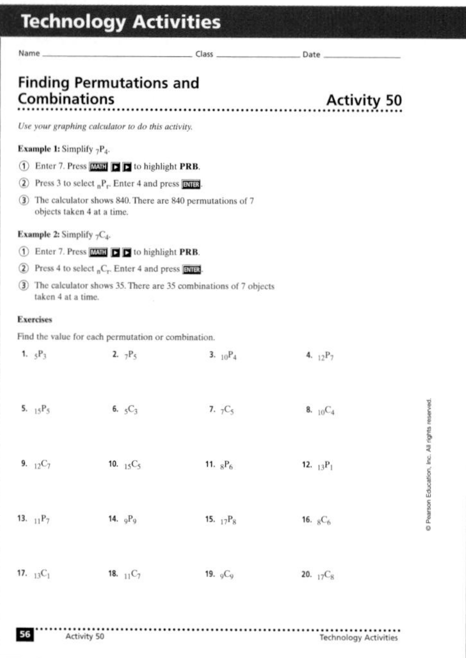

Technology Activities

Name ______________ Class ______________ Date ______________

Finding Permutations and Combinations — Activity 50

Use your graphing calculator to do this activity.

Example 1: Simplify $_7P_4$.

① Enter 7. Press MATH ▶ ▶ to highlight **PRB**.

② Press 3 to select $_nP_r$. Enter 4 and press ENTER.

③ The calculator shows 840. There are 840 permutations of 7 objects taken 4 at a time.

Example 2: Simplify $_7C_4$.

① Enter 7. Press MATH ▶ ▶ to highlight **PRB**.

② Press 4 to select $_nC_r$. Enter 4 and press ENTER.

③ The calculator shows 35. There are 35 combinations of 7 objects taken 4 at a time.

Exercises

Find the value for each permutation or combination.

1. $_5P_3$ 2. $_7P_5$ 3. $_{10}P_4$ 4. $_{12}P_7$

5. $_{15}P_5$ 6. $_5C_3$ 7. $_7C_5$ 8. $_{10}C_4$

9. $_{12}C_7$ 10. $_{15}C_5$ 11. $_8P_6$ 12. $_{13}P_1$

13. $_{11}P_7$ 14. $_9P_9$ 15. $_{17}P_8$ 16. $_8C_6$

17. $_{13}C_1$ 18. $_{11}C_7$ 19. $_9C_9$ 20. $_{17}C_8$

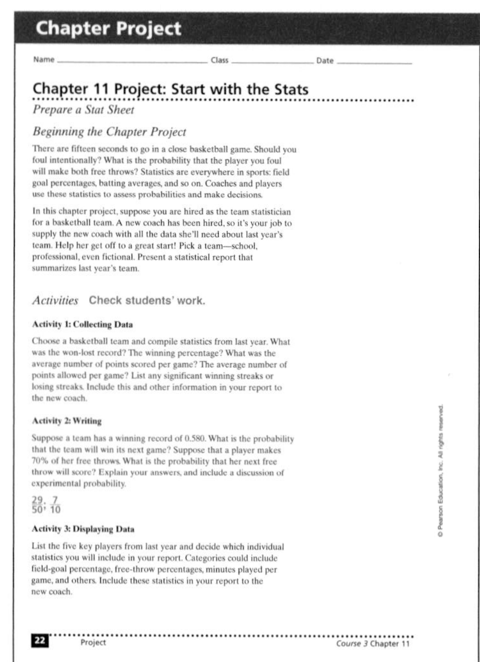

Chapter Project

Name ______________ Class ______________ Date ______________

Chapter 11 Project: Start with the Stats

Prepare a Stat Sheet

Beginning the Chapter Project

There are fifteen seconds to go in a close basketball game. Should you foul intentionally? What is the probability that the player you foul will make both free throws? Statistics are everywhere in sports: field goal percentages, batting averages, and so on. Coaches and players use these statistics to assess probabilities and make decisions.

In this chapter project, suppose you are hired as the team statistician for a basketball team. A new coach has been hired, so it's your job to supply the new coach with all the data she'll need about last year's team. Help her get off to a great start! Pick a team—school, professional, even fictional. Present a statistical report that summarizes last year's team.

Activities Check students' work.

Activity 1: Collecting Data

Choose a basketball team and compile statistics from last year. What was the won-lost record? The winning percentage? What was the average number of points scored per game? The average number of points allowed per game? List any significant winning streaks or losing streaks. Include this and other information in your report to the new coach.

Activity 2: Writing

Suppose a team has a winning record of 0.580. What is the probability that the team will win its next game? Suppose that a player makes 70% of her free throws. What is the probability that her next free throw will score? Explain your answers, and include a discussion of experimental probability.

$\frac{29}{50}$; $\frac{7}{10}$

Activity 3: Displaying Data

List the five key players from last year and decide which individual statistics you will include in your report. Categories could include field-goal percentage, free-throw percentages, minutes played per game, and others. Include these statistics in your report to the new coach.

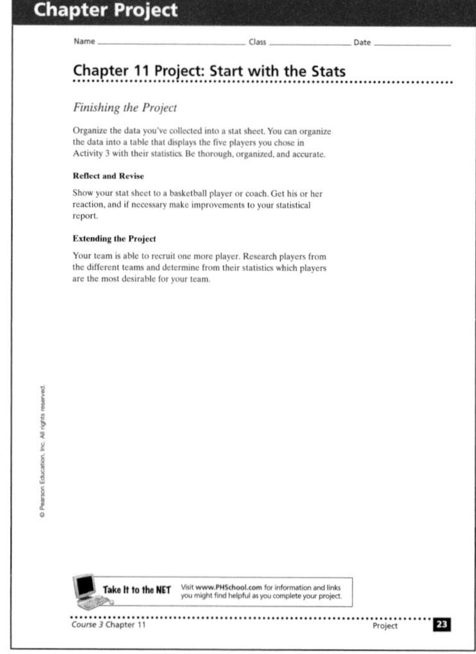

Chapter Project

Name ______________ Class ______________ Date ______________

Chapter 11 Project: Start with the Stats

Finishing the Project

Organize the data you've collected into a stat sheet. You can organize the data into a table that displays the five players you chose in Activity 3 with their statistics. Be thorough, organized, and accurate.

Reflect and Revise

Show your stat sheet to a basketball player or coach. Get his or her reaction, and if necessary make improvements to your statistical report.

Extending the Project

Your team is able to recruit one more player. Research players from the different teams and determine from their statistics which players are the most desirable for your team.

Take It to the NET Visit www.PHSchool.com for information and links you might find helpful as you complete your project.

Chapter Project

Name ______________ Class ______________ Date ______________

Chapter Project Manager

Chapter 11: Start with the Stats

Getting Started

Read about the project. As you work on it, you will need several sheets of paper. If available, a spreadsheet program also can be used. Keep all your work for the project in a folder, along with this Project Manager.

Checklist	Suggestions
❑ Activity 1: collecting	❑ Visit your local library or use the Internet to find the statistics of last seasons' teams.
❑ Activity 2: writing	❑ Review rewriting rational numbers as decimals and percents.
❑ Activity 3: displaying	❑ Use graph paper to make sure your data is listed neatly.
❑ Recommendations	❑ Use pictures from sports magazines to decorate your report.

Scoring Rubric

3 You chose appropriate team and individual statistical categories. Your report is complete, helpful, and accurate.

2 You chose mostly appropriate statistical categories. Your report is helpful and except for some minor errors, is mostly accurate.

1 You give a report that is helpful, but the choices of categories, and the accuracy of the statistics, may need improvement.

0 You leave out or do not complete major elements of the project.

Your Evaluation of Project Evaluate your work, based on the Scoring Rubric.

Teacher's Evaluation of Project

Transparencies

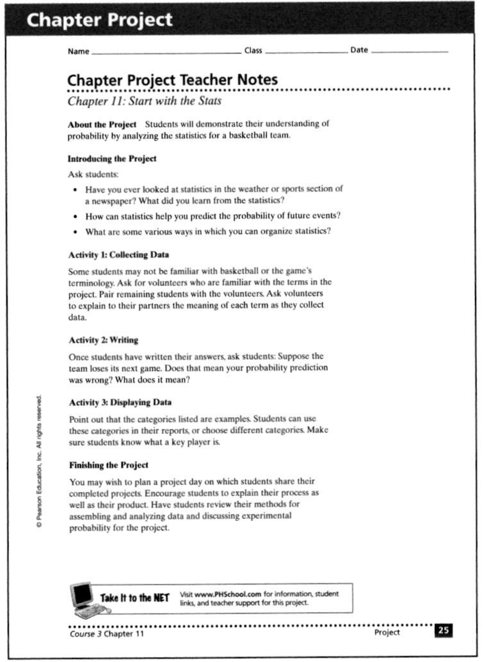

Chapter Project

Name ________ Class ________ Date ________

Chapter Project Teacher Notes

Chapter 11: Start with the Stats

About the Project Students will demonstrate their understanding of probability by analyzing the statistics for a basketball team.

Introducing the Project

Ask students:

- Have you ever looked at statistics in the weather or sports section of a newspaper? What did you learn from the statistics?
- How can statistics help you predict the probability of future events?
- What are some various ways in which you can organize statistics?

Activity 1: Collecting Data

Some students may not be familiar with basketball or the game's terminology. Ask for volunteers who are familiar with the terms in the project. Pair remaining students with the volunteers. Ask volunteers to explain to their partners the meaning of each term as they collect data.

Activity 2: Writing

Once students have written their answers, ask students: Suppose the team loses its next game. Does that mean your probability prediction was wrong? What does it mean?

Activity 3: Displaying Data

Point out that the categories listed are examples. Students can use these categories in their reports, or choose different categories. Make sure students know what a key player is.

Finishing the Project

You may wish to plan a project day on which students share their completed projects. Encourage students to explain their process as well as their product. Have students review their methods for assembling and analyzing data and discussing experimental probability for the project.

Take It to the NET Visit www.PHSchool.com for information, student links, and teacher support for this project.

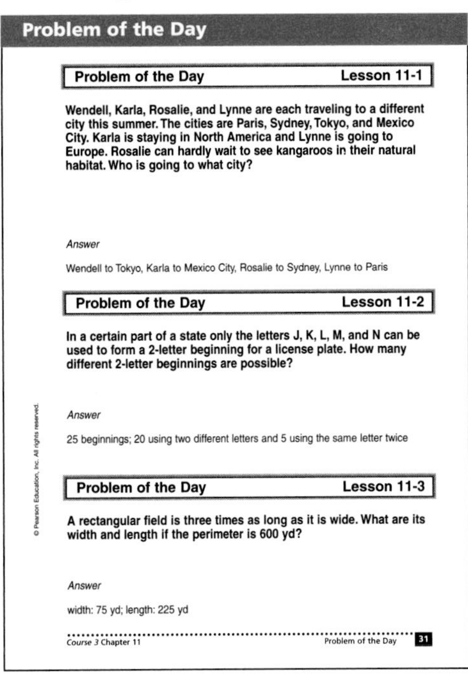

Problem of the Day

Problem of the Day — Lesson 11-1

Wendell, Karla, Rosalie, and Lynne are each traveling to a different city this summer. The cities are Paris, Sydney, Tokyo, and Mexico City. Karla is staying in North America and Lynne is going to Europe. Rosalie can hardly wait to see kangaroos in their natural habitat. Who is going to what city?

Answer

Wendell to Tokyo, Karla to Mexico City, Rosalie to Sydney, Lynne to Paris

Problem of the Day — Lesson 11-2

In a certain part of a state only the letters J, K, L, M, and N can be used to form a 2-letter beginning for a license plate. How many different 2-letter beginnings are possible?

Answer

25 beginnings; 20 using two different letters and 5 using the same letter twice

Problem of the Day — Lesson 11-3

A rectangular field is three times as long as it is wide. What are its width and length if the perimeter is 600 yd?

Answer

width: 75 yd; length: 225 yd

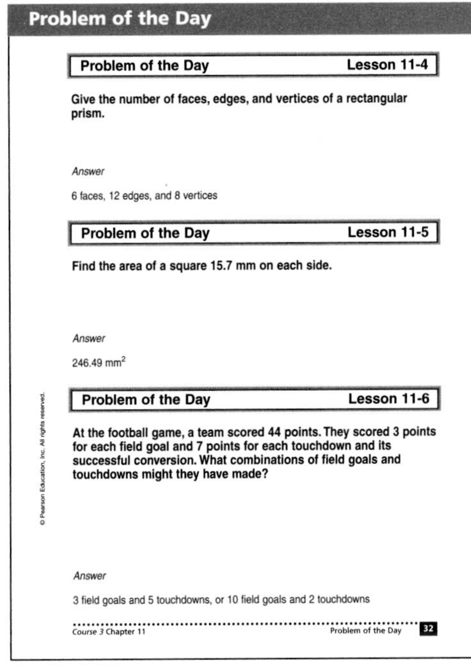

Problem of the Day

Problem of the Day — Lesson 11-4

Give the number of faces, edges, and vertices of a rectangular prism.

Answer

6 faces, 12 edges, and 8 vertices

Problem of the Day — Lesson 11-5

Find the area of a square 15.7 mm on each side.

Answer

246.49 mm^2

Problem of the Day — Lesson 11-6

At the football game, a team scored 44 points. They scored 3 points for each field goal and 7 points for each touchdown and its successful conversion. What combinations of field goals and touchdowns might they have made?

Answer

3 field goals and 5 touchdowns, or 10 field goals and 2 touchdowns

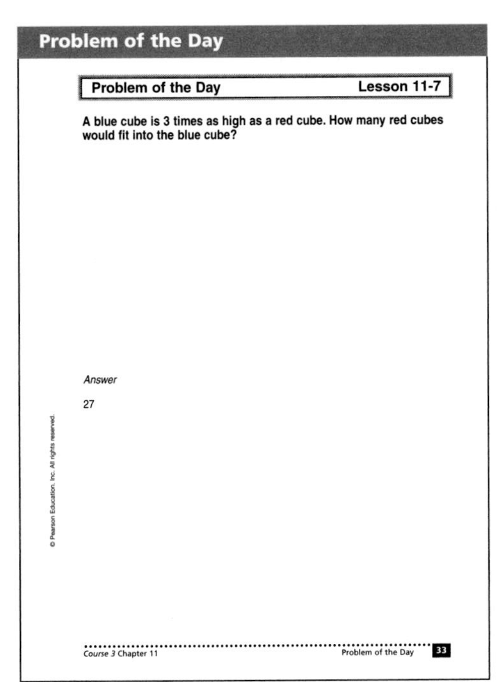

Problem of the Day

Problem of the Day — Lesson 11-7

A blue cube is 3 times as high as a red cube. How many red cubes would fit into the blue cube?

Answer

27

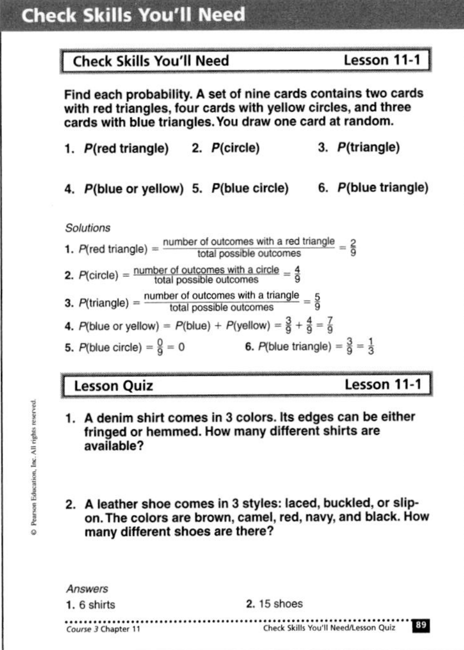

Check Skills You'll Need

Check Skills You'll Need — Lesson 11-1

Find each probability. A set of nine cards contains two cards with red triangles, four cards with yellow circles, and three cards with blue triangles. You draw one card at random.

1. *P*(red triangle) **2.** *P*(circle) **3.** *P*(triangle)

4. *P*(blue or yellow) **5.** *P*(blue circle) **6.** *P*(blue triangle)

Solutions

1. $P(\text{red triangle}) = \frac{\text{number of outcomes with a red triangle}}{\text{total possible outcomes}} = \frac{2}{9}$
2. $P(\text{circle}) = \frac{\text{number of outcomes with a circle}}{\text{total possible outcomes}} = \frac{4}{9}$
3. $P(\text{triangle}) = \frac{\text{number of outcomes with a triangle}}{\text{total possible outcomes}} = \frac{5}{9}$
4. $P(\text{blue or yellow}) = P(\text{blue}) + P(\text{yellow}) = \frac{3}{9} + \frac{4}{9} = \frac{7}{9}$
5. $P(\text{blue circle}) = \frac{0}{9} = 0$
6. $P(\text{blue triangle}) = \frac{3}{9} = \frac{1}{3}$

Lesson Quiz — Lesson 11-1

1. A denim shirt comes in 3 colors. Its edges can be either fringed or hemmed. How many different shirts are available?

2. A leather shoe comes in 3 styles: laced, buckled, or slip-on. The colors are brown, camel, red, navy, and black. How many different shoes are there?

Answers

1. 6 shirts 2. 15 shoes

Sample page; see p. H for complete list.

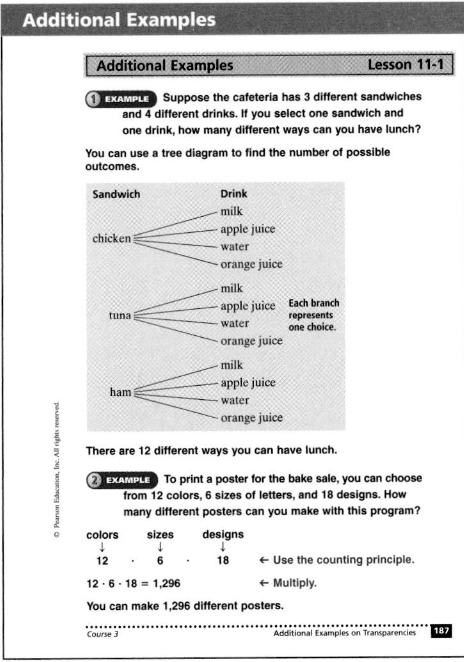

Additional Examples

Additional Examples — Lesson 11-1

1 EXAMPLE **Suppose the cafeteria has 3 different sandwiches and 4 different drinks. If you select one sandwich and one drink, how many different ways can you have lunch?**

You can use a tree diagram to find the number of possible outcomes.

There are 12 different ways you can have lunch.

2 EXAMPLE **To print a poster for the bake sale, you can choose from 12 colors, 6 sizes of letters, and 18 designs. How many different posters can you make with this program?**

colors ↓ 12 · sizes ↓ 6 · designs ↓ 18 ← Use the counting principle.

12 · 6 · 18 = 1,296 ← Multiply.

You can make 1,296 different posters.

Sample page; see p. H for complete list.

Classroom Aid

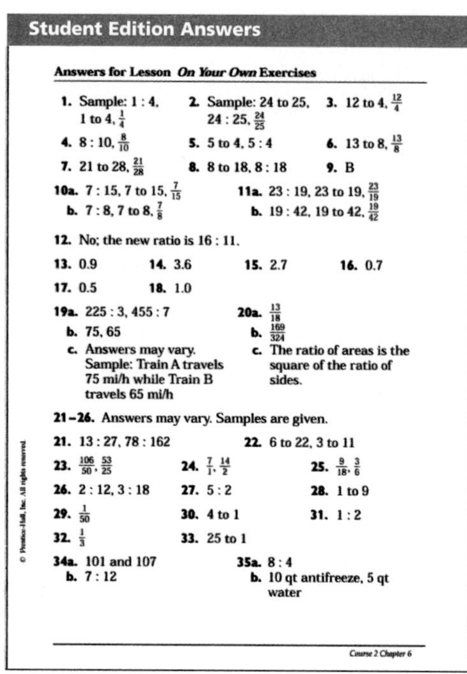

Student Edition Answers

Answers for Lesson *On Your Own* Exercises

1. Sample: 1 : 4, 1 to 4, $\frac{1}{4}$
2. Sample: 24 to 25, 24 : 25, $\frac{24}{25}$
3. 12 to 4, $\frac{12}{4}$
4. 8 : 10, $\frac{8}{10}$
5. 5 to 4, 5 : 4
6. 13 to 8, $\frac{13}{8}$
7. 21 to 28, $\frac{21}{28}$
8. 8 to 18, 8 : 18
9. B

10a. 7 : 15, 7 to 15, $\frac{7}{15}$
b. 7 : 8, 7 to 8, $\frac{7}{8}$

11a. 23 : 19, 23 to 19, $\frac{23}{19}$
b. 19 : 42, 19 to 42, $\frac{19}{42}$

12. No; the new ratio is 16 : 11.
13. 0.9
14. 3.6
15. 2.7
16. 0.7
17. 0.5
18. 1.0

19a. 225 : 3, 455 : 7
b. 75, 65
c. Answers may vary. Sample: Train A travels 75 mi/h while Train B travels 65 mi/h

20a. $\frac{13}{18}$
b. $\frac{169}{324}$
c. The ratio of areas is the square of the ratio of sides.

21–26. Answers may vary. Samples are given.

21. 13 : 27, 78 : 162
22. 6 to 22, 3 to 11
23. $\frac{106}{50}$, $\frac{53}{25}$
24. $\frac{7}{1}$, $\frac{14}{2}$
25. $\frac{9}{18}$, $\frac{3}{6}$
26. 2 : 12, 3 : 18
27. 5 : 2
28. 1 to 9
29. $\frac{1}{50}$
30. 4 to 1
31. 1 : 2
32. $\frac{1}{3}$
33. 25 to 1

34a. 101 and 107
b. 7 : 12

35a. 8 : 4
b. 10 qt antifreeze, 5 qt water

Course 2 Chapter 6

Sample page; see p. H for complete list.

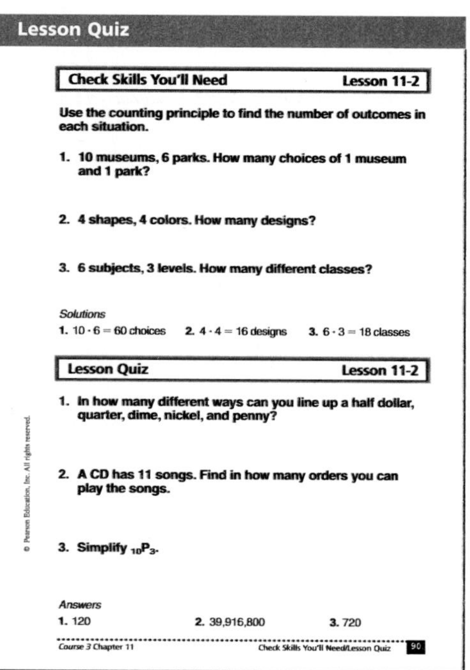

Lesson Quiz

Check Skills You'll Need **Lesson 11-2**

Use the counting principle to find the number of outcomes in each situation.

1. **10 museums, 6 parks. How many choices of 1 museum and 1 park?**
2. **4 shapes, 4 colors. How many designs?**
3. **6 subjects, 3 levels. How many different classes?**

Solutions
1. 10 · 6 = 60 choices 2. 4 · 4 = 16 designs 3. 6 · 3 = 18 classes

Lesson Quiz **Lesson 11-2**

1. **In how many different ways can you line up a half dollar, quarter, dime, nickel, and penny?**
2. **A CD has 11 songs. Find in how many orders you can play the songs.**
3. **Simplify $_{10}P_3$.**

Answers
1. 120 2. 39,916,800 3. 720

Course 3 Chapter 11 Check Skills You'll Need/Lesson Quiz 90

Sample page; see p. H for complete list.

Assessment

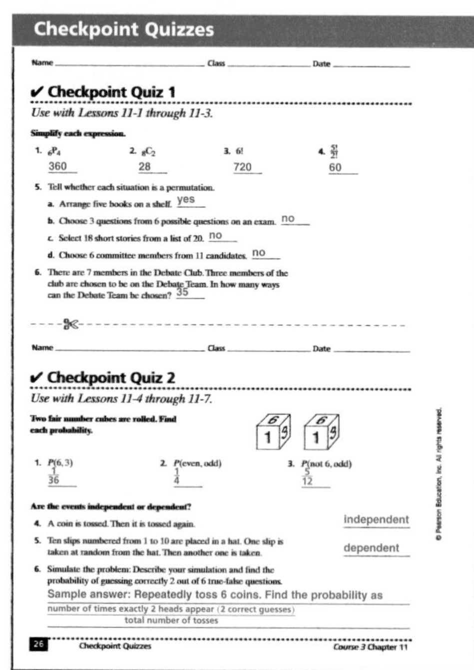

Checkpoint Quizzes

Name ______ Class ______ Date ______

✔ Checkpoint Quiz 1

Use with Lessons 11-1 through 11-3.

Simplify each expression.

1. $_6P_4$ 360
2. $_8C_2$ 28
3. 6! 720
4. $\frac{5!}{2!}$ 60
5. Tell whether each situation is a permutation.
   a. Arrange five books on a shelf. yes
   b. Choose 3 questions from 6 possible questions on an exam. no
   c. Select 18 short stories from a list of 20. no
   d. Choose 6 committee members from 11 candidates. no
6. There are 7 members in the Debate Club. Three members of the club are chosen to be on the Debate Team. In how many ways can the Debate Team be chosen? 35

Name ______ Class ______ Date ______

✔ Checkpoint Quiz 2

Use with Lessons 11-4 through 11-7.

Two fair number cubes are rolled. Find each probability.

1. $P(6, 3)$ $\frac{1}{36}$
2. $P(\text{even, odd})$ $\frac{1}{4}$
3. $P(\text{not 6, odd})$ $\frac{5}{12}$

Are the events independent or dependent?

4. A coin is tossed. Then it is tossed again. independent
5. Ten slips numbered from 1 to 10 are placed in a hat. One slip is taken at random from the hat. Then another one is taken. dependent
6. Simulate the problem: Describe your simulation and find the probability of guessing correctly 2 out of 6 true-false questions.
   Sample answer: Repeatedly toss 6 coins. Find the probability as $\frac{\text{number of times exactly 2 heads appear (2 correct guesses)}}{\text{total number of tosses}}$

26 Checkpoint Quizzes Course 3 Chapter 11

Available in Spanish

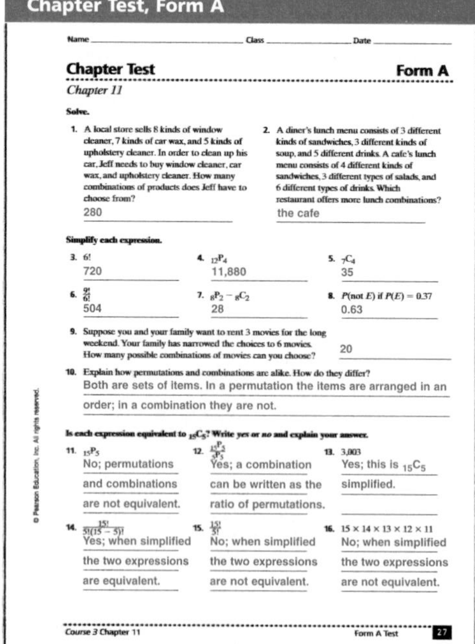

Chapter Test, Form A

Name ______ Class ______ Date ______

Chapter Test **Form A**

Chapter 11

Solve.

1. A local store sells 8 kinds of window cleaner, 7 kinds of car wax, and 5 kinds of upholstery cleaner. In order to clean up his car, Jeff needs to buy window cleaner, car wax, and upholstery cleaner. How many combinations of products does Jeff have to choose from? 280
2. A diner's lunch menu consists of 3 different kinds of sandwiches, 3 different kinds of soup, and 5 different drinks. A cafe's lunch menu consists of 4 different kinds of sandwiches, 3 different types of salads, and 6 different types of drinks. Which restaurant offers more lunch combinations? the cafe

Simplify each expression.

3. 6! 720
4. $_{12}P_4$ 11,880
5. $_7C_4$ 35
6. $\frac{9!}{6!}$ 504
7. $_8P_2 - {_8C_2}$ 28
8. $P(\text{not } E)$ if $P(E) = 0.37$ 0.63
9. Suppose you and your family want to rent 3 movies for the long weekend. Your family has narrowed the choices to 6 movies. How many possible combinations of movies can you choose? 20
10. Explain how permutations and combinations are alike. How do they differ?
    Both are sets of items. In a permutation the items are arranged in an order; in a combination they are not.

Is each expression equivalent to $_{15}C_5$? Write *yes* or *no* and explain your answer.

11. $_{15}P_5$ No; permutations and combinations are not equivalent.
12. $\frac{_{15}P_5}{_5P_5}$ Yes; a combination can be written as the ratio of permutations.
13. 3,003 Yes; this is $_{15}C_5$ simplified.
14. $\frac{15!}{5!(15-5)!}$ Yes; when simplified the two expressions are equivalent.
15. $\frac{15!}{5!}$ No; when simplified the two expressions are not equivalent.
16. $15 \times 14 \times 13 \times 12 \times 11$ No; when simplified the two expressions are not equivalent.

Course 3 Chapter 11 Form A Test 27

Available in Spanish

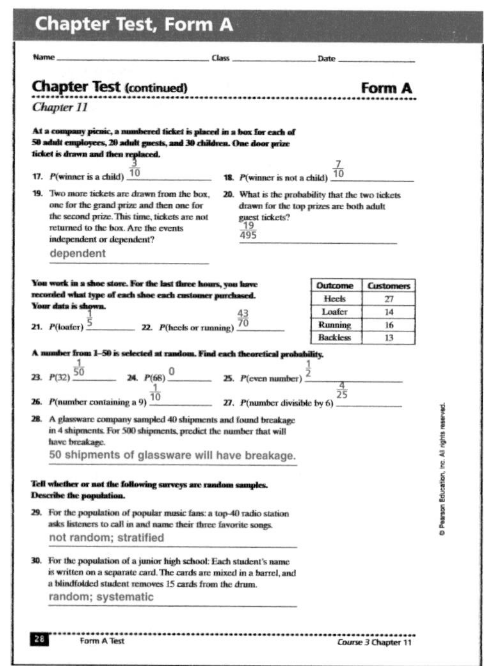

Chapter Test, Form A

Name ______ Class ______ Date ______

Chapter Test (continued) **Form A**

Chapter 11

At a company picnic, a numbered ticket is placed in a box for each of 50 adult employees, 20 adult guests, and 30 children. One door prize ticket is drawn and then replaced.

17. $P(\text{winner is a child})$ $\frac{3}{10}$
18. $P(\text{winner is not a child})$ $\frac{7}{10}$
19. Two more tickets are drawn from the box, one for the grand prize and then one for the second prize. This time, tickets are not returned to the box. Are the events independent or dependent? dependent
20. What is the probability that the two tickets drawn for the top prizes are both adult guest tickets? $\frac{19}{495}$

You work in a shoe store. For the last three hours, you have recorded what type of each shoe each customer purchased. Your data is shown.

Outcome	Customers
Heels	27
Loafer	14
Running	16
Backless	13

21. $P(\text{loafer})$ $\frac{1}{5}$
22. $P(\text{heels or running})$ $\frac{43}{70}$

A number from 1–50 is selected at random. Find each theoretical probability.

23. $P(32)$ $\frac{1}{50}$
24. $P(68)$ 0
25. $P(\text{even number})$ $\frac{1}{2}$
26. $P(\text{number containing a 9})$ $\frac{1}{10}$
27. $P(\text{number divisible by 6})$ $\frac{4}{25}$
28. A glassware company sampled 40 shipments and found breakage in 4 shipments. For 500 shipments, predict the number that will have breakage. 50 shipments of glassware will have breakage.

Tell whether or not the following surveys are random samples. Describe the population.

29. For the population of popular music fans: a top-40 radio station asks listeners to call in and name their three favorite songs. not random; stratified
30. For the population of a junior high school: Each student's name is written on a separate card. The cards are mixed in a barrel, and a blindfolded student removes 15 cards from the drum. random; systematic

28 Form A Test Course 3 Chapter 11

Available in Spanish

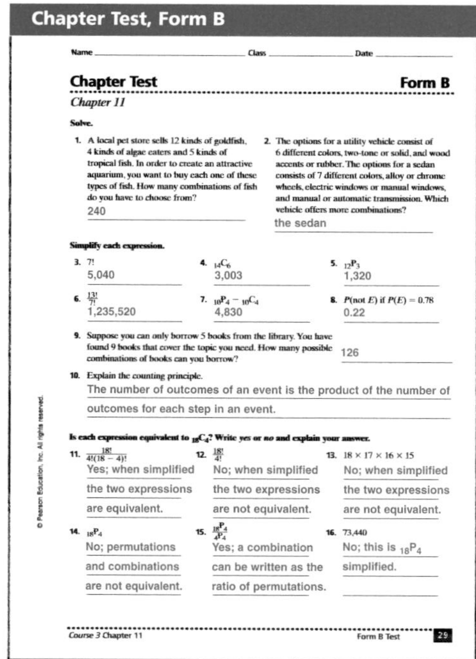

Chapter Test, Form B

Name ____ Class ____ Date ____

Chapter Test **Form B**

Chapter 11

Solve.

1. A local pet store sells 12 kinds of goldfish, 4 kinds of algae eaters and 5 kinds of tropical fish. In order to create an attractive aquarium, you want to buy each one of these types of fish. How many combinations of fish do you have to choose from? 240
2. The options for a utility vehicle consist of 6 different colors, two-tone or solid, and wood accents or rubber. The options for a sedan consists of 7 different colors, alloy or chrome wheels, electric windows or manual windows, and manual or automatic transmission. Which vehicle offers more combinations? the sedan

Simplify each expression.

3. 7! 5,040
4. $_{14}C_6$ 3,003
5. $_{12}P_3$ 1,320
6. $\frac{13!}{7!}$ 1,235,520
7. $_{10}P_4 - {}_{10}C_4$ 4,830
8. $P(\text{not } E)$ if $P(E) = 0.78$ 0.22
9. Suppose you can only borrow 5 books from the library. You have found 9 books that cover the topic you need. How many possible combinations of books can you borrow? 126
10. Explain the counting principle. The number of outcomes of an event is the product of the number of outcomes for each step in an event.

Is each expression equivalent to $_{18}C_4$? Write *yes* or *no* and explain your answer.

11. $\frac{18!}{4!(18-4)!}$ Yes; when simplified the two expressions are equivalent.
12. $\frac{18!}{4!}$ No; when simplified the two expressions are not equivalent.
13. $18 \times 17 \times 16 \times 15$ No; when simplified the two expressions are not equivalent.
14. $_{18}P_4$ No; permutations and combinations are not equivalent.
15. $\frac{_{18}P_4}{_4P_4}$ Yes; a combination can be written as the ratio of permutations.
16. 73,440 No; this is $_{18}P_4$ simplified.

Course 3 Chapter 11 Form B Test 29

Available in Spanish

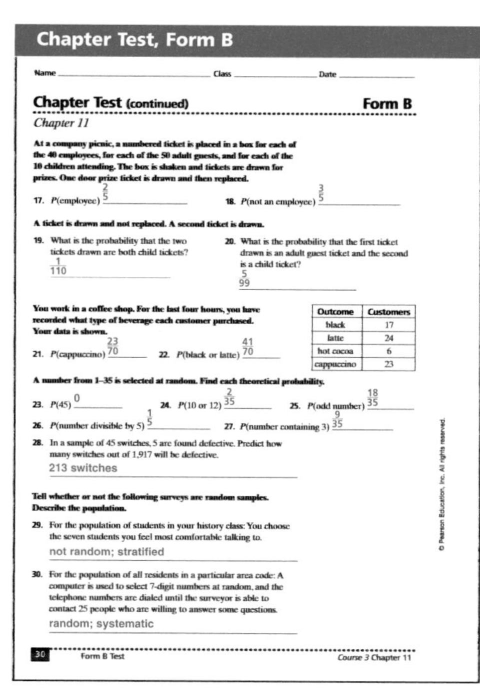

Chapter Test, Form B

Name ____ Class ____ Date ____

Chapter Test (continued) **Form B**

Chapter 11

At a company picnic, a numbered ticket is placed in a box for each of the 40 employees, for each of the 50 adult guests, and for each of the 10 children attending. The box is shaken and tickets are drawn for prizes. One door prize ticket is drawn and then replaced.

17. $P(\text{employee})$ $\frac{2}{5}$
18. $P(\text{not an employee})$ $\frac{3}{5}$

A ticket is drawn and not replaced. A second ticket is drawn.

19. What is the probability that the two tickets drawn are both child tickets? $\frac{1}{110}$
20. What is the probability that the first ticket drawn is an adult guest ticket and the second is a child ticket? $\frac{5}{99}$

You work in a coffee shop. For the last four hours, you have recorded what type of beverage each customer purchased. Your data is shown.

Outcome	Customers
black	17
latte	24
hot cocoa	6
cappuccino	23

21. $P(\text{cappuccino})$ $\frac{23}{70}$
22. $P(\text{black or latte})$ $\frac{41}{70}$

A number from 1–35 is selected at random. Find each theoretical probability.

23. $P(45)$ 0
24. $P(10 \text{ or } 12)$ $\frac{2}{35}$
25. $P(\text{odd number})$ $\frac{18}{35}$
26. $P(\text{number divisible by 5})$ $\frac{1}{5}$
27. $P(\text{number containing 3})$ $\frac{9}{35}$
28. In a sample of 45 switches, 5 are found defective. Predict how many switches out of 1,917 will be defective. 213 switches

Tell whether or not the following surveys are random samples. Describe the population.

29. For the population of students in your history class: You choose the seven students you feel most comfortable talking to. not random; stratified
30. For the population of all residents in a particular area code: A computer is used to select 7-digit numbers at random, and the telephone numbers are dialed until the surveyor is able to contact 25 people who are willing to answer some questions. random; systematic

30 Form B Test Course 3 Chapter 11

Available in Spanish

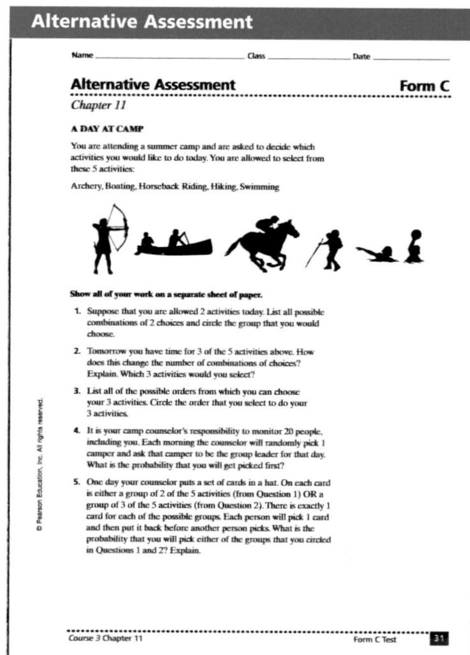

Alternative Assessment

Name ____ Class ____ Date ____

Alternative Assessment **Form C**

Chapter 11

A DAY AT CAMP

You are attending a summer camp and are asked to decide which activities you would like to do today. You are allowed to select from these 5 activities:

Archery, Boating, Horseback Riding, Hiking, Swimming

Show all of your work on a separate sheet of paper.

1. Suppose that you are allowed 2 activities today. List all possible combinations of 2 choices and circle the group that you would choose.
2. Tomorrow you have time for 3 of the 5 activities above. How does this change the number of combinations of choices? Explain. Which 3 activities would you select?
3. List all of the possible orders from which you can choose your 3 activities. Circle the order that you select to do your 3 activities.
4. It is your camp counselor's responsibility to monitor 20 people, including you. Each morning the counselor will randomly pick 1 camper and ask that camper to be the group leader for that day. What is the probability that you will get picked first?
5. One day your counselor puts a set of cards in a hat. On each card is either a group of 2 of the 5 activities (from Question 1) OR a group of 3 of the 5 activities (from Question 2). There is exactly 1 card for each of the possible groups. Each person will pick 1 card and then put it back before another person picks. What is the probability that you will pick either of the groups that you circled in Questions 1 and 2? Explain.

Course 3 Chapter 11 Form C Test 31

Available in Spanish

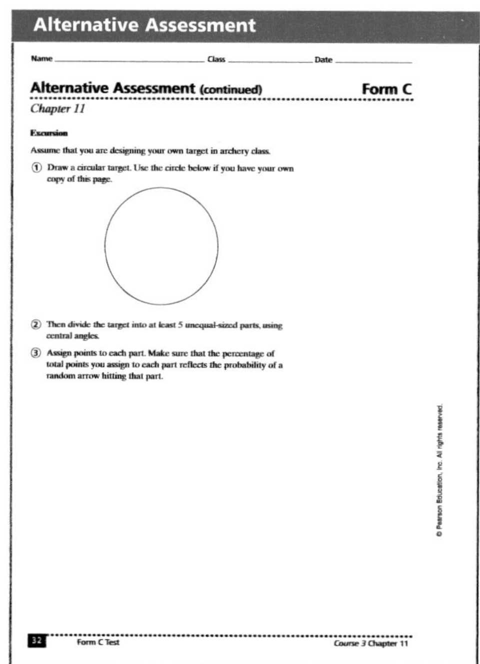

Alternative Assessment

Name ____ Class ____ Date ____

Alternative Assessment (continued) **Form C**

Chapter 11

Excursion

Assume that you are designing your own target in archery class.

① Draw a circular target. Use the circle below if you have your own copy of this page.

② Then divide the target into at least 5 unequal-sized parts, using central angles.

③ Assign points to each part. Make sure that the percentage of total points you assign to each part reflects the probability of a random arrow hitting that part.

32 Form C Test Course 3 Chapter 11

Available in Spanish

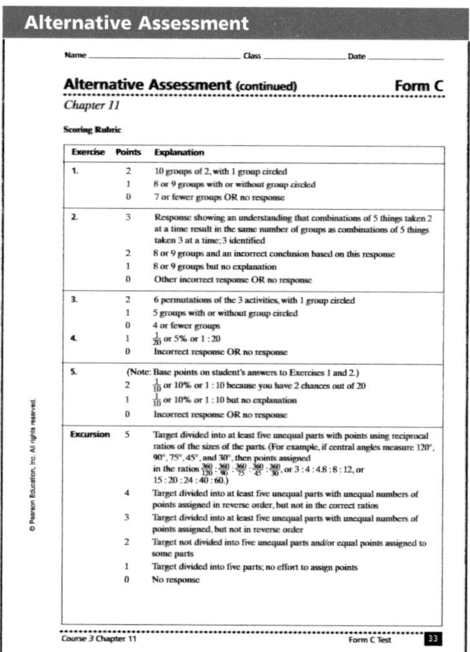

Alternative Assessment

Name ____ Class ____ Date ____

Alternative Assessment (continued) **Form C**

Chapter 11

Scoring Rubric

Exercise	Points	Explanation
1.	2	10 groups of 2, with 1 group circled
	1	8 or 9 groups with or without group circled
	0	7 or fewer groups OR no response
2.	3	Response showing an understanding that combinations of 5 things taken 2 at a time result in the same number of groups as combinations of 5 things taken 3 at a time; 3 identified
	2	8 or 9 groups and an incorrect conclusion based on this response
	1	8 or 9 groups but no explanation
	0	Other incorrect response OR no response
3.	2	6 permutations of the 3 activities, with 1 group circled
	1	5 groups with or without group circled
	0	4 or fewer groups
4.	1	$\frac{1}{20}$ or 5% or 1 : 20
	0	Incorrect response OR no response
5.		(Note: Base points on student's answers to Exercises 1 and 2.)
	2	$\frac{1}{10}$ or 10% or 1 : 10 because you have 2 chances out of 20
	1	$\frac{1}{10}$ or 10% or 1 : 10 but no explanation
	0	Incorrect response OR no response
Excursion	5	Target divided into at least five unequal parts with points using reciprocal ratios of the sizes of the parts. (For example, if central angles measure 120°, 90°, 75°, 45°, and 30°, then points assigned in the ratios $\frac{360}{120} : \frac{360}{90} : \frac{360}{75} : \frac{360}{45} : \frac{360}{30}$, or 3 : 4 : 4.8 : 8 : 12, or 15 : 20 : 24 : 40 : 60.)
	4	Target divided into at least five unequal parts with unequal numbers of points assigned in reverse order, but not in the correct ratios
	3	Target divided into at least five unequal parts with unequal numbers of points assigned, but not in reverse order
	2	Target not divided into five unequal parts and/or equal points assigned to some parts
	1	Target divided into five parts; no effort to assign points
	0	No response

Course 3 Chapter 11 Form C Test 33

Available in Spanish

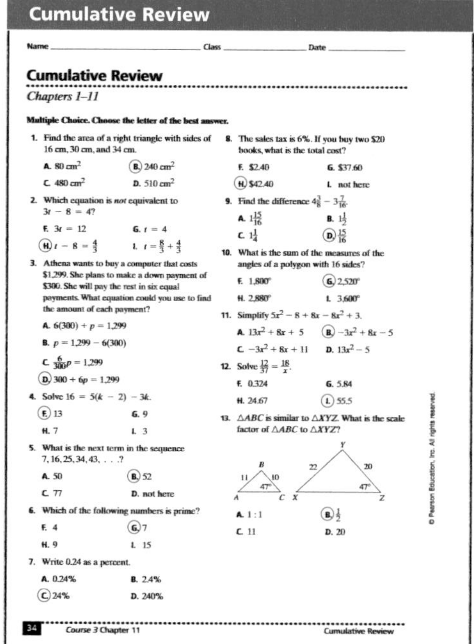

Cumulative Review

Name ____ Class ____ Date ____

Cumulative Review

Chapters 1–11

Multiple Choice. Choose the letter of the best answer.

1. Find the area of a right triangle with sides of 16 cm, 30 cm, and 34 cm.
   A. 80 cm² (B.) 240 cm² C. 480 cm² D. 510 cm²
2. Which equation is *not* equivalent to $3t - 8 = 4$?
   F. $3t = 12$ G. $t = 4$ (H.) $t - 8 = \frac{4}{3}$ I. $t = \frac{8}{3} + \frac{4}{3}$
3. Athena wants to buy a computer that costs $1,299. She plans to make a down payment of $300. She will pay the rest in six equal payments. What equation could you use to find the amount of each payment?
   A. $6(300) + p = 1{,}299$ B. $p = 1{,}299 - 6(300)$ C. $\frac{6}{300}p = 1{,}299$ (D.) $300 + 6p = 1{,}299$
4. Solve $16 = 5(k - 2) - 3k$.
   (F.) 13 G. 9 H. 7 I. 3
5. What is the next term in the sequence 7, 16, 25, 34, 43, . . . ?
   A. 50 (B.) 52 C. 77 D. not here
6. Which of the following numbers is prime?
   F. 4 (G.) 7 H. 9 I. 15
7. Write 0.24 as a percent.
   A. 0.24% B. 2.4% (C.) 24% D. 240%
8. The sales tax is 6%. If you buy two $20 books, what is the total cost?
   F. $2.40 G. $37.60 (H.) $42.40 I. not here
9. Find the difference $4\frac{3}{8} - 3\frac{7}{16}$.
   A. $1\frac{15}{16}$ B. $1\frac{1}{2}$ C. $1\frac{1}{4}$ (D.) $\frac{15}{16}$
10. What is the sum of the measures of the angles of a polygon with 16 sides?
   F. 1,800° (G.) 2,520° H. 2,880° I. 3,600°
11. Simplify $5x^2 - 8 + 8x - 8x^2 + 3$.
   A. $13x^2 + 8x + 5$ (B.) $-3x^2 + 8x - 5$ C. $-3x^2 + 8x + 11$ D. $13x^2 - 5$
12. Solve $\frac{12}{37} = \frac{18}{x}$.
   F. 0.324 G. 5.84 H. 24.67 (I.) 55.5
13. $\triangle ABC$ is similar to $\triangle XYZ$. What is the scale factor of $\triangle ABC$ to $\triangle XYZ$?

   A. 1 : 1 (B.) $\frac{1}{2}$ C. 11 D. 20

34 Course 3 Chapter 11 Cumulative Review

Available in Spanish

Cumulative Review

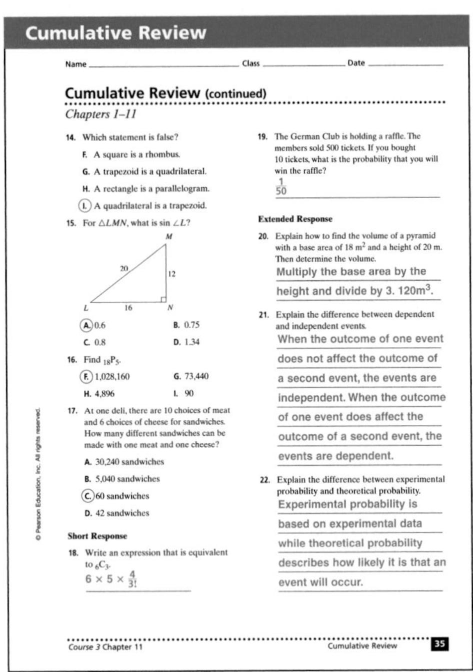

Name ______ Class ______ Date ______

Cumulative Review (continued)

Chapters 1–11

14. Which statement is false?
    - F. A square is a rhombus.
    - G. A trapezoid is a quadrilateral.
    - H. A rectangle is a parallelogram.
    - (I.) A quadrilateral is a trapezoid.
15. For $\triangle LMN$, what is $\sin \angle L$?
    - (A.) 0.6
    - B. 0.75
    - C. 0.8
    - D. 1.34
16. Find ${}_{10}P_5$.
    - (F.) 1,028,160
    - G. 73,440
    - H. 4,896
    - I. 90
17. At one deli, there are 10 choices of meat and 6 choices of cheese for sandwiches. How many different sandwiches can be made with one meat and one cheese?
    - A. 30,240 sandwiches
    - B. 5,040 sandwiches
    - (C.) 60 sandwiches
    - D. 42 sandwiches

Short Response

18. Write an expression that is equivalent to ${}_6C_3$.
    $6 \times 5 \times \frac{4}{3!}$
19. The German Club is holding a raffle. The members sold 500 tickets. If you bought 10 tickets, what is the probability that you will win the raffle?
    $\frac{1}{50}$

Extended Response

20. Explain how to find the volume of a pyramid with a base area of 18 m² and a height of 20 m. Then determine the volume.
    Multiply the base area by the height and divide by 3. 120m³.
21. Explain the difference between dependent and independent events.
    When the outcome of one event does not affect the outcome of a second event, the events are independent. When the outcome of one event does affect the outcome of a second event, the events are dependent.
22. Explain the difference between experimental probability and theoretical probability.
    Experimental probability is based on experimental data while theoretical probability describes how likely it is that an event will occur.

© Pearson Education, Inc. All rights reserved.

Course 3 Chapter 11 Cumulative Review 35

Available in Spanish

Benchmark Test

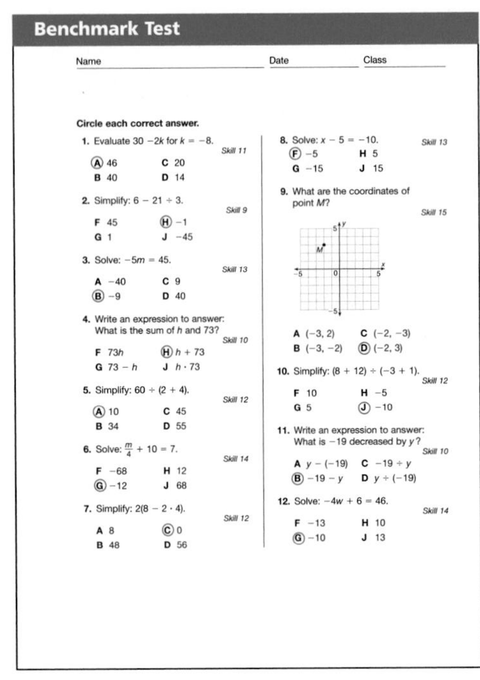

Name ______ Date ______ Class ______

Circle each correct answer.

1. Evaluate $30 - 2k$ for $k = -8$. *Skill 11*
   - (A) 46
   - C 20
   - B 40
   - D 14
2. Simplify: $6 - 21 \div 3$. *Skill 9*
   - F 45
   - (H) −1
   - G 1
   - J −45
3. Solve: $-5m = 45$. *Skill 13*
   - A −40
   - C 9
   - (B) −9
   - D 40
4. Write an expression to answer: What is the sum of h and 73? *Skill 10*
   - F $73h$
   - (H) $h + 73$
   - G $73 - h$
   - J $h \cdot 73$
5. Simplify: $60 \div (2 + 4)$. *Skill 12*
   - (A) 10
   - C 45
   - B 34
   - D 55
6. Solve: $\frac{m}{4} + 10 = 7$. *Skill 14*
   - F −68
   - H 12
   - (G) −12
   - J 68
7. Simplify: $2(8 - 2 \cdot 4)$. *Skill 12*
   - A 8
   - (C) 0
   - B 48
   - D 56
8. Solve: $x - 5 = -10$. *Skill 13*
   - (F) −5
   - H 5
   - G −15
   - J 15
9. What are the coordinates of point M? *Skill 15*
   - A (−3, 2)
   - C (−2, −3)
   - B (−3, −2)
   - (D) (−2, 3)
10. Simplify: $(8 + 12) \div (-3 + 1)$. *Skill 12*
    - F 10
    - H −5
    - G 5
    - (J) −10
11. Write an expression to answer: What is −19 decreased by y? *Skill 10*
    - A $y - (-19)$
    - C $-19 \div y$
    - (B) $-19 - y$
    - D $y \div (-19)$
12. Solve: $-4w + 6 = 46$. *Skill 14*
    - F −13
    - H 10
    - (G) −10
    - J 13

Test-Taking Strategies transparency

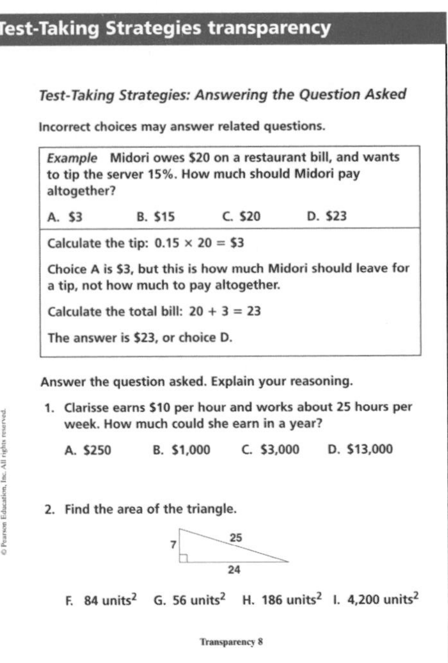

Test-Taking Strategies: Answering the Question Asked

Incorrect choices may answer related questions.

Example Midori owes \$20 on a restaurant bill, and wants to tip the server 15%. How much should Midori pay altogether?

A. \$3 B. \$15 C. \$20 D. \$23

Calculate the tip: 0.15 × 20 = \$3

Choice A is \$3, but this is how much Midori should leave for a tip, not how much to pay altogether.

Calculate the total bill: 20 + 3 = 23

The answer is \$23, or choice D.

Answer the question asked. Explain your reasoning.

1. Clarisse earns \$10 per hour and works about 25 hours per week. How much could she earn in a year?
   A. \$250 B. \$1,000 C. \$3,000 D. \$13,000
2. Find the area of the triangle.
   F. 84 units² G. 56 units² H. 186 units² I. 4,200 units²

© Pearson Education, Inc. All rights reserved.

Transparency 8

On PH Website

Test-Taking Strategies worksheet

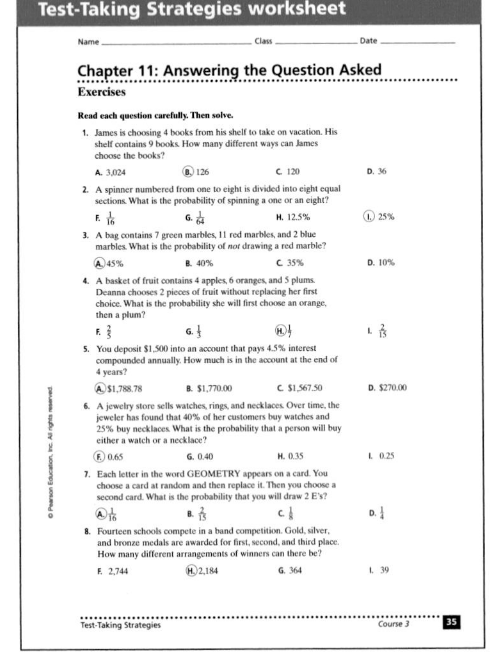

Name ______ Class ______ Date ______

Chapter 11: Answering the Question Asked

Exercises

Read each question carefully. Then solve.

1. James is choosing 4 books from his shelf to take on vacation. His shelf contains 9 books. How many different ways can James choose the books?
   A. 3,024 (B.) 126 C. 120 D. 36
2. A spinner numbered from one to eight is divided into eight equal sections. What is the probability of spinning a one or an eight?
   F. $\frac{1}{16}$ G. $\frac{1}{64}$ H. 12.5% (I.) 25%
3. A bag contains 7 green marbles, 11 red marbles, and 2 blue marbles. What is the probability of *not* drawing a red marble?
   (A.) 45% B. 40% C. 35% D. 10%
4. A basket of fruit contains 4 apples, 6 oranges, and 5 plums. Deanna chooses 2 pieces of fruit without replacing her first choice. What is the probability she will first choose an orange, then a plum?
   F. $\frac{2}{5}$ G. $\frac{1}{3}$ (H.) $\frac{1}{7}$ I. $\frac{2}{15}$
5. You deposit \$1,500 into an account that pays 4.5% interest compounded annually. How much is in the account at the end of 4 years?
   (A.) \$1,788.78 B. \$1,770.00 C. \$1,567.50 D. \$270.00
6. A jewelry store sells watches, rings, and necklaces. Over time, the jeweler has found that 40% of her customers buy watches and 25% buy necklaces. What is the probability that a person will buy either a watch or a necklace?
   (F.) 0.65 G. 0.40 H. 0.35 I. 0.25
7. Each letter in the word GEOMETRY appears on a card. You choose a card at random and then replace it. Then you choose a second card. What is the probability that you will draw 2 E's?
   (A.) $\frac{1}{16}$ B. $\frac{2}{15}$ C. $\frac{1}{8}$ D. $\frac{1}{4}$
8. Fourteen schools compete in a band competition. Gold, silver, and bronze medals are awarded for first, second, and third place. How many different arrangements of winners can there be?
   F. 2,744 (H.) 2,184 G. 364 I. 39

© Pearson Education, Inc. All rights reserved.

Test-Taking Strategies Course 3 35

Home Activities

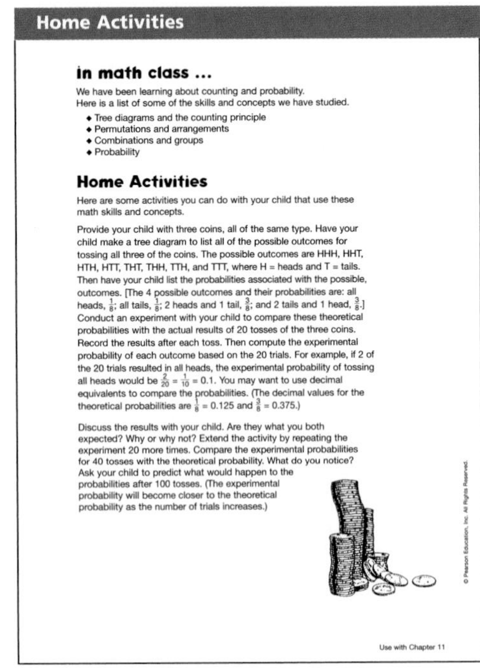

In math class ...

We have been learning about counting and probability. Here is a list of some of the skills and concepts we have studied.

- Tree diagrams and the counting principle
- Permutations and arrangements
- Combinations and groups
- Probability

Home Activities

Here are some activities you can do with your child that use these math skills and concepts.

Provide your child with three coins, all of the same type. Have your child make a tree diagram to list all of the possible outcomes for tossing all three of the coins. The possible outcomes are HHH, HHT, HTH, HTT, THT, THH, TTH, and TTT, where H = heads and T = tails. Then have your child list the probabilities associated with the possible outcomes. [The 4 possible outcomes and their probabilities are: all heads, $\frac{1}{8}$; all tails, $\frac{1}{8}$; 2 heads and 1 tail, $\frac{3}{8}$; and 2 tails and 1 head, $\frac{3}{8}$.] Conduct an experiment with your child to compare these theoretical probabilities with the actual results of 20 tosses of the three coins. Record the results after each toss. Then compute the experimental probability of each outcome based on the 20 trials. For example, if 2 of the 20 trials resulted in all heads, the experimental probability of tossing all heads would be $\frac{2}{20} = \frac{1}{10} = 0.1$. You may want to use decimal equivalents to compare the probabilities. (The decimal values for the theoretical probabilities are $\frac{1}{8} = 0.125$ and $\frac{3}{8} = 0.375$.)

Discuss the results with your child. Are they what you both expected? Why or why not? Extend the activity by repeating the experiment 20 more times. Compare the experimental probabilities for 40 tosses with the theoretical probability. What do you notice? Ask your child to predict what would happen to the probabilities after 100 tosses. (The experimental probability will become closer to the theoretical probability as the number of trials increases.)

© Pearson Education, Inc. All Rights Reserved.

Use with Chapter 11

Available in Spanish;
Web Code: ack-5500

Interdisciplinary Activities

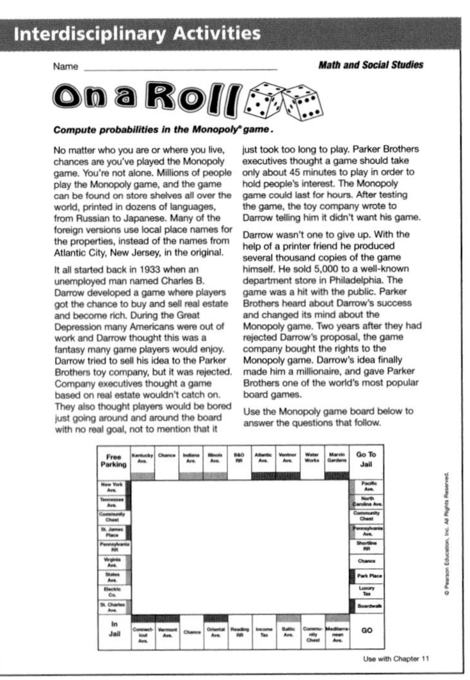

Name ______ *Math and Social Studies*

On a Roll

Compute probabilities in the Monopoly® game.

No matter who you are or where you live, chances are you've played the Monopoly game. You're not alone. Millions of people play the Monopoly game, and the game can be found on store shelves all over the world, printed in dozens of languages, from Russian to Japanese. Many of the foreign versions use local place names for the properties, instead of the names from Atlantic City, New Jersey, in the original.

It all started back in 1933 when an unemployed man named Charles B. Darrow developed a game where players got the chance to buy and sell real estate and become rich. During the Great Depression many Americans were out of work and Darrow thought this was a fantasy many game players would enjoy. Darrow tried to sell his idea to the Parker Brothers toy company, but it was rejected. Company executives thought a game based on real estate wouldn't catch on. They also thought players would be bored just going around and around the board with no real goal, not to mention that it just took too long to play. Parker Brothers executives thought a game should take only about 45 minutes to play in order to hold people's interest. The Monopoly game could last for hours. After testing the game, the toy company wrote to Darrow telling him it didn't want his game.

Darrow wasn't one to give up. With the help of a printer friend he produced several thousand copies of the game himself. He sold 5,000 to a well-known department store in Philadelphia. The game was a hit with the public. Parker Brothers heard about Darrow's success and changed its mind about the Monopoly game. Two years after they had rejected Darrow's proposal, the game company bought the rights to the game. Darrow's idea finally made him a millionaire, and gave Parker Brothers one of the world's most popular board games.

Use the Monopoly game board below to answer the questions that follow.

© Pearson Education, Inc. All Rights Reserved.

Use with Chapter 11

Web Code: ack-5500

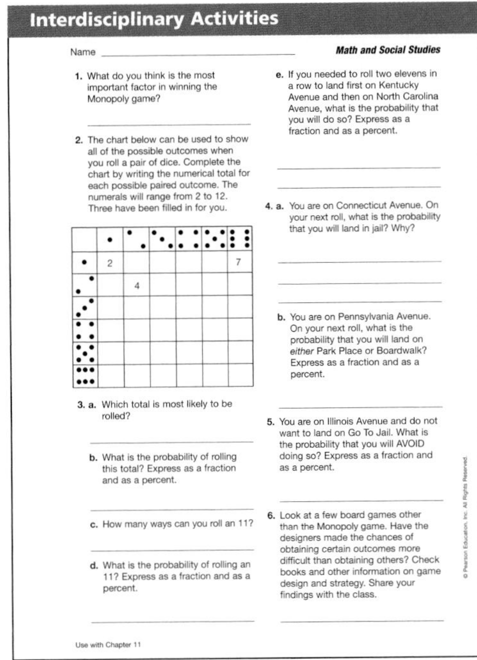

Interdisciplinary Activities

Name ______________________ ***Math and Social Studies***

1. What do you think is the most important factor in winning the Monopoly game?

2. The chart below can be used to show all of the possible outcomes when you roll a pair of dice. Complete the chart by writing the numerical total for each possible paired outcome. The numerals will range from 2 to 12. Three have been filled in for you.

	⚀	⚁	⚂	⚃	⚄	⚅
⚀	2					7
⚁		4				
⚂						
⚃						
⚄						
⚅						

3. a. Which total is most likely to be rolled?

   b. What is the probability of rolling this total? Express as a fraction and as a percent.

   c. How many ways can you roll an 11?

   d. What is the probability of rolling an 11? Express as a fraction and as a percent.

   e. If you needed to roll two elevens in a row to land first on Kentucky Avenue and then on North Carolina Avenue, what is the probability that you will do so? Express as a fraction and as a percent.

4. a. You are on Connecticut Avenue. On your next roll, what is the probability that you will land in jail? Why?

   b. You are on Pennsylvania Avenue. On your next roll, what is the probability that you will land on *either* Park Place or Boardwalk? Express as a fraction and as a percent.

5. You are on Illinois Avenue and do not want to land on Go To Jail. What is the probability that you will AVOID doing so? Express as a fraction and as a percent.

6. Look at a few board games other than the Monopoly game. Have the designers made the chances of obtaining certain outcomes more difficult than obtaining others? Check books and other information on game design and strategy. Share your findings with the class.

Use with Chapter 11

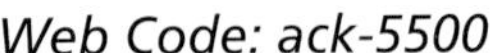

Web Code: ack-5500

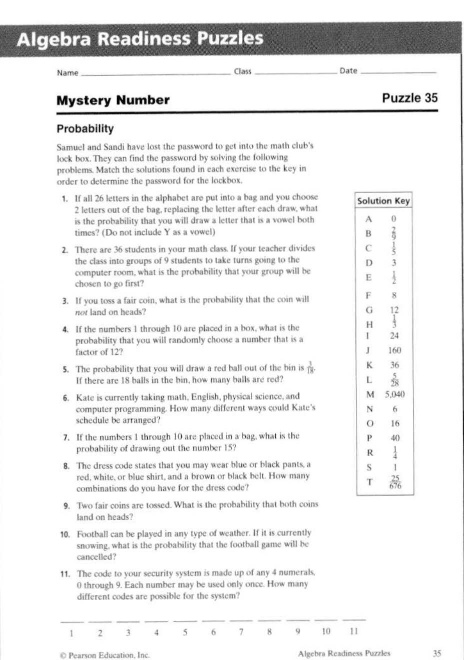

Algebra Readiness Puzzles

Name ______________ Class ______________ Date ______________

Mystery Number — Puzzle 35

Probability

Samuel and Sandi have lost the password to get into the math club's lock box. They can find the password by solving the following problems. Match the solutions found in each exercise to the key in order to determine the password for the lockbox.

1. If all 26 letters in the alphabet are put into a bag and you choose 2 letters out of the bag, replacing the letter after each draw, what is the probability that you will draw a letter that is a vowel both times? (Do not include Y as a vowel)
2. There are 36 students in your math class. If your teacher divides the class into groups of 9 students to take turns going to the computer room, what is the probability that your group will be chosen to go first?
3. If you toss a fair coin, what is the probability that the coin will *not* land on heads?
4. If the numbers 1 through 10 are placed in a box, what is the probability that you will randomly choose a number that is a factor of 12?
5. The probability that you will draw a red ball out of the bin is $\frac{3}{18}$. If there are 18 balls in the bin, how many balls are red?
6. Kate is currently taking math, English, physical science, and computer programming. How many different ways could Kate's schedule be arranged?
7. If the numbers 1 through 10 are placed in a bag, what is the probability of drawing out the number 15?
8. The dress code states that you may wear blue or black pants, a red, white, or blue shirt, and a brown or black belt. How many combinations do you have for the dress code?
9. Two fair coins are tossed. What is the probability that both coins land on heads?
10. Football can be played in any type of weather. If it is currently snowing, what is the probability that the football game will be cancelled?
11. The code to your security system is made up of any 4 numerals, 0 through 9. Each number may be used only once. How many different codes are possible for the system?

Solution Key	
A	0
B	$\frac{2}{9}$
C	$\frac{1}{5}$
D	3
E	$\frac{1}{2}$
F	8
G	12
H	$\frac{1}{3}$
I	24
J	160
K	36
L	$\frac{5}{28}$
M	5,040
N	6
O	16
P	40
R	$\frac{1}{4}$
S	1
T	$\frac{25}{676}$

___ ___ ___ ___ ___ ___ ___ ___ ___ ___ ___
1 2 3 4 5 6 7 8 9 10 11

 Algebra Readiness Puzzles 35

Web Code: ack-5500

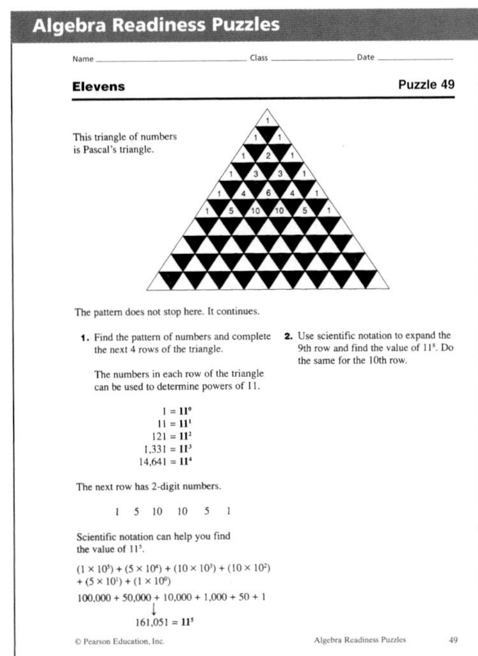

Algebra Readiness Puzzles

Name ______________ Class ______________ Date ______________

Elevens — Puzzle 49

This triangle of numbers is Pascal's triangle.

The pattern does not stop here. It continues.

1. Find the pattern of numbers and complete the next 4 rows of the triangle.

   The numbers in each row of the triangle can be used to determine powers of 11.

   $1 = \mathbf{11^0}$
   $11 = \mathbf{11^1}$
   $121 = \mathbf{11^2}$
   $1{,}331 = \mathbf{11^3}$
   $14{,}641 = \mathbf{11^4}$

   The next row has 2-digit numbers.

   1 5 10 10 5 1

   Scientific notation can help you find the value of 11^5.

   $(1 \times 10^5) + (5 \times 10^4) + (10 \times 10^3) + (10 \times 10^2) + (5 \times 10^1) + (1 \times 10^0)$

   $100{,}000 + 50{,}000 + 10{,}000 + 1{,}000 + 50 + 1$

   $\downarrow$

   $161{,}051 = \mathbf{11^5}$

2. Use scientific notation to expand the 9th row and find the value of 11^8. Do the same for the 10th row.

 Algebra Readiness Puzzles 49

Web Code: ack-5500

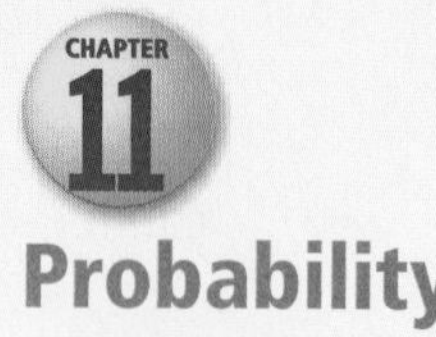

Probability

Chapter 11 Overview

In this chapter, students follow a lesson on counting outcomes by investigating the concepts of permutations and combinations. They learn next about theoretical and experimental probability, and they explore the distinction between independent and dependent events.

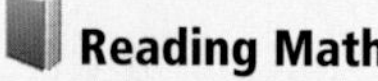

Reading Math

- Understanding Vocabulary, p. 626
- **Vocabulary:** A complete list, plus exercises, in the Chapter Review, p. 628
- **Illustrated Glossary:** Examples for each vocabulary term, plus definitions in English and Spanish, on p. 735

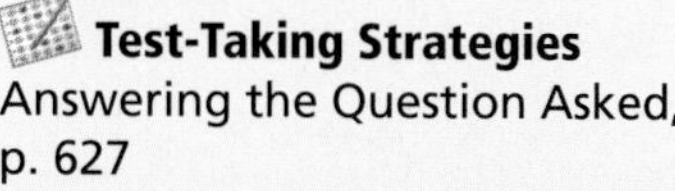

Test-Taking Strategies
Answering the Question Asked, p. 627

Real-World Problem Solving

- **Strategies:** Simulate a Problem and Make an Organized List, pp. 616–619
- **Real-World Snapshots:** Animal Census, pp. 632–633
- **Chapter Project:** Start With the Stats, p. 701

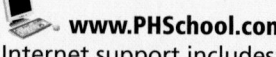

www.PHSchool.com
Internet support includes:

- Self-grading Vocabulary and Chapter 11 Tests
- Activity Masters
- Chapter Project support
- Chapter Planner
- Ch. 11 Math Background
- Ch. 11 Resources

Plus iTEXT

Probability

Lessons

Key Vocabulary

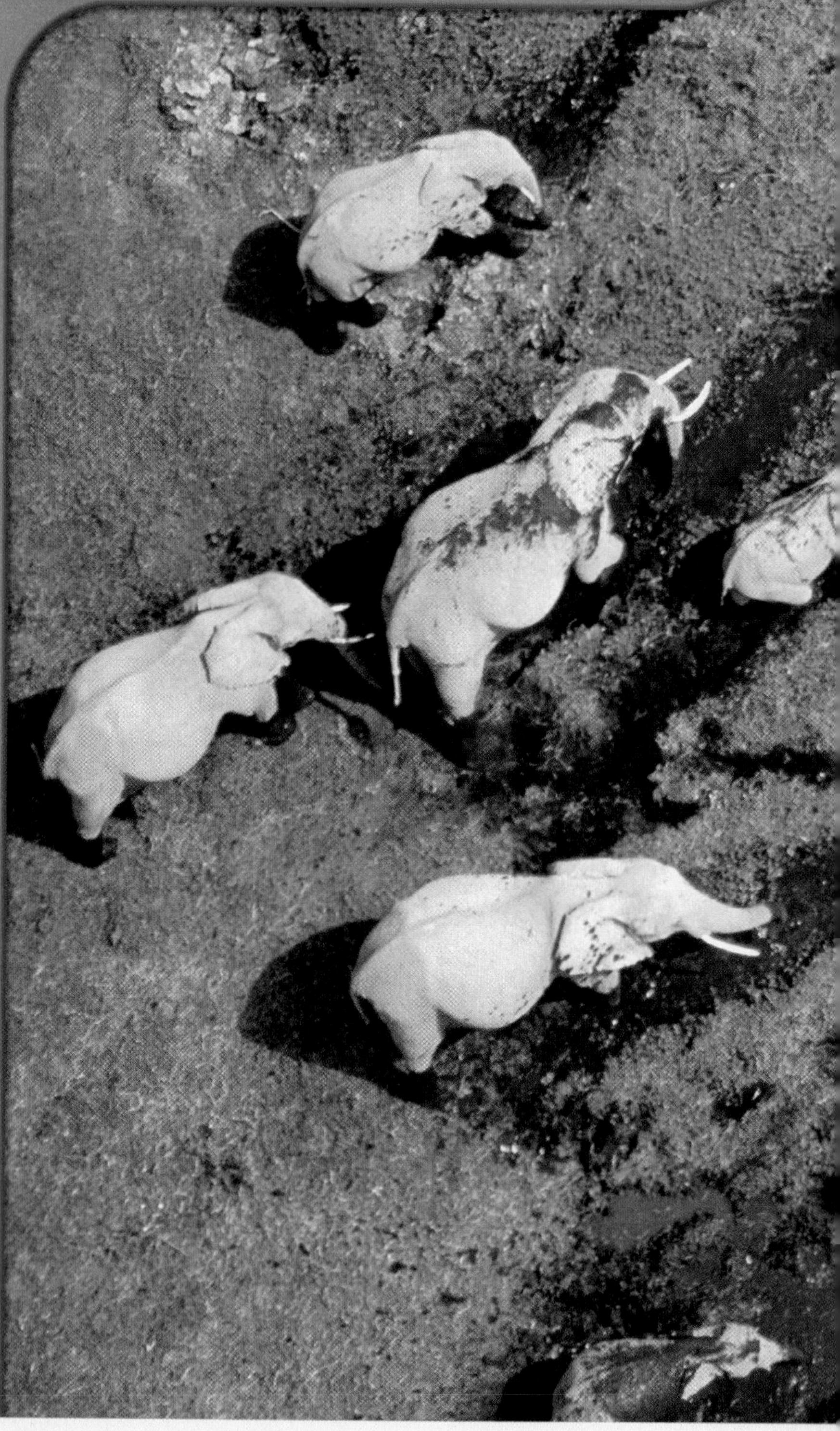

Real-World Snapshots

In addition to being fun to visit, zoos are also important because they save species that are endangered. Sometimes, animals born in zoos are returned to the wild, helping to prevent an end to their species.

Data File **Zoo Populations**

Zoo	Number of Different Animal Species
Denver Zoo	700
Los Angeles Zoo	350
El Paso Zoo	175
Smithsonian National Zoological Park	447
San Antonio Zoo	750
San Diego Zoo	800
St. Louis Zoo	705

SOURCE: Individual Zoos' Websites

You will use the data above throughout this chapter:

- p. 609 Lesson 11-4
- p. 613 Lesson 11-5

Real-World Snapshots On pages 632 and 633, you will solve problems involving capture-recapture.

Teaching Notes

Activating Prior Knowledge

In this chapter, students build on their knowledge of ratios and rates and of applications of proportions. They draw upon their understanding of the concept of probability and of how to find the probability of certain events. Ask questions such as:

- *How would you express the ratio 4:20 in simplest form?* 1:5
- *You roll a 1–6 number cube. What is the probability you will roll an even number?* $\frac{1}{2}$
- *You make 7 of 10 free throws. If you continue to shoot with that rate of success, how many free throws can you expect to make if you shoot 50 of them?* 35

Real-World Snapshots

The data here about zoo populations will be used throughout the chapter. Have a volunteer read the opening sentences and the title of the chart. Focus students on the data in the chart and ask:

- *Which zoo has the fewest number of species of animals?* El Paso Zoo
- *What is the range of the number of different species of animals in these zoos?* 625
- *Which two zoos have about the same number of different species?* Denver and St. Louis

Reading and Math Literacy

11A: Graphic Organizer For use before Lesson 11-1

Study Skill: As you learn new material, it might help to work with other students. They might work problems differently which could make the material easier for you to understand.

Write your answers.

1. What is the chapter title? Probability
2. How many lessons are there in this chapter? 7
3. What is the topic of the Reading Math page? Justifying Statements
4. What is the topic of the Test-Taking Strategy page? Answering the Question Asked
5. Look through the chapter and list four real-world connections that are discussed. Answers will vary.
6. Complete the graphic organizer below as you work through the chapter.
   - In the center, write the title of the chapter.
   - When you begin a lesson, write the lesson name in a rectangle.
   - When you complete a lesson, write a skill or key concept in a circle linked to that lesson block.
   - When you complete the chapter, use this graphic organizer to help you review.

   Check students' diagrams.

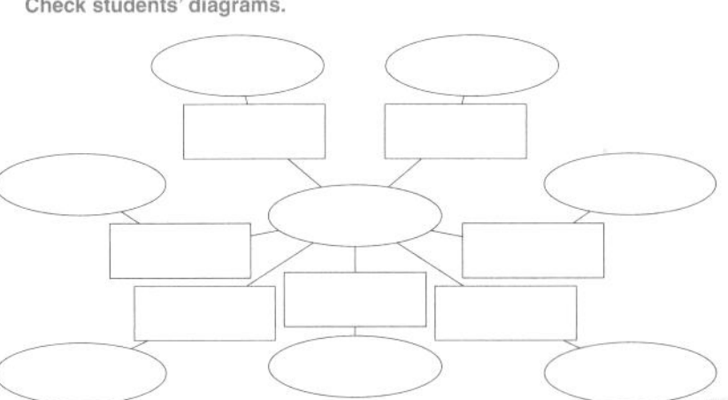

Available in Spanish

Chapter 11: Probability

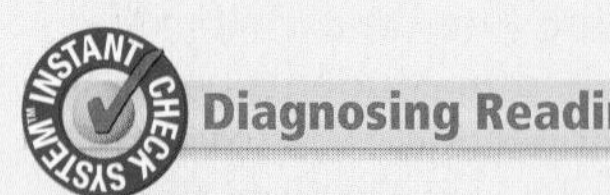

Students will find answers to these exercises in the back of their textbooks.

Prescribing Intervention
For intervention, direct students to:

Multiplying Rational Numbers
Lesson 4-5: Example 1.
Extra Practice, p. 705.

Writing Ratios
Lesson 5-1: Example 1.
Extra Practice, p. 706.

Finding Probabilities
Lesson 6-9: Examples 1, 3, 5.
Extra Practice, p. 707.

Chapter 11 Preview

Where You've Been

- In Chapter 5, you learned about ratios and rates.
- You also explored some applications of proportions.
- In Chapter 6, you learned various methods to find the probability of certain events.

Where You're Going

- In Chapter 11, you will learn about theoretical and experimental probability as well as independent and dependent events.
- Applying what you learn, you will use probability to find the number of combinations of fishing lures that can be used at one time.

Many fly fishermen tie their own flies, which they use as lures.

Instant self-check online and on CD-ROM

Diagnosing Readiness

For help, go to the lesson in green.

Multiplying Rational Numbers (Lesson 4-5)

Find each product.

1. $\frac{3}{7} \cdot \frac{1}{2}$ $\frac{3}{14}$
2. $\frac{1}{6} \cdot \frac{24}{25}$ $\frac{4}{25}$
3. $\frac{9}{14} \cdot \frac{7}{12}$ $\frac{3}{8}$
4. $\frac{2}{9} \cdot \frac{3}{8}$ $\frac{1}{12}$
5. $\frac{8}{9} \cdot \frac{12}{32}$ $\frac{1}{3}$
6. $\frac{27}{34} \cdot \frac{2}{3}$ $\frac{9}{17}$
7. $\frac{10}{17} \cdot \frac{1}{5}$ $\frac{2}{17}$
8. $\frac{3}{4} \cdot \frac{5}{9}$ $\frac{5}{12}$

Writing Ratios (Lesson 5-1)

Write three ratios that each diagram can represent. 9–11. Answers may vary. Samples are given.

9.  $\frac{2}{4}, \frac{4}{2}, \frac{2}{2}$

10. 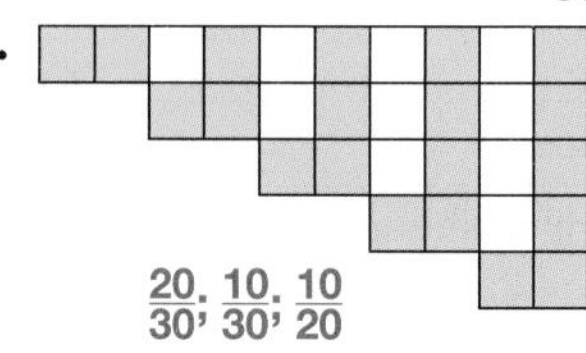 $\frac{20}{30}, \frac{10}{30}, \frac{10}{20}$

11. 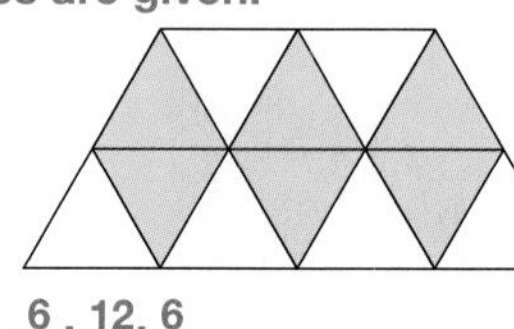 $\frac{6}{12}, \frac{12}{6}, \frac{6}{6}$

Finding Probabilities (Lesson 6-9)

Suppose you spin the spinner once. Find each probability as a fraction in simplest form.

12. P(yellow) $\frac{3}{8}$
13. P(green) $\frac{1}{4}$
14. P(purple) $\frac{1}{8}$
15. P(green or blue) $\frac{1}{2}$
16. P(blue or yellow) $\frac{5}{8}$
17. P(green or purple) $\frac{3}{8}$
18. Suppose you toss a quarter twice. One possible outcome is (heads, tails). Draw a tree diagram to find the sample space.
(heads, heads), (heads, tails), (tails, heads), (tails, tails)

Toss 1	Toss 2
heads	heads
	tails
tails	heads
	tails

11-1 Counting Outcomes

What You'll Learn

To use tree diagrams and the counting principle

. . . And Why

To find the number of possible choices when buying a meal, as in Example 1

✓ Check Skills You'll Need

For help, go to Lesson 6-9.

Find each probability. A set of nine cards contains two cards with red triangles, four cards with yellow circles, and three cards with blue triangles. You draw one card at random.

1. P(red triangle) $\frac{2}{9}$
2. P(circle) $\frac{4}{9}$
3. P(triangle) $\frac{5}{9}$
4. P(blue or yellow) $\frac{7}{9}$
5. P(blue circle) 0
6. P(blue triangle) $\frac{3}{9}$, or $\frac{1}{3}$

OBJECTIVE

Interactive lesson includes instant self-check, tutorials, and activities.

1 Using Tree Diagrams and the Counting Principle

Do you want a small, medium, or large drink? What kind of sandwich? When you buy lunch at school, you have to make choices. Tree diagrams can help you figure out the possibilities.

1 EXAMPLE Using Tree Diagrams

School Lunch Your school cafeteria offers two kinds of sandwiches and three kinds of drinks. If you buy one sandwich and one drink, how many different ways can you choose your lunch?

You can use a tree diagram to find the number of possible outcomes.

Need Help? An *outcome* is any one of the possible results in a given situation.

Sandwich	Drink
chicken	milk
	apple juice
	water
tuna	milk
	apple juice
	water

Each branch represents one choice.

There are 6 different ways you can choose your lunch.

1a. No; if you listed drinks first and sandwiches second you would still have 6 choices.

✓ Check Understanding 1
a. **Reasoning** Does the order in which you list the decisions make a difference? Explain. See above right.
b. Suppose the cafeteria offers four drinks. How many different lunches can you now choose? 8 lunches

11-1

1. Plan

Lesson Preview

✓ Check Skills You'll Need PowerPoint

Finding Probabilities
Lesson 6-9: Examples 1, 3. Extra Practice, p. 707.

Lesson Resources

Teaching Resources
Practice, Reteaching, Enrichment

Reaching All Students
Practice Workbook 11-1
Spanish Practice Workbook 11-1
Guided Problem Solving 11-1

Presentation Assistant Plus!
Transparencies
- Check Skills You'll Need 11-1
- Problem of the Day 11-1
- Additional Examples 11-1
- Student Edition Answers 11-1
- Lesson Quiz 11-1

PH Presentation Pro CD-ROM 11-1

PRENTICE HALL ASSESSMENT SYSTEM

Computer Test Generator CD

Technology
Resource Pro® CD-ROM
Computer Test Generator CD
PH Presentation Pro CD-ROM

www.PHSchool.com
Student Site
- Teacher Web Code: ack-5500
- Self-grading Lesson Quiz

PH SuccessNet Teacher Center
- Lesson Planner
- Resources

Plus iTEXT

Ongoing Assessment and Intervention

Before the Lesson
Diagnose prerequisite skills using:
- Check Skills You'll Need

During the Lesson
Monitor progress using:
- Check Understanding
- Additional Examples
- Test Prep

After the Lesson
Assess knowledge using:
- Lesson Quiz
- Computer Test Generator CD

2. Teach

Math Background

The Counting Principle states that if there are *m* ways of making a first choice and *n* ways of making a second choice, then there are *mn* ways of making the first choice followed by the second choice. You can demonstrate this principle clearly by drawing a tree diagram to show the number of possible outcomes.

Teaching Notes

1 EXAMPLE Auditory Learners

Have students role play an employee in a restaurant taking a food order from a customer, naming the various choices, such as sandwich and drink. Discuss the combinations that can be chosen.

2 EXAMPLE English Learners

Discuss whether students have sent or received an email greeting card. Describe the choices the sender can make, such as music, greeting, and image. Show examples of different *fonts* used in this textbook, such as the shape of the letters used for the text as compared to the titles.

Additional Examples

1. Suppose a cafeteria has 3 different sandwiches and 4 different drinks. If you select one sandwich and one drink, how many different ways can you have lunch? 12
2. To print a poster for the bake sale, you can choose from 12 colors, 6 sizes of letters, and 18 designs. How many different posters can you make with this program? 1,296

Closure

Explain how a tree diagram shows the counting principle. Sample: A tree diagram shows that for each of *m* first choices there are *n* second choices, so the total number of different ways to choose is *m* times *n*.

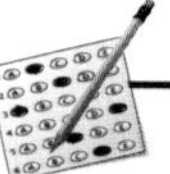

Test-Prep Tip

The counting principle is also known as the fundamental counting principle.

A tree diagram illustrates the counting principle.

Key Concepts **The Counting Principle**

Suppose there are m ways of making one choice and n ways of making a second choice. Then there are $m \cdot n$ ways to make the first choice followed by the second choice.

Example

You have 6 shirts and 5 jeans. You have $6 \cdot 5 = 30$ different outfits.

2 EXAMPLE The Counting Principle

Greeting Cards A greeting card software program offers 24 different greetings, 10 different images, and 8 font styles. How many different cards can you make with this program?

greetings		images		font styles	
↓		↓		↓	
24	·	10	·	8	← Use the counting principle.

$24 \cdot 10 \cdot 8 = 1{,}920$ ← Multiply.

You can make 1,920 different greeting cards.

Check Understanding 2 A software program to design CD covers offers 240 backgrounds, 14 font styles, and 12 song-listing styles. How many different covers can you make? 40,320 covers

EXERCISES

For more practice, see *Extra Practice*.

A Practice by Example

Use a tree diagram to find the number of possible outcomes. Example 1 has been started for you. 1–2. See back of book for diagrams.

Example 1 (page 591)

1. **Dining** A diner offers three choices of entrees, three choices for the first side order, and two choices for the second side order. Find the number of possible meals. 18 possible meals

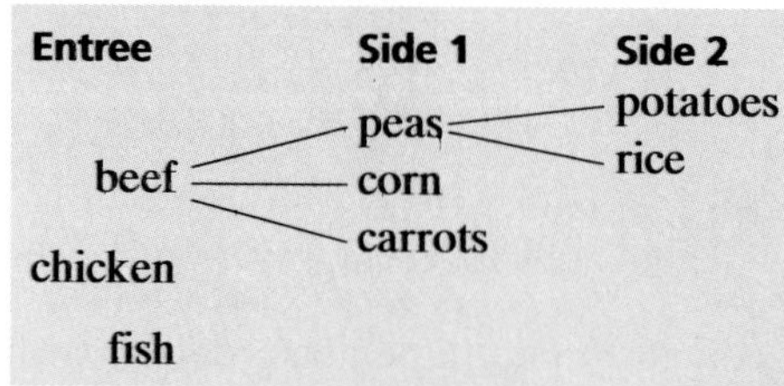

2. **Food** A salad bar offers iceberg and romaine lettuce, with tomatoes, cucumbers, broccoli, and corn as toppings. How many different ways can you make a salad with one type of lettuce and one topping? 8 ways

Reaching All Students

Below Level For Example 1a, have students make a tree diagram that lists the possible drinks (3) followed by the possible sandwiches (2). The diagram shows 3 choices followed by 2 choices and gives the same 6 possible outcomes.	Advanced Learners Suppose there are 2 types of pizza crusts, 3 types of pizza sauce, and t types of toppings. How many different 1-topping pizzas can you make? $6t$	English Learners See note on page 592. Auditory Learners See note on page 592.

Example 2 (page 592)

Use the counting principle to find the number of outcomes in each situation.

3. 2 types, 6 colors. How many roses? 12 roses

4. 15 styles, 7 sizes, 8 rooftops. How many birdhouses? 840 birdhouses

5. 4 sizes, 2 colors. How many bathing suits? 8 bathing suits

B Apply Your Skills

6. **Cars** A car dealer offers a car model with the options in the table at the right. How many different kinds of cars do you have to consider if you choose one style, one transmission, and one color? 48 cars

Style	Sedan, wagon, hatchback
Transmission	Automatic, manual
Color	Red, green, blue, white, gray, black, silver, gold

7. **Carnivals** A carnival has 10 rides and 14 different songs to go with each ride. How many different ride-song combinations are there? 140 combinations

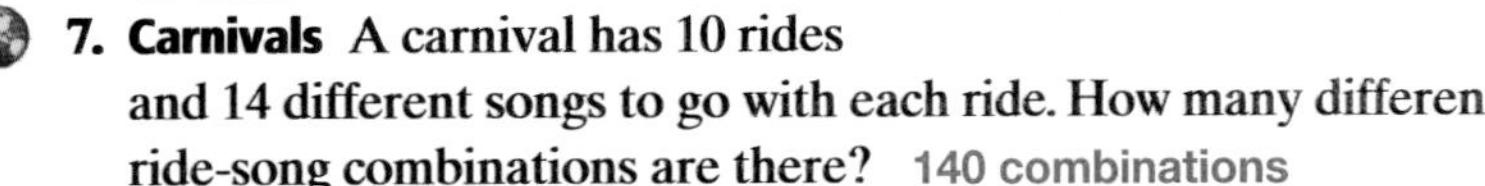

8. Writing in Math Which would be more useful in finding the probability of an event, a tree diagram or the counting principle? Explain.

8. Counting principle; multiplying is faster than drawing a tree diagram.

9. **Shopping** A clothing store sells sweat pants in four sizes and three colors. How many different choices of sweat pants are there? 12 choices

10. **Photographers** You need a roll of film for your 35-mm camera. Your choices are shown below.

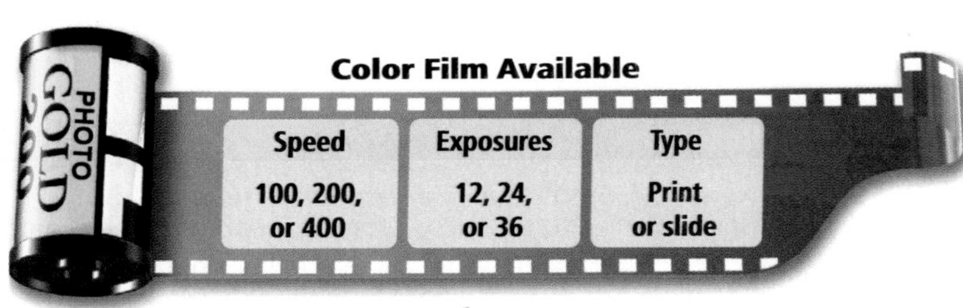

a. How many decisions must you make? 3 decisions

b. Draw a tree diagram to show the choices for a roll of film. How many different kinds of film can you buy? See margin.

c. Number Sense The store is sold out of slide film in 12 exposures. How many choices does this eliminate? Explain. See below left.

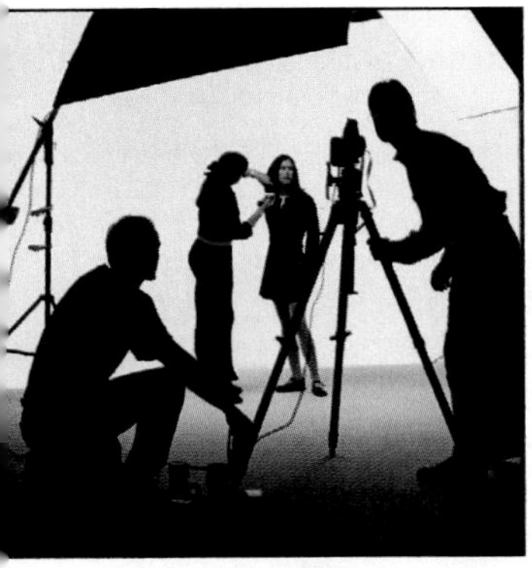

Careers Professional photographers spend hours setting up photo shoots and developing film.

10c. 3 choices; there is 1 slide film in 12 exposures for each of the 3 speeds.

11. Algebra You sell balloons in a different colors and a different shapes.

a. How many different balloons do you sell? a^2 different ballons

b. How many different balloons do you sell if $a = 10$? 100 different balloons

12. Error Analysis A framing store offers 35 frame colors and 12 styles. A student reported that there are 47 different possible frames. What error did the student make? See left.

12. The student added the choices instead of multiplying them. There are 420 possible frames.

13. **Banners** A software program offers 230 fonts and 85 styles to create a banner. How many different banners can you make? 19,550 banners

3. Practice

Assignment Guide

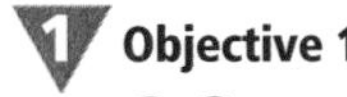

Objective 1

A B Core 1–13

C Extension 14–15

Test Prep 16–19

Mixed Review 20–22

Error Prevention!

Exercises 1–2 Some students may forget to show all of the second choices next to each of the first choices.

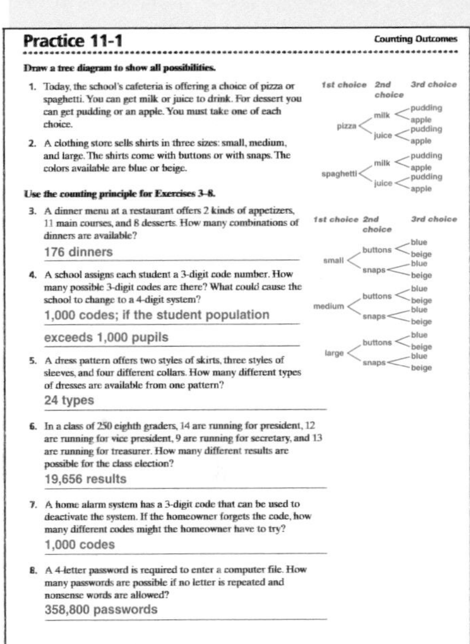

Practice 11-1 Counting Outcomes

Draw a tree diagram to show all possibilities.

1. Today, the school's cafeteria is offering a choice of pizza or spaghetti. You can get milk or juice to drink. For dessert you can get pudding or an apple. You must take one of each choice.

2. A clothing store sells shirts in three sizes: small, medium, and large. The shirts come with buttons or with snaps. The colors available are blue or beige.

Use the counting principle for Exercises 3–8.

3. A dinner menu at a restaurant offers 2 kinds of appetizers, 11 main courses, and 8 desserts. How many combinations of dinners are available? 176 dinners

4. A school assigns each student a 3-digit code number. How many possible 3-digit codes are there? What could cause the school to change to a 4-digit system? 1,000 codes; if the student population exceeds 1,000 pupils

5. A dress pattern offers two styles of skirts, three styles of sleeves, and four different collars. How many different types of dresses are available from one pattern? 24 types

6. In a class of 250 eighth graders, 14 are running for president, 12 are running for vice president, 9 are running for secretary, and 13 are running for treasurer. How many different results are possible for the class election? 19,656 results

7. A home alarm system has a 3-digit code that can be used to deactivate the system. If the homeowner forgets the code, how many different codes might the homeowner have to try? 1,000 codes

8. A 4-letter password is required to enter a computer file. How many passwords are possible if no letter is repeated and nonsense words are allowed? 358,800 passwords

Reteaching 11-1 Counting Outcomes

Andy has 3 pairs of pants: 1 gray, 1 blue, and 1 black. He has 2 shirts: 1 white and 1 red. If Andy picks 1 pair of pants and 1 shirt, how many different outfits does he have?

Andy can choose 1 of 3 pairs of pants and 1 of 2 shirts. A tree diagram can help you count his choices.

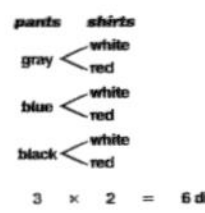

pants shirts
gray white red
blue white red
black white red

3 × 2 = 6 different outfits

The total number of choices is the product of the number of choices for pants and the number of choices for shirts.

You can also use the *counting principle*.

n (first choices) × m (second choices) gives $n \times m$ (total choices)

Andy has 6 different outfits.

Find the total number of choices.

1. Rich is trying to get from San Francisco to San Jose. He needs to stop in San Bruno on the way. There are 3 major roads or freeways from San Francisco to San Bruno and 3 major roads or freeways from San Bruno to San Jose. How many routes can Rich take? 9

2. Ralph wants to have soup and salad for lunch There are 5 kinds of soup and 3 kinds of salad on the menu. He picks one of each. From how many possible combinations can he choose? 15

3. Carla has 4 hats and 4 scarves for winter weather. She picks one of each to wear. How many hat and scarf combinations are there? 6

4. Lorenzo is looking at 5 color markers and 4 types of paper. He picks one of each. How many choices of color and paper does he have? 20

5. Eric has 3 baseballs and 4 bats. From how many possible ball and bat combinations can he choose? 12

6. Ms. Wong is redecorating her office. She has a choice of 3 colors of paint, 4 kinds of curtains, and 4 colors of carpet. How many different ways are there to redecorate? 48

GPS Use the Guided Problem Solving worksheet with Exercise 7.

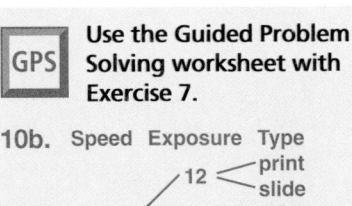

10b. Speed Exposure Type

100 — 12 — print, slide; 24 — print, slide; 36 — print, slide

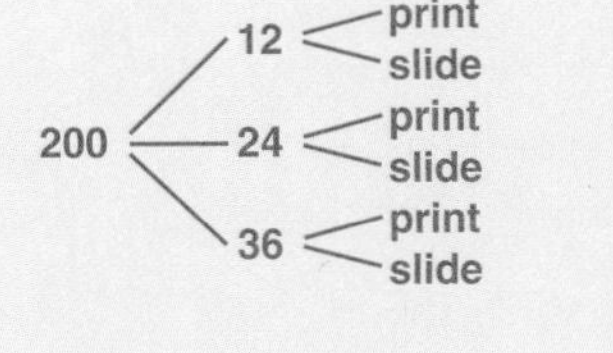

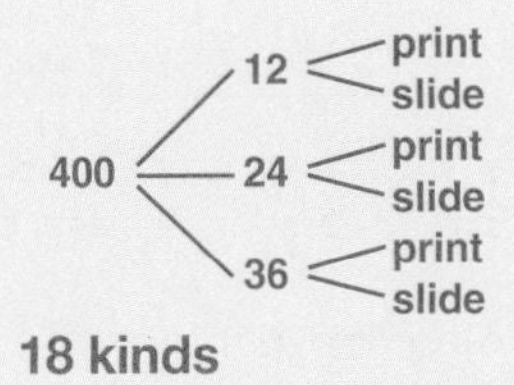

18 kinds

4. Assess

Lesson Quiz 11-1

1. A denim shirt comes in 3 colors. Its edges can be either fringed or hemmed. How many different shirts are available? 6 shirts

2. A leather shoe comes in 3 styles: laced, buckled, or slip-on. The colors are brown, camel, red, navy, and black. How many different shoes are there? 15 shoes

Test Prep

Resources
A sheet of blank grids is available in the *Test-Taking Strategies with Transparencies* booklet. Give copies of this sheet to students so they can practice filling in grids.

For additional practice with a variety of test item formats:
- Test Prep, p. 631
- Test-Taking Strategies, p. 627
- Test-Taking Strategies with Transparencies

Exercise 16 Point out that the number of outcomes is the same as the number of possible choices.

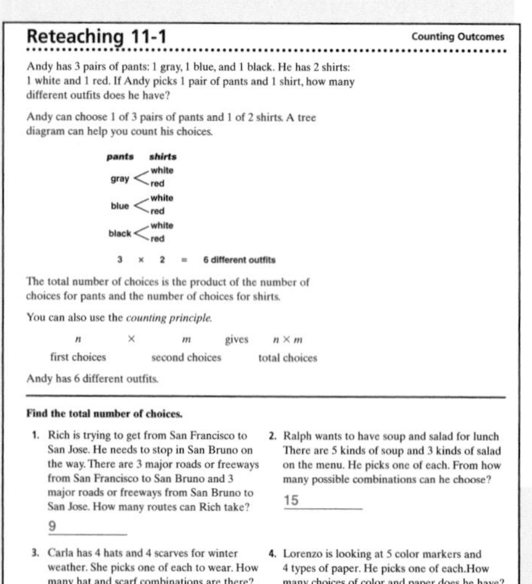

Reteaching 11-1 Counting Outcomes

Andy has 3 pairs of pants: 1 gray, 1 blue, and 1 black. He has 2 shirts: 1 white and 1 red. If Andy picks 1 pair of pants and 1 shirt, how many different outfits does he have?

Andy can choose 1 of 3 pairs of pants and 1 of 2 shirts. A tree diagram can help you count his choices.

The total number of choices is the product of the number of choices for pants and the number of choices for shirts.

You can also use the *counting principle.*

n (first choices) × m (second choices) gives $n \times m$ (total choices)

Andy has 6 different outfits.

Find the total number of choices.

1. Rich is trying to get from San Francisco to San Jose. He needs to stop in San Bruno on the way. There are 3 major roads or freeways from San Francisco to San Bruno and 3 major roads or freeways from San Bruno to San Jose. How many routes can Rich take? 9
2. Ralph wants to have soup and salad for lunch There are 5 kinds of soup and 3 kinds of salad on the menu. He picks one of each. From how many possible combinations can he choose? 15
3. Carla has 4 hats and 4 scarves for winter weather. She picks one of each to wear. How many hat and scarf combinations are there? 6
4. Lorenzo is looking at 5 color markers and 4 types of paper. He picks one of each.How many choices of color and paper does he have? 20
5. Eric has 3 baseballs and 4 bats. From how many possible ball and bat combinations can he choose? 12
6. Ms. Wong is redecorating her office. She has a choice of 3 colors of paint, 4 kinds of curtains, and 4 colors of carpet. How many different ways are there to redecorate? 48

Challenge

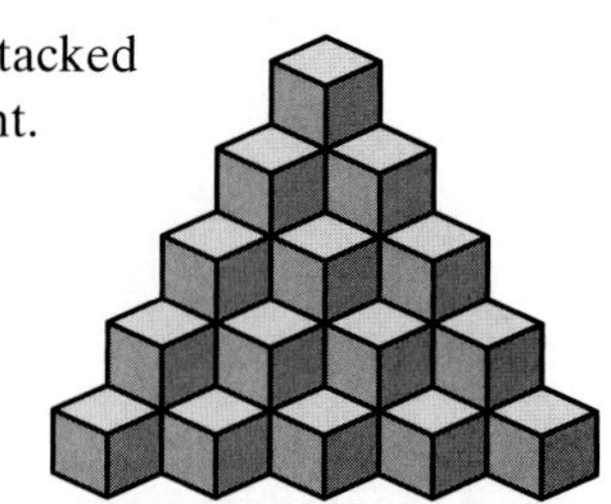

14. **Stretch Your Thinking** Identical cubes are stacked in the corner of a store as shown at the right. How many of the cubes cannot be seen? 20 cubes

15. **Names** A baby book lists 561 names for girls. How many different versions of a first name and a middle name can you select? 314,160 versions

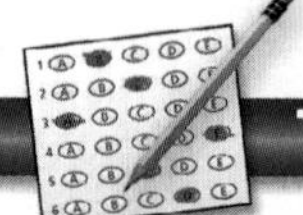

Test Prep

Gridded Response

16. You toss a dime three times. How many outcomes are possible? 8

17. A restaurant offers 12 main courses and 5 types of vegetables. If you choose 1 main course and 1 vegetable, how many different meals can you order? 60

Take It to the NET
Online lesson quiz at **www.PHSchool.com**
Web Code: aca-1101

18. A mall vendor can put a computer-generated picture of you on any of the 30 items that the vendor sells. You can also choose from 15 different backgrounds. How many different items can you buy? 450

19. The gift shop at a beach offers 5 brands of sunscreen and 11 sun hats with various designs. Suppose you want to buy a brand of sunscreen and a hat. How many different choices of sunscreen and hats do you have? 55

Mixed Review

Lesson 10-8

20a. See margin for diagram.

20. a. Use a Venn diagram to find the common factors of 60 and 50. 1, 2, 5, 10
    b. What is the greatest common factor of 60 and 50? 10

Lesson 10-7

Decide which type of graph would be the most appropriate for the data. Explain your choice and then draw the graph. 21–22. See back of book.

21. **Computer Use by 12-Year-Olds**

Types of Use	Time (min)
Games	16
Web sites	7
E-mail	4
School work	9
Other	7

SOURCE: The Kaiser Family Foundation Report

22. **Florida Orange Production**

Year	Boxes of Oranges (thousands)
1960	82,700
1970	142,300
1980	172,400
1990	151,600
2000	223,300

SOURCE: Florida Agricultural Statistics Service

Alternative Assessment

Each student in a pair writes a problem similar to Example 2. Partners trade papers and solve each other's problems two ways: using a tree diagram and using the counting principle. Students then discuss which method they prefer.

20a.

Factors of 60: 3, 4, 6, 12, 15, 20, 30, 60
Both: 1, 2, 5, 10
Factors of 50: 25, 50

11-2 Permutations

What You'll Learn

To find the number of permutations of a set of objects

To use permutation notation

. . . And Why

To find the number of different orders you can play the songs on a CD, as in Example 3

Check Skills You'll Need

For help, go to Lesson 11-1.

Use the counting principle to find the number of outcomes in each situation.

1. 10 museums, 6 parks. How many choices of 1 museum and 1 park? 60 choices
2. 4 shapes, 4 colors. How many designs? 16 designs
3. 6 subjects, 3 levels. How many different classes? 18 classes

New Vocabulary • permutation • factorial

OBJECTIVE 1

Interactive lesson includes instant self-check, tutorials, and activities.

Finding Permutations

Investigation: Counting Arrangements

1. For a school track meet, your math class first chooses a runner for lane 1 and then a runner for lane 2. How many choices do you have for the runner in lane 1? Explain. See left.
2. Once a runner is chosen for lane 1, find the number of choices for the runner in lane 2. one less choice than above
3. Using the counting principle, find the number of ways to choose two students from your class. Answers may vary. Sample: $20 \cdot 19 = 380$ ways
4. A class selects Alexis to run in lane 1 and Chris to run in lane 2. To represent this, they write (Alexis, Chris). What do you think (Chris, Alexis) represents? Chris is the runner in lane 1 and Alexis is the runner in lane 2.
5. Write a rule for determining the number of choices of a runner for lane 1 and a runner for lane 2 for a class size of n students. $n(n - 1)$

1. Answers may vary. Sample: If there are 20 students in a class, then there are 20 ways to choose a runner for lane 1.

In a school track meet, the six runners in the 200-meter dash line up in lanes 1 to 6. Those in the middle lanes have an advantage, so the order of the runners matters.

Sometimes, the order of objects in an arrangement is important. A **permutation** is an arrangement of a set of objects in a particular order.

11-2

1. Plan

Lesson Preview

Check Skills You'll Need

Using the Counting Principle
Lesson 11-1: Example 2. Extra Practice, p. 712.

Lesson Resources

Teaching Resources
Practice, Reteaching, Enrichment

Reaching All Students
Practice Workbook 11-2
Spanish Practice Workbook 11-2
Guided Problem Solving 11-2
Hands-On Activities 42

Presentation Assistant Plus!
Transparencies
- Check Skills You'll Need 11-2
- Problem of the Day 11-2
- Additional Examples 11-2
- Student Edition Answers 11-2
- Lesson Quiz 11-2
- Classroom Aid 11

PH Presentation Pro CD-ROM 11-2

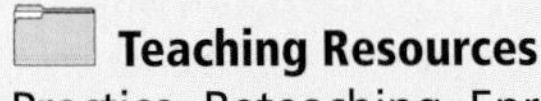

Computer Test Generator CD

Technology
Resource Pro® CD-ROM
Computer Test Generator CD
PH Presentation Pro CD-ROM

www.PHSchool.com
Student Site
- Teacher Web Code: ack-5500
- Self-grading Lesson Quiz
- Graphing Calculator Handbook, Procedure 16

PH SuccessNet Teacher Center
- Lesson Planner
- Resources

Plus 

Ongoing Assessment and Intervention

Before the Lesson
Diagnose prerequisite skills using:
- Check Skills You'll Need

During the Lesson
Monitor progress using:
- Check Understanding
- Additional Examples
- Test Prep

After the Lesson
Assess knowledge using:
- Lesson Quiz
- Computer Test Generator CD

2. Teach

Math Background

As discussed in Lesson 11-1, making the two choices (red, large) is the same as the choice (large, red). The order of the choices makes no difference. A *permutation* is an arrangement of a set of objects in which the order *does* make a difference. The number of permutation of n objects chosen r at a time can be represented by the expression ${}_nP_r$. The value of ${}_nP_n$ is $n!$, which is read as "n factorial." The factorial of a positive integer is the product of all the positive integers less than or equal to that number, so $5! = 5 \cdot 4 \cdot 3 \cdot 2 \cdot 1$ or 120. The value of ${}_nP_r$ is the product of r positive integers from n down, so ${}_7P_3$ is the product of 3 integers, starting with 7. This means that ${}_7P_3 = 7 \cdot 6 \cdot 5$, or 210.

Teaching Notes

Investigation (Optional)
Discuss the difference between the kinds of choice made in Lesson 11-1, where (chicken sandwich, milk) is the same choice as (milk, chicken sandwich) and the kinds of choice here, where (Alexis, Chris) is a different choice from (Chris, Alexis).

1 EXAMPLE Diversity
Ask students who speak languages other than English for words in his or her language for the word *permutation*. Sample: permutatie (Dutch), permutation (French, Danish, German)

2 EXAMPLE Tactile Learners
Have seven volunteers use cards labeled with 1st, 2nd, 3rd, . . . , 7th to model some of these possibilities. Show how there are 7 possible volunteers for the first award, 6 for the second award, and so on.

3 EXAMPLE Inclusion
Some students may not be aware that some CD players allow you to choose the track to be played. Have a student explain how to use such a player.

1 EXAMPLE Permutations Using a Diagram

Real World

Gym In how many ways can Ryan, Emily, and Justin line up in gym class?

Ryan	Emily	Justin	①	(R, E, J)
	Justin	Emily	②	(R, J, E)
Emily	Ryan	Justin	③	(E, R, J)
	Justin	Ryan	④	(E, J, R)
Justin	Ryan	Emily	⑤	(J, R, E)
	Emily	Ryan	⑥	(J, E, R)

Ryan, Emily, and Justin can line up in six different ways. This means that there are six permutations.

1. Yes. In the first lineup, Emily is second and Justin is third. In the second lineup, Justin is second and Emily is third.

Check Understanding 1 **Reasoning** Is the lineup (Ryan, Emily, Justin) different from the lineup (Ryan, Justin, Emily)? Explain. See above left.

2 EXAMPLE Using the Counting Principle

Real World

Awards At a school awards ceremony, the principal will present awards to seven students. How many different ways can the principal give out the awards?

There are seven ways to give out the first award, six ways to give out the second, and so on.

$7 \cdot 6 \cdot 5 \cdot 4 \cdot 3 \cdot 2 \cdot 1 = 5{,}040$ ← Use the counting principle.

There are 5,040 different ways to give out the awards.

Check Understanding 2 **Number Sense** Suppose the principal adds an award. How does this affect the number of different ways to give out the awards?
There are 8 times as many ways, or 40,320.

Calculator Hint
Some calculators have a factorial key. Look on the PRB menu for the ! option.

The solution in Example 2 involves the product of all the integers from 7 to 1. The product of all positive integers less than or equal to a number is a **factorial**. Write 7!, which you read as "seven factorial."

3 EXAMPLE Permutations Using Factorials

Real World

Music Many CD players can vary the order in which songs are played. Your favorite CD has eight songs. Find the number of orders in which the songs can be played.

$8! = 8 \cdot 7 \cdot 6 \cdot 5 \cdot 4 \cdot 3 \cdot 2 \cdot 1 = 40{,}320$ ← Simplify.

The songs can be played in 40,320 different orders or permutations.

Check Understanding 3 Simplify each expression.

a. 2! 2 **b.** 6! 720 **c.** 4! 24

d. Find the number of ways you can arrange ten books on a bookshelf. 3,628,800 ways

Reaching All Students

Below Level	Advanced Learners	Inclusion / Diversity
Have students find the value of 5! and of 7!. 120; 5,040	Is each statement true? Justify your answer. 3! + 4! = 7! no; 3! + 4! = 30; 7! = 5,040 12! ÷ 3! = 4! no; 12! ÷ 3! = 79,833,600; 4! = 24	**Inclusion** See note on page 596. **Diversity** See note on page 596.

OBJECTIVE

2 Using Permutation Notation

A class of 25 students must choose a president and a vice president. There are 25 possible choices for the president. Then there are 24 possible choices for the vice president. So, there are 25 · 24 permutations for choosing a president and a vice president from 25 students. You can write this as $_{25}P_2$.

Reading Math

The expression $_{25}P_2$, represents the number of ways of arranging, in order, 2 items from a set of 25.

Key Concepts **Permutation Notation**

The expression $_nP_r$ represents the number of permutations of n objects chosen r at a time.

Example $_{25}P_2 = 25 \cdot 24 = 600$

↑ 25 objects ↑ groups of 2 (two factors)

4 EXAMPLE Using Permutation Notation

Simplify $_{15}P_3$.

$_{15}P_3 = 15 \cdot 14 \cdot 13$ ← Write the notation as a product of 3 factors, starting with 15.

$= 2{,}730$ ← Simplify.

There are 2,730 permutations of 15 items chosen 3 at a time.

Check Understanding 4 Simplify each expression.

a. $_{12}P_2$ 132 **b.** $_{10}P_4$ 5,040 **c.** $_9P_3$ 504

Real-World Connection

Touching a Van de Graaff generator makes your hair stand up!

You can use permutations to find the number of ways to choose first, second, third, and fourth place in competitions.

5 EXAMPLE Real-World Problem Solving

Science Fair At a school science fair, ribbons are given for first, second, third, and fourth place. There are 20 exhibits in the fair. How many different arrangements of four winning exhibits are possible?

Use a calculator.

Enter 20. Find the PRB menu. Select $_nP_r$.

Enter 4. The display shows 116280.

There are 116,280 different arrangements of four winning exhibits.

Check Understanding 5 **Number Sense** Suppose the school in Example 5 decides to award first, second, and third place only for the science fair. How would you find the number of permutations? How many permutations are there?
Find $_{20}P_3$; 6,840 permutations

4 EXAMPLE Auditory Learners

Have students work with a partner to practice writing an expression such as $_{25}P_2$ and then reading it aloud as "the number of permutations of 25 objects chosen 2 at a time." Ask students to check that their partners have clearly written the numbers as subscripts.

5 EXAMPLE Technology Tip

Point out to students that they enter the first number, 20, *before* they press the nPr key.

Additional Examples

1. In how many ways can four people form a line? 24
2. Suppose you have six invitations to write. In how many different sequences can you write them? 720
3. A CD has nine songs. In how many different orders could you play these songs? 362,880
4. Simplify $_{11}P_5$. 55,440
5. In a spelling contest, trophies are given for first, second, and third places. There are 15 finalists in the contest. How many different arrangements are possible for the winners of the trophies? 2,730

Closure

- *What is a permutation?* An arrangement of a set of objects in a particular order.
- Name at least two ways to find the number of permutations of a set of objects. Use a calculator, make a tree diagram, or use the counting principle.
- Write the notation you could use to show the permutation of t things taken c at a time. $_tP_c$

3. Practice

Assignment Guide

Objective 1

A B Core 1–10, 23, 25

C Extension 28–31

Objective 2

A B Core 11–22, 24, 26–27

C Extension 32–33

Test Prep 34–37

Mixed Review 38–39

Error Prevention!

Exercises 5–16 Ask: *Are you choosing all or some?*

Practice 11-2 — Permutations

Simplify each expression.

1. 6! 720
2. 12! 479,001,600
3. 9! 362,880
4. $\frac{8!}{5!}$ 336
5. $\frac{12!}{3!}$ 79,833,600
6. ${}_9P_5$ 15,120
7. ${}_8P_2$ 56
8. ${}_{10}P_8$ 1,814,400
9. ${}_5P_5$ 120
10. ${}_{15}P_6$ 3,603,600

Use the counting principle to find the number of permutations.

11. In how many ways can all the letters of the word WORK be arranged? 24 ways
12. In how many ways can you arrange seven friends in a row for a photo? 5,040 ways
13. A disk jockey can play eight songs in one time slot. In how many different orders can the eight songs be played? 40,320 orders
14. Melody has nine bowling trophies to arrange in a horizontal line on a shelf. How many arrangements are possible? 362,880 arrangements
15. At a track meet, 42 students entered the 100-m race. In how many ways can first, second, and third places be awarded? 68,880 ways
16. In how many ways can a president, a vice president, and a treasurer be chosen from a group of 15 people running for office? 2,730 ways
17. A car dealer has 38 used cars to sell. Each day two cars are chosen for advertising specials. One car appears in a television commercial and the other appears in a newspaper advertisement. In how many ways can the two cars be chosen? 1,406 ways
18. A bicycle rack outside a classroom has room for six bicycles. In the class, 10 students sometimes ride their bicycles to school. How many different arrangements of bicycles are possible for any given day? 151,200 arrangements
19. A certain type of luggage has room for three initials. How many different 3-letter arrangements of letters with no repetition of the same letter are possible? 15,600 arrangements
20. A roller coaster has room for 10 people. The people sit single file, one after the other. How many different arrangements are possible for 10 passengers on the roller coaster? 3,628,800 arrangements

Reteaching 11-2 — Permutations

The expression 5! is read "5 *factorial*." It means the product of all whole numbers from 5 to 1.

$5! = 5 \cdot 4 \cdot 3 \cdot 2 \cdot 1 = 120$

Example 1: Evaluate $\frac{5!}{3!}$.

Write the products, then simplify.

$\frac{5!}{3!} = \frac{5 \cdot 4 \cdot 3 \cdot 2 \cdot 1}{3 \cdot 2 \cdot 1} = 5 \cdot 4 = 20$

Example 2: How many 3-letter codes can be made from A, B, C, D, E, F, G, H with no repeating letters?

This is a *permutation* problem. Order is important. ABC is different from ACB.

- There are 8 choices for the first letter.
- There are 7 choices for the second letter.
- There are 6 choices for the third letter.

The number of codes possible $= 8 \cdot 7 \cdot 6 = 336$.

You can write this as ${}_8P_3$, meaning the number of permutations of 8 objects chosen 3 at a time.

Simplify each expression.

1. 4! 24
2. 3! 6
3. $\frac{4!}{3!}$ 4
4. $\frac{10!}{8!}$ 90
5. $\frac{9!}{9!}$ 1
6. $5! \times 2!$ 240

Simplify each expression.

7. ${}_6P_3$ 120
8. ${}_5P_2$ 20
9. ${}_{12}P_3$ 1,320
10. ${}_4P_4$ 24
11. ${}_{15}P_2$ 210
12. ${}_6P_4$ 360

Use the counting principle to find the number of permutations.

13. In how many ways can you pick a football center and quarterback from 6 players who try out? ${}_6P_2 = 30$
14. For a meeting agenda, in how many ways can you schedule 3 speakers out of 10 people who would like to speak? ${}_{10}P_3 = 720$

EXERCISES

For more practice, see *Extra Practice*.

A Practice by Example

1–2. See back of book for diagrams.

Use a tree diagram to find the number of permutations.

Example 1 (page 596)

1. Four students are in line to see the school nurse. In how many different ways can the students be positioned in the line? 24 ways

2. Suppose you rent a thriller, a drama, and a comedy from a video store. In how many different orders can you watch the videos? 6 orders

Example 2 (page 596)

Use the counting principle to find the number of permutations.

3. There are nine performers in a charity event. How many different ways can the producer arrange the performers? 362,880 ways

4. Each spring a school holds a speech contest. There are six finalists this year. In how many different orders can the speeches be given? 720 orders

Example 3 (page 596)

Simplify each expression.

5. 5! 120 6. 7! 5,040 7. 9! 362,880 8. 10! 3,628,800 9. 11! 39,916,800

10. A desk organizer is made up of six smaller sections. If you have six different desk items, in how many different ways can you place the items in the organizer? 720 ways

Examples 4, 5 (page 597)

Simplify each expression.

11. ${}_{25}P_3$ 13,800 12. ${}_{18}P_2$ 306 13. ${}_{32}P_3$ 29,760 14. ${}_8P_4$ 1,680 15. ${}_{400}P_2$ 159,600

16. **Education** You have to read 5 of the 42 books on the summer reading list. In how many different ways can you choose five books? 102,080,160 ways

B Apply Your Skills

A bag contains ten blocks. Each block is a different color. Find how many ways you can select the number of blocks given.

17. 3 720 ways 18. 5 30,240 ways 19. 7 604,800 ways 20. 9 3,628,800 ways 21. 10 3,628,800 ways

22. **Dog Shows** Twenty-five dogs enter a dog show. The show awards prizes for first, second, and third place. How many different arrangements of three winners are possible? 13,800 arrangements

GPS

Real-World Connection

Dog obedience and showmanship are judged in dog shows.

23. **Error Analysis** When Spencer simplified 4!, his answer was 10. What error did he make? Explain. See margin.

24. **Surveys** From a list of ten artists, students were asked to list their favorite four in order of preference. In how many different ways can the artists be listed? 5,040 ways

25. a. **Writing in Math** Explain what is meant by 12!. 25a–b. See margin.
b. Describe two different ways you can use a calculator to compute 12!.

Use the Guided Problem Solving worksheet with Exercise 22.

23. He added 4 + 3 + 2 + 1 when he should have multiplied 4 × 3 × 2 × 1.

25a. Multiply 12 by each positive integer less than 12. 12! = 12 × 11 × 10 × 9 × 8 × 7 × 6 × 5 × 4 × 3 × 2 × 1

b. You can multiply 12 by each positive integer less than 12 or you can use the factorial key.

26a. There are 144 possible choices for president, 143 possible choices for vice president, and 142 possible choices for treasurer. So, there are $144 \cdot 143 \cdot 142$, or ${}_{144}P_3$ possible outcomes.

b. $\frac{1}{{}_{144}P_3}$ or $\frac{1}{2,924,064}$

C Challenge

26. a. **Reasoning** An eighth-grade class of 144 students selects a president, a vice president, and a treasurer. Explain why you would use ${}_{144}P_3$ to find the number of possible outcomes.
    b. **Probability** What is the probability of the teacher selecting the same officers at random?

27. **Algebra** You select five out of x different objects. How many different arrangements of the five objects are possible? ${}_{x}P_5$

Simplify each expression.

28. $9! - 5!$ 362,760
29. $2! \cdot 4!$ 48
30. $2! + 6!$ 722
31. $\frac{5!}{3!}$ 20

32. You color rows of 8 squares on graph paper, using a different color for each square in a row. It takes you 45 seconds to color each arrangement. If you use the same 8 colors for each row, how many hours will it take you to color all the possible arrangements? 504 hours

33. **Stretch Your Thinking** Suppose you make $1,000 every time the hands of a clock form a right angle. How much money will you make in 24 hours? $44,000

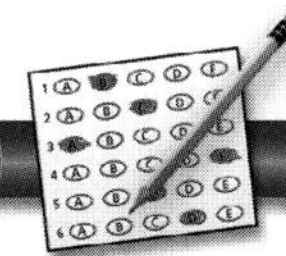

Test Prep

Multiple Choice

34. Simplify 5!. C
    A. 15 B. 24 C. 120 D. 720

35. Simplify ${}_{18}P_3$. I
    F. 15 G. 21 H. 306 I. 4,896

36. A parade has six different floats in line. In how many ways can three of the floats be first, second, and third? D
    A. 4 B. 6 C. 30 D. 120

Take It to the NET
Online lesson quiz at
www.PHSchool.com
Web Code: aca-1102

Short Response

37. Suppose 15 countries compete in an Olympic event. Gold, silver, and bronze medals are awarded. How many different arrangements of winners are there if no country wins more than one medal in this event? Show your work. See margin.

Mixed Review

Lesson 11-1

38. **Sports** In volleyball, you can volley, set, or spike. How many ways can your team make two plays? Use a tree diagram. See margin.

Lesson 10-5

39. **Algebra** Make a scatter plot for the data below. See back of book.

Basketball Shots

Distance From Basket (ft)	5	10	6	12	15	20	18	7
Number of Baskets	10	8	9	7	4	3	4	5

37. [2] ${}_{15}P_3 = 15 \times 14 \times 13$
$= 2,730$
2,730 arrangements
[1] minor computational error OR correct answer without work shown

38. 9 ways

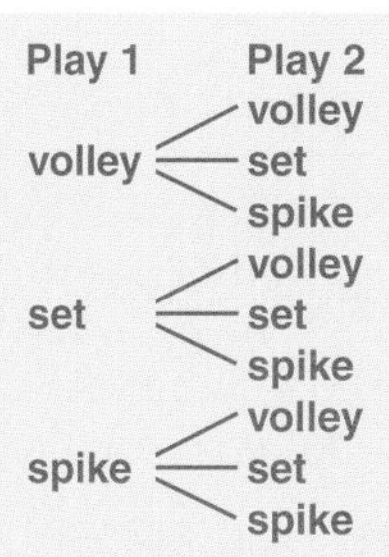

4. Assess

Lesson Quiz 11-2

1. In how many different ways can you line up a half dollar, quarter, dime, nickel, and penny? 120
2. A CD has 11 songs. Find in how many orders you can play the songs. 39,916,800
3. Simplify ${}_{10}P_3$. 720

Alternative Assessment

Have students explain whether or not 30! is the solution for the number of ways to choose a president and vice-president from a class of 30 students. Sample: No, the correct answer is 30×29, or 870, because you are choosing only two students from the 30.

Test Prep

Resources
For additional practice with a variety of test item formats:
- Test Prep, p. 631
- Test-Taking Strategies, p. 627
- Test-Taking Strategies with Transparencies

Exercise 34 Suggest that 5! may be computed mentally by using the commutative property.
Sample: $(5 \cdot 2) \cdot (3 \cdot 4) = 120$

Enrichment 11-2 Permutations

Visual Thinking

Rosa's little sister, Maria, makes solid figures by stacking her play cubes. After all the cubes have been stacked, Rosa paints the outside of each figure Maria made.

1. a. Maria made a wall of cubes as shown in the figure. Complete the table to find how many cubes will have the given number of painted faces.

Number of painted faces	6	5	4	3	2	1	0
Number of cubes	0	0	4	32	64	0	0

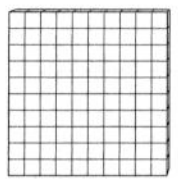

   b. Maria has 26 alphabet stickers (one for each letter). She wants to put one sticker on each cube with 4 painted faces. How many ways can the cube be marked?
   358,800 ways

2. Next, Maria made a large cube like the one shown. Complete the table to find how many small cubes in the figure will have the given number of painted faces.

Number of painted faces	6	5	4	3	2	1	0
Number of cubes	0	0	0	8	96	384	512

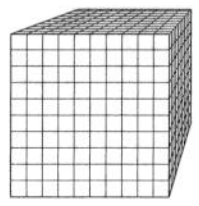

3. Rosa has 5 different colors of paint for the large cube in Exercise 2. She wants to paint each group of small cubes with a given number of faces a different color. For example, she may choose to paint all the cubes with 1 painted face green and those with 2 painted faces blue.
   a. How many different groups of cubes will Rosa paint?
   3 groups
   b. Write an expression for the number of ways Rosa can paint the large cube using permutation notation.
   ${}_{5}P_3$
   c. How many ways can Rosa paint the large cube?
   60 ways

11-3

1. Plan

Lesson Preview

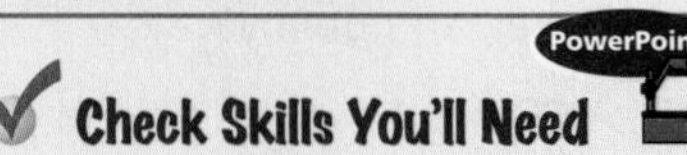

Using Permutation Notation
Lesson 11-2: Example 4. Extra Practice, p. 712.

Lesson Resources

Teaching Resources
Practice, Reteaching, Enrichment
Checkpoint Quiz 1

Reaching All Students
Practice Workbook 11-3
Spanish Practice Workbook 11-3
Reading and Math Literacy 11B
Spanish Reading and Math Literacy 11B
Spanish Checkpoint Quiz 1
Guided Problem Solving 11-3
Technology Activities 50

Presentation Assistant Plus!
Transparencies
- Check Skills You'll Need 11-3
- Problem of the Day 11-3
- Additional Examples 11-3
- Student Edition Answers 11-3
- Lesson Quiz 11-3
- Classroom Aid 11

PH Presentation Pro CD-ROM 11-3

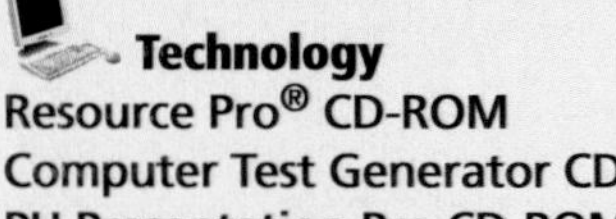

Checkpoint Quiz 1
Computer Test Generator CD

Technology
Resource Pro® CD-ROM
Computer Test Generator CD
PH Presentation Pro CD-ROM

www.PHSchool.com
Student Site
- Teacher Web Code: ack-5500
- Algebra Readiness Puzzle 49
- Self-grading Lesson Quiz
- Graphing Calculator Handbook, Procedure 16

PH SuccessNet Teacher Center
- Lesson Planner
- Resources

Plus 

11-3 Combinations

What You'll Learn

 To find combinations by using a list

 To use combination notation

. . . And Why

To find the number of ways to choose a combination, as in Example 2

Check Skills You'll Need

For help, go to Lesson 11-2.

Simplify each expression.

1. ${}_7P_2$ 42
2. ${}_{10}P_4$ 5,040
3. ${}_8P_8$ 40,320
4. ${}_{52}P_3$ 132,600
5. ${}_{99}P_1$ 99
6. ${}_{14}P_5$ 240,240
7. Suppose a computer password consists of six different digits. How many passwords can there be? 720 passwords

New Vocabulary
- combination

OBJECTIVE 1

 Interactive lesson includes instant self-check, tutorials, and activities.

Finding Combinations

The pair of yogurt toppings, raisins and nuts, is the same as the pair of toppings, nuts and raisins. They form the same combination. A **combination** is a group of items in which the order of the items is *not* considered.

1 EXAMPLE Finding Combinations

Food The table below contains four yogurt toppings. How many different ways can you choose two toppings?

Yogurt Toppings

Topping	Raisins	Nuts	Blueberries	Granola
Letter	R	N	B	G

Use letters to represent the four possible toppings.

Step 1 Make an organized list of all the possible combinations of toppings.

RN	RB	RG
NR	NB	NG
BR	BN	BG
GR	GN	GB

Step 2 Cross out any group that is a duplicate of another.

RN	RB	RG
~~NR~~	NB	NG
~~BR~~	~~BN~~	BG
~~GR~~	~~GN~~	~~GB~~

Need Help?
A group that contains the same items as another group is called a duplicate. Since NR is the same as RN, NR is a duplicate.

Step 3 Count the number of groups that remain.

There are six different ways to choose two toppings.

Ongoing Assessment and Intervention

Before the Lesson
Diagnose prerequisite skills using:
- Check Skills You'll Need

During the Lesson
Monitor progress using:
- Check Understanding
- Additional Examples
- Test Prep

After the Lesson
Assess knowledge using:
- Lesson Quiz
- Computer Test Generator CD
- Chapter Checkpoint 1 (p. 604)

Check Understanding 1 a. How many different groups of three tutors can your teacher choose from four students? Make an organized list to find the number of combinations. See left.

1a. 4 groups; answers may vary. Sample: ABC, ABD, ACD, BCD

b. **Reasoning** Why is Example 1 *not* solved by finding the number of permutations? Explain. The order in which the tutors are picked does not matter, so ABC is the same as BCA.

OBJECTIVE

2 Using Combination Notation

In Example 1, you found the number of combinations by using a list. You can also use permutations to find combinations.

But if order does not matter, the permutation *raisins and nuts* and the permutation *nuts and raisins* represent the same group of toppings. To remove all the duplicate groups, divide by 2!, the number of ways to arrange two toppings.

Reading Math

The expression $_4C_2$ represents the number of ways of choosing 2 items from a set of 4.

$$\text{combinations} = \frac{\text{total number of permutations}}{\text{number of permutations of 2 toppings}} = \frac{4 \cdot 3}{2 \cdot 1} = 6$$

You can write the number of combinations of four yogurt toppings chosen two at a time as $_4C_2$.

Key Concepts Combination Notation

The expression $_nC_r$ represents the number of combinations of n objects chosen r at a time.

$$_nC_r = \frac{_nP_r}{r!}$$

Example $_7C_3 = \frac{_7P_3}{3!} = \frac{7 \cdot 6 \cdot 5}{3 \cdot 2 \cdot 1} = 35$

Real-World Connection

Success in deep-sea fishing involves skill, timing, and proper use of fishing lures.

2 EXAMPLE Using Combination Notation

Real World

Fishing A fishing boat uses 5 fishing lines. Each line holds one lure. There are 12 different lures. How many different combinations of lures can be used at one time?

Find the number of ways you can choose 5 lures from 12.

$_{12}C_5 = \frac{_{12}P_5}{5!}$ ← **Write using combination notation.**

$= \frac{12 \cdot 11 \cdot 10 \cdot 9 \cdot 8}{5 \cdot 4 \cdot 3 \cdot 2 \cdot 1}$ ← **Simplify $_{12}P_5$ and 5!.**

$= 792$ ← **Simplify.**

There are 792 different combinations.

Check Understanding 2 Simplify each expression.

a. $_7C_5$ 21 b. $_8C_4$ 70 c. $_5C_3$ 10

d. **Number Sense** If the fishing boat in Example 2 uses 7 lines rather than 5 lines, are more combinations possible? Explain. No; $_{12}C_7 = {}_{12}C_5$; there are still 792 possible combinations.

Reaching All Students

Below Level Have students find these values. 12! ÷ 5! 3,991,680 (12 · 11 · 10) ÷ 4! 55	**Advanced Learners** Have students write a real-world problem that involves evaluating a combination. Have them challenge classmates to solve the problems.	**English Learners** See note on page 603. **Inclusion** See notes on pages 601 and 603.

2. Teach

Math Background

A *combination* is a group of items in which the order of the items is *not* considered. One way to find the number of combinations is to make an organized list of all the possibilities and eliminate the duplicates (since, for example, *vanilla and nuts* is the same choice as *nuts and vanilla*). The expression $_nC_r$ is read as "the number of combinations of n objects chosen r at a time." Another way to find the number of combinations is to use the formula: $_nC_r = \frac{_nP_r}{r!}$.

Teaching Notes

1 EXAMPLE Inclusion

Some students may have trouble remembering the difference between permutations and combinations. Suggest that they associate *prizes* with *permutations*, usually given in the order of first, second, and so forth. They can associate *combos* (as in food choices) with *combinations*, where order does not matter, since a cheese sandwich with milk is the same as milk with a cheese sandwich.

2 EXAMPLE Diversity

Ask volunteers to share what they know about fishing lures.

Additional Examples

1. How many groups of two can be formed from a committee of six members? 15 groups
2. Find the number of ways you can choose 3 lures from a box of 8 fishing lures. 56 ways

Closure

Explain what the formula $_nC_r = \frac{_nP_r}{r!}$ means. Sample: $_nC_r = \frac{_nP_r}{r!}$ represents the number of combinations of n objects chosen r at a time.

Check Understanding 2d. See back of book.

3. Practice

Assignment Guide

1 Objective 1

A B Core 1–2, 16–18

2 Objective 2

A B Core 3–15, 19–22

C Extension 23–26

Test Prep 27–30

Mixed Review 31–33

Error Prevention!

Exercises 3–12 Point out that the divisor is $r!$ and not just r.

Practice 11-3 — Combinations

Simplify each expression.

1. $_9C_1$ 9
2. $_8C_4$ 70
3. $_{11}C_4$ 330
4. $_{11}C_7$ 330
5. $_4C_4$ 1
6. $_9C_3$ 84
7. $_{12}C_6$ 924
8. $_8C_2$ 28
9. 3 videos from 10 120
10. 2 letters from LOVE 6
11. 4 books from 8 70
12. 5 people from 7 21

Solve.

13. Ten students from a class have volunteered to be on a committee to organize a dance. In how many ways can six be chosen for the committee? 210 ways
14. Twenty-three people try out for extra parts in a play. In how many ways can eight people be chosen to be extras? 490.314 ways
15. A team of nine players is to be chosen from 15 available players. In how many ways can this be done? 5,005 ways
16. In a talent show, five semi-finalists are chosen from 46 entries. In how many ways can the semi-finalists be chosen? 1,370,754 ways
17. At a party there are 12 people present. The host requests that each person present shakes hands exactly once with every other person. How many handshakes are necessary? 66 handshakes
18. In math class there are 24 students. The teacher picks 4 students to serve on the bulletin board committee. How many different committees of 4 are possible? 10,626 committees
19. Five friends, Billi, Joe, Eduardo, Mari, and Xavier, want one photograph taken of each possible pair of friends. Use B, J, E, M, and X, and list all of the pairs that need to be photographed. B, J; B, E; B, M; B, X; J, E; J, M; J, X; E, M; E, X; M, X
20. A team of 3 people is chosen from 8 available players. Describe the number of possible teams using combination notation. $_8C_3$

Reteaching 11-3 — Combinations

Mr. Wisniewski wants to pick 2 students from Minh, Joan, Jim, Esperanza, and Tina to demonstrate an experiment. How many different pairs of students can he choose?

In this *combination* problem, the order of the choice of students does not matter. These are the possibilities:

Minh-Esperanza			
Minh-Jim	Esperanza-Jim		
Minh-Joan	Esperanza-Joan	Jim-Joan	
Minh-Tina	Esperanza-Tina	Jim-Tina	Joan-Tina

There are 10 possible combinations.

The number of combinations of 5 students taken 2 at a time is $_5C_2$ where:

$$_5C_2 = \frac{1}{2!}\,{_5P_2} = \frac{1}{2!} \cdot 5 \cdot 4 = 10$$

In general, the number of combinations of n objects taken r at a time is $_nC_r$ where:

$$_nC_r = \frac{1}{r!} \cdot {_nP_r}$$

Simplify each expression.

1. $_6C_3$ 20
2. $_5C_2$ 10
3. $_7C_5$ 21
4. $_4C_3$ 4
5. $_8C_2$ 28
6. $_6C_4$ 15
7. $_9C_4$ 126
8. $_5C_3$ 10
9. $_6C_5$ 6
10. $_7C_3$ 35
11. $_8C_3$ 56
12. $_9C_3$ 84

Find the number of combinations.

13. In how many ways can Susie choose 3 of 10 books to take with her on a trip? $_{10}C_3 = 120$
14. In how many ways can Rosa select 2 movies to rent out of 6 that she likes? $_6C_2 = 15$
15. In how many ways can Bill pick 2 of his 7 trophies to show his grandfather? $_7C_2 = 21$
16. In how many ways can Mr. Wu choose 5 tulip bulbs out of 15 to plant in a flower bed? $_{15}C_5 = 3{,}003$
17. In how many ways can a town name 5 citizens out of 10 to serve on a committee? $_{10}C_5 = 252$
18. In how many ways can Mrs. Harris pick 3 flowers from 8 for a bouquet? $_8C_3 = 56$

More Than One Way

Your locker contains seven books. You select two books at random. How many different combinations of books can you select?

Nicole's Method

I can use combination notation to solve this problem.

$$_7C_2 = \frac{_7P_2}{2!} \quad \leftarrow \text{Write using combination notation.}$$

$$= \frac{7 \cdot 6}{2 \cdot 1} \quad \leftarrow \text{Simplify } {_7P_2} \text{ and } 2!.$$

$$= 21 \quad \leftarrow \text{Simplify.}$$

You can select 21 different combinations of two books.

Eric's Method

I can use a calculator.

Enter 7. Find the PRB menu. Select $_nC_r$.
Enter 3. The display shows 21.

You can select 21 different combinations of two books.

Choose a Method

You have 12 Web sites you can use to write a research paper. You select 3 sites. How many different combinations of sites you can select? Describe your method. 220 combinations; Check students' methods.

EXERCISES

For more practice, see *Extra Practice*.

A Practice by Example — **Find the number of combinations.**

Example 1 (page 600)

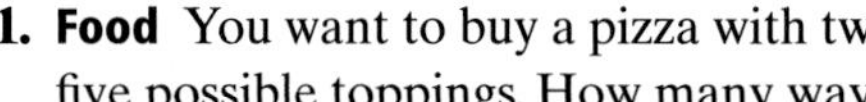

1. **Food** You want to buy a pizza with two toppings. The restaurant offers five possible toppings. How many ways can you choose two toppings? 10 ways
2. **Committees** A school committee has five members. The principal wants to form a subcommittee of three people. How many different groups of three can be formed from the school committee members? 10 groups

Example 2 (page 601)

Simplify each expression.

3. $_7C_4$ 35
4. $_3C_1$ 3
5. $_9C_6$ 84
6. $_8C_5$ 56
7. $_6C_4$ 15
8. $_{16}C_4$ 1,820
9. $_{10}C_9$ 10
10. $_{10}C_1$ 10
11. $_{13}C_{12}$ 13
12. $_{13}C_1$ 13

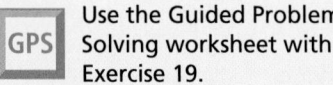

GPS Use the Guided Problem Solving worksheet with Exercise 19.

Apply Your Skills

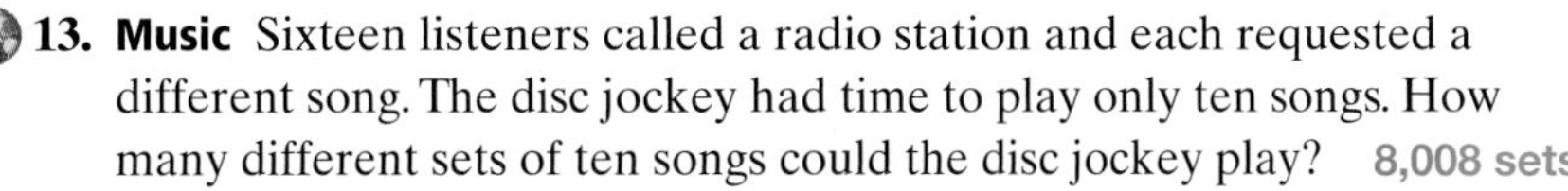

13. **Music** Sixteen listeners called a radio station and each requested a different song. The disc jockey had time to play only ten songs. How many different sets of ten songs could the disc jockey play? 8,008 sets

Real-World Connection
The U.S. Volleyball Junior Olympics is an annual indoor championship.

14. **Sports** Ten teams enter a volleyball tournament. Each team plays every other team once. How many different games are played? 45 games

15. You can bring three people to a party. You have ten friends who would like to go. How many different groups of three people can you bring? 120 groups

Decide if each situation describes a *permutation* or a *combination*.

16. A president and a vice president will be elected from club members. permutation
17. A photographer arranges four children in a row for a group picture. permutation
18. A salad bar offers eight choices of vegetables. combination

19. **Travel** A group of six tourists arrives at the gate fifteen minutes before flight time, but only two seats are available.
    a. How many different groups of two can get on the airplane? 15 groups
    b. How many different groups of four *cannot* get on the airplane? 15 groups

20. **Writing in Math** What is the difference between the number of permutations and the number of combinations of n objects chosen r at a time? Explain. See left.

20. The number of combinations is equal to the number of permutations divided by $r!$

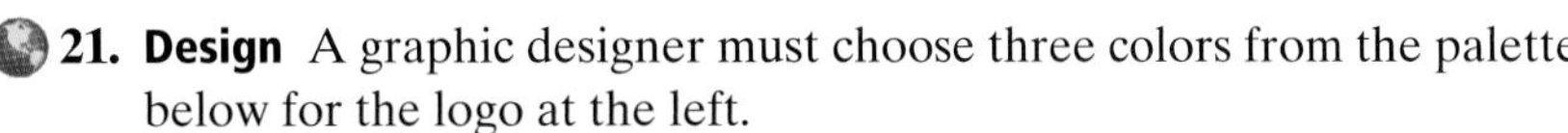

21. **Design** A graphic designer must choose three colors from the palette below for the logo at the left.

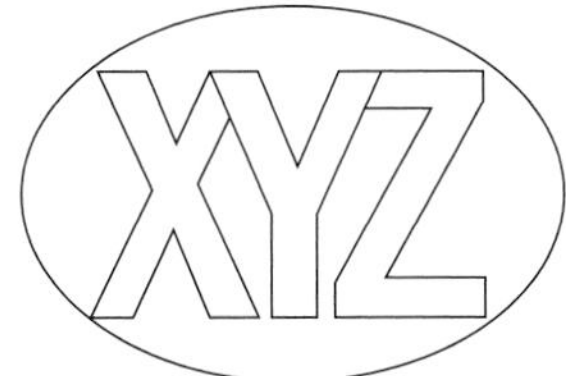

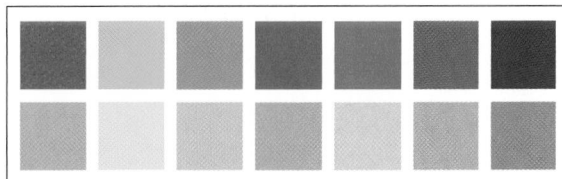

a. How many permutations of three colors are possible?
b. How many combinations of three colors are possible?
c. **Probability** Suppose a customer wants three colors in a specific order for the logo. What is the probability that the designer chooses the correct order of colors at random?

21. a. 2,184 permutations
b. 364 combinations
c. $\frac{1}{2,184}$

22. **Algebra** Write an expression to describe the number of different ways you can choose five objects from x different objects. ${}_xC_5$

Challenge

Simplify each expression.

23. ${}_3C_2 + {}_4C_3$ 7
24. ${}_5C_2 + {}_4C_2$ 16
25. ${}_5C_3 + {}_3C_3$ 11

26. **Stretch Your Thinking** Two numbers are chosen from the digits 3, 4, 5, 6, and 7 without being replaced. What is the probability that the product of the two numbers is a multiple of 4? $\frac{2}{5}$

Inclusion
Exercises 16–18 Review the difference between *permutation* and *combination*.

English Learners
Exercise 21 Discuss what a *palette* of colors is.

4. Assess

Lesson Quiz 11-3

1. How many different ways can two dancers be selected for a dance team out of five candidates? 10
2. Simplify ${}_{10}C_3$. 120

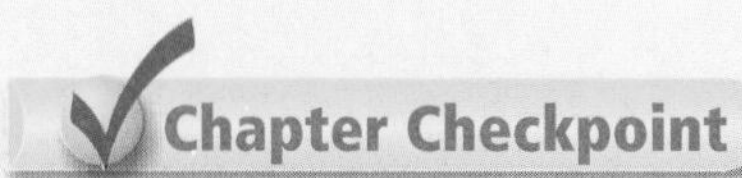

Chapter Checkpoint

To check understanding of Lessons 11-1 to 11-3:

Checkpoint Quiz 1 (p. 604)

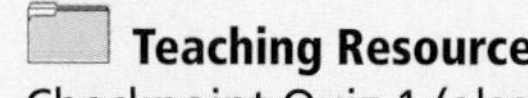

Teaching Resources
Checkpoint Quiz 1 (also in *Prentice Hall Assessment System*)

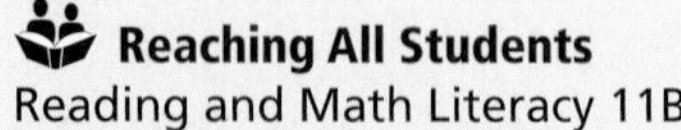

Reaching All Students
Reading and Math Literacy 11B

Spanish versions available

Test Prep

Resources
For additional practice with a variety of test item formats:
- Test Prep, p. 631
- Test-Taking Strategies, p. 627
- Test-Taking Strategies with Transparencies

Enrichment 11-3 — Combinations

Critical Thinking

In how many ways can 9 Senators be selected from among 100 United States Senators to serve on a foreign policy committee?

1. Does the order in which the Senators are chosen matter in this selection process? no
2. Is the question asking you to use combinations or permutations? How do you know? Combinations, because order does not matter.
3. Do you think the number of ways of choosing 9 out of 100 Senators will be a large or small number? Why? Sample answer: Large, because there are many different ways to select 9 Senators from a group of 100.
4. Write and evaluate an expression for the number of ways to choose 9 Senators for a committee. Write your answer in scientific notation. ${}_{100}C_9 = 1.9 \times 10^{12}$
5. a. How many Senators will *not* be needed for the committee? 91 Senators
   b. Write an expression for the number of ways to choose the Senators not needed for the committee from 100 Senators. ${}_{100}C_{91}$
   c. How many ways can you choose the Senators *not* included on the committee? Write your answer in scientific notation. 1.9×10^{12}
   d. How does this number compare to the number of ways to choose 9 Senators for the committee? Explain. The values are the same. Choosing 9 Senators to be included on a committee or 91 Senators *not* to be included on a committee are equivalent decisions.
6. Suppose the Senators decide to expand the committee to 12 members.
   a. Would you expect there to be more ways or fewer ways to select the committee? Explain. Sample answer: More, because there are more combinations of 12 Senators than of 9 Senators.
   b. Use combination notation to write two equivalent expressions for the number of ways to choose a committee of 12 Senators. ${}_{100}C_{12}$; ${}_{100}C_{88}$
   c. In how many ways can a 12-member committee be chosen? Write your answer in scientific notation. 1.1×10^{15}

Test Prep

Multiple Choice

27. What is the value of ${}_{10}C_2$? C
    A. 8 B. 20 C. 45 D. 90
28. A coach selects a team of 9 players from a group of 11 people. How many different combinations are possible? G
    F. 11 G. 55 H. 110 I. 990

Take It to the NET
Online lesson quiz at **www.PHSchool.com**
Web Code: aca-1103

29. A menu has a list of seven appetizers. Your party will choose three. Which of the following represents the number of possible choices? C
    A. $\frac{7!}{3!}$ B. ${}_7P_3$ C. ${}_7C_3$ D. $7! - 3!$

Short Response

30. A store sells 12 types of bread. It wants to display 5 of them on a shelf in front of the deli. How many different combinations are possible? Show your work. See margin.

Mixed Review

Lesson 11-2

31. **Sports** Ten runners compete at a track meet. How many ways can you choose the first, second, third, fourth, and fifth place winners? 30,240 ways

Lesson 10-4

Make a box-and-whisker plot for each set of data. 32–33. See back of book.

32. millions of dollars spent:
    2 9 3 1 7 6 5 8 11 14 9 7 2 1 8 7 6 13 11 10
33. number of employees hired:
    22 24 25 26 32 18 47 54 39 44 41 46 48 50

Checkpoint Quiz 1 — Lessons 11-1 through 11-3

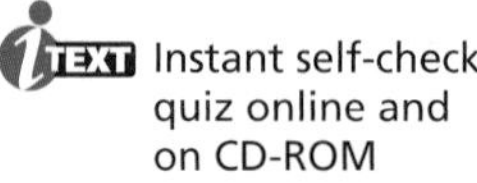

Instant self-check quiz online and on CD-ROM

1. **Gift Baskets** You want to make a gift basket with different types of fruit, toys, and jams. You have five types of fruit, four types of toys, and three types of jam. How many different baskets can you make, using one item from each category? 60 baskets

Simplify each expression.

2. $7!$ 5,040
3. ${}_5P_4$ 120
4. ${}_8P_3$ 336
5. $\frac{9!}{8!}$ 9

6. **Education** At the beginning of the year, your teacher gives you a list of ten possible projects. You must choose two to complete. How many different groups of two projects can you select? 45 groups

Simplify each expression.

7. ${}_7C_6$ 7
8. ${}_8C_2$ 28
9. ${}_9C_4$ 126
10. ${}_{10}C_6$ 210

Alternative Assessment

Use combination notation to solve this problem. There are 13 players on the basketball team. In how many ways can 5 starting players be selected?

$${}_{13}C_5 = \frac{{}_{13}P_5}{5!} = \frac{13 \cdot 12 \cdot 11 \cdot 10 \cdot 9}{5!} = 1,287$$

30. [2] $${}_{12}C_5 = \frac{{}_{12}P_5}{5!} = \frac{12 \cdot 11 \cdot 10 \cdot 9 \cdot 8}{5 \cdot 4 \cdot 3 \cdot 2 \cdot 1} = \frac{95,040}{120} = 792$$
    [1] minor computational error OR correct answer without work shown

Pascal's Triangle

For Use With Lesson 11-3

The structure of Pascal's triangle is described below. You can use Pascal's triangle to find a number of combinations.

Pascal's Triangle

Row	
0	1
1	1 1
2	1 2 1
3	1 3 3 1
4	1 4 6 4 1
5	1 5 10 10 5 1
6	1 6 15 20 15 6 1

The first and last digits in each row are 1.

Find the numbers in each row by adding the two numbers above a number.

EXAMPLE

Find $_5C_2$ using Pascal's triangle.

Row 5 of Pascal's triangle gives all the combinations of the form $_5C_r$.

1	5	10	10	5	1	← row 5
↑	↑	↑	↑	↑	↑	
$_5C_0$	$_5C_1$	$_5C_2$	$_5C_3$	$_5C_4$	$_5C_5$	← all combinations in the form $_5C_r$

So, $_5C_2 = 10$.

EXERCISES

1. Copy Pascal's triangle. Complete two more rows. 1 7 21 35 35 21 7 1; 1 8 28 56 70 56 28 8 1

Use Pascal's triangle to find each combination.

2. $_5C_3$ 10
3. $_6C_4$ 15
4. $_3C_2$ 3
5. $_4C_4$ 1
6. $_2C_2$ 1
7. $_7C_4$ 35

8. a. Write the sum of each row in the triangle. 1, 2, 4, 8, 16, 32, 64
   b. **Algebra** Write the sum of the numbers in row n as a power of two. 2^n
9. **Reasoning** To find how many combinations are possible for six items chosen four at a time, do you use the fourth number in row 6 or the fifth number in row 6? Use the fifth number in the row because the first number corresponds to $_6C_0$.
10. From a committee of eight people, three people are chosen. Use Pascal's triangle to find the total number of combinations. 56 combinations

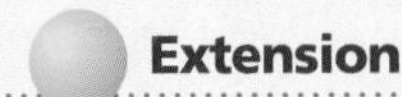

Pascal's Triangle

Pascal's Triangle is an array of numbers named for the 17th century French mathematician and philosopher, Blaise Pascal. The triangle contains many useful patterns. In this feature, students use the triangle to find combinations.

Teaching Notes

Teaching Tip
Tell students that Pascal's Triangle is an array of numbers formulated by a mathematician nearly 400 years ago. The first six rows of the triangle are presented here. Invite students to spend a few minutes examining the rows to look for patterns. Have students share what they discover.

Inclusion
Make sure students understand the distinction between rows and columns. Have them identify the numbers in the second row, the fifth row, and so on.

Teaching Tip
Students can use Pascal's Triangle to find combinations. Work through the Example on the board. Guide students to see that the entries in each row are values of $_nC_r$. You can use row 4 as an example to compare with row 5. For row 4, the entries are the values of $_nC_r$ for $n = 4$ and $r = 0$, 1, 2, 3, and 4.

Exercise 1 Have students work independently. Ask a volunteer to explain how he or she completed rows 7 and 8. Then have students work in pairs on the remaining exercises.

Exercise 9 Students can check their answer by simplifying $_nC_r$ using pencil and paper ($_6C_4 = 15$, the fifth number in row 6).

11-4

1. Plan

Lesson Preview

PowerPoint

 Check Skills You'll Need 

Writing Fractions as Percents
Lesson 6-1: Example 3. Extra Practice, p. 707.

Lesson Resources

 **Teaching Resources**
Practice, Reteaching, Enrichment

Reaching All Students
Practice Workbook 11-4
Spanish Practice Workbook 11-4
Guided Problem Solving 11-4
Hands-On Activities 43, 45–46

Presentation Assistant Plus!
Transparencies
- Check Skills You'll Need 11-4
- Problem of the Day 11-4
- Additional Examples 11-4
- Student Edition Answers 11-4
- Lesson Quiz 11-4

PH Presentation Pro CD-ROM 11-4

Computer Test Generator CD

 **Technology**
Resource Pro® CD-ROM
Computer Test Generator CD
PH Presentation Pro CD-ROM

 **www.PHSchool.com**
Student Site
- Teacher Web Code: ack-5500
- Self-grading Lesson Quiz

PH SuccessNet Teacher Center
- Lesson Planner
- Resources

Plus 

11-4 Theoretical and Experimental Probability

What You'll Learn

 To find experimental probability

 To find the complements and odds of events

. . . And Why

To use experimental probability in science, as in Example 1

✓ Check Skills You'll Need

For help, go to Lesson 6-1.

Write each fraction as a percent. Round to the nearest hundredth of a percent where necessary.

1. $\frac{10}{16}$ 62.5% **2.** $\frac{12}{40}$ 30% **3.** $\frac{70}{175}$ 40% **4.** $\frac{8}{62}$ 12.90%

5. Explain how to write the decimal 0.85 as a percent and as a fraction. See below left.

5. To write 0.85 as a percent, move the decimal point two places to the right and add the % symbol; to write 0.85 as a fraction, drop the decimal point and put 85 over 100. Then write the fraction in lowest terms.

New Vocabulary • experimental probability • theoretical probability • complement • odds in favor • odds against

 Interactive lesson includes instant self-check, tutorials, and activities.

OBJECTIVE 1 Finding Experimental Probability

Investigation: Experimental Probability

- Drop a paper cup from a height of 3 ft. Notice how it lands.
- Copy and complete the table at the right as you repeat the experiment 20 times. 1–3. Check students' work.

Event	Occurrences
Rim up	■
Rim down	■
On its side	■

1. Which event occurs more often than the others?
2. Use the following ratio to show your results: $\frac{\text{number of times event occurs}}{\text{total number of trials}}$.
3. Compare your results to those of your classmates. Did all of your classmates get the same results? Why do you think this is so?

Probability based on experimental data is called **experimental probability.** You find the experimental probability of an event by repeating an experiment, or trial, many times.

Key Concepts **Experimental Probability**

$$P(\text{event}) = \frac{\text{number of times event occurs}}{\text{total number of trials}}$$

Ongoing Assessment and Intervention

Before the Lesson
Diagnose prerequisite skills using:
- Check Skills You'll Need

During the Lesson
Monitor progress using:
- Check Understanding
- Additional Examples
- Test Prep

After the Lesson
Assess knowledge using:
- Lesson Quiz
- Computer Test Generator CD

Real-World Connection

Careers Botanists crossbreed seeds to develop hardier plants.

1 EXAMPLE Finding Experimental Probability

 Real World

Science The scientist Gregor Mendel crossbred green-seed plants and yellow-seed plants. Out of 8,023 crosses, 6,022 plants had yellow seeds and 2,001 had green seeds. Find the probability that a plant has green seeds. Write the probability as a percent.

$P(\text{green}) = \frac{\text{number of plants with green seeds}}{\text{total number of crossbred plants}}$ ← **Write the probability ratio.**

$= \frac{2{,}001}{8{,}023}$ ← **Substitute.**

≈ 0.249 ← **Divide.**

$\approx 25\%$ ← **Round to the nearest percent.**

The experimental probability that a plant has green seeds is about 25%.

Check Understanding 1 Use the table at the right. What is the experimental probability of getting heads after 20 tosses? Write the probability as a fraction, decimal, and percent.

Heads	~~||||~~ |||
Tails	~~||||~~ ~~||||~~ ||

$\frac{2}{5}$; 0.4; 40%

You can toss a coin to find the experimental probability of getting heads. You can also find the theoretical probability without doing any trials because both possible outcomes (heads or tails) are equally likely.

To find the theoretical probability of an event with equally likely outcomes, you use the formula you learned in Chapter 6.

theoretical probability $= P(E) = \frac{\text{number of favorable outcomes}}{\text{total number of possible outcomes}}$

The experimental probability of getting heads is likely to get closer to the theoretical probability the more times you toss the coin.

2 EXAMPLE Identifying the Type of Probability

 Real World

Surveys The table below shows the results of a survey of Mayville residents. Does the survey represent experimental or theoretical probability?

Question 3 on the Town Ballot

Number of People Surveyed	Number of People in Favor	Number of People Not in Favor
100	64	36

The survey records actual responses from Mayville residents. It represents experimental probability.

Check Understanding 2 **Reasoning** Decide whether each probability is *experimental* or *theoretical*. Explain your answers.

a. A bag contains two red marbles and three white marbles. $P(\text{red})$ is $\frac{2}{5}$.

2a. Theoretical; the result is based on the number of possible outcomes.

b. You draw a marble out of a bag, record the color, and replace the marble. After 8 draws, you record 3 red marbles. $P(\text{red})$ is $\frac{3}{8}$.
Experimental; the result is found by repeating an experiment.

Reaching All Students

Below Level Subtract.

$1 - 0.25$ 0.75 $1 - 0.025$ 0.975
$1 - 0.75$ 0.25 $1 - 0.075$ 0.925

Advanced Learners Have students find the theoretical and experimental probabilities of getting an even number when tossing a number cube 50 times. 50%; Experimental probability will vary.

English Learners
See note on page 608.

Diversity
See note on page 607.

2. Teach

Math Background

Probability based on experimental data is called *experimental probability*. The *theoretical probability* of an event, written as *P*(*E*), is the number of favorable outcomes divided by the total number of possible outcomes. For ten trials of tossing a fair coin, the theoretical $P(\text{heads}) = \frac{5}{10}$, or $\frac{1}{2}$. The experimental probability can vary from $\frac{0}{10}$ to $\frac{10}{10}$.

Teaching Notes

Investigation (Optional)
Before students begin, have them agree on how they will hold a cup when they drop it. This will keep the experiments as similar as possible. Point out that there is no "correct" answer; they are trying to determine what happens naturally.

1 EXAMPLE Biology Connection

Have students share what they know about hereditary traits. For example, some students may know that eye color is hereditary.

Diversity
Some students may come from backgrounds that do not approve of gambling. They may not appreciate that probability has many other purposes, such as use in surveys, weather forecasting, sports, and genetics.

2 EXAMPLE Error Prevention

Ask students to find the sum of *in favor* and *not in favor*. 100

Additional Examples

1. A gardener plants 250 sunflower seeds and 210 germinate. Find the experimental probability that a sunflower seed will germinate. 84%
2. The probability of tossing one six-sided number cube and getting a 5 is $\frac{1}{6}$, or about 17%. Is this experimental or theoretical probability? theoretical

3 EXAMPLE English Learners

Help students remember the correct spelling for the *complement* of an event by relating it to the word *complete*. Point out that a *compliment*, or approving remark, has a different spelling.

4 EXAMPLE Sports Connection

Have volunteers describe the game of golf and how it is scored.

Additional Examples

3 Find the probability of *not* rolling a 1 or a 2 with a number cube. $\frac{2}{3}$

4 Suppose you select a pen at random from 3 red ones and 4 blue ones. What are the odds in favor of selecting a red pen? 3 : 4

Closure

- *How does experimental probability differ from theoretical probability?* Sample: Experimental probability is based on experimental data.
- *What is the relationship between the odds in favor of an event and the odds against an event?* Sample: The odds in favor is the inverse ratio of the odds against.

OBJECTIVE

2 Finding Complements and Odds

The **complement** of an event is the opposite of that event. For example, in a coin toss, heads is the complement of tails. The sum of the probabilities of an event and its complement is 1.

Key Concepts — The Complement of an Event

For an event, A, and its complement, not A, $P(A) + P(\text{not } A) = 1$.

To find the probability of a complement, use the following formula:

$$P(\text{not } A) = 1 - P(A)$$

3 EXAMPLE Complements in Probability

Find the probability of *not* rolling a 6 with a number cube. Write the probability as a fraction.

$P(\text{not } 6) = 1 - P(6)$ ← **Write the formula for the complement.**

$= 1 - \frac{1}{6}$ ← **Substitute the probability of rolling a 6.**

$= \frac{5}{6}$ ← **Subtract.**

The probability of *not* rolling a 6 is $\frac{5}{6}$.

Check Understanding 3 What is the probability of *not* rolling a 4 or a 5 on a number cube? $\frac{2}{3}$

Key Concepts — Odds

odds in favor of an event = the ratio of the number of favorable outcomes to the number of unfavorable outcomes

odds against an event = the ratio of the number of unfavorable outcomes to the number of favorable outcomes

Example The odds *in favor* of the spinner landing on red are 1 to 3 or 1:3. The odds *against* the spinner landing on red are 3:1.

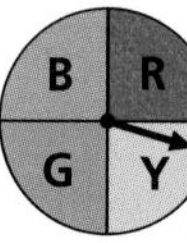

4 EXAMPLE Determining Odds

Miniature Golf Suppose you select a ball at random from the golf balls shown. What are the odds in favor of selecting a yellow ball?

Since two balls are yellow and five are orange, the odds of selecting a yellow ball at random are 2:5.

Check Understanding 4 What are the odds against selecting a yellow ball at random? 5 : 2

EXERCISES

For more practice, see *Extra Practice*.

A Practice by Example

Example 1 (page 607)

Flower Seeds Write each probability as a fraction, a decimal, and a percent. You select 250 seeds from a bag. The results are as follows: 68 marigolds, 94 alyssum, 8 poppies, and the rest are zinnias. Find each experimental probability.

1. P(marigold) $\frac{34}{125}$; 0.272; 27.2%
2. P(alyssum) $\frac{47}{125}$; 0.376; 37.6%
3. P(zinnias) $\frac{8}{25}$; 0.32; 32%
4. P(poppies) $\frac{4}{125}$; 0.032; 3.2%

Example 2 (page 607)

Decide whether each probability is *experimental* or *theoretical*.

5. You toss two pennies 20 times. $P(\text{2 heads}) = \frac{3}{20}$. experimental
6. A spinner is divided into six equal sections. Three sections are green and three sections are blue. P(green) is $\frac{1}{2}$. theoretical

Example 3 (page 608)

A spinner is divided into 12 equal sections numbered from 1 to 12. You spin the spinner once. Find each probability. Write the probability as a fraction.

7. P(not 2) $\frac{11}{12}$
8. P(not odd) $\frac{1}{2}$
9. P(not 3, 5, or 10) $\frac{3}{4}$

Example 4 (page 608)

10. Suppose you have a 12-sided solid numbered 1 to 12. The probability of any side facing upward when the solid is rolled is equally likely. What are the odds in favor of rolling a 7? 1 : 11

B Apply Your Skills

Data Analysis In a survey, a group of children were asked what time they go to bed. The results are shown below. Write each experimental probability as a fraction in simplest form.

Bedtimes of Children

Time (P.M.)	7:30	8:00	8:30	9:00	9:30
Number	24	31	38	42	36

11. P(9:30) $\frac{4}{19}$
12. P(8:30) $\frac{2}{9}$
13. P(7:30–8:30) $\frac{31}{57}$
14. P(not 9:00) $\frac{43}{57}$
15. P(after 8:30) $\frac{26}{57}$
16. P(before 9:30) $\frac{15}{19}$
17. Data File, p. 589 A researcher has a fact sheet for every animal species at the St. Louis Zoo. There are 110 mammal species.
    a. What is the probability of selecting a fact sheet about a mammal? $\frac{22}{141}$
    b. The zoo has two species of pandas. If a mammal fact sheet is chosen, what is the probability that it is about pandas? $\frac{1}{55}$
18. **Writing in Math** What is the difference between experimental and theoretical probability? Explain. See margin.
19. GPS The probability of an event is $\frac{1}{4}$. What are the odds in favor of the event occurring? 1 : 3

Real-World Connection
The population of the giant panda is about 800–1,200 worldwide.

18. Experimental probability is based on running numerous trials or experiments, whereas theoretical probability is based on the mathematical likelihood of events.

GPS Use the Guided Problem Solving worksheet with Exercise 19.

3. Practice

Assignment Guide

Objective 1
A B Core 1–6, 11–13, 15–18
C Extension 20

Objective 2
A B Core 7–10, 14, 19
C Extension 21

Test Prep 22–25
Mixed Review 26–40

Geometry Connection
Exercise 10 Pentagons form the 12 faces of a regular dodecahedron.

Practice 11-4
Theoretical and Experimental Probability

A dart is thrown at the game board shown. Notice that the diameters are at right angles and the slices that are congruent. Find each probability.

1. $P(A)$ $\frac{1}{3}$
2. $P(B)$ $\frac{5}{12}$
3. $P(C)$ $\frac{1}{4}$
4. $P(\text{not } A)$ $\frac{2}{3}$
5. $P(\text{not } B)$ $\frac{7}{12}$
6. $P(\text{not } C)$ $\frac{3}{4}$

The odds in favor of winning a game are 5 to 9.

7. Find the probability of winning the game. $\frac{5}{14}$
8. Find the probability of *not* winning the game. $\frac{9}{14}$

A box of marbles contains 10 red, 12 blue, 15 yellow, and 8 green marbles. A marble is drawn at random. Find each probability.

9. P(red) $\frac{2}{9}$
10. P(blue) $\frac{4}{15}$
11. P(yellow) $\frac{1}{3}$
12. P(green) $\frac{8}{45}$
13. What are the odds in favor of picking a blue marble? 4 to 11
14. What are the odds in favor of picking a green marble? 8 to 37
15. What is the probability of picking a marble that is not yellow? $\frac{2}{3}$
16. What is the probability of picking a marble that is not red? $\frac{7}{9}$

Solve.

17. a. You buy a ticket for the weekly drawing by a community charity. Last week you bought one ticket. Find the probability and odds of winning if 1,200 tickets were bought that week. $\frac{1}{1,200}$; 1 to 1,199
    b. Find the probability and odds of you winning if you bought three tickets and there were 1,200 tickets bought that week. $\frac{1}{400}$; 1 to 399
18. A bakery's bread display case contains wheat and rye bread. If you randomly pick a slice of bread, $P(\text{wheat}) = 0.45$. Find P(rye). If there are 200 slices of bread, how many slices of wheat bread are in the display case? 0.55; 90 slices

Reteaching 11-4
Theoretical and Experimental Probability

You can collect data through observations or experiments and use the data to state the *experimental probability*.

Alan has a coin. He tosses the coin 100 times and gets 60 heads and 40 tails. The experimental probability of getting heads is:

$$P(\text{heads}) = \frac{\text{number of heads}}{\text{number of trials}} = \frac{60}{100} = 0.6$$

Then Sarita calculated the *theoretical probability* of getting heads on one toss of the coin.

$$P(\text{heads}) = \frac{\text{favorable outcomes}}{\text{number of possible outcomes}} = \frac{1}{2} = 0.5$$

Alan thinks that his coin is unfair since the experimental probability is different from the theoretical probability.

Sarita suggests that they run the experiment again. This time they toss 53 heads and 47 tails. This suggests that the coin is more fair than Alan thinks. To form a more convincing conclusion, they should run the test several more times.

Suppose you have a bag with 75 marbles: 15 red, 5 white, 25 green, 20 black, and 10 blue. You draw a marble, note its color, and then put it back. You do this 75 times with these results: 12 red, 9 white, 27 green, 17 black, and 10 blue. Find each probability as a fraction in simplest form.

	1. P(red)	2. P(white)	3. P(green)	4. P(black)	5. P(blue)
Experimental Probability	$\frac{4}{25}$	$\frac{3}{25}$	$\frac{9}{25}$	$\frac{17}{75}$	$\frac{2}{15}$
Theoretical Probability	$\frac{1}{5}$	$\frac{1}{15}$	$\frac{1}{3}$	$\frac{4}{15}$	$\frac{2}{15}$

Suppose you surveyed the students in your class on their favorite juice flavors. Their choices were 6 apple, 10 orange, 1 grapefruit, and 3 mango. Find each probability as a fraction in simplest form.

6. P(apple) $\frac{3}{10}$
7. P(orange) $\frac{1}{2}$
8. P(grapefruit) $\frac{1}{20}$
9. P(not mango) $\frac{17}{20}$

4. Assess

Lesson Quiz 11-4

Use this information to solve the problems: You toss two nickels 50 times, and you get one head and one tail 38 times.

1. Find the experimental probability of getting one head and one tail. 76%
2. Find the probability of getting two heads or two tails. 24%
3. What are the odds in favor of getting exactly one head and one tail? 38 : 12 or 19 : 6

Alternative Assessment

Ask students: *The probability of some event is 45%. What is the probability of the complementary event?* 55% *What are the odds in favor of the event?* 45 : 55 or 9 : 11

Test Prep

Resources
For additional practice with a variety of test item formats:
- Test Prep, p. 631
- Test-Taking Strategies, p. 627
- Test-Taking Strategies with Transparencies

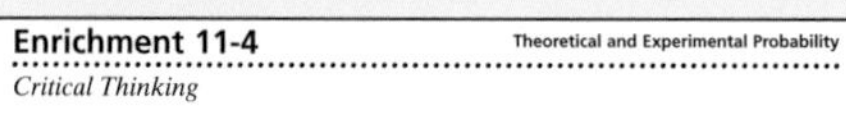

Enrichment 11-4 — Theoretical and Experimental Probability

Critical Thinking

You have learned that the probability of tossing a 4 in one toss of a number cube is $\frac{1}{6}$. What do you think the odds are against tossing a 4? Many people would say it is 6 to 1, but they would be mistaken.

Out of every six tosses of the number cube, you expect to get one 4, and you expect to obtain numbers other than 4 for the remaining five tosses. Therefore, the odds against obtaining a 4 in one toss of a number cube are 5 to 1. The odds in favor of obtaining a 4 in one toss of a number cube are 1 to 5.

- The odds in favor of an event are the ratio of the probability that an event will occur to the probability that the event will not occur. Use this formula. $\frac{P(\text{event})}{1 - P(\text{event})}$
- The odds against the occurrence of the event are the reciprocal of the ratio at the left. $\frac{1 - P(\text{event})}{P(\text{event})}$

Odds and probabilities are closely related. Suppose the odds for an event are 2 to 3, then the probability is $\frac{2}{5}$ because there are two favorable and three unfavorable ways or five possible outcomes.

1. The probability that Tom will win a race is $\frac{1}{10}$. What are the odds in favor of Tom winning the race? 1 to 9
2. What are the odds in favor of tossing a 2 on a number cube? 1 to 5
3. What are the odds in favor of tossing an even number on a number cube? 1 to 1
4. Find the probability of winning a contest if the odds in favor of winning are 3 to 2. $\frac{3}{5}$
5. What are the odds against tossing a number less than 5 on a number cube? 1 to 2
6. You have a set of ten cards, each numbered from 1 through 10. Find the odds in favor of choosing a multiple of 3. 3 to 7
7. Find the probability of spinning *red* if the odds in favor of spinning *red* are 3 to 4. $\frac{3}{7}$
8. You have 1 in 30 chances of being picked at random to lead the Fourth of July parade. What are the odds you will be chosen? 1 to 29
9. Suppose the weather forecast states that there is a 40% chance of rain. What are the odds against having rain? 3 to 2

C Challenge

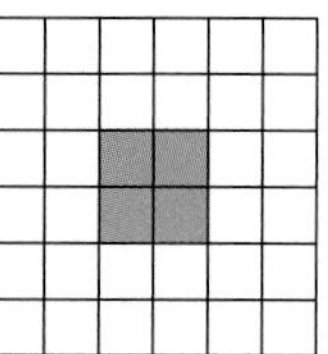

20. Geometry To win a game, you have to toss a coin that lands in the green area of the game board. Suppose the center of the coin lands on the board. What is the theoretical probability that the center of a coin will land in the green area? $\frac{1}{9}$

21. Stretch Your Thinking Two rectangles have perimeters of 144 cm. What is the greatest possible difference between their areas if the lengths and widths of both rectangles are integers? 1,225 cm^2

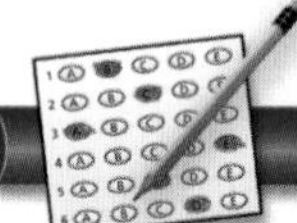

Test Prep

Multiple Choice

22. You roll a number cube. What is the probability of NOT rolling a 3 or 4? D

A. $\frac{1}{6}$ B. $\frac{1}{3}$ C. $\frac{1}{2}$ D. $\frac{2}{3}$

23. You spin a spinner 50 times. It lands on red 8 times, yellow 12 times, green 20 times, and blue 10 times. Based on the results, what is the experimental probability of its landing on green or yellow? I

F. $\frac{6}{25}$ G. $\frac{2}{5}$ H. $\frac{3}{5}$ I. $\frac{16}{25}$

24. You roll a number cube. What are the odds in favor of rolling a 1 or a 5? D

A. 1:5 B. 2:6 C. 5:1 D. 1:2

Extended Response

25. A bag contains 33 green marbles and 25 blue marbles. You select a marble at random from the bag. 25a–c. See margin.

a. Find the theoretical probability of selecting a green marble.
b. Find the theoretical probability of selecting a blue marble.
c. The table at the right shows the results of selecting a marble from the bag, recording the color, and returning the marble to the bag. Find the experimental probability of each color based on the table.

Outcome	Occurrences
Green	41
Blue	35

Take It to the NET
Online lesson quiz at **www.PHSchool.com**
Web Code: aca-1104

Mixed Review

Lesson 11-3 **Simplify each expression.**

26. ${}_7C_2$ 21 **27.** ${}_{11}C_2$ 55 **28.** ${}_{12}C_7$ 792 **29.** ${}_6C_3$ 20 **30.** ${}_{10}C_4$ 210

Lesson 10-6 **Find the measure of the central angle that could represent each percent in a circle graph. Round your answer to the nearest degree.**

31. 25% 90° **32.** 10% 36° **33.** 20% 72° **34.** 15% 54° **35.** 35% 126°

36. 8% 29° **37.** 38% 137° **38.** 50% 180° **39.** 12% 43° **40.** 22% 79°

25. [4] a. $P(\text{green}) = \frac{33}{58}$
b. $P(\text{blue}) = \frac{25}{58}$
c. $P(\text{green}) = \frac{41}{76}$; $P(\text{blue}) = \frac{35}{76}$

[3] correct procedures with one error

[2] correct theoretical probabilities OR correct experimental probabilities

[1] one part correct

11-5 Independent and Dependent Events

What You'll Learn

OBJECTIVE 1 To find the probability of independent events

OBJECTIVE 2 To find the probability of dependent events

. . . And Why

To find the probability of selecting students, as in Example 2

Check Skills You'll Need

For help, go to Lesson 11-4.

A spinner is divided into 8 equal sections that are numbered from 1 to 8. You spin the spinner once. Write each probability in simplest form.

1. $P(\text{not } 3)$ $\frac{7}{8}$
2. $P(\text{a number less than } 7)$ $\frac{3}{4}$
3. $P(\text{not even})$ $\frac{1}{2}$
4. $P(1, 2, 3, 4, \text{ or } 5)$ $\frac{5}{8}$
5. What are the odds in favor of rolling a 2 on a number cube? 1 : 5

New Vocabulary • independent events • dependent events

OBJECTIVE 1

Finding the Probability of Independent Events

Interactive lesson includes instant self-check, tutorials, and activities.

Investigation: Comparing Types of Events

Suppose you have a set of colored cubes. Three are blue, four are green, and three are yellow. You select a cube at random.

1. What is the probability of selecting a green cube? $\frac{2}{5}$
2. Suppose you select a green cube and put it back. What is the probability of selecting a green cube on the second selection? $\frac{2}{5}$
3. Suppose you select a green cube and *do not* put it back. What is the probability of selecting a green cube on the second selection? Explain. $\frac{1}{3}$; because now there are only 3 green cubes left out of 9 total.

Compound events are two or more related events. Suppose you draw a card from a stack of ten cards and replace it. When you draw a second card, there are still ten cards from which to choose. These compound events are independent.

For **independent events,** the outcome of one event does not affect the outcome of a second event.

Key Concepts — Independent Events

If A and B are independent events, then $P(A, \text{then } B) = P(A) \cdot P(B)$.

11-5

1. Plan

Lesson Preview

Check Skills You'll Need (PowerPoint)

Finding Complements in Probability
Lesson 11-4: Example 3. Extra Practice, p. 712.

Lesson Resources

Teaching Resources
Practice, Reteaching, Enrichment

Reaching All Students
Practice Workbook 11-5
Spanish Practice Workbook 11-5
Guided Problem Solving 11-5

Presentation Assistant Plus!
Transparencies
- Check Skills You'll Need 11-5
- Problem of the Day 11-5
- Additional Examples 11-5
- Student Edition Answers 11-5
- Lesson Quiz 11-5

PH Presentation Pro CD-ROM 11-5

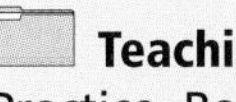

Computer Test Generator CD

Technology
Resource Pro® CD-ROM
Computer Test Generator CD
PH Presentation Pro CD-ROM

www.PHSchool.com
Student Site
- Teacher Web Code: ack-5500
- Algebra Readiness Puzzle 35
- Self-grading Lesson Quiz

PH SuccessNet Teacher Center
- Lesson Planner
- Resources

Plus iTEXT

Ongoing Assessment and Intervention

Before the Lesson
Diagnose prerequisite skills using:
- Check Skills You'll Need

During the Lesson
Monitor progress using:
- Check Understanding
- Additional Examples
- Test Prep

After the Lesson
Assess knowledge using:
- Lesson Quiz
- Computer Test Generator CD

2. Teach

Math Background

Compound events are two or more related events. If the outcome of the first does not affect the outcome of the second, the events are *independent.* If the outcome of the first affects the outcome of the second, the events are *dependent.*

Teaching Notes

Investigation (Optional)
Have students work in pairs, each using a set of cubes (or tiles) and a bag. One student draws the tiles and the other records the results.

1 EXAMPLE Inclusion

Ask: *Would it be possible for the clerk to select the same shirt on the second try?* yes

2 EXAMPLE Tactile Learners

Have students write names on five index cards and experiment with drawing the names and recording the results.

Additional Examples

1. A box contains 3 red marbles and 7 blue ones. You draw a marble at random, replace it, and draw another. Find P(blue and blue). $\frac{49}{100}$
2. From a class of 12 girls and 14 boys, you select two students at random. Find the probability that both students are boys. $\frac{7}{25}$

Closure

Contrast the formulas for finding the probability of independent and dependent events. Sample: For independent events, you multiply $P(A)$ times $P(B)$; for dependent events, you multiply $P(A)$ times $P(B \text{ after } A)$ since the outcome of A affects the outcome for B.

Real-World Connection

The total inventory of shirts in a store is the number of shirts on display plus those in storage.

1 EXAMPLE Probability of Independent Events

Inventory The table at the right shows the colors of 20 soccer shirts in inventory. A clerk selects one shirt at random, puts a price tag on it, replaces it, and selects again. Find the probability that the first shirt is blue and the second is red.

Color	Number of Shirts
Blue	6
Red	4
Black	3
Orange	7

Because the first shirt is replaced, these are independent events.

$P(\text{blue, then red}) = P(\text{blue}) \cdot P(\text{red})$

$= \frac{6}{20} \cdot \frac{4}{20}$ ← Substitute.

$= \frac{24}{400} = \frac{3}{50}$ ← Multiply and simplify.

The probability of choosing a blue and then a red soccer shirt is $\frac{3}{50}$.

Check Understanding 1 Use the data in Example 1 to find P(orange, then black). $\frac{21}{400}$

OBJECTIVE

2 Finding the Probability of Dependent Events

Suppose you draw a card from a stack of ten cards and *do not* replace it. When you draw a second card, there are fewer cards from which to choose. These compound events are dependent. For **dependent events,** the outcome of one event affects the outcome of a second event.

Key Concepts — Dependent Events

If A and B are dependent events, then $P(A, \text{then } B) = P(A) \cdot P(B \text{ after } A)$.

2 EXAMPLE Probability of Dependent Events

School Assembly Two girls and three boys volunteer to speak at a school assembly. Their names are put in a hat. One name is selected at random and not replaced. Then another name is selected. Find P(girl, then girl).

The two events are dependent.

First drawing $P(\text{girl}) = \frac{2}{5}$ ← Two of the five volunteers are girls.

Second drawing $P(\text{girl after girl}) = \frac{1}{4}$ ← One girl is left of four volunteers.

$P(\text{girl, then girl}) = P(\text{girl}) \cdot P(\text{girl after girl})$

$= \frac{2}{5} \cdot \frac{1}{4}$ ← Substitute.

$= \frac{2}{20} = \frac{1}{10}$ ← Multiply and simplify.

The probability that the two girls are selected is $\frac{1}{10}$.

Check Understanding 2 In Example 2, find the probability that a boy and then a girl are selected. $\frac{3}{10}$

Reaching All Students

Below Level Review multiplying and simplifying fractions. Have students simplify $\frac{3}{40} \cdot \frac{10}{21}$. $\frac{1}{28}$

Advanced Learners In Example 2, what is the probability of selecting a boy and then another boy? $\frac{3}{10}$ or 0.3

Inclusion
See notes on pages 612 and 614.

Tactile Learners
See note on page 612.

EXERCISES

For more practice, see *Extra Practice*.

Practice by Example

Example 1 (page 612)

Find each probability. One letter of the alphabet appears on each of 26 cards. You choose a card at random and then replace it. Then you choose a second card. Assume Y is a consonant.

1. $P(\text{I, then a vowel})$ $\frac{5}{676}$
2. $P(\text{Z, then a consonant})$ $\frac{21}{676}$
3. $P(\text{a vowel, then a consonant})$ $\frac{105}{676}$
4. $P(\text{vowel, then vowel})$ $\frac{25}{676}$
5. $P(\text{A, then B})$ $\frac{1}{676}$
6. $P(\text{C, then X})$ $\frac{1}{676}$

Example 2 (page 612)

Find each probability. A bag contains the following marbles: 6 red, 4 orange, 3 yellow, 2 blue, and 5 green. You choose a marble at random and do *not* replace it. Then you select another marble.

7. $P(\text{red, then blue})$ $\frac{3}{95}$
8. $P(\text{red, then yellow})$ $\frac{9}{190}$
9. $P(\text{orange, then blue})$ $\frac{2}{95}$
10. $P(\text{blue, then green})$ $\frac{1}{38}$
11. $P(\text{blue, then yellow})$ $\frac{3}{190}$
12. $P(\text{red, then red})$ $\frac{3}{38}$

Apply Your Skills

Find each probability. Suppose you roll a number cube and spin the spinner at the right. Express your answer as a percent rounded to the nearest tenth.

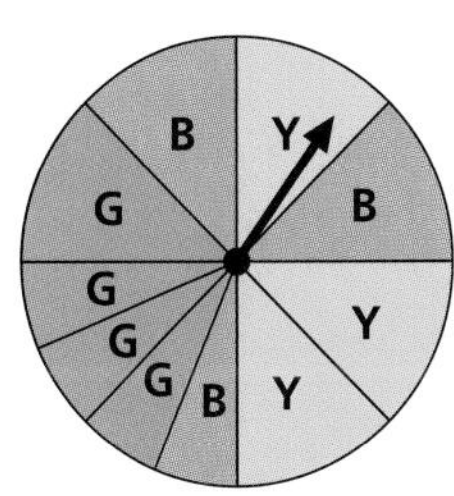

13. $P(\text{3, then green})$ 5.2%
14. $P(\text{prime, then blue})$ 15.6%
15. $P(\text{5, then yellow})$ 6.3%
16. $P(\text{8, then yellow})$ 0%
17. $P(\text{an even number, then green})$ 15.6%

18. a. **School Carnival** For a carnival game, a cube is rolled. Each of its six faces has a different color. To win, you must select the color rolled. Find the probability of playing the carnival game twice and winning both times. $\frac{1}{36}$

    GPS

    b. *Disjoint events* are events with no outcomes in common. To find the probability of two disjoint events, add the probabilities of the individual events. Suppose for the game, you choose red and your friend picks blue. What is the probability that either you or your friend wins? $\frac{2}{6}$ or $\frac{1}{3}$

Real-World Connection

School organizations often hold carnivals to raise money for their schools' needs.

19. a. Data File, p. 589 You plan to visit two different zoos but cannot decide which two to visit. On a piece of paper, you write the name of each zoo in the table. Then you select the names of two zoos at random. Are your selections independent or dependent events? Explain. See margin.

    b. What is $P(\text{Smithsonian, then El Paso})$? $\frac{1}{42}$

20. **Writing in Math** What is the difference between independent and dependent events? Explain. See margin.

GPS Use the Guided Problem Solving worksheet with Exercise 18.

19a. Dependent events; the probability of selecting the second is dependent on what was selected first.

20. For independent events, the outcome of the first event does not affect the outcome of the second event. For dependent events, the outcome of the second event is affected by the outcome of the first event.

3. Practice

Assignment Guide

Objective 1

A B Core 1–6, 13–18

C Extension 26

Objective 2

A B Core 7–12, 19–25

C Extension 27–28

Test Prep 29–32

Mixed Review 33–39

Error Prevention!

Exercise 18 Point out the definition for *disjoint events*.

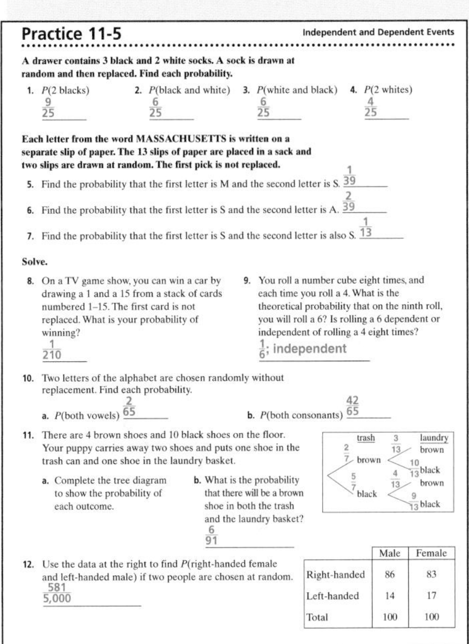

Practice 11-5 Independent and Dependent Events

A drawer contains 3 black and 2 white socks. A sock is drawn at random and then replaced. Find each probability.

1. $P(\text{2 blacks})$ $\frac{9}{25}$
2. $P(\text{black and white})$ $\frac{6}{25}$
3. $P(\text{white and black})$ $\frac{6}{25}$
4. $P(\text{2 whites})$ $\frac{4}{25}$

Each letter from the word MASSACHUSETTS is written on a separate slip of paper. The 13 slips of paper are placed in a sack and two slips are drawn at random. The first pick is not replaced.

5. Find the probability that the first letter is M and the second letter is S. $\frac{1}{39}$
6. Find the probability that the first letter is S and the second letter is A. $\frac{2}{39}$
7. Find the probability that the first letter is S and the second letter is also S. $\frac{1}{13}$

Solve.

8. On a TV game show, you can win a car by drawing a 1 and a 15 from a stack of cards numbered 1–15. The first card is not replaced. What is your probability of winning? $\frac{1}{210}$
9. You roll a number cube eight times, and each time you roll a 4. What is the theoretical probability that on the ninth roll, you will roll a 6? Is rolling a 6 dependent or independent of rolling a 4 eight times? $\frac{1}{6}$; independent
10. Two letters of the alphabet are chosen randomly without replacement. Find each probability.
    a. $P(\text{both vowels})$ $\frac{2}{65}$
    b. $P(\text{both consonants})$ $\frac{42}{65}$
11. There are 4 brown shoes and 10 black shoes on the floor. Your puppy carries away two shoes and puts one shoe in the trash can and one shoe in the laundry basket.
    a. Complete the tree diagram to show the probability of each outcome.
    b. What is the probability that there will be a brown shoe in both the trash and the laundry basket? $\frac{6}{91}$

trash / laundry
$\frac{2}{7}$ brown: $\frac{3}{13}$ brown, $\frac{10}{13}$ black
$\frac{5}{7}$ black: $\frac{4}{13}$ brown, $\frac{9}{13}$ black

12. Use the data at the right to find $P(\text{right-handed female and left-handed male})$ if two people are chosen at random. $\frac{581}{5,000}$

	Male	Female
Right-handed	86	83
Left-handed	14	17
Total	100	100

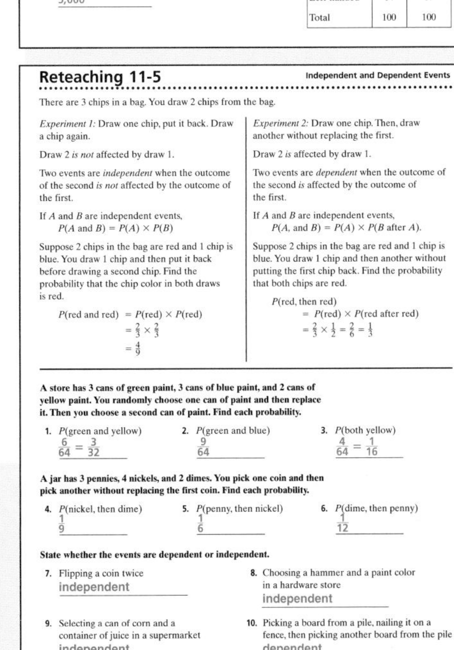

Reteaching 11-5 Independent and Dependent Events

There are 3 chips in a bag. You draw 2 chips from the bag.

Experiment 1: Draw one chip, put it back. Draw a chip again.

Draw 2 *is not* affected by draw 1.

Two events are *independent* when the outcome of the second *is not* affected by the outcome of the first.

If A and B are independent events, $P(A \text{ and } B) = P(A) \times P(B)$

Suppose 2 chips in the bag are red and 1 chip is blue. You draw 1 chip and then put it back before drawing a second chip. Find the probability that the chip color in both draws is red.

$P(\text{red and red}) = P(\text{red}) \times P(\text{red}) = \frac{2}{3} \times \frac{2}{3} = \frac{4}{9}$

Experiment 2: Draw one chip. Then, draw another without replacing the first.

Draw 2 *is* affected by draw 1.

Two events are *dependent* when the outcome of the second *is* affected by the outcome of the first.

If A and B are independent events, $P(A, \text{ and } B) = P(A) \times P(B \text{ after } A)$.

Suppose 2 chips in the bag are red and 1 chip is blue. You draw 1 chip and then another without putting the first chip back. Find the probability that both chips are red.

$P(\text{red, then red}) = P(\text{red}) \times P(\text{red after red}) = \frac{2}{3} \times \frac{1}{2} = \frac{2}{6} = \frac{1}{3}$

A store has 3 cans of green paint, 3 cans of blue paint, and 2 cans of yellow paint. You randomly choose one can of paint and then replace it. Then you choose a second can of paint. Find each probability.

1. $P(\text{green and yellow})$ $\frac{6}{64} = \frac{3}{32}$
2. $P(\text{green and blue})$ $\frac{9}{64}$
3. $P(\text{both yellow})$ $\frac{4}{64} = \frac{1}{16}$

A jar has 3 pennies, 4 nickels, and 2 dimes. You pick one coin and then pick another without replacing the first coin. Find each probability.

4. $P(\text{nickel, then dime})$ $\frac{1}{9}$
5. $P(\text{penny, then nickel})$ $\frac{1}{6}$
6. $P(\text{dime, then penny})$ $\frac{1}{12}$

State whether the events are dependent or independent.

7. Flipping a coin twice — independent
8. Choosing a hammer and a paint color in a hardware store — independent
9. Selecting a can of corn and a container of juice in a supermarket — independent
10. Picking a board from a pile, nailing it on a fence, then picking another board from the pile — dependent

Inclusion
Exercises 29–30 Be sensitive to students who may be color blind.

21–25. See below left.

State whether the events are dependent or independent. Explain.

21. Independent; the outcome of the coin toss does not affect the roll of the cube.
22. Independent; the outcome of the second draw is not dependent on the first draw.
23. Dependent; the second draw is affected by the outcome of the first draw.
24. Independent; the first spin does not affect the second spin.
25. Dependent; the second selection is affected by the first selection.

21. Toss a coin. Then roll a number cube.

22. Select a card. Replace it. Then select another card.

23. Select a card. Do not replace it. Then select another card.

24. Spin a spinner once. Then spin the spinner again.

25. Select a marble from a bag. Put it aside. Then select another marble.

26. **Mazes** Find the probability of a mouse locating the cheese on its first attempt in the maze. Assume the mouse selects each path at random. $\frac{1}{2}$

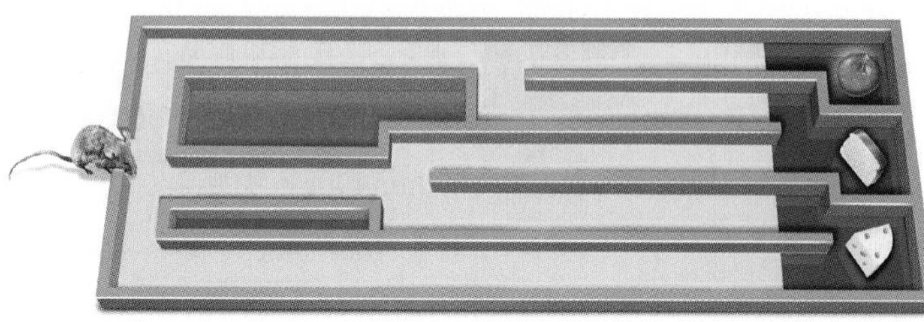

27. **Algebra** If two events are dependent and $P(\text{event}) = \frac{a}{b}$, then what is $P(\text{event, then event})$? $\frac{a(a-1)}{b(b-1)}$

28. **Stretch Your Thinking** Two ants race clockwise around the perimeter of a unit square. They both start at the same vertex. One ant runs at the constant rate of 1 unit per second. The other ant runs at the constant rate of 2 units per second. How far apart will they be after 17 seconds? 1 unit

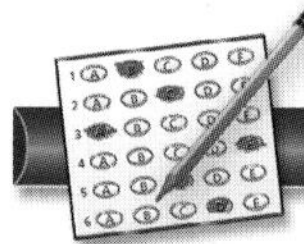

Test Prep

Reading Comprehension **Read the passage and answer the questions below.**

Colorblindness

Most people who are colorblind do not see the world in black and white. In fact, there are many different types of colorblindness. A person who sees only black and white is extremely rare.

Colorblindness occurs when the cones in the retina of the eye are sensitive to a different wavelength of light. One study indicates that 5% of men and 0.5% of women are colorblind.

29. Find the probability of choosing a colorblind man and then another colorblind man. Assume that the two events are independent. $\frac{1}{400}$

30. Find the probability of choosing a colorblind woman and then a woman who is NOT colorblind. Assume that the two events are independent. $\frac{199}{40{,}000}$

Multiple Choice

31. A pack of juice boxes contains 4 apple, 4 cherry, 4 orange, and 4 grape boxes. If you and a friend each select a juice box at random, what is the probability that you will both get grape? B

A. $\frac{3}{64}$ B. $\frac{1}{20}$ C. $\frac{1}{4}$ D. $\frac{1}{2}$

Take It to the NET
Online lesson quiz at
www.PHSchool.com
Web Code: aca-1105

32. Of a set of 10 cards, 3 have red circles, 4 have yellow triangles, and 3 have green diamonds. You choose one card at random and then replace it. Then you choose a second card. What is the probability that both cards have yellow triangles? H

F. $\frac{3}{25}$ G. $\frac{2}{15}$ H. $\frac{4}{25}$ I. $\frac{2}{5}$

Mixed Review

Lesson 11-4

A spinner is divided into 7 equal sections that are numbered from 1 to 7. You spin the spinner once. Find each probability.

33. $P(5)$ $\frac{1}{7}$

34. $P(3 \text{ or } 7)$ $\frac{2}{7}$

35. $P(\text{even number})$ $\frac{3}{7}$

36. $P(\text{not } 8)$ 1

37. $P(\text{not } 5)$ $\frac{6}{7}$

38. $P(\text{odd number})$ $\frac{4}{7}$

Lesson 9-8

39. **Gardening** A gardener has 190 ft of fencing and wants to enclose the greatest possible area for a garden. What dimensions should he use? Draw a diagram and then make a table to find the solution. See margin.

Practice Game

Analyzing Fair Games

What You'll Need

sets of four chips with red on one side and yellow on the other side of each chip, as shown at the right

How To Play

- Decide who is Player A and who is Player B.
- Each player tosses the chips once. If all four chips are the same color, Player A scores a point. If not, Player B scores a point.
- The first player to reach 20 points is the winner.

1. Make an organized list of all possible outcomes. Which is more likely, exactly 1, exactly 2, exactly 3, or exactly 4 red sides up? See margin.
2. **Reasoning** Is this game fair? Explain. See right.
3. Suppose you toss the chips twice. What is the probability that you get exactly 1 red side up twice? $\frac{1}{16}$

2. No. The probability of all the chips being the same color is $\frac{1}{8}$. The probability of all the chips not being the same color is $\frac{7}{8}$. So Player B has a great advantage.

4. Assess

PowerPoint Lesson Quiz 11-5

A bag of marbles contains 2 red, 3 green, and 1 ivory marble. Use this information to solve the problems.

1. You randomly choose one marble, replace it, and then choose a second marble. Find the probability that both are green. $\frac{1}{4}$
2. You randomly choose one marble and then, without replacing the first marble, you choose a second marble. Find the probability that one is ivory and the other is green. $\frac{1}{10}$

Alternative Assessment

Each student in a pair writes one problem that involves independent events and one problem that involves dependent events. Partners trade papers and solve each other's problems.

Test Prep

Resources

For additional practice with a variety of test item formats:

- Test Prep, p. 631
- Test-Taking Strategies, p. 627
- Test-Taking Strategies with Transparencies

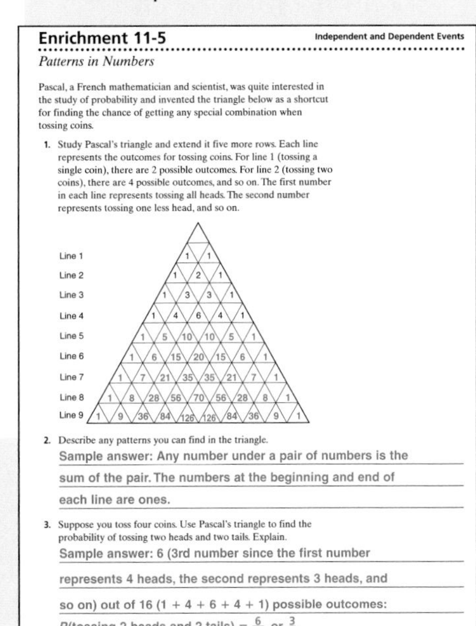

Enrichment 11-5 Independent and Dependent Events

Patterns in Numbers

Pascal, a French mathematician and scientist, was quite interested in the study of probability and invented the triangle below as a shortcut for finding the chance of getting any special combination when tossing coins.

1. Study Pascal's triangle and extend it five more rows. Each line represents the outcomes for tossing coins. For line 1 (tossing a single coin), there are 2 possible outcomes. For line 2 (tossing two coins), there are 4 possible outcomes, and so on. The first number in each line represents tossing all heads. The second number represents tossing one less head, and so on.

2. Describe any patterns you can find in the triangle.
Sample answer: Any number under a pair of numbers is the sum of the pair. The numbers at the beginning and end of each line are ones.

3. Suppose you toss four coins. Use Pascal's triangle to find the probability of tossing two heads and two tails. Explain.
Sample answer: 6 (3rd number since the first number represents 4 heads, the second represents 3 heads, and so on) out of 16 (1 + 4 + 6 + 4 + 1) possible outcomes: $P(\text{tossing 2 heads and 2 tails}) = \frac{6}{16}$, or $\frac{3}{8}$.

39.

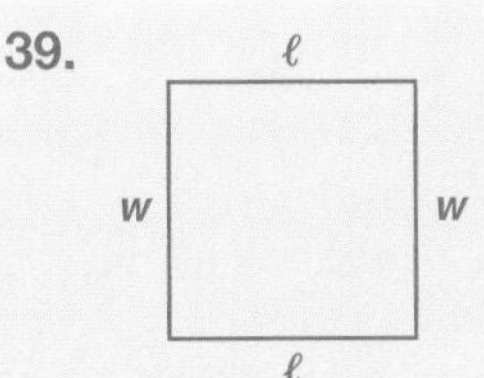

Length (ft)	Width (ft)	Area (ft)
30	65	1,950
35	60	2,100
40	55	2,200
42.5	52.5	2,231.25
45	50	2,250
47.5	47.5	2,256.25
50	45	2,250

47.5 ft by 47.5 ft

Practice Game

1. RRRR, RRRW, RRWR, RRWW, RWRR, RWRW, RWWR, RWWW, WRRR, WRRW, WRWR, WRWW, WWRR, WWRW, WWWR, WWWW; exactly 2

11-6

1. Plan

Lesson Preview

Check Skills You'll Need

Multiplying Rational Numbers
Lesson 4-5: Example 1. Extra Practice, p. 705.

Lesson Resources

Teaching Resources
Practice, Reteaching, Enrichment

Reaching All Students
Practice Workbook 11-6
Spanish Practice Workbook 11-6
Guided Problem Solving 11-6

Presentation Assistant Plus!
Transparencies
- Check Skills You'll Need 11-6
- Problem of the Day 11-6
- Additional Examples 11-6
- Student Edition Answers 11-6
- Lesson Quiz 11-6
- Classroom Aid 11

PH Presentation Pro CD-ROM 11-6

Computer Test Generator CD

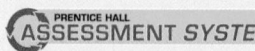

Technology
Resource Pro® CD-ROM
Computer Test Generator CD
PH Presentation Pro CD-ROM

www.PHSchool.com
Student Site
- Teacher Web Code: ack-5500
- Self-grading Lesson Quiz

PH SuccessNet Teacher Center
- Lesson Planner
- Resources

Plus 

Problem Solving

11-6 Simulate a Problem and Make an Organized List

What You'll Learn

To solve a problem using two different methods

. . . And Why

To compare strategies in solving problems, as in Example 1

Check Skills You'll Need

For help, go to Lesson 4-5.

Find each product.

1. $\frac{1}{2} \cdot \frac{2}{3}$ $\frac{1}{3}$
2. $\frac{3}{4} \cdot \frac{1}{6}$ $\frac{1}{8}$
3. $\frac{5}{8} \cdot \frac{6}{7}$ $\frac{15}{28}$
4. $\frac{4}{7} \cdot \frac{3}{5}$ $\frac{12}{35}$
5. $\frac{4}{9} \cdot \frac{1}{6}$ $\frac{2}{27}$
6. $\frac{1}{3} \cdot \frac{10}{14}$ $\frac{5}{21}$
7. Simplify $\frac{2}{3} \cdot \frac{1}{2} \cdot \frac{3}{4}$. $\frac{1}{4}$

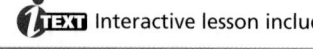

 Interactive lesson includes instant self-check, tutorials, and activities.

OBJECTIVE 1

Solving a Problem Using Two Different Methods

When to Use These Strategies For problems involving probability, you can ***simulate a problem*** by conducting experiments. You can also ***make an organized list*** to find all outcomes that are possible for the situation.

1 EXAMPLE Real-World  Problem Solving

Testing What is the probability of guessing all the answers correctly on a three-question true-false quiz?

Read and Understand Your goal is to find the probability that you will guess the answers to three questions correctly. The probability of guessing correctly for each question is $\frac{1}{2}$.

Plan and Solve

Method 1 Simulate the problem.

Simulate the problem by tossing a coin. Let heads represent a correct guess and tails represent an incorrect guess. Three coin tosses represent the quiz. Simulate 30 quizzes by tossing a coin 90 times.

Circle the quiz simulations where you have three heads.

90 Tosses

HHT	TTH	HTH
(HHH)	TTH	THT
THH	HTH	TTT
HHT	HTT	(HHH)
TTT	THH	THT
HTT	HHT	THH
TTH	(HHH)	HTT
HTT	TTH	THT
THH	(HHH)	TTH
HTH	TTT	HTH

The data shows that from 30 quiz simulations, HHH occurs 4 times.

$$P(\text{3 correct guesses}) = \frac{\text{number of times HHH occurs}}{\text{total number of sets}}$$

$$= \frac{4}{30} \quad \leftarrow \textbf{Substitute.}$$

$$= \frac{2}{15} \quad \leftarrow \textbf{Simplify.}$$

The experimental probability is $\frac{2}{15}$, or about 13.3%.

Ongoing Assessment and Intervention

Before the Lesson
Diagnose prerequisite skills using:
- Check Skills You'll Need

During the Lesson
Monitor progress using:
- Check Understanding
- Additional Examples
- Test Prep

After the Lesson
Assess knowledge using:
- Lesson Quiz
- Computer Test Generator CD

Method 2 Make an organized list.

Make an organized list to find all possible outcomes. The diagram shows one correct guess and one incorrect guess for each question.

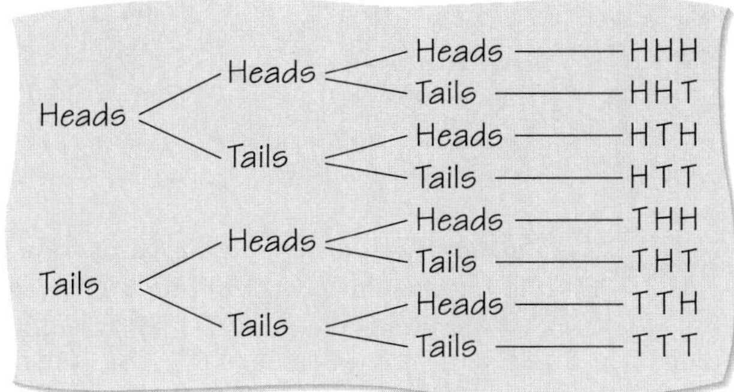

The tree diagram shows that out of eight possible outcomes, there is only one outcome for three correct guesses.

$$P(\text{3 correct}) = \frac{\text{number of times three heads occurs}}{\text{total number of possible outcomes}} = \frac{1}{8}$$

The theoretical probability is $\frac{1}{8}$, or 12.5%.

Need Help?
For help with independent events, go to Lesson 11-5.

Look Back and Check The experimental probability of about 13.3% and the theoretical probability of 12.5% are close in value. Check your results.

$$P(\text{3 correct guesses}) = P(\text{correct}) \cdot P(\text{correct}) \cdot P(\text{correct})$$
$$= \frac{1}{2} \cdot \frac{1}{2} \cdot \frac{1}{2} \quad \leftarrow \text{Substitute.}$$
$$= \frac{1}{8} \quad \leftarrow \text{Multiply.}$$

This is the same probability you found by making an organized list.

Check Understanding 1 What is the probability that a family of three children has two girls and a boy? Assume the probability of each is $\frac{1}{2}$. $\frac{3}{8}$

EXERCISES

For more practice, see *Extra Practice*.

A Practice by Example

Solve by simulating the problem or by making an organized list.

Example 1 (page 616)

1. **License Plates** Suppose a license plate contains three digits. The probability of getting either an even or an odd digit is the same. What is the probability of having a license plate with all even numbers? $\frac{1}{8}$
2. **Testing** A true-false test has five questions. What is the probability of guessing exactly four out of the five answers correctly? $\frac{5}{32}$
3. **Kittens** Your cat is expecting a litter of kittens. The probability of a kitten being either a male or female is $\frac{1}{2}$. What is the probability that a litter of five kittens contains all male kittens? $\frac{1}{32}$

2. Teach

Math Background

Often there is more than one way to approach a problem and more than one way to solve it. Encourage students to consider different strategies before settling on one to solve a problem. Then they have the skills to choose the problem-solving method that makes the most sense to them.

Teaching Notes

Alternative Method
Have students share ideas about how to organize their work both to record data (in the simulation) and to write the organized list (in the second method).

1 EXAMPLE Inclusion
In Method 2, have volunteers review how to convert the fraction $\frac{1}{8}$ into the percent 12.5%. Sample: $1 \div 8 = 0.125 = 12.5\%$

Technology Tip
You might allow students to use a calculator to find the product of the various probabilities.

Additional Examples

1 On a multiple-choice test, each question has 4 possible answers. You know the answers to all but the last two questions on the test. Find the probability of guessing the answers to both questions correctly. theoretical probability = $\frac{1}{16}$ or 6.25%

Closure

What strategies might be useful for solving problems involving probabilities? Sample: Simulate a problem by conducting an experiment or make an organized list to find all possible outcomes.

Reaching All Students

Below Level Convert these fractions to percents. Round answers to the nearest tenth of a percent.
$\frac{4}{15}$ 26.7% $\frac{3}{7}$ 42.9%
$\frac{5}{9}$ 55.6% $\frac{6}{11}$ 54.5%

Advanced Learners What is the theoretical probability of guessing all the answers correctly on a true-false quiz with 5 questions? $\frac{1}{32}$ or about 3%

Inclusion
See note on page 617.
Alternative Method
See note on page 617.

3. Practice

Assignment Guide

 **Objective 1**

A B Core 1–16

C Extension 17–19

Test Prep 20–23

Mixed Review 24–31

Error Prevention!

Exercises 5–10 Point out that the shipping cost is per order, not per box.

Practice 11-6 Problem Solving: Make an Organized List and Simulate a Problem

Solve by making an organized list or by simulating the problem.

1. The probability of a newborn puppy being either a male or female is $\frac{1}{2}$. What is the probability that a litter of 4 puppies contains 3 females?
   $\frac{1}{8}$
2. In a mixed-badminton tournament, each team consists of one boy and one girl. Three boys and three girls signed up for the tournament. How many different badminton games can be played with different mixed-doubles teams?
   18 games

The Coast Guard reports that the probability for calm water each day for the next few days is 50%. You begin a three-day sailing trip. Check students' work.

3. Simulate the situation to find the probability of three days of calm water in a row.
   about 12.5%
4. Simulate the situation to find the probability of only two days of calm water out of the three.
   about 37.5%
5. Simulate the situation to find the probability of only one day of calm water out of the three.
   about 37.5%
6. Simulate the situation to find the probability of no calm water for any of the three days.
   about 12.5%

A soccer player scores a goal on about 1 out of every 6 shots.

7. Explain how you could use a number cube to simulate the player's scoring average.
   Sample answer: Let 1 = goal, 2–6 = no goal.
8. Use your simulation to find the probability of the player making 4 out of 5 of her next attempts.
   Check students' work.

Reteaching 11-6 Problem Solving: Make an Organized List and Simulate a Problem

You can use simulation to estimate solutions to probability problems.

A juice company puts one of the five letters, L, E, M, O, and N, inside the bottle cap. The letters are equally distributed among the caps. If you collect all five letters, you get a bottle of juice at half price. Estimate how many bottles you need to buy to collect all five letters.

Read and Understand What do you want to find? *You want to find how many bottles of juice you need to buy to collect all five letters.*

Plan and Solve Instead of actually buying bottles of juice, develop a simulation. You can use a five-part spinner. Spin until you get all five letters. Keep track of your results.

Show the results of the simulation in a list. You spun the spinner 7 times before you got all five letters. So you estimate that you would have to buy 7 bottles of juice to collect all five letters.

Spins

M L M O E L N

Look Back and Check Would you get the same result if you repeat the simulation?

Solve each problem by making an organized list or by simulating the problem. Describe your method. Check students' answers.

1. There is one of ten team cards inside a box of cereal. The teams are equally distributed among the boxes. Estimate how many boxes of cereal you need to purchase to collect all ten teams.
   Sample answer: Use a set of number cards 1–10 and draw one card at a time from a bag. Then replace the card.
2. There is one of five shapes on the inner wrapper of each granola bar. The symbols are equally distributed among the wrappers. Estimate how many bars you need to buy to collect all five shapes and win a free bar.
   Sample answer: Roll a number cube letting each of the numbers represent a different shape.
3. A gas station gives away one of eight drinking glasses each time you buy a tank of gas. There is an equal chance of getting any one of the glasses. Estimate how many tanks you will have to buy to get all eight glasses.
   Sample answer: Use a spinner with 8 equal parts.
4. A store prints one of 12 different symbols on each receipt. Collect all 12 and you get a 10% discount on your next purchase. Symbols are equally placed among the receipts. Estimate how many receipts you would have to get to collect all 12 symbols.
   Sample answer: Roll a 12-sided number cube, let each number represent a different symbol.

B Apply Your Skills

Need Help?
- Reread the problem.
- Identify the key facts and details.
- Tell the problem in your own words.
- Try a different strategy.
- Check your work.

Strategies

Draw a Diagram
Look for a Pattern
Make a Graph
Make an Organized List
Make a Table
Simulate a Problem
Solve a Simpler Problem
Try, Check, and Revise
Use Logical Reasoning
Work Backward
Write an Equation

13. The first strategy gives an experimental probability, while the second gives the theoretical probability.

Use any strategy to solve each problem. Show your work.

4. The circumference of the peg is 3 in. Will the peg go through the hole? Explain. Yes; the diameter of the peg is $\frac{3}{\pi} \approx 0.95$. Since $0.95 < 1$, the peg will fit in the hole.

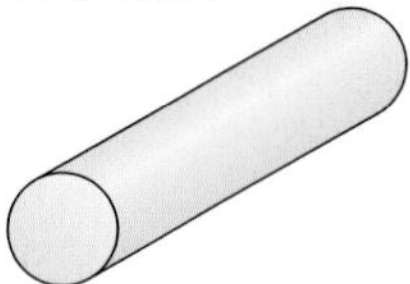

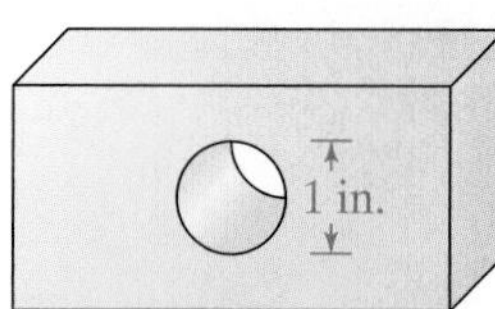

Shopping You order greeting cards from a catalogue. Each box costs $12, and the shipping cost per order is $2. Write an equation and make a graph that represents the total cost. Then find the cost of each order.
5–10. See margin for equation and graph.

5. 2 boxes $26
6. 4 boxes $50
7. 6 boxes $74
8. 9 boxes $110
9. 11 boxes $134
10. 15 boxes $182

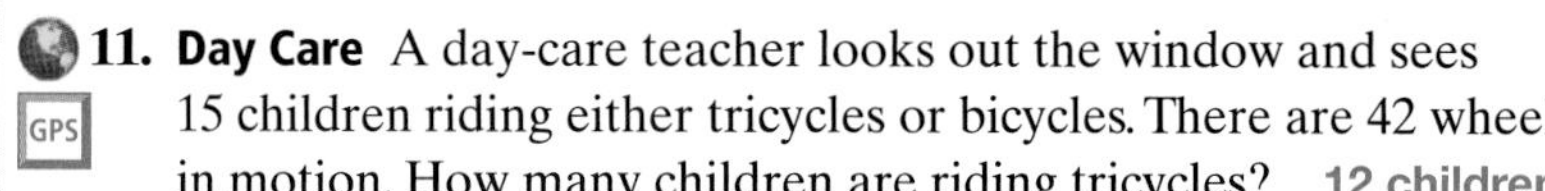

11. **Day Care** GPS A day-care teacher looks out the window and sees 15 children riding either tricycles or bicycles. There are 42 wheels in motion. How many children are riding tricycles? 12 children

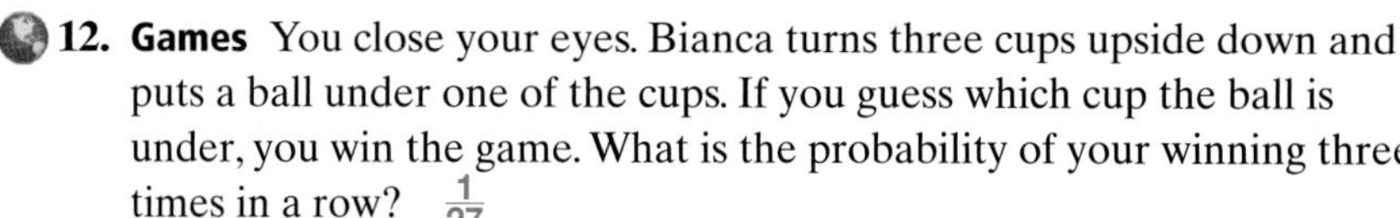

12. **Games** You close your eyes. Bianca turns three cups upside down and puts a ball under one of the cups. If you guess which cup the ball is under, you win the game. What is the probability of your winning three times in a row? $\frac{1}{27}$

13. **Writing in Math** What is the difference between using the strategies *simulate a problem* and *make an organized list* to find probability? Explain. See left.

Recycling On a certain day, customers bring 550 car tires and 76 truck tires to a recycling center.

14. Suppose an employee selects a tire at random to recycle. Find each probability as a percent rounded to the nearest tenth.
    a. *P*(truck tire) 12.1%
    b. *P*(car tire) 87.9%

15. Suppose an employee selects 30 tires at random to recycle. Use a proportion to predict the number of car tires selected. 26 car tires

16. Sketch a graph of the total number of tires recycled in one week. Assume the rate of total tires per day is constant. See back of book.

Use the Guided Problem Solving worksheet with Exercise 11.

5–10. $C = 12x + 2$

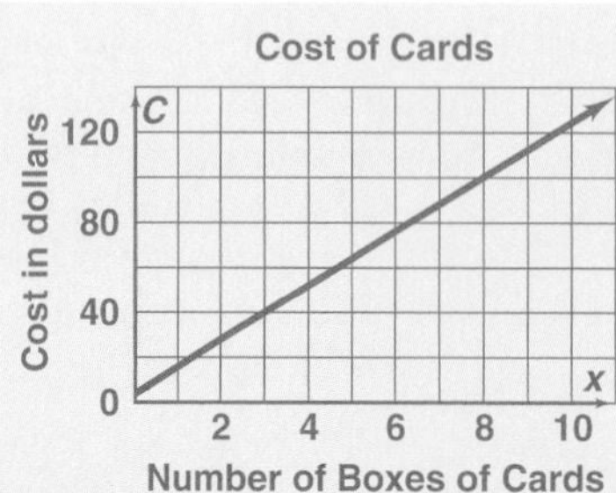

C Challenge 17. **Science** In the United States, there is a 2.9% experimental probability that any one child born is a twin. If there are 118,916 babies born as twins, what is the approximate number of total births? about 4,100,552 births

18. Find the sum of the whole numbers from 1 to 9,999. 49,995,000

19. **Stretch Your Thinking** What is the greatest number of boxes with dimensions $2 \times 2 \times 3$ that can be placed in a box with dimensions $3 \times 4 \times 5$? 4 boxes

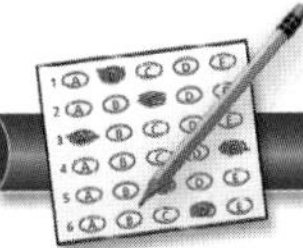

Test Prep

Multiple Choice

20. Suppose you bought 5 red peppers, 5 yellow peppers, and 15 green peppers. You select 1 pepper at random. What is *P*(red pepper)? A

A. $\frac{1}{5}$ B. $\frac{1}{4}$ C. $\frac{1}{3}$ D. $\frac{1}{2}$

Take It to the NET
Online lesson quiz at **www.PHSchool.com**
Web Code: aca-1106

21. You flip a coin twice. What is the probability you get no heads? H

F. $\frac{1}{8}$ G. $\frac{1}{6}$ H. $\frac{1}{4}$ I. $\frac{1}{2}$

22. Cards numbered 0 through 9 are in a bag. What is the probability you pull a card with a number greater than 7? B

A. $\frac{1}{9}$ B. $\frac{1}{5}$ C. $\frac{2}{9}$ D. $\frac{3}{10}$

Short Response

23. You are getting dressed for school. You have 7 shirts and 5 pairs of pants. **(a)** How many different outfits can you make? **(b)** Is this a combination or a permutation? Explain your answer. See margin.

Mixed Review

Lesson 11-5

You roll a standard number cube twice. Find each probability.

24. $P(3, \text{then } 4)$ $\frac{1}{36}$

25. $P(6, \text{then odd})$ $\frac{1}{12}$

26. $P(\text{less than } 5, \text{then } 2)$ $\frac{1}{9}$

27. $P(\text{divisible by } 2, \text{then even})$ $\frac{1}{4}$

Lesson 9-5

Find the lateral area of each figure to the nearest whole unit.

28. 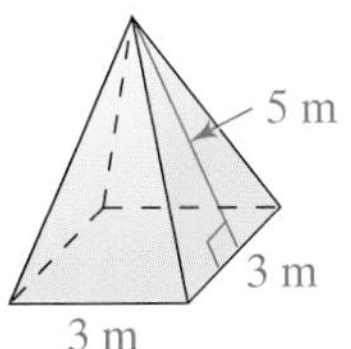

30 m²

29. 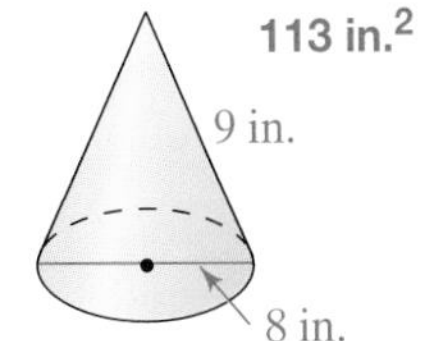

113 in.²

30. 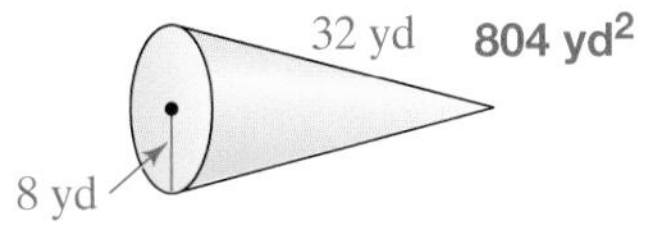

804 yd²

31. 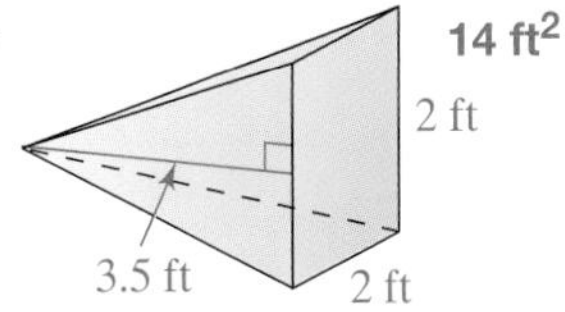

14 ft²

23. [2] 35 outfits; combination since order does not matter

[1] incorrect answer OR incorrect explanation

4. Assess

Lesson Quiz 11-6

1. What is the probability that each of the last four digits of a telephone number is an even number? Sample: Assuming that all digits are equally likely, the theoretical probability is $\frac{1}{16}$.

Alternative Assessment

Each student in a pair writes a problem like the Example that can be solved by using *simulate a problem* and *make an organized list*. Partners trade and solve each other's problem.

Test Prep

Resources

For additional practice with a variety of test item formats:

- Test Prep, p. 631
- Test-Taking Strategies, p. 627
- Test-Taking Strategies with Transparencies

Exercise 22 Point out that the number 7 is not included as a favorable outcome.

Enrichment 11-6 Problem Solving: Make an Organized List and Simulate a Problem

Critical Thinking

A random number table consists of many rows of digits selected at random. Each digit has an equal probability of being selected. You can use the table of random numbers below to simulate an experiment instead of actually performing the experiment.

Row 1	32927	63790	80972	33410	65456
Row 2	18173	00234	84378	04983	91020
Row 3	74362	39890	42822	19514	71085
Row 4	26604	31433	63805	15113	39975

1. Simulate the experiment of tossing a coin 50 times. The first two rows can represent the 50 trials. Assign even numbers and zero to heads and odd numbers to tails. The first twenty have been completed for you.

3 2 9 2 7	6 3 7 9 0	8 0 9 7 2	3 3 4 1 0
T H T H T	H T T T H	H H T T H	T T H T H

a. How many heads did you get? What is the probability?
There are 26 even numbers and zeros, so 26 heads are represented in the experiment. $P(\text{heads}) = \frac{26}{50}$ or $\frac{13}{25}$.

b. How does this result compare with the theoretical probability of tossing a coin?
The theoretical probability is $\frac{1}{2}$ or $\frac{25}{50}$; the simulated probability of $\frac{26}{50}$ is close to $\frac{25}{50}$.

2. Simulate the experiment of tossing a coin 100 times. The four rows of the random numbers above can represent the 100 trials. Again, assign even numbers and zeros to heads and odd numbers to tails.

a. How many heads did you get? What is the probability?
There are 49 even numbers and zeros, so 49 heads are represented in the experiment. $P(\text{heads}) = \frac{49}{100}$.

b. How does this result compare with the theoretical probability of tossing a coin?
The theoretical probability is $\frac{1}{2}$ or $\frac{50}{100}$; the simulated probability of $\frac{49}{100}$ is close to $\frac{50}{100}$.

3. How does the theoretical probability compare to the experimental probability as the number of trials in a simulation increases?
With more trials, the experimental probability becomes closer to the theoretical probability.

Technology

Simulations With Random Numbers

Students may be familiar with how to use spreadsheet software to generate random digits in order to simulate a situation. This feature shows them how to use a graphing calculator to generate the random digits for a simulation.

Optional Materials

- graphing calculator
- Classroom Aid 36

www.PHSchool.com

- Graphing Calculator Handbook, Procedure 15

Teaching Notes

Elicit from students what the advantages are of using a simulation to do a probability experiment. Guide them to appreciate that calculators can generate random digits rapidly.

Inclusion
Remind students that even though they are using a calculator to simulate a situation, the simulation is still only a model, much like the probability experiments with coins and spinners they completed previously. Emphasize, therefore, that the graphing calculator, with its ability to quickly generate random digits, may provide results other than those they would expect, given their prior knowledge of the theoretical probability of outcomes.

Teaching Tip
Work through and discuss the Activity with the whole class. Then provide time for students, working in pairs, to experiment further with generating random digits using the given calculator key sequence.

Exercises
Have partners work together on the exercises. Circulate as students work, checking the results they get from their simulations. Have pairs share and discuss their results with classmates.

Technology Simulations With Random Numbers

For Use With Lesson 11-6

Random numbers can help you simulate some situations. You can use a graphing calculator or a computer to generate random numbers.

To generate a group of ten digits on a graphing calculator, press MATH ▶ ▶ and select the rand option. Each time you press ENTER you will get a different random number. If a random number contains nine digits, use 0 for the tenth digit. When reordering random numbers, ignore the decimal point.

rand	.606334928
rand	.9518983326
rand	.2209784733
rand	.5972865589

Activity

Blood Types About 10% of people in the United States have type B blood. Find the experimental probability that exactly one of the next two donors at a hospital will have type B blood.

Since 10% of the people have type B blood, let 10%, or one out of ten digits, represent this group of people. Let 0 represent type B blood and the remaining nine digits represent the other blood types.

Group the digits of a random number into pairs to represent two donors.

60	63	34	92	80
95	18	98	33	26
22	09	78	47	33
59	72	86	55	89

Any pair with exactly one 0 represents one of two people having type B blood. There are three such pairs in this list.

Based on 20 trials, the experimental probability that exactly one of the next two donors will have type B blood is $\frac{3}{20}$, or 15%.

EXERCISES

Generate your own random numbers to simulate each problem. 1–3. Check students' work.

1. **Blood Types** About 40% of people in the United States have type A blood. Find the experimental probability that exactly one of the next two donors at a blood drive will have type A blood.
2. **Trees** Suppose there is a 50% chance of a tree growing past 50 ft when planted under normal conditions. What is the experimental probability of two trees growing past 50 ft?
3. **Sleep** Data show that people from 14 to 18 years of age dream 20% of the time they are asleep. Suppose a person 14–18 years old is woken up once a night for two nights. What is the experimental probability that the person is dreaming when woken exactly one of the two nights?

11-7 Conducting a Survey

What You'll Learn

 To plan a survey

 To determine biased questions

. . . And Why

To gather reliable information, as in Example 2

Check Skills You'll Need

For help, go to Lesson 11-4.

Find each experimental probability. You survey 20 classmates about their favorite color. The results are 9 blue, 5 red, 2 black, and 4 green. Write each probability as a fraction.

1. P(black) $\frac{1}{10}$ **2.** P(blue) $\frac{9}{20}$ **3.** P(green) $\frac{1}{5}$ **4.** P(red) $\frac{1}{4}$

New Vocabulary • population • sample • random sample • systematic sample • stratified sample • biased questions

 Interactive lesson includes instant self-check, tutorials, and activities.

OBJECTIVE 1 Planning a Survey

Statisticians collect information about specific groups by using a survey. Any group of objects or people in a survey is called a **population.**

Sometimes a population includes too many people to survey. So you look at a sample of the population you want to study to find out the characteristics of the population. A **sample** is a part of the population.

In a **random sample,** each object in the population has an equal chance of being selected.

1 EXAMPLE Determining Random Samples

Tell whether or not the following surveys are random samples. Describe the population of the samples.

a. Game Shows At a game show, five people in the audience are selected to play based on their seat number.

This is a random sample. The population is the audience.

b. Surveys A student interviews several people in his art class to determine the movie star most admired by the students at school.

This is not a random sample. The students in the art class may not represent the views of all the students at school. The population is the students at school.

Check Understanding 1

1a–b. See back of book.

a. Reasoning To find out the type of music people in a city prefer, you survey people who are 18–30 years old. Is the sample random? Explain.

b. Describe the population of the sample in part(a).

Ongoing Assessment and Intervention

Before the Lesson
Diagnose prerequisite skills using:
- Check Skills You'll Need

During the Lesson
Monitor progress using:
- Check Understanding
- Additional Examples
- Test Prep

After the Lesson
Assess knowledge using:
- Lesson Quiz
- Computer Test Generator CD
- Chapter Checkpoint 2 (p. 625)

11-7

1. Plan

Lesson Preview

Check Skills You'll Need
Finding Experimental Probability
Lesson 11-4: Example 1. Extra Practice, p. 712.

Lesson Resources

Teaching Resources
Practice, Reteaching, Enrichment
Checkpoint Quiz 2

Reaching All Students
Practice Workbook 11-7
Spanish Practice Workbook 11-7
Reading and Math Literacy 11C
Spanish Reading and Math Literacy 11C
Spanish Checkpoint Quiz 2
Guided Problem Solving 11-7
Hands-On Activities 44

Presentation Assistant Plus!
Transparencies
- Check Skills You'll Need 11-7
- Problem of the Day 11-7
- Additional Examples 11-7
- Student Edition Answers 11-7
- Lesson Quiz 11-7

PH Presentation Pro CD-ROM 11-7

Checkpoint Quiz 2
Computer Test Generator CD

Technology
Resource Pro® CD-ROM
Computer Test Generator CD
PH Presentation Pro CD-ROM

www.PHSchool.com
Student Site
- Teacher Web Code: ack-5500
- Self-grading Lesson Quiz

PH SuccessNet Teacher Center
- Lesson Planner
- Resources

Plus 

2. Teach

Professional Development

Math Background

A survey collects information about a group of people or objects called a *population*. A *sample* is a part of the population. In a *random sample*, each member of the population has the same chance of being selected as every other member. In a *systematic sample*, each member of the population is selected using a system, such as every 5th member. In a *stratified sample*, the population is separated into groups by a common trait, such as age or grade level, and a random sample is selected from each group. A *biased* survey question is unfair because it makes one answer seem better than another.

Teaching Notes

English Learners
Point out that among humans there are many "populations" among the overall population, such as the teenage population.

1 EXAMPLE Inclusion
Explain that a random sample must meet two tests. First, it must be a part of the population and, second, each member of the population must have an equal chance of being selected.

2 EXAMPLE Auditory Learners
Read aloud the table, which shows sampling methods. Have students practice pronouncing the words *systematic* and *stratified*.

3 EXAMPLE English Learners
Explain that the word *biased* means prejudiced or expressing an opinion.

Diversity
Surveys are very popular in the Unites States. But how popular are they in other countries? Have students who have lived in other countries share their experiences.

Reading Math
Stratify means to separate into groups called strata.

There are other ways to sample a population.

In a **systematic sample,** the members of a survey population are selected using a system of selection that depends on a random number.

In a **stratified sample,** members of the survey population are separated into groups to ensure a balanced sample. Then a random sample is selected from each group.

Methods of Sampling for Conducting Surveys

Name	Sampling Method	Example
Random	Survey a population at random.	Survey people whose names are drawn out of a hat.
Systematic	Select a number n at random. Then survey every nth person.	Select the number 5 at random. Survey every fifth person.
Stratified	Separate a population into smaller groups, each with a certain characteristic. Then survey at random within each group.	Separate a middle school into three groups by grade level. Survey a random sample of students from each grade.

2 EXAMPLE Real-World Problem Solving

Buses You think the school bus makes stops that are too far apart. You want to see if the riders on all the buses agree. Tell whether each survey plan describes a good sample and, if so, name the method of sampling used.

a. Randomly interview 50 people walking on the street.

This sample will probably include people who are not bus riders. It is not a good sample because it is not taken from the population you want to study.

b. Compile a list of all the bus riders by grade level. Put each name on a slip of paper into the appropriate grade-level box. Select ten names from each box to survey.

This is a good sample. It is an example of a stratified sample.

c. Pick four buses at random. Interview every fifth rider boarding the bus.

This is a good sample. It is an example of a systematic sample.

2a. No; it includes people who are not in the population you want to study.

2b. Answers may vary. Sample: Using a group of people who are 12–16 years old, select a number n at random and then survey every nth person.

2c. Systematic; this method does not require that you find information about each person in the survey.

Check Understanding 2 2a–c. See above left.

a. To find out what type of music people 12–16 years old prefer, you survey people at random at a local art museum. Is this a good sample? Explain your reasoning.

b. Describe another survey plan for part (a) that uses systematic or stratified sampling.

c. Reasoning Which survey method is easier to conduct? Explain.

Reaching All Students

Below Level Have students write a biased and an unbiased question on a topic of their own choosing.

Advanced Learners Have students design a survey topic that uses stratified sampling. Sample: polling three different age groups on food preferences

English Learners
See notes on page 622.
Inclusion
See note on page 622.

OBJECTIVE 2

Determining Biased Questions

Unfair questions in a survey are **biased questions.** They make assumptions that may or may not be true. Biased questions can also make one answer seem better than another.

3 EXAMPLE Real-World Problem Solving

In-line Skating Look at the clipboard at the right. Determine whether each question is biased or not. Explain your answer.

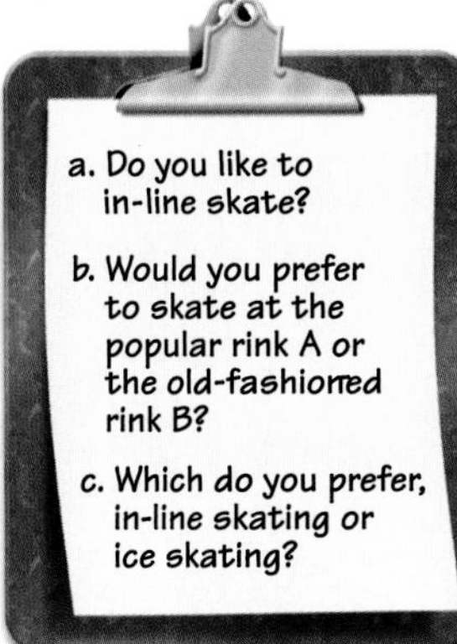

a. Do you like to in-line skate?
b. Would you prefer to skate at the popular rink A or the old-fashioned rink B?
c. Which do you prefer, in-line skating or ice skating?

a. This question is unbiased. It does not try to persuade you one way or the other.

b. This question is biased. It makes in-line skating rink A seem more appealing than skating rink B.

c. This question is biased. It assumes you either in-line skate or ice skate.

Check Understanding 3 **Reasoning** Why would someone want to ask biased questions? Explain. Answers may vary. Sample: A biased survey can give false "evidence" of a particular point of view.

EXERCISES

For more practice, see *Extra Practice.*

A Practice by Example

Example 1 (page 621)

Tell whether or not the following surveys are random samples. Explain your answer and describe the population of samples. 1–4. See margin.

1. Your teacher puts the names of all the students in your class into a box. He selects a class representative by drawing a name out of the box.
2. You survey the last 25 students in the school directory about sports.
3. You want to know how often middle school students buy clothes. You plan to survey every tenth student who arrives at a middle school.
4. Your principal wants to find out what foods to serve at school. The principal interviews 30 students in the eighth grade.

Example 2 (page 622)

Tell whether each survey plan describes a good sample and, if so, name the method of sampling used.

5. A newspaper calls every sixth name in the phone book to find out whether the person likes the paper.
6. A local market surveys every twentieth customer to determine whether they think the store's cashiers are friendly and helpful. This is a good sample; it is an example of systematic sampling.

5. This is not a good sample, because it includes people who do not get the paper.

1. This is a random sample; the population is the students in the class.
2. This is not a random sample; the last 25 students in the directory may not be representative of all of the students in the school.
3. This is not a random sample; students at one middle school may not represent all middle school students.
4. This is not a random sample; students in the eighth grade are not representative of all the students in the school.

Additional Examples

1 Tell whether or not the following surveys are random samples. Describe the population of the samples.

a. To find out how often students in your school go to movies, you select names at random from the school directory to interview. Random; the population is the students in your school.

b. A country radio station asks listeners to call in and give their favorite song. Not random; the population is self-selected country music fans that listen to the radio station.

2 To find the number of tourists in your town, you interview people who are going into the public library. Tell whether this is a good sample and, if so, name the method of sampling used. This sample does not represent the population of tourists in your town, because tourists are not likely to go to the library.

3 Determine whether each question is biased or not. Explain your answer.

a. Do you enjoy modern songs or old songs? Biased; "modern" and "old" are not neutral and descriptive terms.

b. Do you watch more than one hour of television a week? Unbiased; it does not influence the respondent.

Closure

- Explain some important steps in planning a survey. Sample: Identify the population; choose a method for finding a random sample; write unbiased questions; plan how to record the results.
- Explain how to decide whether or not a question is biased. Sample: Read the question carefully to decide whether it makes assumptions or makes one answer seem preferable to another.

3. Practice

Assignment Guide

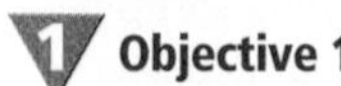

1 Objective 1
- A B Core 1–6, 12–13
- C Extension 14

2 Objective 2
- A B Core 7–11
- C Extension 15–16

Test Prep 17–20
Mixed Review 21–26

Error Prevention!

Exercises 7–11 Have students point out the biased words.

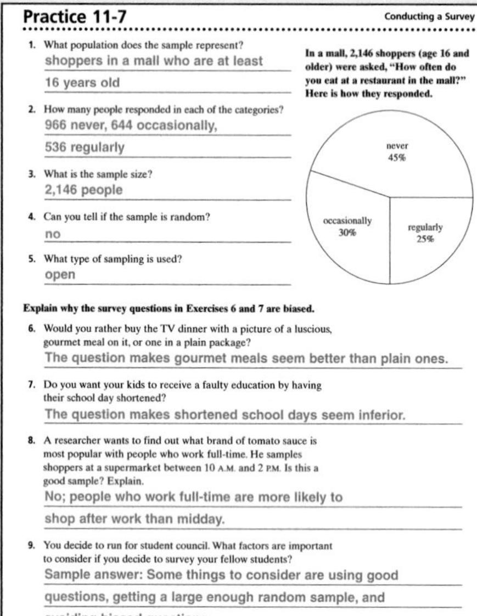

Practice 11-7 — Conducting a Survey

In a mall, 2,146 shoppers (age 16 and older) were asked, "How often do you eat at a restaurant in the mall?" Here is how they responded.

1. What population does the sample represent? shoppers in a mall who are at least 16 years old
2. How many people responded in each of the categories? 966 never, 644 occasionally, 536 regularly
3. What is the sample size? 2,146 people
4. Can you tell if the sample is random? no
5. What type of sampling is used? open

Explain why the survey questions in Exercises 6 and 7 are biased.

6. Would you rather buy the TV dinner with a picture of a luscious, gourmet meal on it, or one in a plain package? The question makes gourmet meals seem better than plain ones.
7. Do you want your kids to receive a faulty education by having their school day shortened? The question makes shortened school days seem inferior.
8. A researcher wants to find out what brand of tomato sauce is most popular with people who work full-time. He samples shoppers at a supermarket between 10 A.M. and 2 P.M. Is this a good sample? Explain. No; people who work full-time are more likely to shop after work than midday.
9. You decide to run for student council. What factors are important to consider if you decide to survey your fellow students? Sample answer: Some things to consider are using good questions, getting a large enough random sample, and avoiding biased questions.

Reteaching 11-7 — Conducting a Survey

In a survey, the entire group is called the *population*. A *sample* is a small part of the population.

For a sample to be fair, it should be *random*. In a random sample, each member of the population has an equal chance of being selected.

- Samples can be either systematic or stratified.

  In a *systematic sample*, members are selected using randomness.

  In a *stratified sample*, members are grouped by similar characteristics.

- Survey questions should be fair, not *biased*. They should not make one answer appear better than another.

  Biased question: Did you hate that movie as much as I did?

  Fair question: What did you think of that movie?

Suppose you want to find out how students feel about new school colors. Tell whether each survey plan describes a good sample. Justify your answer.

1. You interview students while they are in art class. No; the sample includes only students interested in art, not the whole population.
2. You randomly select students from each homeroom in the school. Yes; every student has an equal chance of being selected.

Describe each sample as systematic or stratified.

3. You ask 25 people coming out of 3 different types of movies if they enjoy the movie. stratified
4. You pick 5 names from a hat and ask those people their favorite food. systematic

Explain why each question is biased.

5. Don't you agree that Mrs. Meredith expects too much of her students? Questioner is giving away his or her own feelings.
6. Were you able to follow that boring movie? Question assumes that the movie was boring.

Example 3 (page 623)

Determine whether each question is biased or not. Explain your answer.

7. How do you like your eggs cooked? Biased; it assumes you like eggs.
8. Do you prefer the green chair or the blue chair? Not biased; it does not try to influence your answer.
9. What types of movies have you seen? Not biased; it does not try to influence your answer.

B Apply Your Skills

Open-Ended **Rewrite each biased question as an unbiased question.**

10. Would you rather watch a long baseball game or an exciting figure skating competition? Answers may vary. Sample: Do you prefer to watch baseball, or figure skating, or neither?
11. Do you prefer swimming in a closed-in area, such as a pool, or a more open and challenging area, such as a lake or an ocean? Answers may vary. Sample: Do you prefer to swim in a pool or in the ocean, or neither?

Real-World Connection Market researchers observe focus groups through a one-way mirror.

Market Research **A market research company interviews every hundredth person who registers a car during the year to recommend a fair purchase price for cars at a local dealership. The results are shown below.**

Price Range	Frequency
\$10,000–\$14,999	15
\$15,000–\$19,999	8
\$20,000–\$24,999	12
\$25,000–\$29,999	6

12. What is the population used in the survey plan? See below left.
13. a. What type of sampling is used? systematic
    b. **Probability** Find the experimental probability of a customer choosing the \$20,000–\$24,999 range. $\frac{12}{41}$

C Challenge

14. **Reasoning** Suppose you survey people walking on the street in a city. Of those surveyed, 60% think the city is a great place to visit. If you write a column for a local newspaper, should you report that there is a high probability that a visitor surveyed will love the city? Explain. See margin.
15. **Writing in Math** How do biased surveys affect probability and statistics? Explain. See margin.
16. **Stretch Your Thinking** A line has nonzero slope equal to both the x-intercept and half the y-intercept. What is its equation? $y = -2x - 4$

12. The population is people who register a car during the year.

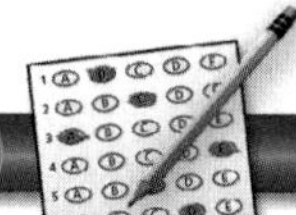

Test Prep

Multiple Choice

17. Which question is NOT biased? C
    - A. Which scary movie do you like best?
    - B. Which sport do you like better, golf or bowling?
    - C. What is your favorite food?
    - D. Would you prefer the beautiful shoes or the plain ones?
18. You sample 50 people who are 12–17 years old and 50 people who are 18–23 years old to see what type of hairstyles they prefer. What type of sampling is this? H
    - F. random
    - G. systematic
    - H. stratified
    - I. biased

Take It to the NET Online lesson quiz at www.PHSchool.com Web Code: aca-1107

Use the Guided Problem Solving worksheet with Exercise 13.

14. No; not everyone walking on the street is a visitor.
15. Answers may vary. Sample: biased surveys may lead to misleading probability values and statistics.

19. You sample every sixth person at an arena to see what type of sports events they watch. What type of sampling is this? B
A. random B. systematic C. stratified D. biased

Short Response

20. You want to find out what type of Web sites students at a college like to visit. You survey people at a local museum. Is this a good sample? Explain your reasoning. See back of book.

Mixed Review

Lesson 11-6

21. Suppose you spin the spinner at the right three times. Make an organized list of all the possible outcomes. Then find the probability of spinning yellow three times in a row. See back of book.

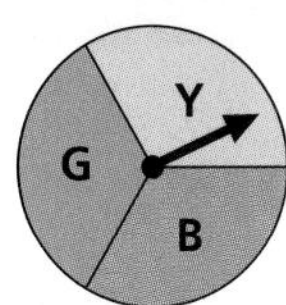

Lesson 11-3

Simplify each expression.

22. ${}_8C_6$ 28
23. ${}_{12}C_3$ 220
24. ${}_{15}C_4$ 1,365
25. ${}_{22}C_2$ 231
26. ${}_{25}C_5$ 53,130

Checkpoint Quiz 2 — Lessons 11-4 through 11-7

Instant self-check quiz online and on CD-ROM

Find each probability. A survey asks eighth graders whether they typically eat certain meals. The results from 1,493 students are shown below. Write each probability as a decimal rounded to the nearest hundredth.

Meals Eaten by 1,493 Eighth Graders

Meal	Breakfast	Lunch	Dinner	Snack
Number of students	1,150	1,403	1,413	1,329

1. P(dinner) 0.95
2. P(lunch) 0.94
3. P(breakfast) 0.77

Find each probability. You place 14 cards marked with the digits 0–13 in a box and select one card at random. You put the card aside and select again. Write each probability as a fraction in simplest form.

4. P(3, then 0) $\frac{1}{182}$
5. P(3, then even) $\frac{1}{26}$
6. P(5, then odd) $\frac{3}{91}$
7. P(2, then not 11) $\frac{6}{91}$

8. Suppose you take a test with five questions. Each question has four choices for answers. You do not know any of the answers. What is the probability you can guess exactly three out of the five questions correctly? Use a spinner to simulate the problem. Check students' work.

9. To find out the type of books people prefer, you survey people at random at a local music store. Is this a good sample? Explain. See left.

9. No; people at the music store are not representative of all the people who read.

10. A store owner surveys every fourth customer to determine what products they like best in the store. Which method of sampling is used? systematic sampling

4. Assess

Lesson Quiz 11-7

You want to find out how many people plan to attend the school pep rally.

1. You survey all students in your science class. Explain why this is not a good sample. Sample: Your science class does not include students from other grades.
2. Explain why this is a biased question: Wouldn't you rather stay home the night of the pep rally? Sample: The question implies that staying home might be a more acceptable choice to the interviewer.

Chapter Checkpoint

To check understanding of Lessons 11-4 to 11-7:

Checkpoint Quiz 2 (p. 625)

Teaching Resources
Checkpoint Quiz 2 (also in *Prentice Hall Assessment System*)

Reaching All Students
Reading and Math Literacy 11C

Spanish versions available

Enrichment 11-7 Conducting a Survey

Decision Making

For each of the following questions, name both the kind of company that would use the question in a survey and the population of the survey. Explain your reasoning for each.

a. Approximately how many times per year do you get a sunburn?
b. How many headaches do you get per year?
c. How many computer video games do you play each week?
d. How long has it been since you've had a burger?

Sample answers: Exercises 2–4

1. Underline the three things you are asked to do for each question.
2. Sunburn is the topic in part *a*. What is the topic in the other parts?
 a. In *b*? headaches b. In *c*? video games c. In *d*? burgers
3. Decide what kind of company would be asking such a question and which population they should survey. Explain your reasoning.
 Part *a* sunscreen co.; outdoor enthusiast; predict sales
 Part *b* pain reliever co.; potential buyers; predict sales
 Part *c* video game co.; teenagers; predict sales
 Part *d* fast food chain; potential patrons; predict sales
4. Would a written or oral questionnaire be a better way to take the survey? Explain why it would better reach your target population.
 Oral; since local populations can be easily targeted and sufficient data gathered.
5. Name both the kind of company that would use the following question in a survey and the population of the survey. Explain your reasoning.
 Do you have a portable CD or tape player?
 Audio distributor; buyers of CDs and tapes; to predict usage for quality control

Test Prep

Resources
For additional practice with a variety of test item formats:
- Test Prep, p. 631
- Test-Taking Strategies, p. 627
- Test-Taking Strategies with Transparencies

Alternative Assessment

Have students describe the difference between a systematic sample and a stratified sample. In a systematic sample, the population is randomly chosen from an entire population. In a stratified sample, the sample is randomly chosen from different subgroups that have similar characteristics.

Understanding Vocabulary

Students who grasp the precision of math vocabulary will improve their ability to fully understand and share mathematical ideas. This feature guides students to use their prior knowledge of everyday meanings of terms to help them comprehend the mathematical meanings of those terms.

Teaching Notes

Elicit from students the value of applying knowledge and understandings they already have to learn new concepts. Discuss that they can more successfully acquire new vocabulary by relating new words to words they already know and use.

Teaching Tip
Remind students to refer as needed to the Illustrated English/Spanish Glossary in the back of their textbooks.

Make an effort to use new math vocabulary often as you work through the textbook lessons. This practice gives students, particularly English language learners, an opportunity to hear the words spoken correctly and in context.

Invite students to add new terms to their personal math dictionaries or to adjust entries that already exist by adding comparisons and other ideas sparked by this feature. Encourage students to include examples—of combinations and permutations, for instance—to accompany the definitions in their dictionaries.

Visual Learners
Students may benefit by using graphic organizers, such as concept maps, to help them process and use new math vocabulary.

Exercises
Have students work with a partner to complete the table. Invite pairs to share their terms, everyday meanings, and math meanings.

Reading Math: Understanding Vocabulary

Many words used in mathematics have an everyday meaning, as well as a specific meaning in mathematics. Knowing the everyday meaning can help you understand the math meaning.

EXAMPLE

Give the everyday meaning and math meaning of each of the following words: population, sample, and combination.

Word	Everyday Meaning	Math Meaning
population	the total number of people living in a region	the total group of people about whom information is wanted
sample	a representative item from a larger group	a part of the population
combination	two or more things put together	a group of items in which the order of items is *not* considered

EXERCISES

Copy and complete the table below. Use a dictionary to look up the everyday meanings of words, if necessary.

	Word	Everyday Meaning	Math Meaning	Answers
1.	permutation	a complete rearrangement	?	1. an arrangement of objects in a particular order
2.	?	?	the outcomes not in an event	2. complement; something that completes
3.	independent	?	?	3. free from influence; outcome of one event does not affect the other
4.	biased	having a strong opinion	?	4. having hidden assumptions or suggesting a preferred answer
5.	random	?	having an equal chance of being selected	5. by chance
6.	systematic	?	selected by a random number	6. orderly
7.	?	arranged in layers	separated into groups and then sampled randomly	7. stratified

Answering the Question Asked

When answering a multiple-choice question, be sure to answer the question asked. Some answer choices may be answers to related questions. So be sure you read the question carefully and check that you have answered it.

For a school assembly, the principal chooses three teachers to sit on the stage. The other seven teachers sit in the audience. How many different groups of three teachers can the principal choose?

A. 6 **B.** 21 **C.** 120 **D.** 720

The principal chooses three teachers from a group of ten. The question is, "How many different groups of three are possible?" In this case, the order in which the principal chooses the teachers does not matter, so use combinations.

Since ${}_{10}C_3 = 120$, the correct choice is C.

Choice A answers the question, "How many ways are there to arrange three people?" $(3! = 3 \cdot 2 \cdot 1 = 6)$

Choice D answers the question, "How many ways are there to select three people from a group of ten, *if order matters?*" $({}_{10}P_3 = 10 \cdot 9 \cdot 8 = 720)$

Choice B simply multiplies the numbers mentioned in the problem. $(3 \cdot 7 = 21)$

EXERCISES

1. Five students reach the final round of a school-wide spelling bee. How many different ways can the five finalists finish? C
   A. 5 **B.** 15 **C.** ${}_5P_5$ **D.** ${}_5C_5$

2. How many groups of three letters can you make from the letters L, O, C, A, T, I, N, G? G
   F. 24 **G.** 56 **H.** 336 **I.** 6,720

3. A restaurant offers a choice of steamed vegetables, a baked potato, or a garden salad with every dinner. Over time, the restaurant has found that 35% of its customers order steamed vegetables, and 55% order a potato. What is the probability that a person will choose either a salad or vegetables? C
   A. 0.10 **B.** 0.35 **C.** 0.45 **D.** 0.90

Answering the Question Asked

This feature alerts students to the importance of reading test questions carefully to make sure that they answer the question asked. It points out the importance of recognizing that some of the answer choices are distractors that answer related questions.

Resources

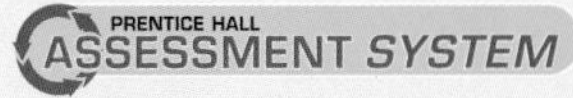

Test-Taking Strategies with Transparencies
- Transparency 8
- Practice master, p. 35

Teaching Notes

Teaching Tip
Students may know that some answer choices on tests are there to catch common mathematical errors. Discuss that other choices are included because they are correct given a *misreading* of the question asked. Stress the importance of reading carefully in order to avoid this trap. Guide students to reread the question to make sure that they have answered it and not a related one.

Test-Taking Strategies With Transparencies

Chapter 11: Answering the Question Asked

Exercises

Read each question carefully. Then solve.

1. James is choosing 4 books from his shelf to take on vacation. His shelf contains 9 books. How many different ways can James choose the books?
   A. 3,024 (B.) 126 C. 120 D. 36
2. A spinner numbered from one to eight is divided into eight equal sections. What is the probability of spinning a one or an eight?
   F. $\frac{1}{16}$ G. $\frac{1}{64}$ H. 12.5% (I.) 25%
3. A bag contains 7 green marbles, 11 red marbles, and 2 blue marbles. What is the probability of *not* drawing a red marble?
   (A.) 45% B. 40% C. 35% D. 10%
4. A basket of fruit contains 4 apples, 6 oranges, and 5 plums. Deanna chooses 2 pieces of fruit without replacing her first choice. What is the probability she will first choose an orange, then a plum?
   F. $\frac{2}{5}$ G. $\frac{1}{3}$ (H.) $\frac{1}{7}$ I. $\frac{2}{15}$
5. You deposit $1,500 into an account that pays 4.5% interest compounded annually. How much is in the account at the end of 4 years?
   (A.) $1,788.78 B. $1,770.00 C. $1,567.50 D. $270.00
6. A jewelry store sells watches, rings, and necklaces. Over time, the jeweler has found that 40% of her customers buy watches and 25% buy necklaces. What is the probability that a person will buy either a watch or a necklace?
   (F.) 0.65 G. 0.40 H. 0.35 I. 0.25
7. Each letter in the word GEOMETRY appears on a card. You choose a card at random and then replace it. Then you choose a second card. What is the probability that you will draw 2 E's?
   (A.) $\frac{1}{16}$ B. $\frac{2}{15}$ C. $\frac{1}{8}$ D. $\frac{1}{4}$
8. Fourteen schools compete in a band competition. Gold, silver, and bronze medals are awarded for first, second, and third place. How many different arrangements of winners can there be?
   F. 2,744 (H.) 2,184 G. 364 I. 39

Resources

Student Edition
Extra Practice, Ch. 11, p. 712
English/Spanish Glossary, p. 735
Table of Symbols, p. 730

Reaching All Students
Reading and Math Literacy 11D
Spanish Reading and Math Literacy 11D

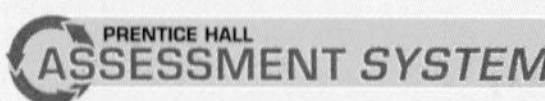

Test Preparation
- Chapter 11 practice in test formats

www.PHSchool.com
Student Site
- Self-grading vocabulary test

PH SuccessNet Teacher Center
- Resources

Plus 

Spanish Reading and Math Literacy

Reading and Math Literacy

11D: Vocabulary For use with the Chapter Review

Study Skill: Take short breaks between assignments. You will be able to concentrate on a new assignment more easily if you take a brief "time out" before starting.

Choose the term that best completes each sentence.

1. A(n) (*event*, *sample*) is one or more possible outcomes.
2. With a (*positive*, *negative*) trend, as one set of values increases, the other set tends to increase.
3. A (*combination*, *permutation*) is an arrangement of items in which the order does not matter.
4. The (*combination*, *complement*) of an event is the opposite of the event.
5. The (*absolute*, *opposite*) value of a number is its distance from 0 on a number line.
6. You can use a (*sample*, *population*) to gather information and make predictions.
7. The (*mean*, *median*) is the middle number in a set of data that has been ordered from least to greatest.
8. The x and y axes divide the coordinate plane into four regions called (*quadrants*, *planes*).
9. You can represent many probability situations using a (*permutation*, *simulation*).
10. Two angles whose sum is 90 degrees are (*complementary*, *supplementary*) angles.
11. Spinning a spinner and then tossing a coin is an example of two (*independent*, *dependent*) events.
12. (*Perpendicular*, *Parallel*) lines are in the same plane and do not intersect.
13. (*Circumference*, *Area*) is the distance around a circle.
14. A (*combination*, *permutation*) is an arrangement of a set of objects in a particular order.

Chapter Review

Vocabulary

biased questions (p. 623)
combination (p. 600)
complement (p. 608)
dependent events (p. 612)
experimental probability (p. 606)
factorial (p. 596)
independent events (p. 611)
odds against (p. 608)
odds in favor (p. 608)
permutation (p. 595)
population (p. 621)
random sample (p. 621)
sample (p. 621)
stratified sample (p. 622)
systematic sample (p. 622)
theoretical probability (p. 607)

Reading Math: Understanding Vocabulary

Take It to the NET
Online vocabulary quiz at **www.PHSchool.com**
Web Code: acj-1151

Choose the correct term to complete each sentence.

1. (Experimental probability, Theoretical probability) describes how likely it is that an event will happen based on all the possible outcomes. theoretical probability
2. People often conduct surveys on a (population, random sample) so that each object in the population has an equal chance of being selected. random sample
3. The (odds, complement) of an event is the opposite of that event. complement
4. To calculate the number of ways a class can line up, you need to find the number of possible (permutations, combinations). permutations
5. When the outcome of one event *does* affect the outcome of a second event, the events are (dependent events, independent events). dependent events

Skills and Concepts

11-1 Objective

- To use tree diagrams and the counting principle

Use the **counting principle** to find the number of outcomes for two or more events. Multiply the number of outcomes for each event.

6. **Cell Phones** A company offers cell phones in four styles and five colors. How many different choices of cell phones are there? 20 choices

11-2 and 11-3 Objectives

- To find the number of permutations of a set of objects
- To use permutation notation
- To find combinations by using a list
- To use combination notation

A **permutation** is an arrangement of a set of objects in a particular order.

$$_{9}P_{4} = 9 \cdot 8 \cdot 7 \cdot 6$$

A **combination** is a group of items in which the order of the items is not important.

$$_{9}C_{4} = \frac{_{9}P_{4}}{4!}$$

7. If 12 people are playing in a tournament and each person plays every other person, how many games will be played? 66 games
8. How many different ways can you choose two magazines from a shelf of ten magazines in a convenience store? 45 ways

11-4 Objectives

- To find experimental probability
- To find the complements and odds of event

You can find the **experimental probability** of an event by using this formula:

$$P(\text{event}) = \frac{\text{number of times event occurs}}{\text{total number of trials}}$$

You can find the **theoretical probability** of an event by using this formula:

$$P(\text{event}) = \frac{\text{number of favorable outcomes}}{\text{total number of possible outcomes}}$$

Toss a coin twice. Complete 30 trials. Record your results. Find each experimental probability. Write each probability as a fraction in simplest form. 9–11. Check students' work.

9. P(heads, then tails) **10.** P(two heads) **11.** P(not two tails)

You have 5 one-dollar bills, 3 five-dollar bills, and 1 ten-dollar bill in your pocket. You select a bill at random. Find the odds in favor of selecting each type of bill.

12. one-dollar bill 5 : 4 **13.** five-dollar bill 1 : 2 **14.** ten-dollar bill 1 : 8

11-5 Objectives

- To find the probability of independent events
- To find the probability of dependent events

When the outcome of one event *does not* affect the outcome of a second event, the events are **independent.** You can find the probability of two independent events by using this formula:

$$P(A, \text{then } B) = P(A) \cdot P(B)$$

If the outcome of one event *does* affect the outcome of a second event, the events are **dependent.** Use the following formula to find the probability:

$$P(A, \text{then } B) = P(A) \cdot P(B \text{ after } A)$$

State whether the events are *dependent* or *independent.* Explain. 15–16. See margin.

15. Roll a number cube. Then roll it again.

16. Pick an item from a bag. Do not replace it. Then pick another item.

11-6 and 11-7 Objectives

- To solve a problem using different methods
- To plan a survey
- To determine biased questions

You can simulate some probability problems by tossing a coin, rolling a number cube, or using a random number table.

A **sample** is part of the population, or group, being studied. In a **random sample,** each item has an equal chance of being selected. **Biased questions** are unfair questions that may influence the answers in a survey.

A triangular solid has an equally likely chance of landing face down on any of its four colored sides: red, white, black, and gray. You toss the solid twice.

17. Make an organized list of all possible outcomes. What is the probability that the gray side faces down twice in a row? See left.

17. WW, WB, WR, WG, BW, BB, BR, BG, RW, RB, RR, RG, GW, GB, GR, GG; $\frac{1}{16}$

18. Simulate the problem. What is the experimental probability that either the black side or the white side faces down twice in a row? Check students' work.

15. Independent; the outcome of the second roll is not dependent on the first roll.

16. Dependent; the probability of the second pick is affected by the first pick.

Alternative Assessment Form C

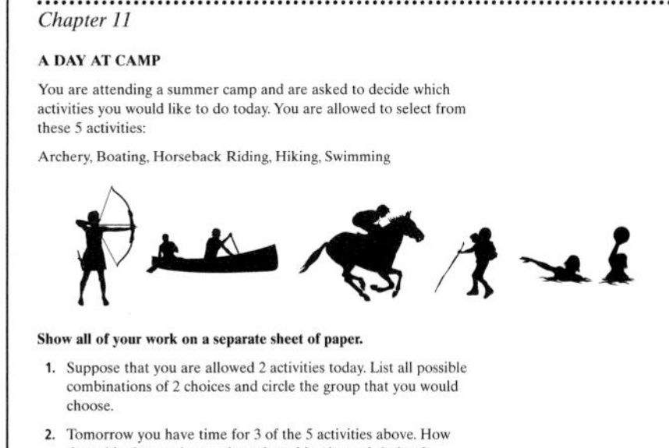

Alternative Assessment **Form C**

Chapter 11

A DAY AT CAMP

You are attending a summer camp and are asked to decide which activities you would like to do today. You are allowed to select from these 5 activities:

Archery, Boating, Horseback Riding, Hiking, Swimming

Show all of your work on a separate sheet of paper.

1. Suppose that you are allowed 2 activities today. List all possible combinations of 2 choices and circle the group that you would choose.
2. Tomorrow you have time for 3 of the 5 activities above. How does this change the number of combinations of choices? Explain. Which 3 activities would you select?
3. List all of the possible orders from which you can choose your 3 activities. Circle the order that you select to do your 3 activities.
4. It is your camp counselor's responsibility to monitor 20 people, including you. Each morning the counselor will randomly pick 1 camper and ask that camper to be the group leader for that day. What is the probability that you will get picked first?
5. One day your counselor puts a set of cards in a hat. On each card is either a group of 2 of the 5 activities (from Question 1) OR a group of 3 of the 5 activities (from Question 2). There is exactly 1 card for each of the possible groups. Each person will pick 1 card and then put it back before another person picks. What is the probability that you will pick either of the groups that you circled in Questions 1 and 2? Explain.

Resources

Teaching Resources
Ch. 11 Test, Forms A & B
Ch. 11 Alternative Assessment, Form C

Reaching All Students
Spanish Ch. 11 Test, Forms A & B
Spanish Ch. 11 Alternative Assessment, Form C

PRENTICE HALL ASSESSMENT SYSTEM

Assessment Resources
- Ch. 11 Test, Forms A & B
- Ch. 11 Alternative Assessment, Form C

Computer Test Generator CD
- Ch. 11 Instant Chapter Test™
- Make your own Ch. 11 test

www.PHSchool.com
Student Site
- Self-grading Ch. 11 test

PH SuccessNet Teacher Center
- Resources

Plus 

Chapter Test – Form B

Chapter Test – Form A

Chapter Test Form A

Chapter 11

Solve.

1. A local store sells 8 kinds of window cleaner, 7 kinds of car wax, and 5 kinds of upholstery cleaner. In order to clean up his car, Jeff needs to buy window cleaner, car wax, and upholstery cleaner. How many combinations of products does Jeff have to choose from? 280
2. A diner's lunch menu consists of 3 different kinds of sandwiches, 3 different kinds of soup, and 5 different drinks. A cafe's lunch menu consists of 4 different kinds of sandwiches, 3 different types of salads, and 6 different types of drinks. Which restaurant offers more lunch combinations? the cafe

Simplify each expression.

3. $6!$ 720
4. ${}_{12}P_4$ 11,880
5. ${}_{7}C_4$ 35
6. $\frac{9!}{6!}$ 504
7. ${}_{8}P_2 - {}_{8}C_2$ 28
8. $P(\text{not } E)$ if $P(E) = 0.37$ 0.63
9. Suppose you and your family want to rent 3 movies for the long weekend. Your family has narrowed the choices to 6 movies. How many possible combinations of movies can you choose? 20
10. Explain how permutations and combinations are alike. How do they differ? Both are sets of items. In a permutation the items are arranged in an order; in a combination they are not.

Is each expression equivalent to ${}_{15}C_5$? Write *yes* or *no* and explain your answer.

11. ${}_{15}P_5$ No; permutations and combinations are not equivalent.
12. $\frac{{}_{15}P_5}{{}_{5}P_5}$ Yes; a combination can be written as the ratio of permutations.
13. 3,003 Yes; this is ${}_{15}C_5$ simplified.
14. $\frac{15!}{5!(15-5)!}$ Yes; when simplified the two expressions are equivalent.
15. $\frac{15!}{5!}$ No; when simplified the two expressions are not equivalent.
16. $15 \times 14 \times 13 \times 12 \times 11$ No; when simplified the two expressions are not equivalent.

Chapter 11 Chapter Test

Take It to the NET
Online chapter test at **www.PHSchool.com**
Web Code: aca-1152

1. **Stationery** A store sells envelopes. They come in cream, purple, and peach colors. The envelopes have five styles. How many different types of envelopes are there? 15 types
2. **License Plates** Which license plate system provides more possible license numbers: four letters and three digits, or seven digits? four letters and three digits

Simplify each expression.

3. $8!$ 40,320
4. ${}_{4}P_3$ 24
5. ${}_{18}C_2$ 153
6. $\frac{6!}{2!}$ 360
7. $P(\text{not } E)$ if $P(E) = 0.53$ 0.47
8. **School Supplies** Suppose you want to buy five different colored notebooks. There are eight colors from which to choose. How many combinations of notebooks are possible? 56 combinations
9. **Writing in Math** Why are there fewer combinations than permutations when selecting from a group of more than 1? Explain. See margin.

Is each expression equivalent to ${}_{12}C_3$? Write *yes* or *no* and explain your answer. 10–13. See margin.

10. ${}_{12}C_9$
11. $\frac{12!}{9!}$
12. $\frac{12 \cdot 11 \cdot 10}{3!}$
13. ${}_{12}P_3$
14. **Reasoning** In the diagram, if events A and B account for all of the possibilities in a sample space, what can you say about $P(B)$? $P(B) = 1 - P(A)$

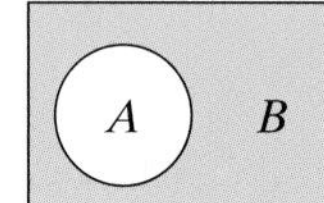

Find each probability. Lucinda has 5 yellow pencils, 6 blue pencils, and 9 green pencils. She picks 1 pencil at random and does not replace it. Then she picks another pencil.

15. $P(\text{yellow then blue})$ $\frac{3}{38}$
16. $P(2 \text{ green})$ $\frac{18}{95}$
17. $P(2 \text{ yellow})$ $\frac{1}{19}$
18. $P(\text{green then blue})$ $\frac{27}{190}$

Food Find each probability. A supermarket polled its customers to see which brand of salsa they preferred. The table below shows the results from the survey.

Preference	Number of Votes
Brand X	92
Brand Y	80
Brand Z	120
No preference	108
Total	**400**

19. $P(\text{Brand X})$ $\frac{23}{100}$
20. $P(\text{Brand Y})$ $\frac{1}{5}$
21. **Repairs** On a recent day, a mechanic found that out of 126 fenders, 7 had cracks. What is the experimental probability that a fender selected at random does *not* have a crack? $\frac{17}{18}$
22. **School** Every day, a teacher randomly selects a row of students to organize the classroom. There are six rows of students. What is the probability that the teacher selects the same row two days in a row? Simulate the problem. Check students' work.

A number from 1 to 100 is selected at random. Find each theoretical probability.

23. $P(85)$ $\frac{1}{100}$
24. $P(105)$ 0
25. $P(\text{number divisible by 9})$ $\frac{11}{100}$
26. $P(\text{number containing a 4})$ $\frac{19}{100}$

Tell whether or not the following surveys are random samples. Describe the population.

27. **Entertainment** A movie theater surveys every tenth person to determine what types of movies its patrons like. See margin.
28. **Games** A computer game company surveys its teenage customers to determine its most popular game. See margin.

9. Answers may vary. Sample: Order does not matter in combinations, so different arrangements of the same outcomes are not counted multiple times.
10. Yes; both equal 220.
11. No; $\frac{12!}{9!}$ is equal to $12 \cdot 11 \cdot 10$, or 1,320.
12. Yes; ${}_{12}C_3 = \frac{12 \cdot 11 \cdot 10}{3 \cdot 2 \cdot 1}$, which is the same as $\frac{12 \cdot 11 \cdot 10}{3!}$.
13. No; ${}_{12}C_3 = \frac{12 \cdot 11 \cdot 10}{3 \cdot 2 \cdot 1}$, but ${}_{12}P_3 = 12 \cdot 11 \cdot 10$.
27. Random; the population is the patrons of the movie theater.

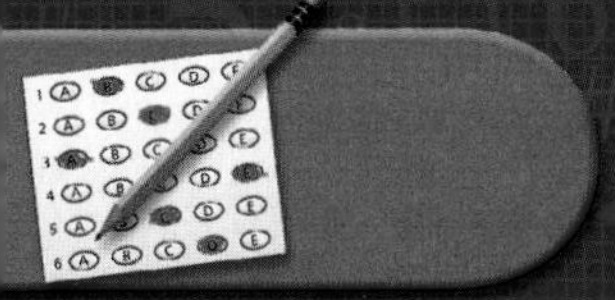

Test Prep

Reading Comprehension

Test Prep

Students must be able to extract information from reading passages, answer multiple-choice questions, and construct responses in order to be successful in current state and national assessments.

Resources

Cumulative Review

Reaching All Students
Spanish Cumulative Review

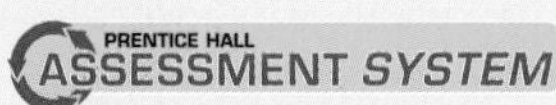

Test Preparation
- Ch. 11 standardized test prep

Assessment Resources
- Cumulative Review

Computer Test Generator CD
- Standardized test prep

www.PHSchool.com
- Standardized test prep
- Resources

Plus iTEXT

Reading Comprehension **Read each passage and answer the questions that follow.**

Mathematical Notes Have you ever wondered how there can still be any songs left to be written? After all, people have been writing music for a very long time, and there are only eight notes in the octave of a scale for songwriters to choose from. Doesn't it seem as though all the new melodies should have been written by now?

For Exercises 1–4, you can use the same note more than once.

1. Suppose you plan to write a song. You use the notes in an octave of a scale. How many different outcomes are there for the first two notes of the song? D
   A. 8 **B.** 16 **C.** 56 **D.** 64
2. How many different ways can you choose the first three notes of a song from the notes in an octave of a scale? I
   F. 6 **G.** 24 **H.** 336 **I.** 512
3. What is the general formula for the number of ways you can write n notes of music choosing from the notes in an octave? D
   A. $8 \cdot 7 \cdot 6 \cdot 5 \cdot 4 \cdot 3 \cdot 2 \cdot 1$
   B. $(n)(n-1)\ldots(3)(2)(1)$
   C. n^8
   D. 8^n
4. How many ways can you choose from eight possible notes to write the first ten notes of a song? F
   F. 8^{10} **G.** 10^8
   H. $10 \cdot 9 \cdot 8$ **I.** 1×10^8

Ecology Club The ecology club at school has 20 members. When the club selects officers, the order of selection matters. When the club selects members to study either recycling, water, land surface, or waste disposal, order does not matter.

5. How many different ways can the ecology club choose a president, a vice president, and a coordinator? C
   A. 380 **B.** 1,140 **C.** 6,840 **D.** 8,000
6. The club plans to go on a field trip. Each member must have a buddy. Which expression represents the number of different ways n members can pair off? I
   F. $(n)(n-1)$ **G.** n^2
   H. $(n)(n-1)\ldots1$ **I.** $\frac{(n)(n-1)}{2}$
7. The club selects 4 people to lead the curriculum groups. How many ways can the club select 4 people? B
   A. 116,280 **B.** 4,845 **C.** 80 **D.** 5
8. Suppose the club gets four more members. In how many more ways can the club select 4 group leaders than in Exercise 7? H
   F. ${}_{24}P_4 - {}_{20}P_4$ **G.** ${}_{24}C_4 + {}_{20}C_4$
   H. ${}_{24}C_4 - {}_{20}C_4$ **I.** ${}_{24}P_4 + {}_{20}P_4$

Cumulative Review

Cumulative Review
Chapters 1–11

Multiple Choice. Choose the letter of the best answer.

1. Find the area of a right triangle with sides of 16 cm, 30 cm, and 34 cm.
   A. 80 cm^2 (B.) 240 cm^2
   C. 480 cm^2 D. 510 cm^2
2. Which equation is *not* equivalent to $3t - 8 = 4$?
   F. $3t = 12$ G. $t = 4$
   (H.) $t - 8 = \frac{4}{3}$ I. $t = \frac{8}{3} + \frac{4}{3}$
3. Athena wants to buy a computer that costs \$1,299. She plans to make a down payment of \$300. She will pay the rest in six equal payments. What equation could you use to find the amount of each payment?
   A. $6(300) + p = 1{,}299$
   B. $p = 1{,}299 - 6(300)$
   C. $\frac{6}{300}p = 1{,}299$
   (D.) $300 + 6p = 1{,}299$
4. Solve $16 = 5(k - 2) - 3k$.
   (F.) 13 G. 9
   H. 7 I. 3
5. What is the next term in the sequence 7, 16, 25, 34, 43, . . .?
   A. 50 (B.) 52
   C. 77 D. not here
6. Which of the following numbers is prime?
   F. 4 (G.) 7
   H. 9 I. 15
7. Write 0.24 as a percent.
   A. 0.24% B. 2.4%
   (C.) 24% D. 240%
8. The sales tax is 6%. If you buy two \$20 books, what is the total cost?
   F. \$2.40 G. \$37.60
   (H.) \$42.40 I. not here
9. Find the difference $4\frac{3}{8} - 3\frac{7}{16}$.
   A. $1\frac{15}{16}$ B. $1\frac{1}{2}$
   C. $1\frac{1}{4}$ (D.) $\frac{15}{16}$
10. What is the sum of the measures of the angles of a polygon with 16 sides?
    F. 1,800° (G.) 2,520°
    H. 2,880° I. 3,600°
11. Simplify $5x^2 - 8 + 8x - 8x^2 + 3$.
    A. $13x^2 + 8x + 5$ (B.) $-3x^2 + 8x - 5$
    C. $-3x^2 + 8x + 11$ D. $13x^2 - 5$
12. Solve $\frac{12}{37} = \frac{18}{x}$.
    F. 0.324 G. 5.84
    H. 24.67 (I.) 55.5
13. $\triangle ABC$ is similar to $\triangle XYZ$. What is the scale factor of $\triangle ABC$ to $\triangle XYZ$?

    A. 1 : 1 (B.) $\frac{1}{2}$
    C. 11 D. 20

Chapter Test

28. Not random; the teenage customers may not represent the views of all the customers of the company; the population is the customers of the company.

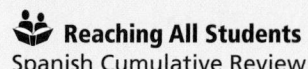

Real-World Snapshots

Animal Census

Students will use data from these two pages to answer the questions posed here in Put It All Together.

Activating Prior Knowledge
Have students discuss what they know about why and how scientists tag animals in the wild.

Teaching Notes

Have a volunteer read aloud the information about capture-recapture for sea turtles, albatrosses, and king penguins. Tell students that in this activity they are going to simulate the way scientists keep track of animal populations.

Social Studies Connection
Tell students that at one time the North American bison population was dropping precipitously, but now the herds are again thriving in places. Invite interested students to learn more about the decline and re-emergence of these large animals, who were once so very important in many ways to Plains Indians like the Cheyenne, Pawnee, and Sioux. Ask them to share with classmates what they find out.

Science Connection
When people think of game preserves, they may think of the large ones in Africa, where lions, wildebeests, giraffes, and other large animals roam freely. But there are many preserves right here in the United States. Have students do research to find out where these preserves are, what purposes they serve, and who runs them.

Real-World Snapshots

Animal Census

Applying Probability Suppose you want to know how many polar bears live in Alaska, or how many cheetahs live in the Serengeti desert. Since it is nearly impossible to count an animal population directly, scientists use a capture-recapture method to estimate populations.

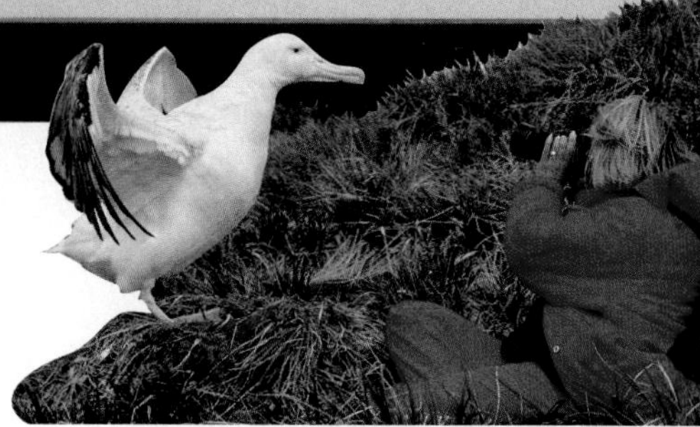

Monitoring the Albatross
Scientists tag albatrosses to study how commercial fishing ventures affect them.

Loggerhead Sea Turtles
Scientists use tags to track sea turtles' movements after nesting, including migration paths and feeding habitats.

King Penguins
Researchers tagged king penguin pairs in a colony of 40,000 penguins to find out how the penguin parents communicated with each other as they incubated their eggs.

632

1. Check students' work.

2a–c. Check students' work.

2d. Answers may vary. Sample: The differences occur due to the random nature of the recapture. It is unlikely that the same number of beans will be recaptured every time.

3. The population is usually not fixed in the wild, because animals can enter or leave the area and new ones may be born or old ones die. Animals may also lose their tags or markings. Scientists might try to control for these factors by closing the area temporarily or doing the second capture soon

Put It All Together

Materials paper bag, dried white beans, permanent marker, graph paper

Work with a partner or in a small group.

- Count out between 250 and 400 beans.
- Record the number and place the beans in the paper bag.
- Exchange bags with another group of students.

1. Use the capture-recapture method below to sample the population. Copy and extend the table. Record your results.
2. a. Make a scatter plot comparing the probability of recapturing a marked bean to the sample size.
   b. Based on your graph, what percent of the total population do you think is marked?
   c. **Estimation** Estimate the population in the bag.
   d. **Writing in Math** Compare your estimate with the number of beans recorded by the group that gave you the bag. Explain any differences.
3. **Reasoning** What real-life factors might make capture-recapture less accurate in the wild? How might scientists control these factors?

Trial Number	Sample Size	Number Recaptured	Percent Recaptured
1	10	2	20%
2	10	■	■
3	10	■	■
4	10	■	■
5	10	■	■
6	20	■	■
7	20	■	■

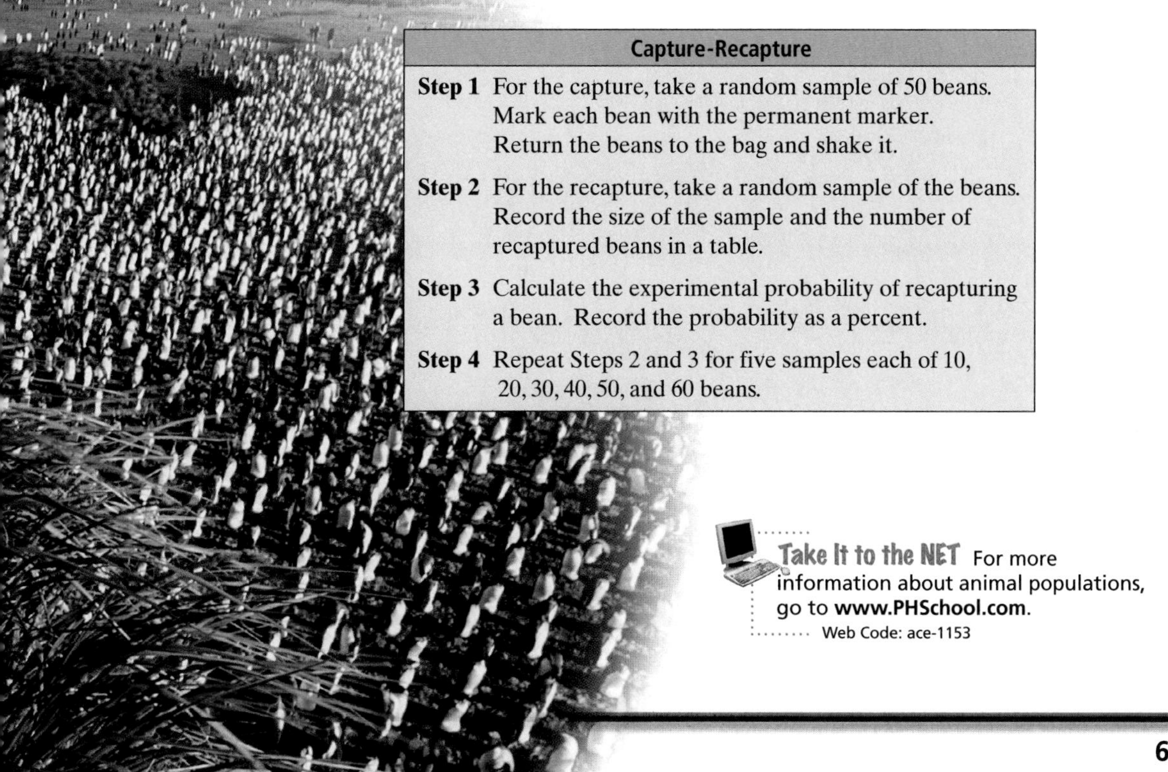

Capture-Recapture	
Step 1	For the capture, take a random sample of 50 beans. Mark each bean with the permanent marker. Return the beans to the bag and shake it.
Step 2	For the recapture, take a random sample of the beans. Record the size of the sample and the number of recaptured beans in a table.
Step 3	Calculate the experimental probability of recapturing a bean. Record the probability as a percent.
Step 4	Repeat Steps 2 and 3 for five samples each of 10, 20, 30, 40, 50, and 60 beans.

Take It to the NET For more information about animal populations, go to **www.PHSchool.com**.
Web Code: ace-1153

after the first. But if the second capture is done too soon, the animals will not have had a chance to mix properly and the results will be skewed.

Put It All Together

Have students work in pairs to do the activities and answer the questions. Guide them to record data as they measure and accumulate it.

Discuss with students that the table started at the right is directly related to the capture-recapture method described in the box at the bottom of the page. To complete the table, students should follow the steps in the box. Guide them to understand that each trial number in the table refers to a recapture. The first step for the partners to take is to collect a random sample of 50 beans and mark the beans.

Teaching Tip
Tell students that while it is important to use permanent markers on the beans, these markers can stain clothing. Guide students to take care when using them.

Inclusion
Discuss ways to equitably share the work in the activity.

Exercise 2 As needed, review what a *scatterplot* is and how to make and interpret one. Discuss how trends can be used to make conjectures about a relationship between two quantities.

CHAPTER 12

Algebraic Relationships

Chapter at a Glance

12-1 Algebra

Sequences *pp. 637–641*

Objectives

1. Describing Sequences
2. Evaluating Algebraic Expressions to Write Sequences

New Vocabulary
sequence, term, arithmetic sequence, common difference, geometric sequence, common ratio

NCTM Standards
1, 2, 5, 6, 7, 8, 9, 10

Local Standards

12-2 Algebra

Functions *pp. 643–647*

Objectives

1. Representing Functions
2. Using Function Notation

New Vocabulary
function, function rule

NCTM Standards
1, 2, 6, 7, 8, 9, 10

Local Standards

12-3 Algebra

Graphing Linear Functions *pp. 648–652*

Objectives

1. Using a Table to Graph a Function
2. Using a Rule to Graph a Function

New Vocabulary
discrete data, continuous data, linear function

Optional Materials
graph paper, ruler

NCTM Standards
1, 5, 6, 7, 8, 9, 10

Local Standards

12-4 Algebra

Writing Rules for Linear Functions *pp. 653–657*

Objectives

1. Writing a Rule From Words
2. Writing a Rule from a Table or Graph

NCTM Standards
1, 2, 6, 7, 8, 9, 10

Local Standards

✓ Checkpoint Quiz 1

12-5 Algebra

Relating Graphs to Events *pp. 658–662*

Objectives

1. Interpreting and Sketching a Graph

Optional Materials
graph paper, watch or clock with second hand

NCTM Standards
1, 2, 5, 6, 7, 8, 9, 10

Local Standards

12-6 Algebra

Nonlinear Functions *pp. 663–667*

Objectives

1. Graphing and Writing Quadratic Functions
2. Graphing Other Nonlinear Functions

New Vocabulary
quadratic function, parabola

Optional Materials
graph paper

NCTM Standards
1, 2, 6, 7, 8, 9, 10

Local Standards

12-7 Problem Solving

Write an Equation *pp. 668–671*

Objectives

1. Solving Problems by Writing an Equation

NCTM Standards
1, 2, 6, 7, 8, 9, 10

Local Standards

✓ Checkpoint Quiz 2

12-8 Algebra

Exploring Polynomials *pp. 673–677*

Objectives

1. Writing Variable Expressions
2. Simplifying Polynomials

New Vocabulary
polynomial, constant

Optional Materials
algebra tiles

NCTM Standards
1, 2, 3, 6, 7, 8, 9, 10

Local Standards

12-9 Algebra

Adding and Subtracting Polynomials *pp. 678–682*

Objectives

1. Adding Polynomials
2. Subtracting Polynomials

New Vocabulary
coefficient

NCTM Standards
1, 2, 3, 6, 7, 8, 9, 10

Local Standards

12-10 Algebra

Multiplying Polynomials *pp. 683–686*

Objectives

1. Multiplying by a Monomial
2. Using Area Models to Multiply Binomials

New Vocabulary
monomial, binomial

NCTM Standards
1, 2, 3, 6, 7, 8, 9, 10

Local Standards

Reaching All Students

Additional Instructional Options in Chapter 12

Reading and Math Literacy

Reading Math

Changing Representations, p. 672

Reading Math hints, pp. 638, 644, 649

Reading Comprehension, p. 662

Understanding Vocabulary, p. 688

Writing in Math

Daily Writing Practice, pp. 640, 646, 651, 656, 661, 665, 666, 670, 676, 681, 685, 690

Above Level

Challenge exercises

pp. 641, 646, 652, 656, 661 667, 670, 677, 681, 686

Hands-On and Technology

Investigations

Exploring Sequences, p. 637

Making and Interpreting a Graph, p. 659

Using Algebra Tiles, p. 673

Technology

Exploring Sequences, p. 642

Activities and Projects

Real-World Snapshots

Applying Polynomials, pp. 694–695

Chapter Project

How Much Dough?, p. 701

Test Prep

Daily Test Prep

pp. 641, 647, 652, 657, 662, 667, 671, 677, 682, 686

Test-Taking Strategies

Work Backward, p. 687

Test Prep

Cumulative Review (Chapters 1–12), pp. 691–693

Chapter Assessment

Checkpoint Quiz

pp. 657, 671

Chapter Review

pp. 688–689

Chapter Test

p. 690

Pacing Options

This chart suggests pacing only for the core lessons and their parts. It is provided as a possible guide. It will help you determine how much time you have in your schedule to cover the additional features and assessment, as described at the left.

Day	Traditional 45-minute class periods	Block 90-minute class periods
1	12-1	12-1 12-2
2	12-2	12-3
3	12-3	12-4
4	12-3	12-5 12-6
5	12-4	12-7 12-8
6	12-4	12-8 12-9
7	12-5	12-9 12-10
8	12-6	12-10
9	12-7	
10	12-8	
11	12-8	
12	12-9	
13	12-9	
14	12-10	
15	12-10	

NCTM STANDARDS 2000

1 Number and Operations
2 Algebra
3 Geometry
4 Measurement
5 Data Analysis and Probability
6 Problem Solving
7 Reasoning and Proof
8 Communication
9 Connections
10 Representation

Math Background

Skills Trace

BEFORE Chapter 12

Course 2 introduced function relationships using tables, word statements, and graphs.

DURING Chapter 12

Course 2 reviews and extends functions to non-linear relationships, and introduces polynomials and operations with polynomials.

AFTER Chapter 12

Throughout this course students use patterns in words, tables, algebraic rules, and graphs.

12-1 Sequences

Math Understandings

- To write an arithmetic sequence, you have to know the number to start with and the common difference, which may be a positive or negative number.
- You can use an algebraic expression, such as $n(n-1)$, to make a sequence by substituting the counting numbers.
- Some sequences, such as 2, 6, 12, 20, . . . , are neither arithmetic nor geometric.

A **sequence** is a set of numbers that follows a pattern. Each number in a sequence is called a **term**, You can find each term of an **arithmetic sequence** by *adding* a fixed number to the previous term. This fixed number is called the **common difference**.

Example: The rule for the arithmetic sequence 2, 6, 10, 14, 18, 22, 26, . . . is: Start with 2 and add 4 repeatedly:

You can find each term of a **geometric sequence** by multiplying the previous term by a fixed number, called the **common ratio**.

Example: The rule for the geometric sequence 2, 6, 18, 54, . . . is: Start with 2 and multiply by 3 repeatedly.

12-2 Functions

Math Understandings

- Some quantities are mathematically related in a special way: for each value of one quantity there is a unique value for the related quantity.

The **function** is a relationship that assigns exactly one output value to each input value. A **function rule** is an equation that describes a function.

Example: Make a table of input/output pairs for $d = \$.05c$.

Input c	6	12	24
Output d	\$.30	\$.60	\$1.20

12-3 Graphing Linear Functions
12-4 Writing Rules for Linear Functions

Math Understandings

- When you graph a function, you place input values along the horizontal axis (x-axis) and output values along the vertical axis (y-axis).
- Discrete data items are separate and values between two data items have no meaning. For example, this list of shoe sizes contains discrete data:
  $4, 4\frac{1}{2}, 5, 5\frac{1}{2}, 6, 6\frac{1}{2}, 7, 7\frac{1}{2}, 8, 8\frac{1}{2}, 9, 9\frac{1}{2}$
- You can write a function rule from a problem stated in words, an equation, values in a table, or in a graph.

Discrete data are data that involve a count of items, such as numbers of people or numbers of cars, and you graph discrete data with a dashed line. **Continuous data** are data where numbers between any two data values have meaning, such as measurements, and you use a solid line to graph continuous data.

A **linear function** is a function whose points lie on a line. You can write linear functions in the form $f(x) = mx + b$ or $y = mx + b$. Then you can used the slope, m, and the y-intercept, b, to graph the function.

Example: Graph the linear function $y = 2x - 3$.

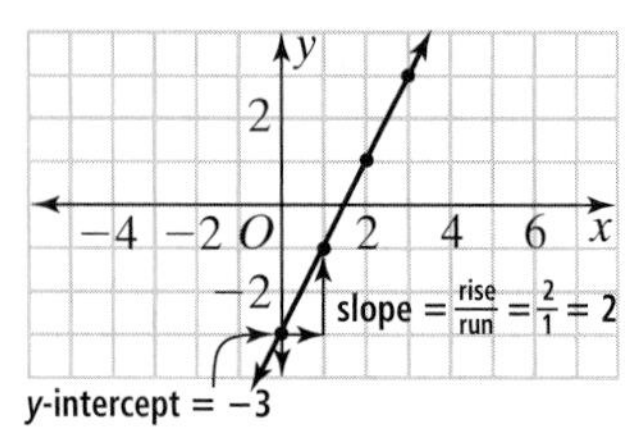

12-5 Relating Graphs to Events

Math Understandings

- A graph can show complex and changing relationships between variables in a simple, visual way.
- When you draw a graph without actual data, you are making a sketch.

The graph at right shows the speed of a commuter train as it makes a morning run.

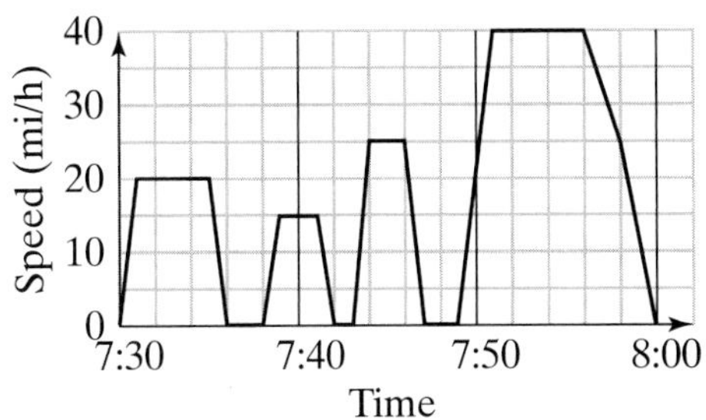

12-6 Nonlinear Functions

Math Understandings

- Some functional relationships are not linear.

One type of nonlinear function is a **quadratic function** of the form $y = ax^2 + bx + c$. The graph of a quadratic function is a U-shaped curve called a **parabola**, which may open upwards or downwards.

12-7 Write an Equation

When a real-world problem cannot be represented with linear equations or linear function rules, you may be able to *write an equation* that is a nonlinear function rule. For example, $y = 2^h$ is one nonlinear function rule for *exponential growth*.

12-8, 12-9 Exploring Polynomials / Adding and Subtracting Polynomials

Math Understandings

- We can use models to make sense of adding and subtracting polynomials.
- The variables and their degrees in a term determine whether terms are like or unlike.
- Polynomials can be simplified by combining like terms.

A **polynomial** is one term, or the sum or difference of two or more terms. For example, $-x^2 + 3x - 4$ is a polynomial in three terms. Each term is separated by a $+$ or a $-$. A term that does not contain a variable, such as -4, is a **constant**. A **coefficient** is a number that is multiplied by a variable, such as 3 in $3x$.

12-10 Multiplying Polynomials

Math Understandings

- You can use an area model to show the product of a monomial and a binomial or the product of two binomials.

A polynomial that has only one term, such as $4a^3$, is a **monomial**. A **binomial** is a polynomial with two terms. You can model the product of two binomials by forming a rectangular array of tiles. The model below shows that $(2x + 1)(3x + 2) = 6x^2 + 7x + 2$.

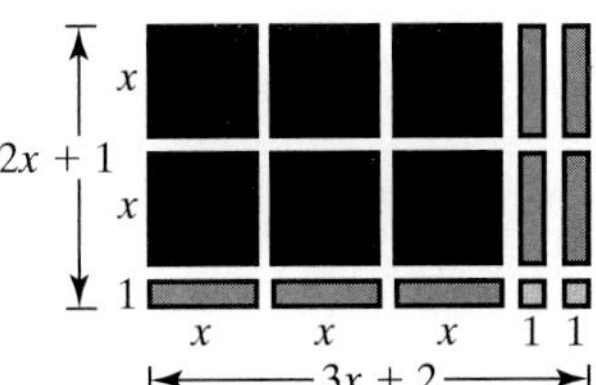

Additional Professional Development Opportunities

Chapter 12 Math Background notes: pp. 638, 644, 649, 654, 659, 664, 669, 674, 679, 684

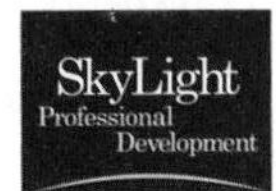

Additional resources available from SkyLight Professional Development:

On-site courses, workshops, summer institutes. Online courses and chat rooms. Videocassettes and books. Visit www.skylightedu.com.

Ongoing Assessment and Intervention

The *Prentice Hall Mathematics* program provides many options for assessment in the Student Edition, Teacher's Edition, and teaching resources. From these options you may choose instructional materials that are appropriate for your students and that support your district's curriculum requirements.

Daily Assessment

Instant Check System™ in Chapter 12

Allows students to check their own learning before, during, and after each lesson.

Diagnosing Readiness before the chapter (p. 636)

Check Skills You'll Need exercises in each lesson (pp. 637, 643, 648, 653, 658, 663, 668, 673, 678, 683)

Check Understanding questions with each Example (pp. 638, 639, 643, 644, 648, 649, 650, 653, 654, 658, 659, 663, 664, 665, 669, 674, 678, 679, 680, 683, 684)

Checkpoint Quiz (pp. 657, 671)

Formal Assessment

Assessment in the Student Text and in Additional Resources

Assess student progress throughout the Course 2 textbook and with blackline masters and CD-ROM.

Student Edition
- Chapter 12 Review, with Vocabulary, Skills, and Concepts Review, pp. 688–689
- Chapter 12 Test, p. 690

Assessment Resources
- Checkpoint Quizzes 1 & 2
- Chapter Test, forms A & B
- Chapter Alternative Assessment

Spanish versions available.

Computer Test Generator CD-ROM
- Instant Chapter Tests™—pre-made tests with items that vary every time you print.
- Online Testing allows you to give tests online and receive progress reports.
- Prepare students by making tests based on standardized test objectives.

Algebra Readiness Tests
- Includes Basic Skills Tests and Concept-Readiness Tests.
- Assess understanding of skills and concepts needed for success in algebra.

Intervention

Skills Intervention Kit

Online Intervention

Integrated within the iText, this online intervention system includes diagnostic tests and prescribed remediation, plus reports to track student mastery.

A *complete* system for the student who is struggling with course-level work

Eight intervention units cover core skills and allow you to:
- **Diagnose** students' gaps in basic skills
- **Prescribe** an individualized course of study
- **Monitor** student progress

Includes print workbooks, tutorial CD-ROM, teacher editions, progress folders, and more. *Available in Spanish.*

How to Use with Chapter 12

12-1 Pre-Algebra Basics, Skill 11
12-6 Pre-Algebra Basics, Skill 20
12-7 Pre-Algebra Basics, Skills 10, 20
12-9 Pre-Algebra Basics, Skills 4–5
12-10 Pre-Algebra Basics, Skill 6

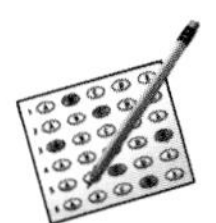

Standardized Test Preparation

The *Prentice Hall Mathematics* program integrates preparation for high-stakes standardized tests in every lesson of the Student Edition and continues this support in the Prentice Hall Assessment System.

Test Prep

In Student Text, Chapter 12

Teaches students strategies and gives them practice with all the test item formats they will encounter on high-stakes tests.

Test Prep exercises in each lesson (pp. 641, 647, 652, 657, 662, 667, 671, 677, 682, 686)

Test-Taking Strategies (p. 687: Work Backward)

Test Prep (pp. 691–693: Cumulative Review, Chapters 1–12)

PRENTICE HALL
ASSESSMENT SYSTEM

A three-step approach to preparing students for high stakes, national, and state exams.

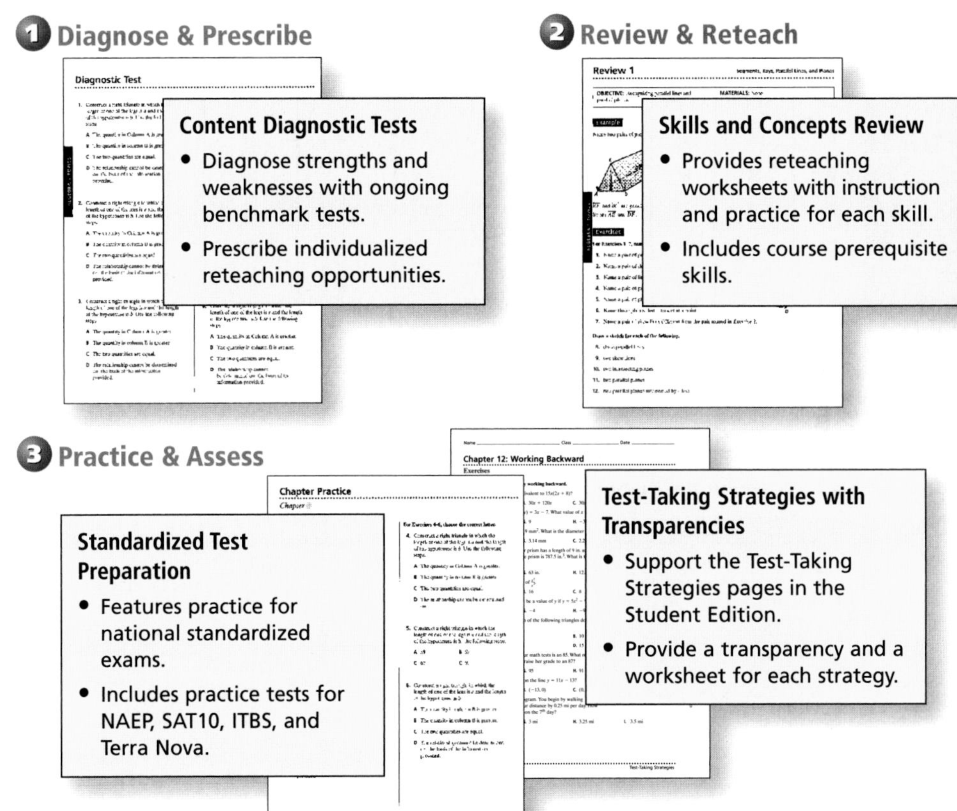
1 Diagnose & Prescribe
Content Diagnostic Tests
• Diagnose strengths and weaknesses with ongoing benchmark tests.
• Prescribe individualized reteaching opportunities.
2 Review & Reteach
Skills and Concepts Review
• Provides reteaching worksheets with instruction and practice for each skill.
• Includes course prerequisite skills.
3 Practice & Assess
Standardized Test Preparation
• Features practice for national standardized exams.
• Includes practice tests for NAEP, SAT10, ITBS, and Terra Nova.
Test-Taking Strategies with Transparencies
• Support the Test-Taking Strategies pages in the Student Edition.
• Provide a transparency and a worksheet for each strategy.

Correlation to Standardized Tests

Lesson		NAEP	CTBS/Terra CAT6	CTBS/Terra Nova	ITBS	SAT10	Local Test
12-1	Sequences	A1a, A1b, A1c	■	■	■	■	
12-2	Functions	A1c, A1d, A1f, A2g		■		■	
12-3	Graphing Linear Functions	A2a, A2b				■	
12-4	Writing Rules for Linear Functions	A1a, A1b, A1c, A2e, A3a		■		■	
12-5	Relating Graphs to Events	A2a					
12-6	Nonlinear Functions	A2g					
12-7	Write an Equation	A3a					
12-8	Exploring Polynomials	A3b					
12-9	Adding and Subtracting Polynomials	A3b					
12-10	Multiplying Polynomials	A3b					

NAEP National Assessment of Educational Progress
CAT6/Terra Nova California Achievement Test, 6th Ed.
CTBS/Terra Nova Comprehensive Test of Basic Skills
ITBS Iowa Test of Basic Skills, Form M.
SAT10 Stanford Achievement Test, 10th Ed.

Program Resources

	Resources in Grab & Go™ Files				Resources for Reaching All Students				Spanish Resources			Presentation Assistant Plus! Transparencies					Presentation Assistant Plus!
	Practice	Reteach	Enrich	Checkpt Quiz	Reading & Math Literacy	Technology Activities	Hands-On Activities	Guided Problem Solving	Practice	Reading & Math Literacy	Checkpt Quiz	Skills Check	Problem of the Day	Additional Examples	Answers to Exercises	Lesson Quiz	Prentice Hall Presentation Pro CD-ROM
12-1	■	■	■		■			■	■	■		■	■	■	■	■	■
12-2	■	■	■					■	■			■	■	■	■	■	■
12-3	■	■	■			■		■	■			■	■	■	■	■	■
12-4	■	■	■	■	■			■	■	■	■	■	■	■	■	■	■
12-5	■	■	■					■	■			■	■	■	■	■	■
12-6	■	■	■			■	■	■	■			■	■	■	■	■	■
12-7	■	■	■	■	■			■	■	■	■	■	■	■	■	■	■
12-8	■	■	■					■	■			■	■	■	■	■	■
12-9	■	■	■					■	■			■	■	■	■	■	■
12-10	■	■	■					■	■			■	■	■	■	■	■
For the Chapter	Chapter Projects, Chapter Tests, Alternative Assessment, Cumulative Review, Cumulative Assessment				**On web site only:** Home Activities, Interdisciplinary Activities, Algebra Readiness Puzzles				Spanish Chapter Tests, Alternative Assessment, Cumulative Review, Cumulative Assessment			Classroom Aid Transparencies					

Also available for use with the chapter:

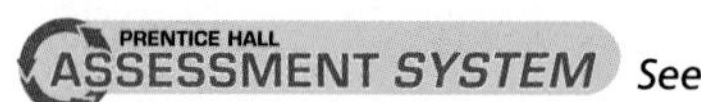

See page 634F.

- Practice Workbook
- Solution Key
- MathNotes folder

- For teacher support and access to student Web materials, use the Web Code abk-5500.
- For additional online and technology resources, see *below.*

Technology

Online and on CD-ROM

Complete Interactive Student Text online and on CD-ROM—with instant feedback assessment, tutorial help, dynamic activities, instructional and real-world videos, audio, and additional practice.

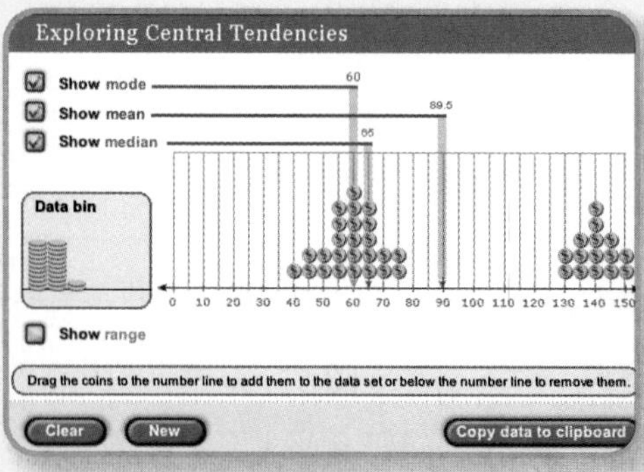

www.PHSchool.com For Students

Use Web codes for easy access to online activities, chapter projects, self-grading lesson quizzes, chapter tests, vocabulary quizzes, updated data sources, graphing calculator procedures, and more.

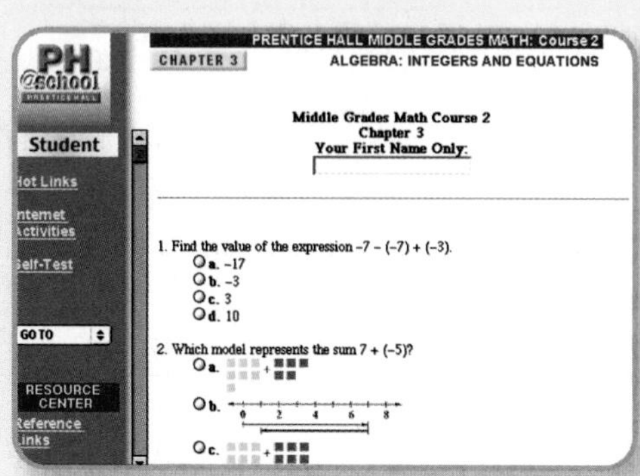

PH SuccessNet For Teachers

Online lesson planning with built-in state correlations, all the teaching resources, complete reference library, your own calendar and Teacher Web page, professional development, and more.

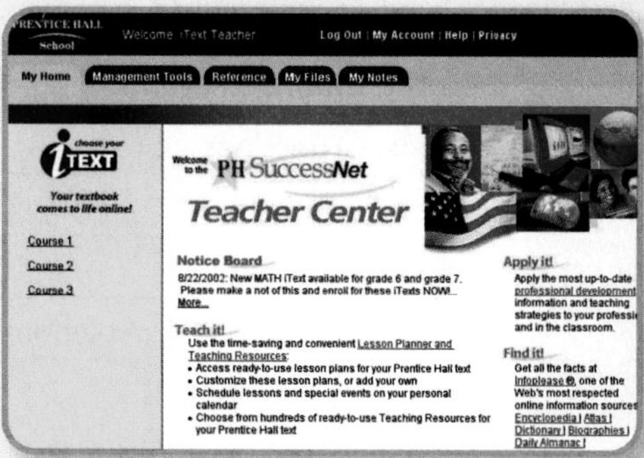

Presentation Assistant Plus!

The *Prentice Hall Presentation Assistant Plus!* provides you with the material you need to teach a lesson from beginning to end. Two easy-to-use formats—Transparencies and PowerPoint®—allow you to present a lesson the way you are most comfortable.

Transparencies

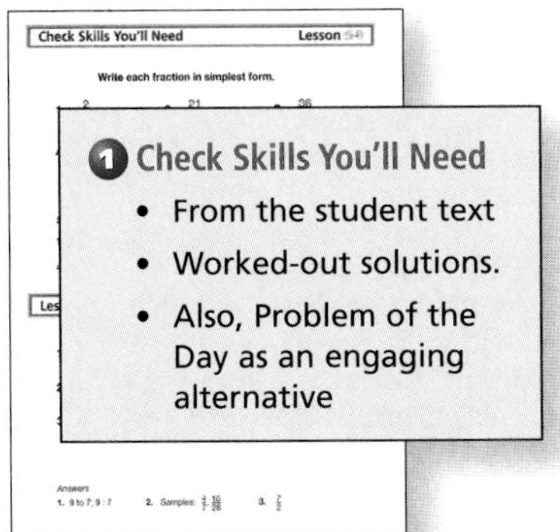

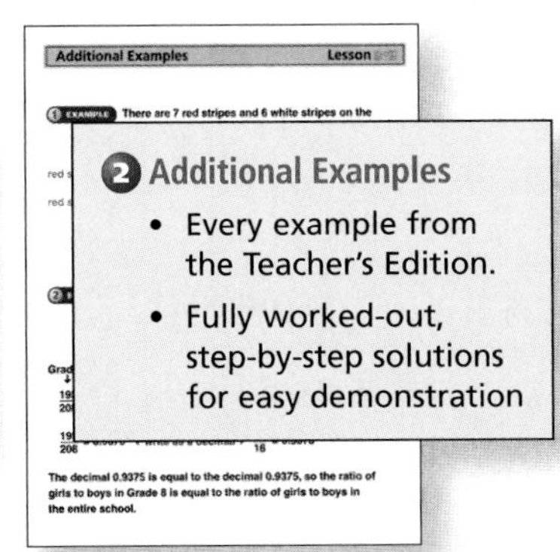

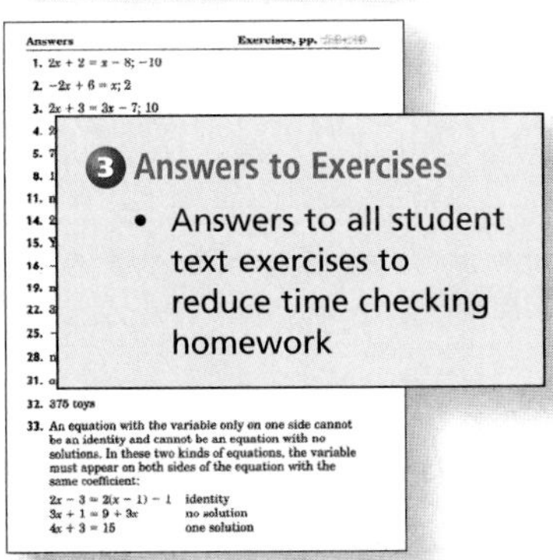

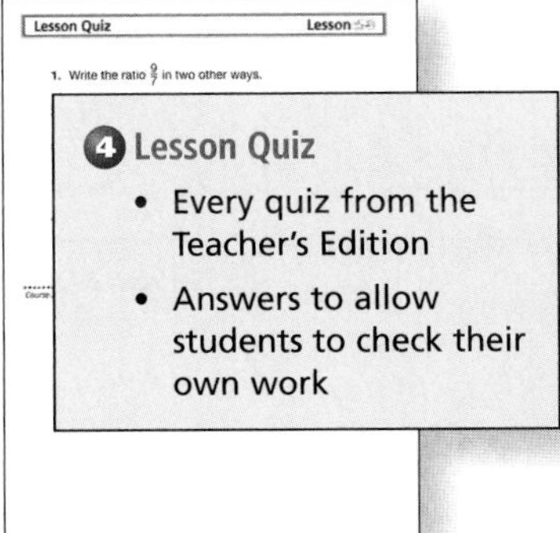

Throughout the Teacher's Edition, this symbol indicates material that is available in the Presentation Assistant Plus!

PowerPoint Prentice Hall Presentation Pro CD-ROM

- Includes all Transparencies.
- Conveniently organized by lesson so you can easily ❶ Introduce, ❷ Teach, ❸ Check Homework, and ❹ Assess each lesson.
- Animated examples allow step-by-step instruction at your own pace.
- Easy to edit so you can create custom presentations.

Teaching Chapter 12 Using Presentation Assistant Plus!

	❶ Introduce	❷ Teach	❸ Check Homework	❹ Assess
	Check Skills You'll Need	Additional Examples	Student Edition Answers	Lesson Quiz
12-1	p. 96	pp. 198–199	✔	p. 96
12-2	p. 97	p. 200	✔	p. 97
12-3	p. 98	pp. 201–202	✔	p. 99
12-4	p. 100	pp. 203–204	✔	p. 100
12-5	p. 101	p. 205	✔	p. 101
12-6	p. 102	pp. 206–208	✔	p. 102
12-7	p. 103	pp. 209–210	✔	p. 103
12-8	p. 104	p. 211	✔	p. 104
12-9	p. 105	pp. 212–213	✔	p. 105
12-10	p. 106	p. 214	✔	p. 106

Prentice Hall Presentation Pro

CD-ROM with dynamic PowerPoint® presentations for every lesson. Helps you introduce and develop concepts, check homework, and assess progress. Part of Presentation Assistant Plus! *(See above.)*

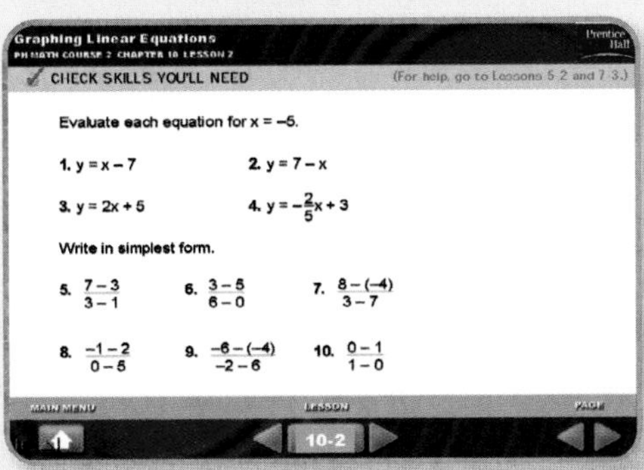

Computer Test Generator

CD-ROM to create practice sheets and tests for course objectives and standardized tests. Includes Instant Chapter Tests™, online testing, and student reports. Part of the PH Assessment System. *(See page 634F.)*

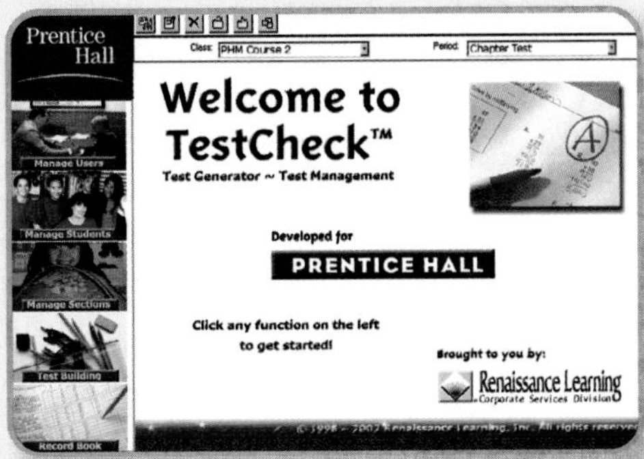

Resource Pro® with Planning Express®

CD-ROM with a lesson planning tool that allows you to import state and local objectives. Includes electronic versions of all the teaching resources.

Chapter Resources

Reading and Math Support

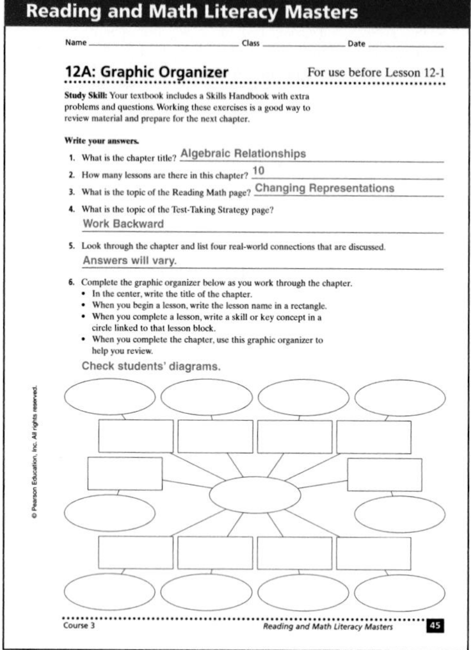

Reading and Math Literacy Masters

Name ____________ Class ____________ Date ____________

12A: Graphic Organizer
For use before Lesson 12-1

Study Skill: Your textbook includes a Skills Handbook with extra problems and questions. Working these exercises is a good way to review material and prepare for the next chapter.

Write your answers.

1. What is the chapter title? Algebraic Relationships
2. How many lessons are there in this chapter? 10
3. What is the topic of the Reading Math page? Changing Representations
4. What is the topic of the Test-Taking Strategy page? Work Backward
5. Look through the chapter and list four real-world connections that are discussed. Answers will vary.
6. Complete the graphic organizer below as you work through the chapter.
   - In the center, write the title of the chapter.
   - When you begin a lesson, write the lesson name in a rectangle.
   - When you complete a lesson, write a skill or key concept in a circle linked to that lesson block.
   - When you complete the chapter, use this graphic organizer to help you review.

Check students' diagrams.

Course 3 Reading and Math Literacy Masters 45

Available in Spanish

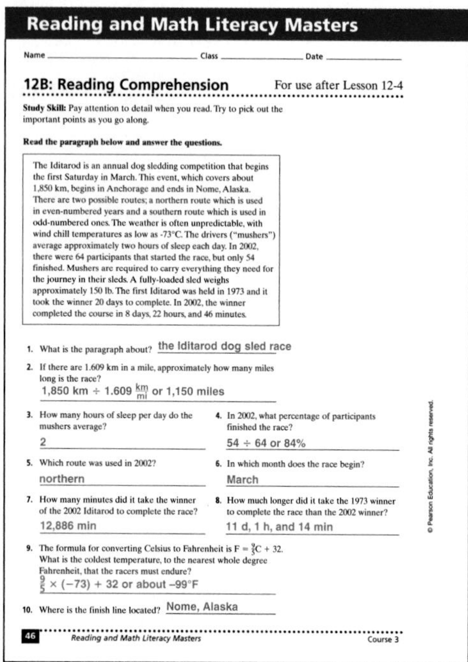

Reading and Math Literacy Masters

Name ____________ Class ____________ Date ____________

12B: Reading Comprehension
For use after Lesson 12-4

Study Skill: Pay attention to detail when you read. Try to pick out the important points as you go along.

Read the paragraph below and answer the questions.

The Iditarod is an annual dog sledding competition that begins the first Saturday in March. This event, which covers about 1,850 km, begins in Anchorage and ends in Nome, Alaska. There are two possible routes; a northern route which is used in even-numbered years and a southern route which is used in odd-numbered ones. The weather is often unpredictable, with wind chill temperatures as low as -73°C. The drivers ("mushers") average approximately two hours of sleep each day. In 2002, there were 64 participants that started the race, but only 54 finished. Mushers are required to carry everything they need for the journey in their sleds. A fully-loaded sled weighs approximately 150 lb. The first Iditarod was held in 1973 and it took the winner 20 days to complete. In 2002, the winner completed the course in 8 days, 22 hours, and 46 minutes.

1. What is the paragraph about? the Iditarod dog sled race
2. If there are 1.609 km in a mile, approximately how many miles long is the race? 1,850 km ÷ 1.609 $\frac{km}{mi}$ or 1,150 miles
3. How many hours of sleep per day do the mushers average? 2
4. In 2002, what percentage of participants finished the race? 54 ÷ 64 or 84%
5. Which route was used in 2002? northern
6. In which month does the race begin? March
7. How many minutes did it take the winner of the 2002 Iditarod to complete the race? 12,886 min
8. How much longer did it take the 1973 winner to complete the race than the 2002 winner? 11 d, 1 h, and 14 min
9. The formula for converting Celsius to Fahrenheit is $F = \frac{9}{5}C + 32$. What is the coldest temperature, to the nearest whole degree Fahrenheit, that the racers must endure? $\frac{9}{5} \times (-73) + 32$ or about −99°F
10. Where is the finish line located? Nome, Alaska

46 Reading and Math Literacy Masters Course 3

Available in Spanish

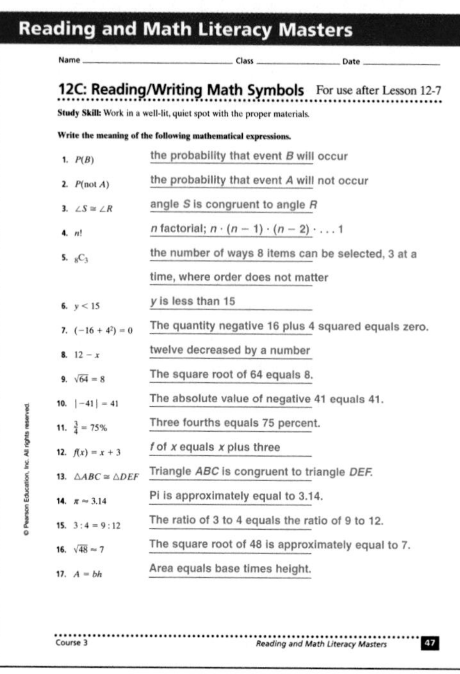

Reading and Math Literacy Masters

Name ____________ Class ____________ Date ____________

12C: Reading/Writing Math Symbols
For use after Lesson 12-7

Study Skill: Work in a well-lit, quiet spot with the proper materials.

Write the meaning of the following mathematical expressions.

1. $P(B)$ — the probability that event B will occur
2. $P(\text{not } A)$ — the probability that event A will not occur
3. $\angle S \cong \angle R$ — angle S is congruent to angle R
4. $n!$ — n factorial; $n \cdot (n-1) \cdot (n-2) \cdot \ldots 1$
5. ${}_8C_3$ — the number of ways 8 items can be selected, 3 at a time, where order does not matter
6. $y < 15$ — y is less than 15
7. $(-16 + 4^2) = 0$ — The quantity negative 16 plus 4 squared equals zero.
8. $12 - x$ — twelve decreased by a number
9. $\sqrt{64} = 8$ — The square root of 64 equals 8.
10. $|-41| = 41$ — The absolute value of negative 41 equals 41.
11. $\frac{3}{4} = 75\%$ — Three fourths equals 75 percent.
12. $f(x) = x + 3$ — f of x equals x plus three
13. $\triangle ABC \cong \triangle DEF$ — Triangle ABC is congruent to triangle DEF.
14. $\pi \approx 3.14$ — Pi is approximately equal to 3.14.
15. $3:4 = 9:12$ — The ratio of 3 to 4 equals the ratio of 9 to 12.
16. $\sqrt{48} \approx 7$ — The square root of 48 is approximately equal to 7.
17. $A = bh$ — Area equals base times height.

Course 3 Reading and Math Literacy Masters 47

Available in Spanish

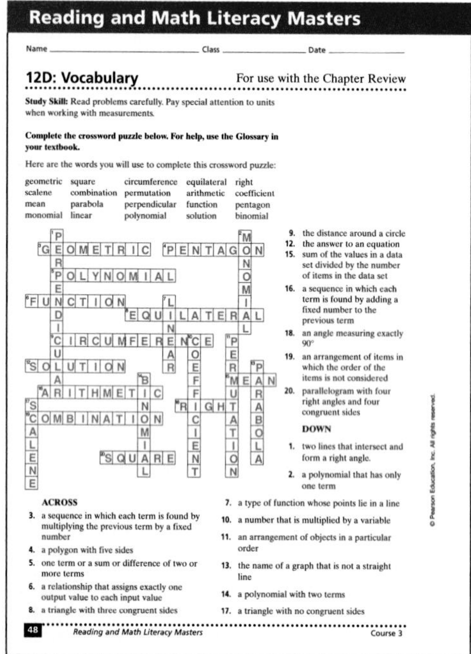

Reading and Math Literacy Masters

Name ____________ Class ____________ Date ____________

12D: Vocabulary
For use with the Chapter Review

Study Skill: Read problems carefully. Pay special attention to units when working with measurements.

Complete the crossword puzzle below. For help, use the Glossary in your textbook.

Here are the words you will use to complete this crossword puzzle:

geometric	square	circumference	equilateral	right
scalene	combination	permutation	arithmetic	coefficient
mean	parabola	perpendicular	function	pentagon
monomial	linear	polynomial	solution	binomial

ACROSS

3. a sequence in which each term is found by multiplying the previous term by a fixed number
4. a polygon with five sides
5. one term or a sum or difference of two or more terms
6. a relationship that assigns exactly one output value to each input value
8. a triangle with three congruent sides
9. the distance around a circle
12. the answer to an equation
15. sum of the values in a data set divided by the number of items in the data set
16. a sequence in which each term is found by adding a fixed number to the previous term
18. an angle measuring exactly 90°
19. an arrangement of items in which the order of the items is not considered
20. parallelogram with four right angles and four congruent sides

DOWN

1. two lines that intersect and form a right angle.
2. a polynomial that has only one term
7. a type of function whose points lie in a line
10. a number that is multiplied by a variable
11. an arrangement of objects in a particular order
13. the name of a graph that is not a straight line
14. a polynomial with two terms
17. a triangle with no congruent sides

48 Reading and Math Literacy Masters Course 3

Available in Spanish

Problem Solving

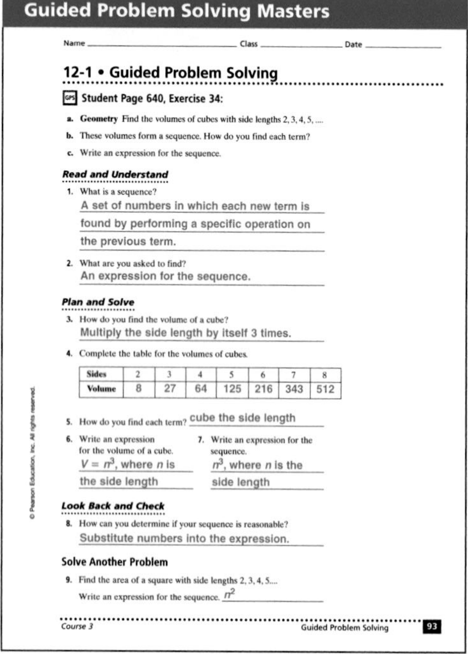

Guided Problem Solving Masters

Name ____________ Class ____________ Date ____________

12-1 • Guided Problem Solving

Student Page 640, Exercise 34:

a. **Geometry** Find the volumes of cubes with side lengths 2, 3, 4, 5, ...
b. These volumes form a sequence. How do you find each term?
c. Write an expression for the sequence.

Read and Understand

1. What is a sequence? A set of numbers in which each new term is found by performing a specific operation on the previous term.
2. What are you asked to find? An expression for the sequence.

Plan and Solve

3. How do you find the volume of a cube? Multiply the side length by itself 3 times.
4. Complete the table for the volumes of cubes.

Sides	2	3	4	5	6	7	8
Volume	8	27	64	125	216	343	512

5. How do you find each term? cube the side length
6. Write an expression for the volume of a cube. $V = n^3$, where n is the side length
7. Write an expression for the sequence. n^3, where n is the side length

Look Back and Check

8. How can you determine if your sequence is reasonable? Substitute numbers into the expression.

Solve Another Problem

9. Find the area of a square with side lengths 2, 3, 4, 5.... Write an expression for the sequence. n^2

Course 3 Guided Problem Solving 93

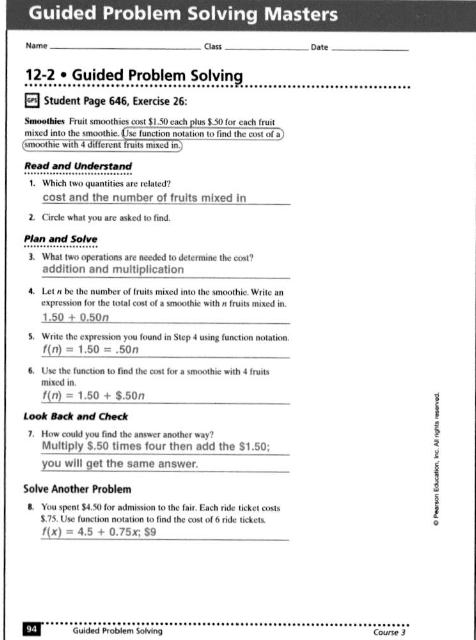

Guided Problem Solving Masters

Name ____________ Class ____________ Date ____________

12-2 • Guided Problem Solving

Student Page 646, Exercise 26:

Smoothies Fruit smoothies cost $1.50 each plus $.50 for each fruit mixed into the smoothie. Use function notation to find the cost of a smoothie with 4 different fruits mixed in.

Read and Understand

1. Which two quantities are related? cost and the number of fruits mixed in
2. Circle what you are asked to find.

Plan and Solve

3. What two operations are needed to determine the cost? addition and multiplication
4. Let n be the number of fruits mixed into the smoothie. Write an expression for the total cost of a smoothie with n fruits mixed in. $1.50 + 0.50n$
5. Write the expression you found in Step 4 using function notation. $f(n) = 1.50 = .50n$
6. Use the function to find the cost for a smoothie with 4 fruits mixed in. $f(n) = 1.50 + \$.50n$

Look Back and Check

7. How could you find the answer another way? Multiply $.50 times four then add the $1.50; you will get the same answer.

Solve Another Problem

8. You spent $4.50 for admission to the fair. Each ride ticket costs $.75. Use function notation to find the cost of 6 ride tickets. $f(x) = 4.5 + 0.75x$; $9

94 Guided Problem Solving Course 3

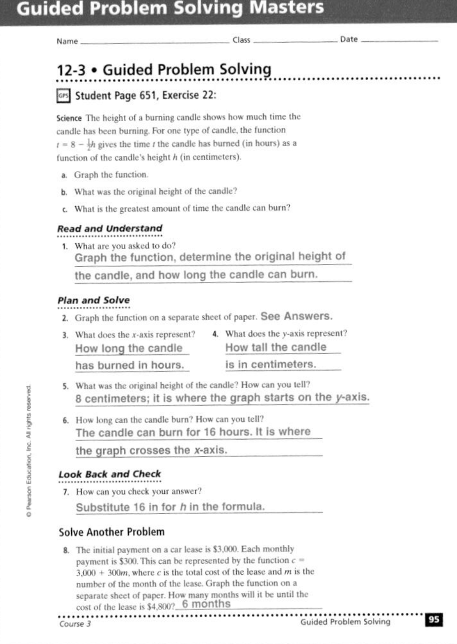

Guided Problem Solving Masters

Name ______ Class ______ Date ______

12-3 • Guided Problem Solving

GPS Student Page 651, Exercise 22:

Science The height of a burning candle shows how much time the candle has been burning. For one type of candle, the function $t = 8 - \frac{1}{2}h$ gives the time t the candle has burned (in hours) as a function of the candle's height h (in centimeters).

a. Graph the function.

b. What was the original height of the candle?

c. What is the greatest amount of time the candle can burn?

Read and Understand

1. What are you asked to do? Graph the function, determine the original height of the candle, and how long the candle can burn.

Plan and Solve

2. Graph the function on a separate sheet of paper. See Answers.
3. What does the x-axis represent? How long the candle has burned in hours.
4. What does the y-axis represent? How tall the candle is in centimeters.
5. What was the original height of the candle? How can you tell? 8 centimeters; it is where the graph starts on the y-axis.
6. How long can the candle burn? How can you tell? The candle can burn for 16 hours. It is where the graph crosses the x-axis.

Look Back and Check

7. How can you check your answer? Substitute 16 in for h in the formula.

Solve Another Problem

8. The initial payment on a car lease is $3,000. Each monthly payment is $300. This can be represented by the function $c = 3{,}000 + 300m$, where c is the total cost of the lease and m is the number of the month of the lease. Graph the function on a separate sheet of paper. How many months will it be until the cost of the lease is $4,800? 6 months

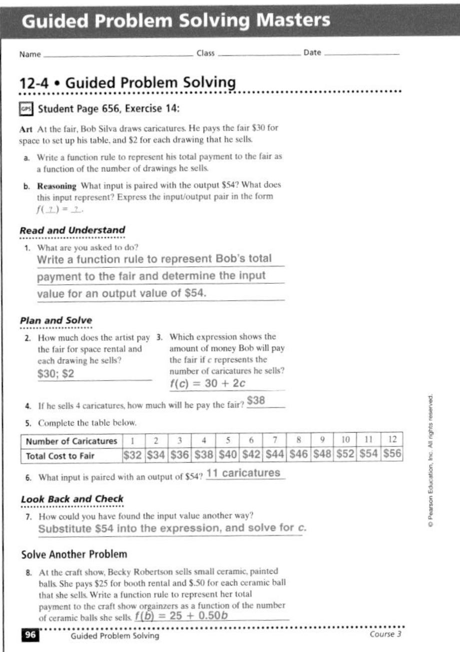

Guided Problem Solving Masters

Name ______ Class ______ Date ______

12-4 • Guided Problem Solving

GPS Student Page 656, Exercise 14:

Art At the fair, Bob Silva draws caricatures. He pays the fair $30 for space to set up his table, and $2 for each drawing that he sells.

a. Write a function rule to represent his total payment to the fair as a function of the number of drawings he sells.

b. **Reasoning** What input is paired with the output $54? What does this input represent? Express the input/output pair in the form $f(\underline{?}) = \underline{?}$.

Read and Understand

1. What are you asked to do? Write a function rule to represent Bob's total payment to the fair and determine the input value for an output value of $54.

Plan and Solve

2. How much does the artist pay the fair for space rental and each drawing he sells? $30; $2
3. Which expression shows the amount of money Bob will pay the fair if c represents the number of caricatures he sells? $f(c) = 30 + 2c$
4. If he sells 4 caricatures, how much will he pay the fair? $38
5. Complete the table below.

Number of Caricatures	1	2	3	4	5	6	7	8	9	10	11	12
Total Cost to Fair	$32	$34	$36	$38	$40	$42	$44	$46	$48	$52	$54	$56

6. What input is paired with an output of $54? 11 caricatures

Look Back and Check

7. How could you have found the input value another way? Substitute $54 into the expression, and solve for c.

Solve Another Problem

8. At the craft show, Becky Robertson sells small ceramic, painted balls. She pays $25 for booth rental and $.50 for each ceramic ball that she sells. Write a function rule to represent her total payment to the craft show orgainzers as a function of the number of ceramic balls she sells. $f(b) = 25 + 0.50b$

Guided Problem Solving Masters

Name ______ Class ______ Date ______

12-5 • Guided Problem Solving

GPS Student Page 660, Exercise 11:

Geometry As the length of the side of a square increases, its area increases. Sketch a graph that shows the area of the square as the side length changes.

Read and Understand

1. Is the length of a side of the square directly or inversely proportional to the area of the square? Explain. Directly; as the length of the side increases, the area increases.
2. What are you being asked to do? Sketch a graph that shows the area of the square as the side length changes.

Plan and Solve

3. What do you know about the lengths of the sides of a square? They are all the same length.
4. What is the formula for the area of a square in terms of one side length? $A = s^2$
5. Complete the chart.

Side length	1	2	3	4	5
Area	1	4	9	16	25

6. Draw a graph with the x-axis labeled "side lengths" and the y-axis labeled "area". Plot each of the values from Step 5, and draw a line connecting the points.

Look Back and Check

7. Another way to find the area of a square is to multiply the length times the width. Are your calculations correct? yes

Solve Another Problem

8. As the length of one side of a square increases by one, its perimeter increases by four. Draw a sketch that shows the perimeter of a square as its side length increases in increments of one. See Answers.

Guided Problem Solving Masters

Name ______ Class ______ Date ______

12-6 • Guided Problem Solving

GPS Student Page 666, Exercise 25:

Gardening Suppose you have 12 yards of fencing to enclose a garden plot like the one shown at the right. Complete the table below to show area as a function of the garden's width. Then graph the function.

Width x

Length

Read and Understand

1. What is the most the perimeter of the garden can be? 12 yards
2. What two things are you being asked to do? Complete the table and graph the function.

Plan and Solve

3. Fill in the lengths of the garden in the table keeping in mind that the total perimeter should equal the total amount of fencing that you have.

Width	Length	Area
1	5	5
2	4	8
3	3	9
4	2	8
5	1	5

4. Now go back to the table in Step 3 and find the area of each, by using the formula $A = lw$.
5. On a separate sheet of paper, graph the function using the widths for the x-values and the areas for the y-values.

Look Back and Check

6. Is your graph reasonable? Using a width of 3.5 yards, what is the area? Does this data fall on the curve? Yes, the point (3.5, 8.75) is on the curve.

Solve Another Problem

7. You are building a rectangular patio and would like to outline the perimeter in brick. If the bricks you have total 40 feet in length, what is the area for the following widths: 6 ft, 8 ft, 10 ft, 12 ft, and 14 ft? 6 ft: 84ft^2; 8 ft: 96 ft^2; 10 ft: 100 ft^2; 12ft: 96 ft^2; 14 ft: 84 ft^2

Guided Problem Solving Masters

Name ______ Class ______ Date ______

12-7 • Guided Problem Solving

GPS Student Page 670, Exercise 6:

Cars The value of a new car decreases as time passes. Suppose your family bought a car for $28,000. The value of the car decreases 20% each year. So each year the value of the car is 80% of the previous year's value. The function is an example of an *exponential* function rule that relates the value of the car to the years that have passed. Use the rule to find the value of the car after 10 years.

Read and Understand

1. What is the initial value of the car? $28,000
2. Each year the value of the car is what percentage of the previous year? 80%
3. Underline what you are asked to find.

Plan and Solve

4. Fill in the table to find the value of the car after the first 2 years.

Years Passed	Value of the car	Pattern
0	\$28,000	\$28,000 = 0.8^0
1	\$28,000 × 0.8 = \$22,400	\$22,400 = \$28,000 × 0.8^1
2	\$28,000 × 0.8 × 0.8 = \$17,920	17,920 = \$28,000 × 0.8^2

5. Based on the chart in Step 4, write an equation that shows the relationship between the number of years that pass and the value of the car. $\$28{,}000 \times 0.8^x$, where x = the number of years.
6. Solve the equation for 10 years (to the nearest cent). $3,006.48

Look Back and Check

7. Check the function rule by solving the rule for the depreciation of the car after five years. Then continue the next two lines of the table in Step 4 to see if the rule is correct. See Answers.

Solve Another Problem

8. An antique Roadster seems to appreciate about 4% in value each year. Your uncle buys a 1932 model for $12,000. What will the car be valued at 8 years after his purchase? Round to the nearest dollar. $16,423

Guided Problem Solving Masters

Name ______ Class ______ Date ______

12-8 • Guided Problem Solving

GPS Student Page 676, Exercise 16:

Science A ball is thrown at a speed of 48 feet per second. Its height in feet, after t seconds, is given by the polynomial $48t - 16t^2$. Evaluate the polynomial to find the height after 3 s.

Read and Understand

1. Circle the polynomial that you are to evaluate.
2. What are you asked to evaluate the polynomial for? the height after 3 seconds

Plan and Solve

3. Rewrite the polynomial substituting the given height for t. $48(3) - 16(3)^2$
4. What operation will you do first? Evaluate the power.
5. Write the expression performing the operation in Step 4. $48(3) - 16(9)$
6. Which operation will you do next? multiply
7. Perform the operations in Step 7 to find your answer. $144 - 144 = 0$

Look Back and Check

8. Is your answer reasonable? How far has the ball traveled before it hits the ground? 144 ft

Solve Another Problem

9. A quarterback throws a football 64 ft per second. Could this pass be caught in the air after 4 seconds? No, because $64(4) - 16(4)^2 = 0$.

Activities and Projects

Guided Problem Solving Masters

Name ____________ Class ________ Date ________

12-9 • Guided Problem Solving

GPS **Student Page 681, Exercise 31:**

Pools The area of a large rectangular deck is $12x^2 + 4x$. A rectangular pool is part of the deck and has an area of $6x^2 - 12x$. Subtract the polynomials to find the area of the deck around the pool.

Read and Understand

1. Circle the information you need to solve the problem.
2. Underline what you are asked to do.

Plan and Solve

3. What is the area of the deck? $12x^2 + 4x$
4. What is the area of the pool? $6x^2 - 12x$
5. What do you need to remember when subtracting polynomials? Add the opposite of each term in the second polynomial.
6. Write the two expressions, using the subtraction sign. $12x^2 + 4x - (6x^2 - 12x)$
7. Add the opposite of each term in the second polynomial. $12x^2 + 4x - 6x^2 + 12x$
8. Group like terms. $12x^2 - 6x^2 + 4x + 12x$
9. Simplify. $6x^2 + 16x$

Look Back and Check

10. How can you check to see if your answer is reasonable? Sample answer: Substitute numbers in each expression, simplify, and subtract to see if you get the same answer as the simplified form.

Solve Another Problem

11. The area of a large rectangular barn is $16x^2 + 6x$. A rectangular workshop is part of the barn and has an area of $4x^2 - 5x$. Subtract the polynomials to find the area of the barn floor remaining. $16x^2 + 6x - (4x^2 - 5x) = 12x^2 + 11x$

Course 3 Guided Problem Solving 101

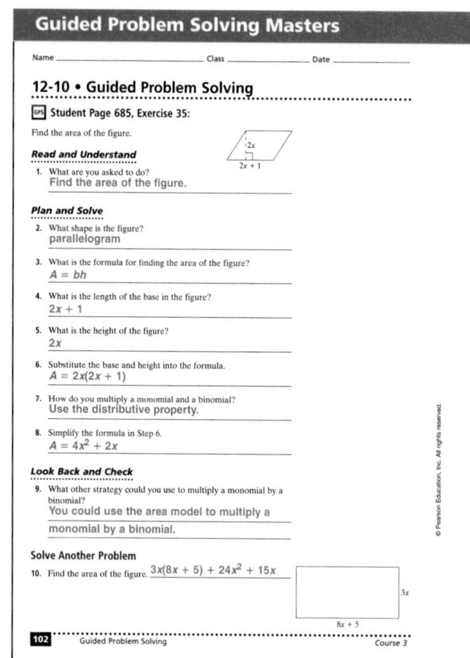

Guided Problem Solving Masters

Name ____________ Class ________ Date ________

12-10 • Guided Problem Solving

GPS **Student Page 685, Exercise 35:**

Find the area of the figure.

Read and Understand

1. What are you asked to do? Find the area of the figure.

Plan and Solve

2. What shape is the figure? parallelogram
3. What is the formula for finding the area of the figure? $A = bh$
4. What is the length of the base in the figure? $2x + 1$
5. What is the height of the figure? $2x$
6. Substitute the base and height into the formula. $A = 2x(2x + 1)$
7. How do you multiply a monomial and a binomial? Use the distributive property.
8. Simplify the formula in Step 6. $A = 4x^2 + 2x$

Look Back and Check

9. What other strategy could you use to multiply a monomial by a binomial? You could use the area model to multiply a monomial by a binomial.

Solve Another Problem

10. Find the area of the figure. $3x(8x + 5) + 24x^2 + 15x$

102 Guided Problem Solving Course 3

Hands-On Activities

Name ____________ Class ________ Date ________

Activity 49: Exponential Decay Curves

Materials needed: number cubes (60 per group)

Work in groups of 5–6 students.

1. a. Copy the table below. You will need only one table per group.

Roll Number	0	1	2	3	4	5	6	7	8	9	10
Number of Dice	60										

   b. Divide the number cubes among the members of your group. Roll all 60 number cubes. Remove any cubes showing a 5 or 6, and set them aside.
   c. Count the number of cubes remaining. Record the number in your group's table, in the Roll Number column labeled "1".
   d. What fraction of the number cubes did you remove?
2. a. Gather up the remaining number cubes. Roll the remaining cubes. Remove any cubes showing a 5 or 6 and set them aside.
   b. Repeat until there is only 1 cube left or you have completed 10 rounds. Record the number of cubes at the end of each roll in the appropriate column of your group's table.
3. Use a graph like the one shown at the right to plot the results of your rolls. The x-axis represents the number of the roll and the y-axis represents the number of dice remaining after each roll. After you have plotted all the information, connect the points. Be sure to label the axes and title the graph.

Dice Remaining: 0, 10, 20, 30, 40, 50, 60
Number of the Roll: 1, 2, 3, 4, 5, 6, 7, 8, 9, 10

4. Compare your group's graph with other groups' graphs in your class. Do all the graphs have a similar shape? Are the graphs linear?
5. Now, as a class, use the results from all the groups to calculate the average of the number of cubes remaining after each roll. Create a new table of the averages and draw a graph like the one you created as a group. Does this graph have a similar shape to the one your group drew?
6. *Optional:* Use a graphing calculator to graph the function, $y = 60\left(\frac{1}{3}\right)^x$. Explain why this graph looks similar to the ones your class created.

Courses 1–3 Hands-On Activities Activity 49 49

Technology Activities

Name ____________ Class ________ Date ________

Graphing Linear Functions — Activity 51

Use your graphing calculator to do this activity.

Example: Graph $y = 2x + 1$.

① Press 2nd [PLOT] **4↓PlotsOff** ENTER to turn off any statistical plots that may have previously been turned on.

② Press Y=. If there are any equations present, delete them by pressing CLEAR.

③ Next to \Y1 =, enter 2 X + 1 and press ENTER.

④ Press 2nd [TABLE]. In the screen you will see a table of x- and y- values for the function, $y = 2x + 1$. (*Note:* You may need to press 2nd [TBLSET] and enter 0 for **TblStart** and 1 for **ΔTbl**.)

⑤ Use your arrow keys to scroll up or down the table of values until you find the value 0 for x. The table indicates that when x has value 0, y has value 1. So, (0, 1) is the y-intercept.

⑥ Scroll up or down to pick another ordered pair on the line. For example, (1, 3). Now that you have the y-intercept (0, 1) and another point on the line (1, 3) you can draw the graph of the function.

⑦ To check that the graph you constructed is correct, press ZOOM **6:Standard**. Does the graph on the screen look like yours? Press TRACE and use the arrow keys to move left and right to check the y-intercept. Press ZOOM **2:Zoom In** to see the intercepts more clearly.

Exercises

Graph each linear function. Label the y-intercept and one other point on the graph.

1. $y = 3x + 4$
2. $y = -2x + 2$
3. $y = -x - 2$

Technology Activities Activity 51 57

Technology Activities

Name ____________ Class ________ Date ________

Graphing Nonlinear Functions — Activity 52

Use your graphing calculator to do this activity.

Example: Graph $y = x^2 = 3$.

① Press 2nd [PLOT] **4↓PlotsOff** ENTER to turn off any statistical plots that may have previously been turned on.

② Press Y=. If there are any equations present, delete them by pressing CLEAR.

③ Next to **\Y1=**, enter X x^2 − 3 and press ENTER.

④ Press ZOOM **6:Standard** to look at the graph of the function. You can see that the graph is a parabola that opens upward.

⑤ Press 2nd [TABLE]. In the screen you see a table of x- and y-values for the function, $y = x^2 - 3$. (*Note:* You may need to press 2nd [TBLSET] and enter 0 for **TblStart** and 1 for **ΔTbl**.)

⑥ Use the arrow keys to scroll up or down the table until you find the least value of y.

Since the parabola opens upward, the least value of y is at the vertex, or minimum point of the parabola. You will find that the least value of y is −3, which occurs when the value of x is 0, so the point (0, −3) is the minimum point of the parabola.

⑦ Scroll up or down to choose two other points on the graph, for example, (3, 6) and (−3, 6). Use these points along with (0, −3) to draw your graph

⑧ To check that the graph you constructed is correct, press ZOOM **6:Standard** again. Does the graph on the screen look like yours? Press TRACE and scroll left and right to see if the coordinates you graphed are on the graph in the calculator window.

Exercises

Graph each linear function. Label the minimum or maximum point on the graph, and two other points.

1. $y = 2x^2 + 1$
2. $y = -x^2 + 4$
3. $y = \frac{1}{2}x^2 - 3$

58 Activity 52 Technology Activities

Chapter Project

Name ____________ Class ________ Date ________

Chapter 12 Project: How Much Dough?

Set Prices for a Product

Beginning the Chapter Project

How much should a pizza cost? Many merchants sell pizzas in a variety of sizes and styles, with many kinds of toppings, so there are many different prices. Do merchants base prices on what they feel customers will pay? Or do they take a mathematical approach and figure costs using area formulas?

In this chapter project, you will investigate pizza prices for a pizza that is available in many sizes. You will look for patterns in the prices and describe the patterns mathematically.

Activities

Activity 1: Collecting Check students' work.

Find prices from a store or restaurant that has at least three sizes of pizza. Record the price of each pizza and the diameter of each different pizza size.

Activity 2: Calculating

Use the data you gathered in Activity 1. Display the sizes and prices of each group of items in a table. Then calculate the area of each different size of pizza. Display your results in a graph.

Activity 3: Analyzing

Using the graph from Activity 2, decide if the graph appears to be linear or nonlinear. Try to write a function rule that models the relationship thatyou see in the graph.

Activity 4: Modeling

Create an alternative pricing scheme. Make a poster showing a menu of prices from the store you used in Activity 1. Then add your own prices. Show a graph that compares both pricing schemes and provide an explanation for why you picked your prices.

32 Project *Course 3* Chapter 12

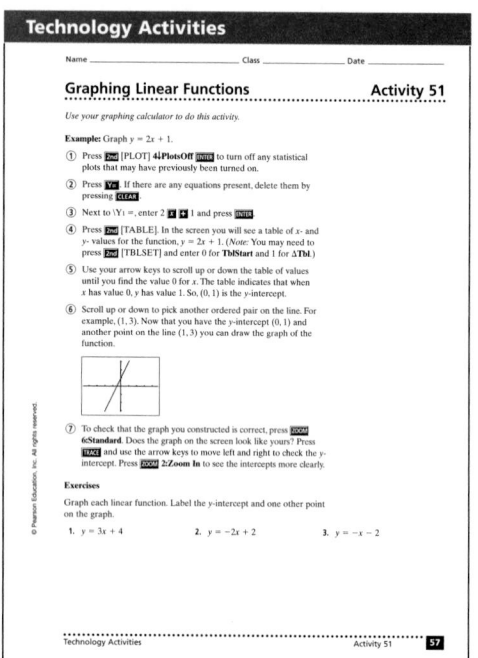

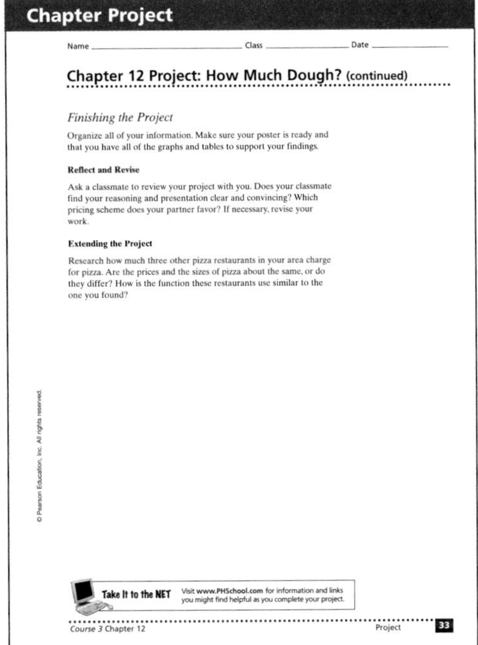

Chapter Project

Name ______________ Class ______________ Date ______________

Chapter 12 Project: How Much Dough? (continued)

Finishing the Project

Organize all of your information. Make sure your poster is ready and that you have all of the graphs and tables to support your findings.

Reflect and Revise

Ask a classmate to review your project with you. Does your classmate find your reasoning and presentation clear and convincing? Which pricing scheme does your partner favor? If necessary, revise your work.

Extending the Project

Research how much three other pizza restaurants in your area charge for pizza. Are the prices and the sizes of pizza about the same, or do they differ? How is the function these restaurants use similar to the one you found?

Take It to the NET Visit www.PHSchool.com for information and links you might find helpful as you complete your project.

Course 3 Chapter 12 Project 33

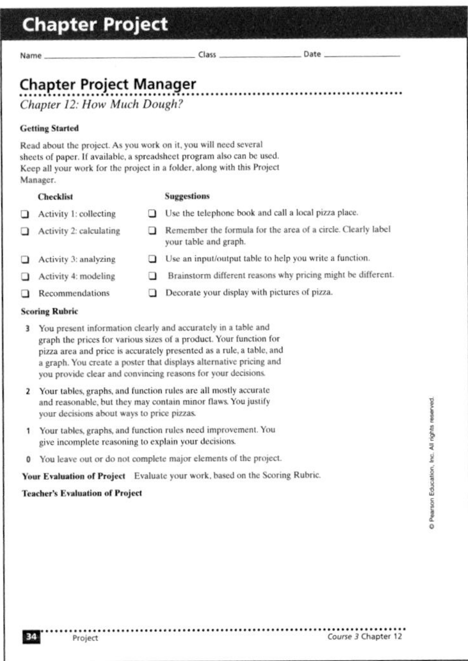

Chapter Project

Name ______________ Class ______________ Date ______________

Chapter Project Manager

Chapter 12: How Much Dough?

Getting Started

Read about the project. As you work on it, you will need several sheets of paper. If available, a spreadsheet program also can be used. Keep all your work for the project in a folder, along with this Project Manager.

Checklist	Suggestions
❑ Activity 1: collecting	❑ Use the telephone book and call a local pizza place.
❑ Activity 2: calculating	❑ Remember the formula for the area of a circle. Clearly label your table and graph.
❑ Activity 3: analyzing	❑ Use an input/output table to help you write a function.
❑ Activity 4: modeling	❑ Brainstorm different reasons why pricing might be different.
❑ Recommendations	❑ Decorate your display with pictures of pizza.

Scoring Rubric

3 You present information clearly and accurately in a table and graph the prices for various sizes of a product. Your function for pizza area and price is accurately presented as a rule, a table, and a graph. You create a poster that displays alternative pricing and you provide clear and convincing reasons for your decisions.

2 Your tables, graphs, and function rules are all mostly accurate and reasonable, but they may contain minor flaws. You justify your decisions about ways to price pizzas.

1 Your tables, graphs, and function rules need improvement. You give incomplete reasoning to explain your decisions.

0 You leave out or do not complete major elements of the project.

Your Evaluation of Project Evaluate your work, based on the Scoring Rubric.

Teacher's Evaluation of Project

34 Project Course 3 Chapter 12

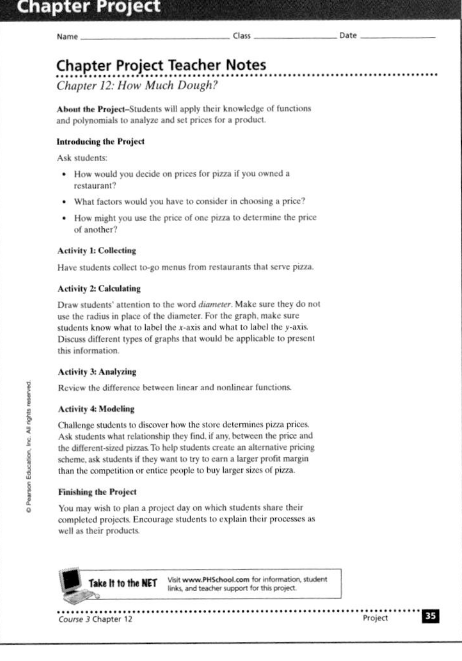

Chapter Project

Name ______________ Class ______________ Date ______________

Chapter Project Teacher Notes

Chapter 12: How Much Dough?

About the Project–Students will apply their knowledge of functions and polynomials to analyze and set prices for a product.

Introducing the Project

Ask students:

- How would you decide on prices for pizza if you owned a restaurant?
- What factors would you have to consider in choosing a price?
- How might you use the price of one pizza to determine the price of another?

Activity 1: Collecting

Have students collect to-go menus from restaurants that serve pizza.

Activity 2: Calculating

Draw students' attention to the word *diameter*. Make sure they do not use the radius in place of the diameter. For the graph, make sure students know what to label the x-axis and what to label the y-axis. Discuss different types of graphs that would be applicable to present this information.

Activity 3: Analyzing

Review the difference between linear and nonlinear functions.

Activity 4: Modeling

Challenge students to discover how the store determines pizza prices. Ask students what relationship they find, if any, between the price and the different-sized pizzas. To help students create an alternative pricing scheme, ask students if they want to try to earn a larger profit margin than the competition or entice people to buy larger sizes of pizza.

Finishing the Project

You may wish to plan a project day on which students share their completed projects. Encourage students to explain their processes as well as their products.

Take It to the NET Visit www.PHSchool.com for information, student links, and teacher support for this project.

Course 3 Chapter 12 Project 35

Transparencies

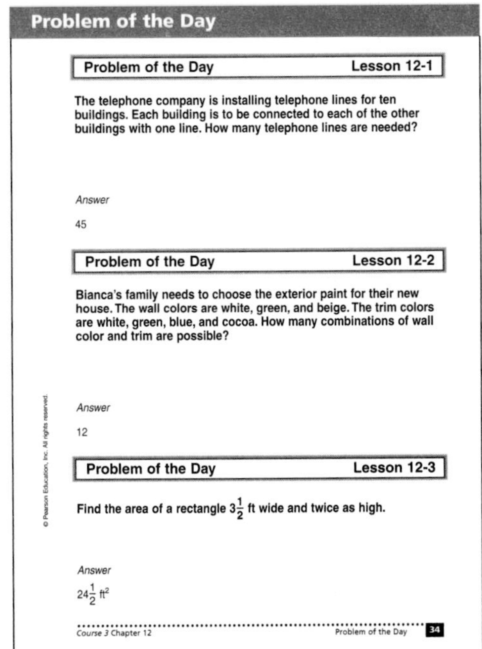

Problem of the Day

Problem of the Day — Lesson 12-1

The telephone company is installing telephone lines for ten buildings. Each building is to be connected to each of the other buildings with one line. How many telephone lines are needed?

Answer

45

Problem of the Day — Lesson 12-2

Bianca's family needs to choose the exterior paint for their new house. The wall colors are white, green, and beige. The trim colors are white, green, blue, and cocoa. How many combinations of wall color and trim are possible?

Answer

12

Problem of the Day — Lesson 12-3

Find the area of a rectangle $3\frac{1}{2}$ ft wide and twice as high.

Answer

$24\frac{1}{2}$ ft^2

Course 3 Chapter 12 Problem of the Day 34

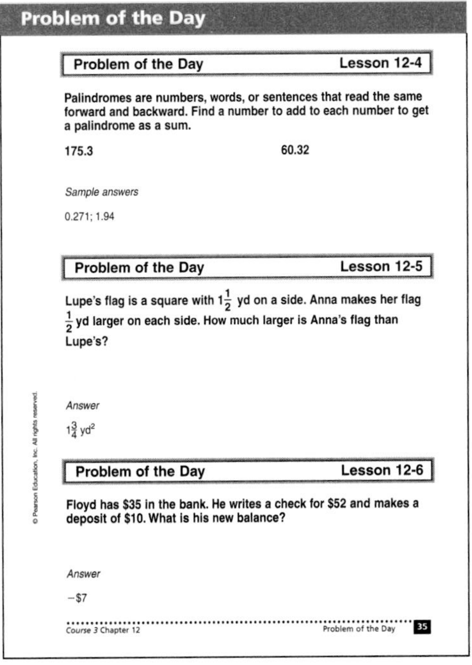

Problem of the Day

Problem of the Day — Lesson 12-4

Palindromes are numbers, words, or sentences that read the same forward and backward. Find a number to add to each number to get a palindrome as a sum.

175.3 60.32

Sample answers

0.271; 1.94

Problem of the Day — Lesson 12-5

Lupe's flag is a square with $1\frac{1}{2}$ yd on a side. Anna makes her flag $\frac{1}{2}$ yd larger on each side. How much larger is Anna's flag than Lupe's?

Answer

$1\frac{3}{4}$ yd^2

Problem of the Day — Lesson 12-6

Floyd has $35 in the bank. He writes a check for $52 and makes a deposit of $10. What is his new balance?

Answer

−$7

Course 3 Chapter 12 Problem of the Day 35

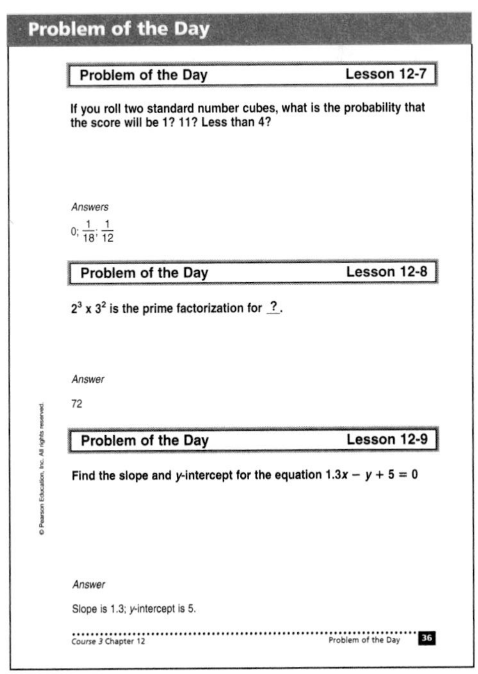

Problem of the Day

Problem of the Day — Lesson 12-7

If you roll two standard number cubes, what is the probability that the score will be 1? 11? Less than 4?

Answers

0; $\frac{1}{18}$; $\frac{1}{12}$

Problem of the Day — Lesson 12-8

$2^3 \times 3^2$ is the prime factorization for __?__.

Answer

72

Problem of the Day — Lesson 12-9

Find the slope and y-intercept for the equation $1.3x - y + 5 = 0$

Answer

Slope is 1.3; y-intercept is 5.

Course 3 Chapter 12 Problem of the Day 36

Problem of the Day

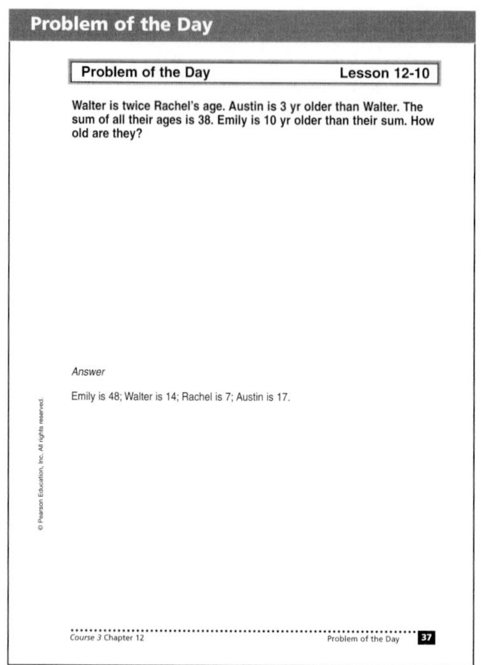

Problem of the Day — **Lesson 12-10**

Walter is twice Rachel's age. Austin is 3 yr older than Walter. The sum of all their ages is 38. Emily is 10 yr older than their sum. How old are they?

Answer

Emily is 48; Walter is 14; Rachel is 7; Austin is 17.

Check Skills You'll Need

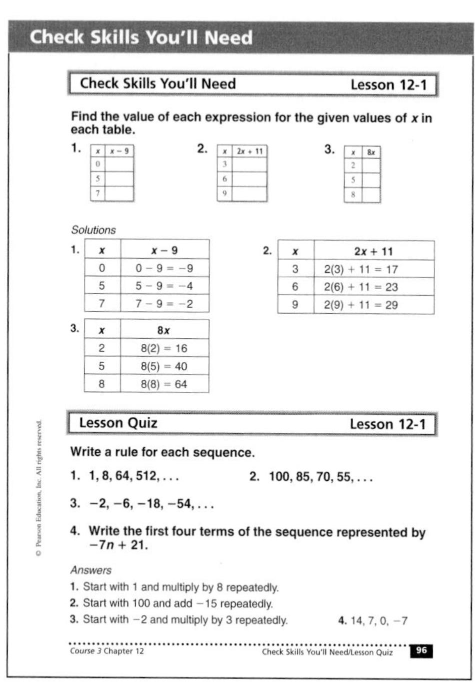

Check Skills You'll Need — **Lesson 12-1**

Find the value of each expression for the given values of x in each table.

1.

x	$x - 9$
0	
5	
7	

2.

x	$2x + 11$
3	
6	
9	

3.

x	$8x$
2	
5	
8	

Solutions

1.

x	$x - 9$
0	$0 - 9 = -9$
5	$5 - 9 = -4$
7	$7 - 9 = -2$

2.

x	$2x + 11$
3	$2(3) + 11 = 17$
6	$2(6) + 11 = 23$
9	$2(9) + 11 = 29$

3.

x	$8x$
2	$8(2) = 16$
5	$8(5) = 40$
8	$8(8) = 64$

Lesson Quiz — **Lesson 12-1**

Write a rule for each sequence.

1. 1, 8, 64, 512, . . .
2. 100, 85, 70, 55, . . .
3. −2, −6, −18, −54, . . .
4. Write the first four terms of the sequence represented by $-7n + 21$.

Answers

1. Start with 1 and multiply by 8 repeatedly.
2. Start with 100 and add −15 repeatedly.
3. Start with −2 and multiply by 3 repeatedly.
4. 14, 7, 0, −7

Sample page; see p. H for complete list.

Additional Examples

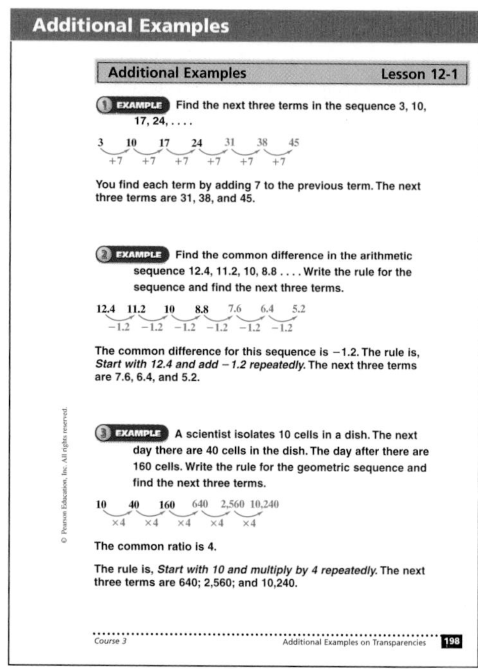

Additional Examples — **Lesson 12-1**

1 EXAMPLE Find the next three terms in the sequence 3, 10, 17, 24, ...

3, 10, 17, 24, 31, 38, 45 (+7 +7 +7 +7 +7 +7)

You find each term by adding 7 to the previous term. The next three terms are 31, 38, and 45.

2 EXAMPLE Find the common difference in the arithmetic sequence 12.4, 11.2, 10, 8.8 . . . . Write the rule for the sequence and find the next three terms.

12.4, 11.2, 10, 8.8, 7.6, 6.4, 5.2 (−1.2 −1.2 −1.2 −1.2 −1.2 −1.2)

The common difference for this sequence is −1.2. The rule is, *Start with 12.4 and add −1.2 repeatedly.* The next three terms are 7.6, 6.4, and 5.2.

3 EXAMPLE A scientist isolates 10 cells in a dish. The next day there are 40 cells in the dish. The day after there are 160 cells. Write the rule for the geometric sequence and find the next three terms.

10, 40, 160, 640, 2,560, 10,240 (×4 ×4 ×4 ×4 ×4)

The common ratio is 4.

The rule is, *Start with 10 and multiply by 4 repeatedly.* The next three terms are 640; 2,560; and 10,240.

Sample page; see p. H for complete list.

Classroom Aid

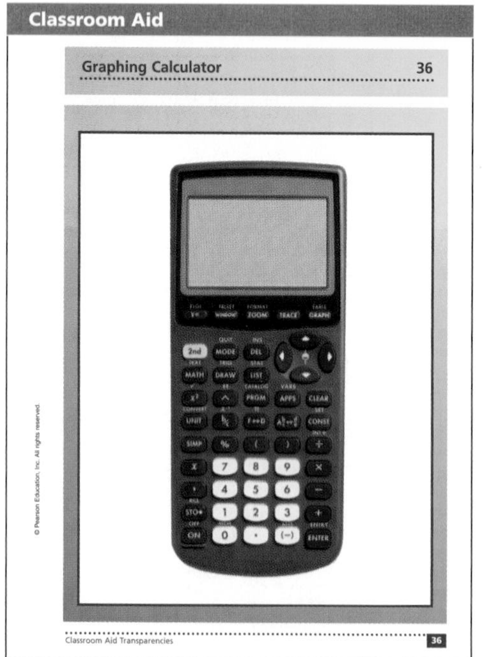

Graphing Calculator 36

Sample page.

Student Edition Answers

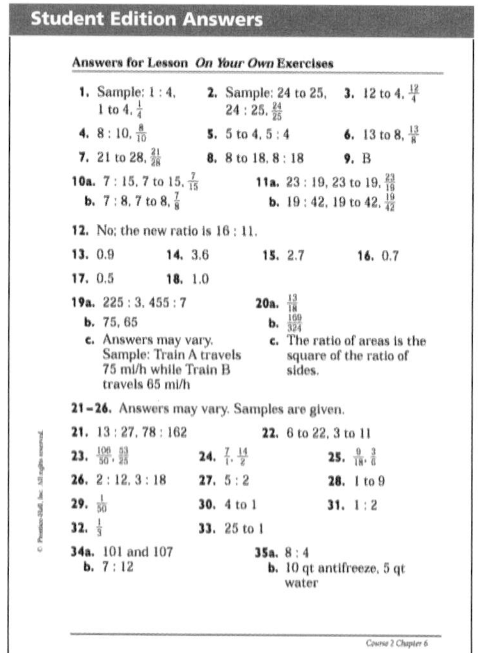

Answers for Lesson *On Your Own* Exercises

1. Sample: 1 : 4, 1 to 4, $\frac{1}{4}$
2. Sample: 24 to 25, 24 : 25, $\frac{24}{25}$
3. 12 to 4, $\frac{12}{4}$
4. 8 : 10, $\frac{8}{10}$
5. 5 to 4, 5 : 4
6. 13 to 8, $\frac{13}{8}$
7. 21 to 28, $\frac{21}{28}$
8. 8 to 18, 8 : 18
9. B

10a. 7 : 15, 7 to 15, $\frac{7}{15}$
 b. 7 : 8, 7 to 8, $\frac{7}{8}$

11a. 23 : 19, 23 to 19, $\frac{23}{19}$
 b. 19 : 42, 19 to 42, $\frac{19}{42}$

12. No; the new ratio is 16 : 11.
13. 0.9
14. 3.6
15. 2.7
16. 0.7
17. 0.5
18. 1.0

19a. 225 : 3, 455 : 7
 b. 75, 65
 c. Answers may vary. Sample: Train A travels 75 mi/h while Train B travels 65 mi/h

20a. $\frac{13}{18}$
 b. $\frac{169}{324}$
 c. The ratio of areas is the square of the ratio of sides.

21–26. Answers may vary. Samples are given.

21. 13 : 27, 78 : 162
22. 6 to 22, 3 to 11
23. $\frac{106}{50}$, $\frac{53}{25}$
24. $\frac{7}{1}$, $\frac{14}{2}$
25. $\frac{9}{18}$, $\frac{3}{6}$
26. 2 : 12, 3 : 18
27. 5 : 2
28. 1 to 9
29. $\frac{1}{50}$
30. 4 to 1
31. 1 : 2
32. $\frac{1}{3}$
33. 25 to 1

34a. 101 and 107
 b. 7 : 12

35a. 8 : 4
 b. 10 qt antifreeze, 5 qt water

Sample page; see p. H for complete list.

Lesson Quiz

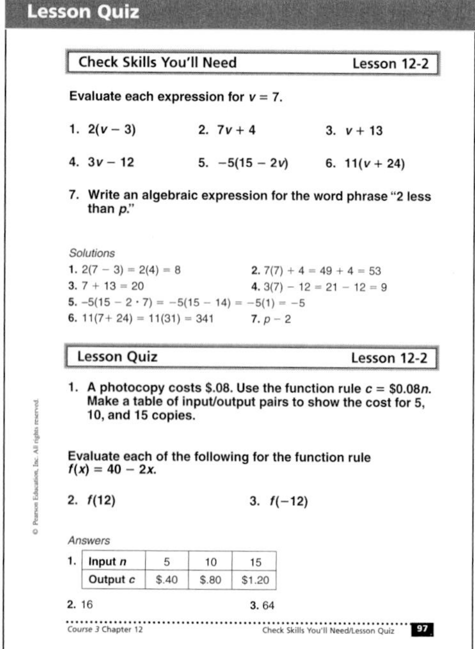

Check Skills You'll Need — **Lesson 12-2**

Evaluate each expression for $v = 7$.

1. $2(v - 3)$
2. $7v + 4$
3. $v + 13$
4. $3v - 12$
5. $-5(15 - 2v)$
6. $11(v + 24)$
7. Write an algebraic expression for the word phrase "2 less than p."

Solutions

1. $2(7 - 3) = 2(4) = 8$
2. $7(7) + 4 = 49 + 4 = 53$
3. $7 + 13 = 20$
4. $3(7) - 12 = 21 - 12 = 9$
5. $-5(15 - 2 \cdot 7) = -5(15 - 14) = -5(1) = -5$
6. $11(7 + 24) = 11(31) = 341$
7. $p - 2$

Lesson Quiz — **Lesson 12-2**

1. A photocopy costs \$.08. Use the function rule $c = \$0.08n$. Make a table of input/output pairs to show the cost for 5, 10, and 15 copies.

Evaluate each of the following for the function rule $f(x) = 40 - 2x$.

2. $f(12)$
3. $f(-12)$

Answers

1.

Input n	5	10	15
Output c	\$.40	\$.80	\$1.20

2. 16
3. 64

Sample page; see p. H for complete list.

Assessment

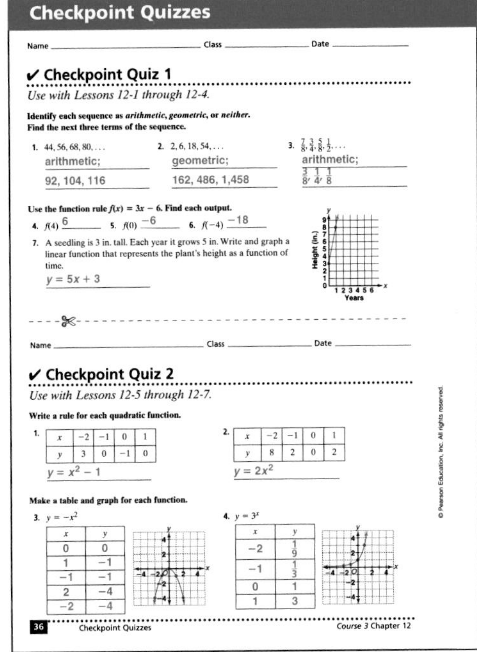
Checkpoint Quizzes

Name ______ Class ______ Date ______

✔ Checkpoint Quiz 1

Use with Lessons 12-1 through 12-4.

Identify each sequence as *arithmetic*, *geometric*, or *neither*. Find the next three terms of the sequence.

1. 44, 56, 68, 80, . . . arithmetic; 92, 104, 116
2. 2, 6, 18, 54, . . . geometric; 162, 486, 1,458
3. $\frac{7}{8}, \frac{3}{4}, \frac{5}{8}, \frac{1}{2}, \ldots$ arithmetic; $\frac{3}{8}, \frac{1}{4}, \frac{1}{8}$

Use the function rule $f(x) = 3x - 6$. Find each output.

4. $f(4)$ 6
5. $f(0)$ −6
6. $f(-4)$ −18
7. A seedling is 3 in. tall. Each year it grows 5 in. Write and graph a linear function that represents the plant's height as a function of time. $y = 5x + 3$

Name ______ Class ______ Date ______

✔ Checkpoint Quiz 2

Use with Lessons 12-5 through 12-7.

Write a rule for each quadratic function.

1.

x	−2	−1	0	1
y	3	0	−1	0

$y = x^2 - 1$

2.

x	−2	−1	0	1
y	8	2	0	2

$y = 2x^2$

Make a table and graph for each function.

3. $y = -x^2$

x	y
0	0
1	−1
−1	−1
2	−4
−2	−4

4. $y = 3^x$

x	y
−2	$\frac{1}{9}$
−1	$\frac{1}{3}$
0	1
1	3

36 Checkpoint Quizzes Course 3 Chapter 12

Available in Spanish

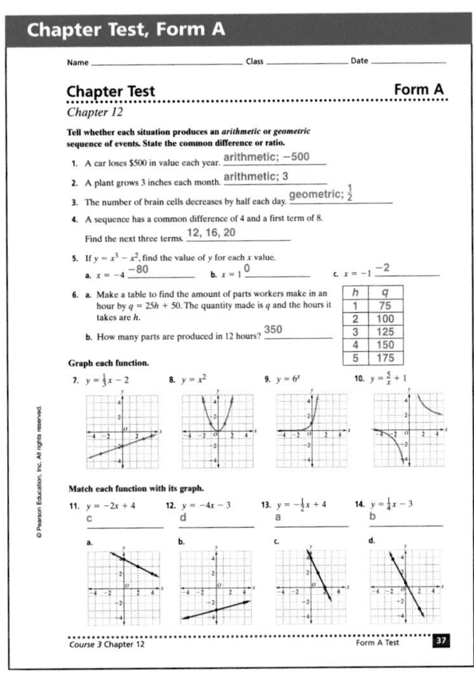
Chapter Test, Form A

Name ______ Class ______ Date ______

Chapter Test Form A

Chapter 12

Tell whether each situation produces an *arithmetic* or *geometric* sequence of events. State the common difference or ratio.

1. A car loses $500 in value each year. arithmetic; −500
2. A plant grows 3 inches each month. arithmetic; 3
3. The number of brain cells decreases by half each day. geometric; $\frac{1}{2}$
4. A sequence has a common difference of 4 and a first term of 8. Find the next three terms. 12, 16, 20
5. If $y = x^3 - x^2$, find the value of y for each x value. a. $x = -4$ −80 b. $x = 1$ 0 c. $x = -1$ −2
6. a. Make a table to find the amount of parts workers make in an hour by $q = 25h + 50$. The quantity made is q and the hours it takes are h.

h	q
1	75
2	100
3	125
4	150
5	175

b. How many parts are produced in 12 hours? 350

Graph each function.

7. $y = \frac{1}{3}x - 2$
8. $y = x^2$
9. $y = 6^x$
10. $y = \frac{2}{x} + 1$

Match each function with its graph.

11. $y = -2x + 4$ c
12. $y = -4x - 3$ d
13. $y = -\frac{1}{2}x + 4$ a
14. $y = \frac{1}{4}x - 3$ b

Course 3 Chapter 12 Form A Test 37

Available in Spanish

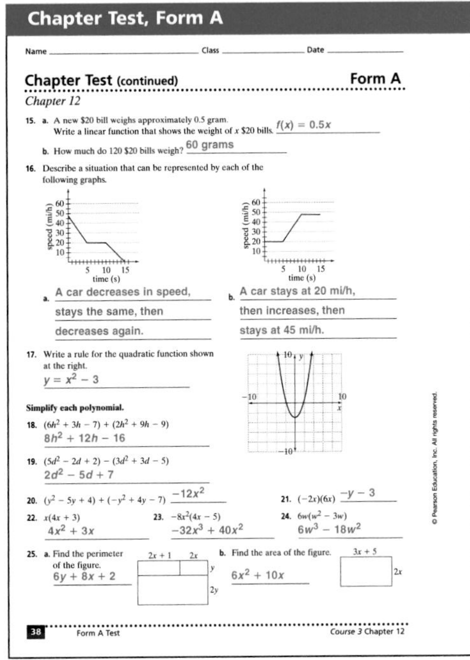
Chapter Test, Form A

Name ______ Class ______ Date ______

Chapter Test (continued) Form A

Chapter 12

15. a. A new $20 bill weighs approximately 0.5 gram. Write a linear function that shows the weight of x $20 bills. $f(x) = 0.5x$
b. How much do 120 $20 bills weigh? 60 grams
16. Describe a situation that can be represented by each of the following graphs.
a. A car decreases in speed, stays the same, then decreases again.
b. A car stays at 20 mi/h, then increases, then stays at 45 mi/h.
17. Write a rule for the quadratic function shown at the right. $y = x^2 - 3$

Simplify each polynomial.

18. $(6h^2 + 3h - 7) + (2h^2 + 9h - 9)$ $8h^2 + 12h - 16$
19. $(5d^2 - 2d + 2) - (3d^2 + 3d - 5)$ $2d^2 - 5d + 7$
20. $(y^2 - 5y + 4) + (-y^2 + 4y - 7)$ $-12x^2$
21. $(-2x)(6x)$ $-y - 3$
22. $x(4x + 3)$ $4x^2 + 3x$
23. $-8x^2(4x - 5)$ $-32x^3 + 40x^2$
24. $6w(w^2 - 3w)$ $6w^3 - 18w^2$
25. a. Find the perimeter of the figure. $6y + 8x + 2$
b. Find the area of the figure. $6x^2 + 10x$

38 Form A Test Course 3 Chapter 12

Available in Spanish

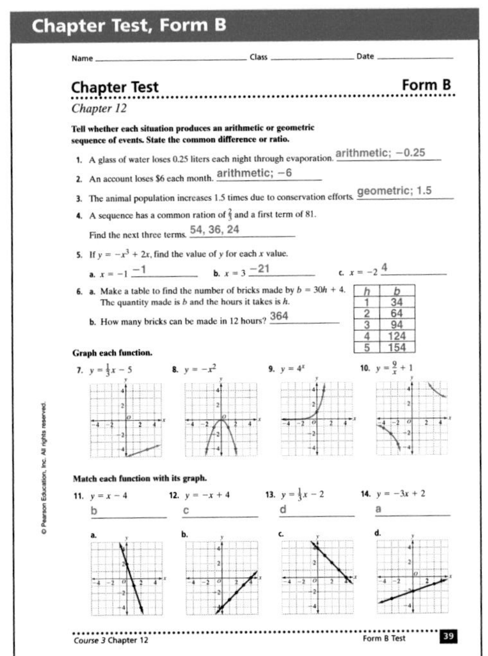
Chapter Test, Form B

Name ______ Class ______ Date ______

Chapter Test Form B

Chapter 12

Tell whether each situation produces an arithmetic or geometric sequence of events. State the common difference or ratio.

1. A glass of water loses 0.25 liters each night through evaporation. arithmetic; −0.25
2. An account loses $6 each month. arithmetic; −6
3. The animal population increases 1.5 times due to conservation efforts. geometric; 1.5
4. A sequence has a common ration of $\frac{2}{3}$ and a first term of 81. Find the next three terms. 54, 36, 24
5. If $y = -x^3 + 2x$, find the value of y for each x value. a. $x = -1$ −1 b. $x = 3$ −21 c. $x = -2$ 4
6. a. Make a table to find the number of bricks made by $b = 30h + 4$. The quantity made is b and the hours it takes is h.

h	b
1	34
2	64
3	94
4	124
5	154

b. How many bricks can be made in 12 hours? 364

Graph each function.

7. $y = \frac{1}{3}x - 5$
8. $y = -x^2$
9. $y = 4^x$
10. $y = \frac{9}{x} + 1$

Match each function with its graph.

11. $y = x - 4$ b
12. $y = -x + 4$ c
13. $y = \frac{1}{3}x - 2$ d
14. $y = -3x + 2$ a

Course 3 Chapter 12 Form B Test 39

Available in Spanish

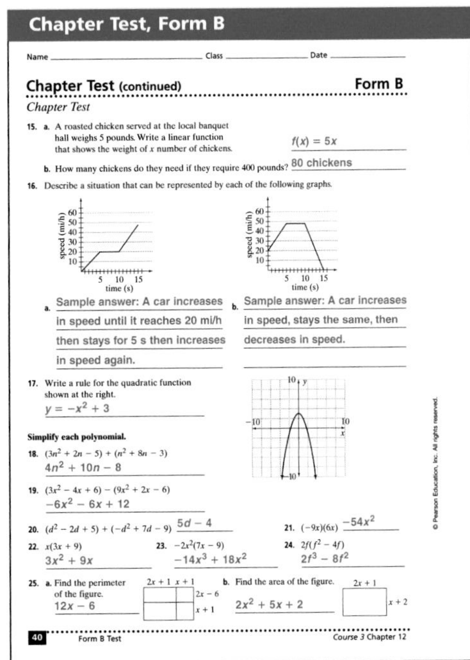
Chapter Test, Form B

Name ______ Class ______ Date ______

Chapter Test (continued) Form B

Chapter Test

15. a. A roasted chicken served at the local banquet hall weighs 5 pounds. Write a linear function that shows the weight of x number of chickens. $f(x) = 5x$
b. How many chickens do they need if they require 400 pounds? 80 chickens
16. Describe a situation that can be represented by each of the following graphs.
a. Sample answer: A car increases in speed until it reaches 20 mi/h then stays for 5 s then increases in speed again.
b. Sample answer: A car increases in speed, stays the same, then decreases in speed.
17. Write a rule for the quadratic function shown at the right. $y = -x^2 + 3$

Simplify each polynomial.

18. $(3n^2 + 2n - 5) + (n^2 + 8n - 3)$ $4n^2 + 10n - 8$
19. $(3x^2 - 4x + 6) - (9x^2 + 2x - 6)$ $-6x^2 - 6x + 12$
20. $(d^2 - 2d + 5) + (-d^2 + 7d - 9)$ $5d - 4$
21. $(-9x)(6x)$ $-54x^2$
22. $x(3x + 9)$ $3x^2 + 9x$
23. $-2x^2(7x - 9)$ $-14x^3 + 18x^2$
24. $2f(f^2 - 4f)$ $2f^3 - 8f^2$
25. a. Find the perimeter of the figure. $12x - 6$
b. Find the area of the figure. $2x^2 + 5x + 2$

40 Form B Test Course 3 Chapter 12

Available in Spanish

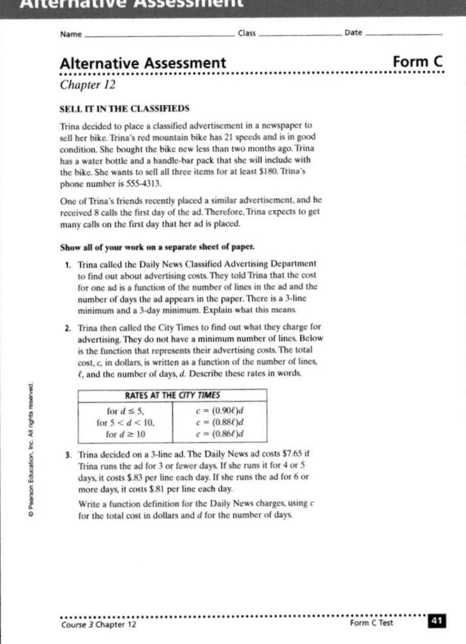
Alternative Assessment

Name ______ Class ______ Date ______

Alternative Assessment Form C

Chapter 12

SELL IT IN THE CLASSIFIEDS

Trina decided to place a classified advertisement in a newspaper to sell her bike. Trina's red mountain bike has 21 speeds and is in good condition. She bought the bike new less than two months ago. Trina has a water bottle and a handle-bar pack that she will include with the bike. She wants to sell all three items for at least $180. Trina's phone number is 555-4313.

One of Trina's friends recently placed a similar advertisement, and he received 8 calls the first day of the ad. Therefore, Trina expects to get many calls on the first day that her ad is placed.

Show all of your work on a separate sheet of paper.

1. Trina called the Daily News Classified Advertising Department to find out about advertising costs. They told Trina that the cost for one ad is a function of the number of lines in the ad and the number of days the ad appears in the paper. There is a 3-line minimum and a 3-day minimum. Explain what this means.
2. Trina then called the City Times to find out what they charge for advertising. They do not have a minimum number of lines. Below is the function that represents their advertising costs. The total cost, c, in dollars, is written as a function of the number of lines, ℓ, and the number of days, d. Describe these rates in words.

RATES AT THE *CITY TIMES*	
for $d \le 5$,	$c = (0.90\ell)d$
for $5 < d < 10$,	$c = (0.88\ell)d$
for $d \ge 10$	$c = (0.86\ell)d$

3. Trina decided on a 3-line ad. The Daily News ad costs $7.65 if Trina runs the ad for 3 or fewer days. If she runs it for 4 or 5 days, it costs $.83 per line each day. If she runs the ad for 6 or more days, it costs $.81 per line each day. Write a function definition for the Daily News charges, using c for the total cost in dollars and d for the number of days.

Course 3 Chapter 12 Form C Test 41

Available in Spanish

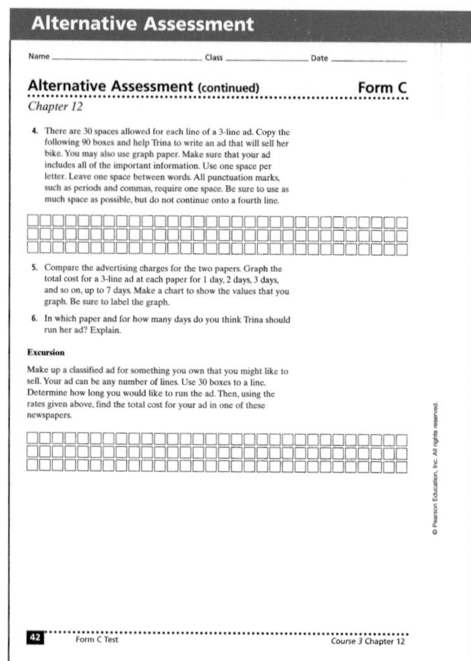

Alternative Assessment

Name ______ Class ______ Date ______

Alternative Assessment (continued) **Form C**

Chapter 12

4. There are 30 spaces allowed for each line of a 3-line ad. Copy the following 90 boxes and help Trina to write an ad that will sell her bike. You may also use graph paper. Make sure that your ad includes all of the important information. Use one space per letter. Leave one space between words. All punctuation marks, such as periods and commas, require one space. Be sure to use as much space as possible, but do not continue onto a fourth line.

5. Compare the advertising charges for the two papers. Graph the total cost for a 3-line ad at each paper for 1 day, 2 days, 3 days, and so on, up to 7 days. Make a chart to show the values that you graph. Be sure to label the graph.

6. In which paper and for how many days do you think Trina should run her ad? Explain.

Excursion

Make up a classified ad for something you own that you might like to sell. Your ad can be any number of lines. Use 30 boxes to a line. Determine how long you would like to run the ad. Then, using the rates given above, find the total cost for your ad in one of these newspapers.

Available in Spanish

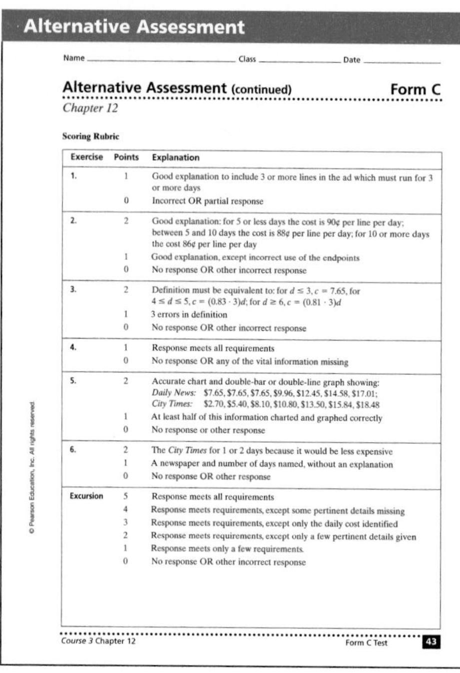

Alternative Assessment

Name ______ Class ______ Date ______

Alternative Assessment (continued) **Form C**

Chapter 12

Scoring Rubric

Exercise	Points	Explanation
1.	1	Good explanation to include 3 or more lines in the ad which must run for 3 or more days
	0	Incorrect OR partial response
2.	2	Good explanation: for 5 or less days the cost is 90¢ per line per day; between 5 and 10 days the cost is 88¢ per line per day; for 10 or more days the cost 86¢ per line per day
	1	Good explanation, except incorrect use of the endpoints
	0	No response OR other incorrect response
3.	2	Definition must be equivalent to: for $d \le 3$, $c = 7.65$, for $4 \le d \le 5$, $c = (0.83 \cdot 3)d$; for $d \ge 6$, $c = (0.81 \cdot 3)d$
	1	3 errors in definition
	0	No response OR other incorrect response
4.	1	Response meets all requirements
	0	No response OR any of the vital information missing
5.	2	Accurate chart and double-bar or double-line graph showing: *Daily News:* \$7.65, \$7.65, \$7.65, \$9.96, \$12.45, \$14.58, \$17.01; *City Times:* \$2.70, \$5.40, \$8.10, \$10.80, \$13.50, \$15.84, \$18.48
	1	At least half of this information charted and graphed correctly
	0	No response or other response
6.	2	The *City Times* for 1 or 2 days because it would be less expensive
	1	A newspaper and number of days named, without an explanation
	0	No response OR other response
Excursion	5	Response meets all requirements
	4	Response meets requirements, except some pertinent details missing
	3	Response meets requirements, except only the daily cost identified
	2	Response meets requirements, except only a few pertinent details given
	1	Response meets only a few requirements.
	0	No response OR other incorrect response

Available in Spanish

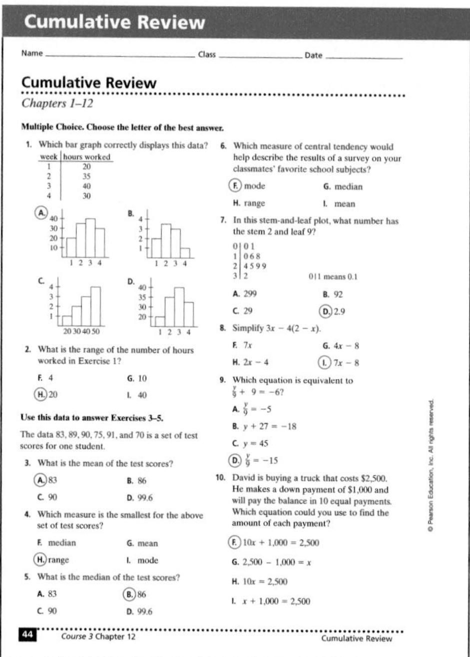

Cumulative Review

Name ______ Class ______ Date ______

Cumulative Review

Chapters 1–12

Multiple Choice. Choose the letter of the best answer.

1. Which bar graph correctly displays this data?

week	hours worked
1	20
2	35
3	40
4	30

Ⓐ B. C. D.

2. What is the range of the number of hours worked in Exercise 1?
F. 4 G. 10 Ⓗ 20 I. 40

Use this data to answer Exercises 3–5.

The data 83, 89, 90, 75, 91, and 70 is a set of test scores for one student.

3. What is the mean of the test scores?
Ⓐ 83 B. 86 C. 90 D. 99.6

4. Which measure is the smallest for the above set of test scores?
F. median G. mean Ⓗ range I. mode

5. What is the median of the test scores?
A. 83 Ⓑ 86 C. 90 D. 99.6

6. Which measure of central tendency would help describe the results of a survey on your classmates' favorite school subjects?
Ⓕ mode G. median H. range I. mean

7. In this stem-and-leaf plot, what number has the stem 2 and leaf 9?

0 | 0 1
1 | 0 6 8
2 | 4 5 9 9
3 | 2
0|1 means 0.1

A. 299 B. 92 C. 29 Ⓓ 2.9

8. Simplify $3x - 4(2 - x)$.
F. $7x$ G. $4x - 8$ H. $2x - 4$ Ⓘ $7x - 8$

9. Which equation is equivalent to $\frac{y}{9} + 9 = -6$?
A. $\frac{y}{9} = -5$ B. $y + 27 = -18$ C. $y = 45$ Ⓓ $\frac{y}{9} = -15$

10. David is buying a truck that costs \$2,500. He makes a down payment of \$1,000 and will pay the balance in 10 equal payments. Which equation could you use to find the amount of each payment?
Ⓕ $10x + 1{,}000 = 2{,}500$
G. $2{,}500 - 1{,}000 = x$
H. $10x = 2{,}500$
I. $x + 1{,}000 = 2{,}500$

Available in Spanish

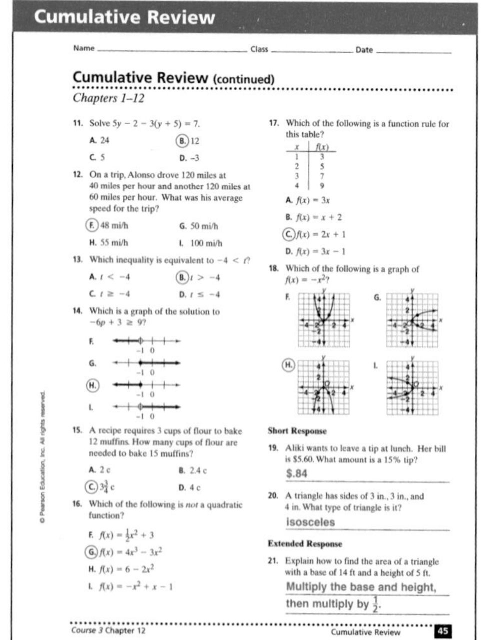

Cumulative Review

Name ______ Class ______ Date ______

Cumulative Review (continued)

Chapters 1–12

11. Solve $5y - 2 - 3(y + 5) = 7$.
A. 24 Ⓑ 12 C. 5 D. −3

12. On a trip, Alonso drove 120 miles at 40 miles per hour and another 120 miles at 60 miles per hour. What was his average speed for the trip?
Ⓕ 48 mi/h G. 50 mi/h H. 55 mi/h I. 100 mi/h

13. Which inequality is equivalent to $-4 < t$?
A. $t < -4$ Ⓑ $t > -4$ C. $t \ge -4$ D. $t \le -4$

14. Which is a graph of the solution to $-6p + 3 \ge 9$?
F. G. Ⓗ I.

15. A recipe requires 3 cups of flour to bake 12 muffins. How many cups of flour are needed to bake 15 muffins?
A. 2 c B. 2.4 c Ⓒ $3\frac{3}{4}$ c D. 4 c

16. Which of the following is *not* a quadratic function?
F. $f(x) = \frac{1}{2}x^2 + 3$
Ⓖ $f(x) = 4x^3 - 3x^2$
H. $f(x) = 6 - 2x^2$
I. $f(x) = -x^2 + x - 1$

17. Which of the following is a function rule for this table?

x	f(x)
1	3
2	5
3	7
4	9

A. $f(x) = 3x$
B. $f(x) = x + 2$
Ⓒ $f(x) = 2x + 1$
D. $f(x) = 3x - 1$

18. Which of the following is a graph of $f(x) = -x^2$?
F. G. Ⓗ I.

Short Response

19. Aliki wants to leave a tip at lunch. Her bill is \$5.60. What amount is a 15% tip?
\$.84

20. A triangle has sides of 3 in., 3 in., and 4 in. What type of triangle is it?
isosceles

Extended Response

21. Explain how to find the area of a triangle with a base of 14 ft and a height of 5 ft.
Multiply the base and height, then multiply by $\frac{1}{2}$.

Available in Spanish

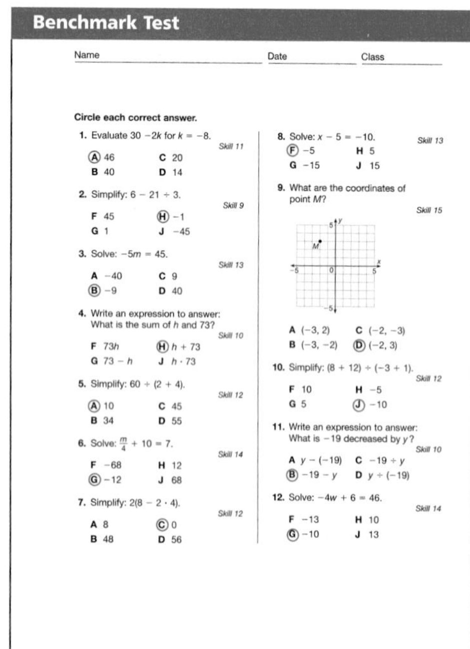

Benchmark Test

Name ______ Date ______ Class ______

Circle each correct answer.

1. Evaluate $30 - 2k$ for $k = -8$. *Skill 11*
Ⓐ 46 C 20 B 40 D 14

2. Simplify: $6 - 21 \div 3$. *Skill 9*
F 45 Ⓗ −1 G 1 J −45

3. Solve: $-5m = 45$. *Skill 13*
A −40 C 9 Ⓑ −9 D 40

4. Write an expression to answer: What is the sum of h and 73? *Skill 10*
F $73h$ Ⓗ $h + 73$ G $73 - h$ J $h \cdot 73$

5. Simplify: $60 \div (2 + 4)$. *Skill 12*
Ⓐ 10 C 45 B 34 D 55

6. Solve: $\frac{m}{4} + 10 = 7$. *Skill 14*
F −68 H 12 Ⓖ −12 J 68

7. Simplify: $2(8 - 2 \cdot 4)$. *Skill 12*
A 8 Ⓒ 0 B 48 D 56

8. Solve: $x - 5 = -10$. *Skill 13*
Ⓕ −5 H 5 G −15 J 15

9. What are the coordinates of point M? *Skill 15*
A (−3, 2) C (−2, −3) B (−3, −2) Ⓓ (−2, 3)

10. Simplify: $(8 + 12) \div (-3 + 1)$. *Skill 12*
F 10 H −5 G 5 Ⓙ −10

11. Write an expression to answer: What is −19 decreased by y? *Skill 10*
A $y - (-19)$ C $-19 \div y$ Ⓑ $-19 - y$ D $y \div (-19)$

12. Solve: $-4w + 6 = 46$. *Skill 14*
F −13 H 10 Ⓖ −10 J 13

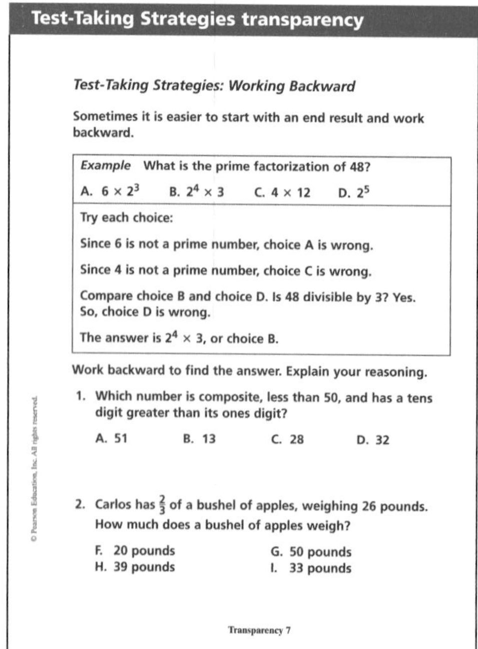

Test-Taking Strategies transparency

Test-Taking Strategies: Working Backward

Sometimes it is easier to start with an end result and work backward.

Example What is the prime factorization of 48?

A. 6×2^3 B. $2^4 \times 3$ C. 4×12 D. 2^5

Try each choice:

Since 6 is not a prime number, choice A is wrong.

Since 4 is not a prime number, choice C is wrong.

Compare choice B and choice D. Is 48 divisible by 3? Yes. So, choice D is wrong.

The answer is $2^4 \times 3$, or choice B.

Work backward to find the answer. Explain your reasoning.

1. Which number is composite, less than 50, and has a tens digit greater than its ones digit?
A. 51 B. 13 C. 28 D. 32

2. Carlos has $\frac{2}{3}$ of a bushel of apples, weighing 26 pounds. How much does a bushel of apples weigh?
F. 20 pounds G. 50 pounds H. 39 pounds I. 33 pounds

Transparency 7

On PH Website

Test-Taking Strategies worksheet

Name ____________ Class ____________ Date ____________

Chapter 12: Working Backward

Exercises

Solve each of the following by working backward.

1. Which polynomial is equivalent to $15x(2x + 8)$?
   A. $30x + 8$ B. $30x + 120x$ (C) $30x^2 + 120x$ D. $30x^2 + 8x$
2. Consider the function $f(y) = 3x - 7$. What value of x will make $f(y) = 20$?
   F. 53 (G) 9 H. −36 I. −80
3. The area of a circle is 15.9 mm^2. What is the diameter of the circle?
   (A) 4.5 mm B. 3.14 mm C. 2.25 mm D. 1.05 mm
4. The base of a rectangular prism has a length of 9 in. and a width of 7 in. The volume of the prism is 787.5 $in.^3$. What is the height of the prism?
   F. 87.5 in. G. 63 in. (H) 12.5 in. I. 7.875 in.
5. If $x^3 = 64$, find the value of $\frac{x^5}{x^3}$.
   A. 1,024 (B) 16 C. 8 D. 4
6. Which number could *not* be a value of y if $y = 5x^2 - 9$?
   F. 11 G. −4 H. −9 (I) −10
7. The side lengths of which of the following triangles do *not* form a right triangle?
   A. 12 cm, 16 cm, 20 cm B. 10 cm, 24 cm, 26 cm
   (C) 8 cm, 10 cm, 12 cm D. 15 cm, 20 cm, 25 cm
8. Jennie's average after four math tests is an 85. What must Jennie score on the fifth test to raise her grade to an 87?
   F. 100 (G) 95 H. 91 I. 87
9. Which ordered pair lies on the line $y = 11x - 13$?
   (A) (2, 9) B. (−13, 0) C. (0, 11) D. (1, 2)
10. You start an exercise program. You begin by walking 1.5 mi the first day and increase your distance by 0.25 mi per day. How many miles do you walk on the 7th day?
    F. 1.75 mi (G) 3 mi H. 3.25 mi I. 3.5 mi

36 Course 3 Test-Taking Strategies

Home Activities

in math class ...

We have been learning about functions and relationships in algebra. Here is a list of some of the skills and concepts we have studied.

- Functions
- Linear functions
- Quadratic functions
- Other functions
- Polynomials
- Adding polynomials
- Subtracting polynomials
- Multiplying monomials and polynomials

Home Activities

Here are some activities you can do with your child that use these math skills and concepts.

Discuss with your child certain situations that may or may not represent functions. A function is a dependent relationship. The amount of your electric bill is a function because the amount of the bill depends on the amount of electricity used. However, the time at which you go to sleep at night is not a function of the time you have to wake up in the morning. Even though you have to wake up at, say, 7:00 each morning, you could have gone to sleep at almost any time. Have your child describe other situations which are functions and some which are not. For example, the charge for a long distance telephone call is a function of the number of minutes you talk. The amount of liquid a glass can hold is not a function of how thirsty you are.

Use with Chapter 12

Available in Spanish; Web Code: ack-5500

Interdisciplinary Activities

Name ____________ ***Math and Science/Technology***

Quick Pitch

Use linear functions to learn about baseball pitches.

Hitting a baseball is one of the hardest skills to master in sports. It is not surprising when you realize that a batter has just a fraction of a second to swing at a small ball whizzing toward home plate at close to 100 miles per hour. In fact, it is so difficult to hit a baseball that the batting averages of even the best hitters in the game are usually not far above .333. So even baseball superstars get a hit only about one third of the times they officially come to bat.

Second Base
Pitcher's Mound
Third Base
First Base
Home Plate
90'
60.5'

SPEED OF BASEBALL PITCHES			
Pitch	Average Speed		Time from Pitcher to Batter (sec)
	mph	feet per second	
Fastball	90	132	
Slider	85	125	
Curveball	75	110	
Change-up	65	95	
Knuckleball	65	95	

In addition to speed, pitchers use a few tricks to keep batters from getting hits. A pitcher who throws the ball at the same velocity and in the same spot all the time won't be successful. Even the worst hitters would adjust and begin to hit the ball hard and often. So pitchers change the speed and location of their pitches constantly, using the basic pitches listed in the table above. They also change the type of pitch they throw. Some of these pitches, like sliders, curves, and knuckleballs, don't move in a straight line but dip, swerve, and flutter.

Use the table and the diagram of the baseball diamond above to answer the questions that follow. Note: the distance from the pitcher's mound to home plate is 60 ft 6 in.

1. List two variables involved when a pitcher throws a baseball toward a hitter. Name one constant. (The variables and the constant are connected with the flight of the ball.)

Use with Chapter 12

Web Code: ack-5500

Interdisciplinary Activities

Name ____________ ***Math and Science/Technology***

2. Which of the variables identified in item 1 is the independent variable? Which is the dependent variable? Explain your answer.
3. a. What is the relationship between the speed of a pitch and the time it takes a ball to travel from pitcher to batter?
   b. Construct a function that expresses the relationship of velocity and distance to time in the pitching of a baseball.
   c. Use the function you constructed above to find t and fill in the table on page 39.
4. Why would changing the speed of consecutive pitches decrease the ability of a batter to hit the baseball?
5. a. An ordinary person might pitch a ball at 40 miles per hour—a pitch speed that would be very easy to hit. How long would it take a ball to get from the pitcher's mound to home plate at that speed?
   b. How much less time does it take for a fastball pitch to reach the batter than a knuckleball?
   c. What is the percent of increase in time?
6. How would you redesign the baseball diamond to help increase the batter's average?
7. The trajectory of a pitched baseball (its exact path including the way it curves) also affects the hitter's ability to hit it. What variables under the control of a pitcher would help to determine the trajectory of the baseball? Do some research to find out how the pitcher alters these variables.

Use with Chapter 12

Web Code: ack-5500

Algebra Readiness Puzzles

Name ____________ Class ____________ Date ____________

A Polynomial Puzzle — Puzzle 36

Algebraic Relationships

Simplify each expression, and show your work. Then match the solution to the corresponding letter to find what Polly the Parrot says when she is tired of eating crackers.

$5x(2x - 11)$	E	$18x + 7y - 6(3x + 2y)$	N
$3x^2 + 4x - 6 + 5x^2 + 7x - 2$	L	$(7x - 2)(4x + 2)$	M
$17x - 8x$	Y	$3x(x + 2)$	P
$12x(4x + y)$	A	$(x + 2)^2$	O

___ $3x^2 + 6x$ ___ $x^2 + 4x + 4$ ___ $8x^2 + 11x - 8$ ___ $8x^2 + 11x - 8$ ___ $9x$

___ $-5y$ ___ $x^2 + 4x + 4$

___ $28x^2 + 6x - 4$ ___ $10x^2 - 55x$ ___ $48x^2 + 12xy$ ___ $8x^2 + 11x - 8$

36 Algebra Readiness Puzzles

Web Code: ack-5500
Sample pages.

Algebra Readiness Puzzles

Name ____________ Class ____________ Date ____________

Binomials and Trinomials — Puzzle 98

A polynomial with exactly two terms is called a **binomial.**
A polynomial with exactly three terms is called a **trinomial.**

Examples

binomials:	$4y + 5$	$x^2 + 2$	$3b^3 + b^2$
	$2 + 6y$	$7 + 8x^2$	$5x^4 + 3x^2$
trinomials:	$x^2 + 2x + 4$	$2x^3 + y + 4$	$2a + 2b + 2c$
	$5 + 2a + a^2$	$3x^2 + x + 2$	$x^2 + 3y + z^3$

Tell whether each expression is a binomial or trinomial.

1. $h^2 + 4h + 3$
2. $6 + t^3$
3. $2x + 12$
4. $f + 5 + 4f^2$
5. Make up a trinomial using the variable y.
6. Make up a binomial using the variable p.

98 Algebra Readiness Puzzles

Web Code: ack-5500

CHAPTER 12

Algebraic Relationships

Chapter 12 Overview

In this chapter, students investigate sequences and both linear and nonlinear functions. They write function rules and then draw graphs for those rules. They also learn about polynomials and add, subtract, and multiply polynomials.

Reading Math

- Changing Representations, p. 672
- **Vocabulary:** A complete list, plus exercises, in the Chapter Review, p. 688
- **Illustrated Glossary:** Examples for each vocabulary term, plus definitions in English and Spanish, on p. 735

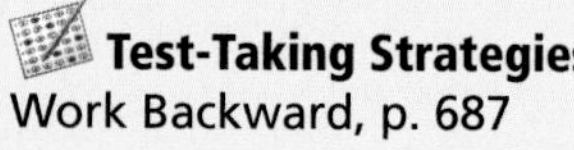

Test-Taking Strategies

Work Backward, p. 687

Real-World Problem Solving

- **Strategies:** Write an Equation, p. 668–671
- **Real-World Snapshots:** Product Pricing, pp. 694–695
- **Chapter Project:** How Much Dough?, p. 701

www.PHSchool.com

Internet support includes:

- Self-grading Vocabulary and Chapter 12 Tests
- Activity Masters
- Chapter Project support
- Chapter Planner
- Ch. 12 Resources

Plus iText

Algebra

CHAPTER 12

Algebraic Relationships

Lessons

Key Vocabulary

- arithmetic sequence (p. 638)
- coefficient (p. 678)
- common difference (p. 638)
- common ratio (p. 638)
- constant (p. 674)
- continuous data (p. 649)
- discrete data (p. 649)
- function (p. 643)
- geometric sequence (p. 638)
- linear function (p. 650)
- monomial (p. 683)
- parabola (p. 663)
- polynomial (p. 674)
- quadratic function (p. 663)

634

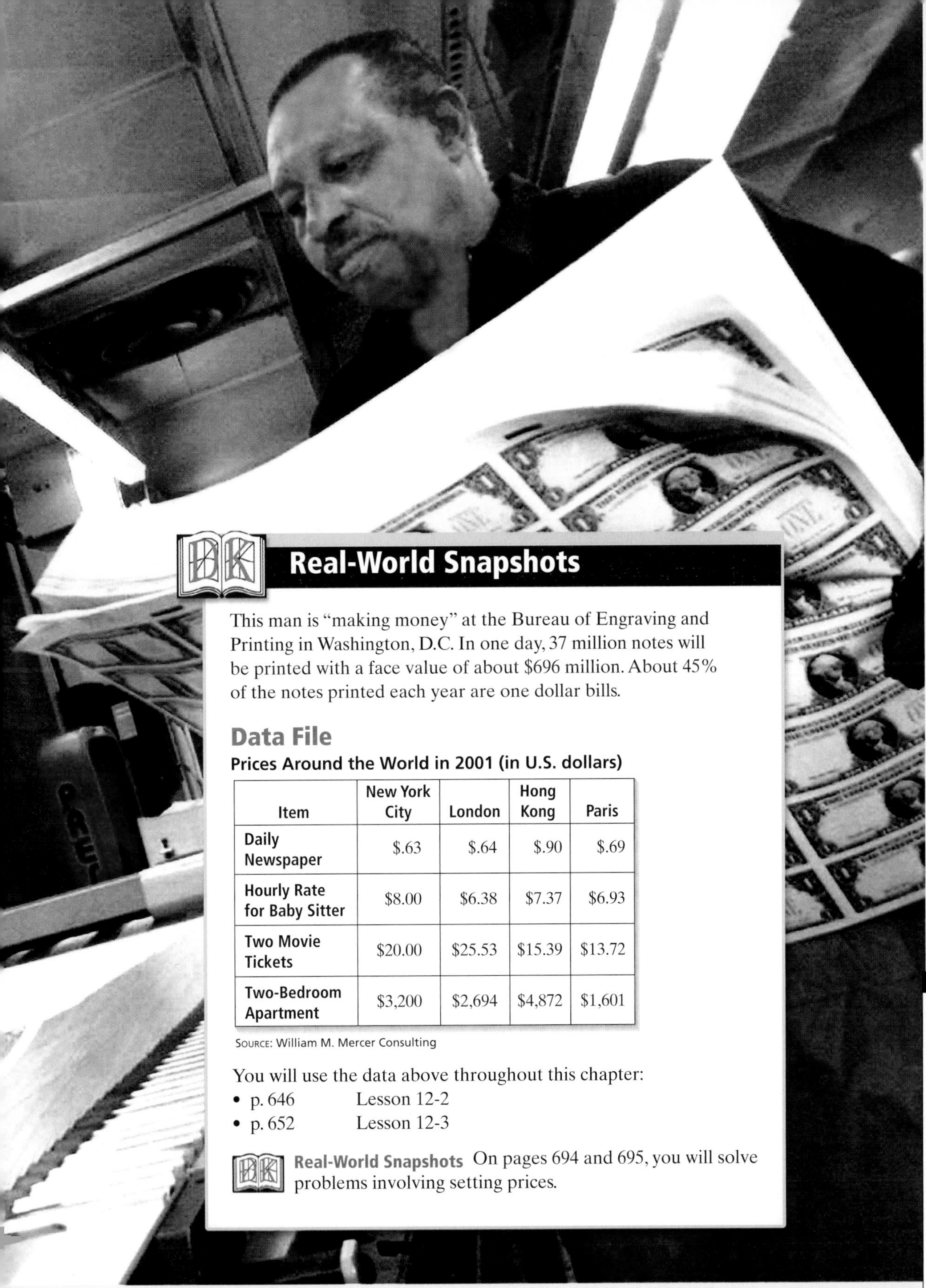

Real-World Snapshots

This man is "making money" at the Bureau of Engraving and Printing in Washington, D.C. In one day, 37 million notes will be printed with a face value of about \$696 million. About 45% of the notes printed each year are one dollar bills.

Data File

Prices Around the World in 2001 (in U.S. dollars)

Item	New York City	London	Hong Kong	Paris
Daily Newspaper	\$.63	\$.64	\$.90	\$.69
Hourly Rate for Baby Sitter	\$8.00	\$6.38	\$7.37	\$6.93
Two Movie Tickets	\$20.00	\$25.53	\$15.39	\$13.72
Two-Bedroom Apartment	\$3,200	\$2,694	\$4,872	\$1,601

SOURCE: William M. Mercer Consulting

You will use the data above throughout this chapter:

- p. 646 Lesson 12-2
- p. 652 Lesson 12-3

Real-World Snapshots On pages 694 and 695, you will solve problems involving setting prices.

Teaching Notes

Activating Prior Knowledge

In this chapter, students build on their knowledge of probability concepts, of graphing, and of equations and expressions. Ask questions such as:

- *Simplify* $12r - 3r = 36$. $r = 4$
- *Simplify* $2^4 \cdot 2^3$. 2^7 or 128

Real-World Snapshots

The data here about prices around the world will be used throughout the chapter. Have a volunteer read the opening sentences and the title of the chart. Focus students on the data in the chart and ask:

- *Where is the price for newspapers the highest?* in Hong Kong
- *Which city has the lowest prices for a two-bedroom apartment?* Paris

Reading and Math Literacy

12A: Graphic Organizer For use before Lesson 12-1

Study Skill: Your textbook includes a Skills Handbook with extra problems and questions. Working these exercises is a good way to review material and prepare for the next chapter.

Write your answers.

1. What is the chapter title? Algebraic Relationships
2. How many lessons are there in this chapter? 10
3. What is the topic of the Reading Math page? Translating Among Representations
4. What is the topic of the Test-Taking Strategy page? Working Backward
5. Look through the chapter and list four real-world connections that are discussed. Answers will vary.
6. Complete the graphic organizer below as you work through the chapter.
   - In the center, write the title of the chapter.
   - When you begin a lesson, write the lesson name in a rectangle.
   - When you complete a lesson, write a skill or key concept in a circle linked to that lesson block.
   - When you complete the chapter, use this graphic organizer to help you review.

   Check students' diagrams.

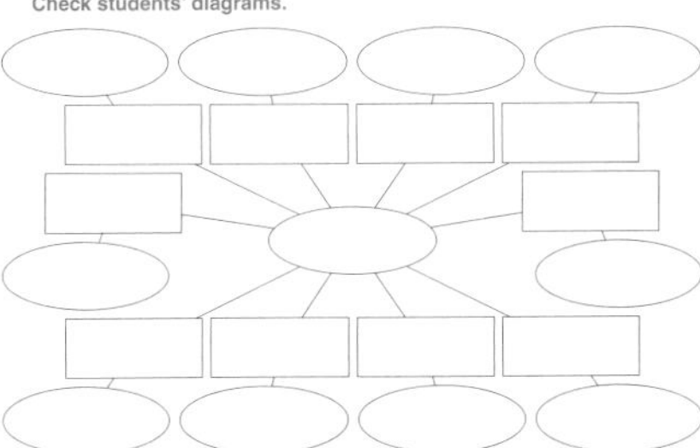

Available in Spanish

Chapter 12: Algebraic Relationships

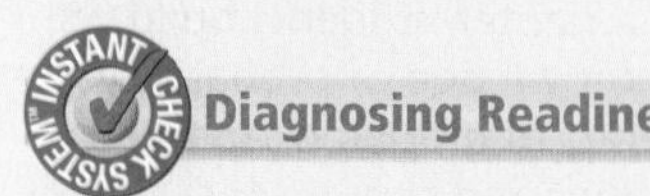

Students will find answers to these exercises in the back of their textbooks.

Prescribing Intervention
For intervention, direct students to:

Simplifying Algebraic Expressions
Lesson 2-3: Examples 3–5.
Extra Practice, p. 703.

Graphing Equations With Two Variables
Lesson 3-2: Example 3.
Extra Practice, p. 704.

Using Graphs of Equations
Lesson 3-6: Examples 1–2.
Extra Practice, p. 704.

Exponents and Multiplication
Lesson 7-2: Example 1.
Extra Practice, p. 708

Chapter 12 Preview

Where You've Been

- In Chapter 11, you learned about probability and conducting surveys.
- You also learned to analyze games and make predictions.

Where You're Going

- In Chapter 12, you will learn about sequences and functions. You will write function rules and draw graphs for these rules. You will also learn about polynomials.
- Applying what you learn, you will graph the relationship between a scuba diver's depth and the atmospheric pressure.

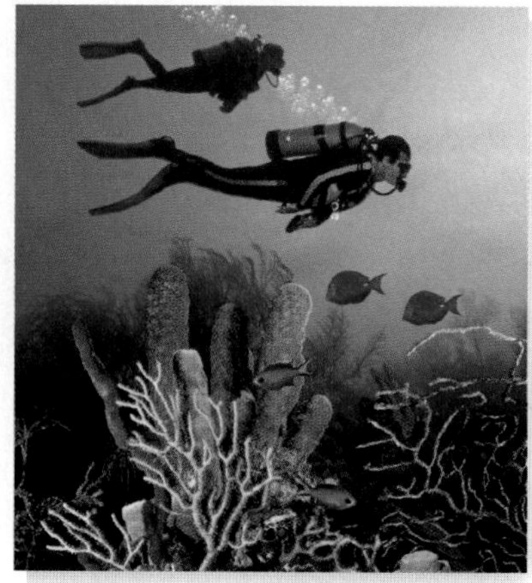

The atmospheric pressure a scuba diver feels depends on how deep the diver swims.

Instant self-check online and on CD-ROM

Diagnosing Readiness

For help, go to the lesson in green.

Simplifying Algebraic Expressions (Lesson 2-3)

Simplify each expression.

1. $13d + 9d - 4$ $22d - 4$

2. $4v + 65 - 11v + 8$ $-7v + 73$

3. $8r + 34 - 2r + 30r$ $36r + 34$

4. $2w - 42 - 7(1 - 9w)$ $65w - 49$

5. $6f - 23g + 3 + 37f$ $43f - 23g + 3$

6. $7t - 6 - 15t + x$ $-8t + x - 6$

Graphing Equations With Two Variables (Lesson 3-2)

Graph each linear equation. 7–9. See margin.

7. $y = \frac{3}{4}x + 2$

8. $y = -7x - 14$

9. $y = \frac{6}{7}x - 4$

Using Graphs of Equations (Lesson 3-6)

Use the graph at the right for Exercises 10–12.

Movie Rentals

(Graph: Cost (dollars), 0–16, vs. Movies, 0–5)

10. a. What is the slope of the line in the graph? 3
b. What does the slope represent? cost per movie

11. Write an equation for the line. $y = 3x$

12. How much would it cost to rent seven movies? \$21

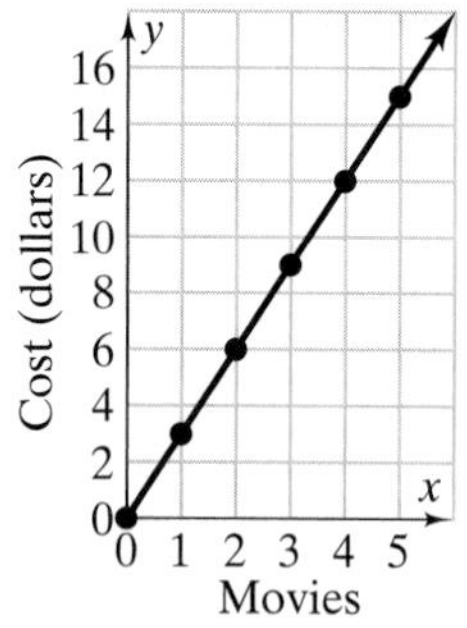

Exponents and Multiplication (Lesson 7-2)

Write each expression using a single exponent.

13. $3^3 \cdot 3^5$ 3^8

14. $5^9 \cdot 5^1$ 5^{10}

15. $12^2 \cdot 12^6$ 12^8

16. $8^4 \cdot 8^{11}$ 8^{15}

17. $1^7 \cdot 1^{23}$ 1^{30}

18. $7^2 \cdot 7^{18} \cdot 7^4$ 7^{24}

19. $20^5 \cdot 20^9 \cdot 20^3$ 20^{17}

20. $6^{10} \cdot 6^{13} \cdot 6^8 \cdot 6^2$ 6^{33}

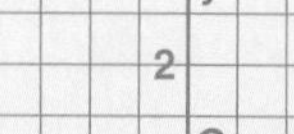

9.

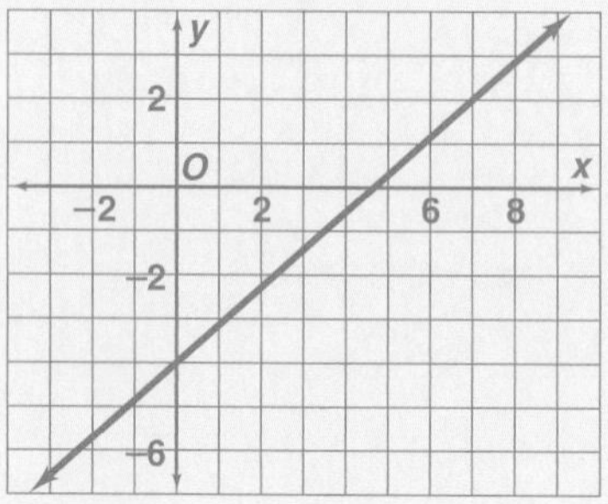

Diagnosing Readiness

7.

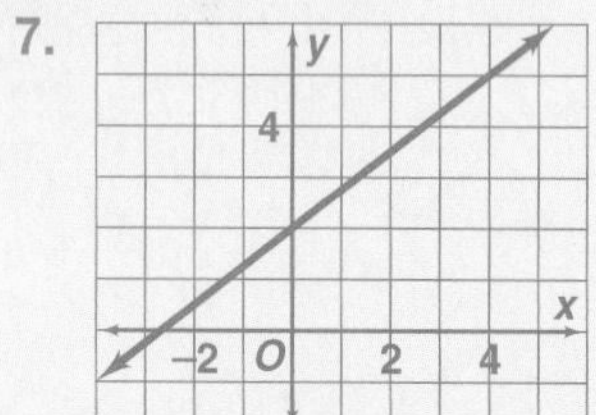

8.

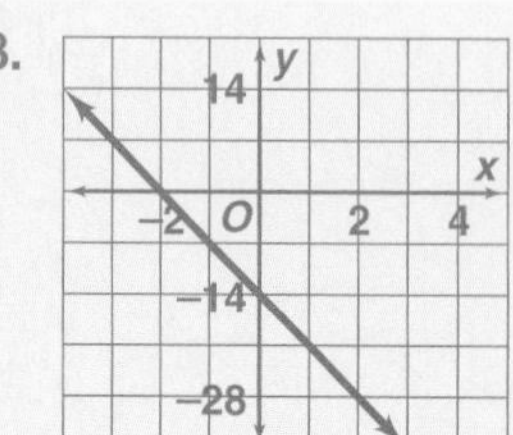

12-1 Sequences

What You'll Learn

To describe sequences

To evaluate an algebraic expression and to write a sequence

. . . And Why

To describe the number of teams in each round of a tournament, as in Example 3

Check Skills You'll Need

For help, go to Lesson 1-1.

Find the value of each expression for the given values of x in each table.

1.

x	$x - 9$
0	■ −9
5	■ −4
7	■ −2

2.

x	$2x + 11$
3	■ 17
6	■ 23
9	■ 29

3.

x	$8x$	
2	■	16
5	■	40
8	■	64

New Vocabulary

- sequence
- term
- arithmetic sequence
- common difference
- geometric sequence
- common ratio

Interactive lesson includes instant self-check, tutorials, and activities.

OBJECTIVE 1

Describing Sequences

Investigation: Exploring Sequences

Suppose you have just paid \$25 to join a baseball-card club for a year. To receive your baseball cards, you must choose one of the three options below.

Option A	Option B	Option C
Receive 230 cards the first month, 250 the second month, 270 the third month, and so on for 12 months	Receive 1 card the first month, 2 cards the second month, 4 cards the third month, 8 cards the fourth month, and so on for 12 months	Receive a total of 4,000 cards when you join

1. How many cards would you receive in one year if you chose Option A? Option B? Option C? 4,080; 4,095; 4,000
2. Which option would you choose? Explain. See left.

2. Answers may vary. Sample: B; the most cards are received by this option.

A **sequence** is a set of numbers that follows a pattern. Here are three different sequences that start with the numbers 2 and 6.

2, 6, 10, 14, . . .
2, 6, 18, 54, . . .
2, 6, 8, 14, . . .

12-1

1. Plan

Lesson Preview

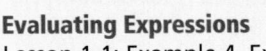

Check Skills You'll Need
Evaluating Expressions
Lesson 1-1: Example 4. Extra Practice, p. 702.

Lesson Resources

Teaching Resources
Practice, Reteaching, Enrichment

Reaching All Students
Practice Workbook 12-1
Spanish Practice Workbook 12-1
Guided Problem Solving 12-1

Presentation Assistant Plus!
Transparencies
- Check Skills You'll Need 12-1
- Problem of the Day 12-1
- Additional Examples 12-1
- Student Edition Answers 12-1
- Lesson Quiz 12-1
- Classroom Aid 36

PH Presentation Pro CD-ROM 12-1

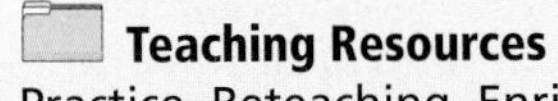

Computer Test Generator CD

Technology
Resource Pro® CD-ROM
Computer Test Generator CD
PH Presentation Pro CD-ROM

www.PHSchool.com
Student Site
- Teacher Web Code: ack-5500
- Algebra Readiness Puzzles 67
- Self-grading Lesson Quiz

PH SuccessNet Teacher Center
- Lesson Planner
- Resources

Ongoing Assessment and Intervention

Before the Lesson
Diagnose prerequisite skills using:
- Check Skills You'll Need

During the Lesson
Monitor progress using:
- Check Understanding
- Additional Examples
- Test Prep

After the Lesson
Assess knowledge using:
- Lesson Quiz
- Computer Test Generator CD

2. Teach

Math Background

A mathematical *sequence* is a set of numbers, separated by commas, that follows a pattern stated in a rule, such as 2, 5, 8, 11, 14, ... In this sequence, 2 is the first *term*, and each new term is formed by adding 3, the *common difference*, to the previous term. *Arithmetic* sequences have a common difference while *geometric* sequences have a *common ratio*. For example, each term in 5, 10, 20, 40, . . . , is found by multiplying the previous term by 2. To write the terms of a sequence, use the first term of a sequence and the rule, often stated as an algebraic expression, such as $n + 3$ for the arithmetic sequence above or $2n$ for the geometric sequence above.

Teaching Notes

Investigation (Optional)
Ask:

- *What is the difference between the number of cards received in one month and the number in the previous month for Option A?* 20 cards
- *What is the ratio between the number of cards received in one month to the number in the previous month for Option B?* 2 : 1

1 EXAMPLE English Learners

Explain that when the word *arithmetic* is an adjective, as in *arithmetic sequence*, it is pronounced with the accent on the third syllable (a-rith-met´-ic). When the same word is used by itself as a noun, it is pronounced with the accent on the second syllable (a-rith´-met-ic).

2 EXAMPLE Error Prevention

Help students see why the common difference is negative by reminding them that the common difference is always added to the previous term.

3 EXAMPLE Auditory Learners

Suggest that students say aloud to themselves, "128 times what number is 64? 64 times what number is 32?" and so forth.

Each number in a sequence is called a **term.** You can often use inductive reasoning to find the terms of a sequence. Recall from Lesson 8-4 that inductive reasoning is making conclusions based on patterns you observe.

1 EXAMPLE Finding Terms of a Sequence

Find the next three terms in the sequence 2, 6, 10, 14, . . .

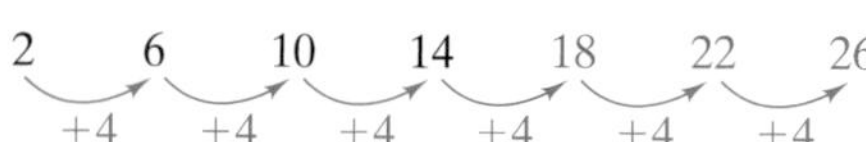

You find each term by adding 4 to the previous term. The next three terms are 18, 22, and 26.

Check Understanding 1 Find the next three terms in each sequence.

a. 5, 12, 19, 26, . . . 33, 40, 47
b. 4, 9, 14, 19, . . . 24, 29, 34
c. 2, 12, 22, 32, . . . 42, 52, 62

Reading Math
You pronounce *arithmetic sequence* as "ar ith MEH tik SEE kwens."

The sequence in Example 1 is an arithmetic sequence. Each term of an **arithmetic sequence** is found by *adding* a fixed number to the previous term. This fixed number is called the **common difference.**

The common difference in Example 1 is 4. The rule for the sequence in Example 1 is, *Start with 2 and add 4 repeatedly*.

2 EXAMPLE Writing a Rule for an Arithmetic Sequence

Find the common difference in the arithmetic sequence 8.3, 7.9, 7.5, 7.1, . . . Write the rule for the sequence and find the next three terms.

8.3 7.9 7.5 7.1 6.7 6.3 5.9
−0.4 −0.4 −0.4 −0.4 −0.4 −0.4

The common difference for this sequence is −0.4. The rule is, *Start with 8.3 and add −0.4 repeatedly*. The next three terms are 6.7, 6.3, and 5.9.

Check Understanding 2 Find the common difference in each arithmetic sequence. Write the rule for each sequence and find the next three terms. 2a–c. See left.

a. 3.2, 3.5, 3.8, 4.1, . . .
b. 6, 4, 2, 0, −2, . . .
c. $9, 8\frac{1}{2}, 8, 7\frac{1}{2}, \ldots$

2a. 0.3; start with 3.2 and add 0.3 repeatedly; 4.4, 4.7, 5.0.
b. −2; start with 6 and add −2 repeatedly; −4, −6, −8.
c. $-\frac{1}{2}$; start with 9 and add $-\frac{1}{2}$ repeatedly; $7, 6\frac{1}{2}, 6$.

The sequence 2, 6, 18, 54, . . . is a geometric sequence. Each term of a **geometric sequence** is found by *multiplying* the previous term by a fixed number. This fixed number is called the **common ratio.**

2 6 18 54
×3 ×3 ×3

The common ratio in this sequence is 3, and the rule is, *Start with 2 and multiply by 3 repeatedly*. The next three terms in the sequence are 162, 486, and 1,458.

Reaching All Students

Below Level	Advanced Learners	
Below Level Ask students to give the next three numbers in this pattern: 2, 4, 6, 8, 10, . . . , and to explain how they know. 12, 14, 16; even numbers or counting by 2s	**Advanced Learners** A 5-in. plant grows 1.5 in. each month. Find its height after 3 months. 9.5 in. Write the rule. Start with 5 and add 1.5 repeatedly.	**English Learners** See note on page 638. **Inclusion** See note on page 639.

Brazil won the 2002 FIFA World Cup soccer tournament.

3 EXAMPLE Writing a Rule for a Geometric Sequence 

Sports The first round of a soccer tournament begins with 128 teams. The following rounds have 64 teams, 32 teams, 16 teams, and so on. Write the rule for the geometric sequence and find the next three terms.

$$128 \quad 64 \quad 32 \quad 16 \quad 8 \quad 4 \quad 2$$
$$\times\tfrac{1}{2} \quad \times\tfrac{1}{2} \quad \times\tfrac{1}{2} \quad \times\tfrac{1}{2} \quad \times\tfrac{1}{2} \quad \times\tfrac{1}{2}$$

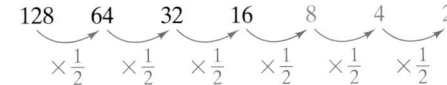

The common ratio is $\frac{1}{2}$.

The rule is, *Start with 128 and multiply by $\frac{1}{2}$ repeatedly*. The next three terms are 8, 4, and 2.

 **Check Understanding** 3 Find the common ratio in each geometric sequence. Write the rule for each sequence and find the next three terms. 3a–c. See below left.

a. 0.1, 1, 10, 100, . . . **b.** 512, 256, 128, 64, . . .

c. Number Sense If you know the first two terms of a sequence, can you determine the rule for the sequence? Explain.

OBJECTIVE

2 Evaluating Algebraic Expressions to Write Sequences

3a. 10; start with 0.1 and multiply by 10 repeatedly; 1,000; 10,000; 100,000.

b. $\frac{1}{2}$; start with 512 and multiply by $\frac{1}{2}$ repeatedly; 32, 16, 8.

c. No; you need at least three to see a pattern.

You can use an algebraic expression to make a sequence. Just evaluate the expression by using the counting numbers 1, 2, 3, . . .

4 EXAMPLE Evaluating Algebraic Expressions

Find the first four terms of the sequence represented by each expression.

a. $n(n + 1)$

Term Number (n)	1	2	3	4
Term of Sequence	$1(1 + 1) = 2$	$2(2 + 1) = 6$	$3(3 + 1) = 12$	$4(4 + 1) = 20$

b. $4 + 3n$

Term Number (n)	1	2	3	4
Term of Sequence	$4 + 3 \cdot 1 = 7$	$4 + 3 \cdot 2 = 10$	$4 + 3 \cdot 3 = 13$	$4 + 3 \cdot 4 = 16$

c. $4 \cdot 3^n$

Term Number (n)	1	2	3	4
Term of Sequence	$4 \cdot 3^1 = 12$	$4 \cdot 3^2 = 36$	$4 \cdot 3^3 = 108$	$4 \cdot 3^4 = 324$

Check Understanding 4 Find the first four terms of the sequence represented by each expression.

a. $n(n - 1)$ 0, 2, 6, 12 **b.** $6 \cdot 2^n$ 12, 24, 48, 96 **c.** $6 + 2n$ 8, 10, 12, 14

4 EXAMPLE **Inclusion**

Make sure students realize that a sequence may be neither arithmetic nor geometric. The pattern for such a sequence has no common difference and no common ratio.

PowerPoint

Additional Examples

1 Find the next three terms in the sequence 3, 10, 17, 24, ... 31, 38, 45

2 Find the common difference in the arithmetic sequence 12.4, 11.2, 10, 8.8, ... Write the rule for the sequence and find the next three terms. −1.2; Start with 12.4 and add −1.2 repeatedly; 7.6, 6.4, 5.2

3 A scientist isolates 10 cells in a dish. The next day there are 40 cells in the dish. The day after there are 160 cells. Write the rule for the geometric sequence and find the next three terms. Start with 10 and multiply by 4 repeatedly; 640; 2,560; 10,240

4 Find the first four terms of the sequence represented by each expression.

a. $(n - 1)n$ 0, 2, 6, 12
b. $1 + 2(n - 1)$ 1, 3, 5, 7
c. $5 \cdot 2^{n+1}$ 20, 40, 80, 160

Closure

- *What is an arithmetic sequence?* a set of numbers that has a common difference between each term
- *What is a geometric sequence?* a set of numbers in which each term is related to the previous term by a common ratio
- *How do you use an algebraic expression to write a sequence?* Substitute the term number for the variable and evaluate. Repeat to find the value of each term of the sequence.

3. Practice

Assignment Guide

1 Objective 1

- A B Core 1–18, 25–33, 35
- C Extension 41

2 Objective 2

- A B Core 19–24, 34, 36
- C Extension 37–40

Test Prep 42–45

Mixed Review 46–49

Geometry Connection

Exercise 34 Ask: *What kind of sequence do the volumes form?* neither arithmetic nor geometric

Practice 12-1 Sequences

Write the rule for each sequence and find the next three terms.

1. 3, 8, 13, 18, 23, 28, 33
   Start with 3 and add 5 repeatedly.
2. 7, 14, 28, 56, 112, 224, 448
   Start with 7 and multiply by 2 repeatedly.
3. 32, 8, 2, $\frac{1}{2}$, $\frac{1}{8}$, $\frac{1}{32}$, $\frac{1}{128}$
   Start with 32 and multiply by $\frac{1}{4}$ repeatedly.
4. 14, 11, 8, 5, 2, −1, −4
   Start with 14 and add −3 repeatedly.
5. 35, 23, 11, −1, −13, −25, −37
   Start with 35 and add −12 repeatedly.
6. 3,000, 300, 30, 3, 0.3, 0.03, 0.003
   Start with 3,000 and multiply by 0.1 repeatedly.

Find the next three terms in each sequence. Identify each as arithmetic, geometric, or neither. For each arithmetic or geometric sequence, find the common difference or ratio.

7. 7.1, 7.5, 7.9, 8.3, ___, ___, ___
   8.7, 9.1, 9.5; arith.; 0.4
8. 5, 6, 8, 11, 15, 20, ___, ___, ___
   26, 33, 41; neither
9. 8,000; 4,000; 2,000; 1,000; ___; ___; ___
   500, 250, 125; geom.; $\frac{1}{2}$
10. 92, 89, 86, 83, ___, ___, ___
    80, 77, 74; arith.; −3
11. −1, 2, −4, 8, ___, ___, ___
    −16, 32, −64; geometric.; −2
12. 2.3, 2.03, 2.003, 2.0003, ___, ___, ___
    2.00003, 2.000003, 2.0000003; neithe
13. 1, 3, 6, 8, 16, 18, 36, ___, ___, ___
    38, 76, 78; neither
14. 140, 133, 126, 119, ___, ___, ___
    112, 105, 98; arith.; −7
15. 3, 9, 27, 81, ___, ___, ___
    243, 729, 2,187; geom.; 3
16. 540, 270, 90, 22.5, ___, ___, ___
    4.5, 0.75, 0.10714285; neither

Tell whether each situation produces an *arithmetic sequence, geometric sequence,* or *neither.*

17. The temperature rises at the rate of 0.75°F per hour. arithmetic
18. A person loses 2 lb each month. arithmetic
19. A toadstool doubles in size each week. geometric
20. A person receives a 6% raise each year. geometric

Find the first four terms of the sequence represented by each expression.

21. $4 \cdot 3^{n+1}$
    12, 36, 108, 324
22. $4 + 3(n-2)$
    −2, 1, 4, 7
23. $n^2(n-1)$
    0, 0, 4, 18

Reteaching 12-1 Sequences

A *sequence* is a set of numbers that follows a pattern.

In an *arithmetic sequence,* each term is found by *adding* a fixed number to the previous term. The number that you add is called the *common difference.*

Example 1: Find the next three terms in the arithmetic sequence: 8, 5, 2, −1, −4, . . .

- The common difference is 5 − 8 = −3.
- Add −3 for the next three terms.

$-4 + (-3) = -7$
$-7 + (-3) = -10$
$-10 + (-3) = -13$

The next three terms are −7, −10, and −13.

In a *geometric sequence,* each term is found by *multiplying* the previous term by a fixed number. The number that you multiply by is called the *common ratio.*

Example 2: Find the next three terms in the geometric sequence: 2, 6, 18, 54, . . .

- The common ratio is $\frac{18}{6} = 3$.
- Multiply by 3 for the next three terms.

$54 \times 3 = 162$
$162 \times 3 = 486$
$486 \times 3 = 1{,}458$

The next three terms are 162, 468, and 1,458.

The sequence: 1, 4, 9, 16, . . . is neither arithmetic nor geometric.

Its pattern is $1^2, 2^2, 3^2, 4^2, \ldots$

Its next three terms are $5^2, 6^2, 7^2$, or 25, 36, 49.

Find the common difference or ratio in each sequence.

1. 2, 6, 10, 14, . . . 4
2. 30, 20, 10, 0, . . . −10
3. −12, −4, 4, 12, . . . 8
4. 6, 12, 24, 48, . . . 2
5. $1, \frac{1}{3}, \frac{1}{9}, \frac{1}{27}$ $\frac{1}{3}$
6. 250, 25, 2.5, 0.25, . . . 0.1

Identify each sequence as *arithmetic, geometric,* or *neither.* Find the next three terms of the sequence.

7. $4, 2, 1, \frac{1}{2} \ldots$
   geometric; $\frac{1}{4}, \frac{1}{8}, \frac{1}{16}$
8. 0.2, 0.4, 0.6, 0.8, . . .
   arithmetic; 1, 1.2, 1.4
9. $1, \frac{1}{4}, \frac{1}{9}, \frac{1}{16}$
   neither; $\frac{1}{25}, \frac{1}{36}, \frac{1}{49}$
10. 70, 50, 30, 10, . . .
    arithmetic; −10, −30, −50
11. 1, 2, 1, 2, 1, 2, . . .
    neither; 1, 2, 1
12. 4, 8, 16, 32, . . .
    geometric; 64, 128, 256

EXERCISES

For more practice, see *Extra Practice.*

A Practice by Example

Find the next three terms in each sequence.

Example 1 (page 638)

1. 0, 2, 4, 6, . . . 8, 10, 12
2. 8, 15, 22, 29, . . . 36, 43, 50
3. 11, 15, 19, 23, . . . 27, 31, 35
4. 4, 7, 10, 13, 16, . . . 19, 22, 25
5. −10, 20, 50, 80, . . . 110, 140, 170
6. −3, 2, 7, 12, . . . 17, 22, 27

Example 2 (page 638)

Find the common difference or ratio in each sequence. Write the rule for each sequence and find the next three terms. 7–18. See margin.

7. −1, 2, 5, 8, . . .
8. 2.8, 2.3, 1.8, 1.3, . . .
9. 22, 15, 8, 1, . . .
10. 20, 17, 14, 11, . . .
11. −12, −8, −4, 0, . . .
12. 1, 2.3, 3.6, 4.9, . . .

Example 3 (page 639)

13. 750, 75, 7.5, 0.75, . . .
14. 100, 200, 400, 800, . . .
15. $1, \frac{1}{2}, \frac{1}{4}, \frac{1}{8}, \ldots$
16. 3, 6, 12, 24, . . .
17. 0.12, 0.36, 1.08, . . .
18. 125, 25, 5, 1, . . .

Example 4 (page 639)

Find the first four terms of the sequence represented by each expression.

19. $5 + 2n$ 7, 9, 11, 13
20. $n(n + 10)$ 11, 24, 39, 56
21. $3 \cdot 2^n$ 6, 12, 24, 48
22. $2 + 2n$ 4, 6, 8, 10
23. $6 \cdot 4^n$ 24; 96; 384; 1,536
24. $5n + 6$ 11, 16, 21, 26

B Apply Your Skills

Identify each sequence as *arithmetic, geometric,* or *neither.* Find the next three terms of the sequence.

25. 2, 2.3, 2.6, 2.9, . . . arithmetic; 3.2, 3.5, 3.8
26. 2, 5, 10, 17, . . . neither; 26, 37, 50
27. 21, 15, 9, 3, . . . arithmetic; −3, −9, −15
28. 2, 6, 18, 54, . . .
29. 2, 1, 0.5, 0.25, . . .
30. 1.1, 1.01, 1.001, . . .

28–30. See back of book.

31. **Movies** In the 1957 movie *The Incredible Shrinking Man,* the main character mysteriously starts shrinking. Suppose his original height is 6 ft and he shrinks 3 in. every day.
    a. How tall is the man at the end of one week? 4 ft 3 in. or 51 in.
    b. How many days would it take for the man to shrink to half his original height? 12 days
    c. Write a rule for the sequence. Start with 72 in. and add −3 repeatedly.

Real-World Connection

Many of the special effects in *The Incredible Shrinking Man* were created by using split screens and oversized props.

Tell whether each situation produces an *arithmetic sequence, geometric sequence,* or *neither.*

32. A baby gains 2 oz every week. arithmetic sequence
33. The time a person bikes each day varies between 30 and 45 minutes. neither
34. a. **Geometry** Find the volumes of cubes with side lengths 2, 3, 4, and 5. a. 8, 27, 64, 125
    b. These volumes form a sequence. How do you find each term? b. Volume is the length of the side cubed.
    c. Write an expression for the sequence. $(n + 1)^3$
35. **Writing in Math** Will an arithmetic sequence that has a negative common difference always contain negative numbers? Explain. Yes; if you start with any number and repeatedly add a negative number, you eventually will end up with negative terms.

Use the Guided Problem Solving worksheet with Exercise 34.

7. 3; start with −1 and add 3 repeatedly; 11, 14, 17.
8. −0.5; start with 2.8 and add −0.5 repeatedly; 0.8, 0.3, −0.2.
9. −7; start with 22 and add −7 repeatedly; −6, −13, −20.
10. −3; start with 20 and add −3 repeatedly; 8, 5, 2.
11. 4; start with −12 and add 4 repeatedly; 4, 8, 12.
12. 1.3; start with 1 and add 1.3 repeatedly; 6.2, 7.5, 8.8.
13. 0.1; start with 750 and multiply by 0.1 repeatedly; 0.075, 0.0075, 0.00075.

14–18. See back of book.

37. 3, 10, 17, 24; arithmetic
38. 400, 200, 100, 50; geometric
39. 2, 0, 0, 2; neither
40. 10, 20, 40, 80; geometric

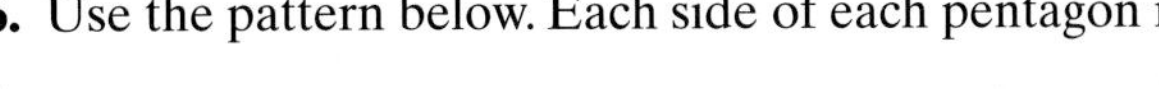

36. Use the pattern below. Each side of each pentagon is one unit long.

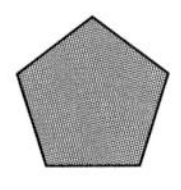
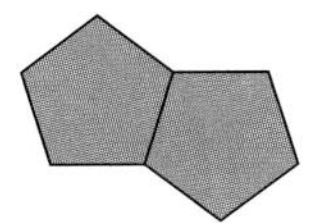
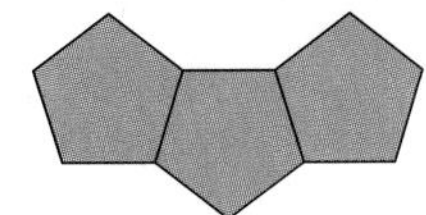

a. Write a sequence of numbers showing how the perimeter of the figure changes with each step. 5, 8, 11, 14, 17, . . .

b. What is the perimeter of a row of ten regular pentagons? Explain how you found your answer. 32; answers may vary. Sample: Start with 5 and add 3 a total of 9 times.

C Challenge

Evaluate each expression for $n = 1, 2, 3,$ and 4. Is the sequence formed *arithmetic, geometric,* or *neither*? 37–40. See above left.

37. $7(n - 1) + 3$ **38.** $400 \cdot \left(\frac{1}{2}\right)^{n-1}$ **39.** $n(n - 5) + 6$ **40.** $5 \cdot 2^n$

41. **Stretch Your Thinking** Jamil bought half as many carnival tickets as Wanda. If Wanda buys 12 more tickets, Jamil will have $\frac{2}{5}$ the number of tickets that Wanda has. How many tickets did Jamil buy? 24 tickets

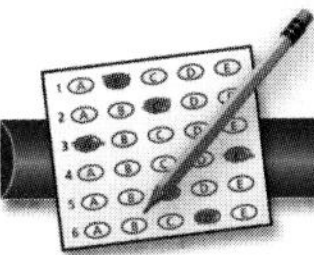

Test Prep

Multiple Choice

42. You start an exercise program. You begin by walking 2 mi the first day and increase your distance by 0.3 mi each day. Which expression represents your distance on the sixth day? C

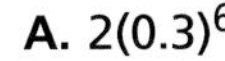

A. $2(0.3)^6$ B. $2 + 6(0.3)$ C. $2 + 5(0.3)$ D. $0.3 + (2)^5$

Take It to the NET
Online lesson quiz at
www.PHSchool.com
Web Code: aca-1201

43. Which expression represents the sequence 13, 16, 19, 22, . . . ? I

F. $4n - 1$ G. $n + 2$ H. $3n$ I. $3n + 10$

44. Find the next term in the sequence 3, 15, 75, 375, . . . D

A. 387 B. 475 C. 1,125 D. 1,875

Short Response

45. In the Fibonacci sequence 1, 1, 2, 3, 5, 8, . . . , you can find each term (after the first two terms) by adding certain terms together. See margin.

a. Write a rule for the sequence.

b. Use the rule to write the next three terms of the sequence.

Mixed Review

Lesson 11-5

Find each probability. A bag contains 7 black paper clips, 2 blue paper clips, and 10 red paper clips. One paper clip is chosen at random and is not replaced. Then a second paper clip is chosen.

46. P(black, then red) $\frac{35}{171}$ **47.** P(red, then blue) $\frac{10}{171}$ **48.** P(blue, then blue) $\frac{1}{171}$

Lesson 10-1

49. Make a frequency table and a line plot for the data below.

hours of exercise each week: 2 9 1 4 5 5 4 6 7 2 3 6 4 4 1

See margin.

45. [2] a. Add the two previous terms to get the next term.
b. 13, 21, 34
[1] minor error in rule OR one incorrect term

49.

Number	1	2	3	4	5	6	7	8	9
Frequency	2	2	1	4	2	2	1	0	1

See back of book for line plot.

4. Assess

Lesson Quiz 12-1

Write a rule for each sequence.

1. 1, 8, 64, 512, . . . Start with 1 and multiply by 8 repeatedly.
2. 100, 85, 70, 55, . . . Start with 100 and add −15 repeatedly.
3. −2, −6, −18, −54, . . . Start with −2 and multiply by 3 repeatedly.
4. Write the first four terms of the sequence represented by $-7n + 21$. 14, 7, 0, −7

Alternative Assessment

Each student in a pair writes an arithmetic sequence. Partners trade papers and find the next three terms and the rule for their partner's sequence. Pairs repeat the activity for a geometric sequence.

Test Prep

Resources

For additional practice with a variety of test item formats:

- Test Prep, p. 691
- Test-Taking Strategies, p. 687
- Test-Taking Strategies with Transparencies

Enrichment 12-1 Sequences

Patterns in Numbers

1. Study the triangle of numbers and describe the numbers in the pattern. The numbers are consecutive odd numbers.

2. Continue the triangle by writing the numbers in the next four rows.

1
3 5
7 9 11
13 15 17 19
21 23 25 27 29
31 33 35 37 39 41
43 45 47 49 51 53 55
57 59 61 63 65 67 69 71
73 75 77 79 81 83 85 87 89
91 93 95 97 99 101 103 105 107 109

3. Find the sum of the numbers in each row. Describe these numbers. 1, 8, 27, 64, 125, 216, 343, 512, 729, and 1,000
They are cubes: $1^3, 2^3, 3^3, 4^3, 5^3, 6^3, 7^3, 8^3, 9^3$, and 10^3.

4. Find the mean (average) of the numbers in each row. Describe these numbers. 1, 4, 9, 16, 25, 36, 49, 64, 81, and 100
They are squares: $1^2, 2^2, 3^2, 4^2, 5^2, 6^2, 7^2, 8^2, 9^2$, and 10^2.

5. Look for the following diagonals in the triangle. List the next four numbers in each sequence.
a. 11, 17, 25, 35, 47, 61, 77, 95
b. 21, 33, 47, 63, 81, 101
c. Describe the pattern. Each number in the sequence increases by two more than the preceding number increased.

6. Does this pattern hold true for the other diagonals in the triangle? yes

Technology

Exploring Sequences

In Lesson 12-1, students investigated sequences and used algebraic expressions to write them. In this activity, they use formulas along with a graphing calculator to generate terms of sequences.

Optional Materials

- graphing calculator
- Classroom Aid 36

Teaching Notes

1 EXAMPLE Teaching Tip

Ask: *What kind of sequence are you generating here? Explain.* A geometric sequence, because each term is found by multiplying the previous term by a fixed number (the common ratio).

2 EXAMPLE Technology Tip

Model the specific keystroke sequences presented. Provide time for students to familiarize themselves with these special keys.

Error Prevention!

Students may press the keys in the wrong order. To help remediate this kind of error, have students work through the examples in pairs, together identifying the keys to press before one partner presses them.

Exercises

Have students work in pairs on the exercises. Before they begin work on Exercises 5–8, have them record the keystrokes they will use to find the sequence of y-values. They can do so taking turns; one partner writes and the other presses the keys. Have pairs compare their sequence rules with other pairs.

Technology — Exploring Sequences

For Use With Lesson 12-1

You can use a graphing calculator to generate a sequence.

1 EXAMPLE Generating Terms of a Sequence

Find the first five terms of the sequence with the rule *Start with 100 and multiply by 0.9 repeatedly.*

Step 1 Press 100 ENTER.

Step 2 Press × 0.9 ENTER.

Step 3 Press ENTER repeatedly.

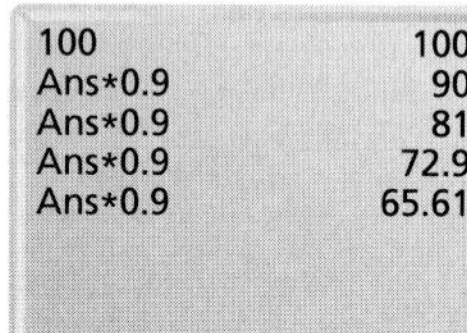

100 100
Ans*0.9 90
Ans*0.9 81
Ans*0.9 72.9
Ans*0.9 65.61

The first five terms are 100, 90, 81, 72.9, and 65.61.

You can also use a formula to make a sequence.

2 EXAMPLE Writing a Rule for a Sequence

Find the sequence of y-values when $y = 3x + 2$ and $x = 1, 2, 3, 4,$ and 5. Then write a rule for the sequence.

Step 1 Press Y= and enter the formula.

Step 2 Use the TBLSET feature.

Step 3 Use the TABLE feature.

Plot1 Plot2 Plot3
\Y1 = 3X+2
\Y2 =
\Y3 =
\Y4 =

TABLE SETUP
TblStart=1
ΔTbl=1
Indpnt: Auto Ask
Depend: Auto Ask

X	Y1
1	5
2	8
3	11
4	14
5	17
6	20
7	23

X=1

The sequence is 5, 8, 11, 14, 17. The rule is, *Start with 5 and add 3 repeatedly.*

EXERCISES

Find the first five terms of each sequence.

1. Start with −3.5; add 0.7 repeatedly. −3.5, −2.8, −2.1, −1.4, −0.7
2. Start with 900; subtract 83 repeatedly. 900, 817, 734, 651, 568
3. Start with 250; multiply by 0.8 repeatedly. 250, 200, 160, 128, 102.4
4. Start with 10; multiply by −1.5 repeatedly. 10, −15, 22.5, −33.75, 50.625

For each formula, find the sequence of y-values when $x = 1, 2, 3, 4,$ and 5. Then write a rule for the sequence. 5–8. See margin.

5. $y = x + 4$
6. $y = 5 \cdot 3^x$
7. $y = -4x + 30$
8. $y = 2x + 4$

Technology

5. 5, 6, 7, 8, 9; start with 5 and add 1 repeatedly.
6. 15, 45, 135, 405, 1,215; start with 15 and multiply by 3 repeatedly.
7. 26, 22, 18, 14, 10; start with 26 and add −4 repeatedly.
8. 6, 8, 10, 12, 14; start with 6 and add 2 repeatedly.

12-2 Functions

What You'll Learn

1. To represent functions with equations and tables
2. To use function notation

. . . And Why

To find the deposit due on containers, as in Example 1

Check Skills You'll Need

For help, go to Lesson 1-1.

Evaluate each expression for $v = 7$.

1. $2(v - 3)$ 8
2. $7v + 4$ 53
3. $v + 13$ 20
4. $3v - 12$ 9
5. $-5(15 - 2v)$ −5
6. $11(v + 24)$ 341
7. Write an algebraic expression for the word phrase "2 less than p." $p - 2$

New Vocabulary
- function
- function rule

OBJECTIVE 1

Representing Functions

To encourage recycling, many states require a nickel deposit on drink containers. The total amount of the deposit you pay depends on the number of containers you buy. You can describe this relationship using an equation with two variables.

$d = \$.05c$ ← input variable: c = number of containers
↑
output variable: d = deposit

A **function** is a relationship that assigns exactly one output value to each input value. A **function rule** is an equation that describes a function.

1 EXAMPLE Representing Functions

Recycling Complete the table of input/output pairs for the function rule $d = \$.05c$ where d represents the deposit and c represents the number of containers.

Input c (number of containers)	Output d (deposit)
6	■ ← $.05 × 6 = $.30
12	■ ← $.05 × 12 = $.60
24	■ ← $.05 × 24 = $1.20

1.

c	d
5	$.50
10	$1.00
15	$1.50

Check Understanding 1 The deposit on each drink container is $.10 in the state of Michigan. Use the function rule $d = \$0.1c$. Make a table of input/output pairs to show the total amount of the deposits on 5, 10, and 15 containers. See above left.

12-2

1. Plan

Lesson Preview

Check Skills You'll Need

Evaluating Algebraic Expressions
Lesson 1-1: Examples 2–3. Extra Practice, p. 702.

Lesson Resources

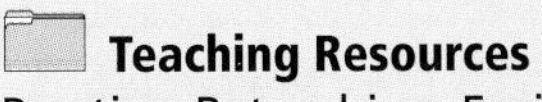

Teaching Resources
Practice, Reteaching, Enrichment

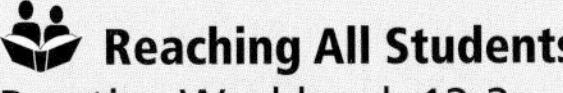

Reaching All Students
Practice Workbook 12-2
Spanish Practice Workbook 12-2
Guided Problem Solving 12-2

Presentation Assistant Plus!
Transparencies
- Check Skills You'll Need 12-2
- Problem of the Day 12-2
- Additional Examples 12-2
- Student Edition Answers 12-2
- Lesson Quiz 12-2

PH Presentation Pro CD-ROM 12-2

PRENTICE HALL ASSESSMENT SYSTEM

Computer Test Generator CD

Technology
Resource Pro® CD-ROM
Computer Test Generator CD
PH Presentation Pro CD-ROM

www.PHSchool.com
Student Site
- Teacher Web Code: ack-5500
- Self-grading Lesson Quiz

PH SuccessNet Teacher Center
- Lesson Planner
- Resources

Plus 

Ongoing Assessment and Intervention

Before the Lesson
Diagnose prerequisite skills using:
- Check Skills You'll Need

During the Lesson
Monitor progress using:
- Check Understanding
- Additional Examples
- Test Prep

After the Lesson
Assess knowledge using:
- Lesson Quiz
- Computer Test Generator CD

2. Teach

Math Background

A mathematical function is a relationship (or set of ordered pairs) that has exactly one y-value for a given x-value. For example, {(2, 3), (2, 4), (2, 5)} is not a function because 2 has more than one matching y-value. But, {(3, 2), (4, 2), (5, 2)} is a function because each x is matched to a single y.

Teaching Notes

2 EXAMPLE Error Prevention

Discuss the differences between $2(x)$ or $x(y)$ and the symbol $f(x)$. Elicit the fact that $f(x)$ does NOT mean the product of f and x.

3 EXAMPLE Inclusion

Point out that students can think of $f(x)$ as being the same as y, so $f(x) = 2x + 7$ is like $y = 2x + 7$ and $f(n) = 2n$ is like $c = 2n$, where c is the cost for n fish.

PowerPoint

Additional Examples

1. Complete the table for $p = 4s$.

Input s	3	5	7	9
Output p	12	20	28	36

2. Use the function rule $f(x) = 3x - 1$. Find the output values $f(2)$, $f(-1)$, and $f(5)$. 5, −4, 14

3. Use functional notation to show the relationship between the total number of cars and the number of tires. Identify your variables. Sample: $f(t) = t \div 4$ where t is the number of tires and $f(t)$ is the number of cars

Closure

- *What is a function?* a relationship that assigns exactly one output value to each input value
- *How can you use function notation to write a function rule?* Write an equation in the form $y =$ but use $f(x)$ for y, the output, and x for the input.

OBJECTIVE 2

Using Function Notation

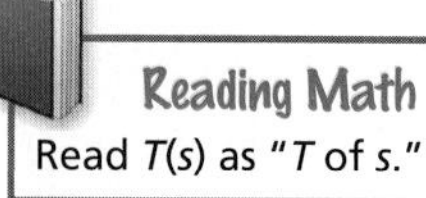

Reading Math
Read $T(s)$ as "T of s."

Function notation is an abbreviation for lengthy word descriptions.

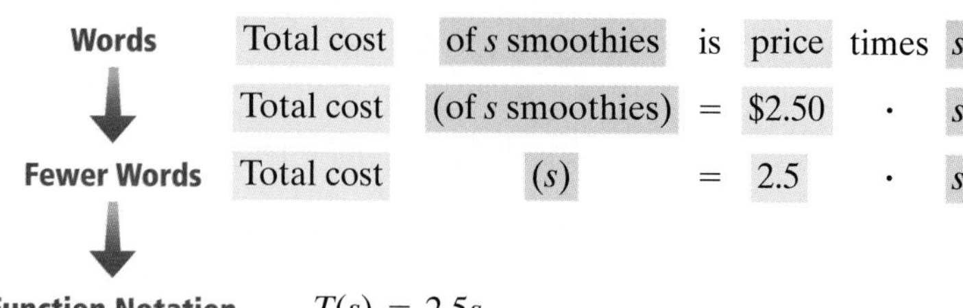

Words	Total cost	of s smoothies	is	price	times	s
	Total cost	(of s smoothies)	=	\$2.50	·	s
Fewer Words	Total cost	(s)	=	2.5	·	s
Function Notation	$T(s) = 2.5s$					

2 EXAMPLE Evaluating a Function Rule

Use the function rule $T(s) = 2.5s$. Find the output value $T(4)$.

$T(s) = 2.5s$ ← **Write the function rule.**
$T(4) = 2.5(4)$ ← **Substitute the input value for s.**
$= 10$ ← **Simplify.**

Check Understanding 2 Use the function rule $f(x) = -4x + 12$. Find each output.
a. $f(-7)$ 40 **b.** $f(3)$ 0 **c.** $f(8)$ −20
d. Number Sense Is the output value of the function rule $f(x) = -4x + 12$ always positive or always negative if the input value is negative? always positive

$T(4)$ means *total cost of 4 smoothies.* Notice that $T(4)$ does *not* mean the product of T and 4. It means the output of the function when the input is 4.

3 EXAMPLE Using Function Notation

Real World

Aquariums Suppose you buy several dwarf gourami fish at \$2 each. Use function notation to show the relationship between the total cost and the number of fish you buy. Identify the variables you use.

Words total cost = \$2 · number of fish bought

Let n = the number of fish bought. ← **input**

Let $f(n)$ = the total cost. ← **output**

Function $f(n) = 2 \cdot n$

$f(n) = 2n$

3a. $f(c) = 4c$ where c is the number of cars you wash and $f(c)$ is the amount of money you make for washing c cars.

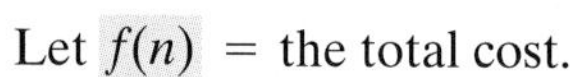

Check Understanding 3 **a.** The money you make (output) is equal to \$4 multiplied by the number of cars you wash (input). Use function notation to show the relationship between the money you make and the number of cars you wash. See above left.
b. Using the function rule in part (a), find $f(6)$. What does this output represent? b. $f(6) = 24$; $f(6)$ is the number of dollars you make if you wash 6 cars.

Reaching All Students

Below Level Discuss familiar relationships that can be expressed as functions, such as the perimeter of a square depends on the length of its sides.

Advanced Learners Have students use functional notation to write expressions for the perimeter of a regular triangle, a pentagon, and an octagon. $f(s) = 3s$; $5s$; $8s$

Inclusion
See note on page 644.
Tactile Learners
See note on page 646.

EXERCISES

For more practice, see *Extra Practice*.

A Practice by Example

Example 1 (page 643)

1. **Hockey** Copy and complete the table of input/output pairs for the function rule $t = \frac{n}{11}$. The variable t represents the number of teams formed in a hockey league. The variable n represents the number of people n who signed up for the league.

Input n (number of people)	Output t (number of teams)
44	■ 4
132	■ 12
165	■ 15

2. **Taxis** The function rule $p = 1.5 + 2m$ represents the taxi fare p in dollars for a ride that is m miles. Make a table of input/output pairs to show the fare if the ride is 2, 6, and 13 miles. See margin.

Example 2 (page 644)

Use the function rule $f(x) = 2x + 3$. Find each output.

3. $f(0)$ 3
4. $f(-2)$ -1
5. $f(2)$ 7
6. $f(10)$ 23
7. $f(-16.7)$ -30.4
8. $f(5.5)$ 14
9. $f(7)$ 17
10. $f(-6.3)$ -9.6
11. $f(32)$ 67
12. $f(-0.09)$ 2.82

Example 3 (page 644)

13. **Energy** For each hour a stereo is on, it uses 0.04 kilowatt-hours of energy. Complete the function rule $E(h) = \underline{?}$ to describe the relationship between the total energy used by the stereo $E(h)$ and the number of hours the stereo is on h. $0.04h$

14. **Groceries** Suppose potatoes cost \$.99 a pound. Complete the function rule $C(p) = \underline{?}$ to describe the relationship between the total cost $C(p)$ and the number of pounds of potatoes you buy p. $0.99p$

B Apply Your Skills

Find $f(-7)$ and $f(7)$ for each function.

15. $f(n) = 10n$ $-70, 70$
16. $f(a) = |a|$ 7, 7
17. $f(t) = t^2$ 49, 49

18. **Laundry** The function $y = 40x$ describes the number of gallons of water used to wash x loads of laundry in a washing machine.
    a. Find the value of y when $x = 0$ and when $x = 6$. What does each output represent? 18a–b. See margin.
    b. The *domain* of a function is all possible input values. The *range* of a function is all possible output values. Which variable, x or y, represents the domain in part (a)? Explain.
    c. What domain value produces a range value of 120? 3

Real-World Connection

The average American household washes 392 loads of laundry each year.

SOURCE: U.S. Dept. of Energy

In a function, each input value can have only one output. Tell whether the data in each table is a function.

19. yes

Input	2	3	4	5	6
Output	5	5	5	5	5

20. no

Input	1	2	2	3	3
Output	1	3	6	9	12

2.

m	p
2	5.50
6	13.50
13	27.50

18a. 0; 240; the total number of gallons of water used to wash x loads of laundry

b. x; the number of loads, which is the input, is the domain.

3. Practice

Assignment Guide

Objective 1
- A B Core 1–2, 22–25
- C Extension 36

Objective 2
- A B Core 3–21, 26–32
- C Extension 33–35

Test Prep 37–42

Mixed Review 43–47

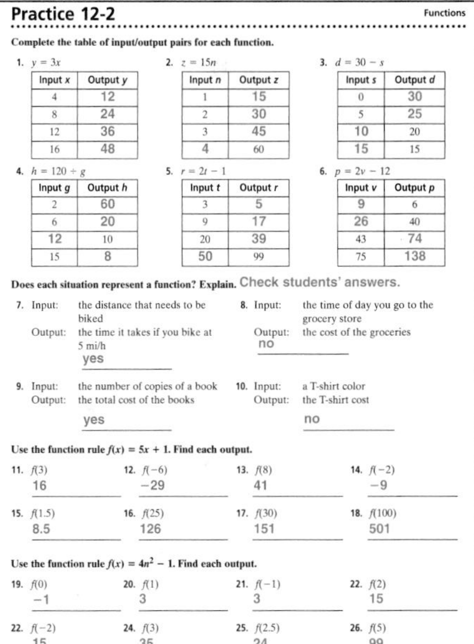

Practice 12-2 Functions

Complete the table of input/output pairs for each function.

1. $y = 3x$

Input x	Output y
4	12
8	24
12	36
16	48

2. $z = 15n$

Input n	Output z
1	15
2	30
3	45
4	60

3. $d = 30 - s$

Input s	Output d
0	30
5	25
10	20
15	15

4. $h = 120 \div g$

Input g	Output h
2	60
6	20
12	10
15	8

5. $r = 2t - 1$

Input t	Output r
3	5
9	17
20	39
50	99

6. $p = 2v - 12$

Input v	Output p
9	6
26	40
43	74
75	138

Does each situation represent a function? Explain. Check students' answers.

7. Input: the distance that needs to be biked
   Output: the time it takes if you bike at 5 mi/h
   yes
8. Input: the time of day you go to the grocery store
   Output: the cost of the groceries
   no
9. Input: the number of copies of a book
   Output: the total cost of the books
   yes
10. Input: a T-shirt color
    Output: the T-shirt cost
    no

Use the function rule $f(x) = 5x + 1$. Find each output.

11. $f(3)$ 16
12. $f(-6)$ -29
13. $f(8)$ 41
14. $f(-2)$ -9
15. $f(1.5)$ 8.5
16. $f(25)$ 126
17. $f(30)$ 151
18. $f(100)$ 501

Use the function rule $f(x) = 4n^2 - 1$. Find each output.

19. $f(0)$ -1
20. $f(1)$ 3
21. $f(-1)$ 3
22. $f(2)$ 15
22. $f(-2)$ 15
24. $f(3)$ 35
25. $f(2.5)$ 24
26. $f(5)$ 99

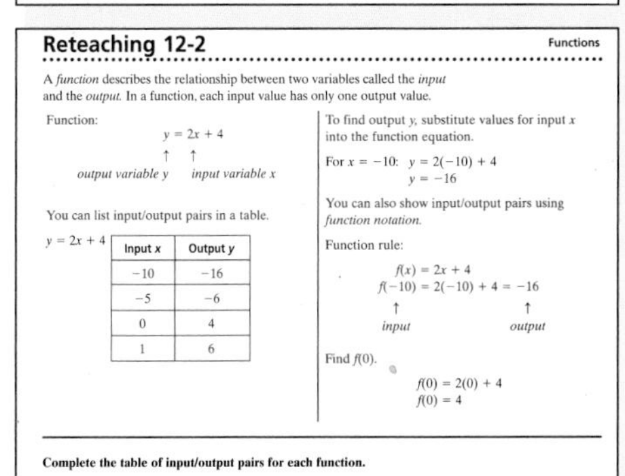

Reteaching 12-2 Functions

A *function* describes the relationship between two variables called the *input* and the *output*. In a function, each input value has only one output value.

Function:

$y = 2x + 4$

↑ output variable y ↑ input variable x

You can list input/output pairs in a table.

$y = 2x + 4$

Input x	Output y
−10	−16
−5	−6
0	4
1	6

To find output y, substitute values for input x into the function equation.

For $x = -10$: $y = 2(-10) + 4$
$y = -16$

You can also show input/output pairs using *function notation*.

Function rule:

$f(x) = 2x + 4$
$f(-10) = 2(-10) + 4 = -16$
↑ *input* ↑ *output*

Find $f(0)$.

$f(0) = 2(0) + 4$
$f(0) = 4$

Complete the table of input/output pairs for each function.

1. $y = 3x$

Input x	Output y
5	15
7	21
9	27
11	33

2. $d = 20r$

Input r	Output d
1	20
2	40
3	60
8	160

3. $y = 25 - 2x$

Input x	Output y
0	25
1	23
2	21
3	19

Use the function rule $f(x) = 3x + 1$. Find each output.

4. $f(0)$ $= 3(\underline{0}) + 1$ $= \underline{1}$
5. $f(1)$ $= 3(\underline{1}) + 1$ $= \underline{4}$
6. $f(2)$ $= 3(\underline{2}) + 1$ $= \underline{7}$
7. $f(-2)$ $= 3(\underline{-2}) + 1$ $= \underline{-5}$
8. $f(5)$ 16
9. $f(-6)$ -17
10. $f(10)$ 31
11. $f(5.5)$ 17.5

Tactile Learners
Exercise 26 Have students create a sign they can post to show the choices and prices.

21. Answers may vary. Sample: (0, −2), (2, 4), (7, 19); each solution (x, y) equals an input/output pair for the function $f(x) = 3x - 2$; $f(0) = -2$, $f(2) = 4$, $f(7) = 19$.

21. **Writing in Math** Find several solutions of the equation $y = 3x - 2$. Explain how these solutions are related to input/output pairs for the function $f(x) = 3x - 2$. Write each solution using function notation. See left.

Copy and complete the table of input/output pairs for each function.

22. $y = 4x$

Input x	Output y
5	■ 20
7	■ 28
9	■ 36
11	■ 44

23. $d = 50t$

Input t	Output d
1	■ 50
2	■ 100
3	■ 150
■ 4	200

24. $y = 20 - 5x$

Input x	Output y
0	■ 20
1	■ 15
■ 2	10
■ 3	5

25. $y = x + 3$

Input x	Output y
12	■ 15
21	■ 24
57	■ 60
■ 42	45

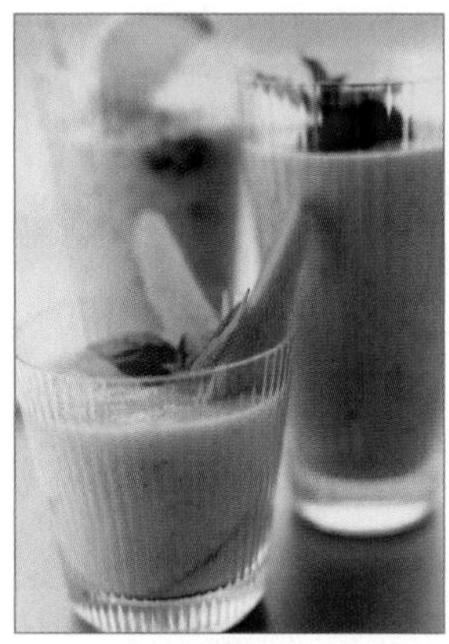

Real-World Connection
In 2001, the sales of the juice and smoothie industry topped $1 billion for the first time.
SOURCE: The Juice and Smoothie Association

26. **Smoothies** Fruit smoothies cost $1.50 each plus $.50 for each fruit mixed into the smoothie. Use function notation to find the cost of a smoothie with 4 different fruits mixed in. $3.50

27. a. Data File, p. 635 A worker in New York City buys newspapers for his office staff. Use function notation to show the relationship between the total cost of the newspapers and the number of newspapers the worker buys. $f(x) = 0.63x$
b. Find $f(15)$. $f(15) = 9.45$
c. Use function notation to show the relationship between the total cost of newspapers in Paris and the number of newspapers bought. $f(x) = 0.69x$
d. Find $f(15)$. $f(15) = 10.35$

28. **Art Supplies** Paintbrushes cost $1.79 each. Use function notation to show the relationship between the total cost and the number of paintbrushes you buy. Use the rule to find the cost of 27 brushes. $C(b) = 1.79b$; $48.33

Use the function rule $f(x) = 3x^2 - 7$. Find each output.

29. $f(0)$ −7
30. $f(-2)$ 5
31. $f(2)$ 5
32. $f(10)$ 293

Challenge

For each function, find $f(1)$, $f(2)$, $f(3)$, and $f(4)$. What type of sequence do these outputs form? 33–35. See left.

33. 96, 92, 88, 84; arithmetic
34. 0.3, 0.03, 0.003, 0.0003; geometric
35. 3, 4, 3, 0; neither

33. $f(n) = 100 - 4n$
34. $f(n) = 3 \cdot 0.1^n$
35. $f(n) = n(4 - n)$

36. **Stretch Your Thinking** Draw a net for a cube that has at most three squares in a line. Write the letters C, U, B, and E in four squares of the net so that when it is folded, the word "CUBE" wraps around the cube. See margin.

Use the Guided Problem Solving worksheet with Exercise 26.

36. Answers may vary. Sample:

	E	
C	U	B

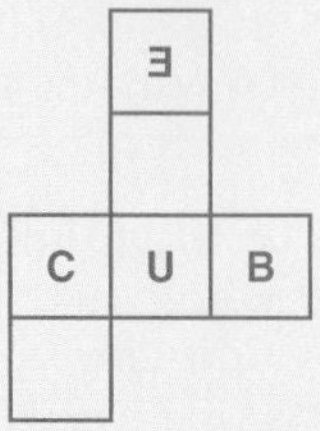

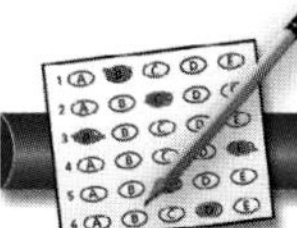

Test Prep

Gridded Response

37. The function $f(r) = \pi r^2$ represents the relationship between the area of a circle and r, the radius of the circle. Find the area in square inches of a circle that has a radius of 12 inches. Round your answer to the nearest square inch. 452

Take It to the NET
Online lesson quiz at **www.PHSchool.com**
Web Code: aca-1202

38. To place an ad in a newspaper, it costs $52 plus $2.50 for each line of the ad. Find the cost in dollars of placing a 7-line ad. 69.50

The function rule $f(x) = x(x + 1)$ represents the product of two consecutive integers. Use the function rule to find each of the following outputs.

39. $f(5)$ 30
40. $f(20)$ 420
41. $f(55)$ 3,080
42. $f(100)$ 10,100

Mixed Review

Lesson 12-1

Find the common difference in each sequence. Write the rule for each sequence, and find the next three terms. 43–46. See margin.

43. $-10, -4, 2, 8, \ldots$
44. $13, 17.5, 22, 26.5, \ldots$
45. $9, 8.2, 7.4, 6.6, \ldots$
46. $\frac{1}{8}, \frac{1}{4}, \frac{3}{8}, \frac{1}{2}, \ldots$

Lesson 11-1

47. **Jeans** A company manufactures blue jeans in 8 waist sizes (28, 30, 32, 34, 36, 38, 40, 42) and 7 lengths (28, 29, 30, 31, 32, 33, 34). How many different types of jeans does the company make? 56 types

Practice Game

What's My Rule?

How to Play

- Player 1 writes a function rule on paper. The other players are not allowed to see this function.
- Make a table like the one at the right. Player 1 writes an input/output pair in the table for the other players to see.
- In turn, each of the other players gives an input and their guess at the corresponding output.
- If a player has a correct input/output pair, the player gets a point and is allowed to guess the function.
- If the player guesses the function correctly, the player gets another point and starts a new round of play.
- Player 1 gets one point each time a player makes an incorrect guess at the function.
- The player with the most points wins.

What's My Rule?

Input	Output
■	■
■	■
■	■
■	■

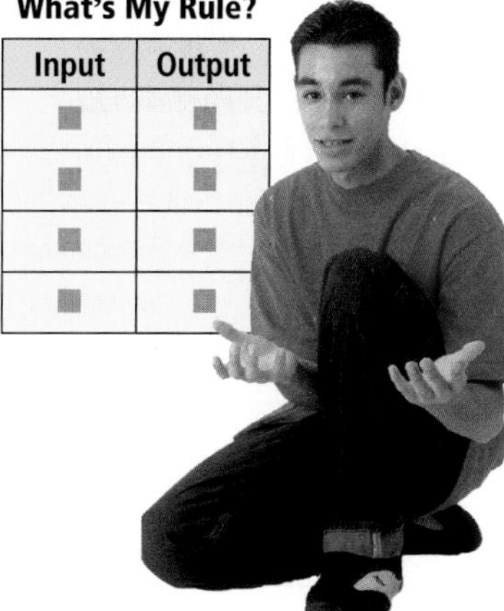

4. Assess

Lesson Quiz 12-2

1. A photocopy costs $.08. Use the function rule $c = \$0.08n$. Make a table of input/output pairs to show the cost for 5, 10, and 15 copies.

Input n	5	10	15
Output c	$.40	$.80	$1.20

Evaluate each of the following for the function rule $f(x) = 40 - 2x$.

2. $f(12)$ 16
3. $f(-12)$ 64

Test Prep

Resources
A sheet of blank grids is available in the *Test-Taking Strategies with Transparencies* booklet. Give copies of this sheet to students so they can practice filling in grids.

For additional practice with a variety of test item formats:
- Test Prep, p. 691
- Test-Taking Strategies, p. 687
- Test-Taking Strategies with Transparencies

46. $\frac{1}{8}$; start with $\frac{1}{8}$ and add $\frac{1}{8}$ repeatedly; $\frac{5}{8}, \frac{3}{4}, \frac{7}{8}$.

Enrichment 12-2 Functions

Patterns in Algebra

Some engineers use the *Rankine* temperature scale in their work. To change a temperature from degrees Fahrenheit to degrees Rankine, you can use the formula $R = 459.67 + F$.

Scientists often use the Celsius temperature scale in their work. To change Celsius temperatures to Rankine temperatures, first change Celsius temperatures to Fahreinheit using the formula $F = \frac{9}{5}C + 32$. Then use the formula above to change to degrees Rankine.

Example: Suppose you want to change 20°C to Rankine.

Step 1: Write as °F. → $F = \frac{9}{5} \cdot 20 + 32$ → $F = 68°$

Step 2: Write as °R. → $R = 459.67 + 68$ → $R = 527.67°$

1. Complete the table.

°Celsius	°Fahrenheit	°Rankine
5	41	500.67
10	50	509.67
15	59	518.67
20	68	527.67
25	77	536.67
30	86	545.67
35	95	554.67

2. Describe the pattern that occurs as each Celsius temperature increases by 5°.
Fahrenheit and Rankine temperatures increase by 9°.

3. How can you combine the two formulas to create a single formula?
Substitute $\frac{9}{5}C + 32$ into the formula $R = 459.67 + F$ for F.
So, $R = 459.67 + \frac{9}{5}C + 32$.

4. Look at the formula you created in Exercise 3. Predict what will happen to the Celsius and Rankine temperatures as the Fahrenheit temperatures increase by 1°. How can you verify your prediction?
Fahrenheit and Rankine temperatures increase by $\frac{9}{5}$.
Verify by comparing temperatures only 1° apart.

43. 6; start with −10 and add 6 repeatedly; 14, 20, 26.
44. 4.5; start with 13 and add 4.5 repeatedly; 31, 35.5, 40.
45. −0.8; start with 9 and add −0.8 repeatedly; 5.8, 5.0, 4.2.

Alternative Assessment

Each student in a pair makes a table of values for a function. Partners exchange tables and use function notation to write their partner's function rule.

12-3

1. Plan

Lesson Preview

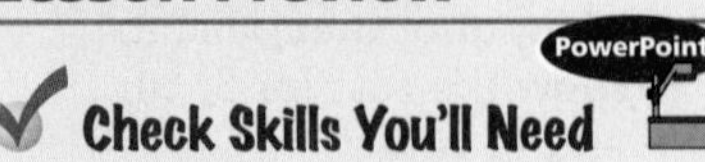

Finding Slope From a Table
Lesson 3-3: Example 4. Extra Practice, p. 704.

Lesson Resources

Optional Materials
- graph paper
- ruler

Teaching Resources
Practice, Reteaching, Enrichment

Reaching All Students
Practice Workbook 12-3
Spanish Practice Workbook 12-3
Guided Problem Solving 12-3
Technology Activities 51

Transparencies
- Check Skills You'll Need 12-3
- Problem of the Day 12-3
- Additional Examples 12-3
- Student Edition Answers 12-3
- Lesson Quiz 12-3
- Classroom Aid 3, 36

PH Presentation Pro CD-ROM 12-3

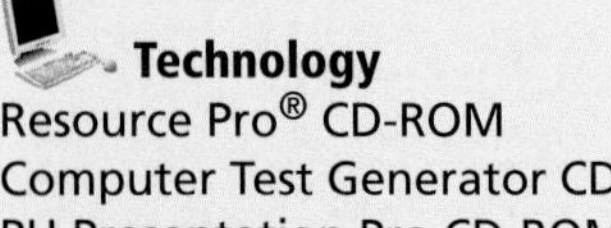

Computer Test Generator CD

Technology
Resource Pro® CD-ROM
Computer Test Generator CD
PH Presentation Pro CD-ROM

www.PHSchool.com
Student Site
- Teacher Web Code: ack-5500
- Self-grading Lesson Quiz

PH SuccessNet Teacher Center
- Lesson Planner
- Resources

Algebra

12-3 Graphing Linear Functions

What You'll Learn

 To use a table to graph a function

 To use a rule to graph a function

. . . And Why

To graph cost as a function of the number of containers, as in Example 2

Check Skills You'll Need

For help, go to Lesson 3-3.

The data in each table are linear. Use the table to find the slope. Then graph the data and each line. 1–2. See back of book.

1.

x	1	2	3	4
y	10	6	2	−2

2.

x	2	5	8	11
y	1	4	7	10

New Vocabulary
- discrete data
- continuous data
- linear function

 Interactive lesson includes instant self-check, tutorials, and activities.

OBJECTIVE 1

Using a Table to Graph a Function

To graph a function, use the coordinate plane. Place input values along the horizontal axis (x-axis) and output values along the vertical axis (y-axis).

1 EXAMPLE Using a Table to Graph a Function

Rock Climbing A rock climber is 200 ft above the base of a cliff. The climber is climbing at a rate of 10 ft per min. Make a table to describe the climber's height above the base of the cliff (output) as a function of the time that has passed (input). Graph the function.

Input: Time (min)	0	1	2	3	4	5
Output: Height (ft)	200	210	220	230	240	250

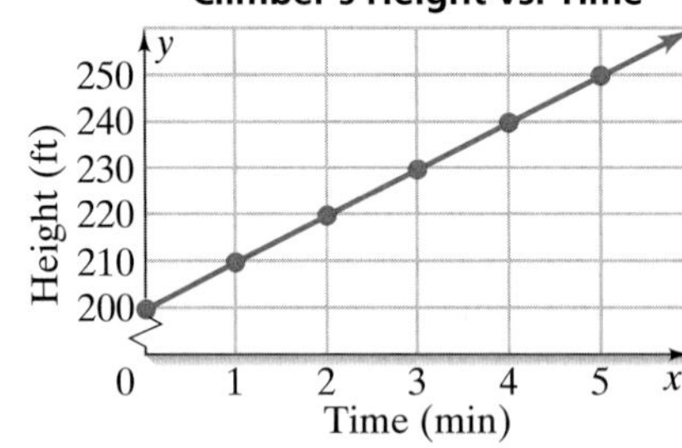

Real-World Connection
Rock climbers use rating systems to determine the difficulty of their routes.

Check Understanding 1 A bamboo plant is 23 cm high and grows 16 cm a day. The plant's height (output) depends on the number of days that have passed (input). Make a table of input/output pairs for the function. Then graph the function.
See back of book.

Ongoing Assessment and Intervention

Before the Lesson
Diagnose prerequisite skills using:
- Check Skills You'll Need

During the Lesson
Monitor progress using:
- Check Understanding
- Additional Examples
- Test Prep

After the Lesson
Assess knowledge using:
- Lesson Quiz
- Computer Test Generator CD

Discrete data are data that involve a count of items, such as numbers of people or numbers of cars. For discrete data, indicate each data item with a point. Connect the points with a dashed line.

Continuous data are data where numbers between any two data values have meaning. Examples of continuous data include measurements of temperature, length, or weight. Use a solid line to indicate continuous data.

2 EXAMPLE Discrete and Continuous Data

Determine whether the data for each function are discrete or continuous. Then make a table and graph each function.

a. Groceries A gallon of milk costs \$2.59. The total cost of g gallons of milk is a function of the price of each gallon of milk.

You cannot buy part of a container, so the data are discrete. Use points for each input value. Connect the points with a dashed line.

Number of Gallons	Total Cost
1	\$2.59
2	\$5.18
3	\$7.77
4	\$10.36

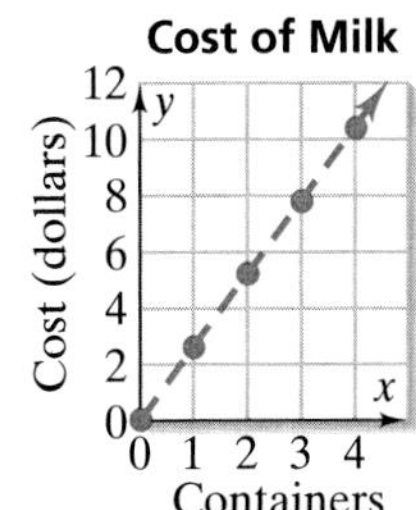

> **Reading Math**
> A dashed line in a graph means not every point on the graph satisfies the conditions of the problem.

b. Fitness During one hour of walking, you burn 257 Calories. The total number of Calories you burn is a function of the number of hours you walk.

You can walk for part of an hour, so the data are continuous. Connect the points with a solid line.

Time (hours)	Number of Calories
1	257
2	514
3	771

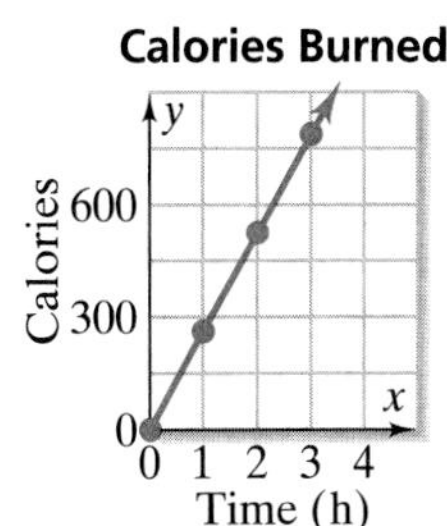

Check Understanding 2 Determine whether the data for each function are discrete or continuous. Then make a table and graph each function. 2a–b. See back of book.

a. Sky Diving The function $h = 4{,}000 - 600m$ represents the height a sky diver is above ground (in feet) after the diver has been falling for m minutes.

b. Tickets The function $c = 15t$ represents the cost (in dollars) of t adult tickets to an aquarium.

Reaching All Students

Below Level Verify with a graphing calculator that the graph of $y = 2x - 3$ from Example 3 remains a line even if the 2 is changed to 3 or 4 or 5 and the 3 is changed to 1 or 6.	**Advanced Learners** Have students use a graphing calculator to compare the graphs of $y = x$, $y = 3x$, $y = 5x$, $y = 6x$. Each line gets steeper.	**English Learners** See note on page 649. **Inclusion** See note on page 650.

2. Teach

Professional Development

Math Background

To graph $f(x)$ in a coordinate plane, graph the input values on the x-axis and the output values, $f(x)$, on the y-axis. *Discrete* data often result from counting and are connected with a dashed line. *Continuous data* often result from measuring and can have values between the graphed points, which are joined with a solid line.

Teaching Notes

1 EXAMPLE English Learners

Discuss the meaning and spelling for *discrete* and *discreet*. Elicit the fact that a discreet person might keep a secret, and discrete points are separate from each other.

Additional Examples

1 Amber earns \$7 per hour. Make a table to describe Amber's earnings (output) as a function of hours she works (input). Graph the function.

Input (hrs)	0	1	2	3	4
Output (\$)	0	7	14	21	28

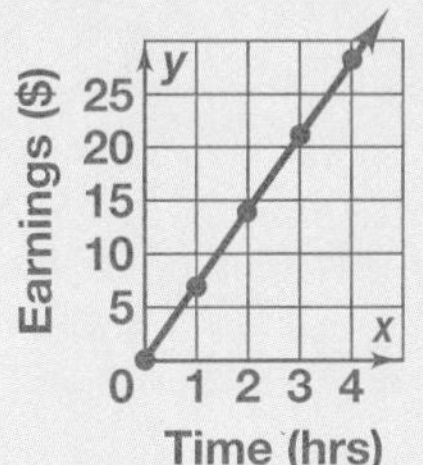

2 Juice costs \$2.19 per gallon. The total cost of g gallons is a function of the price of a single gallon. Determine whether this situation is discrete or continuous. Then make a table and a graph.
discrete

Input g (gal)	1	2	3
Output (\$)	2.19	4.38	6.57

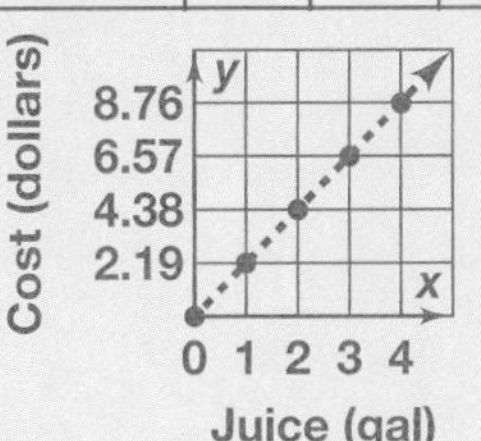

3 EXAMPLE Inclusion

Review graphing equations in the slope-intercept form with these steps: locate b, the y-intercept, on the y-axis; write the slope as a fraction; use the numerator of the fraction as the change in y and the denominator of the fraction as the change in x in order to locate a second point. Then draw the line that connects the points.

Additional Examples

3 Graph the linear function $y = -\frac{4}{3}x + 1$.

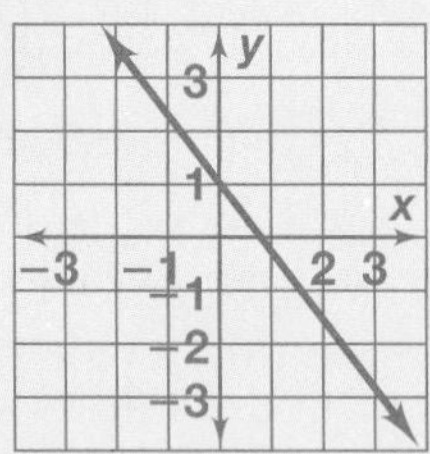

Closure

- Explain how to use a table to graph a function. Plot the input on the x-axis and the output on the y-axis.
- Explain how to use a rule to graph a function. Write the rule in the form $f(x) = mx + b$ and use the y-intercept (b) and the slope m to plot two points. Then draw a line through the points.
- *How do you decide whether to make a solid or dashed line?* Sample: Use a solid line for continuous data and a dashed line for discrete data.

Check Understanding

3c.

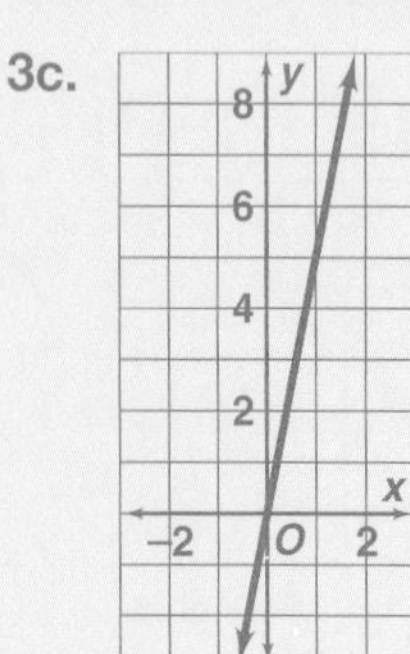

OBJECTIVE 2

Using a Rule to Graph a Function

Need Help?
In the linear equation $y = mx + b$, m represents the slope and b represents the y-intercept.

A **linear function** is a function whose points lie on a line. You can write a linear function in the form $f(x) = mx + b$, or $y = mx + b$. Then you can use the slope and y-intercept to graph the function.

3 EXAMPLE Using a Rule to Graph a Function

Graph the linear function $y = 2x - 3$.

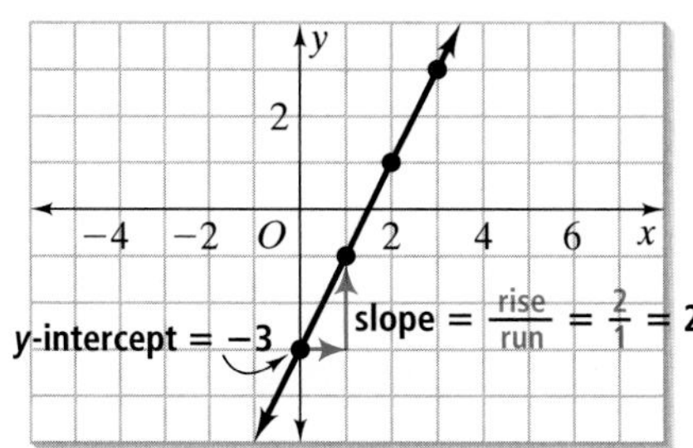

Check Understanding 3 Graph each linear function. 3a–c. See margin.

a. $y = x - 1$ **b.** $y = -\frac{1}{4}x + 3$ **c.** $y = 5x$

EXERCISES

For more practice, see *Extra Practice.*

A Practice by Example

Example 1 (page 648)

Make a table of input/output pairs for each function. Then graph the function. Show only the portion of the graph that makes sense for each situation. Exercise 1 has been started for you. 1–3. See back of book.

1. Internet An Internet company charges a monthly fee of \$4.95 per month plus \$2.50 for each hour you use the Internet. Your monthly bill (output) is a function of the number of hours you use the Internet (input).

Input: number of hours used	0	1	2	3	4	5
Output: monthly bill (dollars)	4.95	7.45	9.95 ■	12.45 ■	14.95 ■	17.45 ■

2. Fuel Suppose gasoline costs \$1.47 per gallon. The cost to fill the gas tank of your car (output) is a function of the number of gallons of gas you fill it with (input).

3. Measurement One pound is equivalent to 2.2046 kilograms. The weight of an object in pounds (output) is a function of the weight of the object in kilograms (input).

3a.

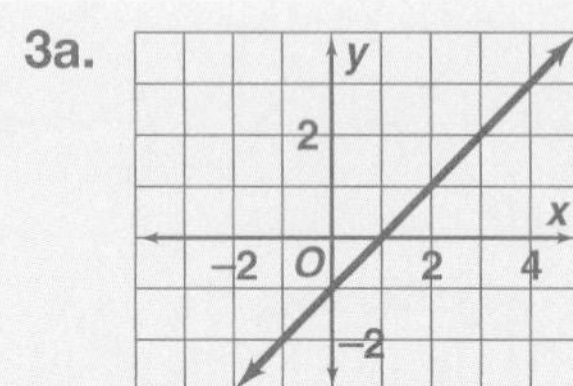

b.

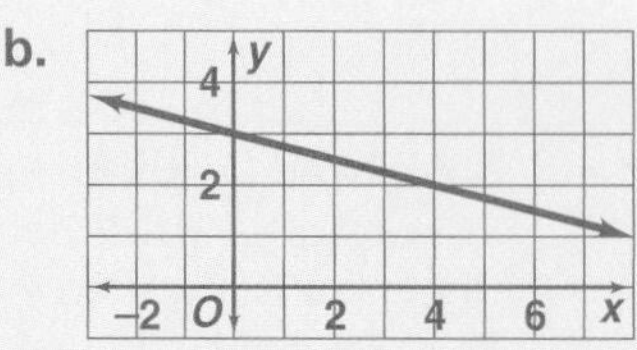

Example 2 (page 649)

Determine whether the data for each function are *discrete* or *continuous*. Then make a table and graph the function. 4–6. See margin.

4. **Shopping** The function $d = 40 - 15x$ represents the amount of money you have left (in dollars) after buying x CDs.

5. **Scuba Diving** The deeper a diver descends, the more pressure the diver feels. The function $p = 1 + 0.03x$ represents the approximate pressure p (in atmospheres) at x feet below sea level.

6. **Temperatures** The function $y = 1.8x + 32$ represents the temperature in degrees Fahrenheit of x degrees Celsius.

Example 3 (page 650)

Graph each linear function. 7–12. See back of book.

7. $y = -2x + 5$ 8. $y = \frac{2}{3}x - 1$ 9. $y = -\frac{3}{5}x - 2$

10. $y = 5x + 3$ 11. $y = 4x$ 12. $y = x + 4$

B Apply Your Skills

Graph each linear function. 13–18. See back of book.

13. $y = -n$ 14. $y = 10 - \frac{4}{5}x$ 15. $2y = 6x + 4$

16. $y = 4(3a + 5)$ 17. $y = 1.5x - 2 + x$ 18. $y = 1.6$

19. **Jeweler** A woman makes earrings and sells them at a jewelry show. She pays \$10.00 to have a table at the show and makes \$20.25 for each pair of earrings she sells. The money she earns (output) is a function of the number of pairs of earrings she sells (input). Make a table and graph the function. See back of book.

20. **Writing in Math** Describe the data for a function in your daily life. Explain why it is a function and define the input and the output. Check students' work.

21. a. **Open-Ended** Write rules for two arithmetic sequences and two geometric sequences. See below left.
    b. Copy and complete the table below for each sequence you wrote. b–c. Check students' work.

x (term number)	1	2	3	4	5
y (term)	■	■	■	■	■

    c. Graph the ordered pairs for each sequence on a separate coordinate plane.
    d. **Reasoning** What do you notice about the graph of each arithmetic sequence? About the graph of each geometric sequence? It is linear; it is not a linear graph.

22. **Science** The height of a burning candle shows how much time the candle has been burning. For one type of candle, the function $h = 8 - \frac{1}{2}t$ gives the candle's height h (in centimeters) as a function of the time t the candle has burned (in hours).
    a. Graph the function. See back of book.
    b. What was the original height of the candle? 8 cm
    c. What is the greatest amount of time the candle can burn? 16 h

GPS

Real-World Connection

Careers Many jewelers have college degrees in jewelry design.

21a. Answers may vary. Samples: Arithmetic sequence: Start with 10 and add 2 repeatedly. Start with 1 and add −4 repeatedly. Geometric sequence: Start with 1 and multiply by 2 repeatedly. Start with −4 and multiply by $-\frac{1}{2}$ repeatedly.

4. discrete

x	d
0	40
1	25
2	10

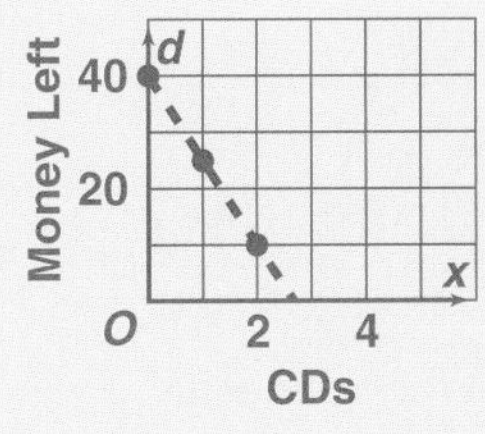

Use the Guided Problem Solving worksheet with Exercise 22.

5–6. See back of book.

3. Practice

Assignment Guide

Objective 1
A B Core 1–6, 23
C Extension 28

Objective 2
A B Core 7–22
C Extension 24–27

Test Prep 29–32
Mixed Review 33–36

Error Prevention!

Exercise 21 Points of geometric sequences cannot be connected with a line.

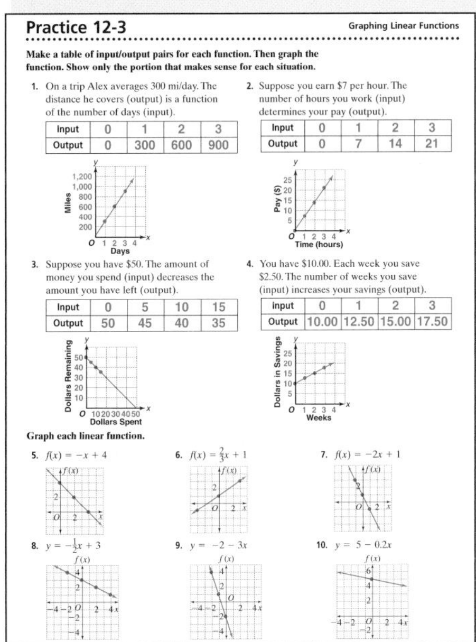

Practice 12-3 Graphing Linear Functions

Make a table of input/output pairs for each function. Then graph the function. Show only the portion that makes sense for each situation.

1. On a trip Alex averages 300 mi/day. The distance he covers (output) is a function of the number of days (input).

Input	0	1	2	3
Output	0	300	600	900

2. Suppose you earn \$7 per hour. The number of hours you work (input) determines your pay (output).

Input	0	1	2	3
Output	0	7	14	21

3. Suppose you have \$50. The amount of money you spend (input) decreases the amount you have left (output).

Input	0	5	10	15
Output	50	45	40	35

4. You have \$10.00. Each week you save \$2.50. The number of weeks you save (input) increases your savings (output).

Input	0	1	2	3
Output	10.00	12.50	15.00	17.50

Graph each linear function.

5. $f(x) = -x + 4$ 6. $f(x) = \frac{2}{3}x + 1$ 7. $f(x) = -2x + 1$

8. $y = -\frac{1}{2}x + 3$ 9. $y = -2 - 3x$ 10. $y = 5 - 0.2x$

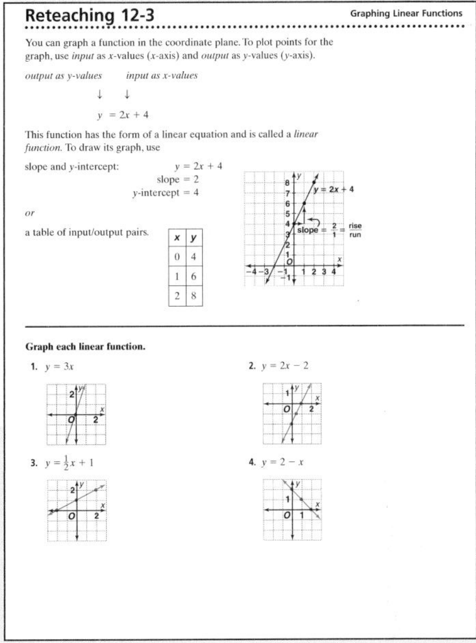

Reteaching 12-3 Graphing Linear Functions

You can graph a function in the coordinate plane. To plot points for the graph, use *input* as x-values (x-axis) and *output* as y-values (y-axis).

output as y-values *input as x-values*

$y = 2x + 4$

This function has the form of a linear equation and is called a *linear function.* To draw its graph, use

slope and y-intercept: $y = 2x + 4$, slope = 2, y-intercept = 4

or

a table of input/output pairs.

x	y
0	4
1	6
2	8

Graph each linear function.

1. $y = 3x$ 2. $y = 2x - 2$

3. $y = \frac{1}{2}x + 1$ 4. $y = 2 - x$

4. Assess

1. A rock climber 150 ft above the base of a cliff climbs at a rate of 5 ft per min. Make a table to describe the climber's height above the cliff base as a function of elapsed time. Graph the function.

Time (min)	0	1	2
Height (ft)	150	155	160

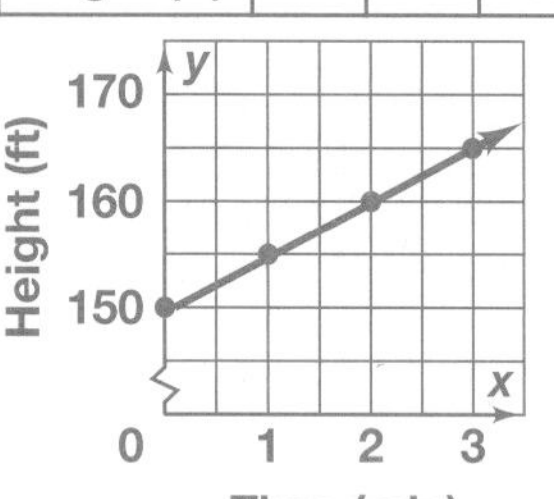

2. Graph the function $y = -3x - 4$.

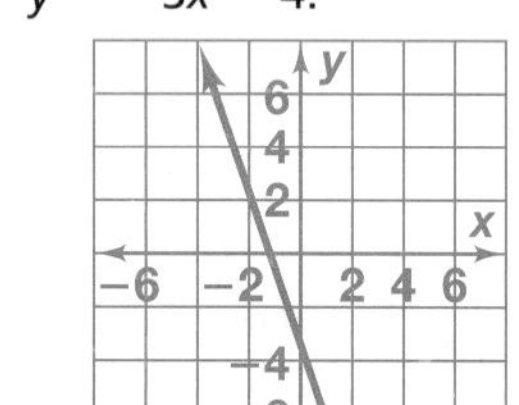

Enrichment 12-3 — Graphing Linear Functions

Critical Thinking

To move some furniture, you decide to rent a moving van for one day. The rental company charges $45 to rent the van plus $.50 for each mile driven.

1. a. Complete the table of input and output values.

Input (*mi*)	10	20	30	40	50
Output ($)	50	55	60	65	70

b. Use your rule and the table of input and output values to make a graph for the cost of renting a van for one day

One Day Rental — Cost in Dollars (0–80); Miles Driven (10 20 30 40 50)

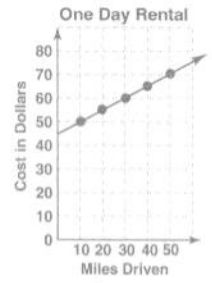

c. You find that you need to make several trips to move all the furniture. Extend your graph cost of renting a van for one day and driving 180 miles.
$135

2. To rent a van for more than one day, the company charges a $50 service fee and $40 for each day. Use of a van for a partial day is charged as a full day.

a. Complete the table of input and output values.

Input (*days*)	2	3	4	5
Output ($)	130	170	210	250

b. Make a graph to show the cost of renting a van for more than one day.

Several Day Rental — Cost in Dollars (110–270); Days (1 2 3 4 5)

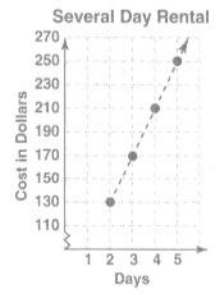

c. Suppose you can move all the furniture in one and a half days. Use your graph to determine how much you will pay for the van.
Renting for one and a half days is the same as renting for two days; $130.

3. a. How does the cost of renting a van for two days compare to the cost of renting a van for one day and driving 180 miles?
It is $5 less.

b. Based on your calculations, would you rather rent a van to move the furniture in one day or take two days to move the furniture?
rent the van for 2 days

23a.

x	y
1	31.91
2	38.29
3	44.67
4	51.05
5	57.43

23. **Data File, p. 635** In London, England, parents of a six-year-old child hire a baby sitter for the evening. They plan to spend money only on two movie tickets and the hourly rate for the baby sitter.
 a. Make a table of input/output values for a function showing the relationship between the number of hours the parents have the baby sitter (input) and the total cost for the evening (output).
 b. Graph the portion of this linear function that makes sense.
 See back of book.

C Challenge

Graph each linear function. 24–26. See back of book.

24. $2y + 3x = 12$ 25. $20 = 5x + 4y$ 26. $x - y = 6$

Nutrition Facts
Serving Size: 8 crackers (31g)
Servings Per Container: about 15

Amount Per Serving	
Calories 140	Calories from Fat 35
	% Daily Value
Total Fat 4g	6%
Saturated Fat 1g	5%
Monounsaturated Fat 1.5g	

27. a. **Nutrition** Using the label at the left, find how many Calories are in one cracker. 17.5 Calories
 b. The number of Calories consumed is a function of the number of crackers eaten. Make a table and a graph for this function.
 See back of book.

28. **Stretch Your Thinking** Keith baked muffins and gave $\frac{3}{4}$ of them to Peter. Peter then gave away a dozen of the muffins to his other friends. Peter ended up with six muffins. How many muffins did Keith bake? 24 muffins

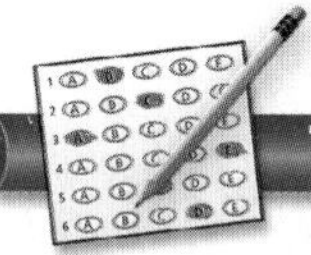

Test Prep

Multiple Choice

29. Which of the following is NOT an input/output pair for the function $y = \frac{7}{5}m - 2$? C
 A. (0, −2) B. (5, 5) C. (7, 7) D. (10, 12)

30. For the function $y = 2x - 7$, which input gives an output of −10? H
 F. $\frac{17}{2}$ G. $\frac{2}{3}$ H. $-\frac{3}{2}$ I. $-\frac{2}{17}$

31. Which of the following is an example of a linear function? D
 A. $y = \frac{2}{3}x^2 - 1$ B. $y = 16 - \frac{1}{x}$
 C. $y = 42x^3 - x + 4$ D. $y = 0.9 + 6.5x$

Take It to the NET
Online lesson quiz at
www.PHSchool.com
Web Code: aca-1203

Short Response

32. Rewrite $y + \frac{2}{3} = -x$ in slope-intercept form. Then graph the function.
 See back of book.

Mixed Review

Lesson 10-4 **Use the box-and-whisker plot at the right to find each of the following.**

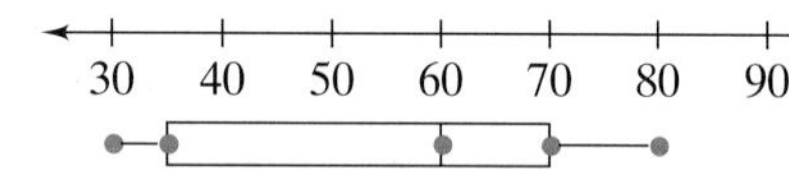

33. the median 60 34. the lower quartile 35 35. the upper quartile 70

Lesson 10-3 36. Make a stem-and-leaf plot for the following set of data.
 8 19 27 36 35 24 6 15 16 24 38 23 20
 See back of book.

Alternative Assessment

Have students work in small groups to list examples of functions. Groups work together to identify each example as discrete or continuous.

Test Prep

Resources
For additional practice with a variety of test item formats:
- Test Prep, p. 691
- Test-Taking Strategies, p. 687
- Test-Taking Strategies with Transparencies

12-4 Writing Rules for Linear Functions

What You'll Learn

 To write a rule from words

 To write a rule from a table or graph

. . . And Why

To write a function for a telephone rate, as in Example 1

Check Skills You'll Need

 For help, go to Lesson 3-4.

Use the graph at the right.

1. Find the slope of the line. $\frac{2}{3}$
2. What is the y-intercept? 0
3. Write the equation of the line in slope-intercept form. $y = \frac{2}{3}x$

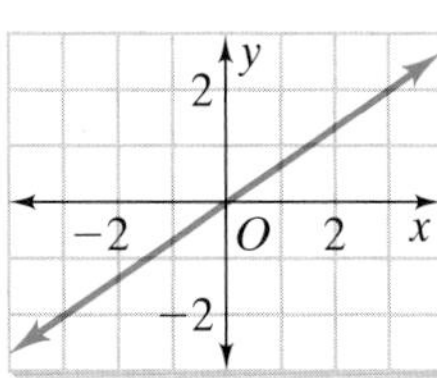

 Interactive lesson includes instant self-check, tutorials, and activities.

OBJECTIVE 1 Writing a Rule From Words

Just as you can translate words to an equation, you can also translate words to a function rule. When writing a function rule, be sure to identify the input and the output.

Real-World Connection

Businesses use toll-free numbers to encourage customers to use their services.

1 EXAMPLE Writing a Rule From Words

 Real World

Toll-Free Numbers Suppose the rate for having a toll-free telephone number is \$2.95 per month plus \$.10 per minute used. Write a function rule to show how the monthly telephone bill depends on the number of minutes used.

Words monthly bill = \$2.95 + \$.10 · number of minutes

Let x = the number of minutes. ← **input**

Let y = the monthly bill. ← **output**

Function $y = 2.95 + 0.1 \cdot x$

$y = 2.95 + 0.1x$

The function rule $y = 2.95 + 0.1x$ shows the monthly bill for x minutes of use.

Check Understanding 1

a. Use the function rule $y = 2.95 + 0.1x$ to find the bill for 520 minutes of use in one month. \$54.95

b. **Funds** A school orchestra is buying music stands. The group has \$298 in its treasury. Each stand costs \$42. Write a function rule to show how the balance in the treasury depends on the number of stands bought. $y = 298 - 42x$

Ongoing Assessment and Intervention

Before the Lesson
Diagnose prerequisite skills using:
- Check Skills You'll Need

During the Lesson
Monitor progress using:
- Check Understanding
- Additional Examples
- Test Prep

After the Lesson
Assess knowledge using:
- Lesson Quiz
- Computer Test Generator CD
- Chapter Checkpoint 1 (p. 657)

12-4

1. Plan

Lesson Preview

Check Skills You'll Need

Writing an Equation From a Graph
Lesson 3-4: Example 4. Extra Practice, p. 704.

Lesson Resources

Teaching Resources
Practice, Reteaching, Enrichment
Checkpoint Quiz 1

Reaching All Students
Practice Workbook 12-4
Spanish Practice Workbook 12-4
Reading and Math Literacy 12B
Spanish Reading and Math Literacy 12B
Spanish Checkpoint Quiz 1
Guided Problem Solving 12-4

Presentation Assistant Plus!
Transparencies
- Check Skills You'll Need 12-4
- Problem of the Day 12-4
- Additional Examples 12-4
- Student Edition Answers 12-4
- Lesson Quiz 12-4

PH Presentation Pro CD-ROM 12-4

PRENTICE HALL ASSESSMENT SYSTEM

Checkpoint Quiz 1
Computer Test Generator CD

Technology
Resource Pro® CD-ROM
Computer Test Generator CD
PH Presentation Pro CD-ROM

www.PHSchool.com
Student Site
- Teacher Web Code: ack-5500
- Algebra Readiness Puzzles 105
- Self-grading Lesson Quiz

PH SuccessNet Teacher Center
- Lesson Planner
- Resources

Plus 

2. Teach

Math Background

Functions can be described in words, tables, graphs, and in equations or function rules. You can write function rules for linear graphs by reading the y-intercept and slope and using $y = mx + b$. To write a function rule for a table of linear data, use the ratio of the changes in the inputs and outputs for the slope and the data point $(0, b)$ to write the function rule.

Teaching Notes

2 EXAMPLE Error Prevention

Make sure students understand that this ratio represents a constant slope. They should not confuse it with the common ratio for a geometric sequence.

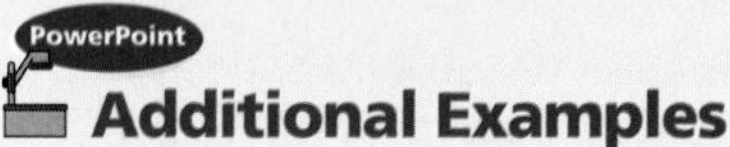

Additional Examples

1. A rate for Internet access is \$15 per month plus \$.25 per hour of use. Write a function rule to show how the monthly bill depends on the number of hours used. $f(x) = 15 + 0.25x$
2. Do the data in the table below represent a linear function? If so, write a rule for the function. $y = 2x + 8$

x	–1	0	1	2	3
y	6	8	10	12	14

3. Use the slope and y-intercept to write a linear function rule for the graph. $y = 2x + 8$

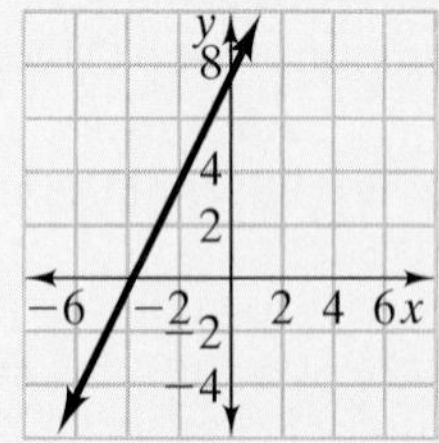

Closure

How can you write a function rule from a graph? Find the slope and y-intercept and substitute into $y = mx + b$.

OBJECTIVE 2

Writing a Rule From a Table or Graph

Values in a table sometimes represent a linear function. If the ratios of the changes in inputs and outputs are the same, the function is linear.

2 EXAMPLE Writing a Rule From a Table

Do the values represent a linear function? If so, write a function rule.

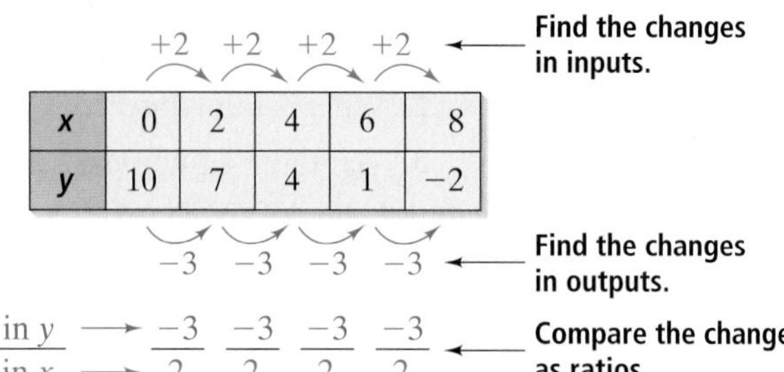

x	0	2	4	6	8
y	10	7	4	1	−2

Find the changes in inputs: +2 +2 +2 +2

Find the changes in outputs: −3 −3 −3 −3

$\frac{\text{Change in } y}{\text{Change in } x} \rightarrow \frac{-3}{2} \quad \frac{-3}{2} \quad \frac{-3}{2} \quad \frac{-3}{2}$ ← **Compare the changes as ratios.**

Since each ratio is the same, the function is linear. Use slope-intercept form to write a function rule.

Need Help?
Slope-intercept form:
$y = mx + b$

According to the table, the point (0, 10) lies on the graph of the function. So the y-intercept is 10. The slope is $-\frac{3}{2}$.

$y = -\frac{3}{2}x + 10$ ← **Substitute $-\frac{3}{2}$ for m and 10 for b.**

Check Understanding 2 Do the values represent a linear function? If so, write a function rule.

a.

x	0	1	2	3	4
y	2	4	7	8	10

no

b.

x	−2	0	2	4	6
y	3	2	1	0	−1

yes; $y = -\frac{1}{2}x + 2$

The slope of a line can be expressed by the equation $\frac{y - y_1}{x - x_1} = m$. You can rewrite this equation as $y - y_1 = m(x - x_1)$. If you know two points on a line or the slope and any point, you can find the equation of the line.

3 EXAMPLE Writing a Rule From a Graph

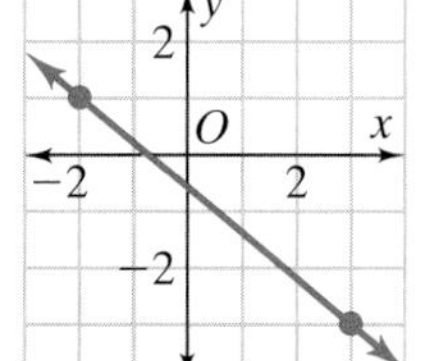

Find the equation of the line in the graph at the left.

Step 1 Find the slope.
Use the points $(3, -3)$ and $(-2, 1)$.

$\text{slope} = \frac{1 - (-3)}{-2 - 3} = -\frac{4}{5}$

Step 2 Use the slope and one point to write an equation.

$y - y_1 = m(x - x_1)$

$y - (-3) = -\frac{4}{5}(x - 3)$ ← **Use the point $(3, -3)$ for (x_1, y_1).**

$y + 3 = -\frac{4}{5}(x - 3)$

Using the point $(3, -3)$, the equation of the line is $y + 3 = -\frac{4}{5}(x - 3)$.

Check Understanding 3 **a.** Use the point $(-2, 1)$ to write another equation for the line in Example 3.
a. $y - 1 = -\frac{4}{5}(x + 2)$
b. Reasoning How many different equations describe one linear function?
b. Answers may vary. Sample: If you use $y - y_1 = m(x - x_1)$, you can write a different equation each time you choose a different point on the line.

Reaching All Students

Below Level A student saved d dollars every month, and her grandmother contributes an equal amount. Write a rule to show the total after 7 months. $T = 7(2d)$

Advanced Learners Ask: *In general, in a problem, is the amount that follows the words "depends on" the input or the output?* input

English Learners
See note on page 656.

Visual Learners
See note on page 655.

EXERCISES

For more practice, see *Extra Practice*.

Ⓐ Practice by Example

Example 1 (page 653)

1. **Sales** Mrs. Savin receives a base salary of \$500, plus a commission of \$1,200 on each car that she sells.
   a. Write a function rule that shows how her total pay y depends on how many cars x she sells. $y = 1{,}200x + 500$
   b. Evaluate the function for $x = 15$. \$18,500

2. **Ecology** Water flows over a dam at a rate of 500 gallons per minute.
   a. Write a function rule that shows how the amount of water over the dam y is a function of the number of minutes x that have passed.
   b. Evaluate the function for $x = 27$.
   a. $y = 500x$
   b. 13,500 gal

3. **Plumbing** A plumber charges \$60 for a house call, plus \$75 for each hour of work.
   a. Write a function rule that shows how the total cost of the plumber's work y depends on the number of hours x the plumber works.
   b. Evaluate the function for $x = 8$.
   a. $y = 75x + 60$
   b. \$660

Example 2 (page 654)

Does each table represent a linear function? If so, write a rule for the function.

4.

x	0	1	2	3
y	8	6	4	2

yes; $y = -2x + 8$

5.

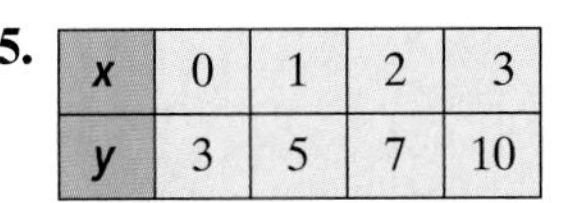

x	0	1	2	3
y	3	5	7	10

no

6.

x	0	3	6	9
y	0	1	3	6

no

7.

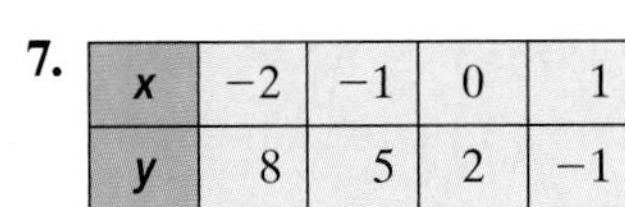

x	−2	−1	0	1
y	8	5	2	−1

yes; $y = -3x + 2$

Example 3 (page 654)

Use the slope and two points to write an equation for each line.

8–11. Answers may vary. Samples are given.

8.

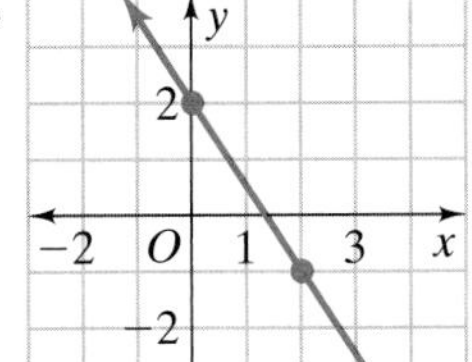

9.

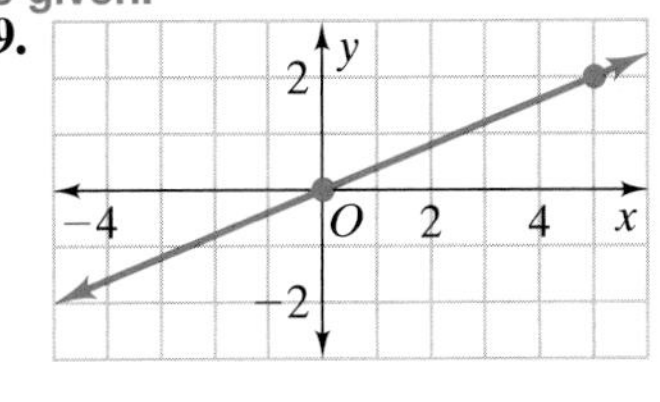

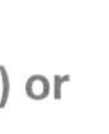

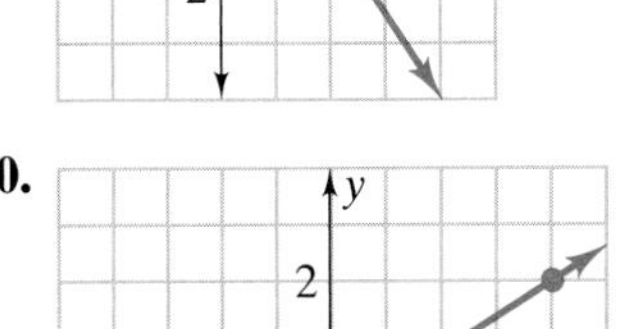

10.

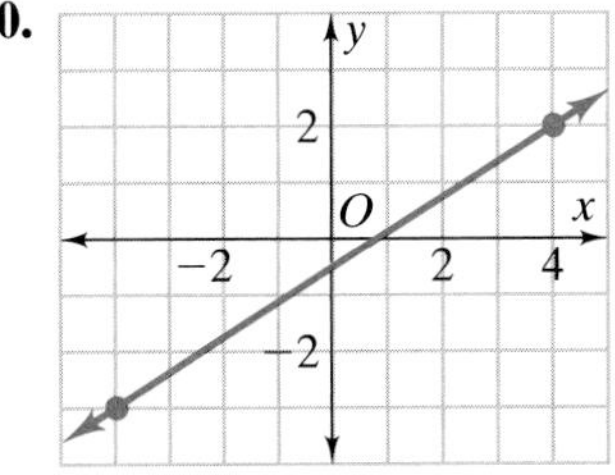

11.

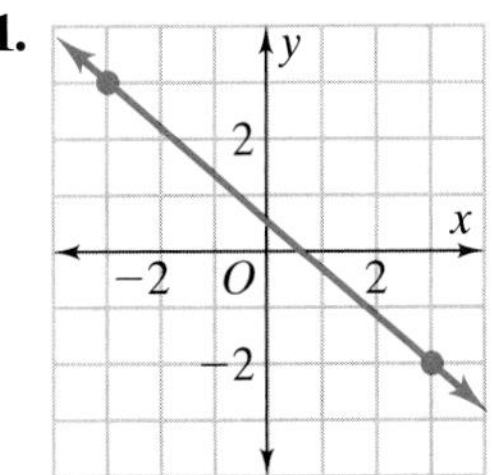

8. $y - 2 = -\frac{3}{2}(x - 0)$ or $y + 1 = -\frac{3}{2}(x - 2)$
9. $y - 0 = \frac{2}{5}(x - 0)$ or $y - 2 = \frac{2}{5}(x - 5)$
10. $y - 2 = \frac{5}{8}(x - 4)$ or $y + 3 = \frac{5}{8}(x + 4)$
11. $y + 2 = -\frac{5}{6}(x - 3)$ or $y - 3 = -\frac{5}{6}(x + 3)$

3. Practice

Assignment Guide

Objective 1

Ⓐ Ⓑ Core 1–3, 12, 14–15

Ⓒ Extension 20

Objective 2

Ⓐ Ⓑ Core 4–11, 13, 16–19

Ⓒ Extension 21

Test Prep 22–25

Mixed Review 26–33

Visual Learners

Exercises 8–11 Before students calculate, ask them to predict the sign and size of the slope.

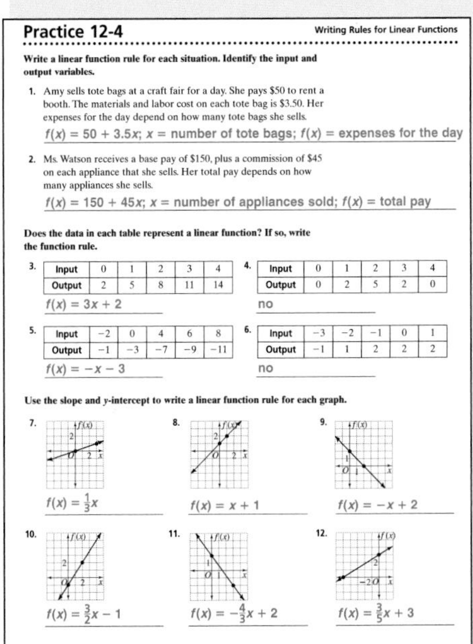

Practice 12-4 — Writing Rules for Linear Functions

Write a linear function rule for each situation. Identify the input and output variables.

1. Amy sells tote bags at a craft fair for a day. She pays \$50 to rent a booth. The materials and labor cost on each tote bag is \$3.50. Her expenses for the day depend on how many tote bags she sells.
   $f(x) = 50 + 3.5x$; x = number of tote bags; $f(x)$ = expenses for the day
2. Ms. Watson receives a base pay of \$150, plus a commission of \$45 on each appliance that she sells. Her total pay depends on how many appliances she sells.
   $f(x) = 150 + 45x$; x = number of appliances sold; $f(x)$ = total pay

Does the data in each table represent a linear function? If so, write the function rule.

3.

Input	0	1	2	3	4
Output	2	5	8	11	14

$f(x) = 3x + 2$

4.

Input	0	1	2	3	4
Output	0	2	5	2	0

no

5.

Input	−2	0	4	6	8
Output	−1	−3	−7	−9	−11

$f(x) = -x - 3$

6.

Input	−3	−2	−1	0	1
Output	−1	1	2	2	2

no

Use the slope and y-intercept to write a linear function rule for each graph.

7. $f(x) = \frac{1}{3}x$
8. $f(x) = x + 1$
9. $f(x) = -x + 2$
10. $f(x) = \frac{3}{2}x - 1$
11. $f(x) = -\frac{4}{3}x + 2$
12. $f(x) = \frac{3}{5}x + 3$

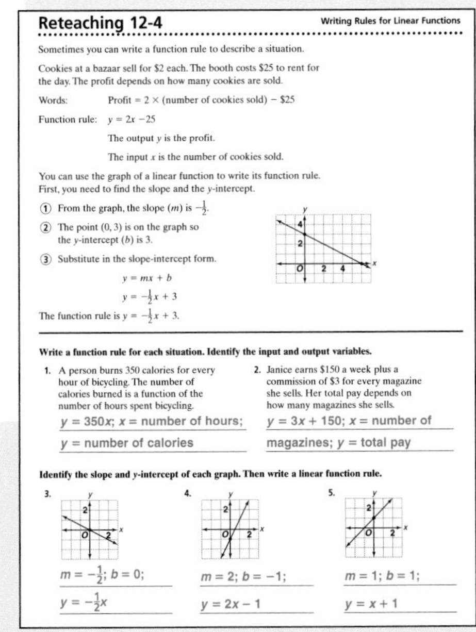

Reteaching 12-4 — Writing Rules for Linear Functions

Sometimes you can write a function rule to describe a situation.

Cookies at a bazaar sell for \$2 each. The booth costs \$25 to rent for the day. The profit depends on how many cookies are sold.

Words: Profit = 2 × (number of cookies sold) − \$25

Function rule: $y = 2x - 25$

The output y is the profit.

The input x is the number of cookies sold.

You can use the graph of a linear function to write its function rule. First, you need to find the slope and the y-intercept.

① From the graph, the slope (m) is $-\frac{1}{2}$.

② The point (0, 3) is on the graph so the y-intercept (b) is 3.

③ Substitute in the slope-intercept form.

$$y = mx + b$$
$$y = -\frac{1}{2}x + 3$$

The function rule is $y = -\frac{1}{2}x + 3$.

Write a function rule for each situation. Identify the input and output variables.

1. A person burns 350 calories for every hour of bicycling. The number of calories burned is a function of the number of hours spent bicycling.
   $y = 350x$; x = number of hours; y = number of calories
2. Janice earns \$150 a week plus a commission of \$3 for every magazine she sells. Her total pay depends on how many magazines she sells.
   $y = 3x + 150$; x = number of magazines; y = total pay

Identify the slope and y-intercept of each graph. Then write a linear function rule.

3. $m = -\frac{1}{2}$; $b = 0$; $y = -\frac{1}{2}x$
4. $m = 2$; $b = -1$; $y = 2x - 1$
5. $m = 1$; $b = 1$; $y = x + 1$

English Learners
Exercise 13 Encourage students to use a table to illustrate their written explanations.

 **Apply Your Skills**

13. Determine the change between each successive input and output value. If the ratios of the change of inputs to the change of outputs are the same, it is a linear function.

 **12. Laundry** Prices at the local laundromat are \$1.25 per load of wash and \$.75 per 20 minutes of drying time. An average load takes 1 hour to dry. Let n = the number of loads of wash.

a. Write a function rule to describe the total cost of washing and drying average loads as a function of the number of loads. $y = 3.50n$

b. Find the output when the input is 3. What does this represent? 10.50; the cost of washing and drying three loads

13. Writing in Math Explain how to determine whether a function is linear by analyzing an input/output table. See left.

Real-World Connection
Caricatures are pictures of people in which certain features are exaggerated for a comic effect.

14. Art At a fair, Bob Silva draws caricatures. He pays the fair \$30 for space to set up his table, and \$2 for each drawing that he sells.

GPS

a. Write a function rule to represent his total payment to the fair as a function of the number of drawings he sells. $y = 30 + 2x$

b. **Reasoning** What input is paired with the output \$54? What does this input represent? Express the input/output pair in the form f(■) = ■. See margin.

15. Geometry Write a function rule for the perimeter p of a square with side length s. $p = 4s$

Find the equation of each line with the given slope and point.

16. slope = $\frac{3}{4}$; $(2, -5)$ $y + 5 = \frac{3}{4}(x - 2)$

17. slope = $-\frac{1}{2}$; $(4, -1)$ $y + 1 = -\frac{1}{2}(x - 4)$

18. slope = $\frac{2}{3}$; $(5, -4)$ $y + 4 = \frac{2}{3}(x - 5)$

The values in each table represent a linear function. Use the slope and two points to write an equation in the form $y = mx + b$.

19.

x	−2	1	4	7
y	5	1	−3	−7

$y = -\frac{4}{3}x + \frac{7}{3}$

20.

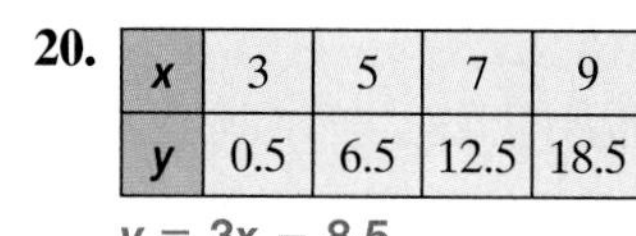

x	3	5	7	9
y	0.5	6.5	12.5	18.5

$y = 3x - 8.5$

Do the data in these tables represent a linear function? If so, write a function rule. If not, explain.

21.

x	0	1	2	3	4
y	1	2	4	5	8

See left.

21. No; the changes in x are always 1, but the changes in y vary from 1 to 3.

22.

x	−10	−5	0	5	10
y	0	3	6	9	12

Yes; equations may vary. Sample: $y = \frac{3}{5}x + 6$

 **Challenge**

23. a. Entertainment A water theme park charges a \$5 entrance fee and \$1 per ride. Write a function rule to show that the cost c depends on the number of rides r. $c = r + 5$

b. The park also offers a plan with a \$10 admission fee and \$.50 per ride. Write a function rule to show the total cost c for r rides. See left.

23b. $c = 0.50r + 10$

c. Graph each function on the same coordinate grid. Which is the best plan for someone who plans to go on many rides? Explain. See margin.

24. Stretch Your Thinking In an eighth-grade class, 80% of the students eat lunch at school. Of those students, 25% bring their lunch. Of those students, 20% buy their drink. What percent of the total number of students in the class bring their lunch *and* buy their drink? 4%

23c.

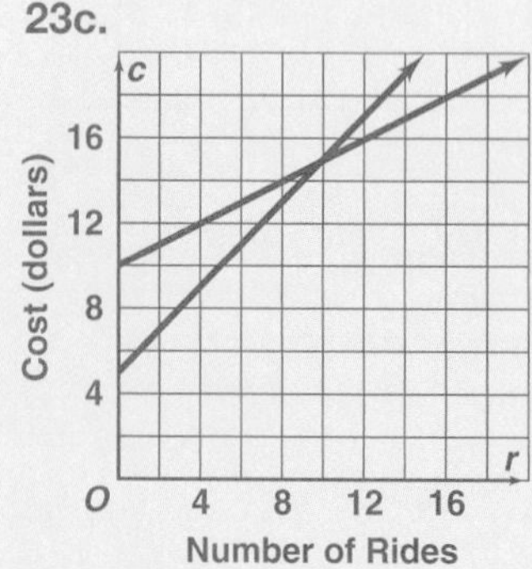

The \$10 plan is best if you want to go on more than 10 rides. With more than 10 rides, the cost/ride on the \$10 plan is cheaper.

14b. When $x = 12$, $y = 54$; the input represents the number of drawings he sold; $f(12) = 54$.

Use the Guided Problem Solving worksheet with Exercise 14.

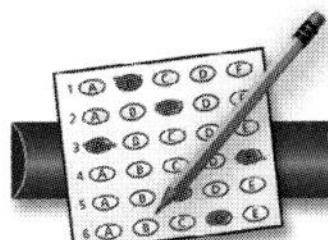

Test Prep

Multiple Choice

25. Which rule represents the data at the right? B
A. $y = 2x + 1$ B. $y = 2x - 1$
C. $y = 3x - 1$ D. $y = 3x + 1$

x	−3	0	3	6
y	−7	−1	5	11

26. A parking meter costs $.25 for 15 minutes. Which function describes the number of quarters a person needs for each hour of parking? G
F. $y = 30x$ G. $y = 4x$ H. $y = 2x$ I. $y = 1.5x$

27. You start with $30. School lunch costs $2 each day. Which function shows the money you have left after x days of buying school lunches? C
A. $y = 30 + 2x$ B. $y = 2 + 30x$
C. $y = 30 - 2x$ D. $y = 2 - 30x$

Extended Response

28. The student council is raising funds by selling hats. They had taken a survey to see how many students would buy the hats at different prices. The results are listed in the table below. See back of book.

Price (dollars)	2	4	6	8	10	12
Number of Buyers	400	325	250	175	100	25

Take It to the NET
Online lesson quiz at **www.PHSchool.com**
Web Code: aca-1204

a. Graph the data. Use the graph to estimate the number of hats that will be sold at $5.
b. Write a function rule to find the number of hats that will be sold at each price. Define the variables you use.

Mixed Review

Lesson 11-3 **Simplify each expression.**

29. ${}_9C_3$ 84 **30.** ${}_7C_5$ 21 **31.** ${}_5C_2$ 10 **32.** ${}_7C_3$ 35

Lesson 11-2 **Simplify each expression.**

33. ${}_6P_3$ 120 **34.** ${}_{12}P_3$ 1,320 **35.** ${}_{15}P_2$ 210 **36.** ${}_4P_4$ 24

Checkpoint Quiz 1 — Lessons 12-1 through 12-4

Instant self-check quiz online and on CD-ROM

Find the next three terms in each sequence.

1. 1, 4, 9, 16, . . . 25, 36, 49
2. 12, 6, 3, 1.5, . . . 0.75, 0.375, 0.1875
3. 12, 23, 34, 45, . . . 56, 67, 78

Use the function rule $f(x) = -3x - 2$. Find each output.

4. $f(-1)$ 1 **5.** $f(5)$ −17 **6.** $f(0)$ −2 **7.** $f(-0.5)$ −0.5 **8.** $f(-10)$ 28

9. Your cousin works at a bookstore and earns $7 per hour. Make a table to describe your cousin's earnings as a function of the hours she works. See back of book.

4. Assess

Lesson Quiz 12-4

1. A telephone company charges $4.95 per month plus $.10 per minute used. Write the rule to show how the monthly bill depends on the minutes used.
$y = 0.1x + 4.95$

2. Write a function rule for the data in the table.
$y = -0.5x + 8$

x	0	2	4	6
y	8	7	6	5

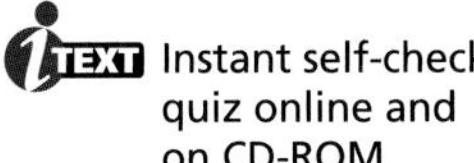

Chapter Checkpoint

To check understanding of Lessons 12-1 to 12-4:

Checkpoint Quiz 1 (p. 657)

Teaching Resources
Checkpoint Quiz 1 (also in *Prentice Hall Assessment System*)

Reaching All Students
Reading and Math Literacy 12B

Spanish versions available

Exercise 23 Remind students that 1 h = 60 min.

Enrichment 12-4 — Writing Rules for Linear Functions

Understanding Relationships

Many situations involve a relationship between two quantities whose values can vary. These relationships can be described using words, tables of values, graphs, or equations.

1. Find the rule that relates x and y in this table. Then find y when $x = 25$.

x	1	2	3	4	5	6
y	4	8	12	16	20	24

Rule: $y = 4x$ $y =$ 100

2. Find the rule that relates x and y in this table. Then find y when $x = 40$.

x	1	2	3	4	5	6
y	5	6	7	8	9	10

Rule: $y = x + 4$ $y =$ 44

3. Find the rule that relates x and y in this table. Then find y when $x = 12$.

x	1	2	3	4	5	6
y	−1	0	1	2	3	4

Rule: $y = x - 2$ $y =$ 10

4. Find the rule that relates x and y in this table. Then find y when $x = 8$.

x	1	$1\frac{1}{2}$	2	$2\frac{1}{2}$	3	$3\frac{1}{2}$
y	5	$7\frac{1}{2}$	10	$12\frac{1}{2}$	15	$17\frac{1}{2}$

Rule: $y = 5x$ $y =$ 40

5. Find the rule that relates x and y in this table. Then find y when $x = 90$.

x	1	2	3	4	5	6
y	−4	−8	−12	−16	−20	−24

Rule: $y = -4x$ $y =$ −360

6. Find the rule that relates x and y in this table. Then find y when $x = 10$.

x	1	2	3	4	5	6
y	1	4	9	16	25	36

Rule: $y = x^2$ $y =$ 100

7. Which of the exercises above is not a linear function? How do you know?
Exercise 6; Sample answer: You can't write the rule in the form $y = mx + b$.

Test Prep

Resources
For additional practice with a variety of test item formats:
- Test Prep, p. 691
- Test-Taking Strategies, p. 687
- Test-Taking Strategies with Transparencies

Alternative Assessment

Each student in a pair writes a function rule and makes a table. Partners trade tables and write the function rule for each other's table.

12-5

1. Plan

Lesson Preview

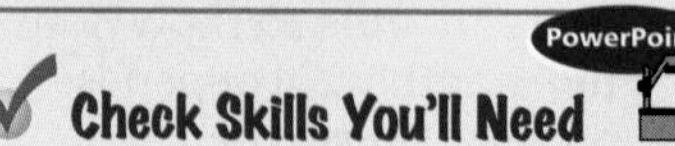

Choosing an Appropriate Graph
Lesson 10-7: Example 2. Extra Practice, p. 711.

Lesson Resources

Optional Materials
- graph paper
- watch or clock with second hand

Teaching Resources
Practice, Reteaching, Enrichment

Reaching All Students
Practice Workbook 12-5
Spanish Practice Workbook 12-5
Guided Problem Solving 12-5

Presentation Assistant Plus!
Transparencies
- Check Skills You'll Need 12-5
- Problem of the Day 12-5
- Additional Examples 12-5
- Student Edition Answers 12-5
- Lesson Quiz 12-5
- Classroom Aid 2

PH Presentation Pro CD-ROM 12-5

Computer Test Generator CD

Resource Pro® CD-ROM
Computer Test Generator CD
PH Presentation Pro CD-ROM

Student Site
- Updated Data
- Teacher Web Code: ack-5500
- Algebra Readiness Puzzles 84
- Self-grading Lesson Quiz

PH SuccessNet Teacher Center
- Lesson Planner
- Resources

Algebra

12-5 Relating Graphs to Events

What You'll Learn

To interpret and to sketch a graph of a situation

. . . And Why

To interpret a graph of the speed of a train, as in Example 1

Check Skills You'll Need

For help, go to Lesson 10-7.

1. Decide which type of graph, a circle graph or a line graph, is appropriate for the data at the right. Explain. Line graph; the data show change over time.
2. Draw the graph. See back of book.
3. What other type of graph could you use to display this data? Explain. Answers may vary. Sample: bar graph.

U.S. Avocado Production

Year	Tons
1999–2000	183,300
2000–2001	239,320
2001–2002	211,300

SOURCE: U.S. Dept. of Agriculture

Interactive lesson includes instant self-check, tutorials, and activities.

OBJECTIVE 1

Interpreting and Sketching a Graph

A graph can show complex relationships between variables in a simple, visual way.

1 EXAMPLE Interpreting a Graph

Real World

Transportation The graph below shows the speed of a commuter train as it makes a morning run.

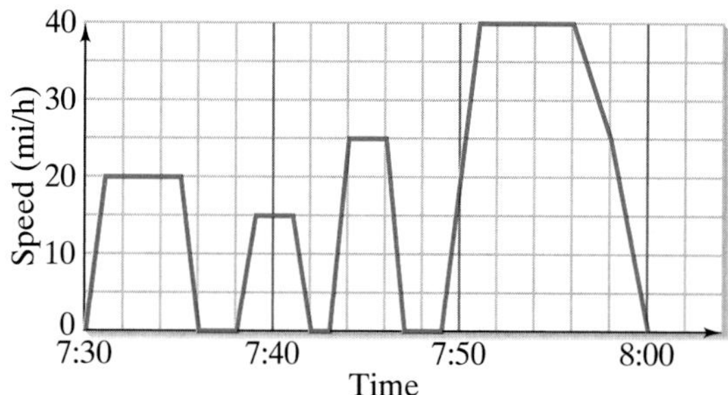

a. How long did the trip take?

Time is shown on the x-axis. The trip lasted 30 minutes, from 7:30 to 8:00.

b. Between which two times did the speed of the train increase the most?

Between 7:49 and 7:51, the speed increased from 0 to 40 mi/h.

Real-World Connection

There are approximately 6,700 miles of subway and commuter-rail tracks in the United States.

SOURCE: U.S. Bureau of Transportation. Go to **www.PHSchool.com** for a data update. Web Code: acg-2041

Check Understanding 1 Use the graph in Example 1.

a. What was the train's fastest speed? 40 mi/h
b. How many stops did the train make between 7:30 and 8:00? 3
c. At 7:57, was the train speeding up or slowing down? slowing down

Ongoing Assessment and Intervention

Before the Lesson
Diagnose prerequisite skills using:
- Check Skills You'll Need

During the Lesson
Monitor progress using:
- Check Understanding
- Additional Examples
- Test Prep

After the Lesson
Assess knowledge using:
- Lesson Quiz
- Computer Test Generator CD

When you draw a graph without actual data, you are making a sketch.

2 EXAMPLE Sketching a Graph

Fitness An athlete measures her pulse rate occasionally during a 50-min workout. The workout includes a 10-min warm-up period and a 5-min cool-down period. Sketch and label a graph showing her pulse rate during her workout.

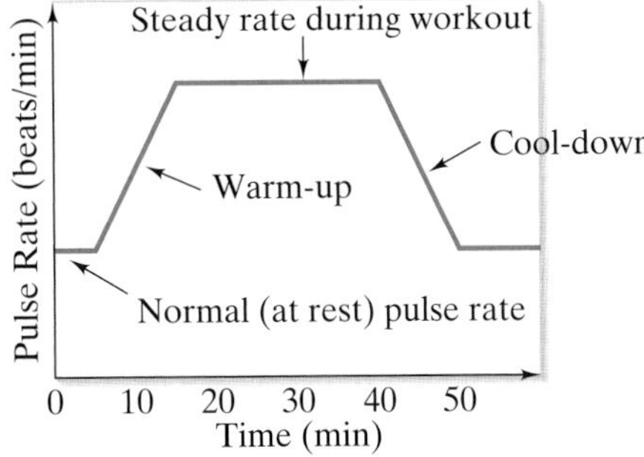

Test-Prep Tip
After you sketch a graph, check to make sure it makes sense with the problem.

Check Understanding 2 a. For 10 min, you walk from home to a park. For 5 min, you watch a ball game in the park. For the last 5 min, you run to your friend's house. Sketch and label a graph showing your distance from home. a. See back of book.

b. **Reasoning** Which section of the graph in part (a) should be steeper, the time you are walking or the time you are running? Explain. See left.

2b. The time when you are running; you cover a greater distance in a shorter period of time when you run, so the slope of the line will be steeper when you are running.

Investigation: Making and Interpreting a Graph

You will need a watch or a clock with a second hand.

1–5. Check students' work.

1. Use the following tongue twister:
   Can you can a can as a canner can can a can?

   Repeat the tongue twister over and over. Have someone count and record the number of times you say the tongue twister after 15 s, 30 s, 45 s, and so on for two minutes.
2. Make a table showing the time intervals in the first column and the number of times you said the tongue twister in the second column.
3. Graph the data.
4. Did you speed up or slow down as you said the tongue twister during the activity? How can you tell from the graph?
5. During which 15-s interval did you say the tongue twister the most? During which 15-s interval did you say the tongue twister the least?

2. Teach

Math Background

Professional Development

Graphs can show complex relationships between variables. Many graphs use time on the x-axis because the other variable depends on time.

Teaching Notes

1 EXAMPLE Error Prevention

Make sure that students recognize which points on the graph mean that the train has stopped.

Investigation (Optional)
Demonstrate the tongue twister and discuss its meaning.

PowerPoint

Additional Examples

1 Use the graph below.

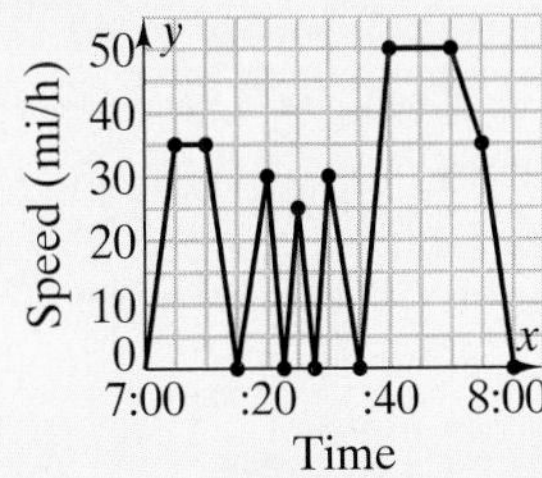

a. How long did the trip take? 1 hr

b. What was the fastest speed? 50 mi/h

2 An athlete jogs for 30 min, sprints for 5 min, and walks for 10 min. Sketch and label a graph showing his speed.

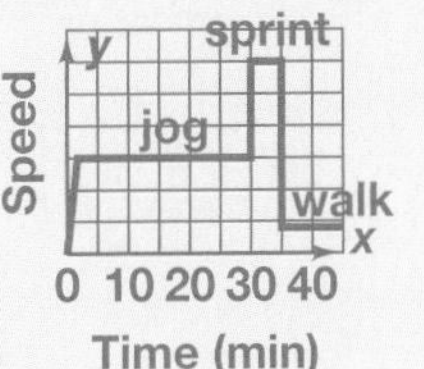

Closure

Explain how to interpret and to sketch the graph of a mail truck making deliveries. Sample: Time is graphed on the x-axis; speed on the y-axis. Points on the x-axis indicate stops. Steep slopes show a rapid increase or decrease in speed.

Reaching All Students

Below Level Have students discuss how to read information from a graph, eliciting the importance of the title, the labels, and the scales.

Advanced Learners Ask students what it means if the graph of a problem appears only in Quadrant I. both variables are always positive

Inclusion
See note on page 660.

Error Prevention
See note on page 659.

3. Practice

Assignment Guide

Objective 1

A B Core 1–23

C Extension 24–26

Test Prep 27–30

Mixed Review 31–37

Inclusion

Exercise 17 Ask a volunteer to explain why this kind of function is named a *step function* (perhaps demonstrating on a staircase).

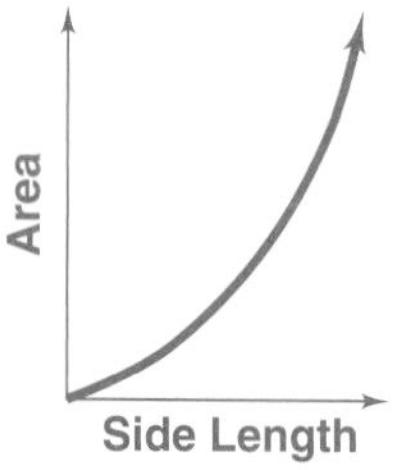

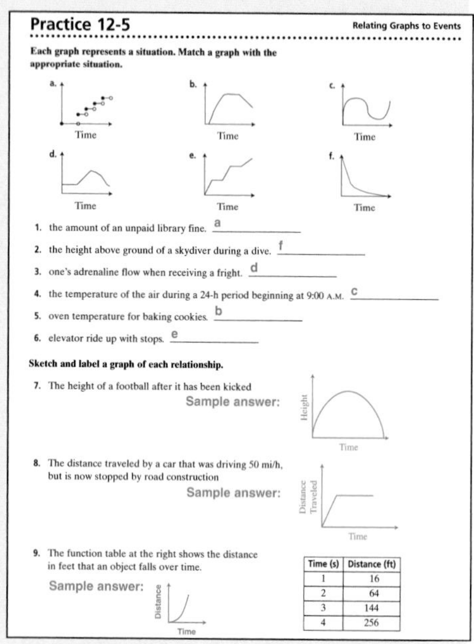

Practice 12-5 — Relating Graphs to Events

Each graph represents a situation. Match a graph with the appropriate situation.

a. Time b. Time c. Time d. Time e. Time f. Time

1. the amount of an unpaid library fine. a
2. the height above ground of a skydiver during a dive. f
3. one's adrenaline flow when receiving a fright. d
4. the temperature of the air during a 24-h period beginning at 9:00 A.M. c
5. oven temperature for baking cookies. b
6. elevator ride up with stops. e

Sketch and label a graph of each relationship.

7. The height of a football after it has been kicked
   Sample answer: (Height vs. Time)
8. The distance traveled by a car that was driving 50 mi/h, but is now stopped by road construction
   Sample answer: (Distance Traveled vs. Time)
9. The function table at the right shows the distance in feet that an object falls over time.
   Sample answer: (Distance vs. Time)

Time (s)	Distance (ft)
1	16
2	64
3	144
4	256

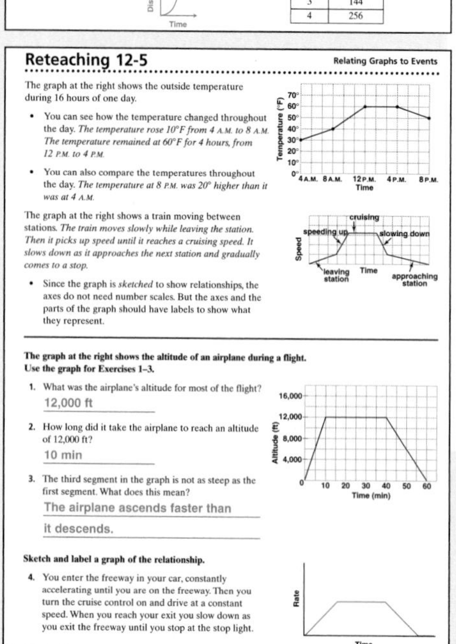

Reteaching 12-5 — Relating Graphs to Events

The graph at the right shows the outside temperature during 16 hours of one day.

- You can see how the temperature changed throughout the day. *The temperature rose 10°F from 4 A.M. to 8 A.M. The temperature remained at 60°F for 4 hours, from 12 P.M. to 4 P.M.*
- You can also compare the temperatures throughout the day. *The temperature at 8 P.M. was 20° higher than it was at 4 A.M.*

The graph at the right shows a train moving between stations. *The train moves slowly while leaving the station. Then it picks up speed until it reaches a cruising speed. It slows down as it approaches the next station and gradually comes to a stop.*

- Since the graph is *sketched* to show relationships, the axes do not need number scales. But the axes and the parts of the graph should have labels to show what they represent.

The graph at the right shows the altitude of an airplane during a flight. Use the graph for Exercises 1–3.

1. What was the airplane's altitude for most of the flight? 12,000 ft
2. How long did it take the airplane to reach an altitude of 12,000 ft? 10 min
3. The third segment in the graph is not as steep as the first segment. What does this mean? The airplane ascends faster than it descends.

Sketch and label a graph of the relationship.

4. You enter the freeway in your car, constantly accelerating until you are on the freeway. Then you turn the cruise control on and drive at a constant speed. When you reach your exit you slow down as you exit the freeway until you stop at the stop light.

9. Altitude; 0 20 40 60; Time (min)

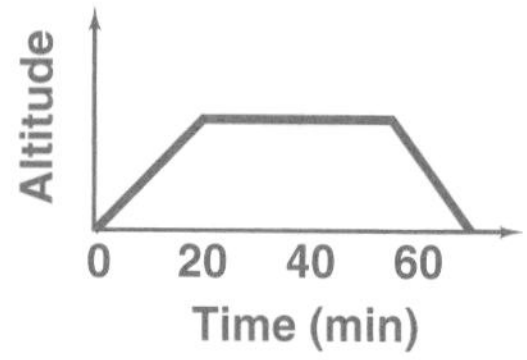

10. Distance; Time

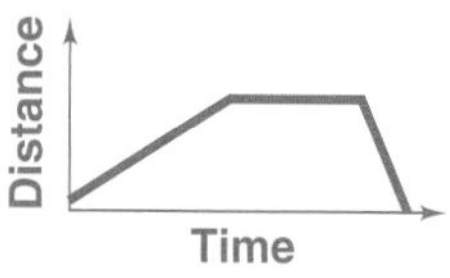

11. Area; Side Length

EXERCISES

For more practice, see *Extra Practice*.

A Practice by Example

Example 1 (page 658)

Swimming **Use the graph at the right for Exercises 1–4.**

Swimming Distance During Olympic Training

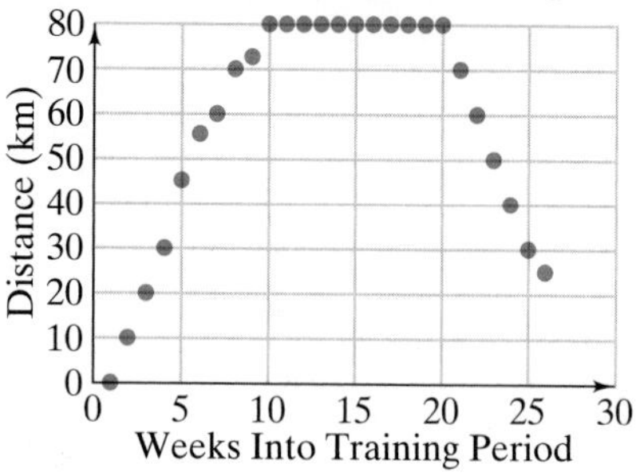

Distance (km); Weeks Into Training Period

1. For how many weeks is the peak training level 80 km/wk? 11 weeks
2. How many weeks does it take to reach the peak training level? 10 weeks
3. Between which two weeks does the greatest increase in swimming distance occur? fourth and fifth weeks
4. Find the change in the average distance between weeks 24 and 25. −10 km

Travel **Use the graph at the right for Exercises 5–7.**

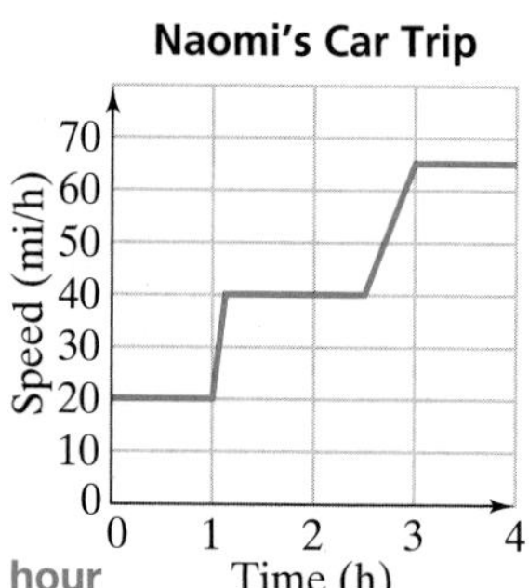

5. a. How fast was Naomi driving during the first hour of her trip? 20 mi/h
   b. How many miles did she travel at this speed? 20 mi
6. a. When did Naomi's speed first increase?
   b. To what speed did it increase? a. after 1 hour b. 40 mi/h
7. a. What was Naomi's final speed at the end of the 4 hours? 65 mi/h
   b. How long did she travel at this speed? 1 hour

Example 2 (page 659)

8. **Temperature** In a 24-hour period, air temperatures rise during the day and cool off during the night. Sketch and label a graph showing the temperature during this 24-hour period. See margin.

9. **Aviation** An airplane flew from Los Angeles to San Francisco in 70 min. The plane took 20 min to reach its cruising altitude. It took 15 min to descend into San Francisco. Sketch and label a graph that shows the plane's altitude during the flight. See above left.

10. **Pets** Haley took her dog Rocky to the park. She walked slowly to the park. She stopped to visit with a friend at the park. Haley and her dog then ran home together. Sketch a graph showing their distance from home throughout the trip. See above left.

B Apply Your Skills

11. **Geometry** As the length of the side of a square increases, its area increases. Sketch a graph that shows the area of the square as the side length changes. See above left.

12. You throw a ball into the air. It lands 4 seconds later. Sketch and label a graph showing the height of the ball during this time. See margin.

GPS Use the Guided Problem Solving worksheet with Exercise 11.

8.

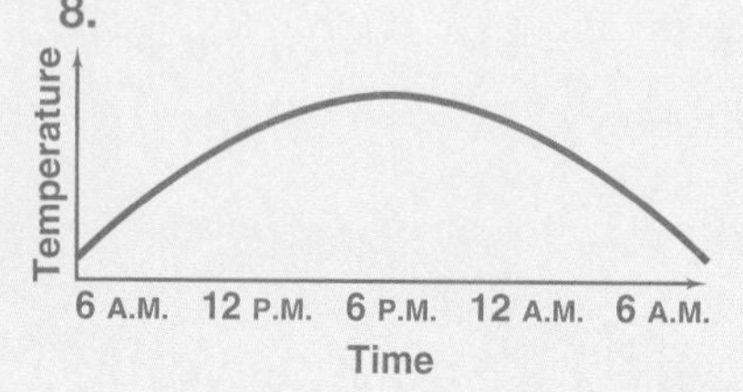

12.

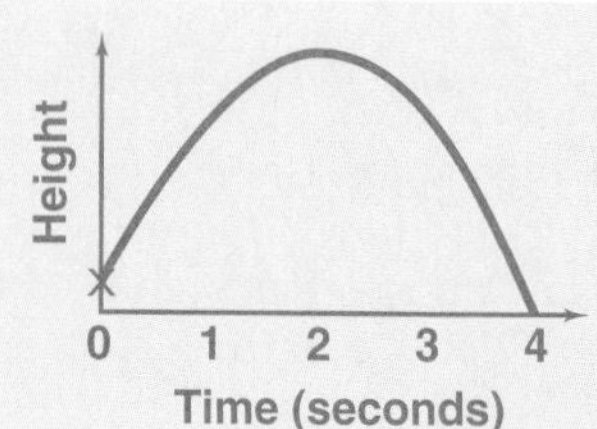

18.

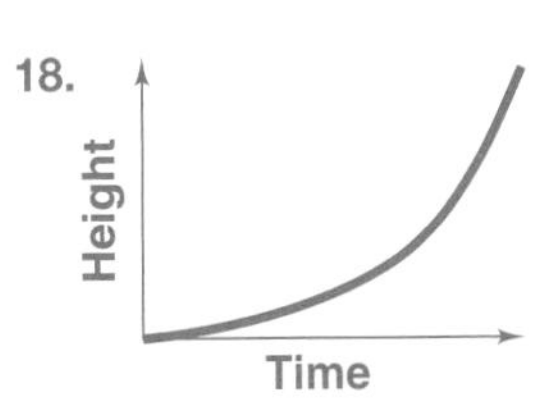

19.

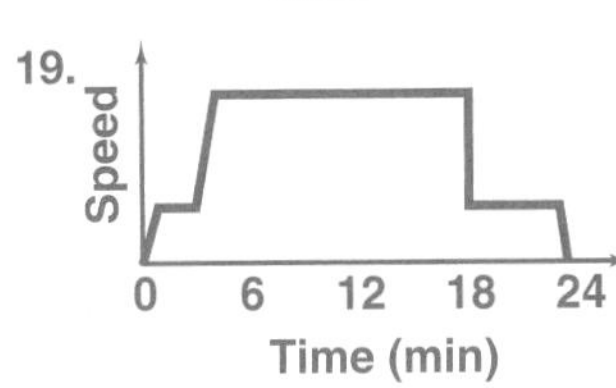

Parking **Use the graph at the right for Exercises 13–17.**

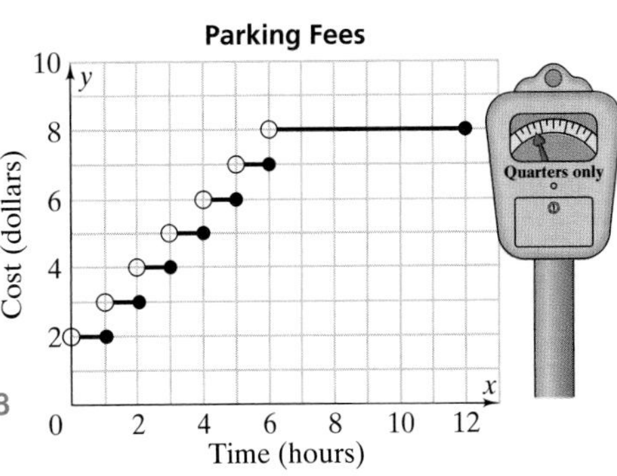

13. What is the rate for the first hour of parking? $2

14. What is the cost to park for $3\frac{1}{2}$ hours? $5

15. What is the maximum cost to park for up to 12 hours? $8

16. What is the cost for each additional hour between 1 and 6 hours? $1

17. **Open-Ended** The graph above shows a *step function.* Sketch a graph of another situation you can represent with a step function. Check students' work.

18. **Chemistry** Water is poured at a constant rate into the container at the left. Sketch a graph of the water level as the container is filled. See above left.

19. **Recreation** A boat travels at low speed for 3 min while leaving a harbor. Then it travels at cruising speed for 15 min. Finally, it travels at low speed for 5 min while entering another harbor. Sketch a graph that shows the boat's speed during the trip. See above left.

25a. The y-intercept represents how far Mr. Lee had traveled (0 miles) before he started his trip.

b. 37.5; Mr. Lee's speed

Use the graph at the right for Exercises 20–23.

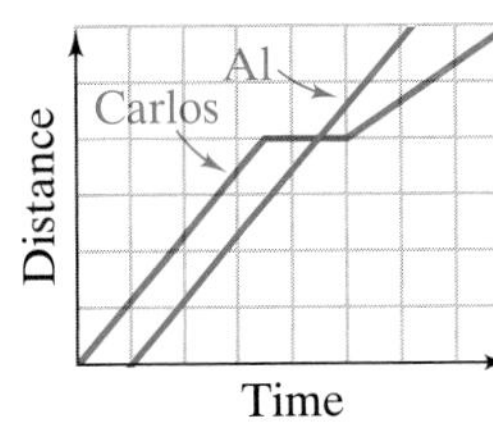

20. Who started the race later? Al

21. Who ran faster? Al

22. Who stopped to tie his shoe? Carlos

23. **Writing in Math** Describe the outcome of the race. Al ran farther in a shorter period of time. Al won.

Challenge

24. Abel, Ben, and Clarissa all left the computer lab at 2:30 P.M. Clarissa walked the fastest and Abel the slowest. At the same time, Daniel and Erin were walking toward the lab. Erin was walking faster than Daniel. Sketch a graph of the students' time along the horizontal axis and the distance from the computer lab along the vertical axis. See margin.

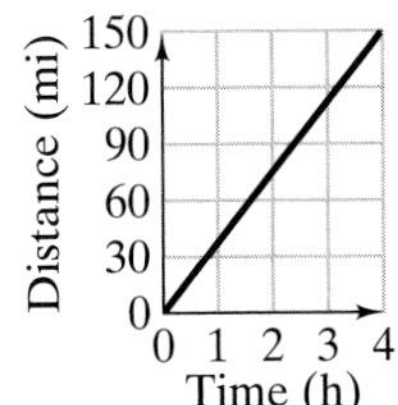

25. **Travel** Mr. Lee took a trip. For 4 hours, he carefully monitored the distance he traveled. At the left is the graph giving his distance traveled as a function of time.

a. What does the y-intercept represent? 25a–b. See above left.

b. Find the slope of the line. What does the slope represent?

c. Write an equation for the line. $y = 37.5x$

26. **Stretch Your Thinking** A bird can fly $\frac{1}{4}$ mile in $\frac{1}{2}$ minute. How far can the bird fly in 5 minutes? 2.5 mi

24. Clarissa, Ben, Abel, Erin, Daniel; Distance From Lab; Time

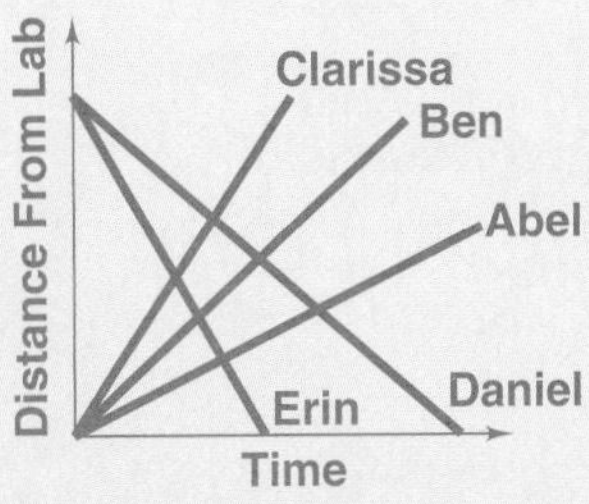

4. Assess

Lesson Quiz 12-5

1. Water is steadily poured into a cone-shaped vase. Sketch and label a graph for the water level as the vase is filled.

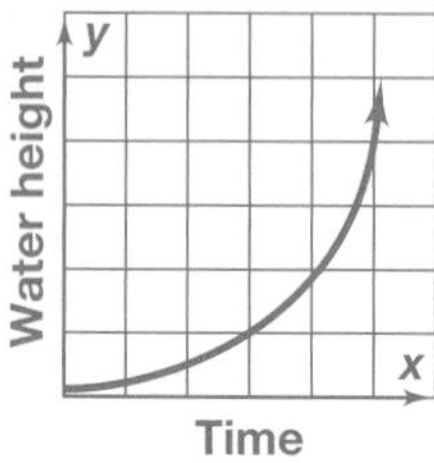

2. Sketch and label a graph for the number of pieces of bread remaining in a loaf of bread as each piece of bread is eaten.

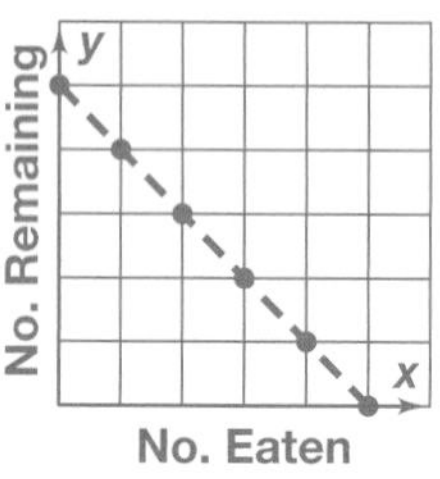

Test Prep

Resources

For additional practice with a variety of test item formats:

- Test Prep, p. 691
- Test-Taking Strategies, p. 687
- Test-Taking Strategies with Transparencies

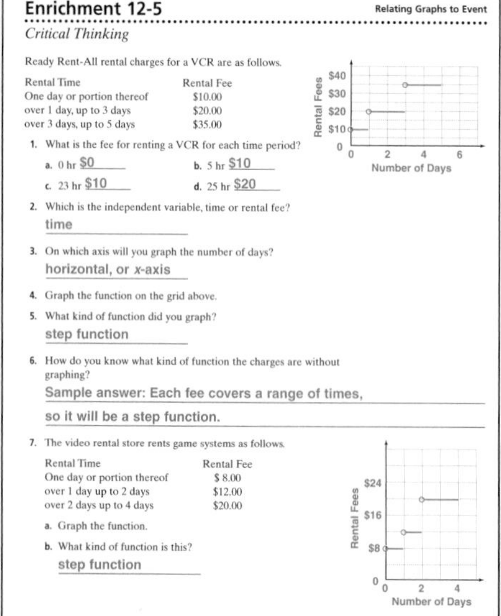

Enrichment 12-5 — Relating Graphs to Event

Critical Thinking

Ready Rent-All rental charges for a VCR are as follows.

Rental Time	Rental Fee
One day or portion thereof	$10.00
over 1 day, up to 3 days	$20.00
over 3 days, up to 5 days	$35.00

1. What is the fee for renting a VCR for each time period?
   a. 0 hr $0 b. 5 hr $10
   c. 23 hr $10 d. 25 hr $20
2. Which is the independent variable, time or rental fee? time
3. On which axis will you graph the number of days? horizontal, or x-axis
4. Graph the function on the grid above.
5. What kind of function did you graph? step function
6. How do you know what kind of function the charges are without graphing? Sample answer: Each fee covers a range of times, so it will be a step function.
7. The video rental store rents game systems as follows.

Rental Time	Rental Fee
One day or portion thereof	$ 8.00
over 1 day up to 2 days	$12.00
over 2 days up to 4 days	$20.00

   a. Graph the function.
   b. What kind of function is this? step function

Rental Fees: $40, $30, $20, $10, 0; Number of Days: 0, 2, 4, 6

Rental Fees: $24, $16, $8, 0; Number of Days: 0, 2, 4

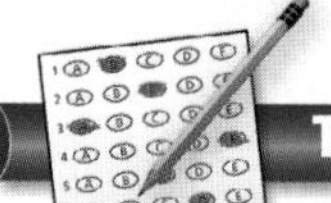

Test Prep

Reading Comprehension **Read the passage and answer the questions below.**

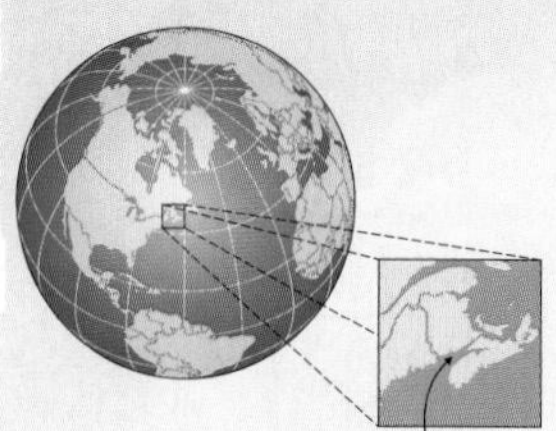

What a Difference!

The tides in the Bay of Fundy are world famous. The difference between the water level at low tide and at high tide averages 39.4 ft, but it can be as much as 70 ft. Situated in Canada between New Brunswick and Nova Scotia, the Bay of Fundy is about 180 mi long and is 35 mi wide on average. Scientists believe that the bay's long, narrow shape accounts for the extreme variation in its tidal range.

27. Explain how the graph at the right describes changes in the water level between low tides at the Bay of Fundy. See margin.
28. Suppose low tide occurs at 3:30 P.M. At what time will the tide have risen 30 ft? 7:30 P.M.

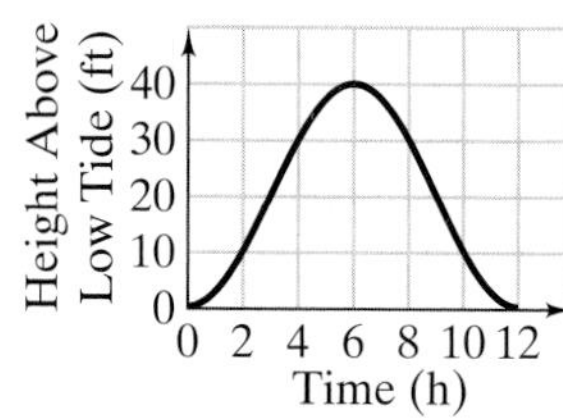

Multiple Choice

29. A boy graphs the distance traveled on a bike ride versus time. Which part of the ride will the steepest part of the graph represent? A
    A. riding downhill B. riding uphill
    C. riding on flat ground D. waiting to cross the street

Take It to the NET
Online lesson quiz at **www.PHSchool.com**
Web Code: aca-1205

30. A student walks home from school, stopping at a friend's house on the way. Which graph could describe the total distance walked? H

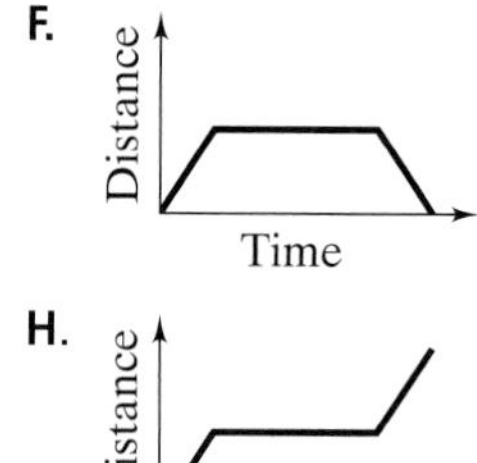

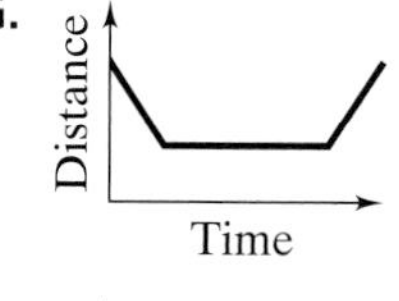

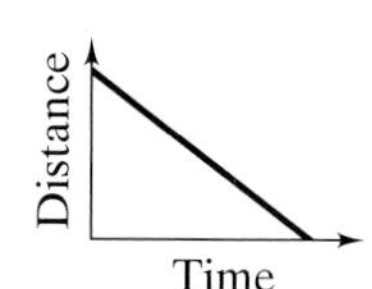

Mixed Review

Lesson 12-2 **Use the function rule $f(x) = 4x - \frac{1}{2}$. Find each output.**

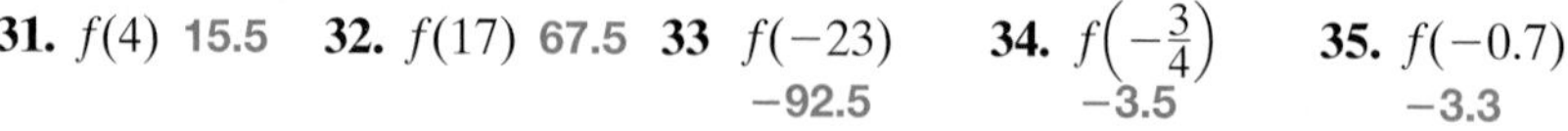

31. $f(4)$ 15.5 32. $f(17)$ 67.5 33 $f(-23)$ −92.5 34. $f\left(-\frac{3}{4}\right)$ −3.5 35. $f(-0.7)$ −3.3

Lesson 11-4 **Decide whether each probability is *experimental* or *theoretical*.**

36. A six-sided number cube is tossed 250 times. $P(\text{rolling a 4})$ is $\frac{37}{250}$. experimental
37. A bag contains 8 pens and 18 pencils. $P(\text{choosing a pen})$ is $\frac{4}{13}$. theoretical

Alternative Assessment

Show students an unlabeled graph with peaks and dips and horizontal stretches. Have students write a story to explain the graph.

27. The water level increases for 6 hours until it peaks; then it lowers for the next 6 hours.

12-6 Nonlinear Functions

Algebra

What You'll Learn

 To graph and write quadratic functions

 To graph other nonlinear functions

. . . And Why

To describe the time needed to complete a task, as in Example 3

For help, go to Lesson 12-3.

Use the table of input/output pairs to graph each linear function.

1.

x	8	4	0	−4	−8
y	1	2	3	4	5

2.

x	0	2	4	6	8
y	6	12	18	24	30

1–2. See back of book.

New Vocabulary • quadratic function • parabola

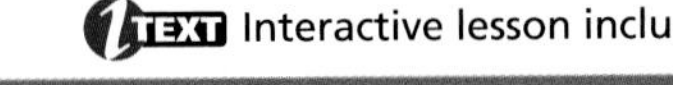

OBJECTIVE 1

Graphing and Writing Quadratic Functions

You have learned about linear functions. There are other types of functions as well. In a **quadratic function,** the greatest power of the variable is 2.

The graph of a quadratic function is a U-shaped curve. The curve may open upward or downward. The curve is called a **parabola.** When you throw a ball into the air, the path the ball follows is a parabola.

After you plot several points on the graph of a quadratic function, connect them with a smooth curve.

1 EXAMPLE Graphing a Quadratic Function

Make a table and graph the quadratic function $y = 4t - t^2$. Use integers from -1 to 5 for inputs.

t	$4t - t^2$			=	y
−1	$4(-1) - (-1)^2$	=	$-4 - 1$	=	−5
0	$4(0) - (0)^2$	=	$0 - 0$	=	0
1	$4(1) - (1)^2$	=	$4 - 1$	=	3
2	$4(2) - (2)^2$	=	$8 - 4$	=	4
3	$4(3) - (3)^2$	=	$12 - 9$	=	3
4	$4(4) - (4)^2$	=	$16 - 16$	=	0
5	$4(5) - (5)^2$	=	$20 - 25$	=	−5

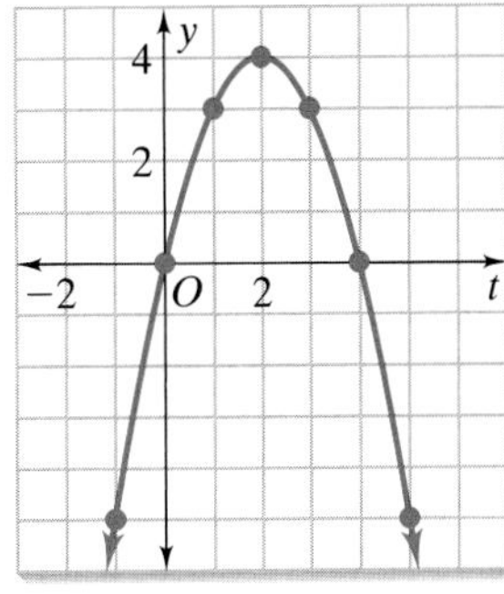

Check Understanding 1 Make a table and graph each quadratic function. 1a–b. See back of book.

a. $y = 2x^2 - 5$ **b.** $y = -x^2 + x$

12-6

1. Plan

Lesson Preview

Check Skills You'll Need

Using a Table to Graph Functions
Lesson 12-3: Example 1. Extra Practice, p. 713.

Lesson Resources

Optional Materials
- graph paper

Teaching Resources
Practice, Reteaching, Enrichment

Reaching All Students
Practice Workbook 12-6
Spanish Practice Workbook 12-6
Guided Problem Solving 12-6
Technology Activities 52

Presentation Assistant Plus!
Transparencies
- Check Skills You'll Need 12-6
- Problem of the Day 12-6
- Additional Examples 12-6
- Student Edition Answers 12-6
- Lesson Quiz 12-6
- Classroom Aid 2–3

PH Presentation Pro CD-ROM 12-6

Computer Test Generator CD

Technology
Resource Pro® CD-ROM
Computer Test Generator CD
PH Presentation Pro CD-ROM

www.PHSchool.com
Student Site
- Teacher Web Code: ack-5500
- Algebra Readiness Puzzles 106
- Self-grading Lesson Quiz

PH SuccessNet Teacher Center
- Lesson Planner
- Resources

Plus 

Ongoing Assessment and Intervention

Before the Lesson
Diagnose prerequisite skills using:
- Check Skills You'll Need

During the Lesson
Monitor progress using:
- Check Understanding
- Additional Examples
- Test Prep

After the Lesson
Assess knowledge using:
- Lesson Quiz
- Computer Test Generator CD

2. Teach

Professional Development

Math Background

Equations of the form $y = mx + b$ always have a graph that is a straight line. Equations of the form $y = ax^2 + bx + c$ ($a \neq 0$) are called *quadratic equations* and have a U-shaped curve called a *parabola*. A parabola opens upward, like a drinking glass, if the coefficient of x^2 is positive ($a > 0$) and opens downward if the coefficient is negative ($a < 0$).

Along with circles and ellipses, parabolas and hyperbolas are called *conic sections* because they result from the intersection of a plane and a right circular double-cone. The *hyperbola* is a two-branched curve and each branch can resemble a parabola, although it has a different mathematical definition.

Teaching Notes

1 EXAMPLE Visual Learners

Point out that the function can also be written in the form $y = -t^2 + 4t$. Have students look at the graph. Ask:

- *What do the arrows at the end of the parabola mean?* The curve extends without stopping.
- *Does this graph show a discrete or a continuous function?* continuous

2 EXAMPLE English Learners

Point out that the words *quadratic function* in the instructions give you a hint that x may be squared.

3 EXAMPLE Technology Tip

To graph this function on a graphing calculator, enter $y = 60 \div x$ and graph. Since y (the number of people) and x (the hours) are both positive, only Quadrant I is relevant.

Error Prevention!

Emphasize that the curve in Example 3 is not simply part of a parabola. The shape is part of a hyperbola, which is mathematically different from a parabola.

You can write function rules for quadratic functions.

2 EXAMPLE Writing a Quadratic Function Rule

x	y
0	3
2	7
3	12
5	28

Write a rule for the quadratic function in the table at the left.

Input x	(Input)^2 x^2	Output y
0	0	3
2	4	7
3	9	12
5	25	28

← **Compare each output to (input)^2. Each output is greater than (input)^2 by 3.**

Words output = (input)^2 + 3

Let x = input.

Let y = output.

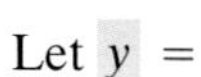

Function $y = x^2 + 3$

So, the function rule is $y = x^2 + 3$.

Check Understanding 2 Write a quadratic function rule for the data in the table. $y = x^2 - 2$

x	−3	−1	0	2	4
y	7	−1	−2	2	14

OBJECTIVE 2 Graphing Other Nonlinear Functions

Other types of nonlinear functions also have curved graphs.

3 EXAMPLE Graphing Other Nonlinear Functions

Real World

Environment Suppose it takes a total of 60 hours of work to clean wildlife damaged by an oil spill. The function $y = \frac{60}{x}$ represents the number of hours (y) each person must work if x people work to clean the wildlife. Make a table and graph the function.

Number of People (x)	Hours per Person (y)
3	$60 \div 3 = 20$
4	$60 \div 4 = 15$
5	$60 \div 5 = 12$
6	$60 \div 6 = 10$
10	$60 \div 10 = 6$

Time for Oil Spill Cleanup

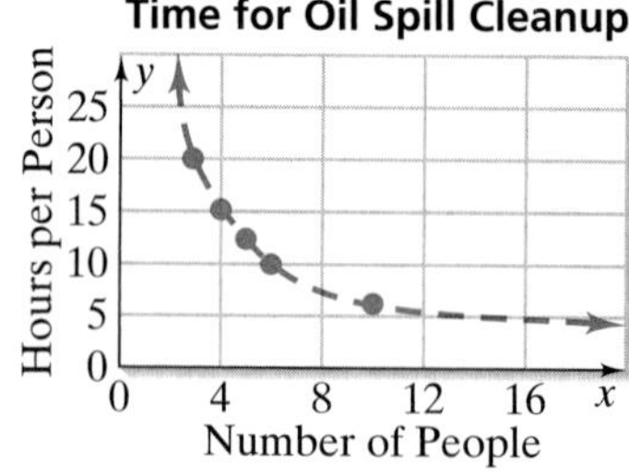

The data are discrete, so the curve is dashed.

Real-World Connection

It takes an average of 45 minutes to clean a bird damaged by an oil spill.

SOURCE: Oiled Wildlife Care Network

Reaching All Students

Below Level Have students use a graphing calculator to see the graphs of the parabolas for the functions in Examples 1 and 2.

Advanced Learners Have students find points for the graph of $xy = 12$. Sample: (3, 4), (4, 3), (−4, −3), (−2, −6), (12, 1), . . .

English Learners See note on page 664.

Visual Learners See note on page 664.

Check Understanding **3** **a.** The function $y = \frac{200}{t}$ relates the time for a 200-mile trip (in hours) to the speed traveled (in miles per hour). Make a table that shows the speed as a function of the number of hours traveled. Then graph the data.

b. Number Sense Does an input of -7 make sense for the function in Example 3? Explain.

3a. See back of book.
b. No; you can't have a negative amount of time.

EXERCISES

For more practice, see *Extra Practice*.

A Practice by Example

Example 1 (page 663)

Make a table and graph each quadratic function. Use integers from –3 to 3 for inputs. 1–6. See back of book.

1. $y = -x^2$ **2.** $y = 2x^2$

3. $y = -8x^2$ **4.** $y = x^2 + 2$

5. $y = -4x^2$ **6.** $y = 9 + 2x^2$

Example 2 (page 664)

Write a quadratic function rule for the data in each table.

7.

x	−10	−5	0	5	10
y	80	5	−20	5	80

$y = x^2 - 20$

8.

x	0	1	2	3	4
y	0	−1	−4	−9	−16

$y = -x^2$

9.

x	0	1	2	3	4
y	5	6	9	14	21

$y = x^2 + 5$

10.

x	−2	−1	0	1	4
y	0	−3	−4	−3	12

$y = x^2 - 4$

Example 3 (page 664)

Make a table and a graph for each function. Use only positive values for *x*. 11–16. See back of book.

11. $y = \frac{10}{x}$ **12.** $y = \frac{8}{x}$ **13.** $y = \frac{20}{x}$

14. $y = \frac{16}{x}$ **15.** $y = \frac{100}{x}$ **16.** $y = \frac{18}{x}$

17. Construction Suppose it takes a total of 225 workdays to build a house. With more workers, the number of days to finish the house decreases. The function $y = \frac{225}{x}$ describes the number of days (y) it will take x people to build the house. Make a table and graph the function. See back of book.

B Apply Your Skills

Make a table and a graph for each quadratic function. Use integers from −3 to 3 for inputs. 18–20. See back of book.

18. $y = -x - 3x^2$ **19.** $y = 2x^2 + 2x + 2$ **20.** $y = x - x^2$

See back of book.

21. a. Graph $y = n^2$ and $y = n^3$ on the same coordinate grid.

b. Writing in Math Describe the similarities and differences in the graphs of the two functions. See left.

21b. Answers may vary. Sample: Both graphs are nonlinear and have positive y values for positive x values. The graph of $y = n^2$ is a parabola but the graph of $y = n^3$ is not.

PowerPoint

Additional Examples

1 Make a table and graph the quadratic function $f(x) = x^2 - 2x$. Use integers from −2 to 4 for inputs.

x	−2	−1	0	1	2	3	4
y	8	3	0	−1	0	3	8

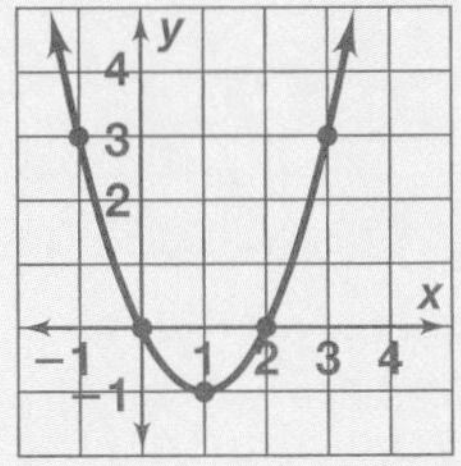

2 Write a quadratic function rule for the data in the table below. $f(x) = x^2 - 3$

Input x	−2	−1	0	1	2
Output y	1	−2	−3	−2	1

3 Suppose a driver is making a 120 mile trip. Make a table and graph this situation using the relationship that 120 ÷ hours for trip = speed for trip. Use 2, 3, 4, 5, and 6 hours for input.

Input t	2	3	4	5	6
Output y	60	40	30	24	20

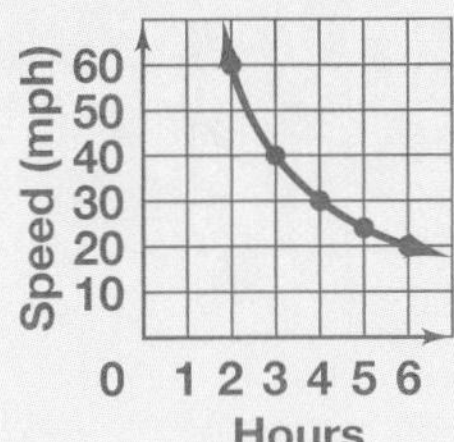

Closure

- *Define a parabola.* a U-shaped curve formed by the graph of a quadratic function
- *How do you write a function rule for a quadratic function represented in a function table?* Find the relationship between each input value and the input value squared and write the corresponding function rule.
- *How do you graph nonlinear functions?* Substitute values for *x* and make a table. Then graph the ordered pairs and connect them in a curve.

3. Practice

Assignment Guide

 **Objective 1**

Ⓐ Ⓑ Core 1–10, 18–20, 22, 25, 27, 29–32, 34

Ⓒ Extension 39

 **Objective 2**

Ⓐ Ⓑ Core 11–17, 21, 23–24, 26, 28, 33

Ⓒ Extension 35–38

Test Prep 40–43
Mixed Review 44–49

Exercise 34 Explain the volume of a bushel: 1 bushel = 16 quarts.

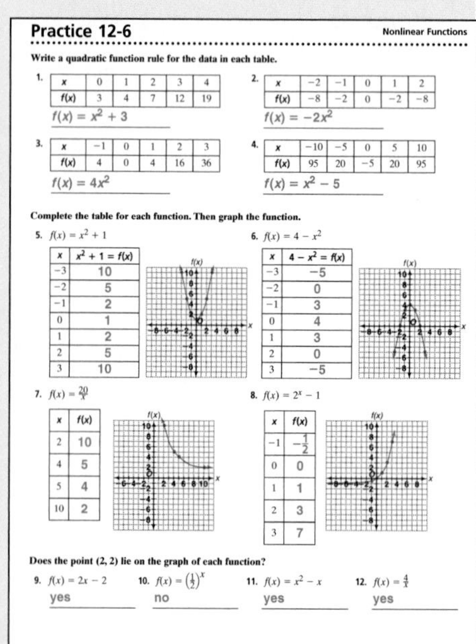

Practice 12-6 — Nonlinear Functions

Write a quadratic function rule for the data in each table.

1.

x	0	1	2	3	4
f(x)	3	4	7	12	19

$f(x) = x^2 + 3$

2.

x	−2	−1	0	1	2
f(x)	−8	−2	0	−2	−8

$f(x) = -2x^2$

3.

x	−1	0	1	2	3
f(x)	4	0	4	16	36

$f(x) = 4x^2$

4.

x	−10	−5	0	5	10
f(x)	95	20	−5	20	95

$f(x) = x^2 - 5$

Complete the table for each function. Then graph the function.

5. $f(x) = x^2 + 1$

x	$x^2 + 1 = f(x)$
−3	10
−2	5
−1	2
0	1
1	2
2	5
3	10

6. $f(x) = 4 - x^2$

x	$4 - x^2 = f(x)$
−3	−5
−2	0
−1	3
0	4
1	3
2	0
3	−5

7. $f(x) = \frac{20}{x}$

x	f(x)
2	10
4	5
5	4
10	2

8. $f(x) = 2^x - 1$

x	f(x)
−1	$-\frac{1}{2}$
0	0
1	1
2	3
3	7

Does the point (2, 2) lie on the graph of each function?

9. $f(x) = 2x - 2$ yes
10. $f(x) = \left(\frac{1}{2}\right)^x$ no
11. $f(x) = x^2 - x$ yes
12. $f(x) = \frac{4}{x}$ yes

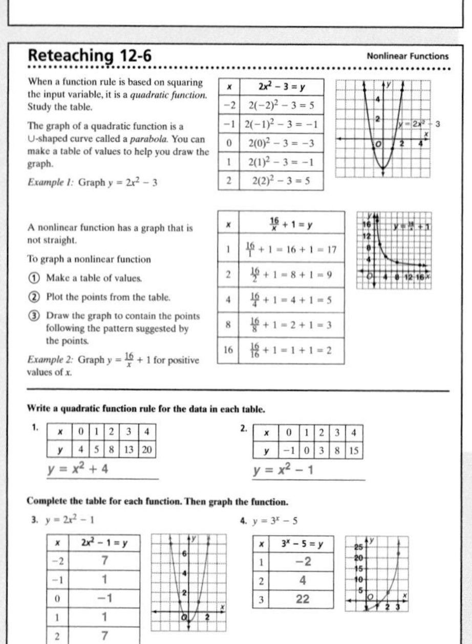

Reteaching 12-6 — Nonlinear Functions

When a function rule is based on squaring the input variable, it is a *quadratic function*. Study the table.

The graph of a quadratic function is a U-shaped curve called a *parabola*. You can make a table of values to help you draw the graph.

Example 1: Graph $y = 2x^2 - 3$

x	$2x^2 - 3 = y$
−2	$2(-2)^2 - 3 = 5$
−1	$2(-1)^2 - 3 = -1$
0	$2(0)^2 - 3 = -3$
1	$2(1)^2 - 3 = -1$
2	$2(2)^2 - 3 = 5$

A nonlinear function has a graph that is not straight.

To graph a nonlinear function

① Make a table of values.
② Plot the points from the table.
③ Draw the graph to contain the points following the pattern suggested by the points.

Example 2: Graph $y = \frac{16}{x} + 1$ for positive values of x.

x	$\frac{16}{x} + 1 = y$
1	$\frac{16}{1} + 1 = 16 + 1 = 17$
2	$\frac{16}{2} + 1 = 8 + 1 = 9$
4	$\frac{16}{4} + 1 = 4 + 1 = 5$
8	$\frac{16}{8} + 1 = 2 + 1 = 3$
16	$\frac{16}{16} + 1 = 1 + 1 = 2$

Write a quadratic function rule for the data in each table.

1.

x	0	1	2	3	4
y	4	5	8	13	20

$y = x^2 + 4$

2.

x	0	1	2	3	4
y	−1	0	3	8	15

$y = x^2 - 1$

Complete the table for each function. Then graph the function.

3. $y = 2x^2 - 1$

x	$2x^2 - 1 = y$
−2	7
−1	1
0	−1
1	1
2	7

4. $y = 3^x - 5$

x	$3^x - 5 = y$
1	−2
2	4
3	22

Copy and complete the table for each function. Then graph the function. Use only positive values for x in Exercise 23. See margin for graphs.

22. $y = x^2 - 2$

x	$x^2 - 2 = y$
0	■ −2
1	■ −1
2	■ 2
3	■ 7

23. $y = \frac{7}{x} + 2$

x	$\frac{7}{x} + 2 = y$
1	■ 9
2	■ 5.5
3	■ $4.\overline{3}$
4	■ 3.75

24. $y = 3 \cdot 2^x$

x	$3 \cdot 2^x = y$
1	■ 6
2	■ 12
3	■ 24
4	■ 48

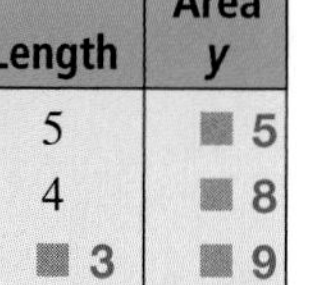

Width x	Length	Area y
1	5	■ 5
2	4	■ 8
3	■ 3	■ 9
4	■ 2	■ 8
5	■ 1	■ 5

25. Gardening Suppose you have 12 yards of fencing to enclose a garden plot like the one shown at the right. Complete the table at the left to show area as a function of the garden's width. Then graph the function. See back of book.

GPS

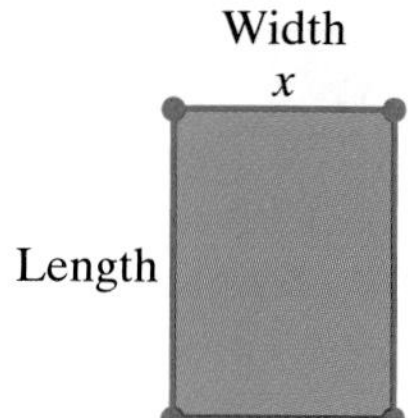

Does the point (3, 5) lie on the graph of each function? Explain. 26–29. See left.

26. $y = 5 \cdot 3^x$ **27.** $y = x^2 - 4$ **28.** $y = \frac{15}{x}$

26. no; $y = 5 \cdot 3^3 = 5 \cdot 27 = 135 \neq 5$

27. yes; $5 = 3^2 - 4$ or $5 = 9 - 4$ or $5 = 5$

28. yes; $5 = \frac{15}{3}$

29. When you square 3 or −3, the result is 9. So each problem is 2(9) − 7, or 11.

29. Writing in Math Suppose $f(x) = 2x^2 - 7$. Explain why $f(3) = f(-3)$.

30. Patterns Consider the pattern of dots below. Then let n = the number of dots in the top row of a figure. Write a function rule that describes the total number of dots in that figure. $D = n^2 - 1$

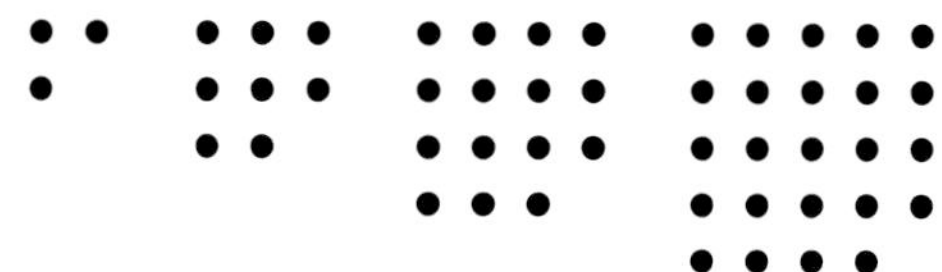

For Exercises 31–33, match each function to its graph at the right.

31. $y = 3x - 2$ III **32.** $y = 3x^2 + 2$ I

33. $y = 2 + 2^x$ II

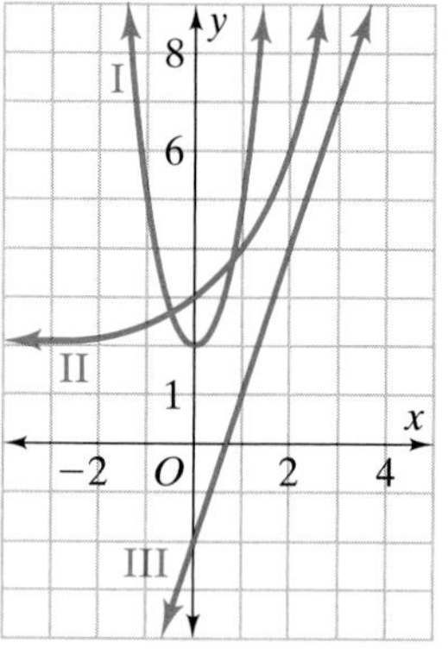

34. Farming The number of bushels of walnuts that a tree produces (output) is a function of the number of trees planted per acre (input). The function rule is $y = -0.01x^2 + 0.8x$.

a. Evaluate the function for 10, 20, 30, 40, 50, and 60 trees per acre. 7, 12, 15, 16, 15, 12

b. Graph the function. Is this data discrete or continuous? See left.

c. Explain how the number of trees planted per acre affects walnut production. When too many trees are planted per acre, production goes down.

34b. The graph is discrete.

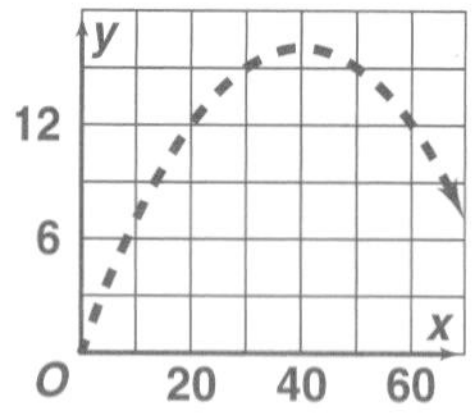

Use the Guided Problem Solving worksheet with Exercise 25.

23.

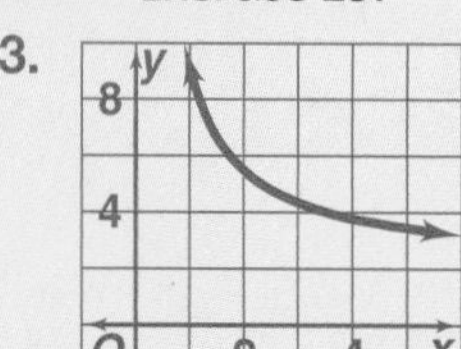

22.

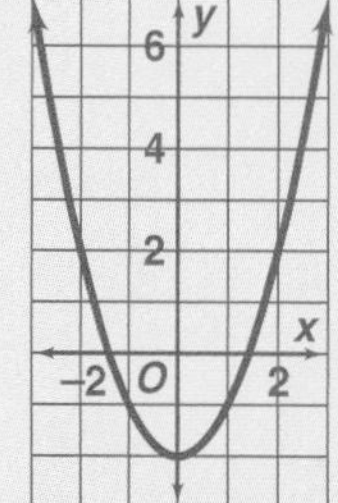

24.

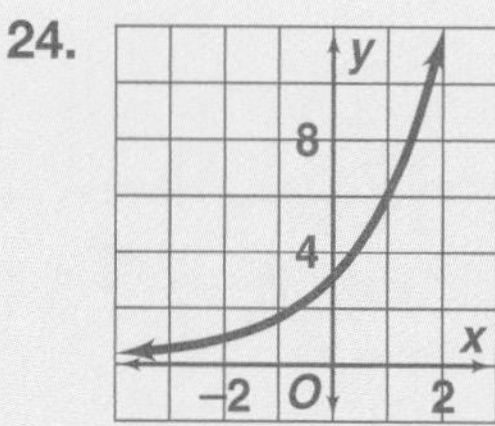

 Challenge

Make a table and a graph for each function. Then compare the graphs.
35–38. See back of book.

35. $y = 3^x$ **36.** $y = 3^{x-2}$ **37.** $y = 3^{x+2}$ **38.** $y = -3^x$

39. **Stretch Your Thinking** A pyramid has 10 edges. How many triangular faces does the pyramid have? 5

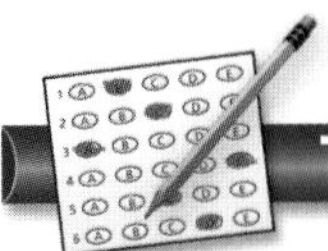

Test Prep

Multiple Choice

40. Which of the following is NOT a quadratic function? D

A. $y = 2x^2 - 3$ B. $y = 5 - 2x^2$
C. $y = -x^2 + x - 1$ D. $y = 4x^3 - 3x^2$

41. The function table at the right describes the distance in feet that a stone falls over time. Which graph best describes the information? H

Time (s)	Distance (ft)
0	0
0.5	4
1	16
1.5	36
2	64

F.
Distance
Time

G.
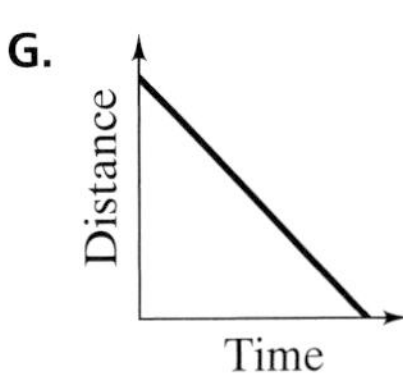

H.
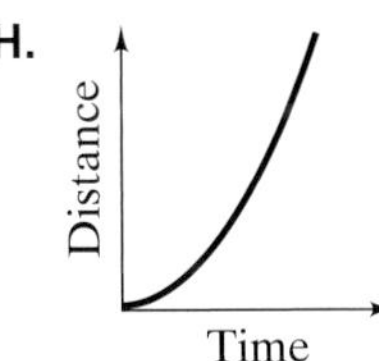

I.
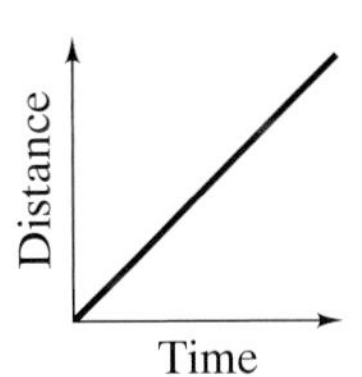

Take It to the NET
Online lesson quiz at
www.PHSchool.com
Web Code: aca-1206

42. Which of the following is a function rule for the table at the right? B

x	0	1	2	3	4
y	0	2	6	12	20

A. $y = 2x$ B. $y = x^2 + x$ C. $y = -2x$ D. $y = 2^x$

Short Response

43. Make a table for the function $y = 3x + 7x^2$. Then graph the function.
See back of book.

Mixed Review

Lesson 12-2

Use the function rule $f(x) = 2x^2 + 5$. Find each output.

44. $f(2)$ 13 **45.** $f(-2)$ 13 **46.** $f(12)$ 293 **47.** $f\left(\frac{1}{2}\right)$ $5\frac{1}{2}$

Lesson 11-7

Determine whether each question is biased or not. Explain your answer.

48. What is your favorite food? Not biased; the question does not make any assumptions about what your favorite food is.

49. Would you rather buy a scooter or a bike? Biased; the question assumes you would want to buy a scooter or a bike.

Test Prep

Resources

For additional practice with a variety of test item formats:

- Test Prep, p. 691
- Test-Taking Strategies, p. 687
- Test-Taking Strategies with Transparencies

4. Assess

Lesson Quiz 12-6

Make a table and graph each function.

1. $y = -x^2 + 4x$

x	0	1	2	3	4
y	0	3	4	3	0

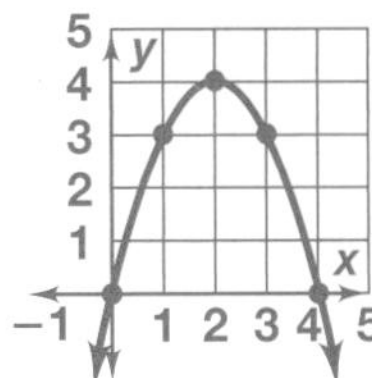

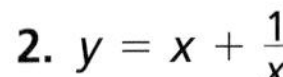

2. $y = x + \frac{1}{x}$

x	1	2	3	4	5
y	2	2.5	$3.\overline{3}$	4.25	5.2

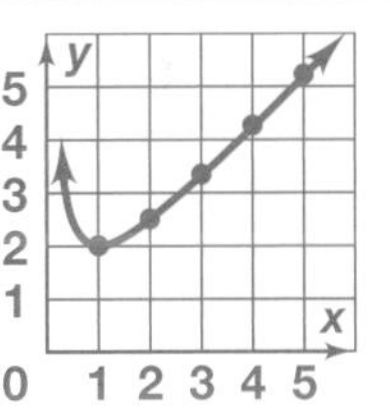

Alternative Assessment

Each student writes a simple quadratic function and makes a table on a separate piece of paper. Partners exchange tables, graph the data, and write the function rule for each other's functions.

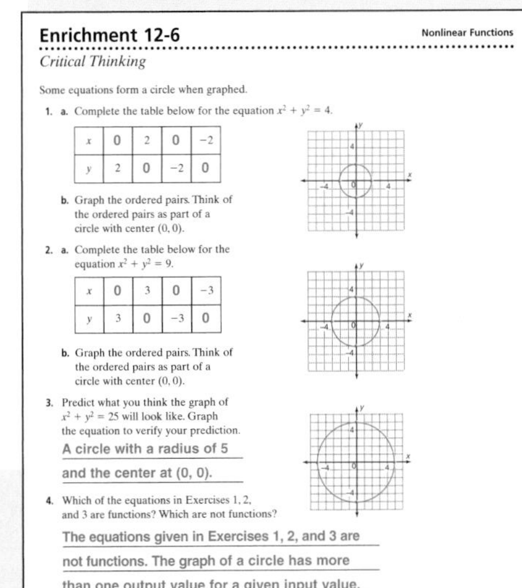

Enrichment 12-6 Nonlinear Functions

Critical Thinking

Some equations form a circle when graphed.

1. a. Complete the table below for the equation $x^2 + y^2 = 4$.

x	0	2	0	−2
y	2	0	−2	0

b. Graph the ordered pairs. Think of the ordered pairs as part of a circle with center (0, 0).

2. a. Complete the table below for the equation $x^2 + y^2 = 9$.

x	0	3	0	−3
y	3	0	−3	0

b. Graph the ordered pairs. Think of the ordered pairs as part of a circle with center (0, 0).

3. Predict what you think the graph of $x^2 + y^2 = 25$ will look like. Graph the equation to verify your prediction.
A circle with a radius of 5 and the center at (0, 0).

4. Which of the equations in Exercises 1, 2, and 3 are functions? Which are not functions?
The equations given in Exercises 1, 2, and 3 are not functions. The graph of a circle has more than one output value for a given input value.

5. Can the equation of a polygon be a function? Explain.
No; when you plot a polygon on a coordinate grid you will notice that there is more than one output value for a given input value.

12-7

1. Plan

Lesson Preview

Check Skills You'll Need

Writing a Quadratic Function Rule
Lesson 12-6: Example 2. Extra Practice, p. 713.

Lesson Resources

Teaching Resources
Practice, Reteaching, Enrichment
Checkpoint Quiz 2

Reaching All Students
Practice Workbook 12-7
Spanish Practice Workbook 12-7
Reading and Math Literacy 12C
Spanish Reading and Math Literacy 12C
Spanish Checkpoint Quiz 2
Guided Problem Solving 12-7

Presentation Assistant Plus!
Transparencies
- Check Skills You'll Need 12-7
- Problem of the Day 12-7
- Additional Examples 12-7
- Student Edition Answers 12-7
- Lesson Quiz 12-7

PH Presentation Pro CD-ROM 12-7

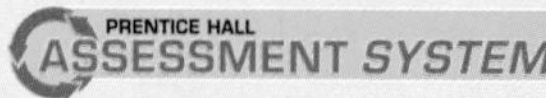

Checkpoint Quiz 2
Computer Test Generator CD

Technology
Resource Pro® CD-ROM
Computer Test Generator CD
PH Presentation Pro CD-ROM

www.PHSchool.com
Student Site
- Teacher Web Code: ack-5500
- Self-grading Lesson Quiz

PH SuccessNet Teacher Center
- Lesson Planner
- Resources

Plus

12-7 Write an Equation

What You'll Learn

To solve problems by writing equations

. . . And Why

To solve a variety of types of problems by writing an equation

Check Skills You'll Need

For help, go to Lesson 12-6.

Write a quadratic function rule for the data in each table.

1.

x	0	1	2	3	4
y	2	3	6	11	18

$y = x^2 + 2$

2.

x	−3	−1	0	1	4
y	6	−2	−3	−2	13

$y = x^2 - 3$

3.

x	−10	−5	0	5	10
y	−10	−2.5	0	−2.5	−10

$y = -\frac{1}{10}x^2$

4.

x	1	2	3	4
y	−3	−12	−27	−48

$y = -3x^2$

Interactive lesson includes instant self-check, tutorials, and activities.

OBJECTIVE 1

Solving Problems by Writing an Equation

When to Use This Strategy Some real-world problems cannot be represented with linear equations or linear function rules. In this lesson, you will write nonlinear function rules for word problems. The following example shows *exponential growth*.

1 EXAMPLE Real-World Problem Solving

Science A bacteria culture starts with one cell. The number of cells doubles every hour. Write a function rule that relates the number of bacteria cells in the culture to the amount of time that has passed. Use the rule to find how many cells there are in the culture after 10 hours and after 20 hours.

Read and Understand The cells in the culture double every hour. The goal is to write a function rule and evaluate the rule for 10 hours and 20 hours.

Plan and Solve Start by making a table that shows the first few hours and the number of cells per hour. Then look for a pattern.

Time Passed	Cells	Pattern
0 h	1	$1 = 2^0$
1 h	$2 \cdot 1 = 2$	$2 = 2 \cdot 1 = 2^1$
2 h	$2 \cdot 2 = 4$	$4 = 2 \cdot 2 \cdot 1 = 2^2$
3 h	$2 \cdot 4 = 8$	$8 = 2 \cdot 2 \cdot 2 \cdot 1 = 2^3$

Notice that each output is equal to 2 raised to the power of the input.

Real-World Connection
E. coli bacteria cultures can double every 20 minutes.

Ongoing Assessment and Intervention

Before the Lesson
Diagnose prerequisite skills using:
- Check Skills You'll Need

During the Lesson
Monitor progress using:
- Check Understanding
- Additional Examples
- Test Prep

After the Lesson
Assess knowledge using:
- Lesson Quiz
- Computer Test Generator CD
- Chapter Checkpoint 2 (p. 671)

Use this pattern to write a function rule.

Words number of bacteria cells is 2 raised to the number of hours

Let h = the number of hours that have passed. ← **input**

Let y = the number of bacteria cells. ← **output**

Function $y = 2^h$ ← **function rule**

Now, use the function rule to find how many cells there will be after 10 hours and after 20 hours.

$y = 2^h$		$y = 2^h$
$= 2^{10}$	← **Substitute the number of hours for *h*.** →	$= 2^{20}$
$= 1,024$	← **Use a calculator.** →	$= 1,048,576$

There will be 1,024 cells after 10 hours, and 1,048,576 cells after 20 hours.

Look Back and Check You can solve a simpler problem to check the function rule. Extend the table for 4 hours and 5 hours and then evaluate the rule for these times.

Time Passed	Cells	Pattern
4 h	$8 \cdot 2 = 16$	$y = 2^4 = 16$
5 h	$16 \cdot 2 = 32$	$y = 2^5 = 32$

The function rule accurately finds the values for 4 hours and 5 hours. ✔

Check Understanding 1 **Science** A bacteria culture starts with 10 cells. The number of cells triples each day. Write a function rule that relates the number of cells in the culture to the amount of time that has passed. Use the rule to find the number of cells after 10 days and after 20 days. $y = 10(3)^d$; 590,490 cells, 3.49×10^{10} cells

EXERCISES

For more practice, see *Extra Practice*.

A Practice by Example

Solve each problem by writing a function rule.

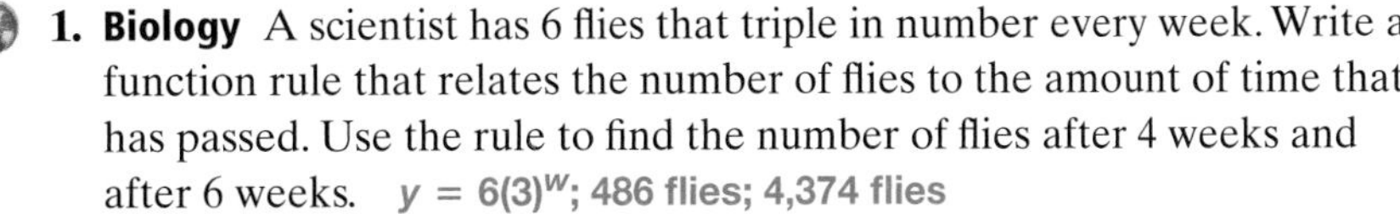

Example 1 (page 668)

1. **Biology** A scientist has 6 flies that triple in number every week. Write a function rule that relates the number of flies to the amount of time that has passed. Use the rule to find the number of flies after 4 weeks and after 6 weeks. $y = 6(3)^w$; 486 flies; 4,374 flies

2. **Savings** Suppose you save \$25 this year. You plan to double the amount you save each year. Write a function rule that relates the amount you save in a given year to the number of years that have passed. Use the rule to find out how much you will save in the fifth year and in the seventh year. $y = 25(2)^x$; \$800, \$3,200

2. Teach

Math Background

Many types of growth and decay, such as bacteria growth and radioactive decay, can be represented by functions where the variable appears as an exponent, as in $y = 2^x$.

Teaching Notes

1 EXAMPLE Error Prevention

Ask:
- *Mathematically, how do you show that a quantity "doubles?"* multiply by 2
- *What symbols can you use to write $2 \times 2 \times 2$ or $2 \times 2 \times 2 \times 2 \times 2$?* 2^3 or 2^5

Technology Tip
On graphing calculators, you can find powers such as 2^{10} by pressing these keys: 2 ^ 10 and then ENTER.

Visual Learners
To demonstrate that these functions are nonlinear, have students graph an exponential function such as $y = 2^x$ on a graphing calculator.

PowerPoint

Additional Examples

1 Suppose you cut a sheet of newspaper in half and stack the two halves. Then you cut this stack in half and stack those pieces, and so on. Write a function rule that relates the number of cuts to the number of pieces of paper in the stack. Use the rule to find how many pieces of paper there are after 8 cuts. $y = 2^x$; 256 pieces of paper

Closure

Explain how to solve problems by writing equations. Sample: Read the problem and make sure you understand all the words and what the problem says. Then make a table that shows the relationships in the problem. Look for a pattern in the table, and use the pattern to write a function rule.

Reaching All Students

Below Level Review exponents by having students find the value of 2^3, 3^2, 4^3, and 5^4. 8, 9, 64, 625	**Advanced Learners** Ask students to write an equation that has the area of a square as its input and the side as the output. $s = \sqrt{A}$	**Diversity** See note on page 670. **Visual Learners** See note on page 669.

3. Practice

Assignment Guide

Objective 1

A B Core 1–8

C Extension 9

Test Prep 10–13

Mixed Review 14–19

Diversity

Exercise 7 Ask if anyone has tasted gumbo or other Creole cooking. Discuss the ingredients and origins.

3. **Elements** A gas under 1 lb of pressure has a volume of 300 ft^3. As the pressure doubles, the amount of volume is halved. Write a function rule that relates the volume of the gas to the pressure applied. Use the rule to find the volume of the gas under 8 lb and under 12 lb of pressure. $V = \frac{300}{p}$; 37.5 ft^3, 25 ft^3

B Apply Your Skills

Use any strategy to solve each problem. Show your work.

Need Help?
- Reread the problem.
- Identify the key facts and details.
- Tell the problem in your own words.
- Try a different strategy.
- Check your work.

4. **Geometry** Suppose you line up multiple squares with side length 1 cm in a straight line, as shown below.

Perimeter	4 cm	6 cm	8 cm

Write a function rule relating the perimeter of the figure to the number of squares that make up the figure. Use the rule to find the perimeter of the figure if there are 10 squares and 25 squares in the figure.
$y = 2n + 2$; 22 cm, 52 cm

5. **Patterns** Examine the list at the right and look for a pattern.

Row 1	1
Row 2	1 3
Row 3	1 3 5
Row 4	1 3 5 7
Row 5	1 3 5 7 9

a. Write the sixth row. 1 3 5 7 9 11
b. What is the last number in the tenth row? In the thirtieth row? 19; 59
c. What is the sum of the numbers in the fifth row? In the tenth row? See left.
d. **Reasoning** How can you find the sum of the numbers in a row when you know the row number? Use the function rule $S = n^2$, where n is the row number.

5c. 25; 100

Strategies

Draw a Diagram
Look for a Pattern
Make a Graph
Make an Organized List
Make a Table
Simulate a Problem
Solve a Simpler Problem
Try, Check, and Revise
Use Logical Reasoning
Work Backward
Write an Equation

6. **Cars** The value of a new car decreases as time passes. Suppose your family bought a new car for $28,000. The value of the car decreases 20% each year. So each year the value of the car is 80% of the previous year's value. This function is an example of *exponential decay*. Write a function rule that relates the value of the car to the years that have passed. Use the rule to find the value of the car after 10 years.
$y = 28{,}000(0.80)^n$; $3,006.48

GPS

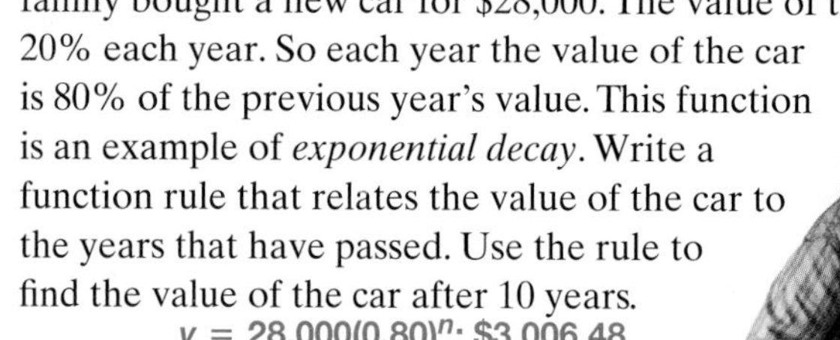

7. **Cooking** A Creole gumbo recipe calls for 1 tsp of thyme and 10 oz of okra. If you use $1\frac{1}{4}$ lb of okra, how many tsp of thyme should you use? 2 tsp

8. a. A photo 3 in. by 5 in. has a border 1 in. wide surrounding it. Find the area of the border. 20 in.^{2}
b. **Writing in Math** Tell how you solved part (a) and explain your strategy. See margin.

C Challenge

9. **Stretch Your Thinking** A teacher took a survey to find how many students owned pets. Of the students who owned pets, 15 had dogs, 14 had cats, and 7 had birds. None of the students had both cats and birds, 8 had dogs and cats, and 3 had dogs and birds. How many students had only dogs? 4 students

Practice 12-7 Problem Solving: Write an Equation

Use any strategy to slove each problem. Show your work.

1. A population of 30 mice is released into a wildlife region. The population triples each year. Write a function rule that relates the number of mice to the amount of time that has passed. Use the rule to find the number of mice after 4 years and 8 years.
$y = 30 \cdot 3^x$; 2,430, 196,830
2. You bought a used car for $6,000. The value of the car will decrease 12% per year. So each year the car is 88% of the previous year's value. Write a function rule that relates the value of the car to the years that have passed. Use the rule to find the value of the car after 6 years.
$y = 6{,}000 \cdot 0.88^x$; $2,786.42
3. The sum of two integers is −44. Their difference is 8. What are the two integers?
−18, −26
4. Margot earns $225 per week plus a commission of 2% on each appliance that she sells. Write a function rule that relates Margot's pay to the number of appliances that she sells. Use the rule to find her pay for a week in which she has sales of $15,234.
$y = 225 + 0.02x$; $529.68
5. The cost of an international long distance phone call is $6.25 for the first minute and $3.75 for each additional minute. What was the total length of a call that cost $28.75?
7 minutes
6. A garden supply shop sells bags of topsoil. The bags come in six sizes: 16, 17, 23, 24, 39, and 40 pounds. The shop will not open or split bags. A greenhouse asks for 100 pounds of topsoil. Can the order be filled with bags in the sizes available? If not, how close can the supply shop come to filling the order?
yes, four 17-pound bags and two 16-pound bags

Reteaching 12-7 Problem Solving: Write an Equation

You can write equations to solve many types of problems.

Read and Understand A bacteria culture starts with 5 cells. The number of cells doubles every day. Write a function rule that relates the number of bacteria cells in the culture to the amount of time that has passed. Use the rule to find the number of cells there are in the culture after 12 days.

What are you asked to do? *Write a function rule that relates bacteria cells to the amount of time that has passed.*

Plan and Solve Start by making a table that shows the first few days and the number of cells per day.

Day	Cells
1	5
2	10
3	20
4	40

Notice that each output is equal to 5 times 2 raised to the power of the input. So, the number of cells is 5 times 2 raised to the number of days. Let d = the number of days that have passed. Let y = the number of bacteria cells.

Function: $y = 5 \cdot 2^d$

Evaluate the function rule to find how many cells there are after 12 days.

$$y = 5 \cdot 2^{12} = 5 \cdot 4{,}096 = 20{,}480$$

Look Back and Check How could you check your answer? *You can solve a simpler problem to check the function rule. Extend the table for 5 and 6 days and then evaluate the rule for these times.*

Solve each problem by writing a function rule.

1. Suppose you save $30 this year. You plan to double the amount you save each year. Write a function rule that relates the amount you save in a given year to the number of years that have passed. Use the rule to find out how much you will save after the sixth year and after the eighth year.
$y = 30 \cdot 2^x$; $1,920; $7,680
2. A population of 10 rabbits is released into a wildlife refuge. The population triples each year. Write a function rule that relates the population of the rabbits to the number of years that have passed. Use the rule to find out how many rabbits will be in the refuge after 5 years.
$y = 10 \cdot 3^x$; 2,430 rabbits

Use the Guided Problem Solving worksheet with Exercise 6.

8b. Answers may vary. Sample: I found the area of the photo without the border and the area of the photo with the border. I then found the difference between the two areas, which is equal to the area of the border. I used the *write an equation* strategy.

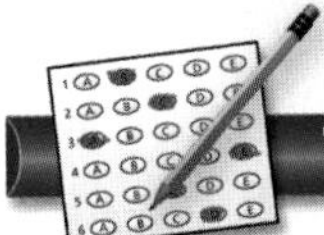

Test Prep

Multiple Choice

10. What is the next term in the sequence 400, −200, 100, −50, . . . ? D
    A. −100 B. −25 C. 0 D. 25

Take It to the NET
Online lesson quiz at **www.PHSchool.com**
Web Code: aca-1207

11. Find the common ratio in the geometric sequence 250, 25, 2.5, 0.25, . . .
    F. 0.001 G. 0.01 H. 0.1 I. 10 H

12. Which of the following is NOT a linear function? B
    A. $y = x$ B. $y = -x + \frac{2}{x}$ C. $y = x - 2x$ D. $y = -2x$

Short Response

13. You ride a scooter slowly up a hill, and then quickly down the other side. You stop at a traffic light, wait for the walk light, and then walk your scooter across the street. Finally you ride home. Sketch and label a graph showing your speed during the time of this ride. See margin.

Mixed Review

Lesson 11-5

Find each probability. A bag contains 10 red, 5 orange, 6 yellow, 1 blue, and 7 green marbles. One marble is chosen at random and *not* replaced. Then a second marble is chosen.

14. P(orange, then orange) $\frac{5}{203}$ or about 0.025 **15.** P(blue, then blue) 0

Lesson 11-3

Simplify each expression.

16. ${}_{15}C_3$ 455 **17.** ${}_{18}C_2$ 153 **18.** ${}_{25}C_4$ 12,650 **19.** ${}_{34}C_2$ 561

Checkpoint Quiz 2 Lessons 12-5 through 12-7

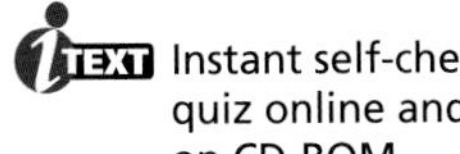

Instant self-check quiz online and on CD-ROM

Write a quadratic function rule for each table.

1.

x	0	1	2	3	4
y	−3	−2	1	6	13

$y = x^2 - 3$

2.

x	−4	−2	0	2	4
y	8	2	0	2	8

$y = \frac{1}{2}x^2$

Make a table and a graph for each function. Use only positive values for *x*.
3–8. See back of book.

3. $y = x^2$ **4.** $y = 10 - x^2$ **5.** $y = \frac{15}{x}$

6. $y = x^2 + 4$ **7.** $y = -3x^2 + 1$ **8.** $y = \frac{36}{x}$

9. Fitness Caitlin jogs for 30 min, sprints for 5 min, and walks for 10 min. Sketch and label a graph showing her speed during her workout.
See back of book.

10. Biology A population of 900 butterflies doubles every year. Write a function rule that relates the number of butterflies to the number of years that have passed. Use the rule to find the number of butterflies after 4 years and after 10 years. $y = 900(2)^x$; 14,400 butterflies, 921,600 butterflies

13. [2] Answers may vary. Sample.

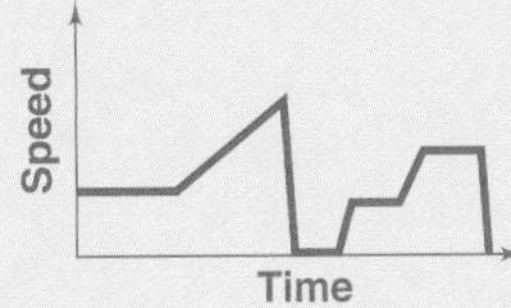

[1] graph drawn with some errors

Test Prep

Resources
For additional practice with a variety of test item formats:
- Test Prep, p. 691
- Test-Taking Strategies, p. 687
- Test-Taking Strategies with Transparencies

4. Assess

Lesson Quiz 12-7

A bacteria culture starts with 25 cells. The number of cells doubles each hour.

1. Write a function rule that relates the number of cells to the number of hours that have passed. $y = 2^t(25)$
2. Find the number of cells after 12 hours. 102,400 cells

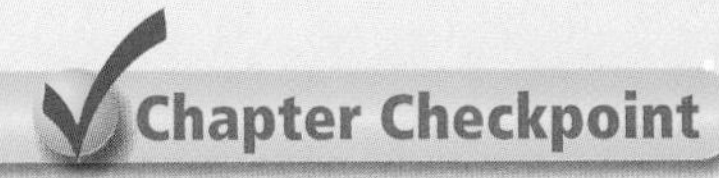

To check understanding of Lessons 12-5 to 12-7:

Checkpoint Quiz 2 (p. 671)

Teaching Resources
Checkpoint Quiz 2 (also in *Prentice Hall Assessment System*)

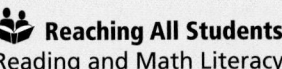

Reaching All Students
Reading and Math Literacy 12C

Spanish versions available

Alternative Assessment

Have students describe the input and output values for one of the first 3 exercises.

Enrichment 12-7 Problem Solving: Write an Equation

Critical Thinking

A team of microbiologists wants to chart the growth of a new strain of bacteria. The cell population appears to double every hour.

1. The first microbiologist starts with one cell. Fill in the table for the number of cells she should expect to find in the population in the first five hours. The first two have been started for you.

Hour	Cells
0	1
1	1 × 2 = 2
2	2 × 2 = 4
3	4 × 2 = 8
4	8 × 2 = 16
5	16 × 2 = 32

2. Write a function to represent the doubling effect shown in the table. $y = 2^x$
3. She examines the bacteria after 25 hours. Use the function from Exercise 2 to find the cell population she should expect at this time. $y = 2^{25}$; 33,554,432 cells
4. After examining the bacteria, the microbiologist determines that the cell population has been doubling every hour as expected. She decides she will stop the experiment after at least 3×10^{13} more cells have grown.
   a. Use your answers to Exercises 2 and 3 to write an equation for the number of cells that will grow in *h* hours after she examines the bacteria. $c = 2^{25+h} - 2^{25} = 2^{25+h} - 33{,}554{,}432$
   b. Solve your equation to find how many more cells will grow 10 hours, 20 hours, and 30 hours after she examines the bacteria. Use scientific notation to express your answers. 3.4×10^{10} cells; 3.5×10^{13} cells; 3.6×10^{16} cells
   c. How many hours after she examines the bacteria can she stop the experiment? 20 hours
5. A second microbiologist had started an experiment with the same bacteria two hours earlier. He also started with one cell.
   a. Modify your equation from Exercise 2 to represent the total cell population for both experiments. (Hint: Write the equation in terms of the number of hours after the first microbiologist started her experiment.) $y = 2^x + 2^{x+2}$
   b. What will the total population of both experiments be 25 hours after the first microbiologist began? Write your answer in scientific notation. 1.7×10^8 cells

Changing Representations

In previous lessons, students interpreted and sketched graphs of linear functions and of nonlinear functions. They have used graphs and tables as well as words and function rules to describe different situations. This feature focuses on the key idea that a math problem can be represented in a variety of different forms.

Teaching Notes

Discuss the idea that the ability to translate information presented in different formats is a key reading skill—not only in mathematics but in the sciences and social sciences, too. Together with students work through the Example, in which they see how the same information about the can collection drive can be given in paragraph form, as well as in a table, a graph, and as a function rule.

Inclusion
Revisit the distinction between discrete and continuous data.

Teaching Tip
Once you have discussed with students the function rule for the Example, ask:

- *If the can collection drive continues, how many cans will the class have collected after 10 days?* 75 cans
- *Which representation of the data works best for finding this answer? Explain.* Sample: Substituting 10 into the function rule is faster than extending the graph or the table to find the answer.

Exercises
Exercise 1 Students might have difficulty translating the information presented in a graph of a quadratic equation.

Exercise 2 Guide students to notice the similarity to the table of values in the Example. Ask pairs to share and discuss their results with the class.

Reading Math: Changing Representations

For Use With Lesson 12-7

There are several ways to show math problems. You can use words, graphs, tables, or function rules. Learning how to translate among these representations can help you solve math problems.

EXAMPLE

Food Drive For one week, Ms. Walker's class collected cans for a food drive for a local shelter. Ms. Walker brought in 15 cans to start the collection. Beginning the next day, the class brought in 6 cans every day. Describe the number of cans collected, c, in d days. Translate your answer into a table, into a graph, and into a function rule.

Table: Make a table with d as the input and c as the output. When $d = 0$, there are 15 cans. The number of cans goes up by 6 each day.

Number of Days, d	0	1	2	3	4	5
Number of Cans, c	15	21	27	33	39	45

Graph: Make a graph of the data with the number of days on the horizontal axis and the number of cans on the vertical axis.

Since the number of cans must be a whole number, the data are discrete. Connect the points with a dashed line.

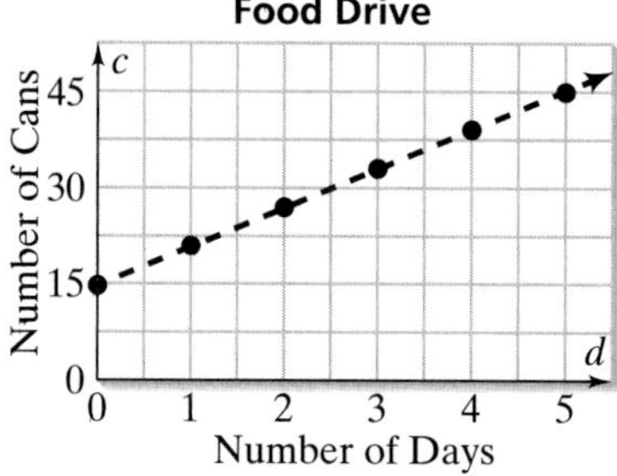

Function Rule: The function is linear because the graph is a line. The y-intercept is 15, and the slope is $\frac{21 - 15}{1 - 0} = 6$. So, the linear function rule is $c = 6d + 15$.

EXERCISES

In Exercises 1–3, one representation of a problem is given. Translate each problem by representing it as a table, as a graph, and as a function rule. 1-3. See margin.

1. 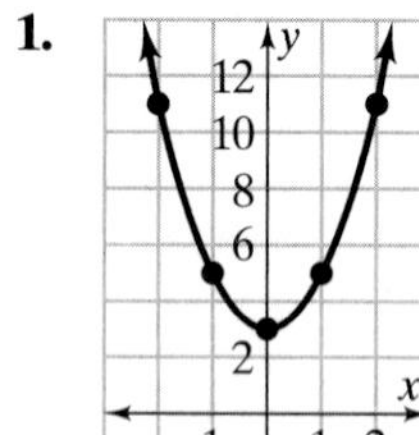

2. $P = 5 \cdot 3^n$

3.

Input	Output
0	10
1	18
2	26
3	34

1. Function rule: $y = 3 + 2x^2$

Table:

x	y
−2	11
−1	5
0	3
1	5
2	11

2–3. See back of book.

Algebra

12-8 Exploring Polynomials

What You'll Learn

 To write variable expressions

 To simplify polynomials

... And Why

To simplify a surface area formula, as in Exercise 17

Check Skills You'll Need

For help, go to Lesson 2-3.

Simplify each expression.

1. $-2 + 2t - 3t$ $-2 - t$
2. $7w - 10 + 5w$ $12w - 10$
3. $3k + 32k - 5$ $35k - 5$
4. $-m + 11c + 6c - 2m$ $-3m + 17c$
5. $7y + 4x - 2y - 2x$ $5y + 2x$
6. $-3v - 7a + 5v - a$ $2v - 8a$

New Vocabulary • polynomial • constant

 Interactive lesson includes instant self-check, tutorials, and activities.

OBJECTIVE 1 **Writing Variable Expressions**

Investigation: Using Algebra Tiles

1. Use algebra tiles to model each step of the number game below. Begin with an x tile to represent the number you choose in Step 1. Check students' work.
   - **Step 1** Choose a number.
   - **Step 2** Multiply the chosen number by 3.
   - **Step 3** Add 4 to the result.
   - **Step 4** Multiply the result by 2.
   - **Step 5** Subtract 2 from the result.
   - **Step 6** Divide the result by 6.
2. How is the number chosen in Step 1 related to the result in Step 6?

2. The number in Step 6 is one more than the number you started with.

You can use algebra tiles like those shown below to model variable expressions.

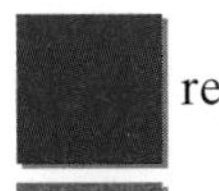

▫ represents 1. ▮ represents x. ■ represents x^2.

▪ represents -1. ▮ represents $-x$. ■ represents $-x^2$.

1 EXAMPLE Writing Variable Expressions

Write a variable expression for the model at the right.

The model shows the expression $-x^2 + 3x - 4$.

12-8

1. Plan

Lesson Preview

PowerPoint

Check Skills You'll Need

Combining Like Terms

Lesson 2-3: Examples 1–3. Extra Practice, p. 703.

Lesson Resources

Optional Materials
- algebra tiles

Teaching Resources
Practice, Reteaching, Enrichment

Reaching All Students
Practice Workbook 12-8
Spanish Practice Workbook 12-8
Guided Problem Solving 12-8

Presentation Assistant Plus!
Transparencies
- Check Skills You'll Need 12-8
- Problem of the Day 12-8
- Additional Examples 12-8
- Student Edition Answers 12-8
- Lesson Quiz 12-8
- Classroom Aid 37

PH Presentation Pro CD-ROM 12-8

Computer Test Generator CD

Technology
Resource Pro® CD-ROM
Computer Test Generator CD
PH Presentation Pro CD-ROM

www.PHSchool.com
Student Site
- Teacher Web Code: ack-5500
- Algebra Readiness Puzzles 98
- Self-grading Lesson Quiz

PH SuccessNet Teacher Center
- Lesson Planner
- Resources

Plus iText

Ongoing Assessment and Intervention

Before the Lesson
Diagnose prerequisite skills using:
- Check Skills You'll Need

During the Lesson
Monitor progress using:
- Check Understanding
- Additional Examples
- Test Prep

After the Lesson
Assess knowledge using:
- Lesson Quiz
- Computer Test Generator CD

2. Teach

Professional Development

Math Background

The *terms* in a variable expression are separated by + or −, so $-2x + 5 - x^2$ has 3 terms. A *polynomial* has one or more terms. A term with no variable, such as 5 in Example 2, is called a *constant* or *constant term*.

When you simplify a polynomial, you use the Commutative, Associative, and Distributive Properties to group together the like terms and combine them.

Like terms have exactly the same variable, or are constant terms, so $-3x$ and $2x$ are like terms and can be combined. However, $3x$ and $3x^2$ are not like terms and cannot be combined.

Teaching Notes

Investigation (Optional)
Remind students that the unit tile (1 tile) is not the same as the x tile. So when they add 4 in Step 3, it is 4 unit tiles they are adding.

1 EXAMPLE Error Prevention

Demonstrate to students that a zero pair consists of two tiles that are the same size but opposite in sign (indicated by a different color).

2 EXAMPLE Auditory Learners

Ask volunteers to explain in their own words with examples the meaning of *term, polynomial,* and *constant.*

3 EXAMPLE Visual Learners

Have a volunteer demonstrate this example on the overhead with transparent tiles.

Teaching Tip
Have students discuss whether they prefer to use tiles or the properties. Ask them to explain their reasons.

Tactile Learners
Point out that students who find that tiles help them can sketch tiles (or even just picture them in their minds) when they are simplifying an expression.

Check Understanding 1 Write a variable expression for each model.

a.  $x^2 - 2x + 2$

b. 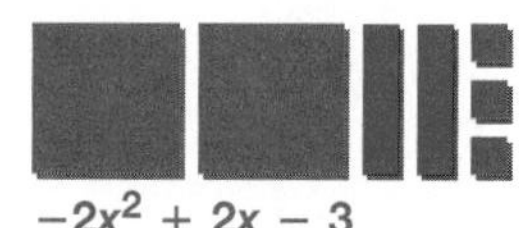 $-2x^2 + 2x - 3$

OBJECTIVE 2

Simplifying Polynomials

The expression $-x^2 + 3x - 4$ has three terms: $-x^2$, $3x$, and -4.
A **polynomial** is one term or the sum or difference of two or more terms.
A term that does not contain a variable, such as -4, is a **constant.**

To simplify a polynomial, combine like terms.

2 EXAMPLE Simplifying Polynomials

Use tiles to simplify the polynomial $2x^2 - 3x - x^2 + 2x + 5$.

Model each term.

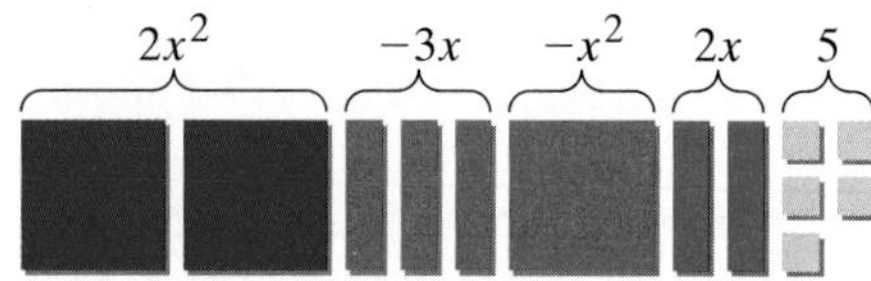

Group like terms together. Remove zero pairs.

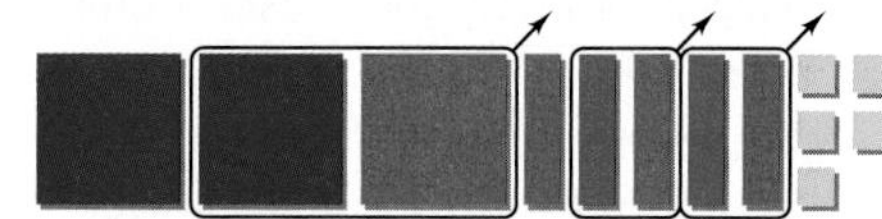

The simplified polynomial is $x^2 - x + 5$.

Need Help?
For help combining like terms, go to Lesson 2-3.

Check Understanding 2 **a.** Draw or use tiles to simplify the polynomial $5x^2 - 4x + 3x - 7x^2 + 6$. $-2x^2 - x + 6$
b. Reasoning Explain why $5x^2$ and $-4x$ are not like terms.
$5x^2$ and $-4x$ do not raise x to the same power.

You can also use properties to simplify polynomials.

3 EXAMPLE Using Properties to Simplify Polynomials

Use properties to simplify the polynomial $3t^2 + 6t - 2t^2 - 9$.

$3t^2 + 6t - 2t^2 - 9 = 3t^2 - 2t^2 + 6t - 9$ ← Use the Commutative Property.
$= (3t^2 - 2t^2) + 6t - 9$ ← Use the Associative Property.
$= (3 - 2)t^2 + 6t - 9$ ← Use the Distributive Property.
$= t^2 + 6t - 9$ ← Simplify.

Check Understanding 3 Use properties to simplify each polynomial.

a. $4g^2 - 5g - 2g^2 + 7g$ $2g^2 + 2g$ **b.** $3y - 5y^2 - y + 7$ $-5y^2 + 2y + 7$

Reaching All Students

Below Level Review the Commutative, Associative, and Distributive Properties and ask students to give examples of each.	**Advanced Learners** Ask students to use algebraic expressions to represent the steps in the Investigation. x, $3x$, $3x + 4$, $2(3x + 4)$, $6x + 8 - 2$, $(6x + 6) \div 6$; $x + 1$	**Visual Learners** See note on page 674. **Tactile Learners** See note on page 674.

More Than One Way

Simplify the polynomial $m^2 - 3m + m^2 + 2m - 1$.

Daryl's Method

I will model the polynomial with algebra tiles.

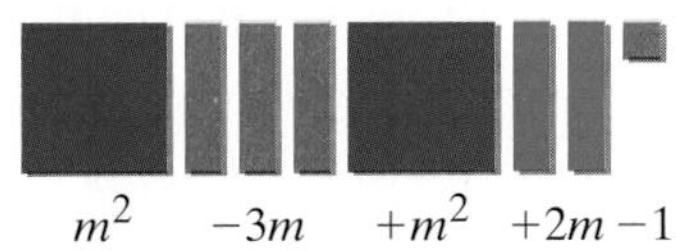

$m^2 \quad -3m \quad +m^2 \quad +2m \; -1$

I will group like terms together and remove zero pairs.

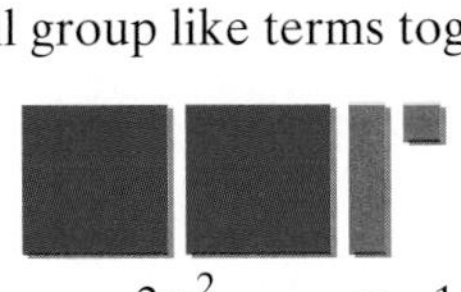

$2m^2 \quad -m - 1$

Michelle's Method

I will simplify the polynomial using properties of numbers.

$m^2 - 3m + m^2 + 2m - 1$

$= m^2 + m^2 - 3m + 2m - 1$ ← Use the Commutative Property.

$= (m^2 + m^2) + (-3m + 2m) - 1$ ← Use the Associative Property.

$= (1 + 1)m^2 + (-3 + 2)m - 1$ ← Use the Distributive Property.

$= 2m^2 - m - 1$ ← Simplify.

Choose a Method

Simplify the polynomial $-2x^2 + 5x - 6x + 5 - 2x^2$. Explain why you chose the method you used. $-4x^2 - x + 5$; Check students' work.

Teaching Tip

Point out that the final simplified version of a polynomial usually has the terms arranged in descending order of the powers of the variable, with the constant term last.

PowerPoint

Additional Examples

1 Write a variable expression for this model. $x^2 - 2x + 3$

2 Use tiles to simplify the polynomial $-x^2 + 3x + 2x^2 + 3 - x - 4$. $x^2 + 2x - 1$

3 Use properties to simplify the polynomial $2b^2 - 2b - 3b^2 + 4 + b - 4$. $-b^2 - b$

Closure

- Explain the parts of a variable expression. Sample: The terms are separated by + or −, and any term that does not contain a variable is a constant.
- *How do you simplify a polynomial?* Sample: Rearrange the terms so the like terms (with the same form of the variable) are together and then combine like terms.

EXERCISES

For more practice, see *Extra Practice.*

A Practice by Example

Example 1 (page 673)

Write a variable expression for each model.

1. 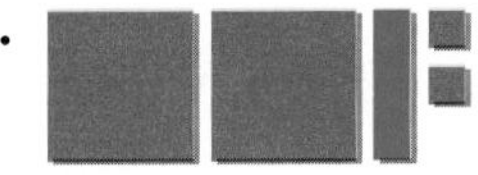 $-2x^2 + x - 2$

2.   $x^2 + 3x - 5$

3.  $2x^2 - 2x + 3$

Example 2 (page 674)

Draw or use tiles to simplify each polynomial.

4. $x^2 + 3x + x^2 + 1 + 2x$ $2x^2 + 5x + 1$

5. $x + 3x^2 + x - 4$ $3x^2 + 2x - 4$

6. $-2 - 2x - 2x^2 + 3x + 3 + 3x^2$ $x^2 + x + 1$

7. $7x - x^2 - 5x + 3x^2$ $2x^2 + 2x$

3. Practice

Assignment Guide

 Objective 1

- A B Core 1–3, 31
- C Extension 36

 Objective 2

- A B Core 4–30
- C Extension 32–35

Test Prep 37–40
Mixed Review 41–46

Geometry Connection
Exercise 17 Use a soup can to show that the surface area includes both ends.

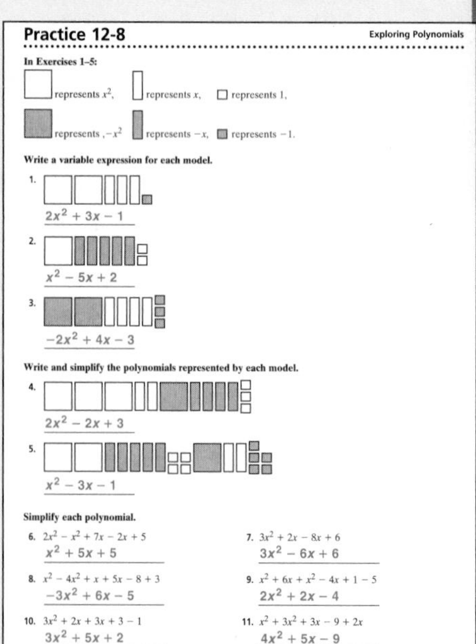

Practice 12-8 — Exploring Polynomials

In Exercises 1–5:

□ represents x^2, ▯ represents x, □ represents 1,
■ represents $-x^2$, ▮ represents $-x$, ■ represents -1.

Write a variable expression for each model.

1. $2x^2 + 3x - 1$
2. $x^2 - 5x + 2$
3. $-2x^2 + 4x - 3$

Write and simplify the polynomials represented by each model.

4. $2x^2 - 2x + 3$
5. $x^2 - 3x - 1$

Simplify each polynomial.

6. $2x^2 - x^2 + 7x - 2x + 5$ — $x^2 + 5x + 5$
7. $3x^2 + 2x - 8x + 6$ — $3x^2 - 6x + 6$
8. $x^2 - 4x^2 + x + 5x - 8 + 3$ — $-3x^2 + 6x - 5$
9. $x^2 + 6x + x^2 - 4x + 1 - 5$ — $2x^2 + 2x - 4$
10. $3x^2 + 2x + 3x + 3 - 1$ — $3x^2 + 5x + 2$
11. $x^2 + 3x^2 + 3x - 9 + 2x$ — $4x^2 + 5x - 9$

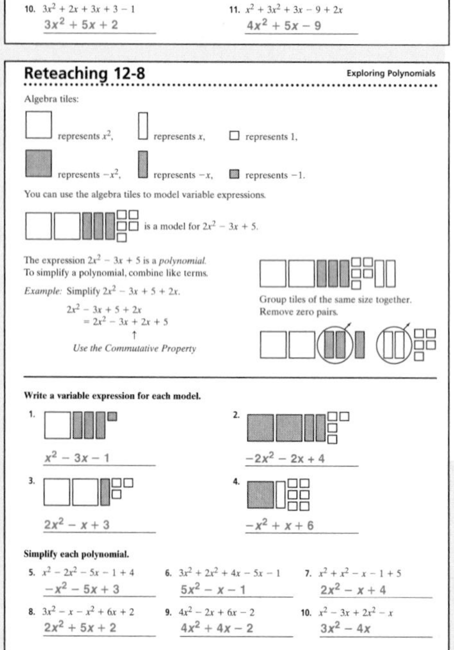

Reteaching 12-8 — Exploring Polynomials

Algebra tiles:

□ represents x^2, ▯ represents x, □ represents 1,
■ represents $-x^2$, ▮ represents $-x$, ■ represents -1.

You can use the algebra tiles to model variable expressions.

is a model for $2x^2 - 3x + 5$.

The expression $2x^2 - 3x + 5$ is a *polynomial.*
To simplify a polynomial, combine like terms.

Example: Simplify $2x^2 - 3x + 5 + 2x$.

$2x^2 - 3x + 5 + 2x$
$= 2x^2 - 3x + 2x + 5$
↑
Use the Commutative Property

Group tiles of the same size together.
Remove zero pairs.

Write a variable expression for each model.

1. $x^2 - 3x - 1$
2. $-2x^2 - 2x + 4$
3. $2x^2 - x + 3$
4. $-x^2 + x + 6$

Simplify each polynomial.

5. $x^2 - 2x^2 - 5x - 1 + 4$ — $-x^2 - 5x + 3$
6. $3x^2 + 2x^2 + 4x - 5x - 1$ — $5x^2 - x - 1$
7. $x^2 + x^2 - x - 1 + 5$ — $2x^2 - x + 4$
8. $3x^2 - x - x^2 + 6x + 2$ — $2x^2 + 5x + 2$
9. $4x^2 - 2x + 6x - 2$ — $4x^2 + 4x - 2$
10. $x^2 - 3x + 2x^2 - x$ — $3x^2 - 4x$

Example 3 (page 674)

Use properties to simplify each polynomial.

8. $3x^2 - 8 + 2x - 4x + 3 - 5x^2$ $-2x^2 - 2x - 5$
9. $3x^2 + 6x - 2 - 4x$ $3x^2 + 2x - 2$
10. $3 - 7x + 3x^2 + 2x^2 + 2x$ $5x^2 - 5x + 3$
11. $4x^2 - 7x - 3x^2 + 9x - 1$ $x^2 + 2x - 1$
12. $-2x^2 - 3x + 1 + 2x + x + 2x^2$ 1
13. $-1 + 2x^2 - 2x + 2 + 3x$ $2x^2 + x + 1$

B Apply Your Skills

Write and simplify the polynomial represented by each model.

14.  $-x^2 + 3$

15.  $x^2 - 2x - 1$

16. **Science** A ball is thrown upward at a speed of 48 feet per second. Its height in feet, after t seconds, is given by the polynomial $48t - 16t^2$. Evaluate the polynomial to find the height after 3 seconds. 0 ft

17. **Geometry** To find the surface area of a cylinder, you can use the polynomial $\pi r^2 + \pi r^2 + \pi dh$, where r is the radius, d the diameter, and h the height of the cylinder. Simplify the polynomial. $2\pi r^2 + \pi dh$

Real-World Connection
The Crystal Bridge conservatory is a cylinder of acrylic and steel, 244 ft long and 70 ft across.

Simplify each polynomial.

18. $-5n + 2n + k + k + 10n$ $7n + 2k$
19. $13 + g - 3r + 10g + 14r$ $11g + 11r + 13$
20. $11c + 9b - 7 - 16b + c - 2$ $-7b + 12c - 9$
21. $9t - p^3 + t + 7t^3 + 7p^3 - 2t^3$ $10t + 6p^3 + 5t^3$

Evaluate each polynomial for $y = 4$.

22. $y^2 + 3y - 10$ 18
23. $2y^2 - y + 3$ 31
24. $-2y - 3y^2$ -56

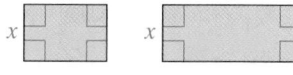

25. a. **Geometry** Write an expression for the area of each rectangle at the right.
    b. Write and simplify an expression for the area of the two rectangles combined. $3x + 5x = 8x$

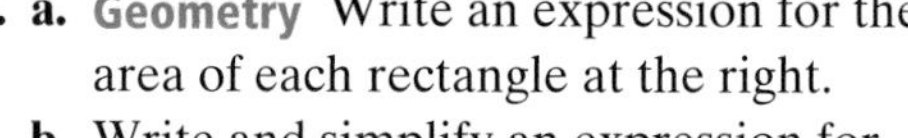

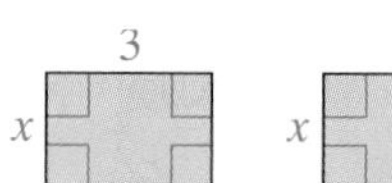

25a. $3x$, $5x$

Find the degree of each polynomial. The degree of a polynomial with one variable is the value of the greatest exponent of the variable that appears in any term. The polynomial $3x^2 + 5x - 6$ has degree 2, since the greatest exponent of x is 2.

26. $-4x^2 + 5x + 1$ 2
27. $3x^3 + 2x^2 - 3x$ 3
28. $2x + 1$ 1
29. $x^5 + 2x^3 - 3x + 1$ 5

30. **Reasoning** What is the degree of a constant expression like 5? Explain. 0; 5 can be written as $5 \cdot x^0$ because $x^0 = 1$.

31. **Writing in Math** Explain how knowing the meaning of the prefix *poly* can help you understand the meanings of words with the prefix *poly*. See above left.

31. Answers may vary. Sample: *polygon, polysyllabic;* the prefix *poly* means "several" or "many".

Use the Guided Problem Solving worksheet with Exercise 16.

Challenge **Simplify each polynomial.**

32. $-3x^2 + 2x - 9xy + 1 - 4y^2$ $-3x^2 + 2x - 9xy - 4y^2 + 1$

33. $11m^2 + 2^2 + 4m^2 + 15m - 3$ $15m^2 + 15m + 1$

34. $-5y^2 - 1 - 8y^2 - 29y - y^2$ $-14y^2 - 29y - 1$

35. $5a^2 + 2ab + 7 + 21ab + 3$ $5a^2 + 23ab + 10$

36. **Stretch Your Thinking** What fraction in simplest form is $\frac{4}{9}$ of its reciprocal? $\frac{2}{3}$, or $-\frac{2}{3}$

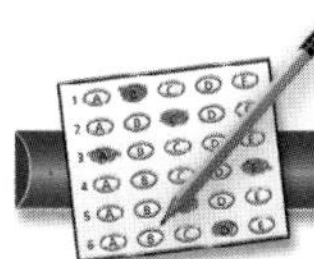

Test Prep

Multiple Choice

37. Simplify the polynomial $n + 5 + 2n$. B

A. $8n$ **B.** $3n + 5$ **C.** $7n$ **D.** $7n^2$

38. Which of the following statements is NOT true about the polynomial $x + 3x + 5x$? H

F. The polynomial can be simplified by combining like terms.
G. The polynomial has no constant.
H. The polynomial is simplified.
I. The polynomial can be simplified to $9x$.

Take It to the NET
Online lesson quiz at **www.PHSchool.com**
Web Code: aca-1208

39. Simplify the polynomial $2s^2 - 2s - 3s^2 + 4 + s - 4$. D

A. $s^2 + 3s$ **B.** $5s^2 + 3s + 8$ **C.** $-s^2 - s + 8$ **D.** $-s^2 - s$

Short Response

40. a. The polynomial $-16t^2 + 100t + 40t$ gives the height, in feet, reached by a display of fireworks in t seconds. Simplify the polynomial. 40a–b. See margin.

b. Find the height of the fireworks 3 seconds after launch.

Mixed Review

Lesson 12-6 **Graph each nonlinear function. Use integers from −3 to 3 for inputs.** 41–44. See margin.

41. $y = 3t^2 - 12$ **42.** $y = m^2 - m$

43. $y = 2x^2 - 2$ **44.** $y = -5x^2 - 9$

Lesson 10-2 **Television** **Use the graph at the right.**

45. About how many hours per week do women ages 18–24 watch television? 22 hours

46. Which age group shows the least difference between men and women? Which shows the greatest difference? 18–24; 55 and older

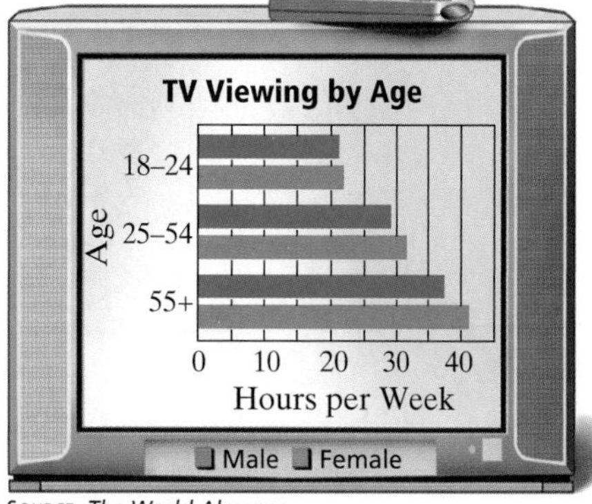

SOURCE: *The World Almanac*

40. [2] a. $-16t^2 + 140t$
b. $-16(3)^2 + 140(3) = -144 + 420 = 276$ ft
[1] one part correct

41.

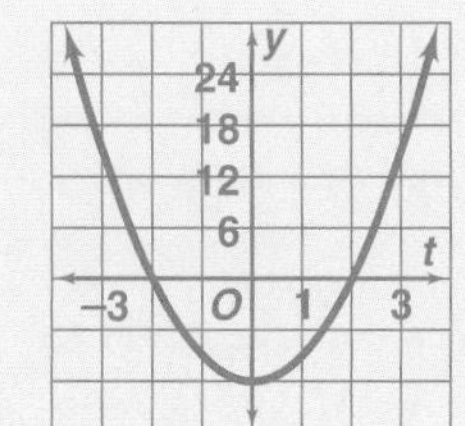

42.

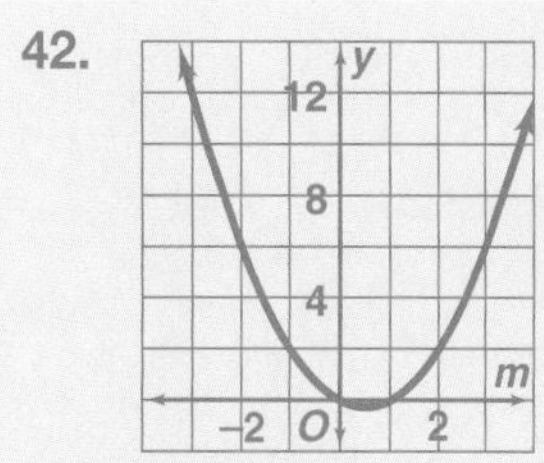

43–44. See back of book.

4. Assess

Lesson Quiz 12-8

1. Write a variable expression for the model. $x^2 - 2x + 4$

2. Simplify the polynomial $4x^2 + 9x - x^2 - 10x - 2$. $3x^2 - x - 2$

Alternative Assessment

Each student in a pair writes a 3-term polynomial in terms of x. Partners work together to combine and simplify their polynomials.

Test Prep

Resources
For additional practice with a variety of test item formats:
- Test Prep, p. 691
- Test-Taking Strategies, p. 687
- Test-Taking Strategies with Transparencies

Exercise 37 Remind students that n is the same as $1n$.

Enrichment 12-8 Exploring Polynomials

Think and Evaluate

The *degree* of a polynomial with one variable is the value of the largest exponent of the variable that appears in any term.

Polynomial	Degree
x and $x - 5$	1
$x^2 + 3x + 2$ and $4x^2 - x$	2
x^3 and $x^3 + x^2 - 2$	3

A polynomial is usually written with the term that has the highest power first, the next highest power second, and so on. This is called *writing a polynomial in descending order.*

Write each polynomial in descending order. What is the degree of the polynomial?

1. $x^2 - 6 + 4x - 10x^3$ $-10x^3 + x^2 + 4x - 6$; degree is 3.
2. $2x + 3x^2 + 9 + x^4$ $x^4 + 3x^2 + 2x + 9$; degree is 4.
3. $5 + 3x + 6x^3 + 2x^2$ $6x^3 + 2x^2 + 3x + 5$; degree is 3.

Simplify each polynomial. What is the degree of the polynomial?

4. $(-9x^2 + 5x^5 - 4x + 3) - (x + 3x^3 - 4x^5 + x^2)$ $9x^5 - 3x^3 - 10x^2 - 5x + 3$; 5
5. $-(2y^9 - 4y - 3y^4 + 6) + (2y^8 + 6y - 3y^3 + 4y^9 + 3)$ $2y^9 + 2y^8 + 3y^4 - 3y^3 + 10y - 3$; 9
6. $4x(2x + 3x^2 - 6 - 2)$ $12x^3 + 8x^2 - 32x$; 3
7. $5x(x + 4x^5 - 2x^5)$ $10x^6 + 5x^2$; 6
8. $-x(4x + 3x^2 - 4) + 2x(4x^4 - 2x^2)$ $8x^5 - 7x^3 - 4x^2 + 4x$; 5

12-9

1. Plan

Lesson Preview

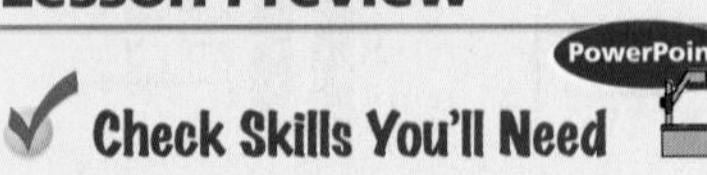

Simplifying Polynomials
Lesson 12-8: Examples 2–3. Extra Practice, p. 713.

Lesson Resources

Teaching Resources
Practice, Reteaching, Enrichment

Reaching All Students
Practice Workbook 12-9
Spanish Practice Workbook 12-9
Guided Problem Solving 12-9

Presentation Assistant Plus!
Transparencies
- Check Skills You'll Need 12-9
- Problem of the Day 12-9
- Additional Examples 12-9
- Student Edition Answers 12-9
- Lesson Quiz 12-9
- Classroom Aid 37

PH Presentation Pro CD-ROM 12-9

Computer Test Generator CD

Technology
Resource Pro® CD-ROM
Computer Test Generator CD
PH Presentation Pro CD-ROM

www.PHSchool.com
Student Site
- Teacher Web Code: ack-5500
- Algebra Readiness Puzzles 64, 99
- Self-grading Lesson Quiz

PH SuccessNet Teacher Center
- Lesson Planner
- Resources

12-9 Adding and Subtracting Polynomials

What You'll Learn

To add polynomials

To subtract polynomials

... And Why

To represent perimeter, as in Example 3

Check Skills You'll Need

For help, go to Lesson 12-8.

Simplify each polynomial.

1. $-p + 2p + 3p$ $4p$
2. $x^2 + 5x - 2x^2$ $-x^2 + 5x$
3. $2y^2 + 3y + (-5y)$ $2y^2 - 2y$
4. $-x + x + 6x^2 - 1$ $6x^2 - 1$
5. $7z - 8z^2 + z + 3z^2$ $8z - 5z^2$
6. $-2 - 10m + 3m + 4$ $2 - 7m$

New Vocabulary • coefficient

Interactive lesson includes instant self-check, tutorials, and activities.

OBJECTIVE 1 Adding Polynomials

A **coefficient** is a number that is multiplied by a variable.

1 EXAMPLE Naming Coefficients

Name the coefficients in each polynomial.

a. $-2y^2 + y - 3$
↓ ↓ ↑ -3 is a constant.
-2 1 ← $y = 1 \cdot y$

The coefficients are -2 and 1.

b. $t^3 - 2t^2 + 5t$
↓ ↓ ↓
1   -2 5

The coefficients are 1, -2, and 5.

> **Need Help?**
> Think of an expression like $8 - 5x$ as $8 + (-5x)$. This will help you identify the coefficient of x as -5.

Check Understanding 1 Name the coefficients in the polynomial $9k^3 + k^2 - k + 5$.   9, 1, −1

To add polynomials, combine the like terms.

2 EXAMPLE Adding Polynomials

Add: $(3n^2 + 3n + 4) + (n^2 - n + 5)$

Method 1 Add using tiles.

$3n^2 + 3n + 4$

$n^2 - n + 5$

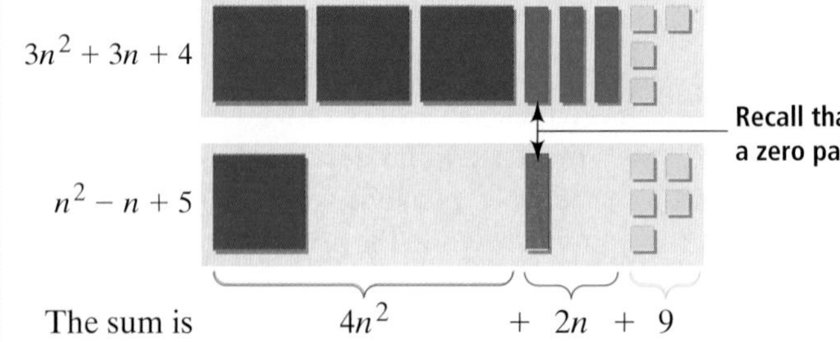

Recall that ▮▮ makes a zero pair.

The sum is $4n^2 + 2n + 9$

Ongoing Assessment and Intervention

Before the Lesson
Diagnose prerequisite skills using:
- Check Skills You'll Need

During the Lesson
Monitor progress using:
- Check Understanding
- Additional Examples
- Test Prep

After the Lesson
Assess knowledge using:
- Lesson Quiz
- Computer Test Generator CD

Method 2 Add using properties.

$(3n^2 + 3n + 4) + (n^2 - n + 5)$

$= (3n^2 + n^2) + (3n - n) + (4 + 5)$ ← Group like terms.

$= (3 + 1)n^2 + (3 - 1)n + (4 + 5)$ ← Use the Distributive Property.

$= 4n^2 + 2n + 9$ ← Simplify.

Check Check the solution in Example 2 by substituting 1 for n.

$(3n^2 + 3n + 4) + (n^2 - n + 5) \stackrel{?}{=} 4n^2 + 2n + 9$

$(3 \cdot 1^2 + 3 \cdot 1 + 4) + (1^2 - 1 + 5) \stackrel{?}{=} 4 \cdot 1^2 + 2 \cdot 1 + 9$ ← Substitute 1 for n.

$(3 + 3 + 4) + (5) \stackrel{?}{=} 4 + 2 + 9$ ← Multiply.

$15 = 15$ ✔ ← Add.

Check Understanding 2 Add.

a. $(x^2 + 3x - 1) + (2x^2 + 4x - 6)$ b. $(-c^2 + 3c - 5) + (4c^2 - c + 7)$

c. Check your solution to part (a). Check students' work.

2a. $3x^2 + 7x - 7$
b. $3c^2 + 2c + 2$

To combine like terms quickly, add the coefficients in the like terms. Remember to use the addition rules for integers.

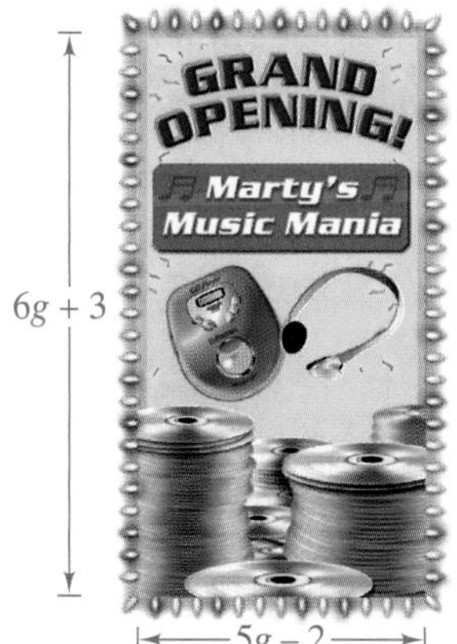

3 EXAMPLE Real-World Problem Solving

Advertising A store is having its grand opening. The owner wants to put a string of lights around the store sign pictured at the left. Write the perimeter of the sign as a polynomial. Then simplify the polynomial to find the length, in feet, of the string of lights needed to go around the sign.

To find the perimeter of the sign, find the sum of the four sides.

perimeter $= (5g - 2) + (5g - 2) + (6g + 3) + (6g + 3)$

$= (5g + 5g + 6g + 6g) + (-2 - 2 + 3 + 3)$ ← Group like terms.

$= 22g + 2$ ← Add the coefficients.

The perimeter of the sign is $(22g + 2)$ ft. The string of lights must be $(22g + 2)$ ft long to go around the sign.

Check Understanding 3 Write the perimeter of each figure as a polynomial. Simplify.

a. 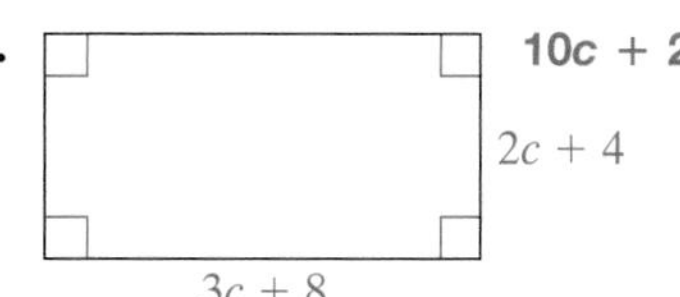

$10c + 24$

b. 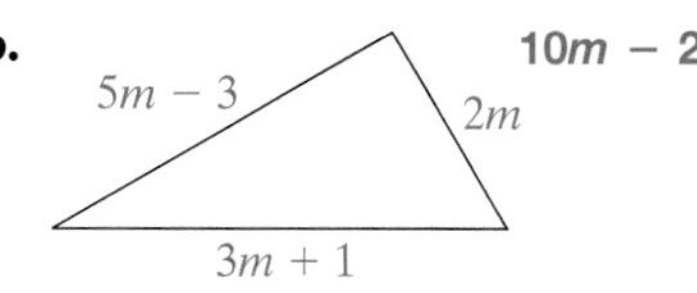

$10m - 2$

c. **Reasoning** The store owner in Example 3 has a 65-ft string of lights. If g is 6, does the owner have enough lights to go completely around the sign? Explain. no; $22(6) + 2 = 134$, $134 > 65$

2. Teach

Math Background

Within a term, such as $3xy^2$, any of the factors of the term can be called a coefficient of the other factors. However, the word *coefficient* is most often used to refer to a numerical factor or coefficient, such as 3 in $3xy^2$.

A term such as x^2 has an understood coefficient of 1, and the term $-x$ has an understood coefficient of -1.

In the variable expression $-(x^2 - 4)$, the entire parentheses has an understood multiplier, or coefficient, of –1. To simplify $-(x^2 - 4)$, take the opposite of every term within the parentheses, resulting in $-x^2 + 4$.

Teaching Notes

1 EXAMPLE English Learners

To help students remember the word *coefficient,* point out that it is more *efficient* to write $y + y + y$ as $3y$.

2 EXAMPLE Teaching Tip

Elicit the fact that adding polynomials is the same process used in simplifying: arrange like terms together and combine.

3 EXAMPLE Inclusion

Ask a student volunteer to explain and demonstrate the meaning of *perimeter.*

PowerPoint

Additional Examples

1. Name the coefficients in each polynomial.
   a. $-5x^2 - x + 7$ $-5, -1$
   b. $4t^3 + 6t^2 - t - 3$ $4, 6, -1$
2. Add: $(5p^2 + 2p + 7) + (2p^2 - p - 5)$. $7p^2 + p + 2$
3. A garden has sides of $3x + 5$, $4x - 2$, $5x + 2$, and $7x - 6$. Write a polynomial to express the length of edging that is needed to go around the garden. $19x - 1$

Reaching All Students

Below Level Review how to add integers, such as $-3 + 5$, $4 - 7$, $-1 + (-3)$. 2, −3, −4	**Advanced Learners** Ask students to explain, using examples, why $y + y^2$ cannot be further simplified. Sample: y and y^2 are not like terms. For instance, you cannot combine inches and square inches.	**English Learners** See note on page 679. **Inclusion** See note on page 679.

4 EXAMPLE Auditory Learners

Remind students that $7x - 2x$ can be rewritten as $7x + (-2x)$ since subtracting is the same as adding the opposite. Students may find it helpful to say to themselves, as they read this example, "$(p^2 - 2p + 5)$ plus the opposite of $2p^2$ plus the opposite of p plus the opposite of -4."

Alternative Method

Some students prefer to perform the subtraction in the vertical format. Make sure they change the subtraction to addition as shown below for Example 4.

Subtraction		*Addition*
$p^2 - 2p + 5$	→	$p^2 - 2p + 5$
$-(2p^2 + p - 4)$	→	$-2p^2 - p + 4$
		$-p^2 - 3p + 9$

Error Prevention!

Students may not take the opposite of every term within the parentheses. Remind them that a coefficient in front of a parentheses multiplies each term within the parentheses.

PowerPoint

Additional Examples

4 Subtract: $(3q^2 - 2q + 4) - (2q^2 - 2q + 3)$. $q^2 + 1$

Closure

- Explain how to add polynomials. Collect the like terms and combine them.
- Explain how subtracting polynomials differs from adding polynomials. Rewrite, changing the subtraction to adding the opposite of each term in the polynomial you are subtracting, and then collect and combine like terms.

OBJECTIVE

2 Subtracting Polynomials

To subtract a polynomial, add the opposite of each term in the second polynomial.

4 EXAMPLE Subtracting Polynomials

Subtract: $(p^2 - 2p + 5) - (2p^2 + p - 4)$

$(p^2 - 2p + 5) - (2p^2 + p - 4)$

$= (p^2 - 2p + 5) + (-2p^2 - p + 4)$ ← **Add the opposite of each term in the second polynomial.**

$= (p^2 - 2p^2) + (-2p - p) + (5 + 4)$ ← **Group like terms.**

$= (1 - 2)p^2 + (-2 - 1)p + (5 + 4)$ ← **Use the Distributive Property.**

$= -p^2 - 3p + 9$ ← **Simplify.**

Check Understanding 4 Subtract. 4a-c. See above left.

a. $(3b^2 + 5b + 7) - (2b^2 + 4b + 6)$ **b.** $(4y^2 - 3y + 1) - (6y^2 - 3y + 3)$

c. Check the solution in Example 4 by substituting 1 for p.

4a. $b^2 + b + 1$

b. $-2y^2 - 2$

c. $(1^2 - 2(1) + 5) - (2(1)^2 + 1 - 4) \stackrel{?}{=} -1^2 - 3(1) + 9$

$4 - (-1) \stackrel{?}{=} -1 - 3 + 9$

$5 = 5$

EXERCISES

For more practice, see *Extra Practice*.

A Practice by Example

Example 1 (page 678)

Name the coefficients in each polynomial.

1. $2x^2 + 3x - 5$ 2, 3 **2.** $-c^2 - c - 1$ −1, −1 **3.** $-4x^2 + 3$ −4

4. $s^2 - 2s - 2$ 1, −2 **5.** $6v^2 - 7v + 12$ 6, −7 **6.** $-11y + 9y - 4$ −11, 9

Example 2 (page 678)

Add. Exercises 7 and 8 have been started for you.

7. $(3m - 7) + (5m + 9)$ $8m + 2$
$= (3m + 5m) + (-7 + 9)$

8. $(x^2 - 4x) + (3x^2 - 2x)$ $4x^2 - 6x$
$= (x^2 + 3x^2) + (-4x - 2x)$

9. $(3p^2 - 2p + 1) + (5p^2 + 4p)$ 9. $8p^2 + 2p + 1$

10. $(7t^2 + t - 3) + (-6t^2 + 3)$ 10. $t^2 + t$

11. $(k^2 + 3k) + (3k^2 - 2k)$ $4k^2 + k$

12. $(2b^2 + b - 3) + (2b^2 - b - 3)$ $4b^2 - 6$

Example 3 (page 679)

Write the perimeter of each figure as a polynomial. Simplify.

13.

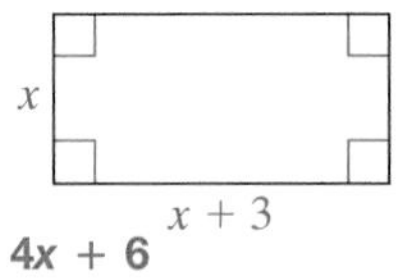

$4x + 6$

14.

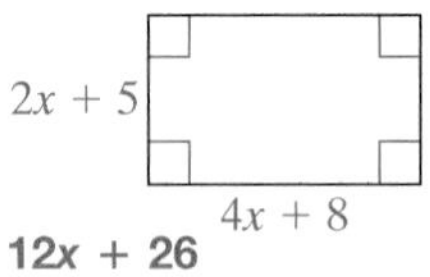

$12x + 26$

15.

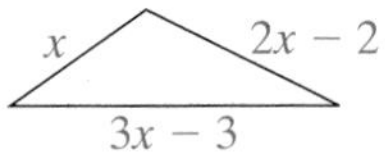

$6x - 5$

Example 4 (page 680)

Subtract. Exercises 16 and 17 have been started for you.

16. $(3y^2 + 7y) - (2y^2 + 5y)$
$= (3y^2 + 7y) + (-2y^2 - 5y)$ $y^2 + 2y$

17. $(2n^2 + 5n + 7) - (n^2 + 3n)$
$= (2n^2 + 5n + 7) + (-n^2 - 3n)$ $n^2 + 2n + 7$

18. $-x^2 - 2x + 7$

19. $e^2 + 8e + 8$

Subtract. 18–19. See left.

18. $(2x^2 + 5x + 7) - (3x^2 + 7x)$

19. $(2e^2 + 5e + 7) - (e^2 - 3e - 1)$

20. $(g^2 + 7) - (3g^2 + 2g + 1)$ $-2g^2 - 2g + 6$

21. $(3r^2 - 4r - 1) - (2r^2 + r - 4)$ $r^2 - 5r + 3$

B Apply Your Skills

22. $12x^3 + 11x^2 + 5x - 4$
23. $-x^3 - 2x^2 + 2x + 5$
24. $3x^3 - 5x^2 + 2x + 3$
25. $x^3 - 9x + 1$
26. Like adding integers, you add the coefficients of like terms; however, unlike adding integers, there are different kinds of terms—some with variables of differing powers and some without variables.

Add or subtract. 22–25. See left.

22. $(12x^3 + 2x^2 - 4) + (9x^2 + 5x)$

23. $(-3x^3 - 2x^2 + 5) + (2x^3 + 2x)$

24. $(3x^3 - 1) - (5x^2 - 2x - 4)$

25. $(x^3 + x^2 + 1) - (x^2 + 9x)$

26. **Writing in Math** How is the process for adding two polynomials like the process for adding two integers? How is it different? See left.

27. a. What polynomial is the opposite of $4x^2 + 2x - 6$? $-4x^2 - 2x + 6$

b. What is the sum of $4x^2 + 2x - 6$ and its opposite? 0

Find the perimeter of each figure.

28. $24d$

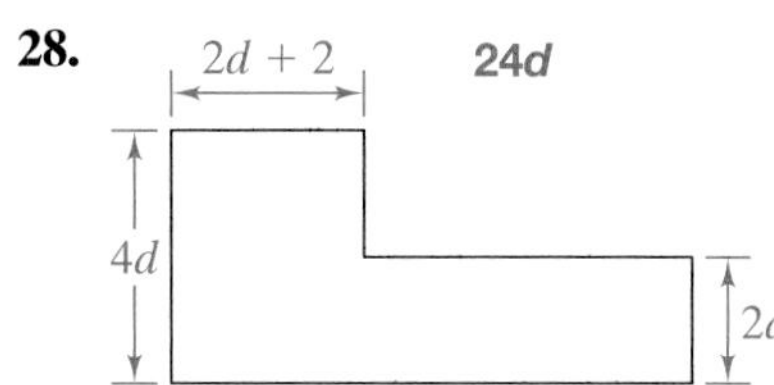

29.

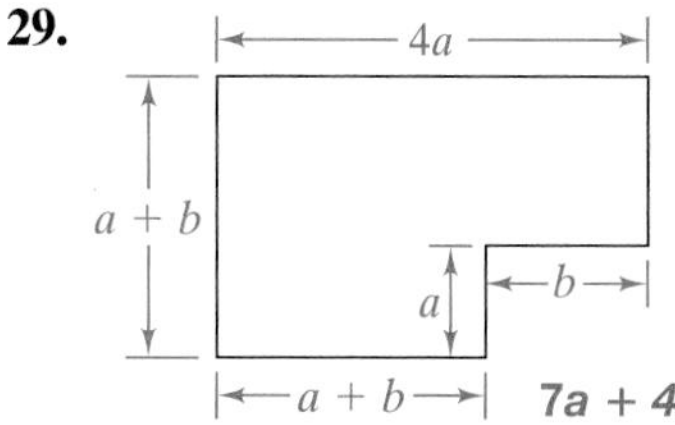

$7a + 4b$

30. The student needs to add the opposite of each term of the second polynomial. $6x^2 + 4x - 2 - 3x^2 + x$

30. **Error Analysis** A student rewrote $(6x^2 + 4x - 2) - (3x^2 - x)$ as $6x^2 + 4x - 2 - 3x^2 - x$. What error did the student make? See left.

31. **Pools** The area of a large rectangular deck is $12x^2 + 4x$. A rectangular pool is set into the deck and has an area of $6x^2 - 12x$. Subtract the polynomials to find the area of the deck around the pool. $6x^2 + 16x$

GPS

32. Write the addition problem modeled below. Then find the sum.

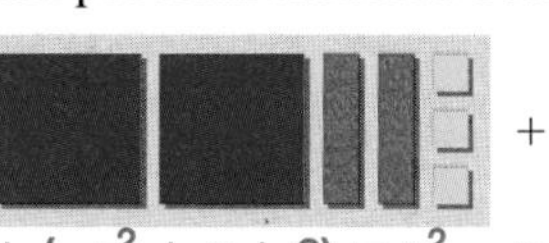

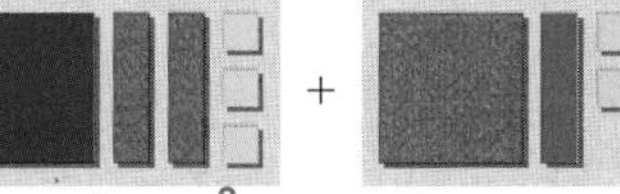

$(2x^2 - 2x + 3) + (-x^2 + x + 2) = x^2 - x + 5$

33. Justify each step.

$(x^2 + 3x - 2) + (3x^2 + 2x + 4)$

a. $(x^2 + 3x^2) + (3x + 2x) + (-2 + 4)$ Comm. and Assoc. Props.

b. $(1 + 3)x^2 + (3 + 2)x + (-2 + 4)$ Distr. Prop.

c. $4x^2 + 5x + 2$ Simplify.

C Challenge

34. a. **Geometry** Write an expression for the area of Figure 1. $\frac{5}{2}x^2$

b. Write an expression for the area of Figure 2. x^2

c. Write and simplify an expression for the total area. $\frac{5}{2}x^2 + x^2$; $\frac{7}{2}x^2$

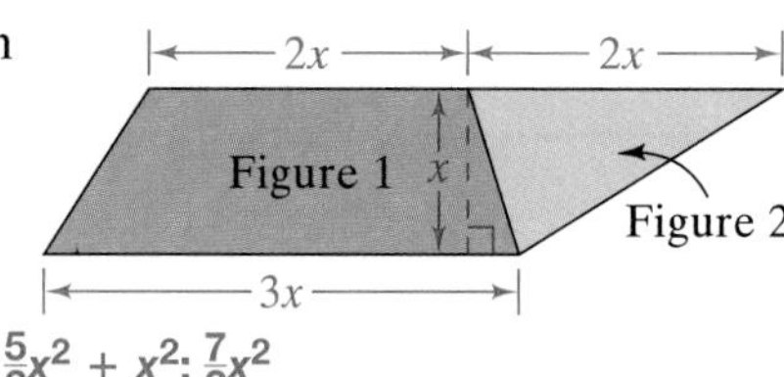

Use the Guided Problem Solving worksheet with Exercise 31.

3. Practice

Assignment Guide

Objective 1

A B Core 1–15, 22–23, 26, 28–30, 32–33

C Extension 34, 37

Objective 2

A B Core 16–21, 24–25, 27, 31

C Extension 35–36, 38

Test Prep 39–43

Mixed Review 44–50

Exercise 38 Ask students who have played darts to explain how the game is played and scored.

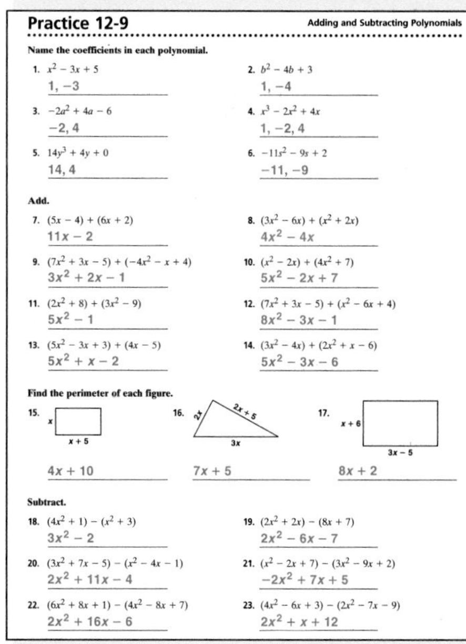

Practice 12-9 Adding and Subtracting Polynomials

Name the coefficients in each polynomial.

1. $x^2 - 3x + 5$ 1, −3
2. $b^2 - 4b + 3$ 1, −4
3. $-2a^2 + 4a - 6$ −2, 4
4. $x^3 - 2x^2 + 4x$ 1, −2, 4
5. $14y^3 + 4y + 0$ 14, 4
6. $-11s^2 - 9s + 2$ −11, −9

Add.

7. $(5x - 4) + (6x + 2)$ $11x - 2$
8. $(3x^2 - 6x) + (x^2 + 2x)$ $4x^2 - 4x$
9. $(7x^2 + 3x - 5) + (-4x^2 - x + 4)$ $3x^2 + 2x - 1$
10. $(x^2 - 2x) + (4x^2 + 7)$ $5x^2 - 2x + 7$
11. $(2x^2 + 8) + (3x^2 - 9)$ $5x^2 - 1$
12. $(7x^2 + 3x - 5) + (x^2 - 6x + 4)$ $8x^2 - 3x - 1$
13. $(5x^2 - 3x + 3) + (4x - 5)$ $5x^2 + x - 2$
14. $(3x^2 - 4x) + (2x^2 + x - 6)$ $5x^2 - 3x - 6$

Find the perimeter of each figure.

15. (rectangle: x, $x + 5$) $4x + 10$
16. (triangle: $2x$, $2x + 5$, $3x$) $7x + 5$
17. (rectangle: $x + 6$, $3x - 5$) $8x + 2$

Subtract.

18. $(4x^2 + 1) - (x^2 + 3)$ $3x^2 - 2$
19. $(2x^2 + 2x) - (8x + 7)$ $2x^2 - 6x - 7$
20. $(3x^2 + 7x - 5) - (x^2 - 4x - 1)$ $2x^2 + 11x - 4$
21. $(x^2 - 2x + 7) - (3x^2 - 9x + 2)$ $-2x^2 + 7x + 5$
22. $(6x^2 + 8x + 1) - (4x^2 - 8x + 7)$ $2x^2 + 16x - 6$
23. $(4x^2 - 6x + 3) - (2x^2 - 7x - 9)$ $2x^2 + x + 12$

Reteaching 12-9 Adding and Subtracting Polynomials

To add polynomials, combine like terms. Add the *coefficients* in the like terms.

Example 1: Add $(3x^2 - 5x - 1)$ and $(x^2 - 6x + 3)$.

$3x^2 - 5x - 1 + x^2 - 6x + 3$ ← Write the sum.
$= (3x^2 + x^2) + (-5x - 6x) + (-1 + 3)$ ← Group like terms.
$= (3 + 1)x^2 + (-5 - 6)x + (-1 + 3)$ ← Use the Distributive Property.
$= 4x^2 - 11x + 2$ ← Add and subtract.

To subtract a polynomial, rewrite the second polynomial to be the opposite and add to the first polynomial.

Example 2: Subtract $(2x^2 + x - 3)$ from $(x^2 - 3x + 1)$.

$(x^2 - 3x + 1) - (2x^2 + x - 3)$
$= (x^2 - 3x + 1) + (-2x^2 - x + 3)$ ← Add the opposite of each term in the second polynomial.
$= (x^2 - 2x^2) + (-3x - x) + (1 + 3)$ ← Group like terms.
$= (1 - 2)x^2 + (-3 - 1)x + (1 + 3)$ ← Use the Distributive Property.
$= -x^2 - 4x + 4$ ← Add and subtract.

Add.

1. $(x^2 + 4x) + (2x^2 - 6x)$ $3x^2 - 2x$
2. $(3x^2 - x - 1) + (2x^2 + 2x - 1)$ $5x^2 + x - 2$
3. $(y^2 - y - 1) + (y^2 + y + 3)$ $2y^2 + 2$
4. $(2y^2 - y) + (y^2 + 3)$ $3y^2 - y + 3$
5. $(2k^2 + 1) + (k^2 - 2k + 5)$ $3k^2 - 2k + 6$
6. $(4n^2 + n - 2) + (n^2 - 3n)$ $5n^2 - 2n - 2$

Subtract.

7. $(2x^2 + 3x) - (x^2 + x)$ $x^2 + 2x$
8. $(3l^2 - 2l + 1) - (2l^2 + l - 3)$ $l^2 - 3l + 4$
9. $(x^2 + 1) - (2x^2 + x - 1)$ $-x^2 - x + 2$
10. $(m^2 - 2m + 6) - (4m^2 - 3)$ $-3m^2 - 2m + 9$
11. $(z^2 - 4z) - (3z^2 + 2z + 1)$ $-2z^2 - 6z - 1$
12. $(p^2 + 6p + 5) - (3p^2 - 2p)$ $-2p^2 + 8p + 5$

4. Assess

Lesson Quiz 12-9

Simplify each polynomial.

1. $(4n^2 + n + 1) + (n^2 + 3n + 1)$ $5n^2 + 4n + 2$
2. $(x^2 - 2x + 6) + (x^2 + 2x - 2)$ $2x^2 + 4$
3. $(a^2 - 7) - (a^2 + 4a - 4)$ $-4a - 3$
4. $(m - 5) + (m^2 - 12) + (6m^2 - 9m)$ $7m^2 - 8m - 17$

Alternative Assessment

Each student in a pair writes a polynomial with three terms: an x^2 term, an x term, and a constant term. Partners work together to find the sum and the differences of their polynomials.

Test Prep

Resources
For additional practice with a variety of test item formats:
- Test Prep, p. 691
- Test-Taking Strategies, p. 687
- Test-Taking Strategies with Transparencies

Exercise 41 Remind students that each term inside the parentheses is multiplied by –1.

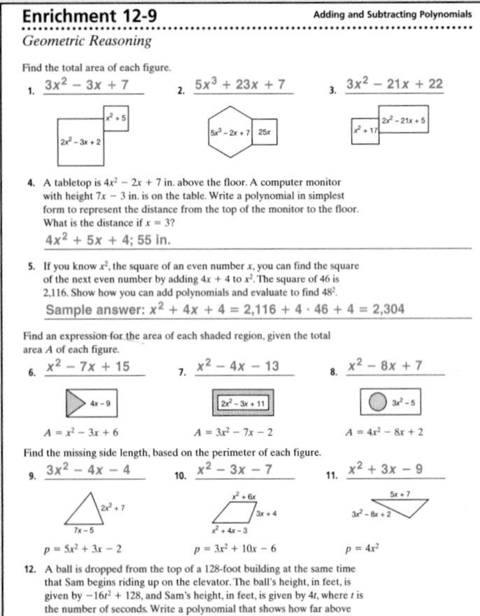

Enrichment 12-9 — Adding and Subtracting Polynomials

Geometric Reasoning

Find the total area of each figure.

1. $3x^2 - 3x + 7$ (figure: $x^2 + 5$; $2x^2 - 3x + 2$)
2. $5x^3 + 23x + 7$ (figure: $5x^3 - 2x + 7$; $25x$)
3. $3x^2 - 21x + 22$ (figure: $x^2 + 17$; $2x^2 - 21x + 5$)
4. A tabletop is $4x^2 - 2x + 7$ in. above the floor. A computer monitor with height $7x - 3$ in. is on the table. Write a polynomial in simplest form to represent the distance from the top of the monitor to the floor. What is the distance if $x = 3$?
   $4x^2 + 5x + 4$; 55 in.
5. If you know x^2, the square of an even number x, you can find the square of the next even number by adding $4x + 4$ to x^2. The square of 46 is 2,116. Show how you can add polynomials and evaluate to find 48^2.
   Sample answer: $x^2 + 4x + 4 = 2{,}116 + 4 \cdot 46 + 4 = 2{,}304$

Find an expression for the area of each shaded region, given the total area A of each figure.

6. $x^2 - 7x + 15$ (figure: $4x - 9$; $A = x^2 - 3x + 6$)
7. $x^2 - 4x - 13$ (figure: $2x^2 - 3x + 11$; $A = 3x^2 - 7x - 2$)
8. $x^2 - 8x + 7$ (figure: $3x^2 - 5$; $A = 4x^2 - 8x + 2$)

Find the missing side length, based on the perimeter of each figure.

9. $3x^2 - 4x - 4$ (figure: $2x^2 + 7$; $7x - 5$; $p = 5x^2 + 3x - 2$)
10. $x^2 - 3x - 7$ (figure: $x^2 + 6x$; $3x + 4$; $x^2 + 4x - 3$; $p = 3x^2 + 10x - 6$)
11. $x^2 + 3x - 9$ (figure: $5x + 7$; $3x^2 - 8x + 2$; $p = 4x^2$)
12. A ball is dropped from the top of a 128-foot building at the same time that Sam begins riding up on the elevator. The ball's height, in feet, is given by $-16t^2 + 128$, and Sam's height, in feet, is given by $4t$, where t is the number of seconds. Write a polynomial that shows how far above Sam the ball is after t seconds.
    $-16t^2 - 4t + 128$

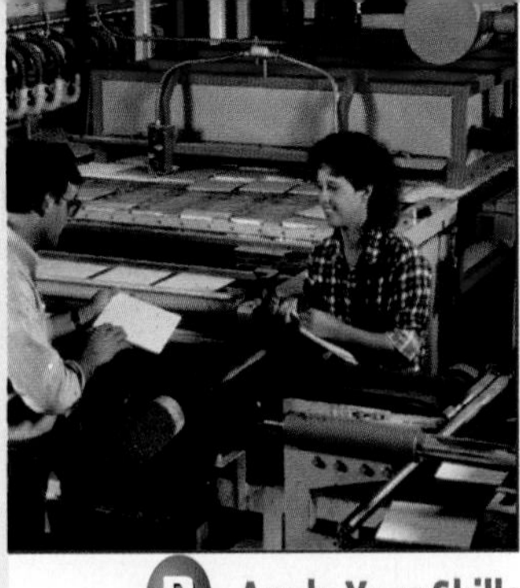

B Apply Your Skills

Careers Businesspeople use polynomials to analyze data.

35. **Business** The polynomial $13x + 400$ represents the expense, in dollars, of producing x items. The polynomial $25x - 30$ represents the income, in dollars, from selling x items. The profit is equal to income minus expenses. Find the polynomial that represents the profit on x items.
    $12x - 430$

Add or subtract.

36. $(3s^3 - 14c^2 + s + c^3 - 7) - (9c^3 - 3s^2 + 8s - c - 10c^2 + 23)$
    $3s^3 + 3s^2 - 7s - 8c^3 - 4c^2 + c - 30$
37. $(17 - 2t^4 - 9g + 3t^2 + g^3 - 15g^2) + (-20t^2 + 11g^3 + 6t^4 - 4g^2)$
    $17 + 4t^4 - 9g - 17t^2 + 12g^3 - 19g^2$
38. **Stretch Your Thinking** When Gil threw 4 darts at a target composed of 2 sections, A and B, 1 landed in A and 3 landed in B. His score was 29. When Ellen threw 3 darts, 1 landed in A and 2 landed in B. Her score was 23. How many points are A and B worth?
    11 and 6

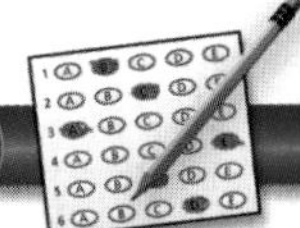

Test Prep

Multiple Choice

39. Add $(3x^2 - 8) + (2x^2 - 3x)$. C
    A. $5x^2 - 11x$ B. $5x^2 + 3x - 8$ C. $5x^2 - 3x - 8$ D. $5x^2 + 5x$
40. What must you add to $5x^2 + 4x$ to get $-x^2 + 5x$? G
    F. $4x^2 + x$ G. $-6x^2 + x$ H. $4x^2 + 9x$ I. $-5x^2$
41. Subtract $(2x^2 - 2x) - (3x^2 + 4 + x)$. A
    A. $-x^2 - 3x - 4$ B. $-x^2 - x + 4$
    C. $-x^2 - x - 4$ D. $x^2 - 3x + 4$
42. What are the coefficients of the polynomial $-4y^2 - 2y + 13$? H
    F. $-4, 2, 13$ G. $-4, -2, 13$ H. $-4, -2$ I. $-4, 2$

Short Response

43. a. Write the perimeter of the figure as a simplified polynomial.
    [2] a. $6a^2 + 8a + 4$
    b. 132
    [1] one part correct

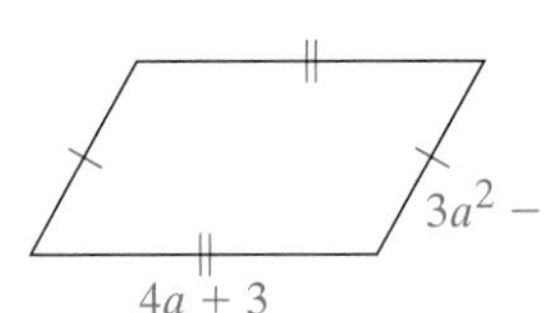

b. Find the perimeter if $a = 4$.

Take It to the NET
Online lesson quiz at www.PHSchool.com
Web Code: aca-1209

Mixed Review

Lesson 12-6 **Make a table and a graph for each function. Use only positive values for x in Exercises 45 and 46.** 44–46. See margin.

44. $y = 4x^2 - 8$
45. $y = \frac{6}{x}$
46. $y = \frac{1}{x}$

Lesson 11-2 **Simplify each expression.**

47. ${}_{20}P_5$ 1,860,480
48. ${}_{8}P_3$ 336
49. ${}_{4}P_2$ 12
50. ${}_{12}P_4$ 11,880

44, 46. See back of book.

45.

x	1	2	3	4	5
y	6	3	2	$\frac{3}{2}$	$\frac{6}{5}$

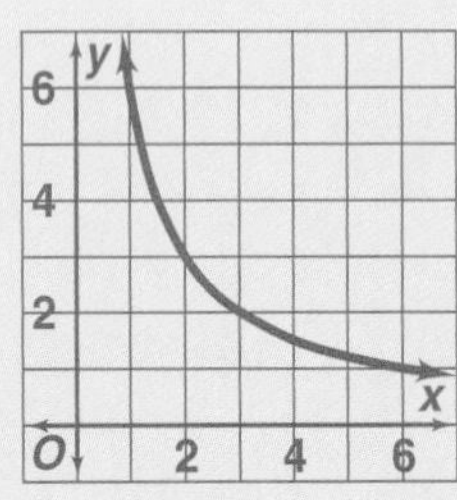

Algebra

12-10 Multiplying Polynomials

What You'll Learn

To multiply by a monomial

To multiply binomials using area models

. . . And Why

To find the area of a rectangle, as in Exercise 24

Check Skills You'll Need

For help, go to Lesson 7-2.

Write each expression using a single exponent.

1. $2^3 \cdot 2^5$ 2^8
2. $a^2 \cdot a$ a^3
3. $n^3 \cdot n^8 \cdot n^4$ n^{15}
4. $(-x^4) \cdot x^{-5} \cdot x^6$ $-x^5$
5. $(-a)^3 \cdot (-a)^7$ $(-a)^{10}$ or a^{10}
6. $(-w)^2 \cdot w^4 \cdot w^{-2}$ w^4

New Vocabulary

- monomial
- binomial

Interactive lesson includes instant self-check, tutorials, and activities.

OBJECTIVE 1 Multiplying by a Monomial

A polynomial that has only one term, such as $4a^3$, is a **monomial.** To multiply monomials, multiply the coefficients and use the properties of exponents.

1 EXAMPLE Multiplying Monomials

Simplify: $(4a^3)(-5a^2)$

$(4a^3)(-5a^2) = (4)(-5) \cdot a^3 \cdot a^2$ ← Use the Commutative Property to rearrange the factors.

$= -20 \cdot a^3 \cdot a^2$ ← Multiply the coefficients.

$= -20a^5$ ← Add the exponents.

Need Help?
To multiply exponents with the same base, add the exponents.

Check Understanding 1 Simplify each expression.

a. $(2y^3)(4y)$ $8y^4$
b. $(-7n^5)(3n^2)$ $-21n^7$
c. $(-2x^4)(-4x^7)$ $8x^{11}$

A **binomial** is a polynomial with two terms. You can use an area model to find the product of a monomial and a binomial.

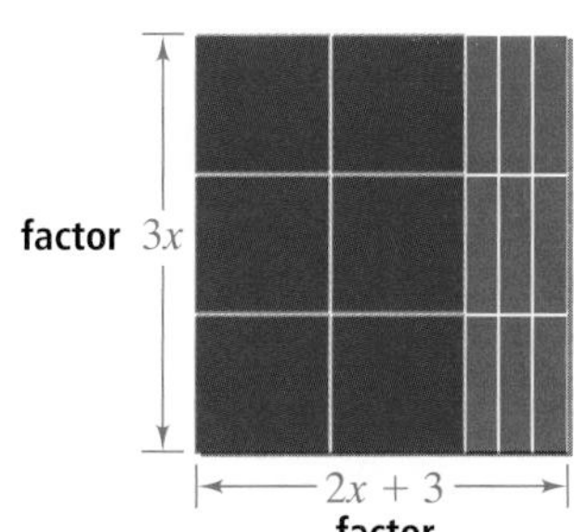

This model shows the product of $3x$ and $2x + 3$.

Since the array of tiles forms a rectangle, the area is the product of the height and the base, or $3x(2x + 3)$.

The area is also the sum of the tiles, or $6x^2 + 9x$.

So, $3x(2x + 3) = 6x^2 + 9x$.

12-10

1. Plan

Lesson Preview

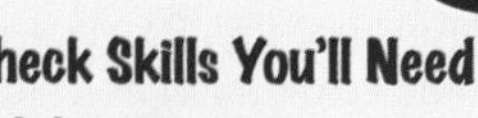

Check Skills You'll Need
Multiplying Powers
Lesson 7-2: Example 1. Extra Practice, p. 708.

Lesson Resources

Teaching Resources
Practice, Reteaching, Enrichment

Reaching All Students
Practice Workbook 12-10
Spanish Practice Workbook 12-10
Guided Problem Solving 12-10

Presentation Assistant Plus!
Transparencies
- Check Skills You'll Need 12-10
- Problem of the Day 12-10
- Additional Examples 12-10
- Student Edition Answers 12-10
- Lesson Quiz 12-10
- Classroom Aid 37

PH Presentation Pro CD 12-10

PRENTICE HALL ASSESSMENT SYSTEM
Computer Test Generator CD

Technology
Resource Pro® CD-ROM
Computer Test Generator CD
PH Presentation Pro CD-ROM

www.PHSchool.com
Student Site
- Teacher Web Code: ack-5500
- Algebra Readiness Puzzles 36, 100, 101, 102, 103, 108
- Self-grading Lesson Quiz

PH SuccessNet Teacher Center
- Lesson Planner
- Resources

Plus iText

Ongoing Assessment and Intervention

Before the Lesson
Diagnose prerequisite skills using:
- Check Skills You'll Need

During the Lesson
Monitor progress using:
- Check Understanding
- Additional Examples
- Test Prep

After the Lesson
Assess knowledge using:
- Lesson Quiz
- Computer Test Generator CD

2. Teach

Math Background

Polynomials can be named according to the number of terms they have. A polynomial with only one term, such as $5xy^2$ or $-b$, is called a *monomial*. Polynomials with two terms, such as $x + 3$ or $y^2 - 3y$, are called *binomials*.

Teaching Notes

Teaching Tip
Review the multiplication of $y^2 \cdot y^3$ by writing $y^2 \cdot y^3 = (y \cdot y) \cdot (y \cdot y \cdot y) = y^{2+3}$ or y^5.

English Learners
Ask students to name other words that use *mono-*, *bi-*, and *poly-*, using a dictionary if necessary. Help them draw the conclusion that *mono-* means "one," *bi-* means "two," and *poly-* means "many."

3 EXAMPLE Alternative Method
Show students that these tiles can be arranged in a different way, as long as they make a rectangle. Make sure that students relate building this rectangle and finding the product to finding the area of a rectangle with dimensions that equal the two binomial expressions.

PowerPoint

Additional Examples

1. Simplify $(3x^2)(-4x^3)$. $-12x^5$
2. Simplify $-2x(4x^3 + 6)$. $-8x^4 - 12x$
3. Use an area model to simplify $(x + 1)(3x + 1)$. $3x^2 + 4x + 1$

Closure

- *How do you multiply two monomials?* Multiply the coefficients and multiply like variables by adding exponents.
- *How do you use an area model to find the product of two binomials?* Use tiles to model the binomials as the length and width of a rectangle and then fill in the rectangle to find the area, which models the product.

You can also use the Distributive Property to find the product of a monomial and a binomial.

2 EXAMPLE Multiplying a Monomial and a Binomial

Simplify: $5n(4n - 6)$

$5n(4n - 6) = 5n \cdot 4n - 5n \cdot 6$ ← Use the Distributive Property.

$= 20n^2 - 30n$ ← Multiply the monomials.

Check Understanding 2 Simplify each expression.

a. $4y(2y + 7)$ $8y^2 + 28y$ **b.** $8b(2b^2 - 9)$ $16b^3 - 72b$ **c.** $3r(5r^4 + 5)$ $15r^5 + 15r$

OBJECTIVE 2

Using Area Models to Multiply Binomials

You can use an area model to find the product of two binomials.

3 EXAMPLE Using Area Models to Multiply Binomials

Simplify: $(2x + 1)(3x + 2)$

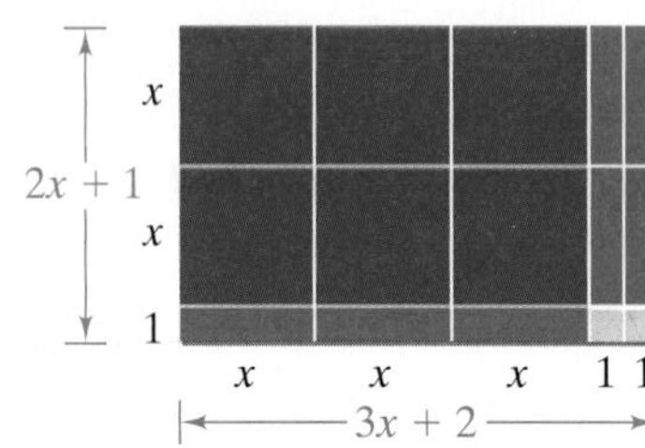

Count each type of tile.

There are six x^2 tiles.

There are seven x tiles.

There are two unit tiles.

So, $(2x + 1)(3x + 2) = 6x^2 + 7x + 2$.

Check Understanding 3 Draw an area model or use algebra tiles to simplify each expression.

a. $(x + 2)(2x + 3)$ **b.** $(3x + 4)(2x + 1)$ **c.** $(x + 1)(2x + 5)$ See left

3a. $2x^2 + 7x + 6$
b. $6x^2 + 11x + 4$
c. $2x^2 + 7x + 5$

d. **Reasoning** Explain why $(2x + 1)(3x + 2)$ does not equal $6x^2 + 2$.
There are six x^2 tiles and two unit tiles, but there are also seven x tiles.

EXERCISES

For more practice, see *Extra Practice*.

A Practice by Example

Example 1 (page 683)

Simplify each expression.

1. $x^5 \cdot x$ x^6
2. $5a \cdot 3a$ $15a^2$
3. $(-8y)(2y)$ $-16y^2$
4. $(-3t^2)(-4t^3)$ $12t^5$
5. $4g^4 \cdot 3g^3$ $12g^7$
6. $(-z^3)(6z^2)$ $-6z^5$
7. $(7x^2)(-2x^3)$ $-14x^5$
8. $(10s^2)(-4s)$ $-40s^3$
9. $(5c^3)(-4c^4)$ $-20c^7$

Reaching All Students

Below Level Review the names of the algebra tile models: x^2, x, and 1, and emphasize that the long side of the x tile does NOT equal a whole number.	**Advanced Learners** Have students relate multiplying 12(13) with $(x + 2)(x + 1)$ to develop a method of multiplying binomials.	**English Learners** See note on page 684. **Alternative Method** See note on page 684.

Example 2 (page 684)

Simplify each expression. Exercises 10 and 11 have been started for you.

10. $a(a - 3) = a \cdot a - a \cdot 3$ $a^2 - 3a$

11. $2m(m - 7) = 2m \cdot m - 2m \cdot 7$ $2m^2 - 14m$

12. $7(3s^2 + 1)$ $21s^2 + 7$

13. $-3y(y^2 - 6y)$ $-3y^3 + 18y^2$

14. $2k(5k - 1)$ $10k^2 - 2k$

15. $-3d^2(d - 4)$ $-3d^3 + 12d^2$

Example 3 (page 684)

State the factors and the product shown in each area model.

16. 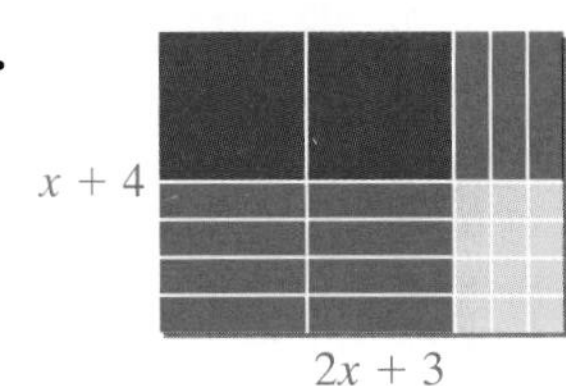

$(x + 4)(2x + 3) = 2x^2 + 11x + 12$

17. 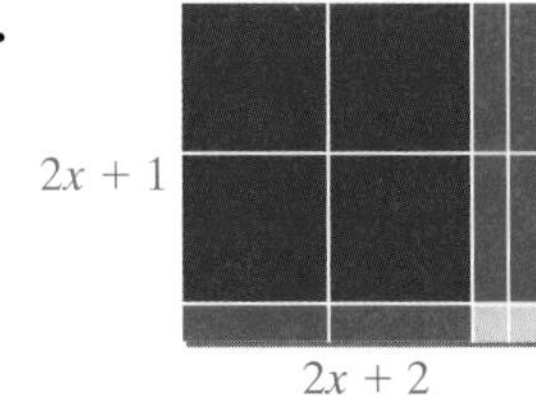

$(2x + 1)(2x + 2) = 4x^2 + 6x + 2$

Draw an area model or use algebra tiles to simplify each expression.

18. $2g(g + 5)$ $2g^2 + 10g$
19. $v(4v + 1)$ $4v^2 + v$
20. $x(3x + 6)$ $3x^2 + 6x$
21. $2r(r + 7)$ $2r^2 + 14r$
22. $3m(m + 3)$ $3m^2 + 9m$
23. $a(2a + 1)$ $2a^2 + a$

B Apply Your Skills

Draw a tile model to find the area of each rectangle.

24. length $= x$
width $= x + 3$
$x^2 + 3x$

25. length $= x$
width $= 2x + 1$
$2x^2 + x$

26. length $= 2x$
width $= x + 2$
$2x^2 + 4x$

Use the Distributive Property to simplify each expression. 27–32. See left

27. $3p(5p^2 + 1)$
28. $-5h(h^2 - 3)$
29. $2n(-3n^2 + 1)$
30. $-8b(3b^2 - 2b)$
31. $7x^2(5x^2 + 4x - 4)$
32. $-w^2(w^2 + 2w - 4)$

27. $15p^3 + 3p$
28. $-5h^3 + 15h$
29. $-6n^3 + 2n$
30. $-24b^3 + 16b^2$
31. $35x^4 + 28x^3 - 28x^2$
32. $-w^4 - 2w^3 + 4w^2$

Find the area of each figure.

33. 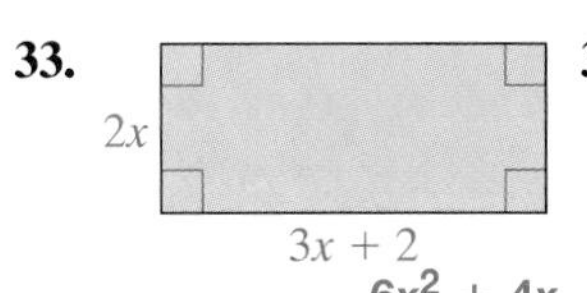

$6x^2 + 4x$

34. 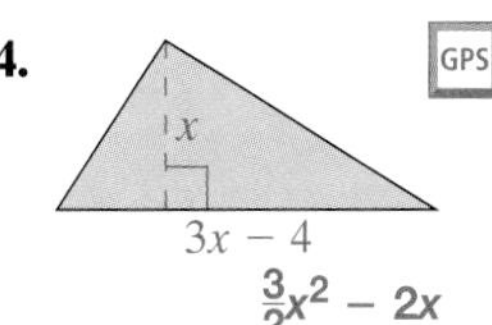

$\frac{3}{2}x^2 - 2x$

GPS 35. 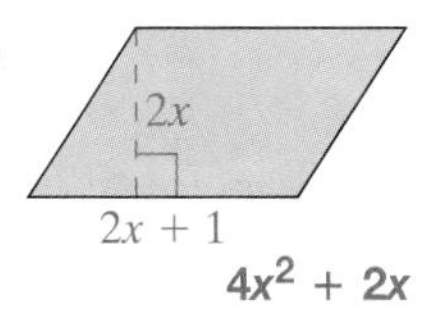

$4x^2 + 2x$

36. **Writing in Math** Explain how to multiply $(x + 1)$ and $(x + 2)$ using an area model.

36. Start with a rectangular area model whose dimensions are $(x + 1)$ and $(x + 2)$. Count each type of tile. There are one x^2 tile, three x tiles, and two unit tiles. The product is $x^2 + 3x + 2$.

37. **Error Analysis** A student rewrote $2x^2(x^2 + 3x - 3)$ as $2x^4 + 3x - 3$. What error did the student make?
The student did not distribute $2x^2$ to the last two terms of the polynomial.

Write an expression for the area of each shaded region.

38. x, $2x$, 3, x $2x^2 + 3x$

39. 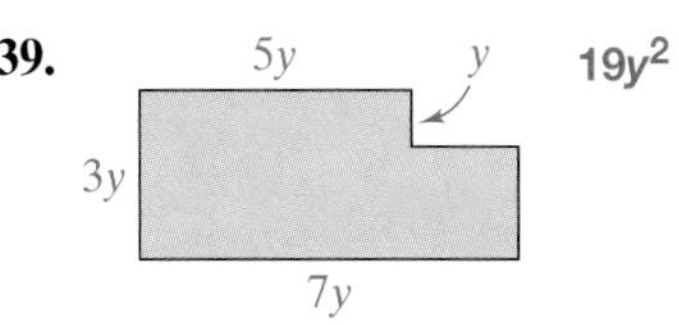

$19y^2$

Use the Guided Problem Solving worksheet with Exercise 35.

3. Practice

Assignment Guide

 Objective 1

A B Core 1–15, 24–35, 37–39

C Extension 43

 Objective 2

A B Core 16–23, 36

C Extension 40–42

Test Prep 44–47
Mixed Review 48–53

Error Prevention!

Exercises 24–26 Remind students that the rectangle must be filled.

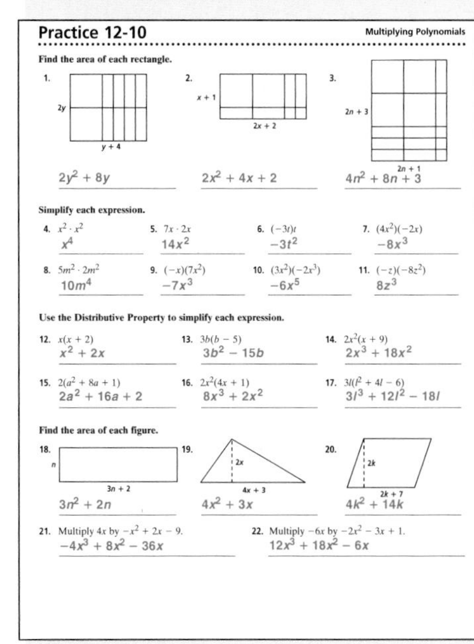

Practice 12-10 Multiplying Polynomials

Find the area of each rectangle.

1. $2y$; $y + 4$ — $2y^2 + 8y$
2. $x + 1$; $2x + 2$ — $2x^2 + 4x + 2$
3. $2n + 3$; $2n + 1$ — $4n^2 + 8n + 3$

Simplify each expression.

4. $x^2 \cdot x^2$ x^4
5. $7x \cdot 2x$ $14x^2$
6. $(-3t)t$ $-3t^2$
7. $(4x^2)(-2x)$ $-8x^3$
8. $5m^2 \cdot 2m^2$ $10m^4$
9. $(-x)(7x^2)$ $-7x^3$
10. $(3x^2)(-2x^3)$ $-6x^5$
11. $(-z)(-8z^2)$ $8z^3$

Use the Distributive Property to simplify each expression.

12. $x(x + 2)$ $x^2 + 2x$
13. $3b(b - 5)$ $3b^2 - 15b$
14. $2x^2(x + 9)$ $2x^3 + 18x^2$
15. $2(a^2 + 8a + 1)$ $2a^2 + 16a + 2$
16. $2x^2(4x + 1)$ $8x^3 + 2x^2$
17. $3l(l^2 + 4l - 6)$ $3l^3 + 12l^2 - 18l$

Find the area of each figure.

18. n; $3n + 2$ — $3n^2 + 2n$
19. $2x$; $4x + 3$ — $4x^2 + 3x$
20. $2k$; $2k + 7$ — $4k^2 + 14k$

21. Multiply $4x$ by $-x^2 + 2x - 9$. $-4x^3 + 8x^2 - 36x$
22. Multiply $-6x$ by $-2x^2 - 3x + 1$. $12x^3 + 18x^2 - 6x$

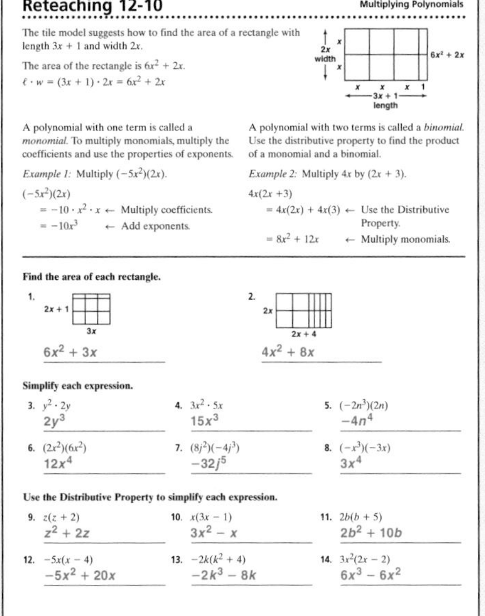

Reteaching 12-10 Multiplying Polynomials

The tile model suggests how to find the area of a rectangle with length $3x + 1$ and width $2x$.

The area of the rectangle is $6x^2 + 2x$.

$\ell \cdot w = (3x + 1) \cdot 2x = 6x^2 + 2x$

A polynomial with one term is called a *monomial.* To multiply monomials, multiply the coefficients and use the properties of exponents.

Example 1: Multiply $(-5x^2)(2x)$.

$(-5x^2)(2x)$
$= -10 \cdot x^2 \cdot x$ ← Multiply coefficients.
$= -10x^3$ ← Add exponents.

A polynomial with two terms is called a *binomial.* Use the distributive property to find the product of a monomial and a binomial.

Example 2: Multiply $4x$ by $(2x + 3)$.

$4x(2x + 3)$
$= 4x(2x) + 4x(3)$ ← Use the Distributive Property.
$= 8x^2 + 12x$ ← Multiply monomials.

Find the area of each rectangle.

1. $2x + 1$; $3x$ — $6x^2 + 3x$
2. $2x$; $2x + 4$ — $4x^2 + 8x$

Simplify each expression.

3. $y^2 \cdot 2y$ $2y^3$
4. $3x^2 \cdot 5x$ $15x^3$
5. $(-2n^3)(2n)$ $-4n^4$
6. $(2x^2)(6x^2)$ $12x^4$
7. $(8j^2)(-4j^3)$ $-32j^5$
8. $(-x^3)(-3x)$ $3x^4$

Use the Distributive Property to simplify each expression.

9. $z(z + 2)$ $z^2 + 2z$
10. $x(3x - 1)$ $3x^2 - x$
11. $2b(b + 5)$ $2b^2 + 10b$
12. $-5x(x - 4)$ $-5x^2 + 20x$
13. $-2k(k^2 + 4)$ $-2k^3 - 8k$
14. $3x^2(2x - 2)$ $6x^3 - 6x^2$

4. Assess

Lesson Quiz 12-10

Simplify each expression.

1. $(-7c^3)(4c)$ $-28c^4$
2. $6y(y^2 - 1)$ $6y^3 - 6y$
3. $x(3x + 2)$ $3x^2 + 2x$
4. $-2m^2(m - 1)$ $-2m^3 + 2m^2$

Alternative Assessment

Together partners decide who writes a binomial in terms of x and who writes a monomial in terms of x. Partners together find the product of the monomial and binomial.

Test Prep

Resources
For additional practice with a variety of test item formats:
- Test Prep, p. 691
- Test-Taking Strategies, p. 687
- Test-Taking Strategies with Transparencies

Exercise 44 Remind students to add the exponents and multiply the coefficients.

47. [2] $(x + 2)(1.5x + x) =$
$(x + 2)(2.5x) =$
$2.5x^2 + 5x$
[1] correct procedure with one computational error OR correct area without work shown

Enrichment 12-10 — Multiplying Polynomials

Patterns in Geometry

Mario is making props and scenery for the school play. For one scene, he needs to make and paint a backdrop in the shape of a house like the one shown to the right. He wants to write an equation to help him determine the amount of backdrop material he will need to construct each house.

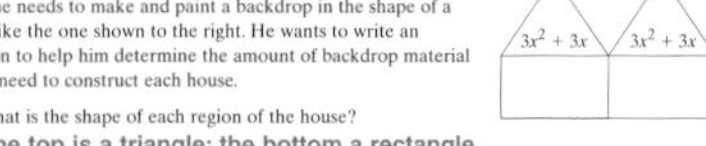

1. What is the shape of each region of the house?
The top is a triangle; the bottom a rectangle.
2. The bottom part of the house has height $x + 1$ ft as labeled above. The length of the house is $3x$ times the height of the bottom part.
   a. Write an expression for the width of the house. $3x(x + 1)$
   b. Evaluate your expression and label the width of the house. $3x^2 + 3x$
3. The height of the house from the ground to the top of the roof is twice the height from the ground to the top of the bottom part.
   a. Write an expression for the total height of the house. $2(x + 1)$
   b. Evaluate your expression and label the total height of the house. $2x + 2$
   c. What is the height of the triangular section of the house? $x + 1$
4. a. Use the formula for the area of a triangle to write and evaluate an expression for the area of the top of the house.
   $A = \frac{1}{2}(3x^2 + 3x)(x + 1) = 1\frac{1}{2}x^3 + 3x^2 + 1\frac{1}{2}x$
   b. Use the formula for the area of a rectangle to write an expression for the area of the base of the house.
   $A = (x + 1)(3x^2 + 3x) = 3x^3 + 6x^2 + 3x$
   c. Write an expression for the total area of the house.
   $(1\frac{1}{2}x^3 + 3x^2 + 1\frac{1}{2}x) + (3x^3 + 6x^2 + 3x) = 4\frac{1}{2}x^3 + 9x^2 + 4\frac{1}{2}x$
5. Mario decides to make $x = 3$ ft. How much material will he need to make a backdrop?
$4\frac{1}{2}(3)^3 + 9(3)^2 + 4\frac{1}{2}(3) = \frac{9}{2}(27) + 9(9) + \frac{9}{2}(3) = 135 + 81 = 216$ ft^2

C Challenge

Find the factors of each polynomial. You can find the factors of a polynomial by finding the GCF of the terms of the polynomial.

Sample

$2a^2 + 6a$ ← The GCF is $2a$.
$2a \cdot a + 2a \cdot 3$ ← Write each term using $2a$ as a factor.
$2a(a + 3)$ ← Use the Distributive Property.

40. $3x^2 + 9$ $3(x^2 + 3)$ **41.** $5y^2 + 10y$ $5y(y + 2)$ **42.** $8a^3 + 4a^2 + 12a$ $4a(2a^2 + a + 3)$

43. **Stretch Your Thinking** It takes 4 hours to fill a swimming pool with the drain closed. It takes 5 hours to drain the same pool. When Joey began to fill the pool, he accidentally left the drain open. How long did it take before the pool was full? 20 hours

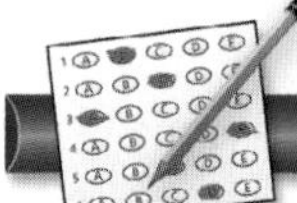

Test Prep

Multiple Choice

44. Which monomial is the product of $(-4x^3) \cdot (-4x^3)$? C
A. $-8x^3$ B. $16x^3$ C. $16x^6$ D. $-8x^6$

45. What number must you multiply $5x + 4$ by to equal $-10x^2 - 8x$? I
F. $-5x$ G. $2x$ H. $5x$ I. $-2x$

46. What is the product of $-3x$ and $x^2 - 2x + 3$? A
A. $-3x^3 + 6x^2 - 9x$ B. $-3x^3 - 6x + 9$
C. $-3x^2 + 6x - 9$ D. $-3x^2 - 2x + 3$

Short Response

Take It to the NET
Online lesson quiz at www.PHSchool.com
Web Code: aca-1210

47. The drawing at the right shows a yard divided into two sections. The left section has a patio, and the right section has a garden. Find the area of the entire yard. Show your work. See margin.

Mixed Review

Lesson 12-4 **Do the data in each table represent a linear function? If so, write a rule for the function.**

48.

x	-1	2	5	8
y	3	-6	-15	-24

yes; $y = -3x$

49.

x	0	1	2	3
y	-2	-4	-16	-32

no

Lesson 12-3 **Graph each linear function.** 50–53. See margin.

50. $y = 7 - 3x$ **51.** $y = 8x + 10$

52. $y = -x + 2$ **53.** $y = 6x - 5$

50.
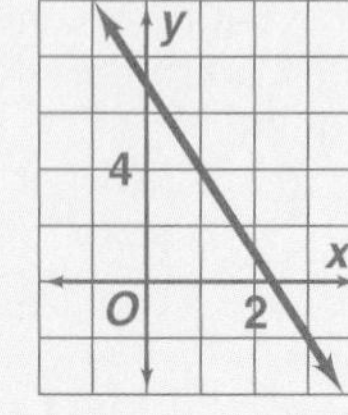

51.
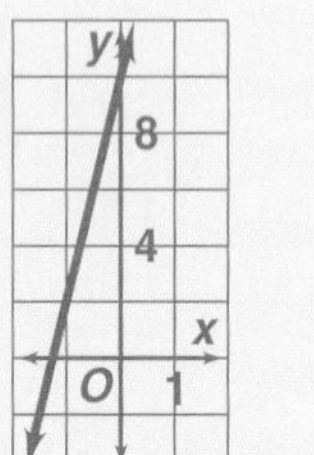

52.
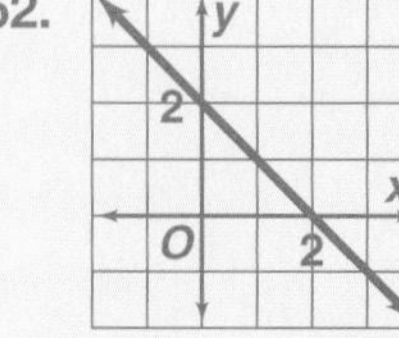

53.
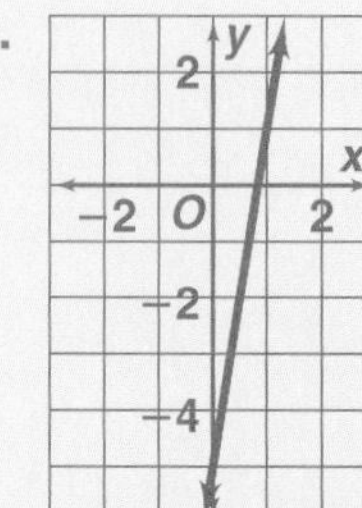

Test-Taking Strategies: Work Backward

One advantage of multiple-choice tests is that the correct answer is among the choices. To get the correct answer, you can use the problem-solving strategy *work backward.*

1 EXAMPLE

Field Trip A school bus can hold 72 passengers. An elementary school uses the function $b = \frac{n}{72}$ to calculate the number of buses needed to transport n students on a field trip. What is the greatest number of students going on the field trip if 6 buses are needed?

A. 288 **B.** 360 **C.** 432 **D.** 504

You can answer the question without solving the equation. Substitute each answer choice for the variable until you find the one that is the solution.

Let $n = 288$. Then $\frac{288}{72} = 4$. Since $4 \neq 6$, A is wrong.

Let $n = 360$. Then $\frac{360}{72} = 5$. Since $5 \neq 6$, B is wrong.

Let $n = 432$. Then $\frac{432}{72} = 6$. Since $6 = 6$, the correct answer is C.

You do not need to try choice D.

2 EXAMPLE

Which polynomial is equivalent to $12x^2 - 28x$?

A. $12x(x - 2)$ **B.** $4x(3x - 7)$ **C.** $4x^2(3 - 7)$ **D.** $6(2x^2 - 4)$

You can multiply each of the answer choices to answer the question.

$12x(x - 2) = 12x^2 - 24x$ This is not equal to $12x^2 - 28x$, so A is wrong.

$4x(3x - 7) = 12x^2 - 28x$ Choice B is correct.

You do not need to test the other two choices.

EXERCISES

Solve each of the following by working backward.

1. The function $f(g) = 33g$ describes the number of miles a car can travel on g gallons of gas. What value of g will make $f(g) = 297$? D

   A. 4 **B.** 14 **C.** 6 **D.** 9

2. Which polynomial is equivalent to $10x + 6x^2$? H

   F. $5(2x + 1)$ **G.** $x(10 + 6)$ **H.** $2x(5 + 3x)$ **I.** $2x^2(3 + 2x)$

Test-Taking Strategies

Work Backward

In general, students can use the work backward strategy effectively when they know a solution but need to find information that led to that solution. This feature guides students to work backward to solve multiple-choice questions.

Resources

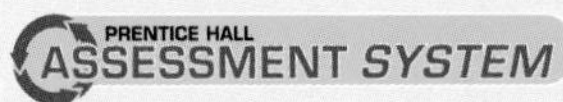

Test-Taking Strategies with Transparencies
- Transparency 7
- Practice master, p. 36

Teaching Notes

Emphasize that students should stop checking answer choices once their substitution results in the desired result.

Discuss that eliminating some answer choices, by estimating or by using number sense, will increase their chances of success on that test question, whether they work backward or apply any other test-taking strategy.

2 EXAMPLE Teaching Tip

Have a volunteer demonstrate how to use mental math and the Distributive Property to solve Example 2.

Test-Taking Strategies With Transparencies

Chapter 12: Work Backward

Exercises

Solve each of the following by working backward.

1. Which polynomial is equivalent to $15x(2x + 8)$?
   A. $30x + 8$ B. $30x + 120x$ (C.) $30x^2 + 120x$ D. $30x^2 + 8x$
2. Consider the function $f(y) = 3x - 7$. What value of x will make $f(y) = 20$?
   F. 53 (G.) 9 H. −36 I. −80
3. The area of a circle is 15.9 mm^2. What is the diameter of the circle?
   (A.) 4.5 mm B. 3.14 mm C. 2.25 mm D. 1.05 mm
4. The base of a rectangular prism has a length of 9 in. and a width of 7 in. The volume of the prism is 787.5 $in.^3$. What is the height of the prism?
   F. 87.5 in. G. 63 in. (H.) 12.5 in. I. 7.875 in.
5. If $x^3 = 64$, find the value of $\frac{x^5}{x^3}$.
   A. 1,024 (B.) 16 C. 8 D. 4
6. Which number could *not* be a value of y if $y = 5x^2 - 9$?
   F. 11 G. −4 H. −9 (I.) −10
7. The side lengths of which of the following triangles do *not* form a right triangle?
   A. 12 cm, 16 cm, 20 cm B. 10 cm, 24 cm, 26 cm
   (C.) 8 cm, 10 cm, 12 cm D. 15 cm, 20 cm, 25 cm
8. Jennie's average after four math tests is an 85. What must Jennie score on the fifth test to raise her grade to an 87?
   F. 100 (G.) 95 H. 91 I. 87
9. Which ordered pair lies on the line $y = 11x - 13$?
   (A.) (2, 9) B. (−13, 0) C. (0, 11) D. (1, 2)
10. You start an exercise program. You begin by walking 1.5 mi the first day and increase your distance by 0.25 mi per day. How many miles do you walk on the 7th day?
    F. 1.75 mi (G.) 3 mi H. 3.25 mi I. 3.5 mi

Resources

Student Edition
Extra Practice, Ch. 12, p. 713
English/Spanish Glossary, p. 735
Table of Symbols, p. 730

 **Reaching All Students**
Reading and Math Literacy 12D
Spanish Reading and Math Literacy 12D

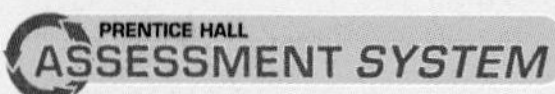

Test Preparation
- Chapter 12 practice in test formats

 **www.PHSchool.com**
Student Site
- Self-grading vocabulary test

PH SuccessNet Teacher Center
- Resources

Plus iTEXT

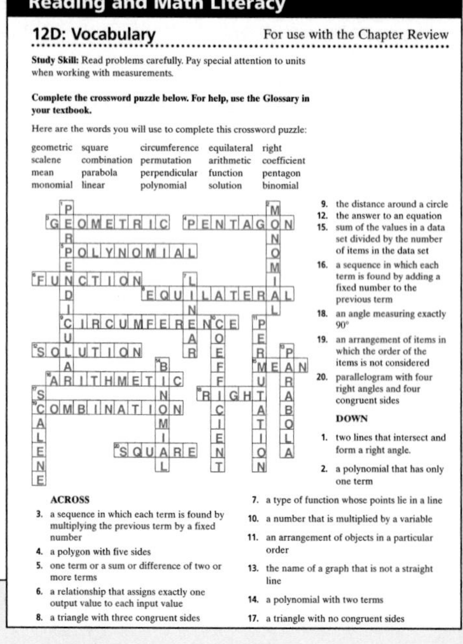

Spanish Reading and Math Literacy

Reading and Math Literacy

12D: Vocabulary For use with the Chapter Review

Study Skill: Read problems carefully. Pay special attention to units when working with measurements.

Complete the crossword puzzle below. For help, use the Glossary in your textbook.

Here are the words you will use to complete this crossword puzzle:

geometric	square	circumference	equilateral	right
scalene	combination	permutation	arithmetic	coefficient
mean	parabola	perpendicular	function	pentagon
monomial	linear	polynomial	solution	binomial

ACROSS

3. a sequence in which each term is found by multiplying the previous term by a fixed number
4. a polygon with five sides
5. one term or a sum or difference of two or more terms
6. a relationship that assigns exactly one output value to each input value
8. a triangle with three congruent sides
9. the distance around a circle
12. the answer to an equation
15. sum of the values in a data set divided by the number of items in the data set
16. a sequence in which each term is found by adding a fixed number to the previous term
18. an angle measuring exactly 90°
19. an arrangement of items in which the order of the items is not considered
20. parallelogram with four right angles and four congruent sides

DOWN

1. two lines that intersect and form a right angle.
2. a polynomial that has only one term
7. a type of function whose points lie in a line
10. a number that is multiplied by a variable
11. an arrangement of objects in a particular order
13. the name of a graph that is not a straight line
14. a polynomial with two terms
17. a triangle with no congruent sides

Chapter Review

Vocabulary

arithmetic sequence (p. 638)	**continuous data** (p. 649)	**monomial** (p. 683)
binomial (p. 683)	**discrete data** (p. 649)	**parabola** (p. 663)
coefficient (p. 678)	**function** (p. 643)	**polynomial** (p. 674)
common difference (p. 638)	**function rule** (p. 643)	**quadratic function** (p. 663)
common ratio (p. 638)	**geometric sequence** (p. 638)	**sequence** (p. 637)
constant (p. 674)	**linear function** (p. 650)	**term** (p. 638)

 **Reading Math: Understanding Vocabulary**

Take It to the NET
Online vocabulary quiz at www.PHSchool.com
Web Code: acj-1251

Match each word on the left with its definition on the right.

1. sequence d — **a.** a U-shaped graph of an equation like $y = x^2 - 2$
2. coefficient c — **b.** a function whose points lie on a line
3. parabola a — **c.** a number that is multiplied by a variable
4. term e — **d.** a set of numbers that follows a pattern
5. linear function b — **e.** each number in a sequence

Skills and Concepts

12-1 Objectives
- To describe sequences
- To evaluate an algebraic expression and to write a sequence

Each term of an **arithmetic sequence** is found by *adding* a fixed number to the previous term. This fixed number is called the **common difference.** Each term of a **geometric sequence** is found by *multiplying* the previous term by a fixed number. This fixed number is called the **common ratio.**

Find the common difference or ratio in each sequence. Write the rule for the sequence and find the next three terms. 6–8. See left.

6. 1,600; 400; 100; 25; . . . **7.** 14, 21, 28, 35, . . . **8.** −1, 2, −4, 8, . . .

6. $\frac{1}{4}$; start with 1,600 and multiply by $\frac{1}{4}$ repeatedly; 6.25, 1.5625, 0.390625.
7. 7; start with 14 and add 7 repeatedly; 42, 49, 56.
8. −2; start with −1 and multiply by −2 repeatedly; −16, 32, −64.

Find the first four terms of the sequence represented by each expression.

9. $14 - 11n$ 3, −8, −19, −30 **10.** $\frac{1}{4}n$ $\frac{1}{4}, \frac{1}{2}, \frac{3}{4}, 1$ **11.** $23 + n$ 24, 25, 26, 27

12-2 Objectives
- To represent functions with equations and tables
- To use function notation

A **function** is a relationship that assigns exactly one output value to each input value. In function notation, $f(3)$ represents the output of function f when the input is 3.

Use the function rule $f(x) = 4x - 7$. Find each output.

12. $f(3)$ 5 **13.** $f(0)$ −7 **14.** $f(-5)$ −27

15. $f(-1)$ −11 **16.** $f\left(\frac{1}{2}\right)$ −5 **17.** $f(11)$ 37

12-3 and 12-4 Objectives

- To use a table to graph a function
- To use a rule to graph a function
- To write a rule from words
- To write a rule from a table or graph

A **linear function** is a function whose points lie on a line.

Graph each linear function. 18–19. See margin.

18. $y = 2.3x - 5$ **19.** $y = -4x + 7$

Do the data in each table represent a linear function? If so, write a rule for the function.

20. yes; $y = \frac{1}{2}x + 1$

x	−4	−2	0	2	4
y	−1	0	1	2	3

21. yes; $y = -3x + 10$

x	0	1	2	3	4
y	10	7	4	1	−2

12-5 and 12-6 Objectives

- To interpret and to sketch a graph of a situation
- To graph and write quadratic functions
- To graph other nonlinear functions

A graph can show complex relationships between variables in a simple, visual way. A **quadratic function** is a function in which the highest power of the variable is 2. Its graph is a U-shaped curve called a **parabola.** Other nonlinear functions also have curved graphs.

22. Baseball A baseball player gets a hit and runs to second base. The next 2 batters strike out. When the next player hits the ball into the outfield, the player on second base runs home. Sketch a graph showing the first player's distance from home plate during the inning. See margin.

Make a table and a graph for each function. Use only positive values for x in Exercise 24. 23–25. See margin.

23. $y = 2x^2 - 4$ **24.** $y = \frac{7}{x}$ **25.** $y = -x^2 + 2$

12-7 Objective

- To solve problems by writing equations

You can write nonlinear function rules to solve many real-world problems.

26. Rabbits Suppose a population of 10 rabbits doubles every year. Write a function rule that relates the rabbit population to the number of years that have passed. Use the rule to find the size of the rabbit population after 10 years. How many rabbits are there after 25 years?
$R = 10(2)^x$; 10,240 rabbits; 335,544,320 rabbits

12-8, 12-9, and 12-10 Objectives

- To write variable expressions
- To simplify polynomials
- To add and subtract polynomials
- To multiply by a monomial
- To multiply binomials

A **polynomial** is an expression like $2x^2 - 3x$. To simplify a polynomial, combine like terms. To add or subtract polynomials, use the rules for integers to combine like terms. To multiply polynomials, use the Distributive Property. To multiply **monomials,** rearrange the factors and use the properties of exponents.

Add, subtract, or multiply. 27–30. See margin.

27. $(8x^2 - 7x + 3) + (3x^2 + x - 5)$ **28.** $(-4x^2 + 7x) + (x^2 - 7x + 3)$

29. $(5x - 4) - (9x + 3)$ **30.** $(2x^2 - 4x + 8) - (x^2 - 5x + 3)$

31. $(-6x)(3x^3)$ $-18x^4$ **32.** $(-2x)(-7x)$ $14x^2$ **33.** $-10x(3x - 2)$ $-30x^2 + 20x$ **34.** $5x(x^2 - 3x)$ $5x^3 - 15x^2$

18.

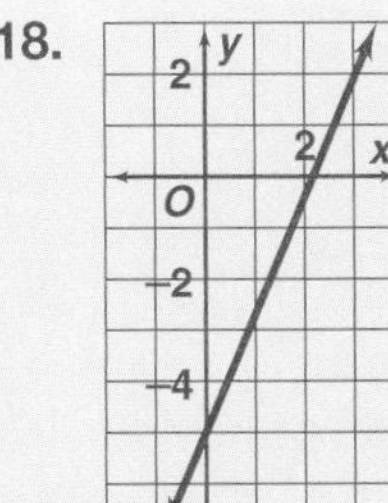

19. See back of book.

22.

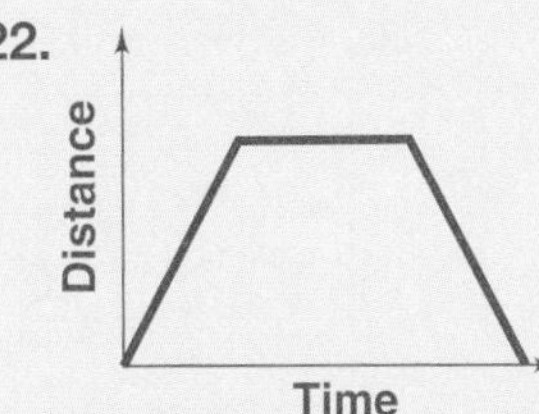

27. $11x^2 - 6x - 2$

28. $-3x^2 + 3$

29. $-4x - 7$

30. $x^2 + x + 5$

23.

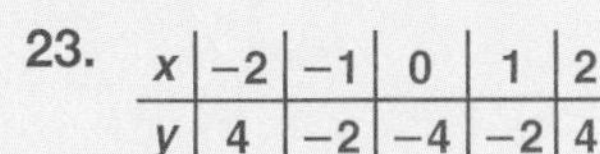

x	−2	−1	0	1	2
y	4	−2	−4	−2	4

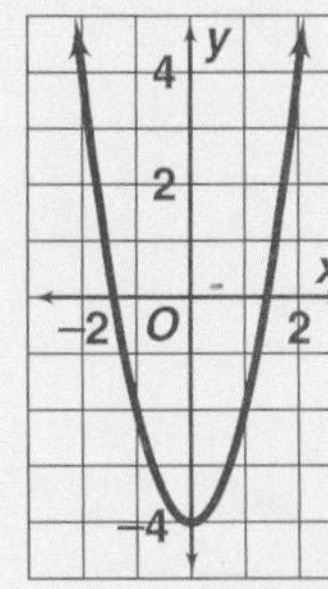

24.

x	1	7	14	21
y	7	1	$\frac{1}{2}$	$\frac{1}{3}$

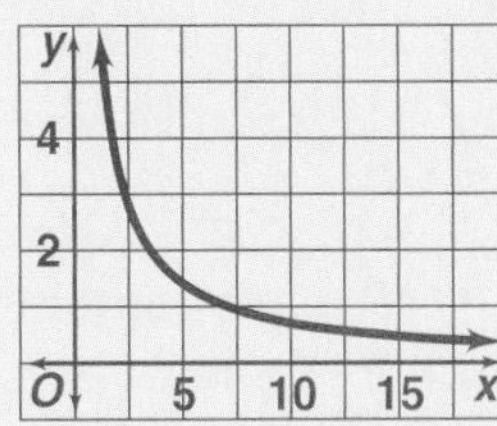

25.

x	−2	−1	0	1	2
y	−2	1	2	1	−2

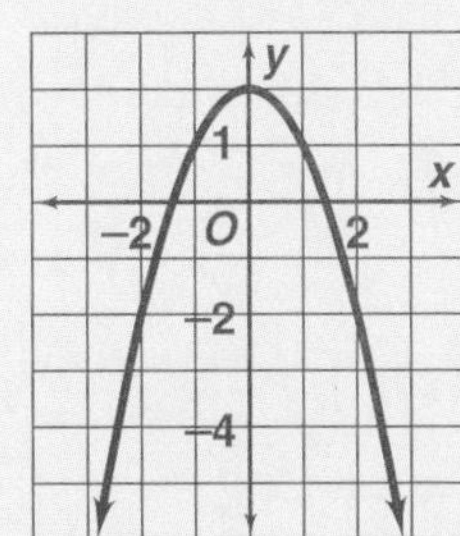

Alternative Assessment Form C

Alternative Assessment Form C

Chapter 12

SELL IT IN THE CLASSIFIEDS

Trina decided to place a classified advertisement in a newspaper to sell her bike. Trina's red mountain bike has 21 speeds and is in good condition. She bought the bike new less than two months ago. Trina has a water bottle and a handle-bar pack that she will include with the bike. She wants to sell all three items for at least $180. Trina's phone number is 555-4313.

One of Trina's friends recently placed a similar advertisement, and he received 8 calls the first day of the ad. Therefore, Trina expects to get many calls on the first day that her ad is placed.

Show all of your work on a separate sheet of paper.

1. Trina called the Daily News Classified Advertising Department to find out about advertising costs. They told Trina that the cost for one ad is a function of the number of lines in the ad and the number of days the ad appears in the paper. There is a 3-line minimum and a 3-day minimum. Explain what this means.
2. Trina then called the City Times to find out what they charge for advertising. They do not have a minimum number of lines. Below is the function that represents their advertising costs. The total cost, c, in dollars, is written as a function of the number of lines, ℓ, and the number of days, d. Describe these rates in words.

RATES AT THE *CITY TIMES*	
for $d \leq 5$,	$c = (0.90\ell)d$
for $5 < d < 10$,	$c = (0.88\ell)d$
for $d \geq 10$	$c = (0.86\ell)d$

3. Trina decided on a 3-line ad. The Daily News ad costs $7.65 if Trina runs the ad for 3 or fewer days. If she runs it for 4 or 5 days, it costs $.83 per line each day. If she runs the ad for 6 or more days, it costs $.81 per line each day.

   Write a function definition for the Daily News charges, using c for the total cost in dollars and d for the number of days.

Resources

Teaching Resources
Ch. 12 Test, Forms A & B
Ch. 12 Alternative Assessment, Form C

Reaching All Students
Spanish Ch. 12 Test, Forms A & B
Spanish Ch. 12 Alternative Assessment, Form C

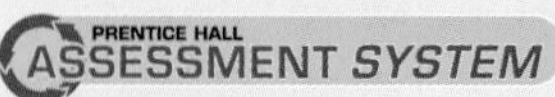

Assessment Resources
- Ch. 12 Test, Forms A & B
- Ch. 12 Alternative Assessment, Form C

Computer Test Generator CD
- Ch. 12 Instant Chapter Test™
- Make your own Ch. 12 test

www.PHSchool.com
Student Site
- Self-grading Ch. 12 test

PH SuccessNet Teacher Center
- Resources

Plus 

7.
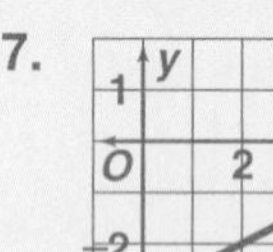
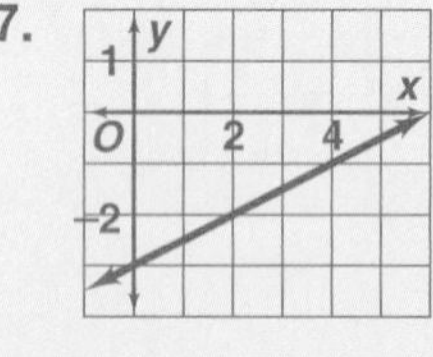

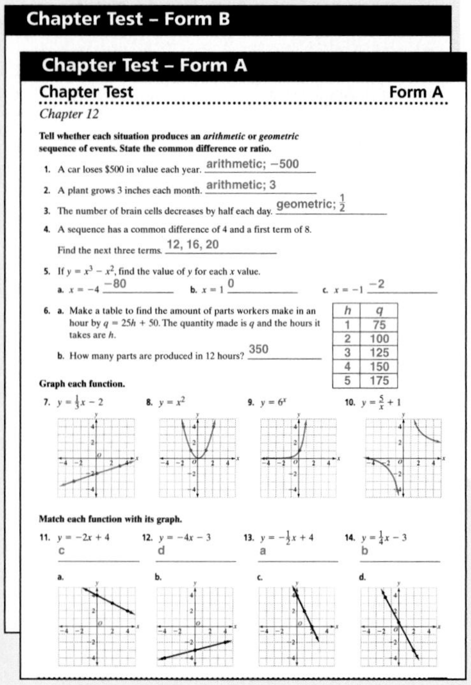

Chapter Test – Form B

Chapter Test – Form A

Chapter Test Form A
Chapter 12

Tell whether each situation produces an *arithmetic* or *geometric* sequence of events. State the common difference or ratio.

1. A car loses $500 in value each year. arithmetic; −500
2. A plant grows 3 inches each month. arithmetic; 3
3. The number of brain cells decreases by half each day. geometric; $\frac{1}{2}$
4. A sequence has a common difference of 4 and a first term of 8. Find the next three terms. 12, 16, 20
5. If $y = x^3 - x^2$, find the value of y for each x value.
   a. $x = -4$ −80 b. $x = 1$ 0 c. $x = -1$ −2
6. a. Make a table to find the amount of parts workers make in an hour by $q = 25h + 50$. The quantity made is q and the hours it takes are h.
   b. How many parts are produced in 12 hours? 350

h	q
1	75
2	100
3	125
4	150
5	175

Graph each function.

7. $y = \frac{1}{3}x - 2$ 8. $y = x^2$ 9. $y = 6^x$ 10. $y = \frac{5}{x} + 1$

Match each function with its graph.

11. $y = -2x + 4$ c 12. $y = -4x - 3$ d 13. $y = -\frac{1}{2}x + 4$ a 14. $y = \frac{1}{4}x - 3$ b

Chapter 12 Chapter Test

For Exercises 1–3, tell whether each situation produces an *arithmetic* or a *geometric sequence.* State the common difference or ratio.

1. A house gains $2,000 in value each year. arithmetic; 2,000
2. A clock loses 30 seconds each hour. arithmetic; −30
3. The number of bacteria in a pond triples each day. geometric; 3
4. A sequence has a common ratio of $\frac{4}{5}$ and a first term of 125. Find the next three terms. 100, 80, 64
5. If $y = -x^2 - 3x$, find the value of y for each x value.
   a. $x = -6$ −18 **b.** $x = 3$ −18 **c.** $x = 0$ 0
6. **a.** Make a table to display the population of a town described by $p = 400t + 5{,}000$. The population is p and the time in years is t.
   b. Find the population after 10 years.
   6a–b. See back of book.

Graph each function. For Exercise 10, use only positive integers as input values. 7–10. See margin.

7. $y = \frac{1}{2}x - 3$
8. $z = t^2$
9. $w = 2^h$
10. $y = \frac{12}{m} + 2$

Match each function with its graph.

11. $y = -x - 1$ IV
12. $y = x^2 + 1$ III
13. $y = x - 1$ II
14. $y = \frac{1}{2}x$ I

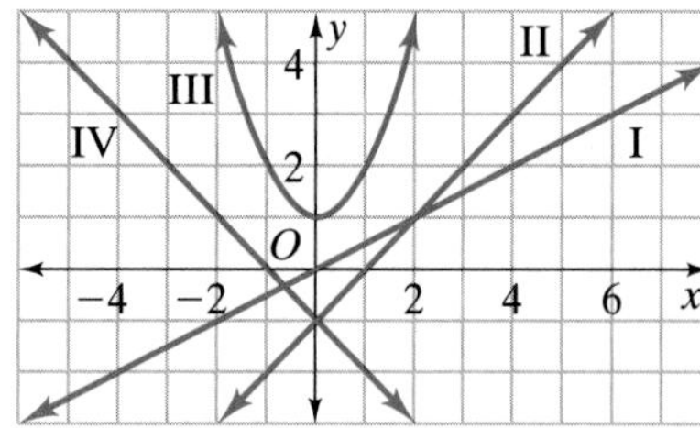

15. **a.** A nickel weighs about 5 grams. Write a function rule for the weight of n nickels. $f(n) = 5n$
    b. How much would $1.00 in nickels weigh? about 100 grams

16. **Writing in Math** Describe a situation that each of the following graphs could represent.

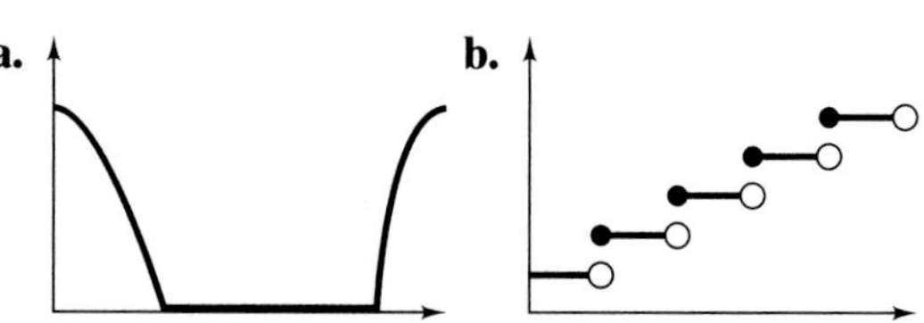

16a–b. Check students' work.

17. Write a rule for the quadratic function below. $y = x^2 + 1$

x	−2	−1	0	1	2
y	5	2	1	2	5

18. **Science** *E. coli* bacteria double their population in 20 minutes. Suppose you start with one *E. coli* cell. Write a function rule to find the number of cells after 2 hours. See margin.
19. Write and simplify the polynomial represented by the model below.
    $2x^2 - x^2 - 2x + 4 - 1 = x^2 - 2x + 3$

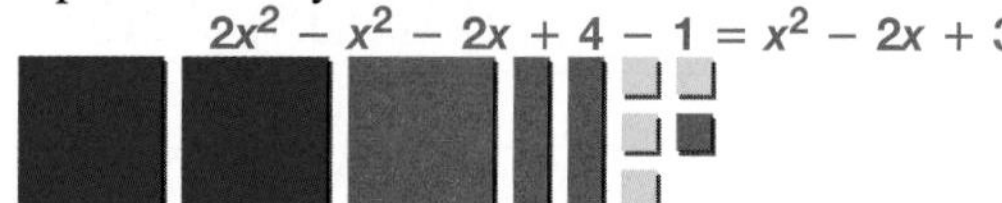

For Exercises 20–26, use tiles or properties to simplify each polynomial. 20–24. See margin.

20. $(5x^2 + 4x - 2) + (3x^2 - 3x - 5)$
21. $(7x^2 - x + 2) - (x^2 + 4x - 4)$
22. $(x^2 - 3x + 5) + (-x^2 + 4x + 4)$
23. $(-9x)(2x)$
24. $x(3x + 5)$
25. $x^2(x + 17)$ $x^3 + 17x^2$
26. $2x(x^2 - 6x)$ $2x^3 - 12x^2$
27. **a.** Find the perimeter of the figure below. $6x - 6$

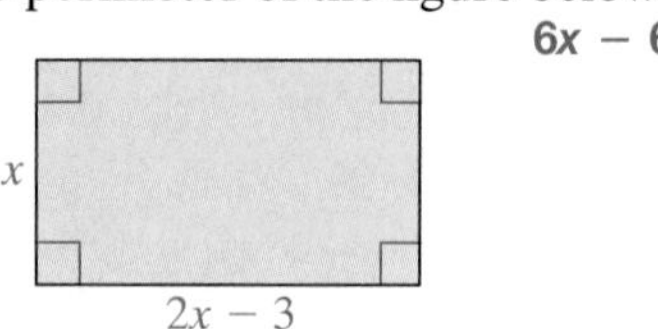

    b. Find the area of the figure. $2x^2 - 3x$

8.
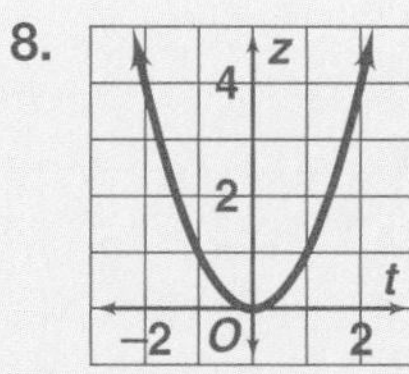

9.
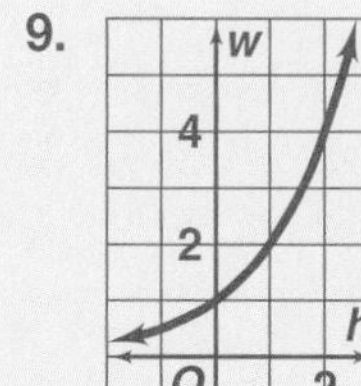

10.
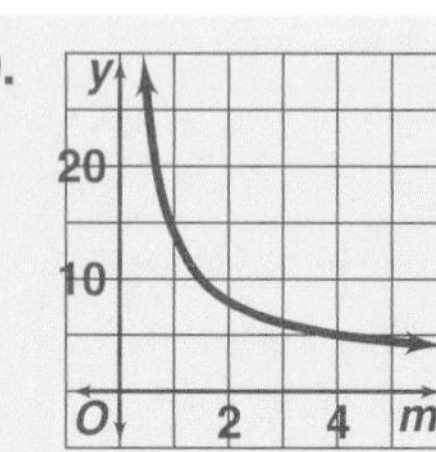

18. $y = 2^x$; 64 cells
20. $8x^2 + x - 7$
21. $6x^2 - 5x + 6$
22. $x + 9$
23–24. See back of book.

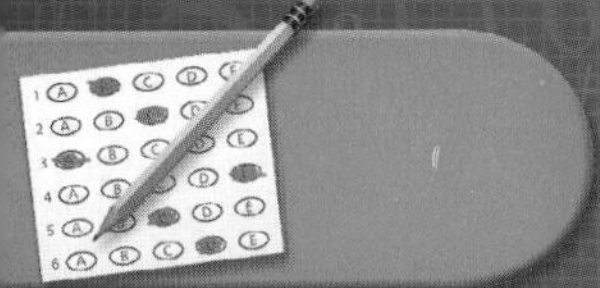

Test Prep

CUMULATIVE REVIEW

CHAPTERS 1–12

Take It to the NET
Online end-of-course test at **www.PHSchool.com**
Web Code: aca-1254

Multiple Choice

For Exercises 1–22, choose the correct letter.

1. You have a set of data that has five items. The median is 14, the mean is 14.8, the mode is 14, and the range is 4. Which could be the correct data set? C
   A. 14, 14, 14, 16, 18 B. 12, 14, 14, 15, 20
   C. 13, 14, 14, 16, 17 D. 12, 13, 14, 16, 16

2. Which proportion could NOT be represented by the model at the right? H 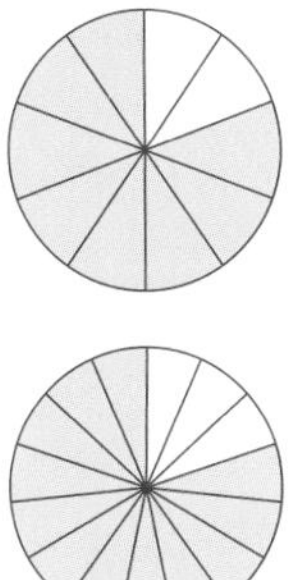
   F. $\frac{12}{15} = \frac{8}{10}$
   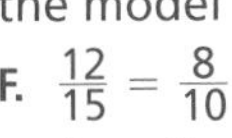
   G. $\frac{2}{8} = \frac{3}{12}$
   H. $\frac{3}{10} = \frac{2}{15}$
   I. $\frac{4}{5} = \frac{8}{10}$

3. Which number could NOT be a value of y if $y = 2x^2 - 3$? D
   A. 15 B. 5 C. −3 D. −5

4. The graph below represents which inequality? F

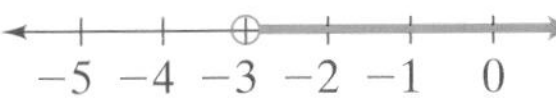

   F. $-\frac{x}{3} < 1$ G. $6z > 18$
   H. $2 + y \leq -1$ I. $-2w \geq -6$

5. Tia has art class every 6th day of school (Monday through Friday). How often does she have art class on Monday? C
   A. every week B. every 5th week
   C. every 6th week D. every 7th week

6. Tate bought 500 grams of hamburger. How many kilograms is this? G
   F. 0.05 kg G. 0.5 kg H. 5 kg I. 50 kg

7. Which of the following triangles is NOT a right triangle? D
   A. 3 cm, 4 cm, 5 cm B. 5.8 ft, 4.0 ft, 4.2 ft
   C. 3.5 m, 12.5 m, 12 m D. 2 yd, 14 yd, 20 yd

8. Which set of numbers could be the side lengths of a right triangle? G
   F. 15, 23, 9 G. 9, $\sqrt{19}$, 10
   H. 8, 14, 22 I. 28, 6, 30

9. Which algebraic expression is NOT equivalent to $2(x - 3)$? D
   A. $2(x) - 2(3)$ B. $2(-3) + 2x$
   C. $(x - 3) + (x - 3)$ D. $2x - 3$

10. Which set of ordered pairs describes the image of the vertices of $\triangle ABC$ after a translation 2 units left and 3 units down? F

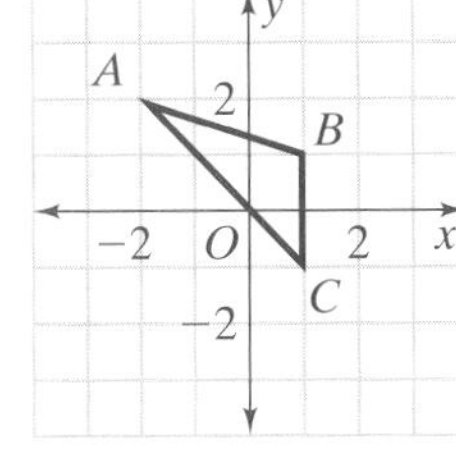

   F. $A'(-4, -1)$, $B'(-1, -2)$, $C'(-1, -4)$
   G. $A'(0, -1)$, $B'(3, -2)$, $C'(3, -4)$
   H. $A'(0, 5)$, $B'(3, 4)$, $C'(3, 2)$
   I. $A'(-4, 5)$, $B'(-1, 4)$, $C'(-1, 2)$

11. How many integers have an absolute value less than 3? C
   A. 3 B. 4 C. 5 D. 6

12. A cubit was a measure used in ancient times. A yard has about 2 cubits. Which of these measurements is about equal to a cubit? H
   F. 1 ft G. 12 in. H. 18 in. I. 2 ft

13. Estimate the shaded area. B
   A. 0.7 units^2
   B. 7 units^2
   C. 17 units^2
   D. 27 units^2

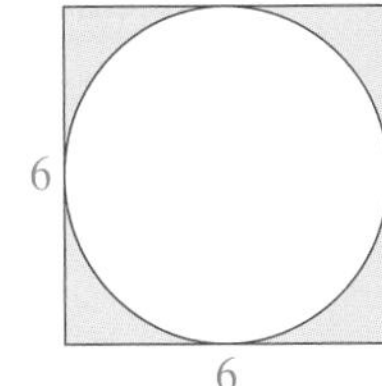

14. There are about 10,550 radio stations in the United States. How is this number written in scientific notation? H
   F. 1.055×10^3 G. 10.55×10^3
   H. 1.055×10^4 I. 10.55×10^4

Item	1	2	3	4	5	6	7	8	9	10	11	12	13	14
Lesson	1-6	5-4	12-6	2-7	8-4	5-2	4-9	4-9	2-3	3-8	1-3	5-2	8-8	7-1

Test Prep

Resources

Teaching Resources
Cumulative Review
Quarter 4 Test, Forms A & B
End-of-Course Test

Reaching All Students
Spanish Cumulative Review
Spanish Quarter 4 Test
Spanish End-of-Course Test

PRENTICE HALL ASSESSMENT SYSTEM

Test Preparation
- Ch. 12 standardized test prep

Assessment Resources
- Cumulative Review
- Quarter 4 Test, Forms A & B
- End-of-Course Test

Computer Test Generator CD
- Standardized test prep

www.PHSchool.com
- Standardized test prep
- Resources

Plus iTEXT

Cumulative Review

Cumulative Review
Chapters 1–12

Multiple Choice. Choose the letter of the best answer.

1. Which bar graph correctly displays this data?

week	hours worked
1	20
2	35
3	40
4	30

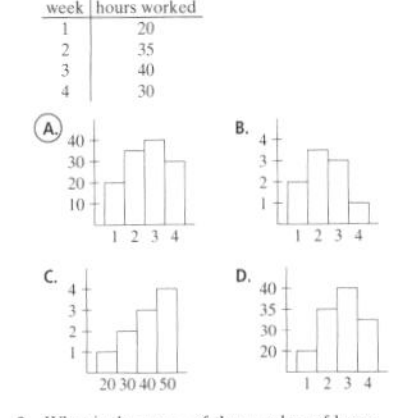

2. What is the range of the number of hours worked in Exercise 1?
   F. 4 G. 10
   (H.) 20 I. 40

Use this data to answer Exercises 3–5.

The data 83, 89, 90, 75, 91, and 70 is a set of test scores for one student.

3. What is the mean of the test scores?
   (A.) 83 B. 86
   C. 90 D. 99.6

4. Which measure is the smallest for the above set of test scores?
   F. median G. mean
   (H.) range I. mode

5. What is the median of the test scores?
   A. 83 (B.) 86
   C. 90 D. 99.6

6. Which measure of central tendency would help describe the results of a survey on your classmates' favorite school subjects?
   (F.) mode G. median
   H. range I. mean

7. In this stem-and-leaf plot, what number has the stem 2 and leaf 9?

0	0 1
1	0 6 8
2	4 5 9 9
3	2

0 | 1 means 0.1

   A. 299 B. 92
   C. 29 (D.) 2.9

8. Simplify $3x - 4(2 - x)$.
   F. $7x$ G. $4x - 8$
   H. $2x - 4$ (I.) $7x - 8$

9. Which equation is equivalent to $\frac{y}{9} + 9 = -6$?
   A. $\frac{y}{9} = -5$
   B. $y + 27 = -18$
   C. $y = 45$
   (D.) $\frac{y}{9} = -15$

10. David is buying a truck that costs \$2,500. He makes a down payment of \$1,000 and will pay the balance in 10 equal payments. Which equation could you use to find the amount of each payment?
   (F.) $10x + 1{,}000 = 2{,}500$
   G. $2{,}500 - 1{,}000 = x$
   H. $10x = 2{,}500$
   I. $x + 1{,}000 = 2{,}500$

15. In how many different orders can 5 out of 8 people be seated in a row of 5 chairs? B
A. 40,320 **B.** 6,720 **C.** 120 **D.** 56

16. In a circle graph, what is the measure of the central angle of a sector that represents 24% of the whole? I
F. 2.4° **G.** 8.64° **H.** 24° **I.** 86.4°

17. Which of the following CANNOT be found from looking at a box-and-whisker plot? C
A. range **B.** median
C. mode **D.** upper quartile

18. In the figure below, the triangles are similar. Find the unknown length h. G

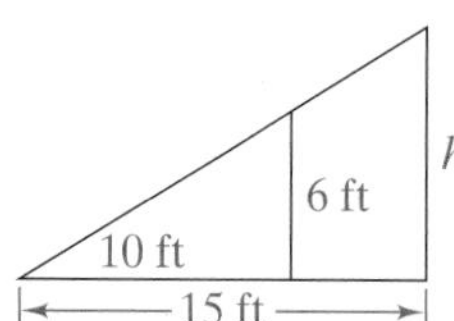

F. 30 ft **G.** 9 ft **H.** 6 ft **I.** 3 ft

19. Jim had $500 in his bank account on Monday. He wrote checks for $200 and $400 on Tuesday and Wednesday. Which of these amounts represents the balance in his account on Thursday? A
A. −$100 **B.** $100
C. $300 **D.** $1,100

20. Which of the following is NOT an example of a prism? I
F. a shoe box **G.** a domino
H. a file cabinet **I.** a soup can

21. Describe the relationship in the scatter plot at the right. B
A. no trend
B. positive trend
C. negative trend
D. positive and negative trend

22. Of the first 50 customers to visit Bagels-R-Us today, 11 order a bagel. If Bagels-R-Us normally has about 880 customers per day, how many bagels can they sell today? F
F. about 16 dozen **G.** about 110
H. about 8 dozen **I.** about 80

Gridded Response

Use the table below for Exercises 23–25.

How Long Students Studied Last Night

Number of Hours	Less than 1	1	2	3	More than 3
Number of Students	15	12	8	3	5

23. How many students were surveyed? 43

24. How many students studied 1 hour or less? 27

25. What percent of the students surveyed studied more than 2 hours? Round to the nearest hundredth of a percent. 18.60

26. How many dollars can you save on your grocery bill if you have 3 coupons, each for $1.00 off, and 2 coupons, each for $2.00 off? 7

27. Jake received these grades on his math tests: 83, 86, 95, 95, 90, 82, 85, 82, 87, 82. What is his median test score? 85.5

28. What is the value of $-3 + x - y$ if $x = -4$ and $y = -8$? 1

29. A triangle with three sides of equal length has a perimeter of $5\frac{1}{4}$ cm. What is the length of one side? 1.75

30. Find the area of the figure below in mm^2. 41

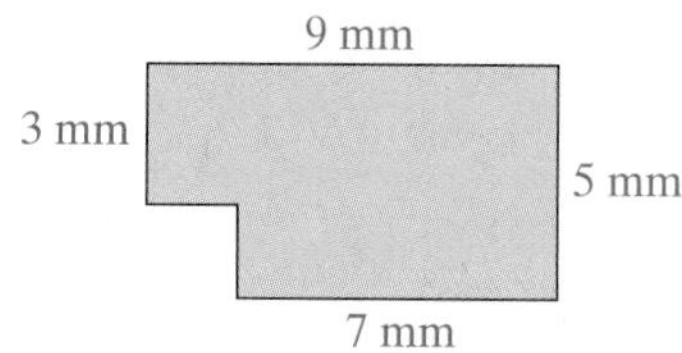

31. A diving board is 4 ft above a pool that is 15 ft deep. The total length of a person's dive is 10 ft. How many feet below the surface of the water did the person dive? 6

32. A copy center charges $.08 per copy. How much would it cost in dollars to make a copy of a one-page song for 250 students in a school? 20

33. A rectangular pyramid has a base area of 126 cm^2 and a height of 23 cm. Find the volume of the pyramid in cm^3. 966

Item	15	16	17	18	19	20	21	22
Lesson	11-2	10-6	10-4	5-5	1-4	9-1	10-5	5-4

Item	23	24	25	26	27	28	29	30	31	32	33
Lesson	10-1	10-1	6-4	1-4	1-6	1-1	8-5	8-8	9-8	4-5	9-7

Short Response 34–42. See margin.

34. Find the lateral area of the square pyramid below. Then find the surface area.

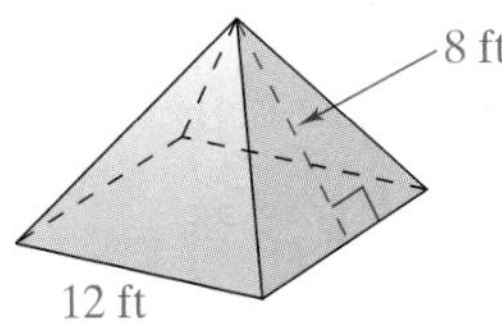

35. Find the percent of markup on a T-shirt that has a store cost of \$4.87 and a selling price of \$15.95. Show your work.

36. a. Graph the function $y = -3x - 1$.
b. What value of x will give $y = 11$?

37. Find the length of a rectangular garden whose perimeter is 32 ft and whose width is 7 ft. Show your work.

38. According to the graph shown, when did the stock fund earn the most? Explain.

Earnings of Two Investments

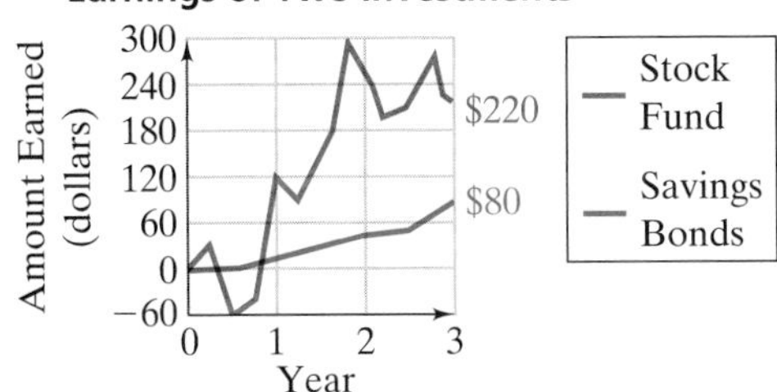

39. Which has a greater volume: a cone with radius 2 cm and height 6 cm, or a cone with height 2 cm and radius 6 cm? Explain.

40. a. What is the next term in the sequence 4, 12, 36, 108, . . . ?
b. What is the common ratio?

41. Find the circumference and the area of the circle. Round to the nearest tenth.

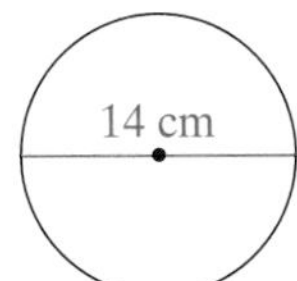

42. Karen swam for a half hour on Monday. She increased her workout by the same number of minutes each day. On Friday, she swam for one hour. Write and solve an equation to find the number of minutes by which Karen increased her daily workout.

Extended Response 43–47. See margin.

43. The total cost to use an in-flight phone on one airline includes a \$3.99 connection fee plus \$3.99 per minute.
a. Write a function rule for the cost of a call using an in-flight phone.
b. Find the cost of a 10-minute in-flight call. Explain your work.
c. Graph the function.

44. a. Draw a net for a cylinder that has a diameter of 4 yd and a height of 7 yd. Label the diameter and height.
b. Find the surface area of the cylinder to the nearest yd^2. Show your work.

45. Boise wants to buy a computer scanner for \$349. He has \$34 and plans to save \$15 each week.
a. Write an equation to show how many weeks Boise must save before he can buy the scanner. Define the variables you use.
b. How long will Boise need to save money to buy the scanner? Justify your reasoning.

46. The diagram below is an architect's plan for a new room in a community center. The architect uses a scale of 1 in. = 20 ft.

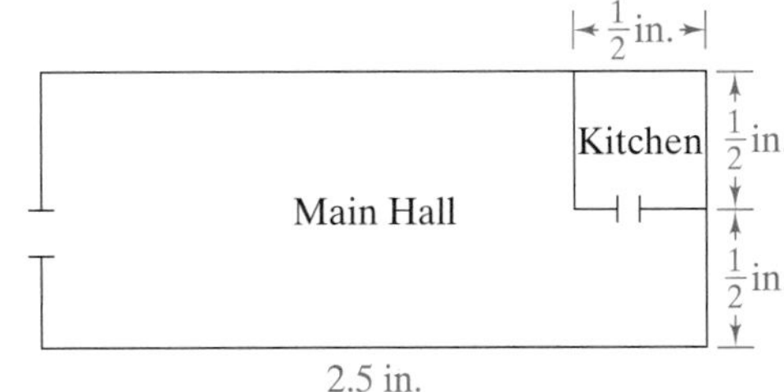

a. How many feet long will the 2.5 in. side of the drawing be in the real building? Justify your reasoning.
b. Find the area of the actual kitchen floor. Show your work.

47. A store pays \$3.50 for a water bottle. The store sells each water bottle for \$6.00.
a. Find the percent of markup on the water bottle. Show your work.
b. How many water bottles can you buy with \$15.00? Show your work.

[1] appropriate method with one computational error OR correct answer without work shown

36. [2] a.

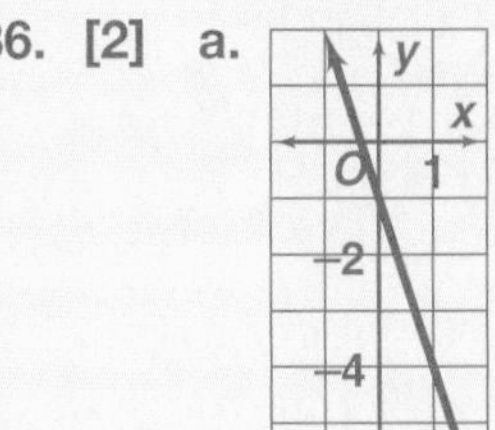

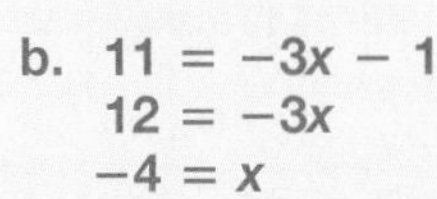

b. $11 = -3x - 1$
$12 = -3x$
$-4 = x$

[1] correct graph OR correct value of x

37. [2] $\ell + \ell + 7 + 7 = 32$
$2\ell + 14 = 32$
$2\ell = 18$
$\ell = 9$
The length is 9 ft.
[1] appropriate methods with one computational error OR correct answer without work shown

38. [2] The stock fund earned the most at about 1.8 years because that is the peak or highest point on the graph.
[1] correct answer without explanation

39. [2] The cone with height 2 cm and radius 6 cm has the greater volume, since $\frac{1}{3}\pi \cdot 6^2 \cdot 2 > \frac{1}{3}\pi \cdot 2^2 \cdot 6$.
[1] correct answer with inadequate explanation

40. [2] a. 324
b. 3
[1] correct term OR correct ratio

41–47. See back of book.

Item	34	35	36	37	38	39	40	41	42	43	44	45	46	47
Lesson	9-5	6-6	12-3	2-5	10-7	9-7	12-1	8-9	2-1	12-4	9-4	2-8	5-7	6-6

Test Prep

34. [2] 192 ft^2; 336 ft^2
[1] only one answer correct

35. [2] markup = selling price − store's cost, \$11.08 = \$15.95 − \$4.87, percent of markup = markup ÷ store's cost, 2.275 ≈ 11.08 ÷ 4.87, the percent of markup is about 227.5%.

Product Pricing

Students will use data from these two pages to answer the questions posed here in Put It All Together.

Activating Prior Knowledge
How do your students listen to music? How do they watch their favorite TV shows and movies? Initiate a class discussion about the distinctions between CDs and cassette tapes, and between DVDs and video tape. Have students compare quality of sound and/or picture, prices, options, product availability, and so on.

Teaching Notes

Have a volunteer read the opening paragraph about interpreting functions to choose the right price to charge for CD players. Invite students to act as consumer advocates and rate today's popular CD players. Which one do students rate as the best? Which is their best buy?

Science Connection
Have interested students find out about the following: What is next on the horizon, technologically speaking, in the world of audio and video? What companies and organizations are leaders in this field? What magazines focus on this kind of data?

Language Art Connection
Invite students to write a compare/contrast essay to summarize their views on (1) whether CDs are better than audio tapes or vinyl records, or (2) whether DVDs are an improvement upon video tapes.

Real-World Snapshots

Product Pricing

Applying Polynomials Suppose you make and sell portable CD/DVD players. You want the price to be high enough for you to make a profit, yet low enough that people will want to buy. Interpreting functions can come in handy when choosing the right price.

Portable Drive
In a CD player, a drive motor spins the disc. A laser system reads the bumps on the CD, and a tracking mechanism moves the laser's beam along the spiral track.

TV Bank
People use banks of TVs to monitor more than one TV station at a time or to see one enlarged image.

694

Put It All Together

1. The equation $n = -2.5p^2 + 39{,}400$ models the relationship between the price, p, of each CD/DVD player and the number sold, n. Copy and extend the table to a price of \$100. Complete the table.
2. Add a column to your table for income from sales, $s = p \times n$, for each price in the table. Record the income for each price.
3. Make a scatter plot comparing the number sold to income.
4. **Writing in Math** Decide on the best price to charge for your CD/DVD player. Find the number you can expect to sell and the income at that price. Explain your choice.
5. **a.** The prices your competitors charge affect your sales. Make adjustments to the price you chose in Exercise 4 based on the prices you think two competitors will charge. Write down your final price.
   b. Exchange prices with two classmates. Calculate the mean of the three prices.
   c. Use your answer to part (b) and the function from Exercise 1. Find the total number of CD/DVD players your three companies will sell.
   d. Assume that the company with the lowest price makes 40% of the sales from part (c), the company with the highest price makes 25% of the sales, and the third company makes 35% of the sales. Calculate the units sold and the total sales for each company. Which company is the most successful? Explain.

Price p	Number Sold n	Sales Income s
\$30	37,150	\$1,114,500
\$35	■	■
\$40	■	■

Take It to the NET For more information about product pricing, go to **www.PHSchool.com**.
Web Code: ace-1253

3. Check students' work.

4. Answers may vary. Sample: The best price is about \$72.50, which yields an income of about \$1,900,400. Prices that are higher or lower than that yield a lower income.

5. Check students' work.

Put It All Together

Have students work in pairs to complete the table, make the scatterplot, and complete the activity.

You may wish to work through the first row in the table with the class. Point out to students that they should continue the first column by writing multiples of \$5. Encourage pairs to work with calculators.

Error Prevention!

Remind students of the order of operations: PEMDAS. Emphasize, accordingly, that in the equation for modeling the relationship between the price of the CD/DVD player and the number sold, students should square the price, *p, before* multiplying it by −2.5.

Exercise 5 Have an extended class discussion about this activity. Elicit that students who choose a price much higher than the optimum will probably find that they have the lowest sales. Discuss that the company with the lowest prices will likely get the most sales but may be hurt if their price is too low compared with the next lowest price.

1–2.

Price (p)	Number of Sales (n)	Sales in Dollars (s)
30	37,150	1,114,500
35	36,338	1,271,813
40	35,400	1,416,000
45	34,338	1,545,188
50	33,150	1,657,500
55	31,838	1,751,063
60	30,400	1,824,000
65	28,838	1,874,438
70	27,150	1,900,500
75	25,338	1,900,313
80	23,400	1,872,000
85	21,338	1,813,688
90	19,150	1,723,500
95	16,838	1,599,563
100	14,400	1,440,000

Weather or Not

Students apply their knowledge of algebraic expression to report on weather temperature data.

Resources

Teaching Resources
Chapter 1 Project Support with Project Manager, Student Activities, Teacher Notes

Teaching Notes

Activating Prior Knowledge
Have students develop a few benchmarks for identifying common Celsius temperatures. Ask:

- *What formula can you use to express Fahrenheit temperatures in degrees Celsius?* Sample: $C = (F - 32) \div 1.8$

Science Connection
Our ability to forecast weather is constantly improving. Ask students to predict the advantages of knowing with confidence what the weather will be weeks rather than hours in advance.

Balancing Act

Students apply their knowledge of equations to explore ways to make a mobile.

Resources

Teaching Resources
Chapter 2 Project Support with Project Manager, Student Activities, Teacher Notes

Teaching Notes

Activating Prior Knowledge
Have students share any experiences they have had constructing mobiles. Ask:

- *What did you do to keep your sculpture in motion?* Answers will vary.

English Learners
Help students understand the meanings of the terms *mobile*, *kinetic*, and *in balance*.

Chapter Projects

Chapter 1 *Integers and Algebraic Expressions*

Would you go swimming in 32° water? Is −2° a good temperature setting for a home freezer? The answer to both questions is "That depends!"

Are you using the Celsius or Fahrenheit scale? Water at 32°C feels like a bath! As for a freezer, −2°C is barely below freezing, while −2°F is a deep freeze! People living in North America use both the Fahrenheit and the Celsius scales, so it pays to know the difference.

Prepare a Report For the chapter project, you will examine weather data for a state or region of your choice. Your final project will be a report on temperature data, using both scales.

Take It to the NET Go to **www.PHSchool.com** for information to help you complete your project.
Web Code: acd-0161

Chapter 2 *Equations and Inequalities*

Mobiles are a popular form of art that you may see anywhere: in people's homes, in large office buildings, and in parks. The objects on a mobile float gently on currents of air. American sculptor Alexander Calder (1898–1976) first popularized mobiles. Calder is considered the founder of kinetic art, or art that is in motion.

Make a Mobile For the chapter project, you will explore techniques for constructing a mobile and use equations to model the relationships involved in the mobile. Your final project will be a finished mobile, along with a written summary telling what you have learned.

Take It to the NET Go to **www.PHSchool.com** for information to help you complete your project.
Web Code: acd-0261

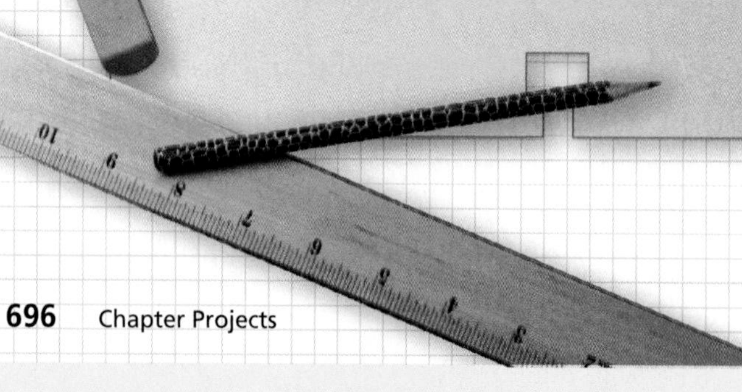

Chapter 3 Graphing in the Coordinate Plane

Have you ever been to a carnival or fair? "Hit the bulls-eye and win a prize!" Is it skill? Or is it luck?

Design a Game Suppose your class is putting on a fair to raise money for a class trip. For the chapter project, you will invent a game in which a ball rolls down a ramp and comes to rest in a target area of your own design. Does a bulls-eye score 10, or maybe 100? Can the players vary the slope of the ramp? You decide, since you make up the rules! Your final project will be the game, along with written rules to play by.

Take It to the NET Go to **www.PHSchool.com** for information to help you complete your project.
Web Code: acd-0361

Chapter 4 Real Numbers

A swirling dragon marks the start of the Chinese New Year. The Chinese calendar is one of several calendars used throughout the world. Each calendar is a unique solution to the problem of how to keep track of time. Even though the calendars are all different, they all work quite well.

Invent a New Calendar For the chapter project, you will invent a new calendar, defining weeks and months as you wish. Will your calendar have 10 months per year? Might it have 5-day weeks? The decisions are up to you. Your final project will be a new calendar and a description of the advantages of your new system.

Take It to the NET Go to **www.PHSchool.com** for information to help you complete your project.
Web Code: acd-0461

Step Right Up!

Students apply their knowledge of slope to design a game in which a ball rolls down a ramp.

Resources

Teaching Resources
Chapter 3 Project Support with Project Manager, Student Activities, Teacher Notes

Teaching Notes

Activating Prior Knowledge
Ask students to suggest ways to start this project. Ask:

- *What features of your game can you vary as you try to improve the design so that the game will work as you wish it to?* **Sample: the slope and length of the ramp, the size and number of targets, the size of the ball, and so on**

A New New Year

Students apply their knowledge of real numbers to invent a new calendar.

Resources

Teaching Resources
Chapter 4 Project Support with Project Manager, Student Activities, Teacher Notes

Teaching Notes

Activating Prior Knowledge
Explain to students that the calendar we use, the Gregorian calendar, dates from 1582. It was an improvement over the Julian calendar that it replaced because it took leap years into account. Ask:

- *What are the origins of the names of our days and months?* **They come from celestial bodies and from mythological gods and goddesses.**

Diversity
The origin of the *day* is a natural consequence of the rising and setting of the sun. However, Native Americans determine a day as the time from one dawn to the next.

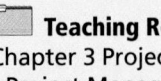

Larger than Life

Students apply their knowledge of proportions to make a scale model.

Resources

Teaching Resources
Chapter 5 Project Support with Project Manager, Student Activities, Teacher Notes

Teaching Notes

Activating Prior Knowledge
Discuss with students what factors they would consider and what tools they would use if they were to make a scale model of the classroom. Ask:

- *How could you use graph paper to help you make a scale model?* **Sample: Draw a floor plan on it using a scale in which an increment on the grid (cm, $\frac{1}{4}$-in., and so on) equals an actual distance.**

Careers
Architects draw and revise floor plans (carefully drawn to scale), or make accurate scale models.

Invest in a Winner

Students apply their knowledge of percents to plan investments.

Resources

Teaching Resources
Chapter 6 Project Support with Project Manager, Student Activities, Teacher Notes

Teaching Notes

Activating Prior Knowledge
Elicit from students what they know about different kinds of investments. Discuss that most investing involves risk. Ask:

- *Why would someone invest in a higher risk investment?* **Sample: Higher risk investments generally offer higher returns.**

English Learners
Pair English language learners with native speakers to help the former with the terms associated with investments.

Chapter 5 *Applications of Proportions*

Mount Rushmore is an example of a scale model that is larger than the objects on which it is based—much larger! Other types of scale models, such as toy trains, dollhouses, and other toys, are smaller than the objects on which they are based.

Build a Scale Model For the chapter project, you will build your own scale model. First, you will choose an object to model. Use your imagination! Your model can be larger or smaller than the actual object—you choose the scale. Then you will select building materials and assemble the model. Your final project will be to present the model to your class, explaining the scale and how you chose the item to model.

Take It to the NET Go to **www.PHSchool.com** for information to help you complete your project.
Web Code: acd-0561

Chapter 6 *Applications of Percent*

You've won! You entered a quiz contest thinking you didn't have a chance, and now you're $5,000 richer! You are looking for a way to double your money in five years. Is that possible?

Explore Ways to Invest Money For the chapter project, you will explore different investments, looking for the best one for your money. Your final project will be to prepare an oral and visual presentation describing your investment choice.

Take It to the NET Go to **www.PHSchool.com** for information to help you complete your project.
Web Code: acd-0661

One Small STEP

Chapter 7 Exponents and Powers

"That's one small step for man; one giant leap for mankind." In June of 1969, Neil Armstrong was the first man to touch the moon's surface. Since then, space travel has exploded, with new missions being launched almost monthly.

Can you even imagine what the space program will be like in 30 more years? How about in 100 years? Take a small step into the future. Pretend you are a travel agent—one who specializes in space travel!

Create a Brochure For the chapter project, you will collect information about two planets, including travel between them, and calculate the approximate distance from Earth to each of them. Your final project will be to design a space-travel brochure that includes interesting and enticing information about travel between the two planets.

Take It to the NET Go to **www.PHSchool.com** for information to help you complete your project.
Web Code: acd-0761

Great Escape

Chapter 8 Geometry

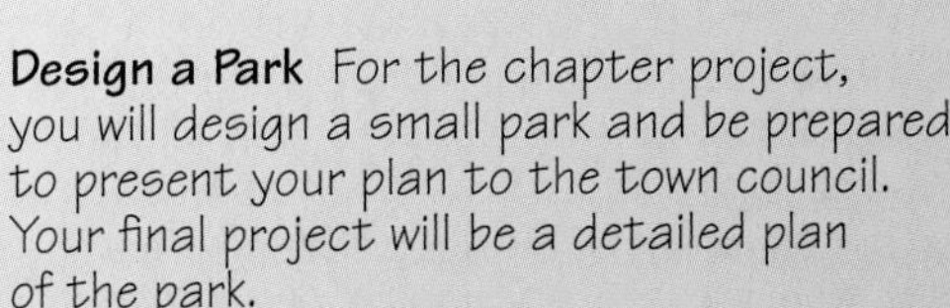

As the summer sun goes down on another hot day, you just have to get outside. Where do you go? To the park! For generations, people in towns and cities have used parks as a place to escape. When properly planned, a park can be the perfect place to relax, meet friends, skate, and be surrounded by natural beauty.

Design a Park For the chapter project, you will design a small park and be prepared to present your plan to the town council. Your final project will be a detailed plan of the park.

Take It to the NET Go to **www.PHSchool.com** for information to help you complete your project.
Web Code: acd-0861

One Small Step . . .

Students apply their knowledge of scientific notation to design a travel brochure.

Resources

Teaching Resources
Chapter 7 Project Support with Project Manager, Student Activities, Teacher Notes

Teaching Notes

Activating Prior Knowledge
Initiate a discussion of potential space travel destinations. Ask:

- *Where can you find the information you need to design your space travel brochure?* **Sample: almanacs, NASA, Internet, science texts, or magazines**

Science Connection
Some planets or moons are likely to be somewhat more hospitable than others for human visits. Have students do research to come up with a preferred list of human-friendly galactic destinations.

Great Escape

Students apply their knowledge of geometry to design a park.

Resources

Teaching Resources
Chapter 8 Project Support with Project Manager, Student Activities, Teacher Notes

Teaching Notes

Activating Prior Knowledge
Have students brainstorm a list of features and facilities they would want a park to have. Ask:

- *What would be a reasonable scale to use for a 8″ by 11″ drawing of a park the same size as your school's grounds?* **Sample: 1 in. = 40 ft**

Careers
Landscape architects are trained to design and oversee the construction of parks and other public spaces.

A Better Way

Students apply their knowledge of geometry and measurement to design a cereal package.

Resources

Teaching Resources
Chapter 9 Project Support with Project Manager, Student Activities, Teacher Notes

Teaching Notes

Activating Prior Knowledge
Initiate a discussion of what food manufacturers consider when designing packages for their product. Ask:

- *What purposes does packaging serve other than to hold a product and display or stack it?* **Sample: to provide advertising space and space for required nutritional information and other information**

News Flash

Students apply their knowledge of using graphs to illustrate a news story.

Resources

Teaching Resources
Chapter 10 Project Support with Project Manager, Student Activities, Teacher Notes

Teaching Notes

Activating Prior Knowledge
Discuss what kinds of news stories benefit by having a graph accompany them. Ask:

- *What kind of graph might you use to accompany a story about budget problems a city faces? Explain.* **Sample: circle graph, which shows how parts relate to a whole**

English Learners
Invite students acquiring English to use a newspaper written in their native language. Pair them with native English speakers who can help them interpret a news story.

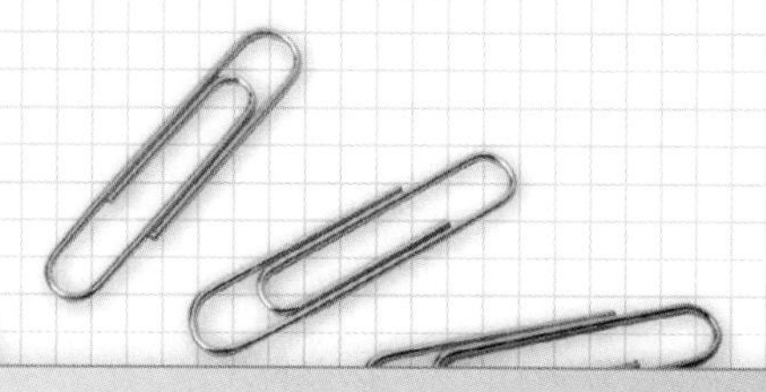

A Better Way

Chapter 9 Geometry and Measurement

Stop by the cereal section of your local supermarket. There are dozens of brands! Now check out the packaging. Most cereals are packaged in the same way: in cardboard rectangular boxes that are high and wide, but not deep.

Is this a waste of cardboard? Can you design a better package? You can . . . because now, you're in charge!

Design Packaging for Cereal For the chapter project, you will redesign the packaging of your favorite cereal. Your final project will be a new and different-shaped cardboard package that still holds the same volume as the original.

Take It to the NET Go to **www.PHSchool.com** for information to help you complete your project.
Web Code: acd-0961

News Flash

Chapter 10 Using Graphs to Analyze Data

What type of news catches your eye? Do you notice graphs and charts in news magazines and newspapers? If a picture is worth a thousand words, a graph is worth a thousand numbers! Reporters use graphs to summarize data and to tell a story clearly and simply. Do they always do it accurately?

Create a Graph for a News Article For the chapter project, you will analyze graphs and charts that appear in the news. For your final project, using a topic that you choose, you will write a news article and illustrate it with an appropriate graph.

Take It to the NET Go to **www.PHSchool.com** for information to help you complete your project.
Web Code: acd-1061

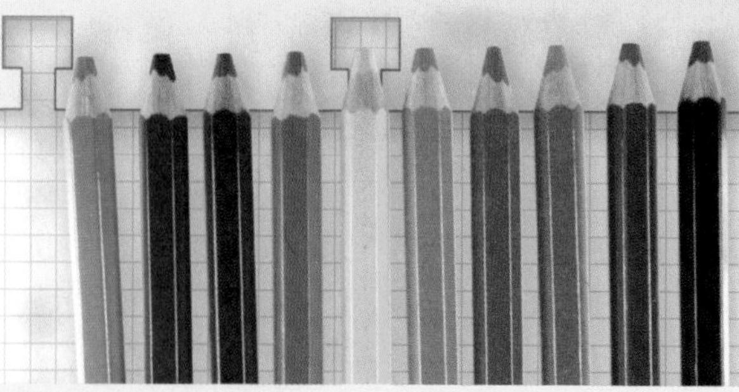

Chapter 11 Probability

There are fifteen seconds to go in a close basketball game. Should you foul intentionally? What is the probability that the player you foul will make both free throws? Statistics are everywhere in sports: field-goal percentages, batting averages, and so on. Coaches and players use these statistics to assess probabilities and make decisions.

Prepare a Stat Sheet Suppose you are a statistician for a basketball team. Pick any team—school, professional, even fictional. For the chapter project, you will gather data on five key players from the team. For your final project, you will present a statistical report that summarizes these basketball players' season last year.

Take It to the NET Go to **www.PHSchool.com** for information to help you complete your project.
Web Code: acd-1161

Chapter 12 Algebraic Relationships

How much should a pizza cost? Many restaurants sell pizzas in a variety of sizes and types, with many different kinds of toppings. Do restaurants base their prices on what they think their customers will be willing to pay for different sizes? Or do they take a mathematical approach and figure their costs using area formulas?

Set Prices for a Product For the chapter project, you will investigate prices for a product that is available in many sizes. You will look for patterns in the prices and describe the patterns mathematically. Then you will use this analysis to decide on prices for new products. Your final project will be a written proposal for setting pizza prices.

Take It to the NET Go to **www.PHSchool.com** for information to help you complete your project.
Web Code: acd-1261

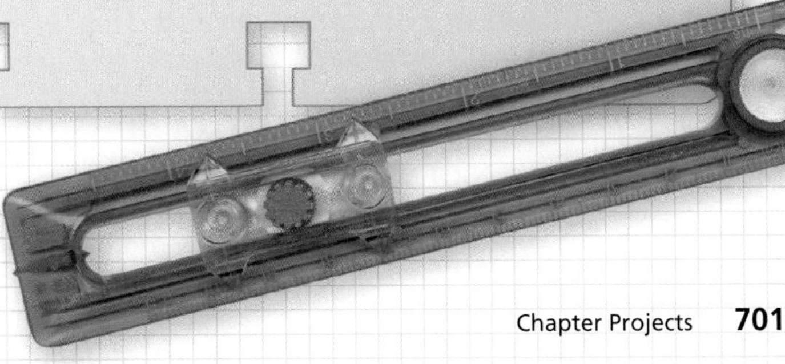

Start With the Stats

Students apply their knowledge of probability to prepare a statistical report for a coach.

Resources

Teaching Resources
Chapter 11 Project Support with Project Manager, Student Activities, Teacher Notes

Teaching Notes

Activating Prior Knowledge
Have students discuss key basketball statistics for the level of the sport they choose. Ask:

- *Which statistical information would the coach most want to know?* **Accept any answers students can justify.**

Physical Education Connection
Discuss that, with the advent of the computer, statistics have played an increasingly important role in collegiate and professional sports.

How Much Dough?

Students apply their knowledge of algebraic relationships to analyze product pricing.

Resources

Teaching Resources
Chapter 12 Project Support with Project Manager, Student Activities, Teacher Notes

Teaching Notes

Activating Prior Knowledge
Have students brainstorm a list of products they buy that are sold in different sizes. Ask:

- *What size/price patterns might you expect to find for foods that come in different sizes?* **Sample: unit prices based on volume or weight**

Consumer Connection
Initiate a class discussion about factors they, as shoppers, consider when making purchases.

Chapter 1

Extra Practice

Lesson 1-1 **Evaluate each expression for $n = 2, m = 3$, and $t = 5$.**

1. $3t - 4n$ 7
2. $13 - (m + n)$ 8
3. $\frac{m + t}{n}$ 4
4. $7 + mt$ 22

Lesson 1-2 **Use the problem-solving plan to solve this problem.**

5. You have some sports cards, and you give 8 cards to Alice. Alice then gives 4 of her cards to Bill. Finally, Bill gives 10 of his cards to you. All of you now have 14 cards. Find how many cards each of you had at the beginning of the trades. Me: 12; Alice: 10; Bill: 20

Lesson 1-3 **Compare. Write <, >, or =.**

6. -7 ■ 7 <
7. 32 ■ $|-32|$ =
8. $|-9|$ ■ -3 >
9. $|-8|$ ■ $|-6|$ >

Lessons 1-4 and 1-5 **Simplify each expression.**

10. $-6 + 4$ −2
11. $-4 + (-5)$ −9
12. $-2 - 6$ −8
13. $-8 - (-5)$ −3
14. $15 - (-8)$ 23
15. $99 + (-101)$ −2
16. $-3 \cdot 4$ −12
17. $-15 \cdot (-5)$ 75
18. $2 \cdot (-7) \cdot 5$ −70
19. $\frac{-12}{6}$ −2
20. $\frac{-80}{-16}$ 5
21. $\frac{16}{-8}$ −2

Lesson 1-6 **Find the mean, median, mode, and range of each data set. Where necessary, round to the nearest hundredth.**

22. goals per game: 1 1 1 2 2 4 4 2.14, 2, 1, 3
23. golf score: −2 −3 2 5 0 3 7 1.71, 2, no mode, 10
24. words spelled correctly: 7 7 8 8 8 9 10 10 8.38, 8, 8, 3
25. customers served: 7 7 7 9 11 12 8.83, 8, 7, 5

Lesson 1-7 **Simplify or evaluate each expression.**

26. $-3^2 - (-8)$ −1
27. $3 + 4^2 - 15$ 4
28. $(-2)^3 + 4 \div 2 - 3$ −9
29. $(3 - 4)^5 - 17 + 1^{12}$ −17
30. $2r^2 + 6r + 3$ for $r = -6$ 39
31. $|c| + (-c)^2$ for $c = 4$ 20
32. $-c^3 + 2c^2 - c + 8$ for $c = -3$ 56
33. $-3a + 4b^2$ for $a = 3$ and $b = -2$ 7
34. $x^3 + x^2 + x + 1$ for $x = 10$ 1,111
35. $1 + 2y + 3y^2$ for $y = -1$ 2

Lesson 1-8 **Identify each property.**

36. $2(11) + 2(4) = 2(11 + 4)$ Distr. Prop.
37. $(3 + 4) + 5 = 3 + (4 + 5)$ Assoc. Prop. of Add.
38. $2n + p = p + 2n$ Comm. Prop. of Add.
39. $(3 + m)(-7) = -21 - 7m$ Distr. Prop.
40. $(12 \cdot 5) \cdot 100 = 12 \cdot (5 \cdot 100)$ Assoc. Prop. of Mult.
41. $c + 0 = c$ Ident. Prop. of Add.

Chapter 2 Extra Practice

Lesson 2-1 Solve each equation.

1. $x - 6 = -15$ −9
2. $-12 = m + 8$ −20
3. $1.5 = m - 3.2$ 4.7
4. $x + 10 = 10$ 0
5. $\frac{b}{7} = 9$ 63
6. $-3w = 360$ −120
7. $144 = -6k$ −24
8. $20 = \frac{h}{-10}$ −200

Lesson 2-2 Solve each equation.

9. $6n + 3 = 21$ 3
10. $10 = \frac{m}{5} + 2$ 40
11. $-b + 2 = -\frac{1}{2}$ $2\frac{1}{2}$
12. $7g - 4 = 10$ 2
13. $5d + 10 = 25$ 3
14. $-10 = 2 + 6w$ −2
15. $15 = -k + 18$ 3
16. $4x - 2 = 8$ $2\frac{1}{2}$

Lesson 2-3 Simplify each expression.

17. $6x + 4 - 3x$ $3x + 4$
18. $7(h - 5)$ $7h - 35$
19. $2(x + 1) + 5$ $2x + 7$
20. $-5 + 3p - p$ $-5 + 2p$

Lesson 2-4 Write and solve an equation to answer each question.

21. Five less than three times a number is sixteen more than two times the number. What is the number? $3x - 5 = 16 + 2x$; 21

22. **Savings** Hugo received $100 for his birthday. He then saved $20 per week until he had a total of $460 to buy a digital camera. How many weeks did it take him to save the money? $100 + 20x = 460$; 18

Lesson 2-5 Use either one of the strategies *draw a diagram* or *write an equation* to solve this problem.

23. **Entertainment** José watches $\frac{1}{3}$ of a movie at home and then decides to finish watching it later. If he has watched 35 minutes of the movie, how long is the movie? Answers may vary. Sample: $\frac{1}{3}x = 35$; $x = 105$ minutes

Lesson 2-6 Write and graph an inequality for each word sentence. 24–28. See margin for graphs.

24. y is no greater than 12. $y \le 12$
25. t is at most −7. $t \le -7$
26. You must be at least 18 years old to vote. $x \ge 18$
27. The weight the bag can hold is less than 8 lb. $x < 8$
28. The minimum temperature for the mixture is −10°. $x \ge -10$

Lessons 2-7 and 2-8 Solve each inequality.

29. $3x > -42$ $x > -14$
30. $-2h \le 10$ $h \ge -5$
31. $\frac{t}{-2} < -7$ $t > 14$
32. $\frac{y}{-5} \ge 12$ $y \le -60$
33. $-t < 6$ $t > -6$
34. $12m \ge -72$ $m \ge -6$
35. $20 > -5w$ $w > -4$
36. $-16 \le \frac{x}{4}$ $x \ge -64$
37. $3w - 5 \le -11$ $w \le -2$
38. $8 + 4d > 12$ $d > 1$
39. $\frac{r}{-4} - 3 > -6$ $r < 12$
40. $8 - \frac{b}{5} > 13$ $b < -25$

24. 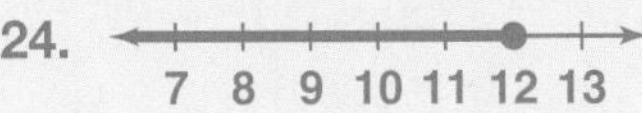

25. −11 −10 −9 −8 −7 −6 −5

26. 16 17 18 19 20 21 22

27. 4 5 6 7 8 9 10

28. −12 −11 −10 −9 −8 −7 −6

Extra Practice

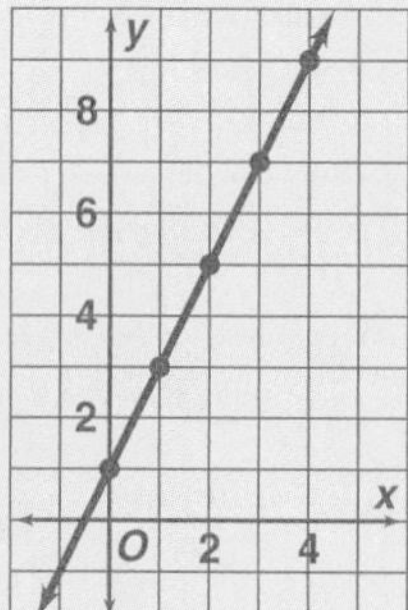

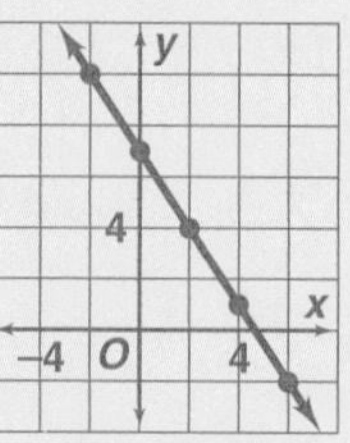

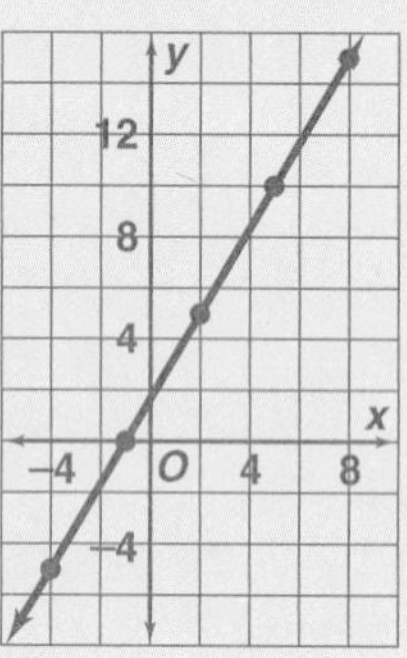

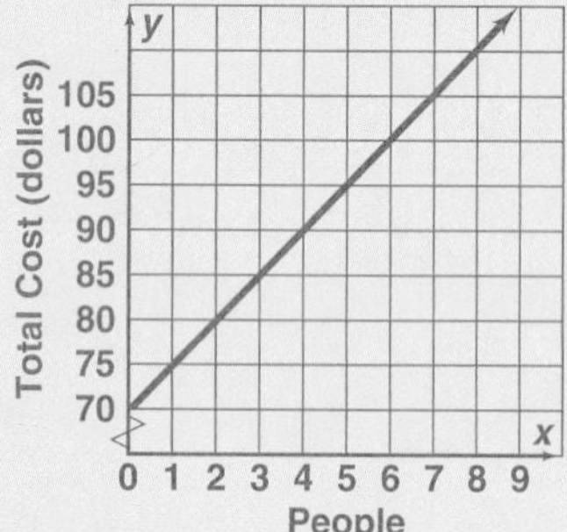

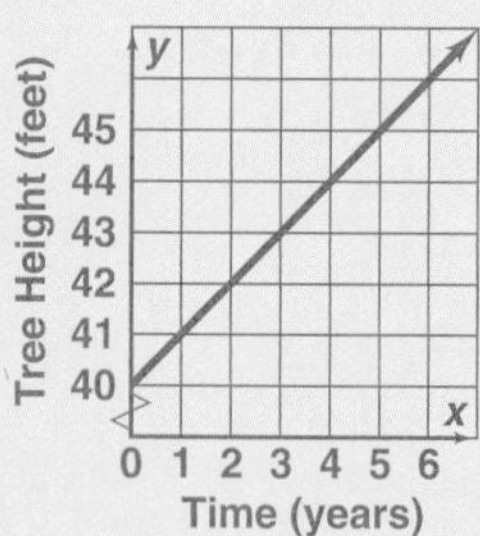

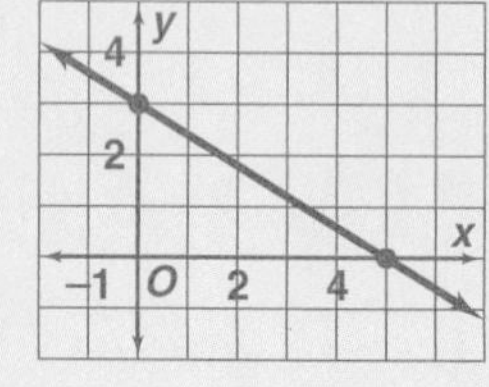

Chapter 3 Extra Practice

● **Lesson 3-1** **Name the coordinates of each point in the graph.**

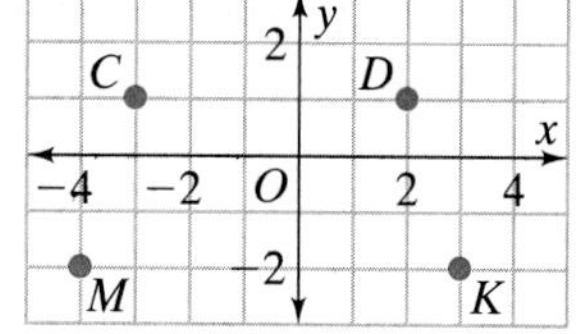

1. C (−3, 1) **2.** D (2, 1) **3.** K (3, −2) **4.** M (−4, −2)

● **Lessons 3-2 and 3-4** **Identify the slope and y-intercept. Then graph each linear equation.** 5–8. See margin for graphs.

5. $y = 3x - 2$ 3; −2 **6.** $y = x + 5$ 1; 5 **7.** $y = \frac{2}{3}x$ $\frac{2}{3}$, 0 **8.** $y = -\frac{3}{4}x + 6$ $-\frac{3}{4}$; 6

● **Lesson 3-3** **The data in each table are linear. Use the table to find the slope. Then graph the data and each line.** 9–11. See margin for graphs.

9.

x	0	1	2	3	4
y	1	3	5	7	9

2

10.

x	−2	0	2	4	6
y	10	7	4	1	−2

$-\frac{3}{2}$

11.

x	−4	−1	2	5	8
y	−5	0	5	10	15

$\frac{5}{3}$

● **Lesson 3-5** **Use the strategies *write an equation* and *make a graph* to model each situation.** 12–13. See margin for graphs.

12. Museums For large groups, a museum charges an initial fee of $70 and $5 for each person. Write an equation and make a graph that represents the total cost. $y = 5x + 70$

13. Trees A tree has an initial height of 40 feet when planted. It grows one foot every year. Write an equation and make a graph that represents how much the tree grows over time. $y = x + 40$

● **Lesson 3-6** **Graph each equation by using the x- and y-intercepts.** 14–17. See margin.

14. $3x + 5y = 15$ **15.** $2x - 7y = 28$ **16.** $x + y = 7$ **17.** $4x - 3y = -12$

● **Lesson 3-7** **Solve each system of equations by graphing. Check the solution.** 18–20. See margin for graphs.

18. $y = x + 7$, $y = 2x + 8$ (−1, 6)

19. $y = x - 1$, $y = 3x - 1$ (0, −1)

20. $y = 4x + 1$, $y = x + 4$ (1, 5)

● **Lessons 3-8 to 3-10** **Copy the figure shown below for Exercises 21–23. Then draw its image after each transformation.** 21–23. See margin.

21. translation 3 units right and 1 unit down

22. reflection over the y-axis

23. rotation 270° about the origin

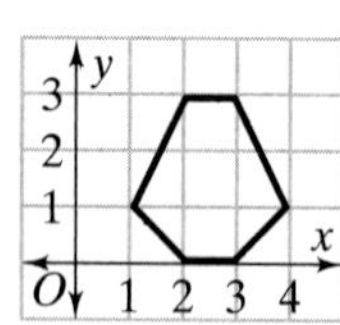

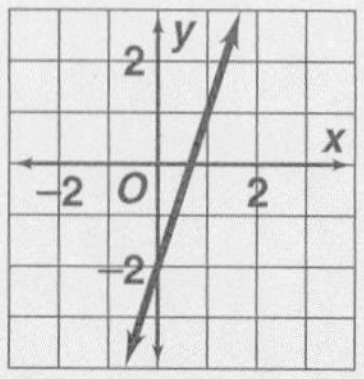

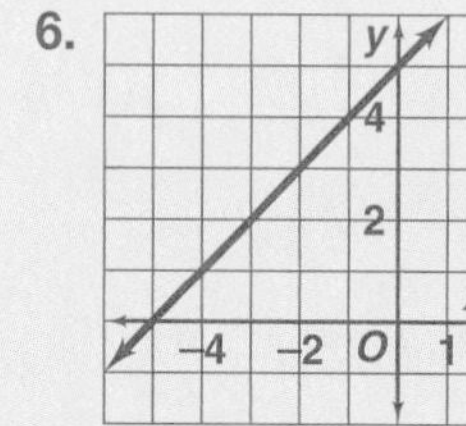

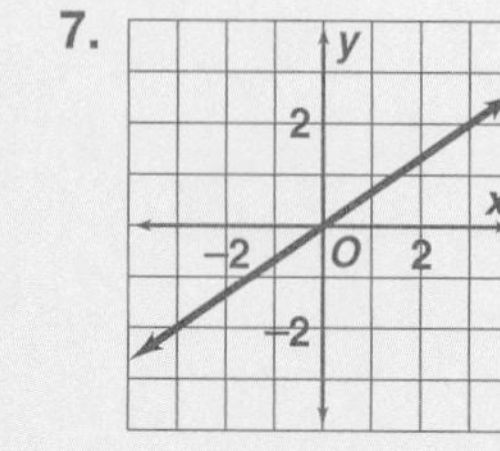

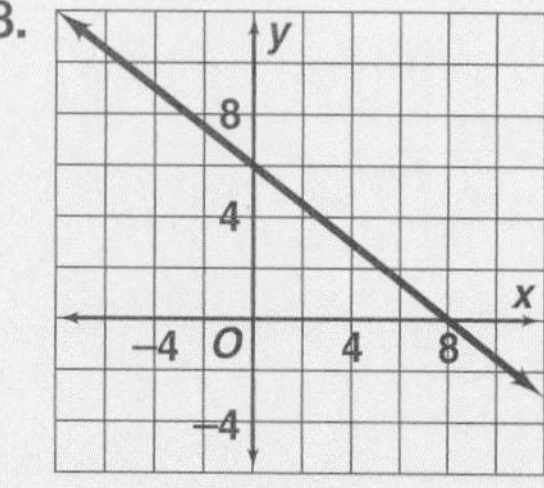

Chapter 4 Extra Practice

34. Irrational; the decimal does not repeat.

35. Rational; 25 is a perfect square.

36. Irrational; 26 is not a perfect square.

37. Rational; the decimal repeats.

Extra Practice

Lesson 4-1 Find the GCF of each pair of numbers using prime factorization.

1. 9, 33 3 **2.** 7, 15 1 **3.** 6, 24 6 **4.** 4, 18 2 **5.** 22, 121 11

Lesson 4-2 Write each fraction in simplest form.

6. $\frac{20}{25}$ $\frac{4}{5}$ **7.** $\frac{7}{77}$ $\frac{1}{11}$ **8.** $\frac{40}{48}$ $\frac{5}{6}$ **9.** $-\frac{15}{35}$ $-\frac{3}{7}$ **10.** $-\frac{9}{42}$ $-\frac{3}{14}$

Write each decimal as a mixed number or fraction in simplest form.

11. 0.45 $\frac{9}{20}$ **12.** 12.2 $12\frac{1}{5}$ **13.** 8.6 $8\frac{3}{5}$ **14.** $0.\overline{8}$ $\frac{8}{9}$ **15.** $0.\overline{72}$ $\frac{8}{11}$

Lesson 4-3 Compare. Write <, >, or =.

16. $\frac{25}{36}$ ■ $0.69\overline{4}$ = **17.** 2.7 ■ $\frac{10}{3}$ < **18.** −4.3 ■ −4.2 < **19.** $-\frac{17}{5}$ ■ −15.9 >

Lesson 4-4 Find each sum or difference. Write your answer as a mixed number or fraction in simplest form.

20. $-\frac{3}{8} + \frac{7}{8}$ $\frac{1}{2}$ **21.** $-\frac{5}{18} + \left(-\frac{1}{6}\right)$ $-\frac{4}{9}$ **22.** $12\frac{1}{3} - 6\frac{2}{3}$ $5\frac{2}{3}$ **23.** $3\frac{1}{2} - \left(-\frac{11}{14}\right)$ $4\frac{2}{7}$ **24.** $-\frac{1}{21} + \frac{5}{14}$ $\frac{13}{42}$

Lesson 4-5 Find each product or quotient. Write each answer as a fraction or mixed number in simplest form.

25. $-\frac{3}{7} \cdot \frac{5}{9}$ $-\frac{5}{21}$ **26.** $-4\frac{5}{24} \cdot (-6)$ $25\frac{1}{4}$ **27.** $-2\frac{1}{2} \div 6$ $-\frac{5}{12}$ **28.** $-25 \div \frac{5}{7}$ −35 **29.** $\frac{2}{3} \div 1\frac{8}{9}$ $\frac{6}{17}$

Lesson 4-6 Solve each formula for the variable indicated in red.

30. $V = \frac{1}{3}Bh$ $h = \frac{3V}{B}$ **31.** $I = prt$ $r = \frac{I}{pt}$ **32.** $C = 44 + ab$ $b = \frac{C - 44}{a}$

Lesson 4-7 Use either one of the strategies *try, check, and revise* or *work backward* to solve this problem.

33. If you start with a number, subtract 4, multiply by $\frac{1}{4}$, add 6, and then divide by 2, the result is 10. What is the number? 60

Lesson 4-8 Identify each number as *rational* or *irrational*. Explain. 34–37. See margin.

34. 1.020304 . . . **35.** $\sqrt{25}$ **36.** $\sqrt{26}$ **37.** $5.63\overline{663}$

Lesson 4-9

38. Construction How high can you build your tree house if you have a 12-ft ladder that must be placed 3 ft from the tree for stability? Round to the nearest tenth. 11.6 ft

19. 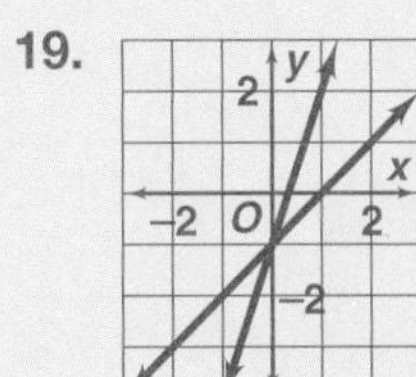

20. 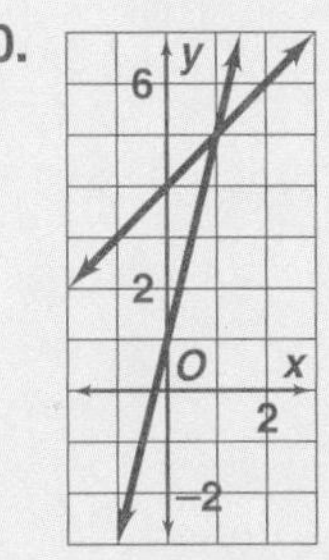

21. 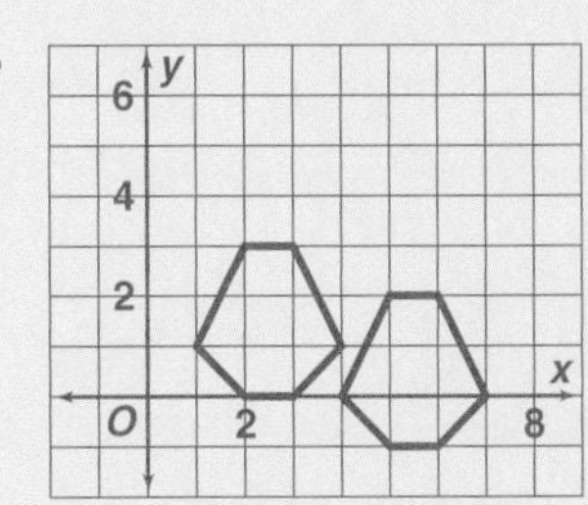

22. 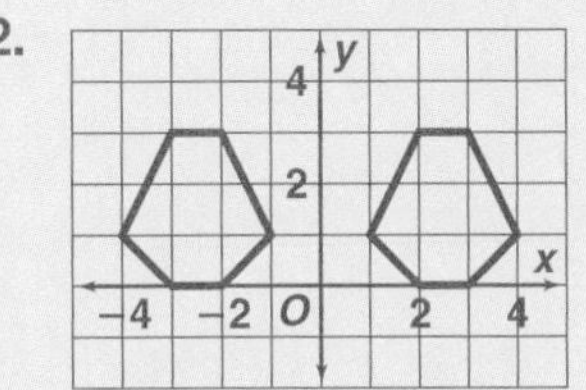

23. 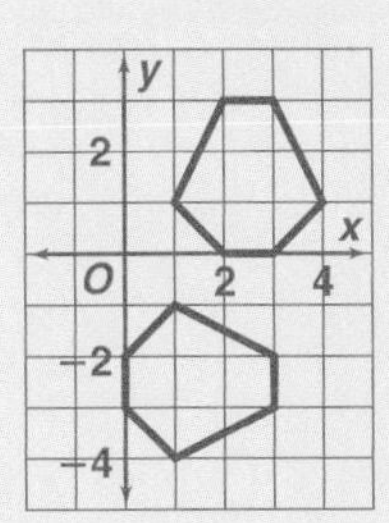

15. 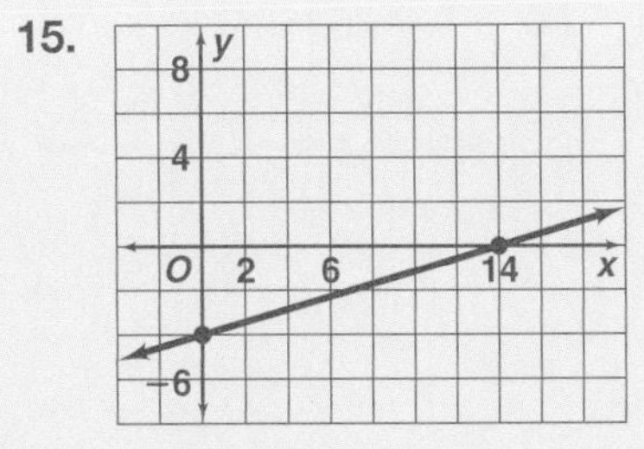

16. 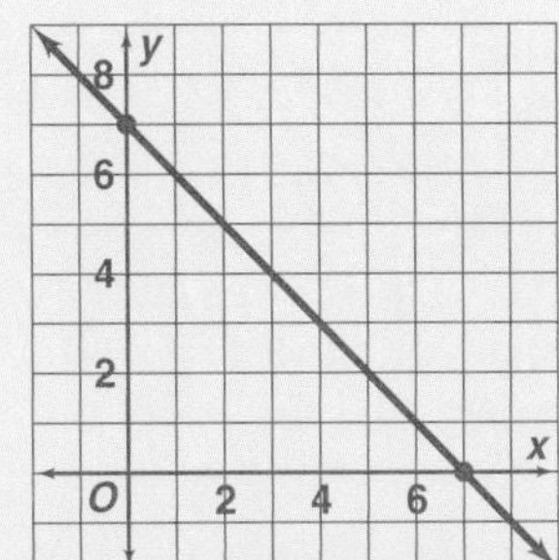

17. 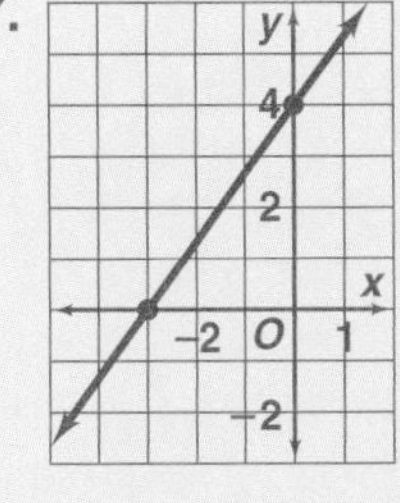

18. 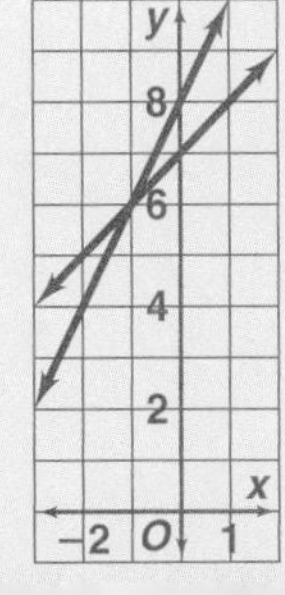

17. $A'(-3, 6), B'(-3, -3),$ $C'(3, -3)$

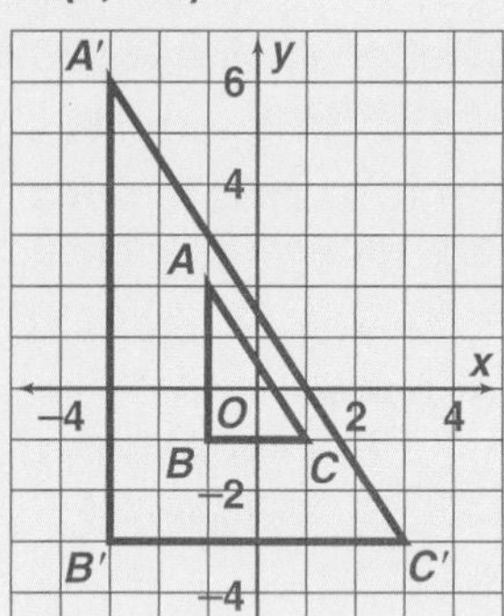

Extra Practice

Lesson 5-1 **Find each unit rate.**

1. 240 mi on 8 gal 30 mi/gal
2. \$3.50 for 10 oz \$.35/oz
3. 450 mi in 9 h 50 mph
4. \$18 for 12 cans \$1.50/can

Lesson 5-2 **Use dimensional analysis to convert each measure.**

5. 3.5 mi = ■ ft 18,480
6. 7.2 km = ■ m 7,200
7. 80 oz = ■ lb 5
8. 120 fl oz = ■ gal 0.9375

Lesson 5-3 **Use the strategy *write an equation* to solve this problem.**

9. **Lemonade** To make watermelon lemonade, you mix watermelon puree, lemon juice, and water in the ratio 12 : 1 : 2. You want to make 5 cups of lemonade. How many cups of each ingredient is needed? 4 c puree, $\frac{1}{3}$ c juice, $\frac{2}{3}$ c water

Lesson 5-4 **Solve each proportion.**

10. $\frac{4}{7} = \frac{x}{21}$ 12
11. $\frac{3}{x} = \frac{18}{9}$ $1\frac{1}{2}$
12. $\frac{x}{10} = \frac{8}{15}$ $5\frac{1}{3}$
13. $\frac{3}{5} = \frac{2}{x}$ $3\frac{1}{3}$

Lesson 5-5 **Exercises 14–16 show pairs of similar polygons. Find the unknown lengths.**

14.

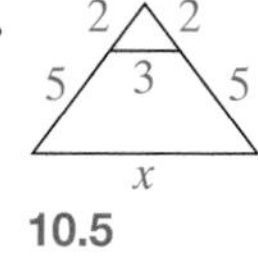

10.5

15.

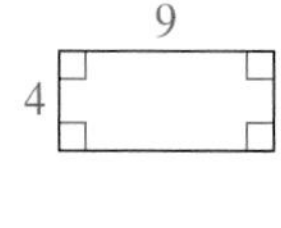

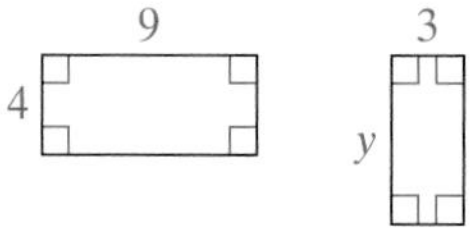

3

y

6.75

16.

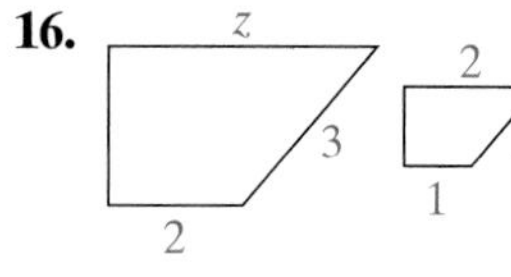

$y = 1.5, z = 4$

Lesson 5-6

17. Graph $\triangle ABC$ with vertices $A(-1, 2)$, $B(-1, -1)$, and $C(1, -1)$. Find the coordinates of its image after a dilation with a scale factor of 3. See margin.

Lesson 5-7

18. **Maps** The scale of a map is 1 in. : 30 mi. What is the actual distance between two cities that are $2\frac{2}{3}$ in. apart on the map? 80 mi

Lesson 5-8

19. A student is 5 ft tall and casts a shadow 12 ft long. A flagpole casts a shadow 25 ft long. Find the height of the flagpole to the nearest tenth. 10.4 ft

Lesson 5-9

20. **Ramps** A wheelchair ramp is 36 in. long and makes an angle of 3° with the floor. Find the height of the upper edge of the ramp. Round to the nearest tenth. 1.9 in.

Chapter 6 Extra Practice

Lesson 6-1 Write each number as a decimal, a fraction, and a percent.

1. 0.3 $0.3, \frac{3}{10}, 30\%$
2. 21% $0.21, \frac{21}{100}, 21\%$
3. 3.47 $3.47, 3\frac{47}{100}, 347\%$
4. 0.004 $0.004, \frac{1}{250}, 0.40\%$
5. $\frac{3}{20}$ $0.15, \frac{3}{20}, 15\%$
6. $\frac{1}{3}$ $0.\overline{3}, \frac{1}{3}, 33\frac{1}{3}\%$
7. 0.62% $0.0062, \frac{31}{5{,}000}, 0.62\%$
8. $2\frac{1}{2}$ $2.5, 2\frac{1}{2}, 250\%$

Lesson 6-2 Estimate each percent.

9. 28% of 99 about 28
10. 7% of 93 about 7
11. 48% of 32 about 16
12. 125% of 84 about 105

Lessons 6-3 and 6-4 Solve each problem.

13. 18% of 36 is ■. 6.48
14. 44 is ■% of 22. 200
15. 145 is 15% of ■. $966.\overline{6}$
16. 0.4 is ■% of 5. 8
17. 0.09% of 1,024 is ■. 0.9216
18. 215% of 20 is ■. 43

Lesson 6-5 Find each percent of change. Round your answer to the nearest tenth of a percent where necessary.

19. 16 to 20 25%
20. 320 to 542 69.4%
21. 1 to 4 300%
22. 20 to 3 −85%
23. On May 29, 2003, in Boston, Massachusetts, there were 15 daylight hours. On November 9 of that same year, there were 10 daylight hours. Find the percent decrease in the number of daylight hours. $33\frac{1}{3}\%$

Lesson 6-6

24. **a.** Daniel ordered a shipment of $18.00 sunglasses for his store. He marked them up 50%. What is the selling price? $27.00
    b. Unfortunately, the sunglasses weren't selling, so he marked them down to $22.95. What was the percent of discount? 15%

Lesson 6-7 Use the strategy *write an equation* to solve this problem.

25. **Exercise** Your grandmother walked 2.5 miles each day this week. Next week, she wants to walk between 10% and 20% more miles each day than last week. Find the minimum and maximum number of miles she must walk to reach this goal. 2.75 miles; 3 miles

Lesson 6-8 Find the final balance in each account to the nearest cent.

26. $165 at $4\frac{1}{2}\%$ simple interest for 2 yr $179.85
27. $350 at $5\frac{1}{4}\%$ compounded annually for 3 yr $408.07

Lesson 6-9 Suppose you toss a coin twice. Find each probability.

28. P(no heads) $\frac{1}{4}$
29. P(exactly one head) $\frac{1}{2}$
30. P(at least one head) $\frac{3}{4}$

Extra Practice

Extra Practice

Chapter 7

Extra Practice

Lesson 7-1 Write each number in scientific notation.

1. 400,000,000 4×10^8 **2.** 8,570,000 8.57×10^6 **3.** 40,000 4×10^4 **4.** 19,000,000 1.9×10^7

Lessons 7-2 and 7-3 Write each expression using a single exponent.

5. $4^8 \cdot 4^{10}$ 4^{18} **6.** $(-9)^2 \cdot (-9)^4$ $(-9)^6$ **7.** $3.2^8 \cdot 3.2^3$ $(3.2)^{11}$ **8.** $7^t \cdot 7^{3t}$ 7^{4t}

9. $\frac{4^7}{4^5}$ 4^2 **10.** $\frac{8.1^{15}}{8.1^{12}}$ 8.1^3 **11.** $\frac{(-654)^{10}}{(-654)^1}$ $(-654)^9$ **12.** $\frac{2^{3x}}{2^x}$ 2^{2x}

Write each number in standard form.

13. 4×10^{-3} 0.004 **14.** 2.6×10^{-5} 0.000026 **15.** 1.03×10^{-2} 0.0103 **16.** 5.05×10^{-3} 0.00505

Write each number in scientific notation.

17. 0.003 3×10^{-3} **18.** 0.0105 1.05×10^{-2} **19.** 0.04 4×10^{-2} **20.** 0.0000104 1.04×10^{-5}

Multiply. Write each result in scientific notation.

21. $(3 \times 10^4)(2 \times 10^{12})$ 6×10^{16} **22.** $(5 \times 10^9)(7 \times 10^3)$ 3.5×10^{13} **23.** $12(1.6 \times 10^{-4})$ 1.92×10^{-3} **24.** $45.5(2 \times 10^{-6})$ 9.1×10^{-5}

Simplify each expression.

25. $(-142)^0$ 1 **26.** $(4c)^{-1}$ $\frac{1}{4c}$ **27.** 7^{-w} $\frac{1}{7^w}$ **28.** $(-3)^{-5}$ $\frac{1}{(-3)^5}$

Lesson 7-4 Simplify each expression.

29. $(a^4)^7$ a^{28} **30.** $(5^a)^9$ 5^{9a} **31.** $(2x^7)^3$ $8x^{21}$ **32.** $(w^3x^5)^7$ $w^{21}x^{35}$

33. $(3n)^3$ $27n^3$ **34.** $(2a)^4$ $16a^4$ **35.** $(2 \times 10^5)^0$ 1 **36.** $(3 \times 10^5)^2$ 9×10^{10}

Lesson 7-5 Use the strategy *write an equation* to solve this problem.

37. If you travel at 2.5×10^3 centimeters per second, how long will it take you to go 1 kilometer? 40 seconds

Lesson 7-6 Write the decimal value for each binary number.

38. 1111_2 15 **39.** 1101_2 13 **40.** 110011_2 51 **41.** 111000_2 56

Write each decimal number as a binary number.

42. 22 10110_2 **43.** 31 11111_2 **44.** 50 110010_2 **45.** 64 1000000_2

Chapter 8

Extra Practice

Lesson 8-1 For Exercises 1–3, use the diagram at the right.

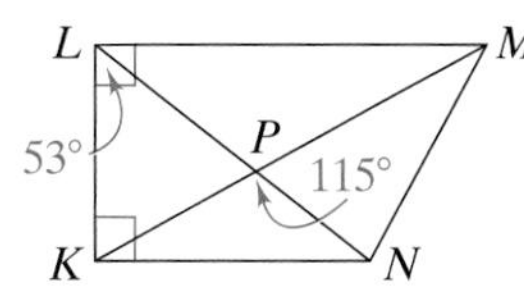

1. Find the measure of the complement of $\angle PLK$. 37°

2. Name a pair of vertical angles. Answers may vary. Sample: $\angle LPM$ and $\angle KPN$

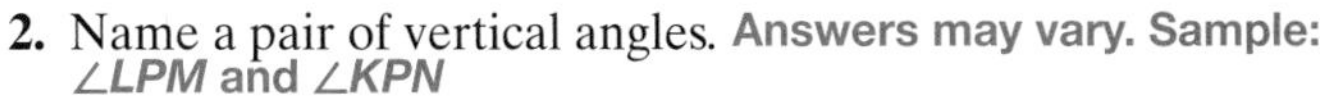

3. Find the measures of $\angle LPM$ and $\angle MPN$. 115°, 65°

Lesson 8-2 In the diagram at the right, $\ell \parallel m$.

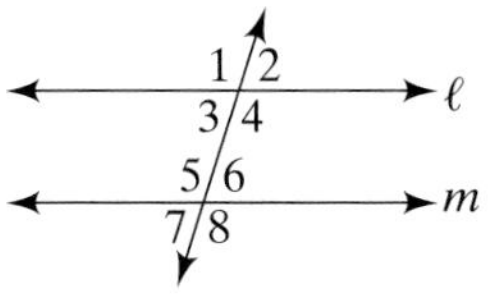

4. Identify a pair of alternate interior angles. Answers may vary. Sample: $\angle 3$ and $\angle 6$

5. If $m\angle 1 = 108°$, find the measure of each numbered angle. $\angle 2 = 72°$, $\angle 3 = 72°$, $\angle 4 = 108°$, $\angle 5 = 108°$, $\angle 6 = 72°$, $\angle 7 = 72°$, $\angle 8 = 108°$

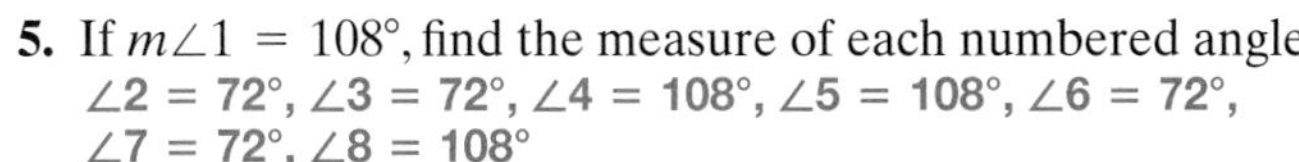

Lesson 8-3 Explain why each pair of triangles is congruent.

6.

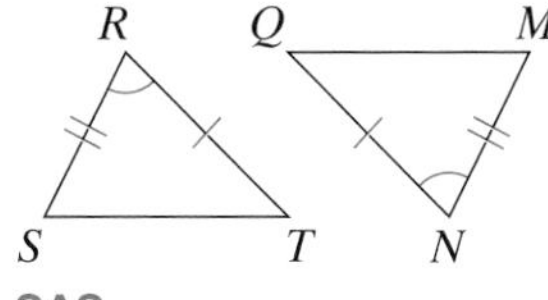

SAS

7.

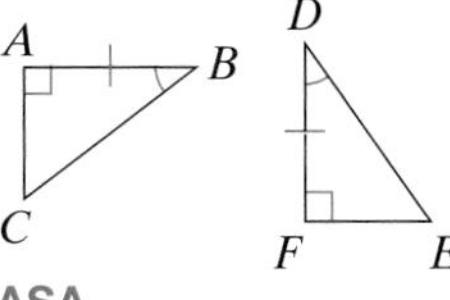

ASA

8.

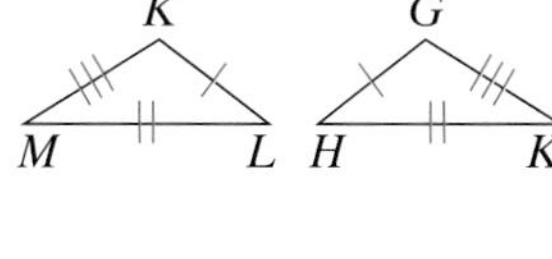

SSS

Lesson 8-4 Use the strategies *solve a simpler problem* and *look for a pattern* to solve this problem.

9. You can draw two lines to intersect at one point and three lines to intersect at three points. What is the largest number of points at which five lines can intersect? 10 points

Lesson 8-5 Determine the best name for each quadrilateral.

10.

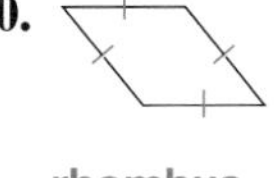

rhombus

11.

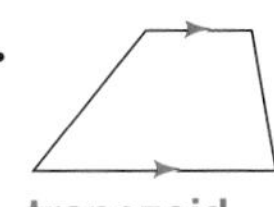

trapezoid

12.

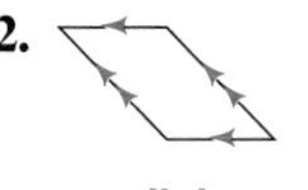

parallelogram

13.

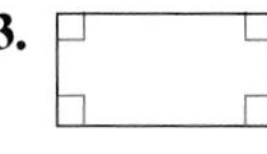

rectangle

Lesson 8-6 Find the sum of the interior angles of each polygon.

14. rhombus 360° **15.** hexagon 720° **16.** triangle 180° **17.** pentagon 540° **18.** trapezoid 360°

Lessons 8-7 and 8-8 Find the area of each figure. Round to the nearest tenth.

19. parallelogram: $b = 6$ m and $h = 12$ m 72 m^2 **20.** circle: $d = 5.5$ in. 23.8 in.^{2}

Lesson 8-9

21. Draw an angle and label it $\angle A$. Construct $\angle B$ congruent to $\angle A$. Check students' work.

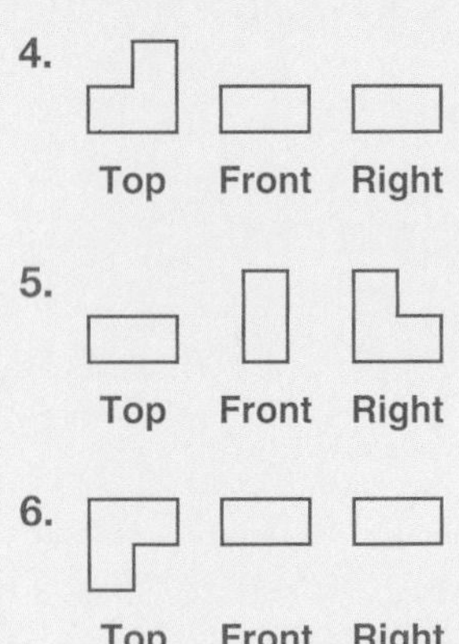

Chapter 9 Extra Practice

Lesson 9-1 For each figure, describe the base(s), name the figure, and name the part labeled $\overline{PQ}$.

1. 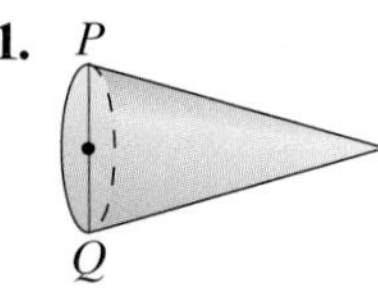

circle; cone, diameter

2. 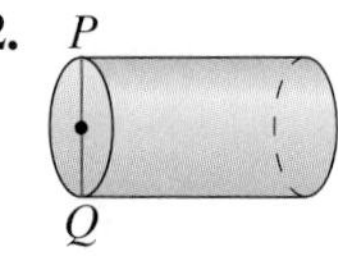

circle; cylinder, diameter

3. 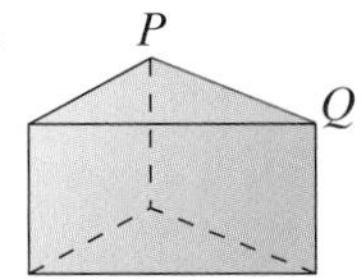

triangle; triangular prism, edge

Lesson 9-2 Draw the top, front, and right views of each figure. 4–6. See margin.

4. 

5. 

6. 

Lesson 9-3

7. Identify the solid that the net at the right forms. cone

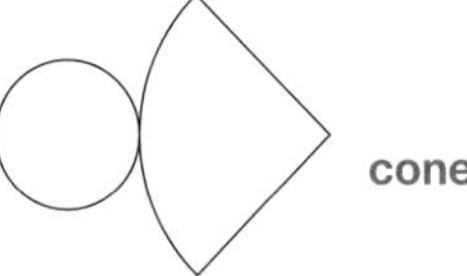

Lessons 9-4 and 9-6 Find (a) the surface area and (b) the volume of each figure. Round to the nearest whole unit.

8. cube with edge length 1.2 m 9 m^2; 2 m^3
9. rectangular prism 10 cm × 15 cm × 18 cm $1{,}200\text{ cm}^2$; $2{,}700\text{ cm}^3$
10. cylinder with radius 1 ft and height 8 ft 57 ft^2; 25 ft^3
11. cylinder with diameter 6 in. and height 4 in. 132 in.^2; 113 in.^3

Lessons 9-5 and 9-7 Find (a) the surface area and (b) the volume of each figure with the given characteristics. Round to the nearest whole unit.

12. a square pyramid with a height of 4 in., a slant height of 5 in., and a base area of 36 in.^2 96 in.^2; 48 in.^3
13. a cone with a diameter of 12 cm, a height of 8 cm, and a slant height of 10 cm 302 cm^2; 302 cm^3

Lesson 9-8 Use the strategies *draw a diagram* and *make a table* to solve this problem. Round to the nearest tenth.

14. Each side of one cube is 10 cm. A second cube has a volume twice that of the first. Find the length of each side of the second cube. 12.6 cm

Lesson 9-9

15. **Cans** A can of tomatoes has a volume of 245 mL and a diameter of 5 cm. Find the volume of a similar can with a diameter of 6 cm. 423.36 mL

16. A cone has a radius of 4 ft and a surface area of 150 ft^2. Find the surface area of a similar cone with a radius of 7 ft. 459.375 ft^2

Chapter 10 Extra Practice

Lessons 10-1 and 10-2 **For Exercises 1–3, use the following data set.**

Hours spent waiting:
1.8 1.7 1.4 1.2 1.7 1.7 1.7 1.7 1.5 1.9 1.6 1.6 1.5 1.3 1.4

1. Find the mean, the median, and the mode of the data set. 1.58, 1.6, 1.7
2. Make a frequency table and a histogram for the data set. Use intervals of equal size to group the data. See margin.
3. Make a line plot for the data set. See margin.

Lessons 10-3 and 10-4 **Use the stem-and-leaf plot for Exercises 4 and 5.**

7	0 3 4
8	2 5
9	3 6 7 8

Key: 7 | 0 means 7.0

4. Find the mode and median of the data set. no mode, 8.5
5. Make a box-and-whisker plot for the data set. See margin.

Lesson 10-5 **In each scatter plot, describe the type of trend: *positive, negative,* or *no trend.***

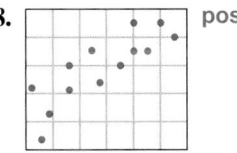

6. negative

7. 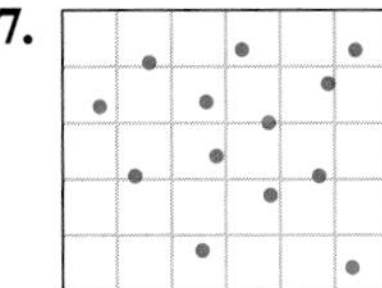
no trend

8. positive

Lesson 10-6

9. Make a circle graph for the set of data at the right. See margin.

U.S. Service Academy 2001 Enrollment

School	Enrollment
Army	4,152
Navy	4,297
Air Force	4,365
Coast Guard	919
Merchant Marine	931

SOURCE: *College Board Handbook*

Lesson 10-7 **Choose the appropriate graph to display each set of data. Explain your choice.**

10. circle graph or scatter plot?
parts of a monthly budget Circle graph; it shows parts of the whole budget.
11. line graph or scatter plot?
changes in temperature in one week Scatter plot; it compares two sets of data, and the data may not be linear.
12. box-and-whisker plot or double bar graph?
number of girls and number of boys in three classes Double bar graph; it shows the comparison of two sets of data.

Lesson 10-8 **Use the strategies *draw a diagram* and *use logical reasoning* to solve this problem.**

13. In a class of 21 students, 14 take Spanish, 10 take French, and 5 take both languages. How many students do not take either language? 2 students

2.

Waiting Time

Minutes	Tally	Frequency
1.2–1.3	II	2
1.4–1.5	IIII	4
1.6–1.7	~~IIII~~ II	7
1.8–1.9	II	2

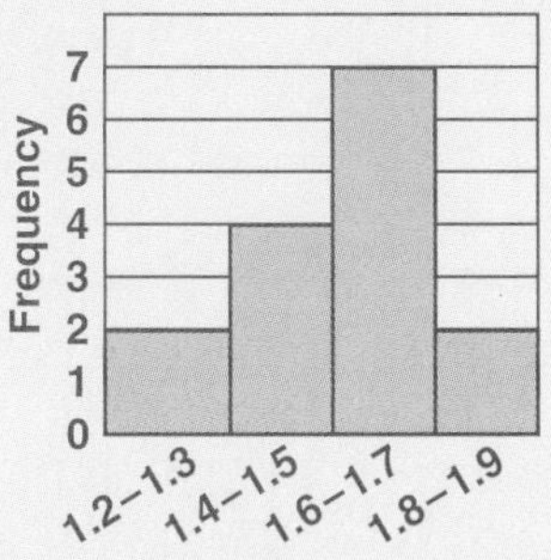

3.

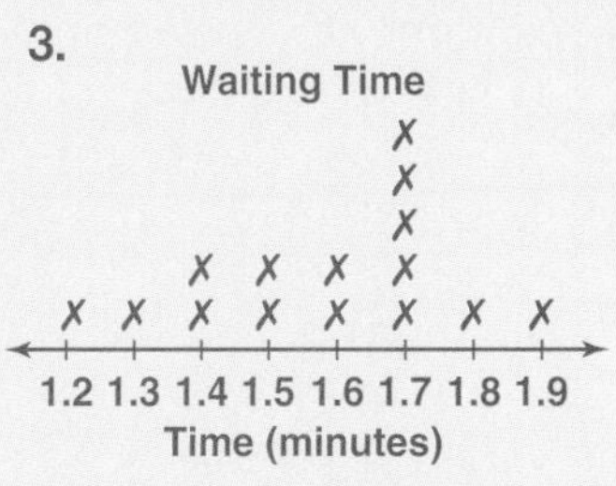

5.

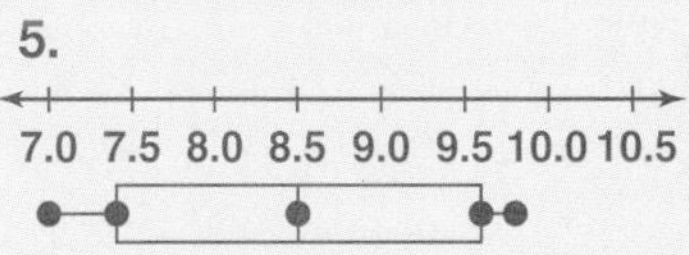

9.

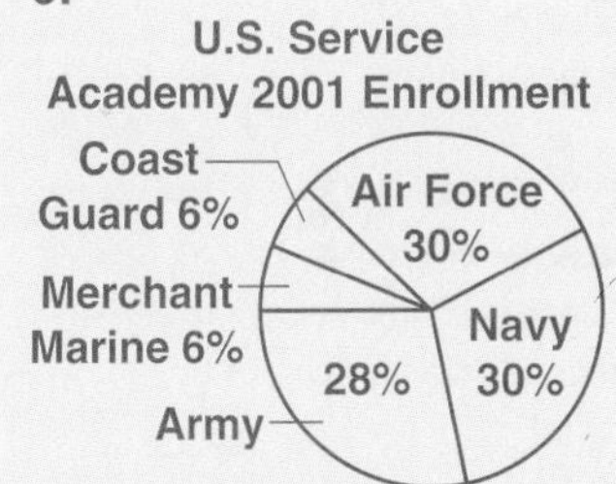

Extra Practice

Chapter 11 Extra Practice

Lesson 11-1 **Use the counting principle to find the number of possible outcomes in each situation.**

1. 3 sizes, 6 toppings. How many pizzas? 18 pizzas
2. 6 lengths, 3 arm styles, 10 fabrics. How many sofas? 180 sofas
3. 7 colors, 4 sizes, 5 fonts. How many jerseys? 140 jerseys

Lessons 11-2 and 11-3 **Simplify each expression.**

4. 4! 24 **5.** 8! 40,320 **6.** ${}_6P_3$ 120 **7.** ${}_{17}P_2$ 272 **8.** ${}_{24}P_4$ 255,024

9. ${}_{18}P_5$ 1,028,160 **10.** ${}_7C_4$ 35 **11.** ${}_{16}C_2$ 120 **12.** ${}_{19}C_7$ 50,388 **13.** ${}_{24}C_2$ 276

14. You need to choose a team of 5 players from 15 potential players. In how many ways can you do this? 3,003 ways

Lesson 11-4 **Find each experimental probability.** Suppose you write North, South, East, and West on separate pieces of paper. You select a piece of paper at random, record the result, replace the paper, and select again. The results of 20 trials are shown.

Location	Number Selected
North	7
South	5
East	3
West	5

15. P(West) $\frac{1}{4}$ **16.** P(South or East) $\frac{2}{5}$ **17.** P(not North) $\frac{13}{20}$

18. What is the theoretical probability of selecting North? $\frac{1}{4}$

19. Which event or events have the same experimental probability as the theoretical probability? South and West

Lesson 11-5 **Find each probability. Assume Y is a consonant.** A spinner is divided into 26 equal sections. Each section is labeled with a letter of the alphabet. Suppose you spin the spinner once and then roll a number cube.

20. P(M, then 2) $\frac{1}{156}$ **21.** P(C, then prime) $\frac{1}{52}$ **22.** P(vowel, then odd) $\frac{5}{52}$ **23.** P(consonant, then 5) $\frac{7}{52}$

Lesson 11-6 **Use the strategies *make an organized list* and *simulate a problem* to solve this problem.**

24. **Basketball** The probability that Carl will make a foul shot is $\frac{1}{2}$. Find the probability that he will make at least 2 out of his next 3 foul shots. Check students' work.

Lesson 11-7 **Determine whether each question is biased or not. Explain.**

25. What is your favorite food?
Unbiased; the question does not favor an answer.

26. How much homework do you do each night?
Biased; the question assumes that the person interviewed does homework and that homework is done every night.

Chapter 12

Extra Practice

Lesson 12-1 Find the common difference or ratio in each sequence. Write the rule for each sequence and find the next three terms. 1–4. See margin.

1. 4, 16, 64, . . . **2.** −5, −3, −1, . . . **3.** $1, \frac{5}{6}, \frac{2}{3}, \frac{1}{2}, \ldots$ **4.** 12, 6, 3, . . .

Lesson 12-2 Use the function rule $f(x) = 2x - 1$. Find each output.

5. $f(1)$ 1 **6.** $f(0)$ −1 **7.** $f(-3)$ −7 **8.** $f(\frac{1}{2})$ 0

Lesson 12-3 Make a table of input/output pairs for each function. Then graph the function. 9–12. See margin.

9. $y = 3x$ **10.** $y = -2x + 3$ **11.** $y = \frac{3}{5}x + 1$ **12.** $y = 4$

Lesson 12-4 Do the data in each table represent a linear function? If so, write a rule for the function.

13.

x	0	1	2	3	4
y	8	6	4	2	0

yes; $y = -2x + 8$

14.

x	−3	−1	1	3	5
y	0	1	2	3	4

yes; $y = \frac{1}{2}x + \frac{3}{2}$

15.

x	0	3	6	9	12
y	0	2	4	7	10

no

Lesson 12-5

16. The library charges 25 cents each day a book is overdue. After 5 days, the library charges 50 cents a day. Sketch and label a graph that shows the total charge each day a book is overdue. See margin.

Lesson 12-6 Make a table and a graph for each quadratic function. Use integers from −4 to 4 for inputs. 17–20. See back of book.

17. $y = x^2 + 2$ **18.** $y = -2x^2$ **19.** $y = 3x^2$ **20.** $y = -x^2 + 3$

Lesson 12-7 Use the strategy *write an equation* to solve this problem.

21. Sales Suppose you sold 5 paintings this year. You hope to double the number of paintings you sell each year. Write a function rule that relates the number of paintings sold to the number of years passed. Use your rule to find the number of paintings you will sell in the fourth year. $y = 5 \cdot 2^t$; 80 paintings

Lessons 12-8 to 12-10 Simplify each expression.

22. $x^2 - 5x + 3x + 4$ $x^2 - 2x + 4$

23. $-x^2 + 2x^2 - 6x + 3 - 2$ $x^2 - 6x + 1$

24. $(2x^2 - x + 1) - (4x^2 - 3)$ $-2x^2 - x + 4$

25. $(-4x^2)(3x^4)$ $-12x^6$

26. $(6x)(-2x)$ $-12x^2$

27. $4x^2(2x - 7)$ $8x^3 - 28x^2$

Extra Practice

1. 4; start with 4 and multiply by 4 repeatedly; 256, 1,024, 4,096
2. 2; start with −5 and add 2 repeatedly; 1, 3, 5
3. $-\frac{1}{6}$; start with 1 and add $-\frac{1}{6}$ repeatedly; $\frac{1}{3}, \frac{1}{6}, 0$
4. $\frac{1}{2}$; start with 12 and multiply by $\frac{1}{2}$ repeatedly; $\frac{3}{2}, \frac{3}{4}, \frac{3}{8}$
9. Answers may vary. Sample:

x	−1	0	1	2
y	−3	0	3	6

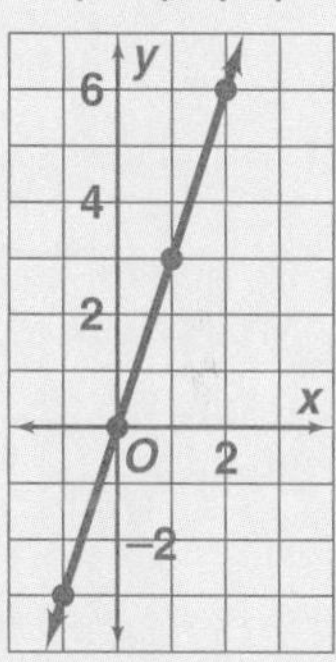

10. Answers may vary. Sample:

x	−1	0	1	2
y	5	3	1	−1

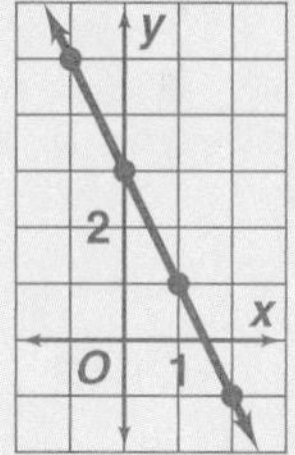

11. Answers may vary. Sample:

x	−5	0	5
y	−2	1	4

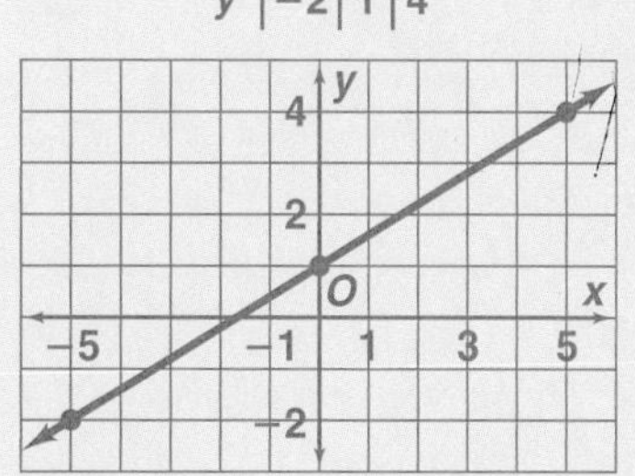

12. Answers may vary. Sample:

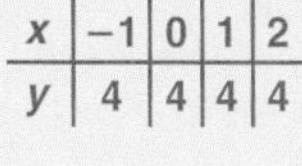

x	−1	0	1	2
y	4	4	4	4

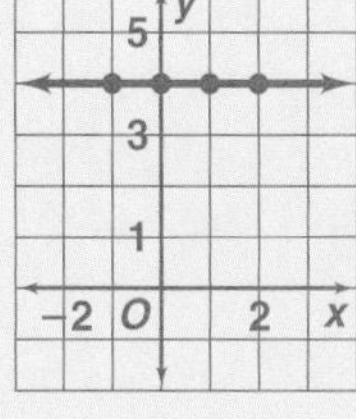

16.

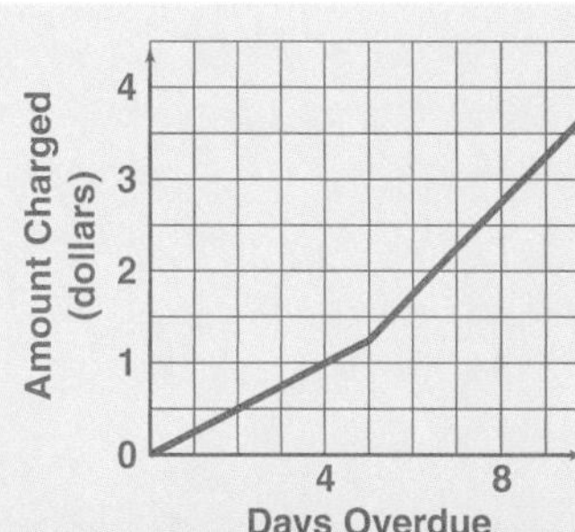

13. six hundredths
14. four and seven tenths
15. eleven hundred-thousandths
16. nine tenths
17. twelve thousandths
18. fifty-nine millionths
19. forty-two ten-thousandths
20. six and twenty-nine thousand one hundred eighty-six millionths

Skills Handbook

Decimals and Place Value

Each digit in a whole number or a decimal has both a place and a value. The value of any place is one tenth the value of the place to its left. The chart below can help you read and write decimals. It shows the place and value of the number 2,401,262,830.750191.

billions	hundred millions	ten millions	millions	hundred thousands	ten thousands	thousands	hundreds	tens	ones	.	tenths	hundredths	thousandths	ten-thousandths	hundred-thousandths	millionths
2	4	0	1	2	6	2	8	3	0	.	7	5	0	1	9	1

EXAMPLE

a. What is the value of the digit 8 in the number above?

The digit 8 is in the hundreds place. So, its value is 8 hundreds.

b. Write 2.006 in words.

The digit 6 is in the thousandths place. The answer is two and six thousandths.

c. Write five and thirty-four ten-thousandths as a decimal.

Ten-thousandths is 4 places to the right of the decimal point. So, the decimal will have 4 places after the decimal point. The answer is 5.0034.

EXERCISES

Use the chart above. Write the value of each digit.

1. the digit 9 hundred-thousandths
2. the digit 7 tenths
3. the digit 5 hundredths
4. the digit 6 ten thousands
5. the digit 4 hundred millions
6. the digit 3 tens

Write a decimal for the given words.

7. forty-one ten-thousandths 0.0041
8. eighteen and five hundred four thousandths 18.504
9. eight millionths 0.000008
10. seven and sixty-three hundred-thousandths 7.00063
11. twelve thousandths 0.012
12. sixty-five and two hundred one thousandths 65.201

Write each decimal in words. 13–20. See margin.

13. 0.06
14. 4.7
15. 0.00011
16. 0.9
17. 0.012
18. 0.000059
19. 0.0042
20. 6.029186

Comparing and Ordering Decimals

To compare two decimals, use the symbols < (is less than), > (is greater than), or = (is equal to). When you compare, start at the left and compare the digits.

1 EXAMPLE

Use <, >, or = to compare the decimals.

a. 0.1 ■ 0.06

1 tenth > 0 tenths, so 0.1 > 0.06

b. 2.4583 ■ 2.48

5 hundredths < 8 hundredths, so 2.4583 < 2.48

c. 0.30026 ■ 0.03026

3 tenths > 0 tenths, so 0.30026 > 0.03026

2 EXAMPLE

Draw number lines to compare the decimals.

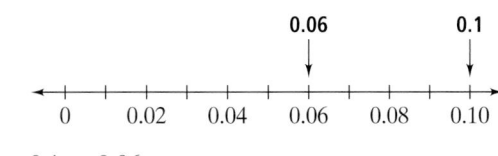

a. 0.1 ■ 0.06

0.06 0.1

0 0.02 0.04 0.06 0.08 0.10

0.1 > 0.06

b. 2.4583 ■ 2.48

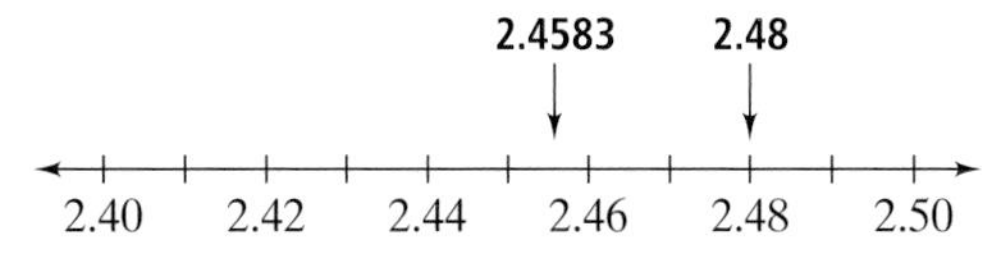

2.4583 < 2.48

EXERCISES

Use <, >, or = to compare the decimals. Draw number lines if you wish.

1. 0.003 ■ 0.02 <
2. 84.2 ■ 842 <
3. 0.162 ■ 0.106 >
4. 0.0659 ■ 0.6059 <
5. 2.13 ■ 2.99 <
6. 3.53 ■ 3.529 >
7. 2.01 ■ 2.010 =
8. 0.00072 ■ 0.07002 <
9. 0.458 ■ 0.4589 <
10. 8.627 ■ 8.649 <
11. 0.0019 ■ 0.0002 >
12. 0.19321 ■ 0.19231 >

Write the decimals in order from least to greatest. 13–22. See margin.

13. 2.31, 0.231, 23.1, 0.23, 3.21
14. 1.02, 1.002, 1.2, 1.11, 1.021
15. 0.02, 0.002, 0.22, 0.222, 2.22
16. 55.5, 555.5, 55.555, 5.5555
17. 0.07, 0.007, 0.7, 0.71, 0.72
18. 2.78, 2.7001, 2.701, 2.71, 2.7
19. 7, 7.3264, 7.3, 7.3246, 7.0324
20. 0.0101, 0.0099, 0.011, 0.00019
21. 0.8, 0.83, 0.08, 0.083, 0.082
22. 4.6, 4.61, 4.601, 4.602, 4.6002, 4.62

13. 0.23, 0.231, 2.31, 3.21, 23.1
14. 1.002, 1.02, 1.021, 1.11, 1.2
15. 0.002, 0.02, 0.22, 0.222, 2.22
16. 5.5555, 55.5, 55.555, 555.5
17. 0.007, 0.07, 0.7, 0.71, 0.72
18. 2.7, 2.7001, 2.701, 2.71, 2.78
19. 7, 7.0324, 7.3, 7.3246, 7.3264
20. 0.00019, 0.0099, 0.0101, 0.011
21. 0.08, 0.082, 0.083, 0.8, 0.83
22. 4.6, 4.6002, 4.601, 4.602, 4.61, 4.62

21. 7.06
22. 6
23. 1,520
24. 0.9195
25. 4.2
26. 240
27. 400
28. 3.49537
29. 8.1
30. 1
31. 410
32. 33,000,000
33. 2.58
34. 860
35. 19
36. 900
37. 7,700
38. 25.660
39. 980,000,000
40. 30
41. 0.00377
42. 0.1
43. 12.8
44. 1,759,000
45. 21,000

Rounding

When you round to a particular place, look at the digit to the right of that place. If it is 5 or more, the digit in the place you are rounding to will increase by 1. If it is less than 5, the digit in the place you are rounding to will stay the same.

EXAMPLE

a. Round 1.627 to the nearest whole number.

The digit to the right of the units place is 6, so 1.627 rounds up to 2.

b. Round 12,034 to the nearest thousand.

The digit to the right of the thousands place is 0, so 12,034 rounds down to 12,000.

c. Round 2.7195 to the nearest hundredth.

The digit to the right of the hundredths place is 9, so 2.7195 rounds up to 2.72.

d. Round 0.060521 to the place of the underlined digit.

The digit to the right of 5 is 2, so 0.060521 rounds down to 0.0605.

EXERCISES

Round to the nearest thousand.

1. 105,099 105,000 **2.** 10,400 10,000 **3.** 79,527,826 79,528,000 **4.** 79,932 80,000 **5.** 4,312,349 4,312,000

Round to the nearest whole number.

6. 135.91 136 **7.** 3.001095 3 **8.** 96.912 97 **9.** 101.167 101 **10.** 299.9 300

Round to the nearest tenth.

11. 82.01 82.0 **12.** 4.67522 4.7 **13.** 20.397 20.4 **14.** 399.95 400.0 **15.** 129.98 130.0

Round to the nearest hundredth.

16. 13.458 13.46 **17.** 96.4045 96.40 **18.** 0.699 0.70 **19.** 4.234 4.23 **20.** 12.09531 12.10

Round to the place of the underlined digit. 21–45. See margin.

21. 7.0615 **22.** 5.77125 **23.** 1,522 **24.** 0.91952 **25.** 4.243

26. 236.001 **27.** 352 **28.** 3.495366 **29.** 8.07092 **30.** 0.6008

31. 409 **32.** 32,951,888 **33.** 2.5784 **34.** 862 **35.** 19.32

36. 918 **37.** 7,735 **38.** 25.66047 **39.** 983,240,631 **40.** 27

41. 0.003771 **42.** 0.0649 **43.** 12.777 **44.** 1,759,230 **45.** 20,908

Adding and Subtracting Decimals

You add or subtract decimals just as you do whole numbers. You line up the decimal points and then add or subtract. If you wish, you can use zeros to make the columns even.

EXAMPLE

Find each sum or difference.

a. 37.6 + 8.431

$$\begin{array}{r} 37.6 \\ +\ 8.431 \\ \hline \end{array} \rightarrow \begin{array}{r} 37.600 \\ +\ 8.431 \\ \hline 46.031 \end{array}$$

b. 8 − 4.593

$$\begin{array}{r} 8. \\ -\ 4.593 \\ \hline \end{array} \rightarrow \begin{array}{r} 8.000 \\ -\ 4.593 \\ \hline 3.407 \end{array}$$

c. 8.3 + 2.99 + 17.5

$$\begin{array}{r} 8.3 \\ 2.99 \\ +\ 17.5 \\ \hline \end{array} \rightarrow \begin{array}{r} 8.30 \\ 2.99 \\ +\ 17.50 \\ \hline 28.79 \end{array}$$

EXERCISES

Find each sum or difference.

1. 39.7 − 36.03 3.67

2. 1.08 − 0.9 0.18

3. 6.784 + 0.528 7.312

4. 5.01 − 0.87 4.14

5. 13.02 + 23.107 36.127

6. 8.634 + 1.409 10.043

7. 2.1 − 0.5 1.6

8. 8.23 − 3.1 5.13

9. 1.05 + 12.9 13.95

10. 2.60 + 23.107 25.707

11. 0.1 + 58.21 + 1.9 60.21

12. 12.2 + 3.06 + 0.5 15.76

13. 9.42 + 3.6 + 21.003 34.023

14. 15.22 + 7.4 + 8.125 30.745

15. 3.7 + 20.06 + 16.19 39.95

16. 12.22 + 9.8 + 2.375 24.395

17. 76.39 − 8.47 67.92

18. 8.7 + 17.03 25.73

19. 32.403 + 12.06 44.463

20. 20.5 + 11.45 31.95

21. 8.9 − 4.45 4.45

22. 1.245 + 5.8 7.045

23. 3.9 + 6.57 10.47

24. 14.81 − 8.6 6.21

25. 11.9 − 2.06 9.84

26. 3.45 + 4.061 7.511

27. 8.29 + 4.3 12.59

28. 7.06 − 4.235 2.825

29. 6.02 + 4.005 10.025

30. 7.05 − 3.5 3.55

31. 1.18 + 3.015 4.195

32. 2.304 − 0.87 1.434

33. 5.002 − 3.45 1.552

34. 6.8 + 3.57 10.37

35. 0.23 + 0.091 0.321

36. 0.5 − 0.18 0.32

37. 8.3 + 2.99 + 17.52 28.81

38. 9.5 + 12.32 + 6.4 28.22

39. 4.521 + 1.8 + 3.07 9.391

40. 3.602 + 9.4 + 24 37.002

41. 11.6 + 8.05 + 5.13 24.78

42. 7.023 + 1.48 + 3.9 12.403

43. 57 + 0.6327 + 189.007 246.6397

44. 741 + 6.08 + 0.0309 747.1109

45. 0.045 + 16.32 + 8.6 24.965

46. 4.27 + 6.18 + 0.91 11.36

47. 3.856 + 14.01 + 1.72 19.586

48. 11.45 + 3.79 + 23.861 39.101

Skills Handbook

Multiplying Decimals

Multiply decimals as you would whole numbers. Then place the decimal point in the product. To do this, add the number of decimal places in the factors.

1 EXAMPLE

Multiply 0.068 × 2.3.

Step 1 Multiply decimals without the decimal point.

$$\begin{array}{r} 0.068 \\ \times\ 2.3 \\ \hline \end{array} \qquad \begin{array}{r} 68 \\ \times\ 23 \\ \hline 204 \\ +\ 1360 \\ \hline 1564 \end{array}$$

Step 2 Place the decimal point.

$$\begin{array}{rl} 0.068 & \leftarrow \text{three decimal places} \\ \times\ 2.3 & \leftarrow \text{one decimal place} \\ \hline 204 & \\ +\ 1360 & \\ \hline 0.1564 & \leftarrow \text{four decimal places} \end{array}$$

2 EXAMPLE

Find each product.

a. 3.12 × 0.9

$$\begin{array}{r} 3.12 \\ \times\ 0.9 \\ \hline 2.808 \end{array}$$

b. 5.75 × 42

$$\begin{array}{r} 5.75 \\ \times\ 42 \\ \hline 1150 \\ +\ 23000 \\ \hline 241.50 \end{array}$$

c. 0.964 × 0.28

$$\begin{array}{r} 0.964 \\ \times\ 0.28 \\ \hline 7712 \\ +\ 19280 \\ \hline 0.26992 \end{array}$$

EXERCISES

Multiply.

1. 1.48 × 3.6 **5.328**
2. 191.1 × 3.4 **649.74**
3. 0.05 × 43 **2.15**
4. 0.27 × 5 **1.35**
5. 1.36 × 3.8 **5.168**

6. 6.23 × 0.21 **1.3083**
7. 0.512 × 0.76 **0.38912**
8. 0.04 × 7 **0.28**
9. 0.136 × 8.4 **1.1424**
10. 3 × 0.05 **0.15**

11. 2.07 × 1.004 **2.07828**
12. 0.12 × 61 **7.32**
13. 3.2 × 0.15 **0.48**
14. 0.74 × 0.23 **0.1702**

15. 2.6 × 0.14 **0.364**
16. 0.77 × 51 **39.27**
17. 9.3 × 0.706 **6.5658**
18. 71.13 × 0.4 **28.452**

19. 0.42 × 98 **41.16**
20. 6.3 × 85 **535.5**
21. 45 × 0.028 **1.26**
22. 76 × 3.3 **250.8**

23. 9 × 1.35 **12.15**
24. 4.56 × 7 **31.92**
25. 5 × 2.41 **12.05**
26. 704 × 0.3 **211.2**

27. 8.003 × 0.6 **4.8018**
28. 42.2 × 0.9 **37.98**
29. 0.6 × 30.02 **18.012**
30. 0.05 × 11.8 **0.59**

Zeros in a Product

When you multiply with decimals, you may have to write one or more zeros to the left of a product before you can place the decimal point.

1 EXAMPLE

Multiply 0.06 × 0.015.

Step 1 Multiply.

$$\begin{array}{r} 0.015 \\ \times\ 0.06 \\ \hline 90 \end{array}$$

Step 2 Place the decimal point.

$$\begin{array}{r} 0.015 \\ \times\ 0.06 \\ \hline 0.00090 \end{array}$$

← three decimal places (0.015)
← two decimal places (0.06)
← The product should have five decimal places, so you must write three zeros before placing the decimal point. (0.00090)

2 EXAMPLE

a. 0.02 × 1.3

$$\begin{array}{r} 1.3 \\ \times\ 0.02 \\ \hline 0.026 \end{array}$$

b. 0.012 × 2.4

$$\begin{array}{r} 2.4 \\ \times\ 0.012 \\ \hline 48 \\ +\ 240 \\ \hline 0.0288 \end{array}$$

c. 0.022 × 0.051

$$\begin{array}{r} 0.051 \\ \times\ 0.022 \\ \hline 102 \\ +\ 1020 \\ \hline 0.001122 \end{array}$$

Skills Handbook

Skills Handbook

EXERCISES

Multiply.

1. 0.03 × 0.9 0.027
2. 0.06 × 0.5 0.03
3. 2.4 × 0.03 0.072
4. 7 × 0.01 0.07
5. 0.05 × 0.05 0.0025
6. 0.016 × 0.12 0.00192
7. 0.031 × 0.08 0.00248
8. 0.03 × 0.2 0.006
9. 0.27 × 0.033 0.00891
10. 0.014 × 0.25 0.0035

11. 0.003 × 0.55 0.00165
12. 0.01 × 0.74 0.0074
13. 0.47 × 0.08 0.0376
14. 0.76 × 0.1 0.076
15. 0.3 × 0.27 0.081
16. 0.19 × 0.05 0.0095
17. 0.018 × 0.04 0.00072
18. 0.43 × 0.2 0.086
19. 0.03 × 0.03 0.0009
20. 4.003 × 0.02 0.08006
21. 0.5 × 0.08 0.04
22. 0.06 × 0.7 0.042
23. 0.047 × 0.008 0.000376
24. 0.05 × 0.06 0.003
25. 0.03 × 0.4 0.012
26. 0.05 × 0.036 0.0018
27. 0.4 × 0.23 0.092
28. 0.3 × 0.017 0.0051
29. 0.3 × 0.24 0.072
30. 0.67 × 0.09 0.0603
31. 3.02 × 0.006 0.01812
32. 0.31 × 0.08 0.0248
33. 0.14 × 0.05 0.007
34. 0.07 × 0.85 0.0595

Dividing Decimals by Whole Numbers

When you divide a decimal by a whole number, the decimal point in the quotient goes directly above the decimal point in the dividend. You may need extra zeros to place the decimal point.

Divide 2.432 ÷ 32.

Step 1 Divide.

```
      76
 32)2.432
   - 2 24
      192
    - 192
        0
```

Step 2 Place the decimal point.

```
   0.076   ← You need two extra zeros to get the
 32)2.432     decimal point in the correct place.
   - 2 24
      192
    - 192
        0
```

2 EXAMPLE

a. 37.6 ÷ 8

```
   4.7
 8)37.6
  - 32
     5 6
   - 5 6
       0
```

b. 39.33 ÷ 69

```
     0.57
 69)39.33
   - 34 5
      4 83
    - 4 83
         0
```

c. 4.482 ÷ 54

```
    0.083
 54)4.482
   - 4 32
      162
    - 162
        0
```

EXERCISES

Divide.

1. 17.92 ÷ 7 2.56	**2.** 16.5 ÷ 5 3.3	**3.** 6.984 ÷ 9 0.776	**4.** 91.44 ÷ 6 15.24
5. 35.16 ÷ 4 8.79	**6.** 8.848 ÷ 56 0.158	**7.** 2.42 ÷ 22 0.11	**8.** 1,723.8 ÷ 26 66.3
9. 15.272 ÷ 83 0.184	**10.** 26.91 ÷ 39 0.69	**11.** 14.49 ÷ 7 2.07	**12.** 10.53 ÷ 9 1.17
13. 17.52 ÷ 2 8.76	**14.** 37.14 ÷ 6 6.19	**15.** 0.1352 ÷ 8 0.0169	**16.** 0.0324 ÷ 9 0.0036
17. 0.0882 ÷ 6 0.0147	**18.** 0.8682 ÷ 6 0.1447	**19.** 12.342 ÷ 22 0.561	**20.** 29.792 ÷ 32 0.931
21. 22.568 ÷ 26 0.868	**22.** 11.340 ÷ 36 0.315	**23.** 45.918 ÷ 18 2.551	**24.** 79.599 ÷ 13 6.123
25. 59.7 ÷ 15 3.98	**26.** 74.664 ÷ 12 6.222	**27.** 2.1 ÷ 84 0.025	**28.** 89.378 ÷ 67 1.334
29. 0.0672 ÷ 48 0.0014	**30.** 171.031 ÷ 53 3.227	**31.** 79.53 ÷ 11 7.23	**32.** 3.2 ÷ 8 0.4
33. 0.378 ÷ 5 0.0756	**34.** 9.76 ÷ 32 0.305	**35.** 0.133 ÷ 7 0.019	**36.** 61.915 ÷ 35 1.769

Multiplying and Dividing by Powers of Ten

You can use shortcuts to multiply or divide by powers of ten.

When you multiply by...	Move the decimal point ...
10,000	4 places to the right.
1,000	3 places to the right.
100	2 places to the right.
10	1 place to the right.
0.1	1 place to the left.
0.01	2 places to the left.
0.001	3 places to the left.

When you divide by...	Move the decimal point ...
10,000	4 places to the left.
1,000	3 places to the left.
100	2 places to the left.
10	1 place to the left.
0.1	1 place to the right.
0.01	2 places to the right.
0.001	3 places to the right.

Skills Handbook

1 EXAMPLE

Multiply.

a. 0.7×0.001

Move the decimal point three places to the left. 0.000.7

$0.7 \times 0.001 = 0.0007$

b. 0.934×100

Move the decimal point two places to the right. 0.93.4

$0.934 \times 100 = 93.4$

2 EXAMPLE

Divide.

a. $0.605 \div 100$

Move the decimal point two places to the left. 0.00.605

$0.605 \div 100 = 0.00605$

b. $0.38 \div 0.001$

Move the decimal point three places to the right. 0.380.

$0.38 \div 0.001 = 380$

EXERCISES

Multiply or divide.

1. $10{,}000 \times 0.056$ 560
2. 0.001×0.09 0.00009
3. 5.2×10 52
4. $0.03 \times 1{,}000$ 30
5. $236.7 \div 0.1$ 2,367
6. $45.28 \div 10$ 4.528
7. $0.9 \div 1{,}000$ 0.0009
8. $1.07 \div 0.01$ 107
9. 100×0.08 8
10. $1.03 \times 10{,}000$ 10,300
11. 1.803×0.001 0.001803
12. 4.1×100 410
13. $13.7 \div 0.001$ 13,700
14. $203.05 \div 0.01$ 20,305
15. $4.7 \div 10$ 0.47
16. $0.05 \div 100$ 0.0005
17. 23.6×0.01 0.236
18. $1{,}000 \times 0.12$ 120
19. $5.02 \div 0.01$ 502
20. $0.27 \div 0.01$ 27

Dividing Decimals by Decimals

To divide with a decimal divisor, multiply it by the smallest power of ten that will make the divisor a whole number. Then multiply the dividend by that same power of ten.

EXAMPLE

Find each quotient.

a. $3.348 \div 6.2$

Multiply by 10.

$$\begin{array}{r} 0.54 \\ 6.2\overline{)3.3.48} \\ -3\,1\,0 \\ \hline 2\,48 \\ -2\,48 \\ \hline 0 \end{array}$$

b. $2.4885 \div 0.35$

Multiply by 100.

$$\begin{array}{r} 7.11 \\ 0.35\overline{)2.48.85} \\ -2\,45 \\ \hline 3\,8 \\ -3\,5 \\ \hline 35 \\ -35 \\ \hline 0 \end{array}$$

c. $0.0576 \div 0.012$

Multiply by 1,000.

$$\begin{array}{r} 4.8 \\ 0.012\overline{)0.057.6} \\ -48 \\ \hline 9\,6 \\ -9\,6 \\ \hline 0 \end{array}$$

EXERCISES

Divide.

1. $268.8 \div 3.2$ 84
2. $123.5 \div 1.9$ 65
3. $135.6 \div 0.3$ 452
4. $170.2 \div 2.3$ 74
5. $252.8 \div 7.9$ 32
6. $10.26 \div 5.7$ 1.8
7. $71.53 \div 2.3$ 31.1
8. $16.12 \div 3.1$ 5.2
9. $24.18 \div 7.8$ 3.1
10. $14.49 \div 6.3$ 2.3
11. $134.42 \div 5.17$ 26
12. $89.96 \div 3.46$ 26
13. $160.58 \div 5.18$ 31
14. $106.59 \div 6.27$ 17
15. $62.4 \div 3.9$ 16
16. $260.4 \div 8.4$ 31
17. $316.8 \div 7.2$ 44
18. $162.4 \div 2.9$ 56
19. $1.512 \div 0.54$ 2.8
20. $3.225 \div 0.43$ 7.5
21. $2.484 \div 0.69$ 3.6
22. $511.5 \div 5.5$ 93
23. $0.992 \div 0.8$ 1.24
24. $4.53 \div 0.05$ 90.6
25. $3.498 \div 0.06$ 58.3
26. $59.2 \div 0.8$ 74
27. $2.198 \div 0.07$ 31.4
28. $14.28 \div 0.7$ 20.4
29. $1.98 \div 0.5$ 3.96
30. $26.36 \div 0.04$ 659
31. $3.922 \div 7.4$ 0.53
32. $23.52 \div 0.98$ 24
33. $71.25 \div 7.5$ 9.5
34. $114.7 \div 3.7$ 31
35. $0.832 \div 0.52$ 1.6
36. $1.125 \div 0.09$ 12.5
37. $9.666 \div 2.7$ 3.58
38. $1.456 \div 9.1$ 0.16
39. $0.4374 \div 1.8$ 0.243

Zeros in Decimal Division

When you are dividing by a decimal, sometimes you need to use extra zeros in the dividend or the quotient, or both.

1 EXAMPLE

Divide 0.045 ÷ 3.6.

Step 1 Multiply by 10.

3.6)0.0.45

Step 2 Divide.

```
     125
36)0.4500
  −36
    90
   −72
    180
   −180
      0
```

Step 3 Place the decimal point.

```
  0.0125
36)0.4500
  −36
    90
   −72
    180
   −180
      0
```

2 EXAMPLE

Find each quotient.

a. 0.4428 ÷ 8.2

Multiply by 10.

8.2)0.4.428 = 0.054

b. 0.00434 ÷ 0.07

Multiply by 100.

0.07.)0.00.434 = 0.062

c. 0.00306 ÷ 0.072

Multiply by 1,000.

0.072.)0.003.0600 = 0.0425

EXERCISES

Divide. 1–32. See margin.

1. 0.0023 ÷ 0.05	**2.** 0.000162 ÷ 0.02	**3.** 0.009 ÷ 0.12	**4.** 0.021 ÷ 2.5
5. 0.0019 ÷ 0.2	**6.** 0.9 ÷ 0.8	**7.** 0.000175 ÷ 0.07	**8.** 0.142 ÷ 0.04
9. 0.0017 ÷ 0.02	**10.** 0.003 ÷ 0.6	**11.** 0.0105 ÷ 0.7	**12.** 0.034 ÷ 0.05
13. 0.00056 ÷ 0.16	**14.** 0.0612 ÷ 7.2	**15.** 0.217 ÷ 3.1	**16.** 0.052 ÷ 0.8
17. 0.000924 ÷ 0.44	**18.** 0.05796 ÷ 0.63	**19.** 0.00123 ÷ 8.2	**20.** 0.0954 ÷ 0.09
21. 0.0084 ÷ 1.4	**22.** 0.259 ÷ 3.5	**23.** 0.00468 ÷ 0.52	**24.** 0.104 ÷ 0.05
25. 0.00063 ÷ 0.18	**26.** 0.011 ÷ 0.25	**27.** 0.3069 ÷ 9.3	**28.** 0.00045 ÷ 0.3
29. 0.6497 ÷ 8.9	**30.** 0.00246 ÷ 0.06	**31.** 0.00168 ÷ 0.3	**32.** 0.00816 ÷ 3.4

1. 0.046
2. 0.0081
3. 0.075
4. 0.0084
5. 0.0095
6. 1.125
7. 0.0025
8. 3.55
9. 0.085
10. 0.005
11. 0.015
12. 0.68
13. 0.0035
14. 0.0085
15. 0.07
16. 0.065
17. 0.0021
18. 0.092
19. 0.00015
20. 1.06
21. 0.006
22. 0.074
23. 0.009
24. 2.08
25. 0.0035
26. 0.044
27. 0.033
28. 0.0015
29. 0.073
30. 0.041
31. 0.0056
32. 0.0024

Mixed Numbers and Improper Fractions

A fraction, such as $\frac{10}{7}$, in which the numerator is greater than or equal to the denominator is an improper fraction. You can write an improper fraction as a mixed number that shows the sum of a whole number and a fraction.

Sometimes it is necessary to do the opposite and write a mixed number as an improper fraction.

EXAMPLE

a. Write $\frac{11}{5}$ as a mixed number.

$\frac{11}{5} \rightarrow$ $5\overline{)11}$ with quotient 2 ← **whole number**

$-\ 10$

1 ← **remainder**

$\frac{11}{5} = 2\frac{1}{5}$ ← **whole number +** $\frac{\textbf{remainder}}{\textbf{denominator}}$

b. Write $2\frac{5}{6}$ as an improper fraction.

$2\frac{5}{6} = 2 + \frac{5}{6}$

$= \frac{12}{6} + \frac{5}{6}$ ← **Write 2 as $\frac{12}{6}$.**

$= \frac{12 + 5}{6}$ ← **Add the numerators.**

$= \frac{17}{6}$

$2\frac{5}{6} = \frac{17}{6}$ ← **Simplify.**

EXERCISES

Write each improper fraction as a mixed number.

1. $\frac{7}{5}$ $1\frac{2}{5}$	**2.** $\frac{9}{2}$ $4\frac{1}{2}$	**3.** $\frac{13}{4}$ $3\frac{1}{4}$	**4.** $\frac{21}{5}$ $4\frac{1}{5}$	**5.** $\frac{13}{10}$ $1\frac{3}{10}$
6. $\frac{49}{5}$ $9\frac{4}{5}$	**7.** $\frac{21}{8}$ $2\frac{5}{8}$	**8.** $\frac{13}{7}$ $1\frac{6}{7}$	**9.** $\frac{17}{5}$ $3\frac{2}{5}$	**10.** $\frac{49}{6}$ $8\frac{1}{6}$
11. $\frac{17}{4}$ $4\frac{1}{4}$	**12.** $\frac{5}{2}$ $2\frac{1}{2}$	**13.** $\frac{27}{5}$ $5\frac{2}{5}$	**14.** $\frac{12}{9}$ $1\frac{1}{3}$	**15.** $\frac{30}{8}$ $3\frac{3}{4}$
16. $\frac{37}{12}$ $3\frac{1}{12}$	**17.** $\frac{8}{6}$ $1\frac{1}{3}$	**18.** $\frac{19}{12}$ $1\frac{7}{12}$	**19.** $\frac{45}{10}$ $4\frac{1}{2}$	**20.** $\frac{15}{12}$ $1\frac{1}{4}$
21. $\frac{11}{2}$ $5\frac{1}{2}$	**22.** $\frac{20}{6}$ $3\frac{1}{3}$	**23.** $\frac{34}{8}$ $4\frac{1}{4}$	**24.** $\frac{21}{9}$ $2\frac{1}{3}$	**25.** $\frac{42}{4}$ $10\frac{1}{2}$

Write each mixed number as an improper fraction.

26. $1\frac{1}{2}$ $\frac{3}{2}$	**27.** $2\frac{2}{3}$ $\frac{8}{3}$	**28.** $1\frac{1}{12}$ $\frac{13}{12}$	**29.** $3\frac{1}{5}$ $\frac{16}{5}$	**30.** $2\frac{2}{7}$ $\frac{16}{7}$
31. $4\frac{1}{2}$ $\frac{9}{2}$	**32.** $2\frac{7}{8}$ $\frac{23}{8}$	**33.** $1\frac{2}{9}$ $\frac{11}{9}$	**34.** $5\frac{1}{5}$ $\frac{26}{5}$	**35.** $4\frac{7}{9}$ $\frac{43}{9}$
36. $9\frac{1}{4}$ $\frac{37}{4}$	**37.** $2\frac{3}{8}$ $\frac{19}{8}$	**38.** $7\frac{7}{8}$ $\frac{63}{8}$	**39.** $1\frac{5}{12}$ $\frac{17}{12}$	**40.** $3\frac{3}{7}$ $\frac{24}{7}$
41. $6\frac{1}{2}$ $\frac{13}{2}$	**42.** $3\frac{1}{10}$ $\frac{31}{10}$	**43.** $4\frac{6}{7}$ $\frac{34}{7}$	**44.** $8\frac{1}{8}$ $\frac{65}{8}$	**45.** $6\frac{1}{3}$ $\frac{19}{3}$

Adding and Subtracting Fractions With Like Denominators

When you add or subtract fractions with the same denominator, add or subtract the numerators and then write the answer over the denominator.

1 EXAMPLE

Add or subtract. Write the answers in simplest form.

a. $\frac{5}{8} + \frac{7}{8}$

$\frac{5}{8} + \frac{7}{8} = \frac{5+7}{8} = \frac{12}{8} = 1\frac{4}{8} = 1\frac{1}{2}$

b. $\frac{11}{12} - \frac{2}{12}$

$\frac{11}{12} - \frac{2}{12} = \frac{11-2}{12} = \frac{9}{12} = \frac{3}{4}$

To add or subtract mixed numbers, add or subtract the fractions first. Then add or subtract the whole numbers.

2 EXAMPLE

Add or subtract. Write the answers in simplest form.

a. $3\frac{4}{6} + 2\frac{5}{6}$

$$\begin{array}{r} 3\frac{4}{6} \\ +2\frac{5}{6} \\ \hline 5\frac{9}{6} \end{array} = 5 + 1 + \frac{3}{6} = 6\frac{1}{2}$$

b. $6\frac{1}{4} - 1\frac{3}{4}$ ← Rewrite 6 as $5\frac{4}{4}$ and add it to $\frac{1}{4}$.

$$\begin{array}{r} 6\frac{1}{4} \\ -1\frac{3}{4} \\ \hline \end{array} \rightarrow \begin{array}{r} 5\frac{5}{4} \\ -1\frac{3}{4} \\ \hline 4\frac{2}{4} \end{array} = 4\frac{1}{2}$$

EXERCISES

Add or subtract. Write the answers in simplest form.

1. $\frac{4}{5} + \frac{3}{5}$ $1\frac{2}{5}$
2. $\frac{2}{6} - \frac{1}{6}$ $\frac{1}{6}$
3. $\frac{2}{7} + \frac{2}{7}$ $\frac{4}{7}$
4. $\frac{7}{8} + \frac{2}{8}$ $1\frac{1}{8}$
5. $1\frac{2}{5} - \frac{1}{5}$ $1\frac{1}{5}$

6. $\frac{3}{6} - \frac{1}{6}$ $\frac{1}{3}$
7. $\frac{6}{8} - \frac{3}{8}$ $\frac{3}{8}$
8. $\frac{2}{9} + \frac{1}{9}$ $\frac{1}{3}$
9. $\frac{4}{5} - \frac{1}{5}$ $\frac{3}{5}$
10. $\frac{5}{9} + \frac{7}{9}$ $1\frac{1}{3}$

11. $9\frac{1}{3} - 8\frac{1}{3}$ 1
12. $8\frac{6}{7} - 4\frac{2}{7}$ $4\frac{4}{7}$
13. $3\frac{1}{10} + 1\frac{3}{10}$ $4\frac{2}{5}$
14. $2\frac{2}{9} + 3\frac{4}{9}$ $5\frac{2}{3}$

15. $4\frac{5}{12} - 3\frac{1}{12}$ $1\frac{1}{3}$
16. $9\frac{5}{9} + 6\frac{7}{9}$ $16\frac{1}{3}$
17. $5\frac{7}{8} + 2\frac{3}{8}$ $8\frac{1}{4}$
18. $4\frac{4}{7} - 2\frac{1}{7}$ $2\frac{3}{7}$

19. $9\frac{3}{4} + 1\frac{3}{4}$ $11\frac{1}{2}$
20. $8\frac{2}{3} - 4\frac{1}{3}$ $4\frac{1}{3}$
21. $8\frac{7}{10} + 2\frac{3}{10}$ 11
22. $1\frac{4}{5} + 3\frac{3}{5}$ $5\frac{2}{5}$

23. $7\frac{1}{5} - 2\frac{3}{5}$ $4\frac{3}{5}$
24. $4\frac{1}{3} - 1\frac{2}{3}$ $2\frac{2}{3}$
25. $4\frac{3}{8} - 3\frac{5}{8}$ $\frac{3}{4}$
26. $5\frac{1}{12} - 2\frac{7}{12}$ $2\frac{1}{2}$

Skills Handbook

Classifying and Measuring Angles

Recall that an angle is a geometric figure formed by two rays with a common endpoint. The rays are sides of the angle and the endpoint is the vertex of the angle. You can name the angle at the right in three different ways: $\angle A$, $\angle BAC$, or $\angle CAB$.

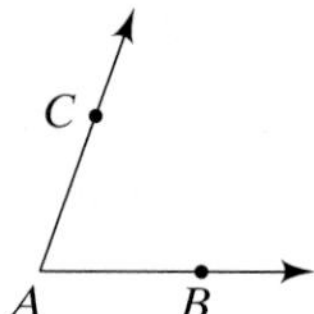

Classify angles by their measures.

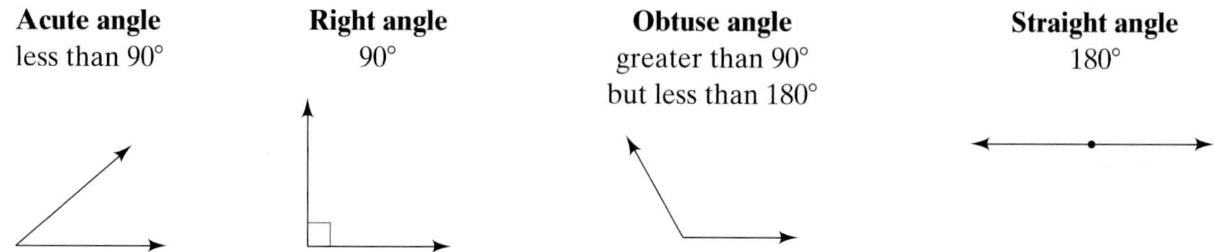

EXAMPLE

Measure the angle. Classify it as *acute, right, obtuse,* or *straight.*

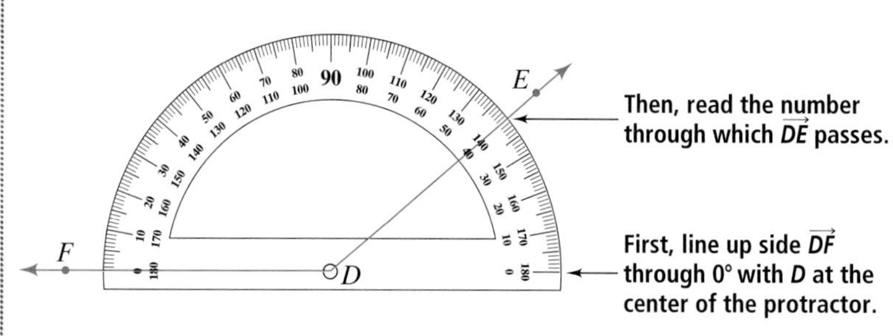

The measure of the angle is 140°. The angle is obtuse.

EXERCISES

1–4. Measures may vary. Samples are given.

Measure each angle. Classify it as *acute, right, obtuse,* or *straight.*

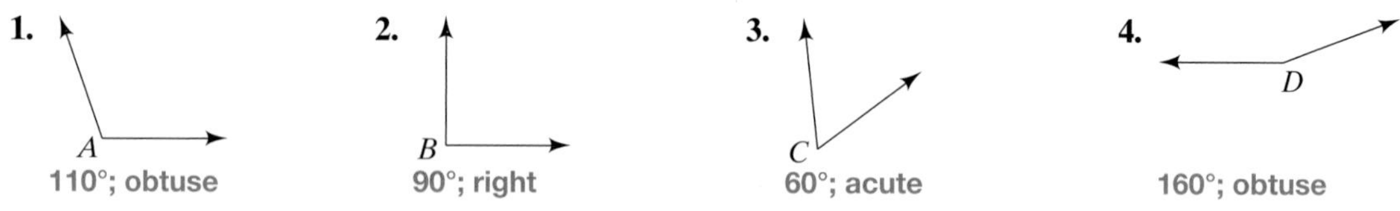

Classify each angle as *acute, right, obtuse,* or *straight.*

5. 30° acute **6.** 45° acute **7.** 95° obtuse **8.** 180° straight **9.** 140° obtuse **10.** 170° obtuse

Bar Graphs

Use bar graphs to compare amounts. The horizontal axis shows the categories and the vertical axis shows the amounts. A multiple bar graph includes a key.

Draw a bar graph for the data in the table at the right.

Place the categories (in the first column) on the horizontal scale. Place the amounts (in the second and third columns) on the vertical scale. Include a key to the two price categories.

List and Sale Prices

Item	List	Sale
Pocket PC	$450	$400
Digital Camera	$500	$350
Minidisc Player/Recorder	$230	$180

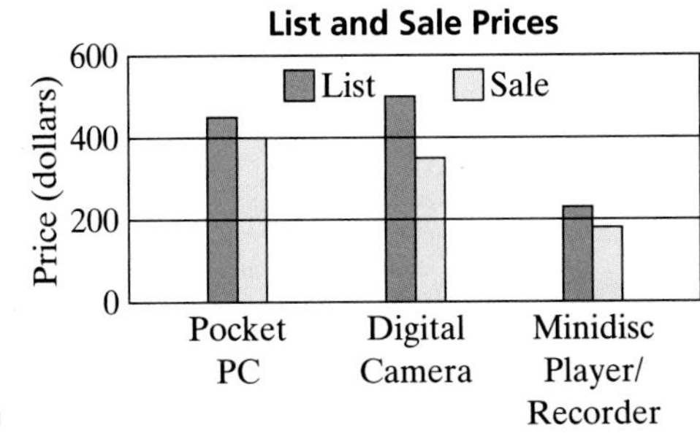

EXERCISES

Draw a bar graph for each set of data. 1–2. See margin.

1. **Meat Consumption (pounds per person per year)**

Beef	Chicken	Pork	Turkey
62.9	53.9	46.7	13.7

SOURCE: U.S. Department of Agriculture. Go to **www.PHSchool.com** for a data update. Web Code: acg-2041

2. **Pets in Students' Homes**

Number of Pets	0	1	2	3	more than 3
Number of Students	11	16	9	11	6

Draw a multiple bar graph for the set of data. 3–4. See margin.

3. **Weekly Leisure Time (hours)**

Activity	Sports	Reading	Working
Anna	12	8	12
Tobi	6	12	10

4. **Average SAT Math and Verbal Scores**

Year	1998	1999	2000
Math	511	514	514
Verbal	505	505	506

SOURCE: U.S. Dept. of Education. Go to **www.PHSchool.com** for a data update. Web Code: acg-2041

1.

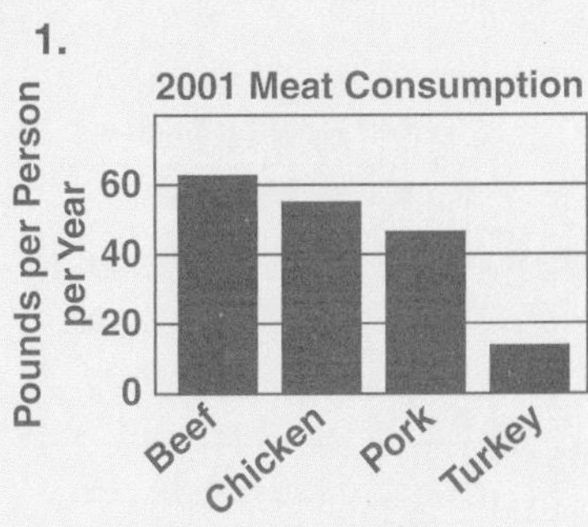

2.

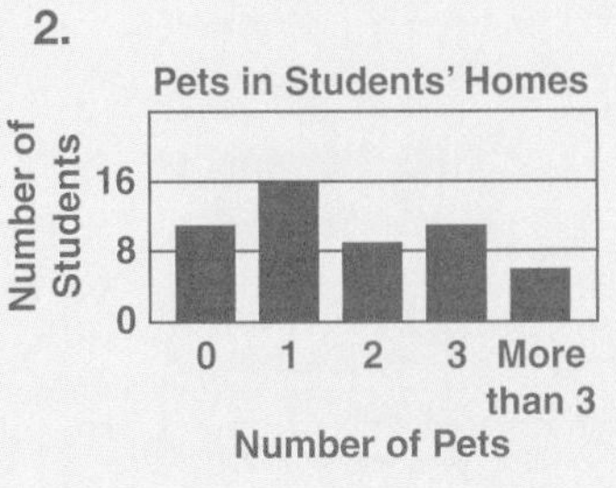

3.

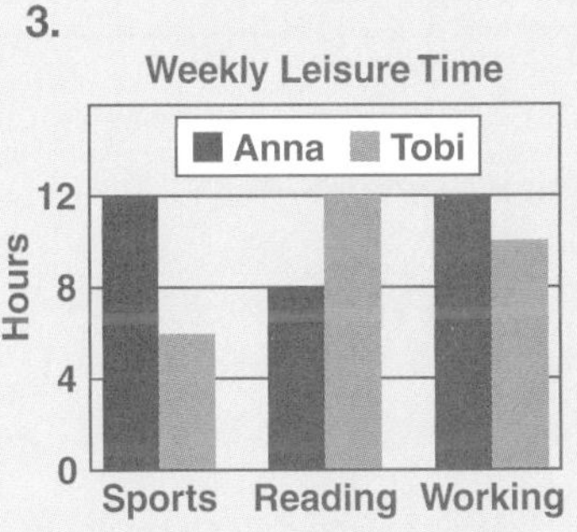

4.

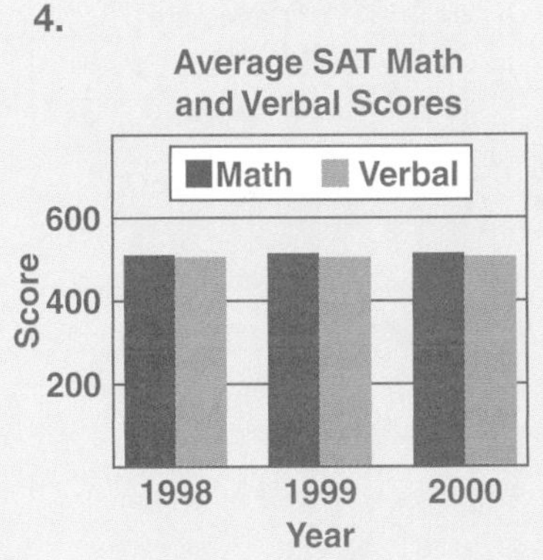

Skills Handbook

1.

Average Baseball and Hockey Salaries

Baseball
Hockey

Salary (Millions of Dollars)

2.5
2.0
1.5
1.0
0.5
0

1998 1999 2000 2001

Year

2.

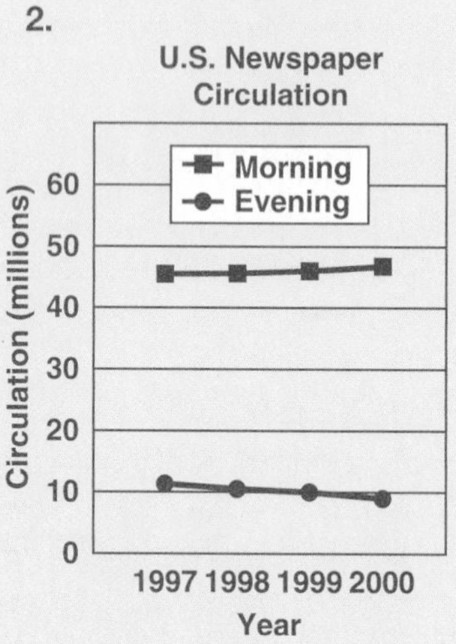

3.

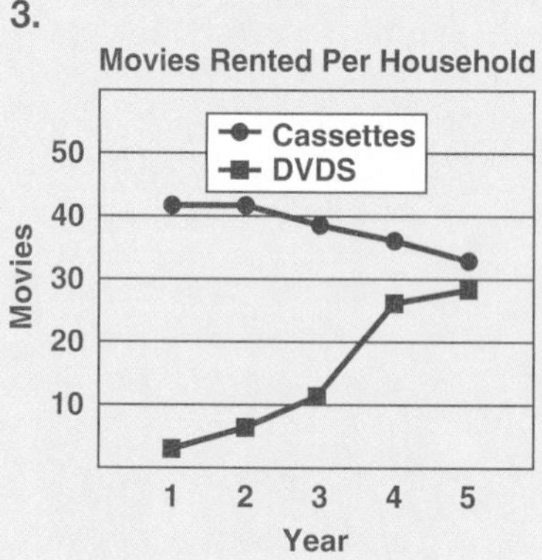

4.

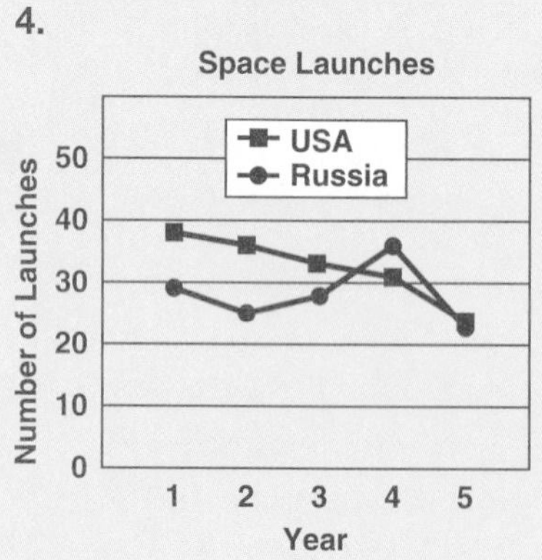

Line Graphs

Use line graphs to show changes over time. A multiple line graph shows more than one category changing over time. Use the same vertical scale for both categories.

EXAMPLE

Display the data in the table below in a line graph.

Monthly Average Temperatures (°F)

Month	J	F	M	A	M	J	J	A	S	O	N	D
Houston, Texas	50	54	61	68	75	80	83	82	78	70	61	54
Chicago, Illinois	21	25	37	49	59	69	73	72	64	53	40	27

SOURCE: National Climatic Data Center. Go to **www.PHSchool.com** for a data update. Web Code: acg-2041

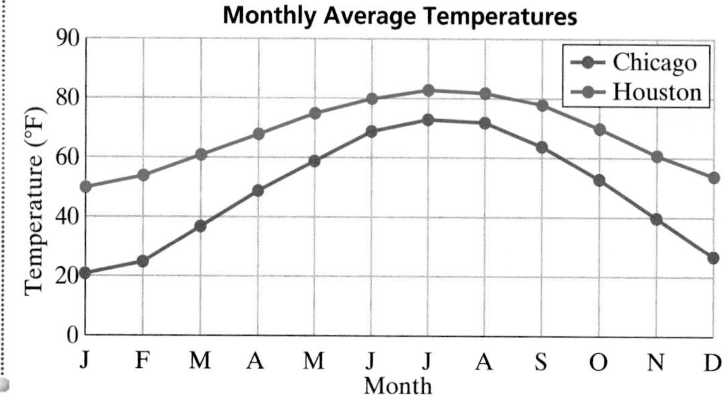

EXERCISES

Draw multiple line graphs for the data below. 1–4. See margin.

1. **Average Baseball and Hockey Salaries (millions of dollars)**

Year	1998	1999	2000	2001
Baseball	1.4	1.6	1.9	2.1
Hockey	1.3	1.4	1.4	1.6

SOURCE: Major League Baseball Players Association and National Hockey League

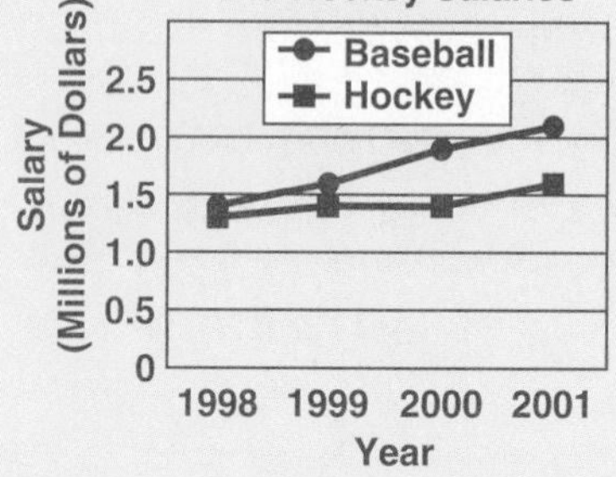

2. **U.S. Newspaper Circulation (millions)**

Year	1997	1998	1999	2000
Morning	45.4	45.6	46.0	46.8
Evening	11.3	10.5	10.0	9.0

SOURCE: U.S. Census Bureau. Go to **www.PHSchool.com** for a data update. Web Code: acg-2041

3. **Movies Rented per Household**

Year	1	2	3	4	5
Videos	40.8	40.1	38.9	35.2	33.8
DVDs	3.1	8.5	10.9	25.4	29.9

4. **Space Launches**

Year	1	2	3	4	5
United States	38	36	33	31	24
Russia	29	25	28	36	23

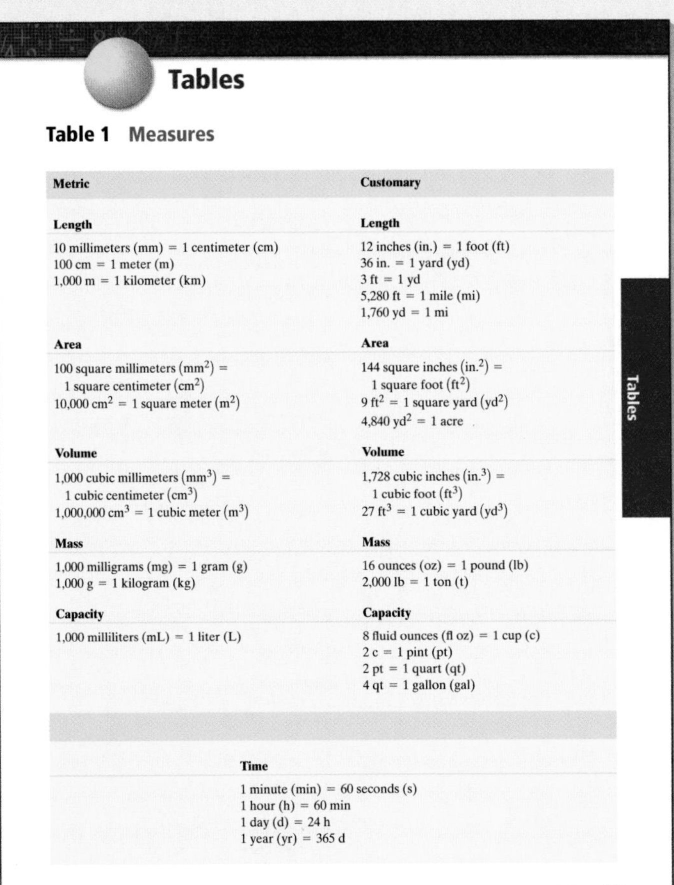

Tables

Table 1 Measures

Metric	Customary
Length	**Length**
10 millimeters (mm) = 1 centimeter (cm) 100 cm = 1 meter (m) 1,000 m = 1 kilometer (km)	12 inches (in.) = 1 foot (ft) 36 in. = 1 yard (yd) 3 ft = 1 yd 5,280 ft = 1 mile (mi) 1,760 yd = 1 mi
Area	**Area**
100 square millimeters (mm^2) = 1 square centimeter (cm^2) 10,000 cm^2 = 1 square meter (m^2)	144 square inches ($in.^2$) = 1 square foot (ft^2) 9 ft^2 = 1 square yard (yd^2) 4,840 yd^2 = 1 acre
Volume	**Volume**
1,000 cubic millimeters (mm^3) = 1 cubic centimeter (cm^3) 1,000,000 cm^3 = 1 cubic meter (m^3)	1,728 cubic inches ($in.^3$) = 1 cubic foot (ft^3) 27 ft^3 = 1 cubic yard (yd^3)
Mass	**Mass**
1,000 milligrams (mg) = 1 gram (g) 1,000 g = 1 kilogram (kg)	16 ounces (oz) = 1 pound (lb) 2,000 lb = 1 ton (t)
Capacity	**Capacity**
1,000 milliliters (mL) = 1 liter (L)	8 fluid ounces (fl oz) = 1 cup (c) 2 c = 1 pint (pt) 2 pt = 1 quart (qt) 4 qt = 1 gallon (gal)

Time
1 minute (min) = 60 seconds (s) 1 hour (h) = 60 min 1 day (d) = 24 h 1 year (yr) = 365 d

Tables

Table 2 Reading Math Symbols

Symbol	Meaning	Page
$+$	plus (addition)	p. 5
$-$	minus (subtraction)	p. 5
$\times, \cdot$	times (multiplication)	p. 5
$\div, \overline{)}$	divide (division)	p. 5
$=$	is equal to	p. 6
( )	parentheses for grouping	p. 7
[ ]	brackets for grouping	p. 7
$-a$	opposite of a	p. 16
. . .	and so on	p. 16
°	degrees	p. 16
$\lvert a \rvert$	absolute value of a	p. 17
$<$	is less than	p. 19
$>$	is greater than	p. 19
$\approx$	is approximately equal to	p. 35
a^n	nth power of a	p. 39
$\stackrel{?}{=}$	Is the statement true?	p. 62
$\leq$	is less than or equal to	p. 90
$\geq$	is greater than or equal to	p. 90
$\neq$	is not equal to	p. 90
(a, b)	ordered pair with x-coordinate a and y-coordinate b	p. 118
b	y-intercept	p. 137
m	slope of a line	p. 137
A'	image of A, A prime	p. 157
$\triangle ABC$	triangle with vertices A, B, and C	p. 158
$\rightarrow$	arrow notation	p. 158
$\overline{AB}$	segment AB	p. 167
$\frac{b}{a}$	reciprocal of $\frac{a}{b}$	p. 206
A	area	p. 212
ℓ	length	p. 212
w	width	p. 212
h	height	p. 212
b_1, b_2	base lengths of a trapezoid	p. 212
d	distance	p. 213
r	rate	p. 213
t	time	p. 213
P	perimeter	p. 213
$\sqrt{x}$	nonnegative square root of x	p. 221
π	pi, an irrational number, approximately equal to 3.14	p. 223
$a : b, \frac{a}{b}$	ratio of a to b	p. 243
$\cong$	is congruent to	p. 265
$\sim$	is similar to	p. 265
$\angle A$	angle with vertex A	p. 265
AB	length of segment $\overline{AB}$	p. 265
$\angle ABC$	angle with sides $\overrightarrow{BA}$ and $\overrightarrow{BC}$	p. 268
$\overrightarrow{AB}$	ray AB	p. 271
$\sin A$	sine of $\angle A$	p. 287
$\cos A$	cosine of $\angle A$	p. 287
$\tan A$	tangent of $\angle A$	p. 292
%	percent	p. 303
P(event)	probability of an event	p. 349
$m\angle ABC$	measure of angle ABC	p. 407
$\overleftrightarrow{AB}$	line AB	p. 409
$\parallel$	is parallel to	p. 415
b	base length	p. 441
C	circumference	p. 447
d	diameter	p. 447
r	radius	p. 447
S.A.	surface area	p. 488
B	area of base	p. 489
L.A.	lateral area	p. 489
ℓ	slant height	p. 494
V	volume	p. 500
$n!$	n factorial	p. 596
$_nP_r$	permutations of n things taken r at a time	p. 597
$_nC_r$	combinations of n things taken r at a time	p. 601
$f(n)$	the function value at n, f of n	p. 644
$\perp$	is perpendicular to	p. 761

Tables

Table 3 Squares and Square Roots

Number n	Square n^2	Positive Square Root $\sqrt{n}$	Number n	Square n^2	Positive Square Root $\sqrt{n}$
1	1	1.000	51	2,601	7.141
2	4	1.414	52	2,704	7.211
3	9	1.732	53	2,809	7.280
4	16	2.000	54	2,916	7.348
5	25	2.236	55	3,025	7.416
6	36	2.449	56	3,136	7.483
7	49	2.646	57	3,249	7.550
8	64	2.828	58	3,364	7.616
9	81	3.000	59	3,481	7.681
10	100	3.162	60	3,600	7.746
11	121	3.317	61	3,721	7.810
12	144	3.464	62	3,844	7.874
13	169	3.606	63	3,969	7.937
14	196	3.742	64	4,096	8.000
15	225	3.873	65	4,225	8.062
16	256	4.000	66	4,356	8.124
17	289	4.123	67	4,489	8.185
18	324	4.243	68	4,624	8.246
19	361	4.359	69	4,761	8.307
20	400	4.472	70	4,900	8.367
21	441	4.583	71	5,041	8.426
22	484	4.690	72	5,184	8.485
23	529	4.796	73	5,329	8.544
24	576	4.899	74	5,476	8.602
25	625	5.000	75	5,625	8.660
26	676	5.099	76	5,776	8.718
27	729	5.196	77	5,929	8.775
28	784	5.292	78	6,084	8.832
29	841	5.385	79	6,241	8.888
30	900	5.477	80	6,400	8.944
31	961	5.568	81	6,561	9.000
32	1,024	5.657	82	6,724	9.055
33	1,089	5.745	83	6,889	9.110
34	1,156	5.831	84	7,056	9.165
35	1,225	5.916	85	7,225	9.220
36	1,296	6.000	86	7,396	9.274
37	1,369	6.083	87	7,569	9.327
38	1,444	6.164	88	7,744	9.381
39	1,521	6.245	89	7,921	9.434
40	1,600	6.325	90	8,100	9.487
41	1,681	6.403	91	8,281	9.539
42	1,764	6.481	92	8,464	9.592
43	1,849	6.557	93	8,649	9.644
44	1,936	6.633	94	8,836	9.695
45	2,025	6.708	95	9,025	9.747
46	2,116	6.782	96	9,216	9.798
47	2,209	6.856	97	9,409	9.849
48	2,304	6.928	98	9,604	9.899
49	2,401	7.000	99	9,801	9.950
50	2,500	7.071	100	10,000	10.000

Table 4 Trigonometric Ratios

Angle	Sine	Cosine	Tangent	Angle	Sine	Cosine	Tangent
1°	0.0175	0.9998	0.0175	46°	0.7193	0.6947	1.0355
2°	0.0349	0.9994	0.0349	47°	0.7314	0.6820	1.0724
3°	0.0523	0.9986	0.0524	48°	0.7431	0.6691	1.1106
4°	0.0698	0.9976	0.0699	49°	0.7547	0.6561	1.1504
5°	0.0872	0.9962	0.0875	50°	0.7660	0.6428	1.1918
6°	0.1045	0.9945	0.1051	51°	0.7771	0.6293	1.2349
7°	0.1219	0.9925	0.1228	52°	0.7880	0.6157	1.2799
8°	0.1392	0.9903	0.1405	53°	0.7986	0.6018	1.3270
9°	0.1564	0.9877	0.1584	54°	0.8090	0.5878	1.3764
10°	0.1736	0.9848	0.1763	55°	0.8192	0.5736	1.4281
11°	0.1908	0.9816	0.1944	56°	0.8290	0.5592	1.4826
12°	0.2079	0.9781	0.2126	57°	0.8387	0.5446	1.5399
13°	0.2250	0.9744	0.2309	58°	0.8480	0.5299	1.6003
14°	0.2419	0.9703	0.2493	59°	0.8572	0.5150	1.6643
15°	0.2588	0.9659	0.2679	60°	0.8660	0.5000	1.7321
16°	0.2756	0.9613	0.2867	61°	0.8746	0.4848	1.8040
17°	0.2924	0.9563	0.3057	62°	0.8829	0.4695	1.8807
18°	0.3090	0.9511	0.3249	63°	0.8910	0.4540	1.9626
19°	0.3256	0.9455	0.3443	64°	0.8988	0.4384	2.0503
20°	0.3420	0.9397	0.3640	65°	0.9063	0.4226	2.1445
21°	0.3584	0.9336	0.3839	66°	0.9135	0.4067	2.2460
22°	0.3746	0.9272	0.4040	67°	0.9205	0.3907	2.3559
23°	0.3907	0.9205	0.4245	68°	0.9272	0.3746	2.4751
24°	0.4067	0.9135	0.4452	69°	0.9336	0.3584	2.6051
25°	0.4226	0.9063	0.4663	70°	0.9397	0.3420	2.7475
26°	0.4384	0.8988	0.4877	71°	0.9455	0.3256	2.9042
27°	0.4540	0.8910	0.5095	72°	0.9511	0.3090	3.0777
28°	0.4695	0.8829	0.5317	73°	0.9563	0.2924	3.2709
29°	0.4848	0.8746	0.5543	74°	0.9613	0.2756	3.4874
30°	0.5000	0.8660	0.5774	75°	0.9659	0.2588	3.7321
31°	0.5150	0.8572	0.6009	76°	0.9703	0.2419	4.0108
32°	0.5299	0.8480	0.6249	77°	0.9744	0.2250	4.3315
33°	0.5446	0.8387	0.6494	78°	0.9781	0.2079	4.7046
34°	0.5592	0.8290	0.6745	79°	0.9816	0.1908	5.1446
35°	0.5736	0.8192	0.7002	80°	0.9848	0.1736	5.6713
36°	0.5878	0.8090	0.7265	81°	0.9877	0.1564	6.3138
37°	0.6018	0.7986	0.7536	82°	0.9903	0.1392	7.1154
38°	0.6157	0.7880	0.7813	83°	0.9925	0.1219	8.1443
39°	0.6293	0.7771	0.8098	84°	0.9945	0.1045	9.5144
40°	0.6428	0.7660	0.8391	85°	0.9962	0.0872	11.4301
41°	0.6561	0.7547	0.8693	86°	0.9976	0.0698	14.3007
42°	0.6691	0.7431	0.9004	87°	0.9986	0.0523	19.0811
43°	0.6820	0.7314	0.9325	88°	0.9994	0.0349	28.6363
44°	0.6947	0.7193	0.9657	89°	0.9998	0.0175	57.2900
45°	0.7071	0.7071	1.0000	90°	1.0000	0.0000	

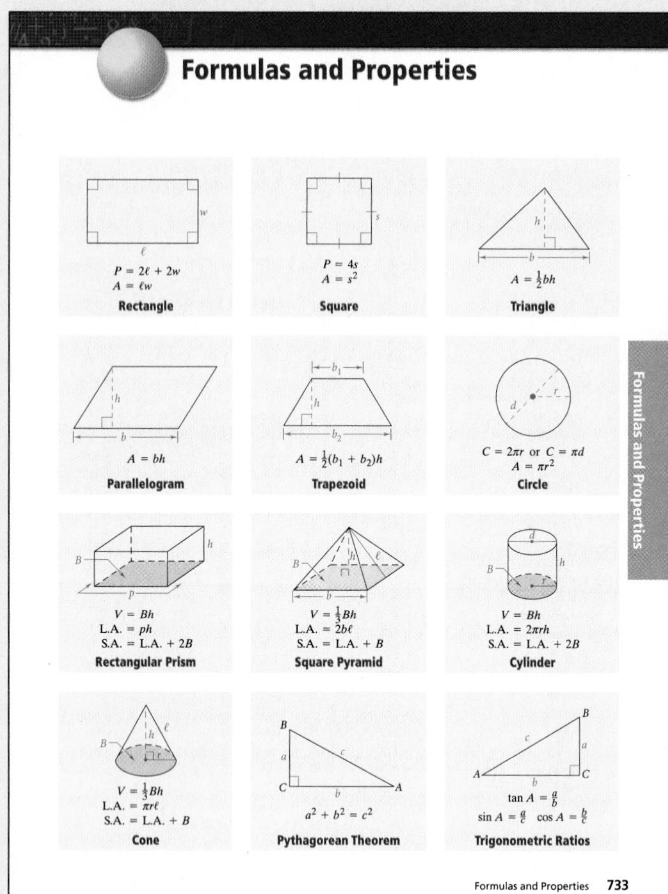

Formulas and Properties
$P = 2\ell + 2w$
$A = \ell w$
Rectangle
$P = 4s$
$A = s^2$
Square
$A = \frac{1}{2}bh$
Triangle
$A = bh$
Parallelogram
$A = \frac{1}{2}(b_1 + b_2)h$
Trapezoid
$C = 2\pi r$ or $C = \pi d$
$A = \pi r^2$
Circle
$V = Bh$
L.A. = ph
S.A. = L.A. + $2B$
Rectangular Prism
$V = \frac{1}{3}Bh$
L.A. = $2b\ell$
S.A. = L.A. + B
Square Pyramid
$V = Bh$
L.A. = $2\pi rh$
S.A. = L.A. + $2B$
Cylinder
$V = \frac{1}{3}Bh$
L.A. = $\pi r\ell$
S.A. = L.A. + B
Cone
$a^2 + b^2 = c^2$
Pythagorean Theorem
$\tan A = \frac{a}{b}$
$\sin A = \frac{a}{c}$ $\cos A = \frac{b}{c}$
Trigonometric Ratios
Formulas and Properties
Formulas and Properties 733

Properties of Real Numbers

Unless otherwise stated, the variables a, b, c, and d used in these properties can be replaced with any number represented on a number line.

Identity Properties

Addition $a + 0 = a$ and $0 + a = a$

Multiplication $a \cdot 1 = a$ and $1 \cdot a = a$

Commutative Properties

Addition $a + b = b + a$

Multiplication $a \cdot b = b \cdot a$

Associative Properties

Addition $(a + b) + c = a + (b + c)$

Multiplication $(a \cdot b) \cdot c = a \cdot (b \cdot c)$

Inverse Properties

Addition

$a + (-a) = 0$ and $-a + a = 0$

Multiplication

$a \cdot \frac{1}{a} = 1$ and $\frac{1}{a} \cdot a = 1$ $(a \neq 0)$

Distributive Properties

$a(b + c) = ab + ac$ $(b + c)a = ba + ca$

$a(b - c) = ab - ac$ $(b - c)a = ba - ca$

Properties of Equality

Addition If $a = b$, then $a + c = b + c$.

Subtraction If $a = b$, then $a - c = b - c$.

Multiplication If $a = b$, then $a \cdot c = b \cdot c$.

Division If $a = b$, and $c \neq 0$, then $\frac{a}{c} = \frac{b}{c}$.

Substitution If $a = b$, then b can replace a in any expression.

Reflexive $a = a$

Symmetric If $a = b$, then $b = a$.

Transitive If $a = b$ and $b = c$, then $a = c$.

Cross Product Property

$\frac{a}{c} = \frac{b}{d}$ is equivalent to $ad = bc$.

Zero-Product Property

If $ab = 0$, then $a = 0$ or $b = 0$.

Closure Property

$a + b$ is a unique real number.

ab is a unique real number.

Density Property

Between any two rational numbers, there is at least one other rational number.

Properties of Inequality

Addition If $a > b$, then $a + c > b + c$.
If $a < b$, then $a + c < b + c$.

Subtraction If $a > b$, then $a - c > b - c$.
If $a < b$, then $a - c < b - c$.

Multiplication

If $a > b$ and $c > 0$, then $ac > bc$.
If $a < b$ and $c > 0$, then $ac < bc$.
If $a > b$ and $c < 0$, then $ac < bc$.
If $a < b$ and $c < 0$, then $ac > bc$.

Division

If $a > b$ and $c > 0$, then $\frac{a}{c} > \frac{b}{c}$.
If $a < b$ and $c > 0$, then $\frac{a}{c} < \frac{b}{c}$.
If $a > b$ and $c < 0$, then $\frac{a}{c} < \frac{b}{c}$.
If $a < b$ and $c < 0$, then $\frac{a}{c} > \frac{b}{c}$.

Transitive

If $a > b$ and $b > c$, then $a > c$.

Comparative

If $a = b + c$ and $c > 0$, then $a > b$.

Properties of Exponents

For any nonzero number a and any integers m and n:

Zero Exponent $a^0 = 1$

Negative Exponent $a^{-n} = \frac{1}{a^n}$

Product of Powers $a^m \cdot a^n = a^{m+n}$

Quotient of Powers $\frac{a^m}{a^n} = a^{m-n}$

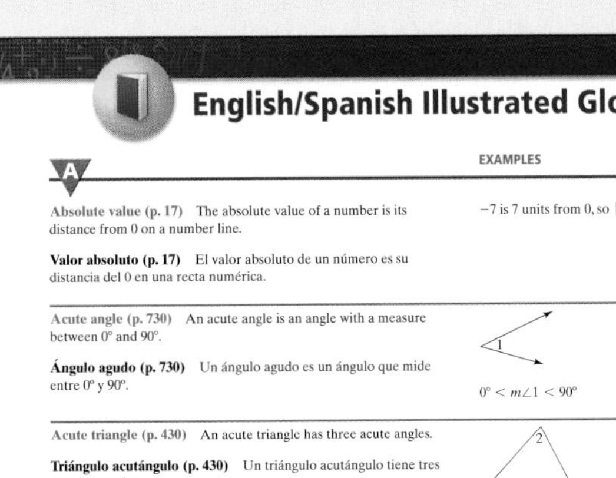

English/Spanish Illustrated Glossary

A

EXAMPLES

Absolute value (p. 17) The absolute value of a number is its distance from 0 on a number line.

Valor absoluto (p. 17) El valor absoluto de un número es su distancia del 0 en una recta numérica.

-7 is 7 units from 0, so $|-7| = 7$.

Acute angle (p. 730) An acute angle is an angle with a measure between 0° and 90°.

Ángulo agudo (p. 730) Un ángulo agudo es un ángulo que mide entre 0° y 90°.

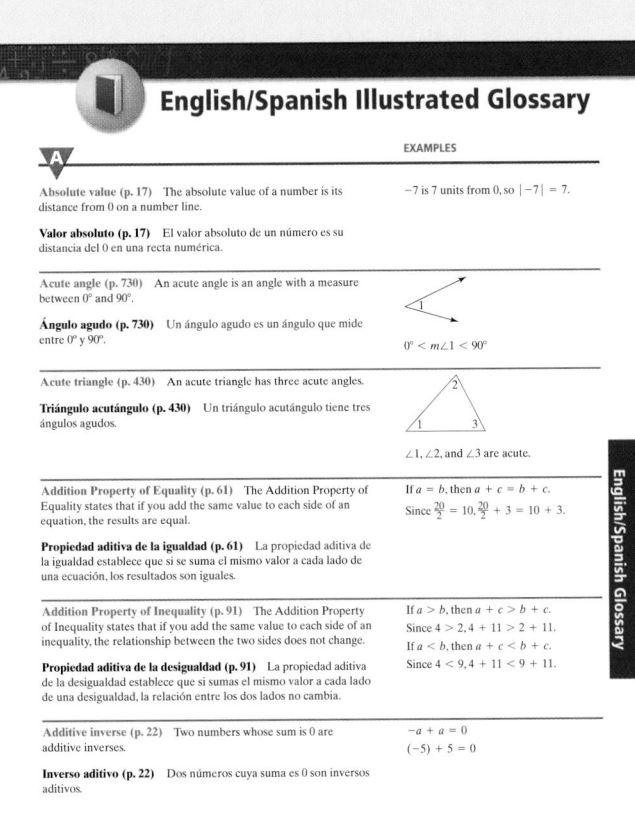

$0° < m\angle 1 < 90°$

Acute triangle (p. 430) An acute triangle has three acute angles.

Triángulo acutángulo (p. 430) Un triángulo acutángulo tiene tres ángulos agudos.

$\angle 1$, $\angle 2$, and $\angle 3$ are acute.

Addition Property of Equality (p. 61) The Addition Property of Equality states that if you add the same value to each side of an equation, the results are equal.

Propiedad aditiva de la igualdad (p. 61) La propiedad aditiva de la igualdad establece que si se suma el mismo valor a cada lado de una ecuación, los resultados son iguales.

If $a = b$, then $a + c = b + c$.
Since $\frac{20}{2} = 10$, $\frac{20}{2} + 3 = 10 + 3$.

Addition Property of Inequality (p. 91) The Addition Property of Inequality states that if you add the same value to each side of an inequality, the relationship between the two sides does not change.

Propiedad aditiva de la desigualdad (p. 91) La propiedad aditiva de la desigualdad establece que si sumas el mismo valor a cada lado de una desigualdad, la relación entre los dos lados no cambia.

If $a > b$, then $a + c > b + c$.
Since $4 > 2$, $4 + 11 > 2 + 11$.
If $a < b$, then $a + c < b + c$.
Since $4 < 9$, $4 + 11 < 9 + 11$.

Additive inverse (p. 22) Two numbers whose sum is 0 are additive inverses.

Inverso aditivo (p. 22) Dos números cuya suma es 0 son inversos aditivos.

$-a + a = 0$
$(-5) + 5 = 0$

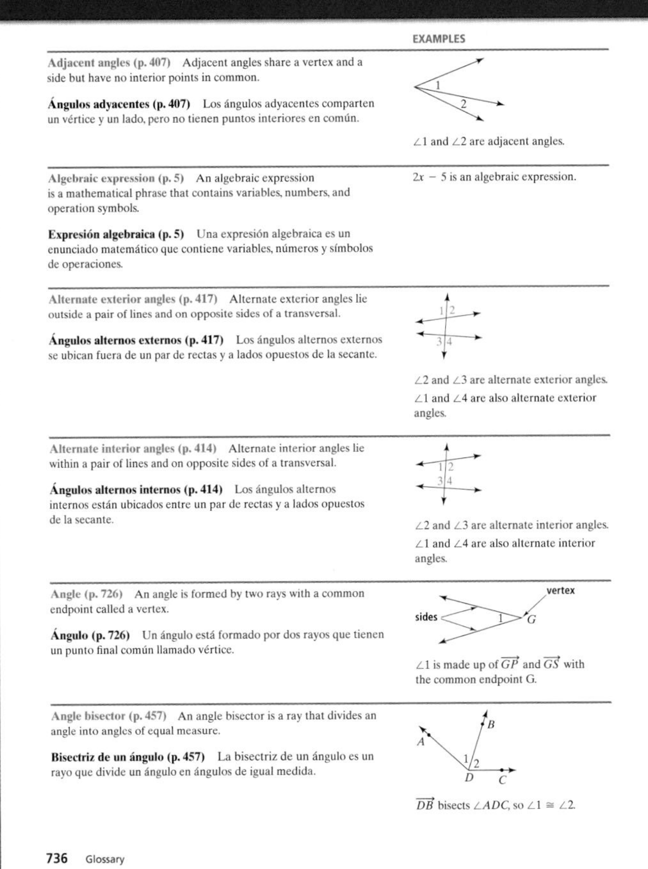

EXAMPLES

Adjacent angles (p. 407) Adjacent angles share a vertex and a side but have no interior points in common.

Ángulos adyacentes (p. 407) Los ángulos adyacentes comparten un vértice y un lado, pero no tienen puntos interiores en común.

$\angle 1$ and $\angle 2$ are adjacent angles.

Algebraic expression (p. 5) An algebraic expression is a mathematical phrase that contains variables, numbers, and operation symbols.

Expresión algebraica (p. 5) Una expresión algebraica es un enunciado matemático que contiene variables, números y símbolos de operaciones.

$2x - 5$ is an algebraic expression.

Alternate exterior angles (p. 417) Alternate exterior angles lie outside a pair of lines and on opposite sides of a transversal.

Ángulos alternos externos (p. 417) Los ángulos alternos externos se ubican fuera de un par de rectas y a lados opuestos de la secante.

$\angle 2$ and $\angle 3$ are alternate exterior angles.
$\angle 1$ and $\angle 4$ are also alternate exterior angles.

Alternate interior angles (p. 414) Alternate interior angles lie within a pair of lines and on opposite sides of a transversal.

Ángulos alternos internos (p. 414) Los ángulos alternos internos están ubicados entre un par de rectas y a lados opuestos de la secante.

$\angle 2$ and $\angle 3$ are alternate interior angles.
$\angle 1$ and $\angle 4$ are also alternate interior angles.

Angle (p. 726) An angle is formed by two rays with a common endpoint called a vertex.

Ángulo (p. 726) Un ángulo está formado por dos rayos que tienen un punto final común llamado vértice.

$\angle 1$ is made up of $\overrightarrow{GP}$ and $\overrightarrow{GS}$ with the common endpoint G.

Angle bisector (p. 457) An angle bisector is a ray that divides an angle into angles of equal measure.

Bisectriz de un ángulo (p. 457) La bisectriz de un ángulo es un rayo que divide un ángulo en ángulos de igual medida.

$\overrightarrow{DB}$ bisects $\angle ADC$, so $\angle 1 \cong \angle 2$.

EXAMPLES

Angle of rotation (p. 171) The angle of rotation is the number of degrees that a figure rotates.

Ángulo de rotación (p. 171) El ángulo de rotación es el número de grados que se rota una figura.

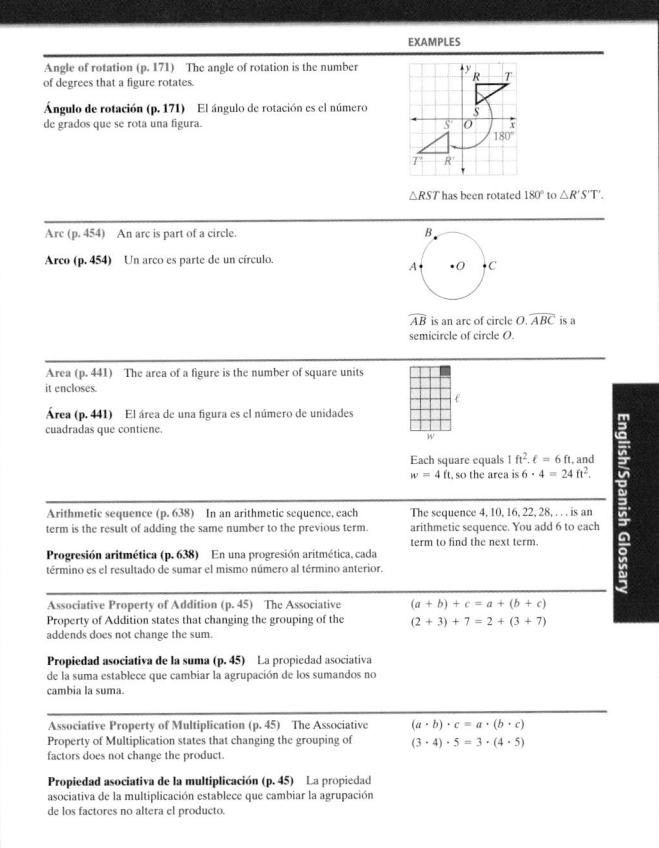

$\triangle RST$ has been rotated 180° to $\triangle R'S'T'$.

Arc (p. 454) An arc is part of a circle.

Arco (p. 454) Un arco es parte de un círculo.

$\overset{\frown}{AB}$ is an arc of circle O. $\overset{\frown}{ABC}$ is a semicircle of circle O.

Area (p. 441) The area of a figure is the number of square units it encloses.

Área (p. 441) El área de una figura es el número de unidades cuadradas que contiene.

Each square equals 1 ft^2. $\ell = 6$ ft, and $w = 4$ ft, so the area is $6 \cdot 4 = 24$ ft^2.

Arithmetic sequence (p. 638) In an arithmetic sequence, each term is the result of adding the same number to the previous term.

Progresión aritmética (p. 638) En una progresión aritmética, cada término es el resultado de sumar el mismo número al término anterior.

The sequence 4, 10, 16, 22, 28, . . . is an arithmetic sequence. You add 6 to each term to find the next term.

Associative Property of Addition (p. 45) The Associative Property of Addition states that changing the grouping of the addends does not change the sum.

Propiedad asociativa de la suma (p. 45) La propiedad asociativa de la suma establece que cambiar la agrupación de los sumandos no cambia la suma.

$(a + b) + c = a + (b + c)$
$(2 + 3) + 7 = 2 + (3 + 7)$

Associative Property of Multiplication (p. 45) The Associative Property of Multiplication states that changing the grouping of factors does not change the product.

Propiedad asociativa de la multiplicación (p. 45) La propiedad asociativa de la multiplicación establece que cambiar la agrupación de los factores no altera el producto.

$(a \cdot b) \cdot c = a \cdot (b \cdot c)$
$(3 \cdot 4) \cdot 5 = 3 \cdot (4 \cdot 5)$

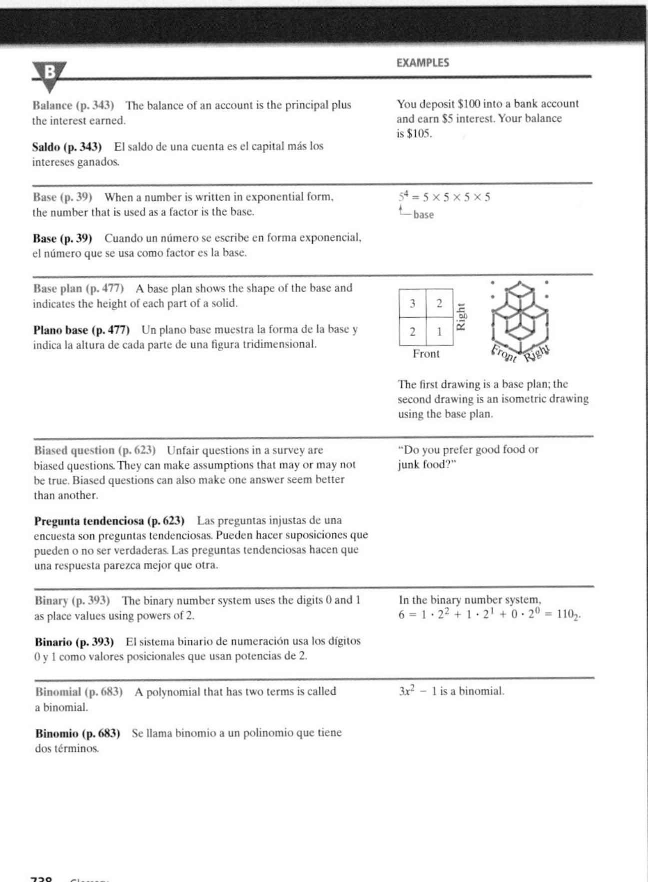

B

EXAMPLES

Balance (p. 343) The balance of an account is the principal plus the interest earned.

Saldo (p. 343) El saldo de una cuenta es el capital más los intereses ganados.

You deposit $100 into a bank account and earn $5 interest. Your balance is $105.

Base (p. 39) When a number is written in exponential form, the number that is used as a factor is the base.

Base (p. 39) Cuando un número se escribe en forma exponencial, el número que se usa como factor es la base.

$5^4 = 5 \times 5 \times 5 \times 5$
base

Base plan (p. 477) A base plan shows the shape of the base and indicates the height of each part of a solid.

Plano base (p. 477) Un plano base muestra la forma de la base y indica la altura de cada parte de una figura tridimensional.

The first drawing is a base plan; the second drawing is an isometric drawing using the base plan.

Biased question (p. 623) Unfair questions in a survey are biased questions. They can make assumptions that may or may not be true. Biased questions can also make one answer seem better than another.

Pregunta tendenciosa (p. 623) Las preguntas injustas de una encuesta son preguntas tendenciosas. Pueden hacer suposiciones que pueden o no ser verdaderas. Las preguntas tendenciosas hacen que una respuesta parezca mejor que otra.

"Do you prefer good food or junk food?"

Binary (p. 393) The binary number system uses the digits 0 and 1 as place values using powers of 2.

Binario (p. 393) El sistema binario de numeración usa los dígitos 0 y 1 como valores posicionales que usan potencias de 2.

In the binary number system, $6 = 1 \cdot 2^2 + 1 \cdot 2^1 + 0 \cdot 2^0 = 110_2$.

Binomial (p. 683) A polynomial that has two terms is called a binomial.

Binomio (p. 683) Se llama binomio a un polinomio que tiene dos términos.

$3x^2 - 1$ is a binomial.

	EXAMPLES
Box-and-whisker plot (p. 552) A box-and-whisker plot is a graph that summarizes a data set using five key values. There is a box in the middle and "whiskers" at either side. The quartiles divide the data into four equal parts. **Gráfica de caja y brazos (p. 552)** Una gráfica de caja y brazos es un diagrama que resume un conjunto de datos usando cinco valores clave. Hay una caja en el centro y extensiones a cada lado. Los cuartiles dividen los datos en cuatro partes iguales.	16 24 32 40 The box-and-whisker plot above uses these data: 16 19 26 26 27 29 30 31 34 34 38 39 40

C

Center of a circle (p. 447) A circle is named by its center. **Centro de un círculo (p. 447)** Un círculo es denominado por su centro.	O• Circle O
Center of a sphere (p. 511) See *Sphere*. **Centro de una esfera (p. 511)** Ver *Sphere*.	
Center of rotation (p. 170) The center of rotation is a fixed point about which a figure is rotated. **Centro de rotación (p. 170)** El centro de rotación es un punto fijo alrededor del cual se rota una figura.	center of rotation O is the center of rotation.
Central angle (p. 564) A central angle is an angle whose vertex is the center of a circle. The sum of the measures of the central angles is 360°. **Ángulo central (p. 564)** Un ángulo central es un ángulo cuyo vértice es el centro de un círculo. La suma de las medidas de los ángulos centrales es 360°.	$\angle AOB$ is a central angle of circle O.

English/Spanish Glossary

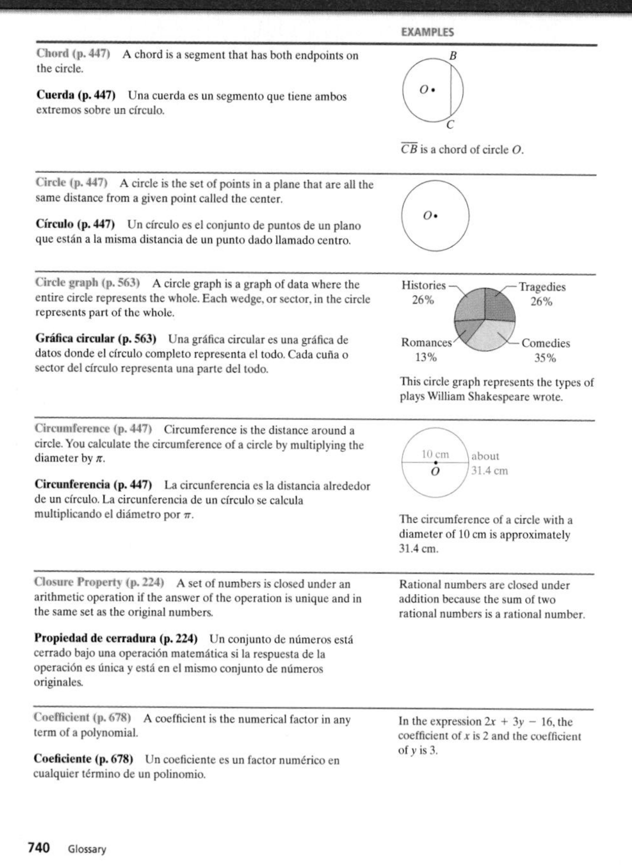

	EXAMPLES
Chord (p. 447) A chord is a segment that has both endpoints on the circle. **Cuerda (p. 447)** Una cuerda es un segmento que tiene ambos extremos sobre un círculo.	$\overline{CB}$ is a chord of circle O.
Circle (p. 447) A circle is the set of points in a plane that are all the same distance from a given point called the center. **Círculo (p. 447)** Un círculo es el conjunto de puntos de un plano que están a la misma distancia de un punto dado llamado centro.	O•
Circle graph (p. 563) A circle graph is a graph of data where the entire circle represents the whole. Each wedge, or sector, in the circle represents part of the whole. **Gráfica circular (p. 563)** Una gráfica circular es una gráfica de datos donde el círculo completo representa el todo. Cada cuña o sector del círculo representa una parte del todo.	Histories 26%, Tragedies 26%, Romances 13%, Comedies 35% This circle graph represents the types of plays William Shakespeare wrote.
Circumference (p. 447) Circumference is the distance around a circle. You calculate the circumference of a circle by multiplying the diameter by π. **Circunferencia (p. 447)** La circunferencia es la distancia alrededor de un círculo. La circunferencia de un círculo se calcula multiplicando el diámetro por π.	10 cm, about 31.4 cm The circumference of a circle with a diameter of 10 cm is approximately 31.4 cm.
Closure Property (p. 224) A set of numbers is closed under an arithmetic operation if the answer of the operation is unique and in the same set as the original numbers. **Propiedad de cerradura (p. 224)** Un conjunto de números está cerrado bajo una operación matemática si la respuesta de la operación es única y está en el mismo conjunto de números originales.	Rational numbers are closed under addition because the sum of two rational numbers is a rational number.
Coefficient (p. 678) A coefficient is the numerical factor in any term of a polynomial. **Coeficiente (p. 678)** Un coeficiente es un factor numérico en cualquier término de un polinomio.	In the expression $2x + 3y - 16$, the coefficient of x is 2 and the coefficient of y is 3.

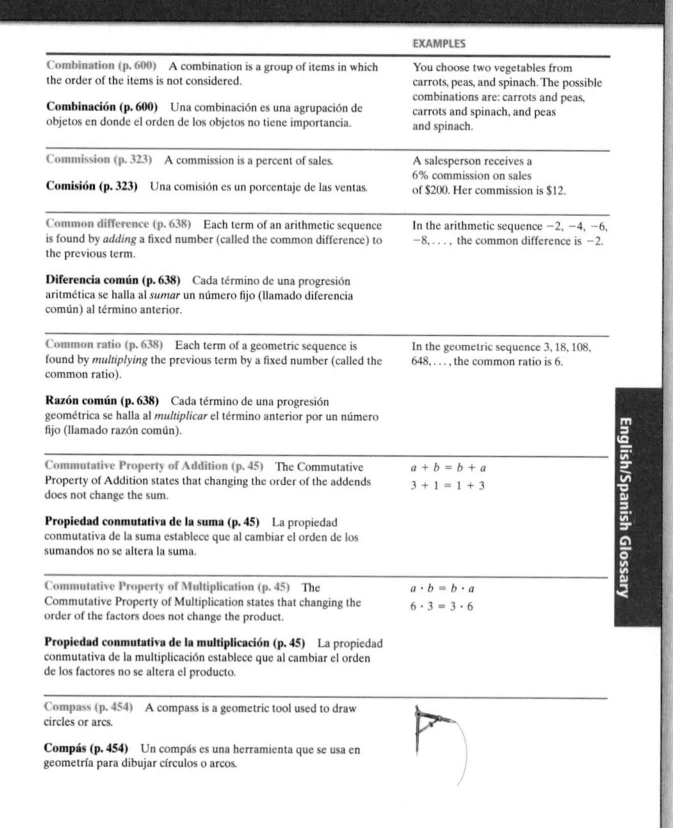

	EXAMPLES
Combination (p. 600) A combination is a group of items in which the order of the items is not considered. **Combinación (p. 600)** Una combinación es una agrupación de objetos en donde el orden de los objetos no tiene importancia.	You choose two vegetables from carrots, peas, and spinach. The possible combinations are: carrots and peas, carrots and spinach, and peas and spinach.
Commission (p. 323) A commission is a percent of sales. **Comisión (p. 323)** Una comisión es un porcentaje de las ventas.	A salesperson receives a 6% commission on sales of \$200. Her commission is \$12.
Common difference (p. 638) Each term of an arithmetic sequence is found by *adding* a fixed number (called the common difference) to the previous term. **Diferencia común (p. 638)** Cada término de una progresión aritmética se halla al *sumar* un número fijo (llamado diferencia común) al término anterior.	In the arithmetic sequence $-2, -4, -6, -8, \ldots$, the common difference is -2.
Common ratio (p. 638) Each term of a geometric sequence is found by *multiplying* the previous term by a fixed number (called the common ratio). **Razón común (p. 638)** Cada término de una progresión geométrica se halla al *multiplicar* el término anterior por un número fijo (llamado razón común).	In the geometric sequence 3, 18, 108, 648, . . . , the common ratio is 6.
Commutative Property of Addition (p. 45) The Commutative Property of Addition states that changing the order of the addends does not change the sum. **Propiedad conmutativa de la suma (p. 45)** La propiedad conmutativa de la suma establece que al cambiar el orden de los sumandos no se altera la suma.	$a + b = b + a$ $3 + 1 = 1 + 3$
Commutative Property of Multiplication (p. 45) The Commutative Property of Multiplication states that changing the order of the factors does not change the product. **Propiedad conmutativa de la multiplicación (p. 45)** La propiedad conmutativa de la multiplicación establece que al cambiar el orden de los factores no se altera el producto.	$a \cdot b = b \cdot a$ $6 \cdot 3 = 3 \cdot 6$
Compass (p. 454) A compass is a geometric tool used to draw circles or arcs. **Compás (p. 454)** Un compás es una herramienta que se usa en geometría para dibujar círculos o arcos.	

English/Spanish Glossary

	EXAMPLES
Compatible numbers (p. 309) Compatible numbers are numbers that are easy to compute mentally. **Números compatibles (p. 309)** Los números compatibles son números con los que se puede calcular mentalmente con facilidad.	Estimate $151 \div 14.6$. $151 \approx 150$, $14.6 \approx 15$ $150 \div 15 = 10$ $151 \div 14.6 \approx 10$
Complement (p. 608) The complement of an event is the collection of outcomes not contained in the event. **Complemento (p. 608)** El complemento de un suceso es la colección de resultados que el suceso no incluye.	The event *no rain* is the complement of the event *rain*.
Complementary (p. 408) Two angles are complementary if the sum of their measures is 90°. **Complementario (p. 408)** Dos ángulos son complementarios si la suma de sus medidas es 90°.	$\angle BCA$ and $\angle CAB$ are complementary angles.
Composite number (p. 186) A composite number is a whole number greater than 1 with more than two factors. **Número compuesto (p. 186)** Un número compuesto es un número entero mayor que 1, que tiene más de dos factores.	24 is a composite number that has 1, 2, 3, 4, 6, 8, 12, and 24 as factors.
Compound event (p. 614) A compound event is an event that consists of two or more events. The probability of a compound event can be found by multiplying the probability of one event by the probability of a second event. **Suceso compuesto (p. 614)** Un suceso compuesto es un suceso que está formado por dos o más sucesos. La probabilidad de un suceso compuesto se puede hallar al multiplicar la probabilidad de un suceso por la probabilidad de un segundo suceso.	If $P(A) = \frac{1}{3}$ and $P(B) = \frac{1}{2}$, then $P(A, \text{then } B) = \frac{1}{3} \cdot \frac{1}{2} = \frac{1}{6}$, when A and B are independent events.
Compound interest (p. 343) Compound interest is interest paid on the original principal and on any interest that has been left in the account. You can use the formula $B = p(1 + r)^n$ where B is the balance in the account, p is the principal, r is the annual interest rate, and n is the number of years that the account earns interest. **Interés compuesto (p. 343)** El interés compuesto es el interés que se paga sobre el principal original y sobre cualquier interés que ha quedado en la cuenta. Se puede usar la fórmula $S = p(1 + i)^t$ donde S es el saldo en la cuenta, p es el principal, i es la tasa de interés anual y t es el tiempo en años en que la cuenta gana interés.	You deposit \$500 in an account earning 5% annual interest. The balance after six years is $500(1 + 0.05)^6$, or \$670.05.

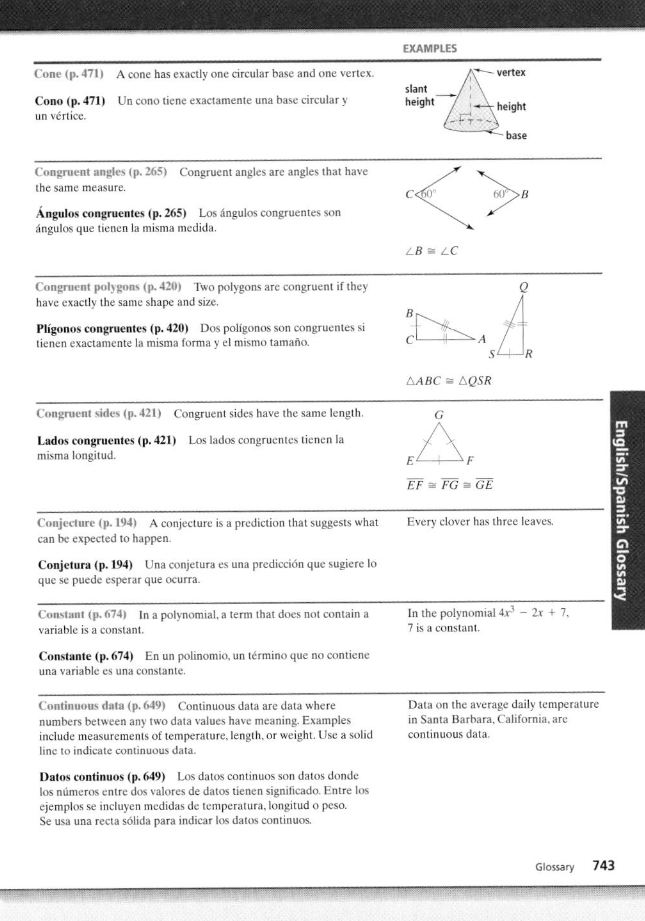
EXAMPLES

Cone (p. 471) A cone has exactly one circular base and one vertex.

Cono (p. 471) Un cono tiene exactamente una base circular y un vértice.

Congruent angles (p. 265) Congruent angles are angles that have the same measure.

Ángulos congruentes (p. 265) Los ángulos congruentes son ángulos que tienen la misma medida.

$\angle B \cong \angle C$

Congruent polygons (p. 420) Two polygons are congruent if they have exactly the same shape and size.

Plígonos congruentes (p. 420) Dos polígonos son congruentes si tienen exactamente la misma forma y el mismo tamaño.

$\triangle ABC \cong \triangle QSR$

Congruent sides (p. 421) Congruent sides have the same length.

Lados congruentes (p. 421) Los lados congruentes tienen la misma longitud.

$\overline{EF} \cong \overline{FG} \cong \overline{GE}$

Conjecture (p. 194) A conjecture is a prediction that suggests what can be expected to happen.

Conjetura (p. 194) Una conjetura es una predicción que sugiere lo que se puede esperar que ocurra.

Every clover has three leaves.

Constant (p. 674) In a polynomial, a term that does not contain a variable is a constant.

Constante (p. 674) En un polinomio, un término que no contiene una variable es una constante.

In the polynomial $4x^3 - 2x + 7$, 7 is a constant.

Continuous data (p. 649) Continuous data are data where numbers between any two data values have meaning. Examples include measurements of temperature, length, or weight. Use a solid line to indicate continuous data.

Datos continuos (p. 649) Los datos continuos son datos donde los números entre dos valores de datos tienen significado. Entre los ejemplos se incluyen medidas de temperatura, longitud o peso. Se usa una recta sólida para indicar los datos continuos.

Data on the average daily temperature in Santa Barbara, California, are continuous data.

English/Spanish Glossary

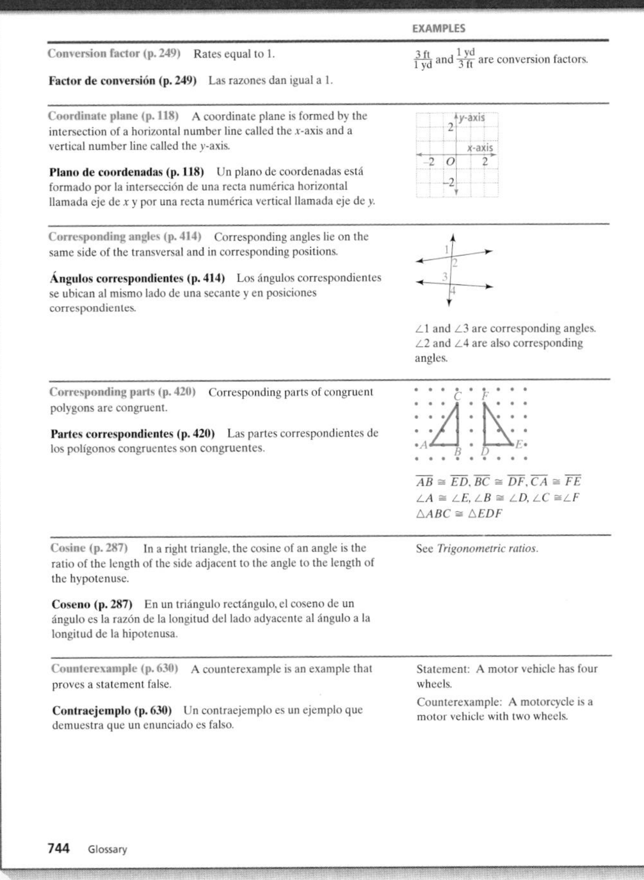
EXAMPLES

Conversion factor (p. 249) Rates equal to 1.

Factor de conversión (p. 249) Las razones dan igual a 1.

$\frac{3 \text{ ft}}{1 \text{ yd}}$ and $\frac{1 \text{ yd}}{3 \text{ ft}}$ are conversion factors.

Coordinate plane (p. 118) A coordinate plane is formed by the intersection of a horizontal number line called the x-axis and a vertical number line called the y-axis.

Plano de coordenadas (p. 118) Un plano de coordenadas está formado por la intersección de una recta numérica horizontal llamada eje de x y por una recta numérica vertical llamada eje de y.

Corresponding angles (p. 414) Corresponding angles lie on the same side of the transversal and in corresponding positions.

Ángulos correspondientes (p. 414) Los ángulos correspondientes se ubican al mismo lado de una secante y en posiciones correspondientes.

$\angle 1$ and $\angle 3$ are corresponding angles. $\angle 2$ and $\angle 4$ are also corresponding angles.

Corresponding parts (p. 420) Corresponding parts of congruent polygons are congruent.

Partes correspondientes (p. 420) Las partes correspondientes de los polígonos congruentes son congruentes.

$\overline{AB} \cong \overline{ED}, \overline{BC} \cong \overline{DF}, \overline{CA} \cong \overline{FE}$
$\angle A \cong \angle E, \angle B \cong \angle D, \angle C \cong \angle F$
$\triangle ABC \cong \triangle EDF$

Cosine (p. 287) In a right triangle, the cosine of an angle is the ratio of the length of the side adjacent to the angle to the length of the hypotenuse.

Coseno (p. 287) En un triángulo rectángulo, el coseno de un ángulo es la razón de la longitud del lado adyacente al ángulo a la longitud de la hipotenusa.

See *Trigonometric ratios*.

Counterexample (p. 630) A counterexample is an example that proves a statement false.

Contraejemplo (p. 630) Un contraejemplo es un ejemplo que demuestra que un enunciado es falso.

Statement: A motor vehicle has four wheels.

Counterexample: A motorcycle is a motor vehicle with two wheels.

EXAMPLES

Counting principle (p. 592) Suppose there are m ways of making one choice and n ways of making a second choice. Then there are $m \cdot n$ ways to make the first choice followed by the second.

Principio de conteo (p. 592) Supongamos que hay m maneras de hacer una elección en una primera situación y n maneras de hacer una elección en una segunda situación. Entonces hay $m \cdot n$ maneras de hacer la primera elección seguida por la segunda.

Toss a coin and roll a standard number cube. The total number of possible outcomes is $2 \cdot 6 = 12$.

Cross products (p. 259) For two ratios, the cross products are found by multiplying the denominator of one ratio by the numerator of the other ratio.

Productos cruzados (p. 259) En dos razones, los productos cruzados se hallan al multiplicar el denominador de una razón por el numerador de la otra razón.

In the proportion $\frac{2}{5} = \frac{10}{25}$, the cross products are $2 \cdot 25$ and $5 \cdot 10$.

Cube (p. 477) A cube is a rectangular prism whose faces are all squares.

Cubo (p. 477) Un cubo es un prisma rectangular cuyas caras son todas cuandras.

Cylinder (p. 471) A cylinder has two bases that are parallel, congruent circles.

Cilindro (p. 471) Un cilindro tiene dos bases paralelas que son círculos congruentes.

base
height
base

D

Deductive reasoning (p. 415) A process of reasoning logically from given facts to a conclusion is called deductive reasoning.

Razonamiento deductivo (p. 415) El proceso de razonar lógicamente para llegar a una conclusión a partir de datos dados se llama razonamiento deductivo.

Dependent events (p. 613) When the outcome of one event *does* affect the outcome of a second event, the events are dependent events.

Sucesos dependientes (p. 613) Cuando el resultado de un suceso afecta el resultado de un segundo suceso, los sucesos son dependientes.

Suppose you remove two marbles, one after the other, from a bag. If you do not replace the first marble before removing the second marble, the events are dependent.

English/Spanish Glossary

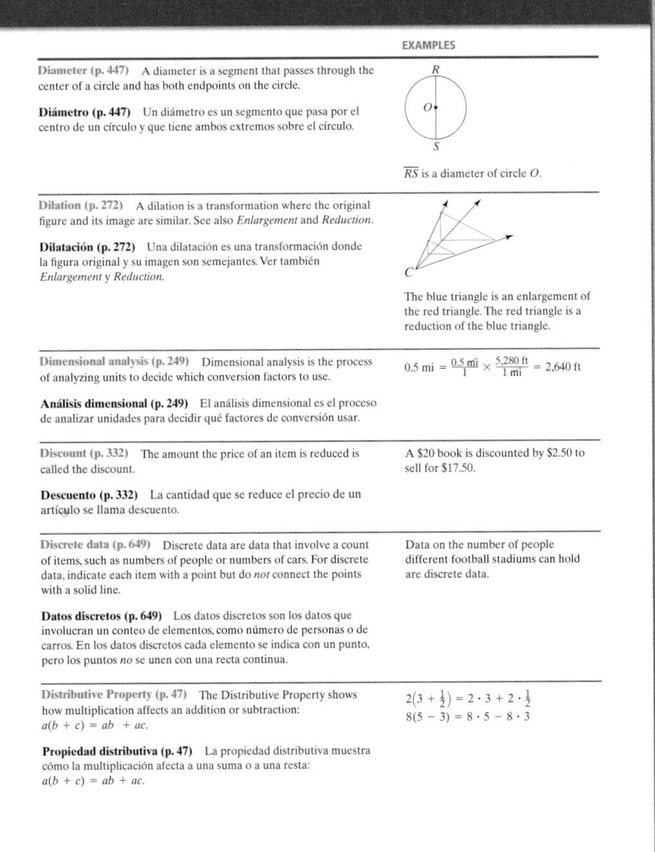
EXAMPLES

Diameter (p. 447) A diameter is a segment that passes through the center of a circle and has both endpoints on the circle.

Diámetro (p. 447) Un diámetro es un segmento que pasa por el centro de un círculo y que tiene ambos extremos sobre el círculo.

$\overline{RS}$ is a diameter of circle O.

Dilation (p. 272) A dilation is a transformation where the original figure and its image are similar. See also *Enlargement* and *Reduction*.

Dilatación (p. 272) Una dilatación es una transformación donde la figura original y su imagen son semejantes. Ver también *Enlargement* y *Reduction*.

The blue triangle is an enlargement of the red triangle. The red triangle is a reduction of the blue triangle.

Dimensional analysis (p. 249) Dimensional analysis is the process of analyzing units to decide which conversion factors to use.

Análisis dimensional (p. 249) El análisis dimensional es el proceso de analizar unidades para decidir qué factores de conversión usar.

$0.5 \text{ mi} = \frac{0.5 \text{ mi}}{1} \times \frac{5{,}280 \text{ ft}}{1 \text{ mi}} = 2{,}640 \text{ ft}$

Discount (p. 332) The amount the price of an item is reduced is called the discount.

Descuento (p. 332) La cantidad que se reduce el precio de un artículo se llama descuento.

A $20 book is discounted by $2.50 to sell for $17.50.

Discrete data (p. 649) Discrete data are data that involve a count of items, such as numbers of people or numbers of cars. For discrete data, indicate each item with a point but do *not* connect the points with a solid line.

Datos discretos (p. 649) Los datos discretos son los datos que involucran un conteo de elementos, como número de personas o de carros. En los datos discretos cada elemento se indica con un punto, pero los puntos *no* se unen con una recta continua.

Data on the number of people different football stadiums can hold are discrete data.

Distributive Property (p. 47) The Distributive Property shows how multiplication affects an addition or subtraction: $a(b + c) = ab + ac$.

Propiedad distributiva (p. 47) La propiedad distributiva muestra cómo la multiplicación afecta a una suma o a una resta: $a(b + c) = ab + ac$.

$2\left(3 + \frac{1}{2}\right) = 2 \cdot 3 + 2 \cdot \frac{1}{2}$
$8(5 - 3) = 8 \cdot 5 - 8 \cdot 3$

English/Spanish Glossary

EXAMPLES

Divisible (p. 185) A number is divisible by a second whole number if the first number can be divided by the second number with a remainder of 0.

Divisible (p. 185) Un número es divisible por un segundo número entero si el primer número se puede dividir por el segundo número y el residuo es cero.

Example: 16 is divisible by 1, 2, 4, 8, and 16.

Division Property of Equality (p. 63) The Division Property of Equality states that if you divide each side of an equation by the same nonzero number, the sides remain equal.

Propiedad de división de la igualdad (p. 63) La propiedad de división de la igualdad establece que si cada lado de una ecuación se divide por el mismo número distinto de cero, los dos lados se mantienen iguales.

Example: If $a = b$ and $c \neq 0$, then $\frac{a}{c} = \frac{b}{c}$.
Since $3 \cdot 2 = 6$, $\frac{3 \cdot 2}{2} = \frac{6}{2}$.

Division Property of Inequality (p. 97) The Division Property of Inequality states that if you divide an inequality by a positive number, the direction of the inequality is unchanged. If you divide an inequality by a negative number, *reverse* the direction of the inequality sign.

Propiedad de división de la desigualdad (p. 97) La propiedad de división de la desigualdad establece que si se divide una desigualdad por un número positivo, la dirección de la desigualdad no cambia. Si se divide una desigualdad por un número negativo, se *invierte* la dirección del signo de desigualdad.

Example:
If $a > b$ and $c > 0$, then $\frac{a}{c} > \frac{b}{c}$.
Since $2 > 1$ and $3 > 0$, $\frac{2}{3} > \frac{1}{3}$.
If $a < b$ and $c > 0$, then $\frac{a}{c} < \frac{b}{c}$.
Since $2 < 4$ and $3 > 0$, $\frac{2}{3} < \frac{4}{3}$.
If $a > b$ and $c < 0$, then $\frac{a}{c} < \frac{b}{c}$.
Since $2 > 1$ and $-4 < 0$, $\frac{2}{-4} < \frac{1}{-4}$.
If $a < b$ and $c < 0$, then $\frac{a}{c} > \frac{b}{c}$.
Since $2 < 4$ and $-4 < 0$, $\frac{2}{-4} > \frac{4}{-4}$.

English/Spanish Glossary

E

Edge (p. 472) An edge is a segment formed by the intersection of two faces of a three-dimensional figure.

Arista (p. 472) Una arista es un segmento formado por la intersección de dos caras de una figura tridimensional.

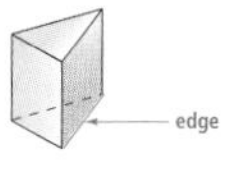

Enlargement (p. 273) A dilation with a scale factor greater than 1 is an enlargement.

Aumento (p. 273) Una dilatación con un factor de escala mayor que 1 es un aumento.

Example: See *Dilation*.

Equation (p. 61) An equation is a mathematical sentence with an equal sign.

Ecuación (p. 61) Una ecuación es una oración matemática con un signo igual.

Example: $2(3 + 5) = 16$ and $x + 10 = 8$ are examples of equations.

EXAMPLES

Equilateral triangle (p. 430) An equilateral triangle is a triangle with three congruent sides.

Triángulo equilátero (p. 430) Un triángulo equilátero es un triángulo que tiene tres lados congruentes.

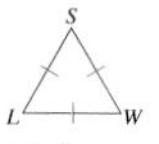

$\triangle SWL$ is an equilateral triangle.

Evaluating expressions (p. 6) To evaluate an algebraic expression, replace each variable with a number. Then follow the order of operations to simplify the expression.

Evaluación de expresiones (p. 6) Para evaluar una expresión algebraica, se reemplaza cada variable con un número. Luego se sigue el orden de las operaciones para simplificar la expresión.

Example: To evaluate the expression $3x + 2$ for $x = 4$, substitute 4 for x.
$3x + 2 = 3(4) + 2 = 12 + 2 = 14$

Event (p. 349) A collection of possible outcomes is an event.

Suceso (p. 349) Un suceso es un grupo de resultados posibles.

Example: When you toss a coin, "heads" is a possible outcome.

Expanded form (p. 393) The expanded form of a number is the sum that shows the place and value of each digit.

Forma desarrollada (p. 393) La forma desarrollada de un número es la suma que muestra el lugar y valor de cada dígito.

Example: The expanded form of the base-10 number 136 is
$(1 \cdot 10^2) + (3 \cdot 10^1) + (6 \cdot 10^0)$
See also *Standard form*.

Experimental probability (p. 606) Probability based on experimental data is called experimental probability. You find the experimental probability of an event by repeating an experiment, or a trial, many times, and using the following ratio.

$P(\text{event}) = \frac{\text{number of times event occurs}}{\text{total number of trials}}$

Probabilidad experimental (p. 606) La probabilidad experimental es la probabilidad que se basa en datos experimentales. La probabilidad experimental de un suceso se halla al repetir un experimento, o prueba, muchas veces y usar la siguiente razón.

$P(\text{suceso}) = \frac{\text{número de veces que ocurre un suceso}}{\text{número total de pruebas}}$

Example: Suppose a basketball player makes 19 baskets in 28 attempts. The experimental probability that the player makes a basket is $\frac{19}{28} \approx 68\%$.

Exponent (p. 39) An exponent tells how many times a number, or base, is used as a factor.

Exponente (p. 39) Un exponente dice cuántas veces se usa como factor un número o base.

Example: (exponent)
$3^4 = 3 \times 3 \times 3 \times 3$
Read 3^4 as "three to the fourth power."

Exterior angle of a polygon (p. 435) The exterior angle of a polygon is an angle formed by a side and an extension of an adjacent side.

Ángulo exterior de un polígono (p. 435) El ángulo exterior de un polígono es el ángulo formado por un lado y una extensión del lado adyacente.

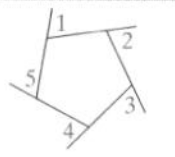

Angles 1, 2, 3, 4, and 5 are exterior angles of the polygon.

EXAMPLES

F

Faces (p. 471) The flat surfaces of a solid are called faces.

Caras (p. 471) Las superficies planas de un sólido se llaman caras.

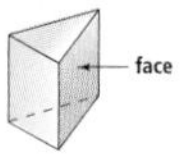

Factor (p. 39) A factor is an integer that divides another integer with a remainder of 0.

Divisor (p. 39) Un divisor es un número entero que divide a otro número entero y el residuo es cero.

Example: 1, 2, 3, 4, 6, 12, 18, and 36 are factors of 36.

Factorial (p. 596) The product of all positive integers less than or equal to a number is a factorial.

Factorial (p. 596) Un factorial es el producto de todos los enteros positivos menores o iguales que un número.

Example: $5! = 5 \cdot 4 \cdot 3 \cdot 2 \cdot 1 = 120$

Formula (p. 212) A formula is a rule that shows the relationship between two or more quantities.

Fórmula (p. 212) Una fórmula es una regla que muestra la relación entre dos o más cantidades.

Example: The formula $P = 2\ell + 2w$ gives the perimeter of a rectangle in terms of its length and width.

Frequency (p. 533) The number of times a data item occurs is the frequency of the item.

Frecuencia (p. 533) El número de veces que un dato ocurre es la frecuencia del dato.

Example: In the data set 2 4 3 2 2 5 10 9 5 2 6, the frequency of 2 is 4.

Frequency table (p. 533) A frequency table lists the frequency of each item in a set of data.

Tabla de frecuencia (p. 533) Una tabla de frecuencia indica la frecuencia de cada elemento en un conjunto de datos.

Household Telephones

Phones	Tally	Frequency
1	卌 III	8
2	卌 I	6
3	IIII	4

This frequency table shows the number of household telephones for a class of students.

English/Spanish Glossary

Function (p. 643) A function is a relationship that assigns exactly one output value for each input value.

Función (p. 643) Una función es una relación que asigna exactamente un valor resultante a cada valor inicial.

Example: Earned income is a function of the number of hours worked w. If you earn \$6/h, then your income can be expressed by the function $f(w) = 6w$.

EXAMPLES

Function rule (p. 643) A function rule is an equation that describes a function.

Regla de una función (p. 643) Una regla de una función es una ecuación que describe una función.

Example: The function rule that describes the cost c of buying x movie tickets that cost \$9 each is $c = 9x$.

G

Geometric sequence (p. 638) In a geometric sequence, each term is the result of multiplying the previous term by the same number.

Progresión geométrica (p. 638) En una progresión geométrica, cada término es el resultado de la multiplicación del término anterior por el mismo número.

Example: The sequence 1, 3, 9, 27, 81, . . . is a geometric sequence. You multiply each term by 3 to find the next term.

Graph of an equation (p. 123) The graph of an equation is the graph of all the points whose coordinates are solutions of the equation.

Gráfica de una ecuación (p. 123) La gráfica de una ecuación es la gráfica de todos los puntos cuyas coordenadas son soluciones a la ecuación.

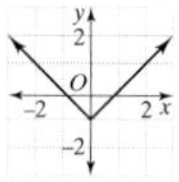

The coordinates of all the points on the graph satisfy the equation $y = |x| - 1$.

Graph of an inequality (p. 90) The graph of an inequality containing a variable shows all the solutions that satisfy the inequality.

Gráfica de una desigualdad (p. 90) La gráfica de una desigualdad que contiene una variable muestra todas las soluciones que satisfacen la desigualdad.

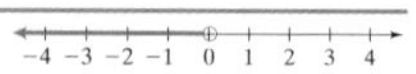

The graph shows the inequality $x < 0$.

Greatest common factor (GCF) (p. 187) The greatest common factor of two or more numbers is the greatest number that is a factor of all of the numbers.

Máximo común divisor (MCD) (p. 187) El máximo común divisor de dos o más números es el mayor número que es divisor de todos los números.

Example: The GCF of 12 and 30 is 6.

Greatest possible error (p. 487) The greatest possible error of a measurement is half the unit of measure to which the measurement has been rounded.

Máximo error posible (p. 487) El máximo error posible de una medición es la mitad de la unidad de medida a la cual se ha redondeado la medición.

Example: The measurement 400 kg is rounded to the nearest hundred kilograms. So, the greatest possible error is 50 kg.

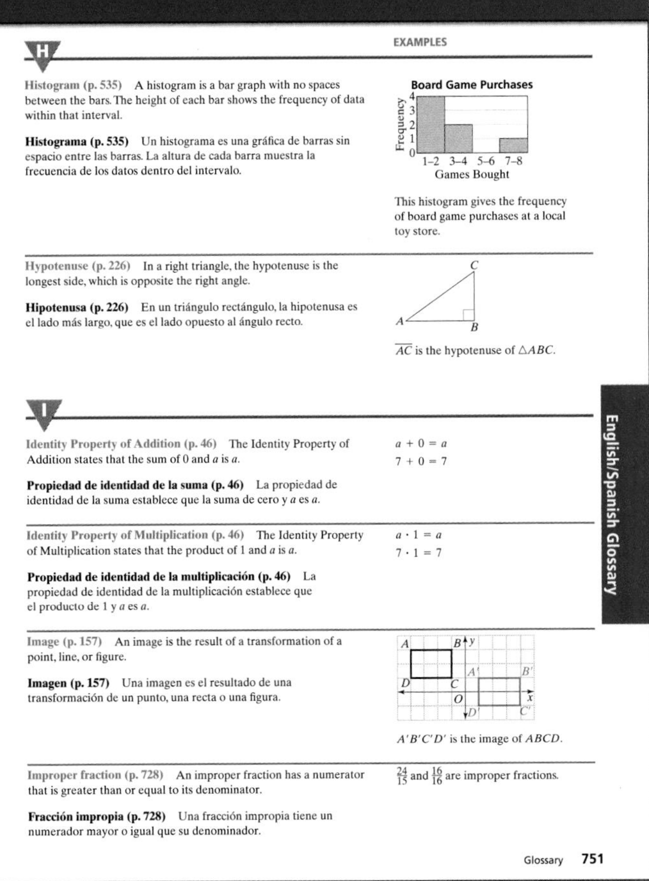

EXAMPLES

H

Histogram (p. 535) A histogram is a bar graph with no spaces between the bars. The height of each bar shows the frequency of data within that interval.

Histograma (p. 535) Un histograma es una gráfica de barras sin espacio entre las barras. La altura de cada barra muestra la frecuencia de los datos dentro del intervalo.

This histogram gives the frequency of board game purchases at a local toy store.

Hypotenuse (p. 226) In a right triangle, the hypotenuse is the longest side, which is opposite the right angle.

Hipotenusa (p. 226) En un triángulo rectángulo, la hipotenusa es el lado más largo, que es el lado opuesto al ángulo recto.

$\overline{AC}$ is the hypotenuse of $\triangle ABC$.

I

Identity Property of Addition (p. 46) The Identity Property of Addition states that the sum of 0 and a is a.

Propiedad de identidad de la suma (p. 46) La propiedad de identidad de la suma establece que la suma de cero y a es a.

$a + 0 = a$
$7 + 0 = 7$

Identity Property of Multiplication (p. 46) The Identity Property of Multiplication states that the product of 1 and a is a.

Propiedad de identidad de la multiplicación (p. 46) La propiedad de identidad de la multiplicación establece que el producto de 1 y a es a.

$a \cdot 1 = a$
$7 \cdot 1 = 7$

Image (p. 157) An image is the result of a transformation of a point, line, or figure.

Imagen (p. 157) Una imagen es el resultado de una transformación de un punto, una recta o una figura.

$A'B'C'D'$ is the image of $ABCD$.

Improper fraction (p. 728) An improper fraction has a numerator that is greater than or equal to its denominator.

Fracción impropia (p. 728) Una fracción impropia tiene un numerador mayor o igual que su denominador.

$\frac{24}{15}$ and $\frac{16}{16}$ are improper fractions.

English/Spanish Glossary

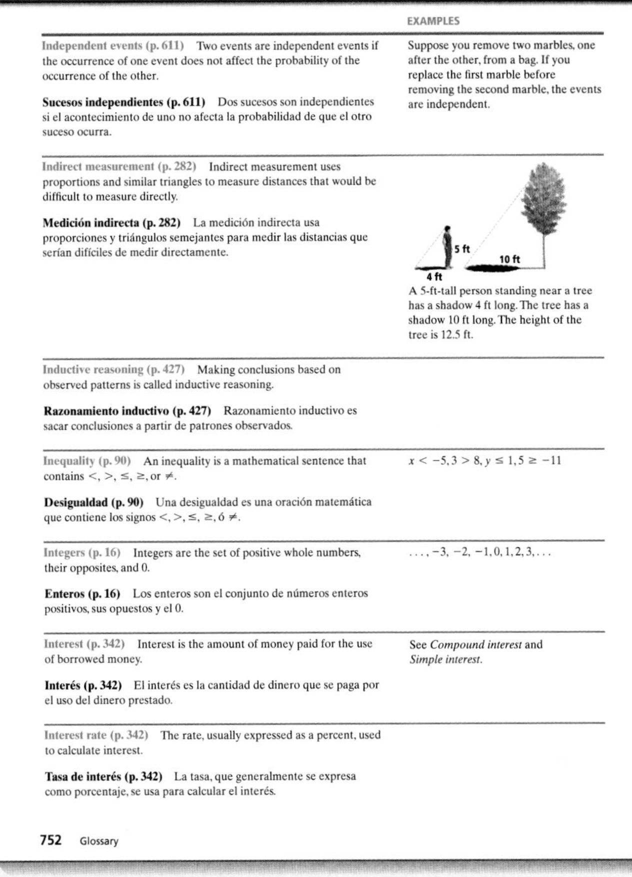

EXAMPLES

Independent events (p. 611) Two events are independent events if the occurrence of one event does not affect the probability of the occurrence of the other.

Sucesos independientes (p. 611) Dos sucesos son independientes si el acontecimiento de uno no afecta la probabilidad de que el otro suceso ocurra.

Suppose you remove two marbles, one after the other, from a bag. If you replace the first marble before removing the second marble, the events are independent.

Indirect measurement (p. 282) Indirect measurement uses proportions and similar triangles to measure distances that would be difficult to measure directly.

Medición indirecta (p. 282) La medición indirecta usa proporciones y triángulos semejantes para medir las distancias que serían difíciles de medir directamente.

A 5-ft-tall person standing near a tree has a shadow 4 ft long. The tree has a shadow 10 ft long. The height of the tree is 12.5 ft.

Inductive reasoning (p. 427) Making conclusions based on observed patterns is called inductive reasoning.

Razonamiento inductivo (p. 427) Razonamiento inductivo es sacar conclusiones a partir de patrones observados.

Inequality (p. 90) An inequality is a mathematical sentence that contains $<, >, \leq, \geq$, or $\neq$.

Desigualdad (p. 90) Una desigualdad es una oración matemática que contiene los signos $<, >, \leq, \geq$, ó $\neq$.

$x < -5, 3 > 8, y \leq 1, 5 \geq -11$

Integers (p. 16) Integers are the set of positive whole numbers, their opposites, and 0.

Enteros (p. 16) Los enteros son el conjunto de números enteros positivos, sus opuestos y el 0.

$\ldots, -3, -2, -1, 0, 1, 2, 3, \ldots$

Interest (p. 342) Interest is the amount of money paid for the use of borrowed money.

Interés (p. 342) El interés es la cantidad de dinero que se paga por el uso del dinero prestado.

See *Compound interest* and *Simple interest*.

Interest rate (p. 342) The rate, usually expressed as a percent, used to calculate interest.

Tasa de interés (p. 342) La tasa, que generalmente se expresa como porcentaje, se usa para calcular el interés.

EXAMPLES

Interior angle (p. 436) Interior angles are the angles inside a polygon at its vertices.

Ángulo interior (p. 436) Los ángulos interiores son los ángulos que están en la parte interna de los vértices de un polígono.

Interior angles

Inverse operations (p. 62) Inverse operations are operations that undo each other.

Operaciones inversas (p. 62) Las operaciones inversas son las operaciones que se anulan entre ellas.

Addition and subtraction are inverse operations.

Irrational number (p. 222) An irrational number is a number that cannot be written as the ratio of two integers. In decimal form, an irrational number cannot be written as a terminating or repeating decimal.

Número irracional (p. 222) Un número irracional es un número que no se puede escribir como una razón de dos enteros. Como decimal, un número irracional no se puede escribir como decimal finito o periódico.

The numbers π and 2.41592653 . . . are irrational numbers.

Irregular polygon (p. 438) An irregular polygon is a polygon with sides that are not all congruent and/or angles that are not all congruent.

Polígono irregular (p. 438) Un polígono irregular es un polígono que tiene lados que no son todos congruentes y/o ángulos que no son todos congruentes.

$KLMN$ is an irregular polygon.

Isolate (p. 62) To isolate the variable means to get the variable alone on one side of an equation.

Despejar (p. 62) Despejar la variable quiere decir dejar la variable sola a un lado de la ecuación.

To isolate y on one side of the equation $y - 2x = 4$, add $2x$ to each side. The equation becomes $y = 4 + 2x$.

Isometric view (p. 477) An isometric view is a corner view of a solid. It is usually drawn on isometric dot paper. An isometric view allows you to see the top, front, and side of an object in the same drawing.

Vista isométrica (p. 477) Una vista isométrica es una vista desde una esquina de un sólido. Generalmente se dibuja sobre papel isométrico de puntos. Una vista isométrica permite ver la parte de arriba, del frente y del lado de un objeto en un mismo dibujo.

Front Right

English/Spanish Glossary

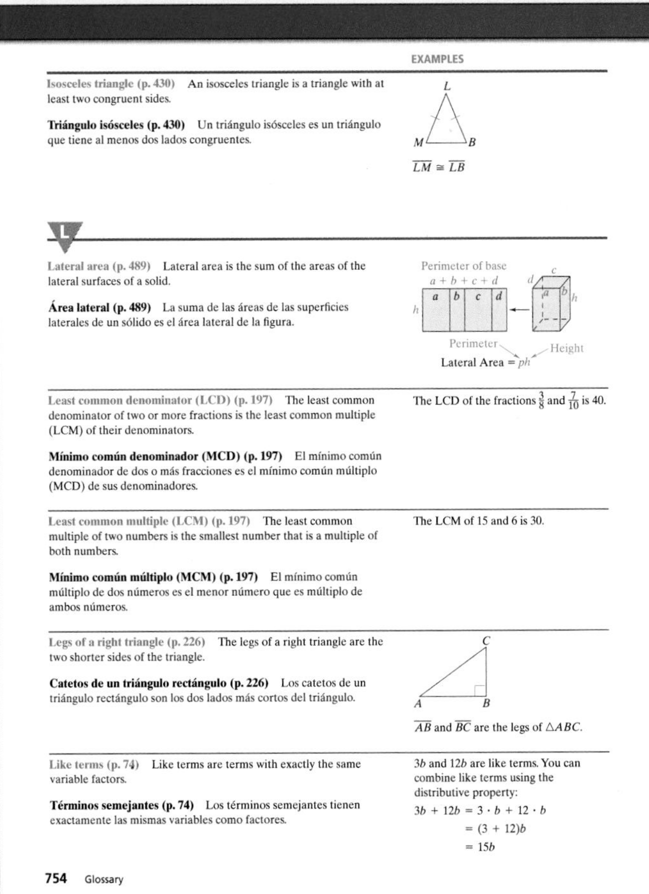

EXAMPLES

Isosceles triangle (p. 430) An isosceles triangle is a triangle with at least two congruent sides.

Triángulo isósceles (p. 430) Un triángulo isósceles es un triángulo que tiene al menos dos lados congruentes.

$\overline{LM} \cong \overline{LB}$

L

Lateral area (p. 489) Lateral area is the sum of the areas of the lateral surfaces of a solid.

Área lateral (p. 489) La suma de las áreas de las superficies laterales de un sólido es el área lateral de la figura.

Lateral Area = ph

Least common denominator (LCD) (p. 197) The least common denominator of two or more fractions is the least common multiple (LCM) of their denominators.

Mínimo común denominador (MCD) (p. 197) El mínimo común denominador de dos o más fracciones es el mínimo común múltiplo (MCD) de sus denominadores.

The LCD of the fractions $\frac{3}{8}$ and $\frac{7}{10}$ is 40.

Least common multiple (LCM) (p. 197) The least common multiple of two numbers is the smallest number that is a multiple of both numbers.

Mínimo común múltiplo (MCM) (p. 197) El mínimo común múltiplo de dos números es el menor número que es múltiplo de ambos números.

The LCM of 15 and 6 is 30.

Legs of a right triangle (p. 226) The legs of a right triangle are the two shorter sides of the triangle.

Catetos de un triángulo rectángulo (p. 226) Los catetos de un triángulo rectángulo son los dos lados más cortos del triángulo.

$\overline{AB}$ and $\overline{BC}$ are the legs of $\triangle ABC$.

Like terms (p. 74) Like terms are terms with exactly the same variable factors.

Términos semejantes (p. 74) Los términos semejantes tienen exactamente las mismas variables como factores.

$3b$ and $12b$ are like terms. You can combine like terms using the distributive property:

$3b + 12b = 3 \cdot b + 12 \cdot b$
$= (3 + 12)b$
$= 15b$

English/Spanish Glossary

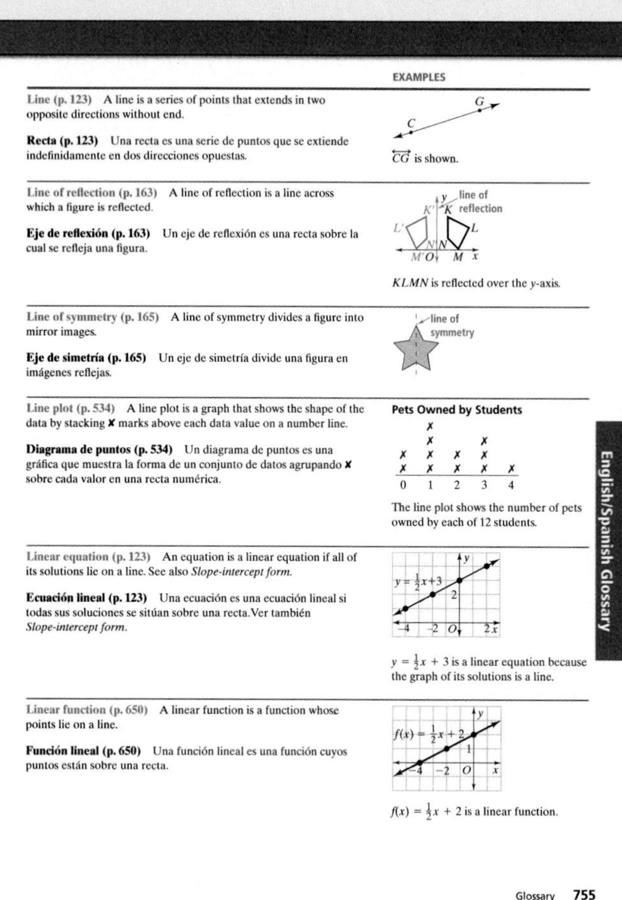

EXAMPLES

Line (p. 123) A line is a series of points that extends in two opposite directions without end.

Recta (p. 123) Una recta es una serie de puntos que se extiende indefinidamente en dos direcciones opuestas.

$\overleftrightarrow{CG}$ is shown.

Line of reflection (p. 163) A line of reflection is a line across which a figure is reflected.

Eje de reflexión (p. 163) Un eje de reflexión es una recta sobre la cual se refleja una figura.

KLMN is reflected over the *y*-axis.

Line of symmetry (p. 165) A line of symmetry divides a figure into mirror images.

Eje de simetría (p. 165) Un eje de simetría divide una figura en imágenes reflejas.

Line plot (p. 534) A line plot is a graph that shows the shape of the data by stacking ✗ marks above each data value on a number line.

Diagrama de puntos (p. 534) Un diagrama de puntos es una gráfica que muestra la forma de un conjunto de datos agrupando ✗ sobre cada valor en una recta numérica.

Pets Owned by Students

The line plot shows the number of pets owned by each of 12 students.

Linear equation (p. 123) An equation is a linear equation if all of its solutions lie on a line. See also *Slope-intercept form.*

Ecuación lineal (p. 123) Una ecuación es una ecuación lineal si todas sus soluciones se sitúan sobre una recta. Ver también *Slope-intercept form.*

$y = \frac{1}{2}x + 3$ is a linear equation because the graph of its solutions is a line.

Linear function (p. 650) A linear function is a function whose points lie on a line.

Función lineal (p. 650) Una función lineal es una función cuyos puntos están sobre una recta.

$f(x) = \frac{1}{2}x + 2$ is a linear function.

English/Spanish Glossary

Glossary 755

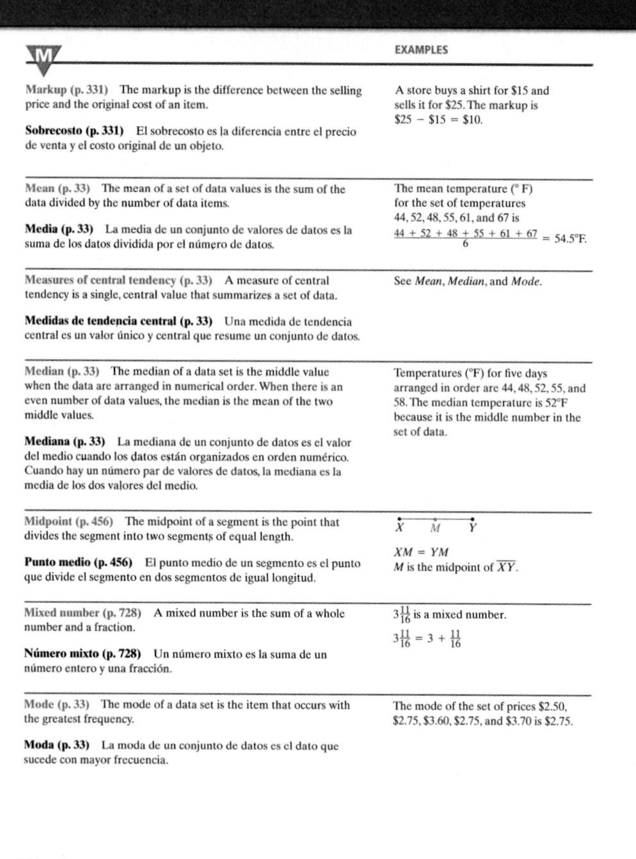

M

EXAMPLES

Markup (p. 331) The markup is the difference between the selling price and the original cost of an item.

Sobrecosto (p. 331) El sobrecosto es la diferencia entre el precio de venta y el costo original de un objeto.

A store buys a shirt for $15 and sells it for $25. The markup is $25 − $15 = $10.

Mean (p. 33) The mean of a set of data values is the sum of the data divided by the number of data items.

Media (p. 33) La media de un conjunto de valores de datos es la suma de los datos dividida por el número de datos.

The mean temperature (° F) for the set of temperatures 44, 52, 48, 55, 61, and 67 is $\frac{44 + 52 + 48 + 55 + 61 + 67}{6} = 54.5°F$.

Measures of central tendency (p. 33) A measure of central tendency is a single, central value that summarizes a set of data.

Medidas de tendencia central (p. 33) Una medida de tendencia central es un valor único y central que resume un conjunto de datos.

See *Mean*, *Median*, and *Mode*.

Median (p. 33) The median of a data set is the middle value when the data are arranged in numerical order. When there is an even number of data values, the median is the mean of the two middle values.

Mediana (p. 33) La mediana de un conjunto de datos es el valor del medio cuando los datos están organizados en orden numérico. Cuando hay un número par de valores de datos, la mediana es la media de los dos valores del medio.

Temperatures (°F) for five days arranged in order are 44, 48, 52, 55, and 58. The median temperature is 52°F because it is the middle number in the set of data.

Midpoint (p. 456) The midpoint of a segment is the point that divides the segment into two segments of equal length.

Punto medio (p. 456) El punto medio de un segmento es el punto que divide el segmento en dos segmentos de igual longitud.

$XM = YM$
M is the midpoint of $\overline{XY}$.

Mixed number (p. 728) A mixed number is the sum of a whole number and a fraction.

Número mixto (p. 728) Un número mixto es la suma de un número entero y una fracción.

$3\frac{11}{16}$ is a mixed number.
$3\frac{11}{16} = 3 + \frac{11}{16}$

Mode (p. 33) The mode of a data set is the item that occurs with the greatest frequency.

Moda (p. 33) La moda de un conjunto de datos es el dato que sucede con mayor frecuencia.

The mode of the set of prices $2.50, $2.75, $3.60, $2.75, and $3.70 is $2.75.

756 Glossary

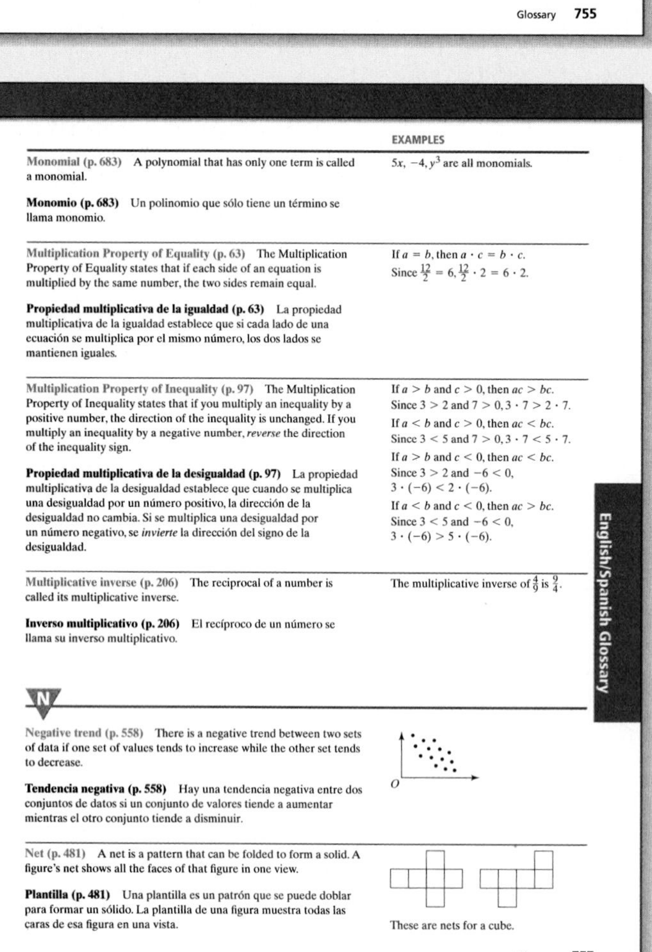

EXAMPLES

Monomial (p. 683) A polynomial that has only one term is called a monomial.

Monomio (p. 683) Un polinomio que sólo tiene un término se llama monomio.

$5x$, -4, y^3 are all monomials.

Multiplication Property of Equality (p. 63) The Multiplication Property of Equality states that if each side of an equation is multiplied by the same number, the two sides remain equal.

Propiedad multiplicativa de la igualdad (p. 63) La propiedad multiplicativa de la igualdad establece que si cada lado de una ecuación se multiplica por el mismo número, los dos lados se mantienen iguales.

If $a = b$, then $a \cdot c = b \cdot c$.
Since $\frac{12}{2} = 6$, $\frac{12}{2} \cdot 2 = 6 \cdot 2$.

Multiplication Property of Inequality (p. 97) The Multiplication Property of Inequality states that if you multiply an inequality by a positive number, the direction of the inequality is unchanged. If you multiply an inequality by a negative number, *reverse* the direction of the inequality sign.

Propiedad multiplicativa de la desigualdad (p. 97) La propiedad multiplicativa de la desigualdad establece que cuando se multiplica una desigualdad por un número positivo, la dirección de la desigualdad no cambia. Si se multiplica una desigualdad por un número negativo, se *invierte* la dirección del signo de la desigualdad.

If $a > b$ and $c > 0$, then $ac > bc$.
Since $3 > 2$ and $7 > 0$, $3 \cdot 7 > 2 \cdot 7$.
If $a < b$ and $c > 0$, then $ac < bc$.
Since $3 < 5$ and $7 > 0$, $3 \cdot 7 < 5 \cdot 7$.
If $a > b$ and $c < 0$, then $ac < bc$.
Since $3 > 2$ and $-6 < 0$, $3 \cdot (-6) < 2 \cdot (-6)$.
If $a < b$ and $c < 0$, then $ac > bc$.
Since $3 < 5$ and $-6 < 0$, $3 \cdot (-6) > 5 \cdot (-6)$.

Multiplicative inverse (p. 206) The reciprocal of a number is called its multiplicative inverse.

Inverso multiplicativo (p. 206) El recíproco de un número se llama su inverso multiplicativo.

The multiplicative inverse of $\frac{4}{9}$ is $\frac{9}{4}$.

N

Negative trend (p. 558) There is a negative trend between two sets of data if one set of values tends to increase while the other set tends to decrease.

Tendencia negativa (p. 558) Hay una tendencia negativa entre dos conjuntos de datos si un conjunto de valores tiende a aumentar mientras el otro conjunto tiende a disminuir.

Net (p. 481) A net is a pattern that can be folded to form a solid. A figure's net shows all the faces of that figure in one view.

Plantilla (p. 481) Una plantilla es un patrón que se puede doblar para formar un sólido. La plantilla de una figura muestra todas las caras de esa figura en una vista.

These are nets for a cube.

English/Spanish Glossary

Glossary 757

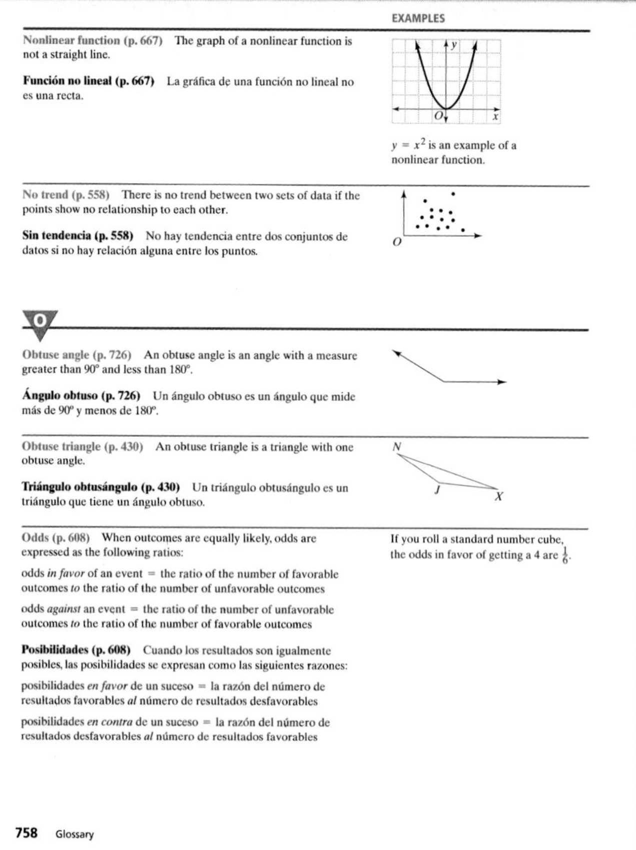

EXAMPLES

Nonlinear function (p. 667) The graph of a nonlinear function is not a straight line.

Función no lineal (p. 667) La gráfica de una función no lineal no es una recta.

$y = x^2$ is an example of a nonlinear function.

No trend (p. 558) There is no trend between two sets of data if the points show no relationship to each other.

Sin tendencia (p. 558) No hay tendencia entre dos conjuntos de datos si no hay relación alguna entre los puntos.

O

Obtuse angle (p. 726) An obtuse angle is an angle with a measure greater than 90° and less than 180°.

Ángulo obtuso (p. 726) Un ángulo obtuso es un ángulo que mide más de 90° y menos de 180°.

Obtuse triangle (p. 430) An obtuse triangle is a triangle with one obtuse angle.

Triángulo obtusángulo (p. 430) Un triángulo obtusángulo es un triángulo que tiene un ángulo obtuso.

Odds (p. 608) When outcomes are equally likely, odds are expressed as the following ratios:

odds *in favor* of an event = the ratio of the number of favorable outcomes *to* the ratio of the number of unfavorable outcomes

odds *against* an event = the ratio of the number of unfavorable outcomes *to* the ratio of the number of favorable outcomes

Posibilidades (p. 608) Cuando los resultados son igualmente posibles, las posibilidades se expresan como las siguientes razones:

posibilidades *en favor* de un suceso = la razón del número de resultados favorables *al* número de resultados desfavorables

posibilidades *en contra* de un suceso = la razón del número de resultados desfavorables *al* número de resultados favorables

If you roll a standard number cube, the odds in favor of getting a 4 are $\frac{1}{6}$.

758 Glossary

EXAMPLES

Opposites (p. 16) Opposites are two numbers that are the same distance from 0 on a number line, but in opposite directions.

Opuestos (p. 16) Opuestos son dos números que están a la misma distancia del cero en una recta numérica, pero en direcciones opuestas.

17 and −17 are opposites.

Ordered pair (p. 118) An ordered pair identifies the location of a point. The x-coordinate shows a point's position left or right of the y-axis. The y-coordinate shows a point's position up or down from the x-axis.

Par ordenado (p. 118) Un par ordenado identifica la ubicación de un punto. La coordenada x muestra la posición de un punto a la izquierda o derecha del eje de y. La coordenada y muestra la posición de un punto arriba o abajo del eje de x.

The x-coordinate of the point $(-2, 1)$ is -2, and the y-coordinate is 1.

Order of operations (pp. 6, 40)
1. Work inside grouping symbols.
2. Simplify the exponents.
3. Multiply and divide in order from left to right.
4. Add and subtract in order from left to right.

Orden de las operaciones (pp. 6, 40)
1. Trabaja dentro de los signos de agrupación.
2. Simplifica los exponentes.
3. Multiplica y divide en orden de izquierda a derecha.
4. Suma y resta en orden de izquierda a derecha.

$2^3(7 - 4) = 2^3 \cdot 3 = 8 \cdot 3 = 24$

Origin (p. 118) The origin is the point of intersection of the x- and y-axes in a coordinate plane.

Origen (p. 118) El origen es el punto de intersección de los ejes de x y de y en un plano de coordenadas.

The ordered pair that describes the origin is (0, 0).

Outcome (p. 349) An outcome is any of the possible results that can occur in an experiment.

Resultado (p. 349) Un resultado es cualquiera de los posibles desenlaces que pueden ocurrir en un experimento.

The outcomes of rolling a standard number cube are 1, 2, 3, 4, 5, and 6.

Outlier (p. 35) An outlier is a data item that is much higher or much lower than the other items in a data set.

Valor extremo (p. 35) Un valor extremo es un dato que es mucho más alto o más bajo que los demás datos de un conjunto de datos.

An outlier in the data set 6, 7, 9, 10, 11, 12, 14, and 52 is 52.

English/Spanish Glossary

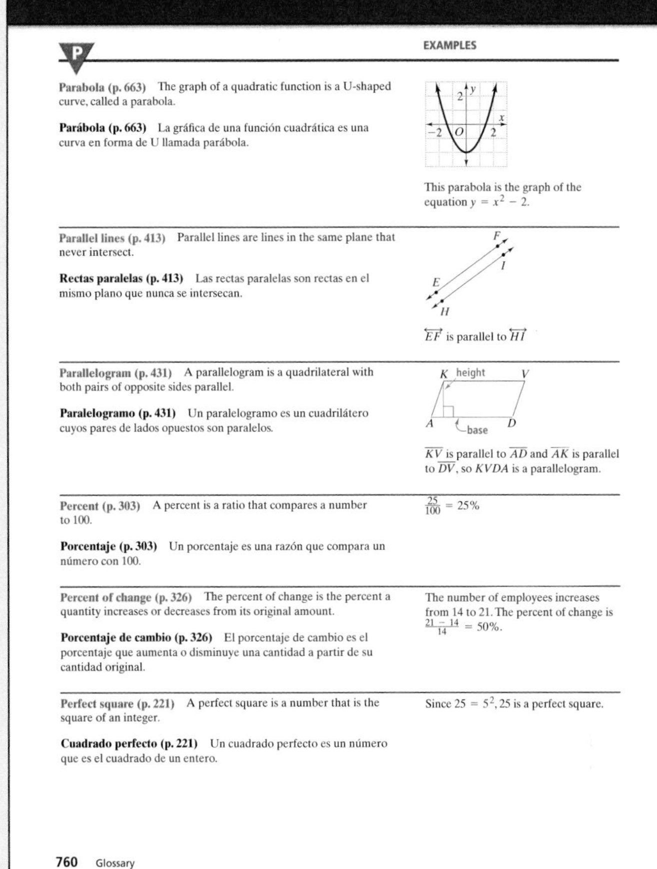

P

EXAMPLES

Parabola (p. 663) The graph of a quadratic function is a U-shaped curve, called a parabola.

Parábola (p. 663) La gráfica de una función cuadrática es una curva en forma de U llamada parábola.

This parabola is the graph of the equation $y = x^2 - 2$.

Parallel lines (p. 413) Parallel lines are lines in the same plane that never intersect.

Rectas paralelas (p. 413) Las rectas paralelas son rectas en el mismo plano que nunca se intersecan.

$\overleftrightarrow{EF}$ is parallel to $\overleftrightarrow{HI}$

Parallelogram (p. 431) A parallelogram is a quadrilateral with both pairs of opposite sides parallel.

Paralelogramo (p. 431) Un paralelogramo es un cuadrilátero cuyos pares de lados opuestos son paralelos.

$\overline{KV}$ is parallel to $\overline{AD}$ and $\overline{AK}$ is parallel to $\overline{DV}$, so $KVDA$ is a parallelogram.

Percent (p. 303) A percent is a ratio that compares a number to 100.

Porcentaje (p. 303) Un porcentaje es una razón que compara un número con 100.

$\frac{25}{100} = 25\%$

Percent of change (p. 326) The percent of change is the percent a quantity increases or decreases from its original amount.

Porcentaje de cambio (p. 326) El porcentaje de cambio es el porcentaje que aumenta o disminuye una cantidad a partir de su cantidad original.

The number of employees increases from 14 to 21. The percent of change is $\frac{21 - 14}{14} = 50\%$.

Perfect square (p. 221) A perfect square is a number that is the square of an integer.

Cuadrado perfecto (p. 221) Un cuadrado perfecto es un número que es el cuadrado de un entero.

Since $25 = 5^2$, 25 is a perfect square.

EXAMPLES

Perimeter (p. 212) The perimeter of a figure is the distance around the figure.

Perímetro (p. 212) El perímetro de una figura es la distancia alrededor de la figura.

The perimeter of rectangle $ABCD$ is 12 ft.

Permutation (p. 595) A permutation is an arrangement of objects in a particular order.

Permutación (p. 595) Una permutación es un arreglo de objetos en un orden particular.

The permutations of the letters W, A, and X, are WAX, WXA, AXW, AWX, XWA, and XAW.

Perpendicular bisector (p. 456) A perpendicular bisector is a segment bisector that is perpendicular to the segment.

Mediatriz (p. 456) Una mediatriz es una bisectriz de un segmento que es perpendicular a ese segmento.

$\overleftrightarrow{MK} \perp \overline{AB}$, $AM = MB$. $\overleftrightarrow{MK}$ is the perpendicular bisector of $\overline{AB}$.

Perpendicular lines (p. 409) Perpendicular lines intersect to form right angles.

Rectas perpendiculares (p. 409) Las rectas perpendiculares se intersecan para formar ángulos rectos.

$\overleftrightarrow{DE} \perp \overleftrightarrow{RS}$

Pi (p. 447) Pi (π) is the ratio of the circumference C of any circle to its diameter d.

Pi (p. 447) Pi (π) es la razón de la circunferencia C de cualquier círculo a su diámetro d.

$\pi = \frac{C}{d}$

Plane (p. 118) A plane is a flat surface that extends indefinitely in all directions.

Plano (p. 118) Un plano es la superficie plana que se extiende indefinidamente en todas las direcciones.

$DEFG$ is a plane.

Point (p. 118) A point is a location that has no size.

Punto (p. 118) Un punto es una ubicación que no tiene tamaño.

A is a point.

Polygon (p. 265) A polygon is a closed figure formed by three or more line segments that do not cross.

Polígono (p. 265) Un polígono es una figura cerrada que está formada por tres o más segmentos de recta que no se cruzan.

English/Spanish Glossary

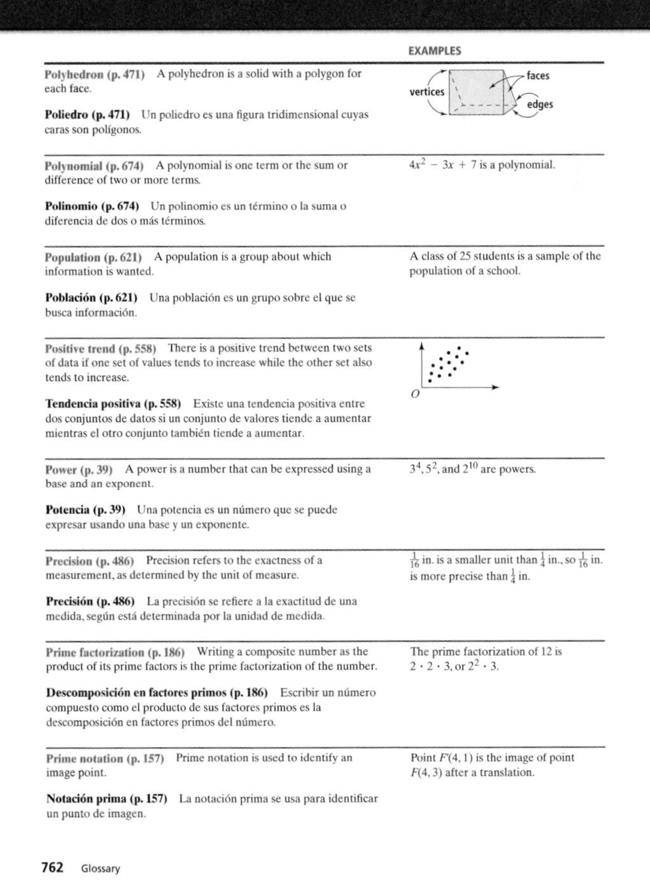

EXAMPLES

Polyhedron (p. 471) A polyhedron is a solid with a polygon for each face.

Poliedro (p. 471) Un poliedro es una figura tridimensional cuyas caras son polígonos.

Polynomial (p. 674) A polynomial is one term or the sum or difference of two or more terms.

Polinomio (p. 674) Un polinomio es un término o la suma o diferencia de dos o más términos.

$4x^2 - 3x + 7$ is a polynomial.

Population (p. 621) A population is a group about which information is wanted.

Población (p. 621) Una población es un grupo sobre el que se busca información.

A class of 25 students is a sample of the population of a school.

Positive trend (p. 558) There is a positive trend between two sets of data if one set of values tends to increase while the other set also tends to increase.

Tendencia positiva (p. 558) Existe una tendencia positiva entre dos conjuntos de datos si un conjunto de valores tiende a aumentar mientras el otro conjunto también tiende a aumentar.

Power (p. 39) A power is a number that can be expressed using a base and an exponent.

Potencia (p. 39) Una potencia es un número que se puede expresar usando una base y un exponente.

3^4, 5^2, and 2^{10} are powers.

Precision (p. 486) Precision refers to the exactness of a measurement, as determined by the unit of measure.

Precisión (p. 486) La precisión se refiere a la exactitud de una medida, según está determinada por la unidad de medida.

$\frac{1}{16}$ in. is a smaller unit than $\frac{1}{4}$ in., so $\frac{1}{16}$ in. is more precise than $\frac{1}{4}$ in.

Prime factorization (p. 186) Writing a composite number as the product of its prime factors is the prime factorization of the number.

Descomposición en factores primos (p. 186) Escribir un número compuesto como el producto de sus factores primos es la descomposición en factores primos del número.

The prime factorization of 12 is $2 \cdot 2 \cdot 3$, or $2^2 \cdot 3$.

Prime notation (p. 157) Prime notation is used to identify an image point.

Notación prima (p. 157) La notación prima se usa para identificar un punto de imagen.

Point $F'(4, 1)$ is the image of point $F(4, 3)$ after a translation.

English/Spanish Glossary

EXAMPLES

Prime number (p. 186) A prime number is a whole number with exactly two factors, 1 and the number itself.

13 is a prime number because its only factors are 1 and 13.

Número primo (p. 186) Un número primo es un entero que tiene exactamente dos factores, 1 y el mismo número.

Principal (p. 342) Principal is the original amount deposited or borrowed.

You deposit \$500 in a savings account. Your principal is \$500.

Capital (p. 342) El capital es el monto original que se deposita o se toma prestado.

Prism (p. 471) A prism is a solid with two parallel and congruent polygonal faces called bases. A prism is named for the shape of its base.

Rectangular Prism   Triangular Prism

Prisma (p. 471) Un prisma es un sólido que tiene dos caras poligonales paralelas y congruentes llamadas bases. Un prisma recibe su nombre por la forma de su base.

Probability of an event (p. 349) When outcomes are equally likely: $P(E) = \frac{\text{number of favorable outcomes}}{\text{total number of possible outcomes}}$.

The probability of rolling a 4 on a number cube is $\frac{1}{6}$.
See also *Experimental probability* and *Theoretical probability*.

Probabilidad de un suceso (p. 349) Cuando los resultados son igualmente posibles: $P(E) = \frac{\text{número de resultados favorables}}{\text{número total de resultados posibles}}$.

Proportion (p. 259) A proportion is an equation stating that two ratios are equal.

$\frac{3}{12} = \frac{9}{36}$ is a proportion.

Proporción (p. 259) Una proporción es una ecuación que establece que dos razones son iguales.

Pyramid (p. 471) A pyramid is a solid with triangular faces that meet at a vertex and a base that is a polygon. A pyramid is named for the shape of its base.

height, bases, slant height
Triangular   Square

Pirámide (p. 471) Una pirámide es una figura tridimensional que tiene caras triangulares que coinciden en un vértice y una base que es un polígono. Una pirámide recibe su nombre por la forma de su base.

Pythagorean Theorem (p. 226) In any right triangle, the sum of the squares of the lengths of the legs (a and b) is equal to the square of the length of the hypotenuse (c): $a^2 + b^2 = c^2$.

A, C, B; 3, 4, 5

The right triangle has leg lengths 3 and 4 and hypotenuse length 5.
$3^2 + 4^2 = 5^2$

Teorema de Pitágoras (p. 226) En cualquier triángulo rectángulo, la suma del cuadrado de la longitud de los catetos (a y b) es igual al cuadrado de la longitud de la hipotenusa (c): $a^2 + b^2 = c^2$.

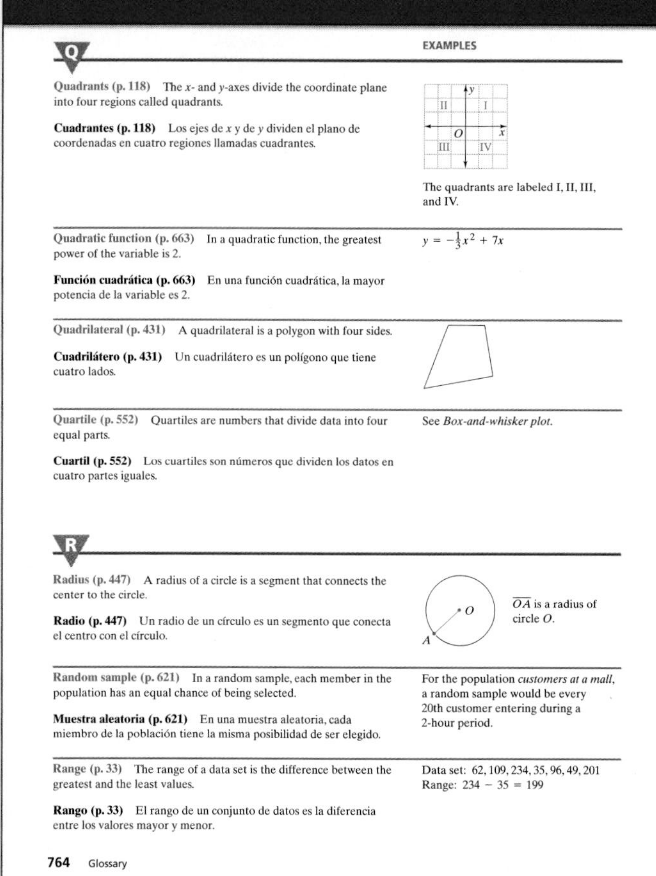

Q

EXAMPLES

Quadrants (p. 118) The x- and y-axes divide the coordinate plane into four regions called quadrants.

The quadrants are labeled I, II, III, and IV.

Cuadrantes (p. 118) Los ejes de x y de y dividen el plano de coordenadas en cuatro regiones llamadas cuadrantes.

Quadratic function (p. 663) In a quadratic function, the greatest power of the variable is 2.

$y = -\frac{1}{3}x^2 + 7x$

Función cuadrática (p. 663) En una función cuadrática, la mayor potencia de la variable es 2.

Quadrilateral (p. 431) A quadrilateral is a polygon with four sides.

Cuadrilátero (p. 431) Un cuadrilátero es un polígono que tiene cuatro lados.

Quartile (p. 552) Quartiles are numbers that divide data into four equal parts.

See *Box-and-whisker plot*.

Cuartil (p. 552) Los cuartiles son números que dividen los datos en cuatro partes iguales.

R

Radius (p. 447) A radius of a circle is a segment that connects the center to the circle.

$\overline{OA}$ is a radius of circle O.

Radio (p. 447) Un radio de un círculo es un segmento que conecta el centro con el círculo.

Random sample (p. 621) In a random sample, each member in the population has an equal chance of being selected.

For the population *customers at a mall*, a random sample would be every 20th customer entering during a 2-hour period.

Muestra aleatoria (p. 621) En una muestra aleatoria, cada miembro de la población tiene la misma posibilidad de ser elegido.

Range (p. 33) The range of a data set is the difference between the greatest and the least values.

Data set: 62, 109, 234, 35, 96, 49, 201
Range: $234 - 35 = 199$

Rango (p. 33) El rango de un conjunto de datos es la diferencia entre los valores mayor y menor.

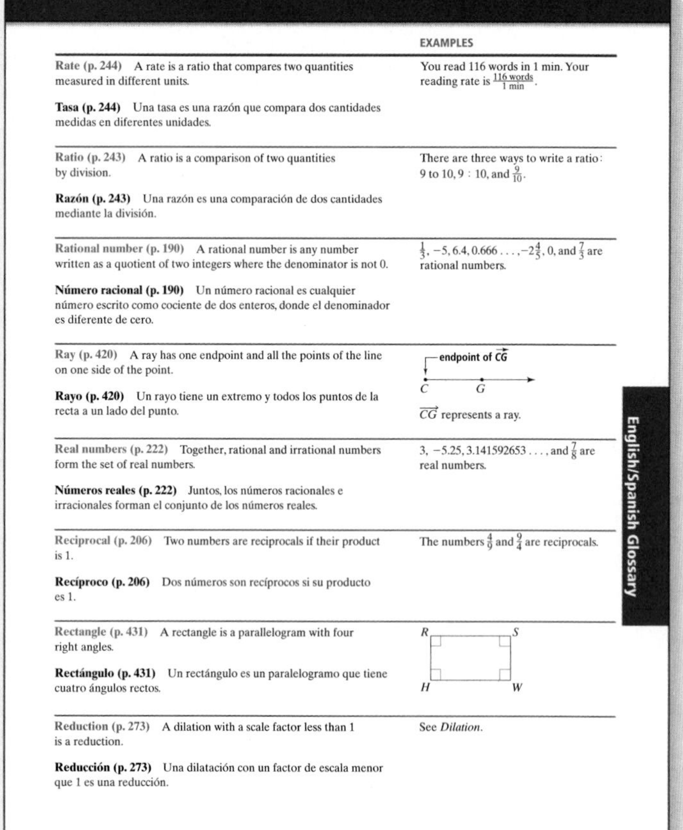

EXAMPLES

Rate (p. 244) A rate is a ratio that compares two quantities measured in different units.

You read 116 words in 1 min. Your reading rate is $\frac{116 \text{ words}}{1 \text{ min}}$.

Tasa (p. 244) Una tasa es una razón que compara dos cantidades medidas en diferentes unidades.

Ratio (p. 243) A ratio is a comparison of two quantities by division.

There are three ways to write a ratio: 9 to 10, 9 : 10, and $\frac{9}{10}$.

Razón (p. 243) Una razón es una comparación de dos cantidades mediante la división.

Rational number (p. 190) A rational number is any number written as a quotient of two integers where the denominator is not 0.

$\frac{1}{3}, -5, 6.4, 0.666\ldots, -2\frac{4}{5}, 0$, and $\frac{7}{3}$ are rational numbers.

Número racional (p. 190) Un número racional es cualquier número escrito como cociente de dos enteros, donde el denominador es diferente de cero.

Ray (p. 420) A ray has one endpoint and all the points of the line on one side of the point.

$\overrightarrow{CG}$ represents a ray.

Rayo (p. 420) Un rayo tiene un extremo y todos los puntos de la recta a un lado del punto.

Real numbers (p. 222) Together, rational and irrational numbers form the set of real numbers.

$3, -5.25, 3.141592653\ldots$, and $\frac{7}{8}$ are real numbers.

Números reales (p. 222) Juntos, los números racionales e irracionales forman el conjunto de los números reales.

Reciprocal (p. 206) Two numbers are reciprocals if their product is 1.

The numbers $\frac{4}{9}$ and $\frac{9}{4}$ are reciprocals.

Recíproco (p. 206) Dos números son recíprocos si su producto es 1.

Rectangle (p. 431) A rectangle is a parallelogram with four right angles.

Rectángulo (p. 431) Un rectángulo es un paralelogramo que tiene cuatro ángulos rectos.

Reduction (p. 273) A dilation with a scale factor less than 1 is a reduction.

See *Dilation*.

Reducción (p. 273) Una dilatación con un factor de escala menor que 1 es una reducción.

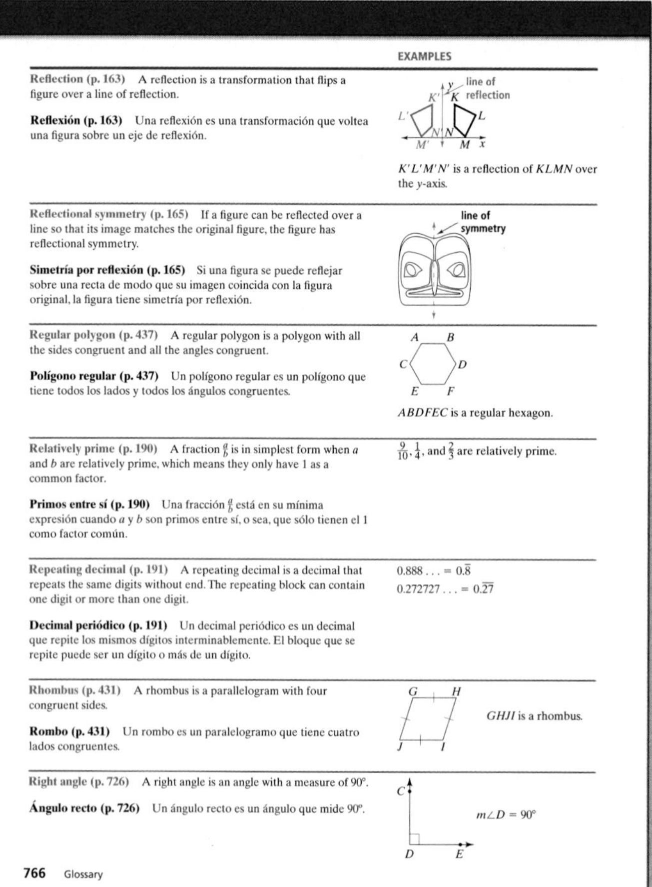

EXAMPLES

Reflection (p. 163) A reflection is a transformation that flips a figure over a line of reflection.

$K'L'M'N'$ is a reflection of $KLMN$ over the y-axis.

Reflexión (p. 163) Una reflexión es una transformación que voltea una figura sobre un eje de reflexión.

Reflectional symmetry (p. 165) If a figure can be reflected over a line so that its image matches the original figure, the figure has reflectional symmetry.

Simetría por reflexión (p. 165) Si una figura se puede reflejar sobre una recta de modo que su imagen coincida con la figura original, la figura tiene simetría por reflexión.

Regular polygon (p. 437) A regular polygon is a polygon with all the sides congruent and all the angles congruent.

$ABDFEC$ is a regular hexagon.

Polígono regular (p. 437) Un polígono regular es un polígono que tiene todos los lados y todos los ángulos congruentes.

Relatively prime (p. 190) A fraction $\frac{a}{b}$ is in simplest form when a and b are relatively prime, which means they only have 1 as a common factor.

$\frac{9}{10}, \frac{1}{4}$, and $\frac{2}{3}$ are relatively prime.

Primos entre sí (p. 190) Una fracción $\frac{a}{b}$ está en su mínima expresión cuando a y b son primos entre sí, o sea, que sólo tienen el 1 como factor común.

Repeating decimal (p. 191) A repeating decimal is a decimal that repeats the same digits without end. The repeating block can contain one digit or more than one digit.

$0.888\ldots = 0.\overline{8}$
$0.272727\ldots = 0.\overline{27}$

Decimal periódico (p. 191) Un decimal periódico es un decimal que repite los mismos dígitos interminablemente. El bloque que se repite puede ser un dígito o más de un dígito.

Rhombus (p. 431) A rhombus is a parallelogram with four congruent sides.

$GHJI$ is a rhombus.

Rombo (p. 431) Un rombo es un paralelogramo que tiene cuatro lados congruentes.

Right angle (p. 726) A right angle is an angle with a measure of 90°.

$m\angle D = 90°$

Ángulo recto (p. 726) Un ángulo recto es un ángulo que mide 90°.

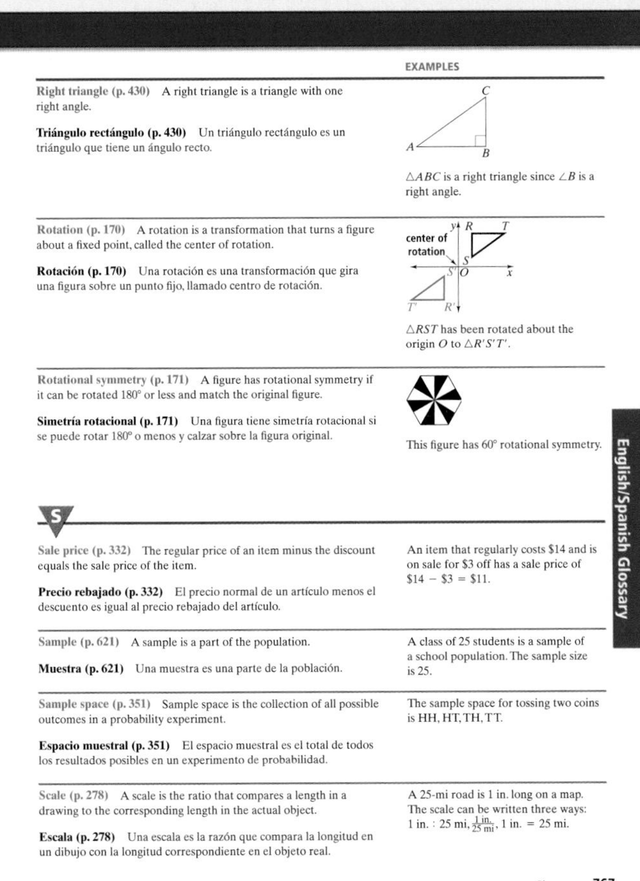

EXAMPLES

Right triangle (p. 430) A right triangle is a triangle with one right angle.

Triángulo rectángulo (p. 430) Un triángulo rectángulo es un triángulo que tiene un ángulo recto.

$\triangle ABC$ is a right triangle since $\angle B$ is a right angle.

Rotation (p. 170) A rotation is a transformation that turns a figure about a fixed point, called the center of rotation.

Rotación (p. 170) Una rotación es una transformación que gira una figura sobre un punto fijo, llamado centro de rotación.

center of rotation

$\triangle RST$ has been rotated about the origin O to $\triangle R'S'T'$.

Rotational symmetry (p. 171) A figure has rotational symmetry if it can be rotated 180° or less and match the original figure.

Simetría rotacional (p. 171) Una figura tiene simetría rotacional si se puede rotar 180° o menos y calzar sobre la figura original.

This figure has 60° rotational symmetry.

S

Sale price (p. 332) The regular price of an item minus the discount equals the sale price of the item.

Precio rebajado (p. 332) El precio normal de un artículo menos el descuento es igual al precio rebajado del artículo.

An item that regularly costs \$14 and is on sale for \$3 off has a sale price of \$14 − \$3 = \$11.

Sample (p. 621) A sample is a part of the population.

Muestra (p. 621) Una muestra es una parte de la población.

A class of 25 students is a sample of a school population. The sample size is 25.

Sample space (p. 351) Sample space is the collection of all possible outcomes in a probability experiment.

Espacio muestral (p. 351) El espacio muestral es el total de todos los resultados posibles en un experimento de probabilidad.

The sample space for tossing two coins is HH, HT, TH, TT.

Scale (p. 278) A scale is the ratio that compares a length in a drawing to the corresponding length in the actual object.

Escala (p. 278) Una escala es la razón que compara la longitud en un dibujo con la longitud correspondiente en el objeto real.

A 25-mi road is 1 in. long on a map. The scale can be written three ways: 1 in. : 25 mi, $\frac{1 \text{ in.}}{25 \text{ mi}}$, 1 in. = 25 mi.

English/Spanish Glossary

EXAMPLES

Scale factor (p. 272) The ratio of the dimensions of the image to the dimensions of the original figure is called a scale factor.

Factor de escala (p. 272) La razón de las dimensiones de una imagen a las dimensiones de la figura original se llama el factor de escala.

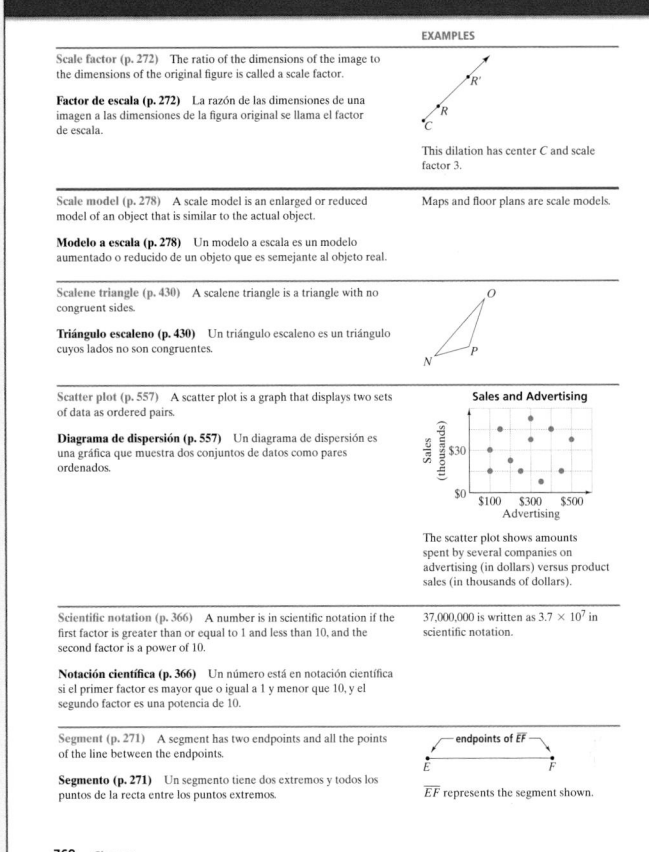

This dilation has center C and scale factor 3.

Scale model (p. 278) A scale model is an enlarged or reduced model of an object that is similar to the actual object.

Modelo a escala (p. 278) Un modelo a escala es un modelo aumentado o reducido de un objeto que es semejante al objeto real.

Maps and floor plans are scale models.

Scalene triangle (p. 430) A scalene triangle is a triangle with no congruent sides.

Triángulo escaleno (p. 430) Un triángulo escaleno es un triángulo cuyos lados no son congruentes.

Scatter plot (p. 557) A scatter plot is a graph that displays two sets of data as ordered pairs.

Diagrama de dispersión (p. 557) Un diagrama de dispersión es una gráfica que muestra dos conjuntos de datos como pares ordenados.

Sales and Advertising

Sales (thousands): \$0, \$30; Advertising: \$100, \$300, \$500

The scatter plot shows amounts spent by several companies on advertising (in dollars) versus product sales (in thousands of dollars).

Scientific notation (p. 366) A number is in scientific notation if the first factor is greater than or equal to 1 and less than 10, and the second factor is a power of 10.

Notación científica (p. 366) Un número está en notación científica si el primer factor es mayor que o igual a 1 y menor que 10, y el segundo factor es una potencia de 10.

37,000,000 is written as 3.7×10^7 in scientific notation.

Segment (p. 271) A segment has two endpoints and all the points of the line between the endpoints.

Segmento (p. 271) Un segmento tiene dos extremos y todos los puntos de la recta entre los puntos extremos.

endpoints of $\overline{EF}$

$\overline{EF}$ represents the segment shown.

EXAMPLES

Segment bisector (p. 456) A segment bisector is a line, segment, or ray that goes through the midpoint of a segment.

Mediatriz de un segmento (p. 456) Una mediatriz de un segmento es una recta, segmento o rayo que pasa por el punto medio de un segmento.

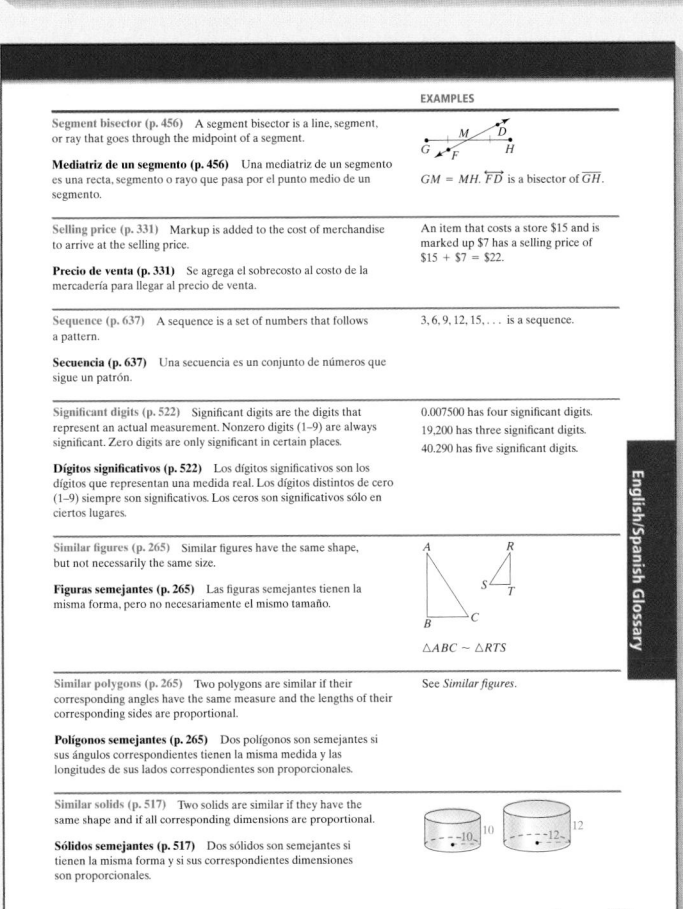

$GM = MH$. $\overleftrightarrow{FD}$ is a bisector of $\overline{GH}$.

Selling price (p. 331) Markup is added to the cost of merchandise to arrive at the selling price.

Precio de venta (p. 331) Se agrega el sobrecosto al costo de la mercadería para llegar al precio de venta.

An item that costs a store \$15 and is marked up \$7 has a selling price of \$15 + \$7 = \$22.

Sequence (p. 637) A sequence is a set of numbers that follows a pattern.

Secuencia (p. 637) Una secuencia es un conjunto de números que sigue un patrón.

3, 6, 9, 12, 15, . . . is a sequence.

Significant digits (p. 522) Significant digits are the digits that represent an actual measurement. Nonzero digits (1–9) are always significant. Zero digits are only significant in certain places.

Dígitos significativos (p. 522) Los dígitos significativos son los dígitos que representan una medida real. Los dígitos distintos de cero (1–9) siempre son significativos. Los ceros son significativos sólo en ciertos lugares.

0.007500 has four significant digits.
19,200 has three significant digits.
40.290 has five significant digits.

Similar figures (p. 265) Similar figures have the same shape, but not necessarily the same size.

Figuras semejantes (p. 265) Las figuras semejantes tienen la misma forma, pero no necesariamente el mismo tamaño.

$\triangle ABC \sim \triangle RTS$

Similar polygons (p. 265) Two polygons are similar if their corresponding angles have the same measure and the lengths of their corresponding sides are proportional.

Polígonos semejantes (p. 265) Dos polígonos son semejantes si sus ángulos correspondientes tienen la misma medida y las longitudes de sus lados correspondientes son proporcionales.

See *Similar figures*.

Similar solids (p. 517) Two solids are similar if they have the same shape and if all corresponding dimensions are proportional.

Sólidos semejantes (p. 517) Dos sólidos son semejantes si tienen la misma forma y si sus correspondientes dimensiones son proporcionales.

English/Spanish Glossary

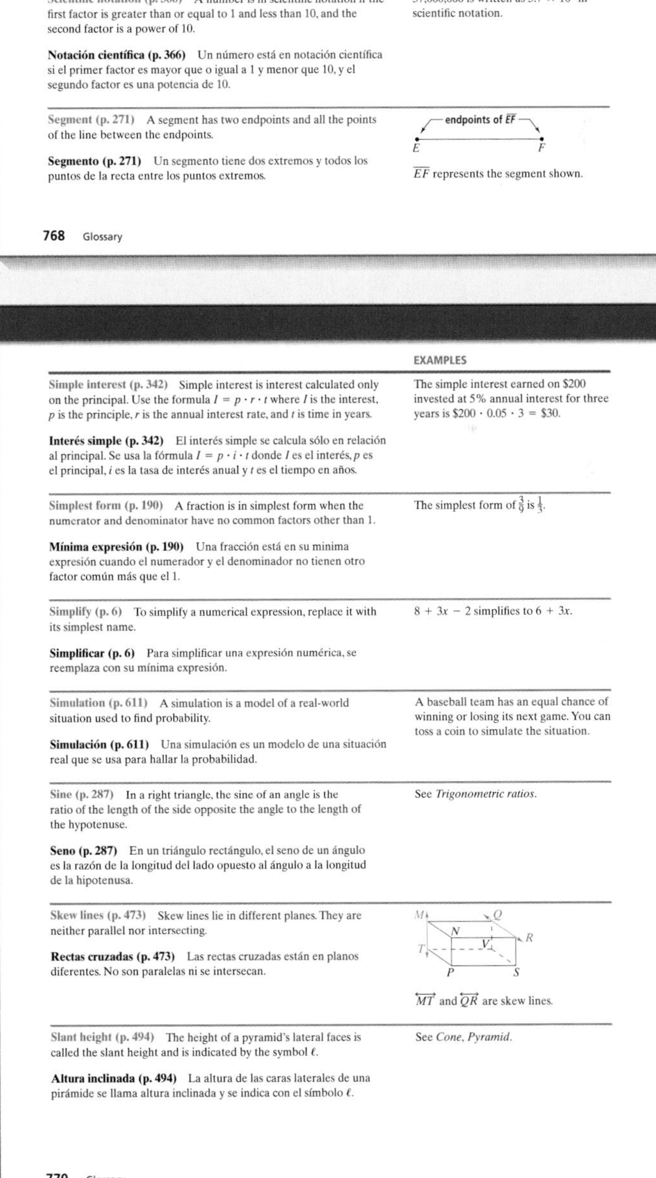

EXAMPLES

Simple interest (p. 342) Simple interest is interest calculated only on the principal. Use the formula $I = p \cdot r \cdot t$ where I is the interest, p is the principle, r is the annual interest rate, and t is time in years.

Interés simple (p. 342) El interés simple se calcula sólo en relación al principal. Se usa la fórmula $I = p \cdot i \cdot t$ donde I es el interés, p es el principal, i es la tasa de interés anual y t es el tiempo en años.

The simple interest earned on \$200 invested at 5% annual interest for three years is \$200 · 0.05 · 3 = \$30.

Simplest form (p. 190) A fraction is in simplest form when the numerator and denominator have no common factors other than 1.

Mínima expresión (p. 190) Una fracción está en su mínima expresión cuando el numerador y el denominador no tienen otro factor común más que el 1.

The simplest form of $\frac{3}{9}$ is $\frac{1}{3}$.

Simplify (p. 6) To simplify a numerical expression, replace it with its simplest name.

Simplificar (p. 6) Para simplificar una expresión numérica, se reemplaza con su mínima expresión.

$8 + 3x - 2$ simplifies to $6 + 3x$.

Simulation (p. 611) A simulation is a model of a real-world situation used to find probability.

Simulación (p. 611) Una simulación es un modelo de una situación real que se usa para hallar la probabilidad.

A baseball team has an equal chance of winning or losing its next game. You can toss a coin to simulate the situation.

Sine (p. 287) In a right triangle, the sine of an angle is the ratio of the length of the side opposite the angle to the length of the hypotenuse.

Seno (p. 287) En un triángulo rectángulo, el seno de un ángulo es la razón de la longitud del lado opuesto al ángulo a la longitud de la hipotenusa.

See *Trigonometric ratios*.

Skew lines (p. 473) Skew lines lie in different planes. They are neither parallel nor intersecting.

Rectas cruzadas (p. 473) Las rectas cruzadas están en planos diferentes. No son paralelas ni se intersecan.

$\overleftrightarrow{MT}$ and $\overleftrightarrow{QR}$ are skew lines.

Slant height (p. 494) The height of a pyramid's lateral faces is called the slant height and is indicated by the symbol ℓ.

Altura inclinada (p. 494) La altura de las caras laterales de una pirámide se llama altura inclinada y se indica con el símbolo ℓ.

See *Cone*, *Pyramid*.

English/Spanish Glossary

EXAMPLES

Slope (p. 128) Slope is a ratio that describes steepness.

$$\text{Slope} = \frac{\text{vertical change}}{\text{horizontal change}} = \frac{\text{rise}}{\text{run}}$$

Pendiente (p. 128) La pendiente es la razón que describe la inclinación.

$$\text{Pendiente} = \frac{\text{cambio vertical}}{\text{cambio horizontal}} = \frac{\text{elevación}}{\text{desplazamiento}}$$

Slope of a line (p. 128)

$$\text{Slope} = \frac{\text{change in } y \text{ coordinates}}{\text{change in } x \text{ coordinates}} = \frac{\text{rise}}{\text{run}}$$

Pendiente de una recta (p. 128)

$$\text{Pendiente} = \frac{\text{cambio en la coordenada } y}{\text{cambio en la coordenada } x} = \frac{\text{elevación}}{\text{desplazamiento}}$$

y, 2, O, rise: 2, run: 4, 4, x

The slope of the given line is $\frac{2}{4} = \frac{1}{2}$.

Slope-intercept form (p. 137) An equation written in the form $y = mx + b$ is in slope-intercept form. The graph is a line with slope m and y-intercept b.

Forma pendiente intercepto (p. 137) Una ecuación escrita en la forma $y = mx + b$ está en la forma pendiente intercepto. La gráfica es una recta en la que m es la pendiente y b es el intercepto y.

The equation $y = 2x + 1$ is written in slope-intercept form with $m = 2$ and $b = 1$.

Solid (p. 471) Solids, or three-dimensional figures, are objects that do not line in a plane. They have length, width, and height.

Sólido (p. 471) Las figuras tridimensionales, o sólidos, son los objetos que no están en un sólo plano. Tienen longitud, anchura y altura.

A cylinder, a cone, and a rectangular prism are all solids.

Solution (pp. 62, 90) A solution is any value or values that make an equation or inequality true.

Solución (pp. 62, 90) Una solución es cualquier valor o valores que hacen que una ecuación o una desigualdad sea verdadera.

4 is the solution of $x + 5 = 9$.
7 is a solution of $x < 15$.

Sphere (p. 511) A sphere is the set of all points in space that are the same distance from a center point.

Esfera (p. 511) Una esfera es el conjunto de todos los puntos en el espacio que están a la misma distancia de un punto central.

Square (p. 431) A square is a parallelogram with four right angles and four congruent sides.

Cuadrado (p. 431) Un cuadrado es un paralelogramo que tiene cuatro ángulos rectos y cuatro lados congruentes.

Q, 5 cm, R, 5 cm, 5 cm, S, 5 cm, T

$QRTS$ is a square. $\angle Q$, $\angle R$, $\angle T$, and $\angle S$ are right angles, and $\overline{QR} = \overline{RT} = \overline{TS} = \overline{SQ}$.

EXAMPLES

Square root (p. 221) The square root of a number is a number that when multiplied by itself is equal to the original number.

Raíz cuadrada (p. 221) La raíz cuadrada de un número es un número que cuando se multiplica por sí mismo es igual al número original.

$\sqrt{9} = 3$ because $3^2 = 9$.

Standard form (p. 365) A number written using digits and place value is in standard form. See also *Expanded form*.

Forma normal (p. 365) Un número escrito usando dígitos y valor posicional está en forma normal. Ver también *Expanded form*.

The standard form of 8.9×10^5 is 890,000.

Stem-and-leaf plot (p. 546) A stem-and-leaf plot is a display that shows numeric data arranged in order. Each data item is broken into a stem (digit or digits on the left) and a leaf (digit on the right).

Diagrama de tallo y hojas (p. 546) Un diagrama de tallo y hojas es una muestra de datos numéricos arreglados en orden. Cada dato se divide en un tallo (dígito o dígitos a la izquierda) y hoja (dígito a la derecha).

stem	leaves
27	7
28	5 6 8
29	6 9
30	8

Key: 27 | 7 means 27.7

This stem-and-leaf plot displays recorded times in a race. The stem represents the whole number of seconds. The leaves represent tenths of a second.

Straight angle (p. 726) A straight angle is an angle with a measure of 180°.

Ángulo llano (p. 726) Un ángulo llano es un ángulo que mide 180°.

180°, T, P, L

$m\angle TPL = 180°$

Stratified sample (p. 622) In a stratified sample, members of the survey population are separated into groups with similar characteristics. Then a random sample is selected from each group.

Muestra estratificada (p. 622) En una muestra estratificada, los miembros de la población estudiada se separan en grupos o estratos con características similares. Luego, se selecciona una muestra aleatoria de cada grupo o estrato.

In a sample, people are separated into the age groups 11–20 years old, 21–30 years old, and 31–40 years old to see what topics they like to look for on the Internet.

Subtraction Property of Equality (p. 61) The Subtraction Property of Equality states that if the same number is subtracted from each side of an equation, the results are equal.

Propiedad sustractiva de la igualdad (p. 61) La propiedad sustractiva de la igualdad establece que si se resta el mismo número a cada lado de una ecuación, los resultados son iguales.

If $a = b$, then $a - c = b - c$.
Since $\frac{20}{2} = 10$, $\frac{20}{2} - 3 = 10 - 3$.

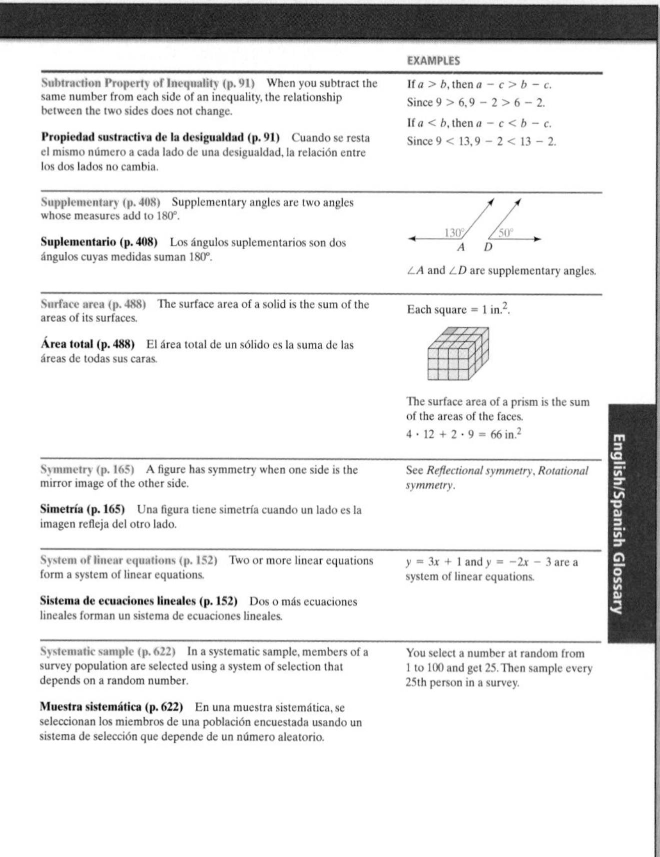

EXAMPLES

Subtraction Property of Inequality (p. 91) When you subtract the same number from each side of an inequality, the relationship between the two sides does not change.

Propiedad sustractiva de la desigualdad (p. 91) Cuando se resta el mismo número a cada lado de una desigualdad, la relación entre los dos lados no cambia.

If $a > b$, then $a - c > b - c$.
Since $9 > 6$, $9 - 2 > 6 - 2$.
If $a < b$, then $a - c < b - c$.
Since $9 < 13$, $9 - 2 < 13 - 2$.

Supplementary (p. 408) Supplementary angles are two angles whose measures add to 180°.

Suplementario (p. 408) Los ángulos suplementarios son dos ángulos cuyas medidas suman 180°.

130°, 50°, A, D

$\angle A$ and $\angle D$ are supplementary angles.

Surface area (p. 488) The surface area of a solid is the sum of the areas of its surfaces.

Área total (p. 488) El área total de un sólido es la suma de las áreas de todas sus caras.

Each square = 1 in.^{2}.

The surface area of a prism is the sum of the areas of the faces.
$4 \cdot 12 + 2 \cdot 9 = 66$ in.^{2}

Symmetry (p. 165) A figure has symmetry when one side is the mirror image of the other side.

Simetría (p. 165) Una figura tiene simetría cuando un lado es la imagen refleja del otro lado.

See *Reflectional symmetry*, *Rotational symmetry*.

System of linear equations (p. 152) Two or more linear equations form a system of linear equations.

Sistema de ecuaciones lineales (p. 152) Dos o más ecuaciones lineales forman un sistema de ecuaciones lineales.

$y = 3x + 1$ and $y = -2x - 3$ are a system of linear equations.

Systematic sample (p. 622) In a systematic sample, members of a survey population are selected using a system of selection that depends on a random number.

Muestra sistemática (p. 622) En una muestra sistemática, se seleccionan los miembros de una población encuestada usando un sistema de selección que depende de un número aleatorio.

You select a number at random from 1 to 100 and get 25. Then sample every 25th person in a survey.

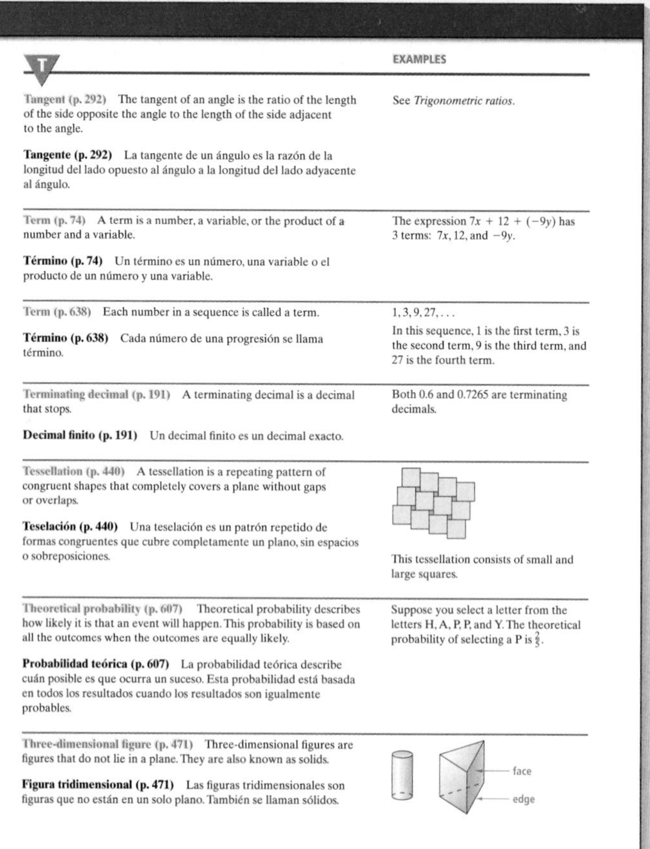

T

EXAMPLES

Tangent (p. 292) The tangent of an angle is the ratio of the length of the side opposite the angle to the length of the side adjacent to the angle.

Tangente (p. 292) La tangente de un ángulo es la razón de la longitud del lado opuesto al ángulo a la longitud del lado adyacente al ángulo.

See *Trigonometric ratios*.

Term (p. 74) A term is a number, a variable, or the product of a number and a variable.

Término (p. 74) Un término es un número, una variable o el producto de un número y una variable.

The expression $7x + 12 + (-9y)$ has 3 terms: $7x$, 12, and $-9y$.

Term (p. 638) Each number in a sequence is called a term.

Término (p. 638) Cada número de una progresión se llama término.

1, 3, 9, 27, . . .
In this sequence, 1 is the first term, 3 is the second term, 9 is the third term, and 27 is the fourth term.

Terminating decimal (p. 191) A terminating decimal is a decimal that stops.

Decimal finito (p. 191) Un decimal finito es un decimal exacto.

Both 0.6 and 0.7265 are terminating decimals.

Tessellation (p. 440) A tessellation is a repeating pattern of congruent shapes that completely covers a plane without gaps or overlaps.

Teselación (p. 440) Una teselación es un patrón repetido de formas congruentes que cubre completamente un plano, sin espacios o sobreposiciones.

This tessellation consists of small and large squares.

Theoretical probability (p. 607) Theoretical probability describes how likely it is that an event will happen. This probability is based on all the outcomes when the outcomes are equally likely.

Probabilidad teórica (p. 607) La probabilidad teórica describe cuán posible es que ocurra un suceso. Esta probabilidad está basada en todos los resultados cuando los resultados son igualmente probables.

Suppose you select a letter from the letters H, A, P, P, and Y. The theoretical probability of selecting a P is $\frac{2}{5}$.

Three-dimensional figure (p. 471) Three-dimensional figures are figures that do not lie in a plane. They are also known as solids.

Figura tridimensional (p. 471) Las figuras tridimensionales son figuras que no están en un solo plano. También se llaman sólidos.

face, edge

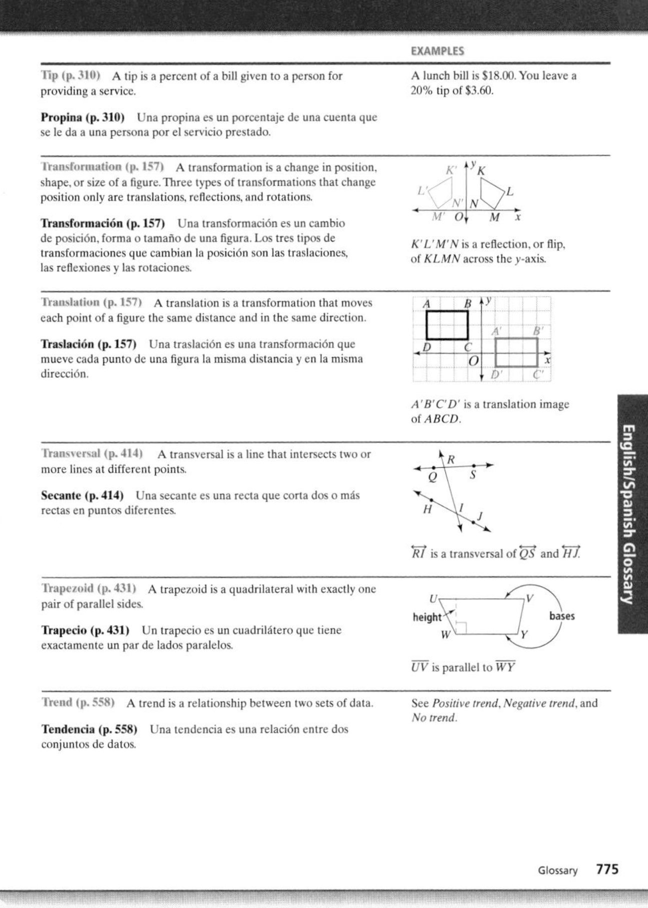

EXAMPLES

Tip (p. 310) A tip is a percent of a bill given to a person for providing a service.

Propina (p. 310) Una propina es un porcentaje de una cuenta que se le da a una persona por el servicio prestado.

A lunch bill is $18.00. You leave a 20% tip of $3.60.

Transformation (p. 157) A transformation is a change in position, shape, or size of a figure. Three types of transformations that change position only are translations, reflections, and rotations.

Transformación (p. 157) Una transformación es un cambio de posición, forma o tamaño de una figura. Los tres tipos de transformaciones que cambian la posición son las traslaciones, las reflexiones y las rotaciones.

$K'L'M'N$ is a reflection, or flip, of $KLMN$ across the y-axis.

Translation (p. 157) A translation is a transformation that moves each point of a figure the same distance and in the same direction.

Traslación (p. 157) Una traslación es una transformación que mueve cada punto de una figura la misma distancia y en la misma dirección.

$A'B'C'D'$ is a translation image of $ABCD$.

Transversal (p. 414) A transversal is a line that intersects two or more lines at different points.

Secante (p. 414) Una secante es una recta que corta dos o más rectas en puntos diferentes.

$\overleftrightarrow{RI}$ is a transversal of $\overleftrightarrow{QS}$ and $\overleftrightarrow{HJ}$.

Trapezoid (p. 431) A trapezoid is a quadrilateral with exactly one pair of parallel sides.

Trapecio (p. 431) Un trapecio es un cuadrilátero que tiene exactamente un par de lados paralelos.

$\overline{UV}$ is parallel to $\overline{WY}$

Trend (p. 558) A trend is a relationship between two sets of data.

Tendencia (p. 558) Una tendencia es una relación entre dos conjuntos de datos.

See *Positive trend*, *Negative trend*, and *No trend*.

English/Spanish Glossary

Glossary 775

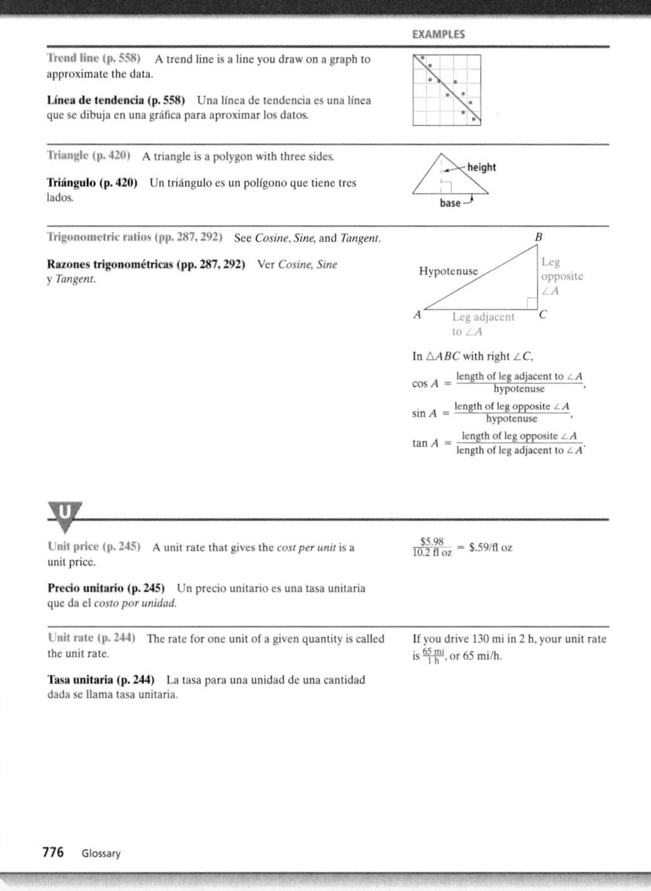

EXAMPLES

Trend line (p. 558) A trend line is a line you draw on a graph to approximate the data.

Línea de tendencia (p. 558) Una línea de tendencia es una línea que se dibuja en una gráfica para aproximar los datos.

Triangle (p. 420) A triangle is a polygon with three sides.

Triángulo (p. 420) Un triángulo es un polígono que tiene tres lados.

Trigonometric ratios (pp. 287, 292) See *Cosine*, *Sine*, and *Tangent*.

Razones trigonométricas (pp. 287, 292) Ver *Cosine*, *Sine* y *Tangent*.

In $\triangle ABC$ with right $\angle C$,

$\cos A = \frac{\text{length of leg adjacent to } \angle A}{\text{hypotenuse}}$,

$\sin A = \frac{\text{length of leg opposite } \angle A}{\text{hypotenuse}}$,

$\tan A = \frac{\text{length of leg opposite } \angle A}{\text{length of leg adjacent to } \angle A}$.

U

Unit price (p. 245) A unit rate that gives the *cost per unit* is a unit price.

Precio unitario (p. 245) Un precio unitario es una tasa unitaria que da el *costo por unidad*.

$\frac{\$5.98}{10.2 \text{ fl oz}} = \$.59/\text{fl oz}$

Unit rate (p. 244) The rate for one unit of a given quantity is called the unit rate.

Tasa unitaria (p. 244) La tasa para una unidad de una cantidad dada se llama tasa unitaria.

If you drive 130 mi in 2 h, your unit rate is $\frac{65 \text{ mi}}{1 \text{ h}}$, or 65 mi/h.

776 Glossary

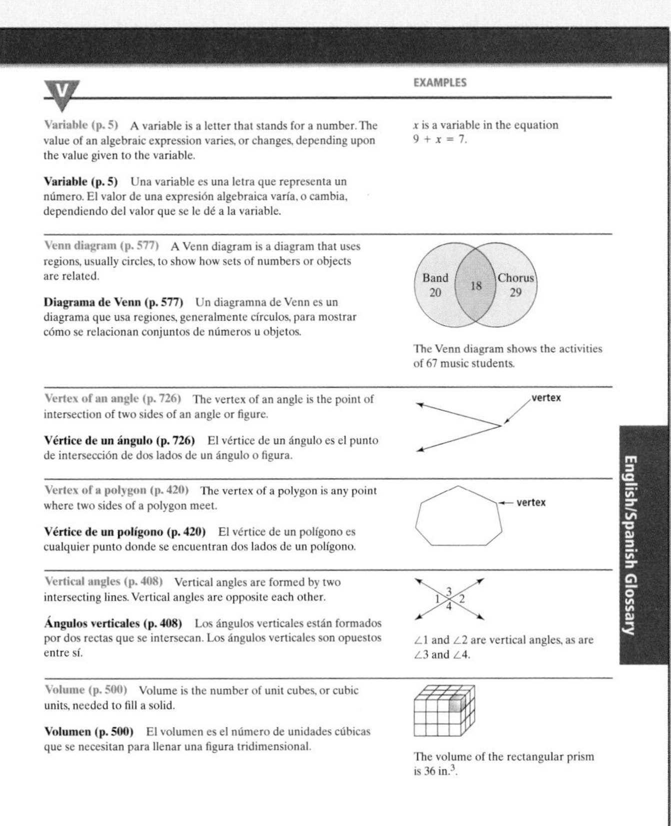

EXAMPLES

V

Variable (p. 5) A variable is a letter that stands for a number. The value of an algebraic expression varies, or changes, depending upon the value given to the variable.

Variable (p. 5) Una variable es una letra que representa un número. El valor de una expresión algebraica varía, o cambia, dependiendo del valor que se le dé a la variable.

x is a variable in the equation $9 + x = 7$.

Venn diagram (p. 577) A Venn diagram is a diagram that uses regions, usually circles, to show how sets of numbers or objects are related.

Diagrama de Venn (p. 577) Un diagramna de Venn es un diagrama que usa regiones, generalmente círculos, para mostrar cómo se relacionan conjuntos de números u objetos.

The Venn diagram shows the activities of 67 music students.

Vertex of an angle (p. 726) The vertex of an angle is the point of intersection of two sides of an angle or figure.

Vértice de un ángulo (p. 726) El vértice de un ángulo es el punto de intersección de dos lados de un ángulo o figura.

Vertex of a polygon (p. 420) The vertex of a polygon is any point where two sides of a polygon meet.

Vértice de un polígono (p. 420) El vértice de un polígono es cualquier punto donde se encuentran dos lados de un polígono.

Vertical angles (p. 408) Vertical angles are formed by two intersecting lines. Vertical angles are opposite each other.

Ángulos verticales (p. 408) Los ángulos verticales están formados por dos rectas que se intersecan. Los ángulos verticales son opuestos entre sí.

$\angle 1$ and $\angle 2$ are vertical angles, as are $\angle 3$ and $\angle 4$.

Volume (p. 500) Volume is the number of unit cubes, or cubic units, needed to fill a solid.

Volumen (p. 500) El volumen es el número de unidades cúbicas que se necesitan para llenar una figura tridimensional.

The volume of the rectangular prism is 36 in.^{3}.

English/Spanish Glossary

Glossary 777

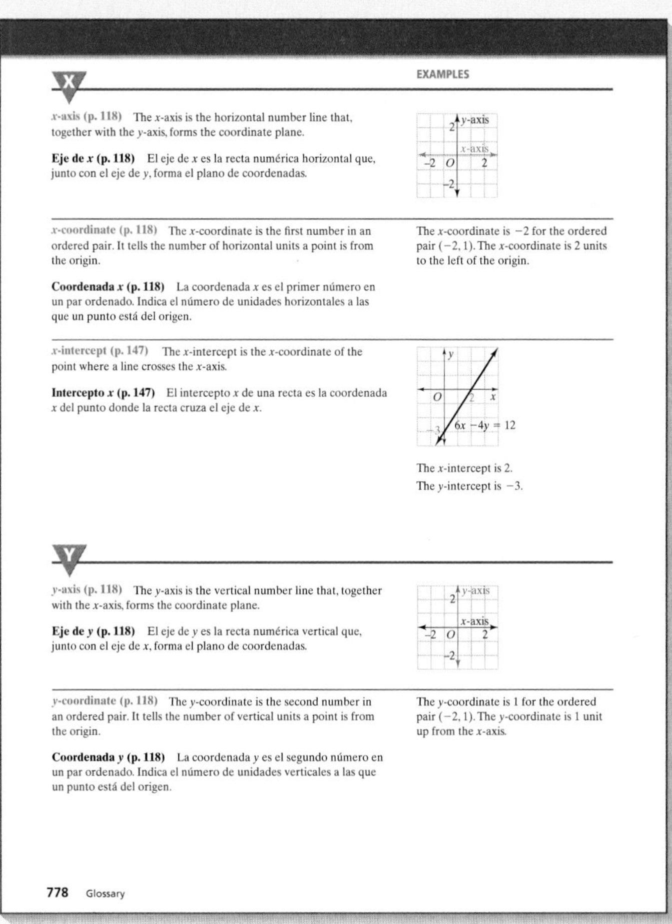

EXAMPLES

X

x-axis (p. 118) The x-axis is the horizontal number line that, together with the y-axis, forms the coordinate plane.

Eje de x (p. 118) El eje de x es la recta numérica horizontal que, junto con el eje de y, forma el plano de coordenadas.

x-coordinate (p. 118) The x-coordinate is the first number in an ordered pair. It tells the number of horizontal units a point is from the origin.

Coordenada x (p. 118) La coordenada x es el primer número en un par ordenado. Indica el número de unidades horizontales a las que un punto está del origen.

The x-coordinate is -2 for the ordered pair $(-2, 1)$. The x-coordinate is 2 units to the left of the origin.

x-intercept (p. 147) The x-intercept is the x-coordinate of the point where a line crosses the x-axis.

Intercepto x (p. 147) El intercepto x de una recta es la coordenada x del punto donde la recta cruza el eje de x.

The x-intercept is 2.
The y-intercept is -3.

Y

y-axis (p. 118) The y-axis is the vertical number line that, together with the x-axis, forms the coordinate plane.

Eje de y (p. 118) El eje de y es la recta numérica vertical que, junto con el eje de x, forma el plano de coordenadas.

y-coordinate (p. 118) The y-coordinate is the second number in an ordered pair. It tells the number of vertical units a point is from the origin.

Coordenada y (p. 118) La coordenada y es el segundo número en un par ordenado. Indica el número de unidades verticales a las que un punto está del origen.

The y-coordinate is 1 for the ordered pair $(-2, 1)$. The y-coordinate is 1 unit up from the x-axis.

778 Glossary

English/Spanish Glossary

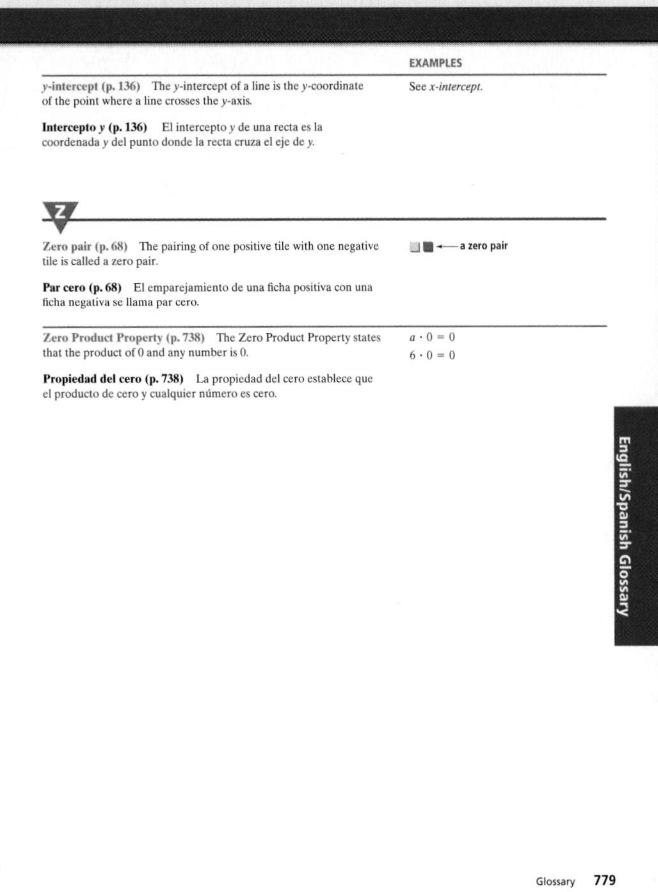

EXAMPLES

y-intercept (p. 136) The *y*-intercept of a line is the *y*-coordinate of the point where a line crosses the *y*-axis.

Intercepto *y* (p. 136) El intercepto *y* de una recta es la coordenada *y* del punto donde la recta cruza el eje de *y*.

See *x-intercept*.

Z

Zero pair (p. 68) The pairing of one positive tile with one negative tile is called a zero pair.

Par cero (p. 68) El emparejamiento de una ficha positiva con una ficha negativa se llama par cero.

Zero Product Property (p. 738) The Zero Product Property states that the product of 0 and any number is 0.

Propiedad del cero (p. 738) La propiedad del cero establece que el producto de cero y cualquier número es cero.

$a \cdot 0 = 0$
$6 \cdot 0 = 0$

English/Spanish Glossary

Glossary 779

Answers to Instant Check System™

Chapter 1

Diagnosing Readiness p. 4

1. < **2.** = **3.** < **4.** < **5.** > **6.** > **7.** < **8.** < **9.** > **10.** 1.234 **11.** 0.96 **12.** 7.29 **13.** 47.3 **14.** 1.88 **15.** 10.16 **16.** 0.68 **17.** 14.7 **18.** 15.52 **19.** 0.0138 **20.** 22.53 **21.** 8.512 **22.** 5.68 **23.** 11.52 **24.** 0.092 **25.** 8.95 **26.** 3.19 **27.** 0.044

Lesson 1-1 pp. 5–7

Check Skills You'll Need **1.** 9.6 **2.** 18.6 **3.** 11.25 **4.** 11.1 **5.** 6.5 **6.** 270

Check Understanding **1.** Answers may vary. Sample: Let c = the cost of a hat; $15c$ **2.** 5 **3a.** 40 **b.** 24 **4a.** 12, 14, 16, 18 **b.** 7, 35, 63, 91 **c.** 1, 10, 16, 25

Lesson 1-2 pp. 12–13

Check Skills You'll Need **1.** $q - 2$ **2.** $2b + 4$ **3.** $m - 7$ **4.** $8 - 2n$ **5.** $x + 6$ **6.** $\frac{y}{3}$

Check Understanding **1.** 1,730 ft

Lesson 1-3 pp. 16–18

Check Skills You'll Need **1.** 11 **2.** 19 **3.** 14 **4.** 15 **5.** 12 **6.** 14 **7.** 3 **8.** 1

Check Understanding **1a.** −5 −4 −3 −2 −1 0 1 2 3 **b.** halfway between −2 and −3 **2a.** 7 **b.** 7 **c.** 13 **d.** 15 **3a.** 15 **b.** 27.2 **c.** $5|-x|$ **4.** −5, 0, 4 **5.** Africa; −11 has a greater absolute value than −9.

Lesson 1-4 pp. 22–27

Check Skills You'll Need **1.** 28 **2.** 19 **3.** 2 **4.** 38 **5.** 6 **6.** 3 **7.** 2 **8.** 38 **9.** 20

Check Understanding **1a.** 4 **b.** negative **2a.** −8 **b.** negative **3a.** −42 **b.** −80 **c.** 81 **4a.** 12 **b.** −12 **c.** −200 **5.** −181 **6.** −2

Checkpoint Quiz 1 **1.** Let n = a number; $-3n$. **2.** Let n = a number; $\frac{n}{12}$. **3.** 304 **4.** −7 **5.** −64 **6.** 37 **7.** 43 **8.** −21 **9.** 12 **10.** −37 + (−16.5); −53.5

Lesson 1-5 pp. 28–30

Check Skills You'll Need **1.** −6 **2.** −16 **3.** −15 **4.** −36 **5.** −4 **6.** −16 **7.** −12

Check Understanding **1a.** −24 **b.** 24 **c.** 161 **d.** −9 **e.** a negative times a negative **2a.** 144 **b.** −16 **c.** −448 **3.** \$6 **4.** −36

Lesson 1-6 pp. 33–35

Check Skills You'll Need **1.** −6 **2.** −7 **3.** −11 **4.** −8 **5.** 8 **6.** −74

Check Understanding **1a.** $2.58\overline{3}$; 1.5; 11 **b.** The mean goes down to 2, the median stays at 1.5, and there is no mode. **2.** 8.9 **3a.** 1; it lowers the mean about 1.4. **b.** −18; it lowers the mean about 1.8. **4a–c.** Answers may vary. Samples are given. **4a.** Median; there may be outliers. **b.** Mode; favorite cereals are not numerical. **c.** Mean; there are no outliers of ages in my class.

Lesson 1-7 pp. 39–43

Check Skills You'll Need **1.** 16 **2.** 27 **3.** 16 **4.** 4 **5.** −125 **6.** 81 **7.** −8 **8.** 1

Check Understanding **1a.** $6^2 \cdot 7^6$ **b.** $9^2a^4b^2$ **2a.** 81 **b.** −81 **c.** −343 **d.** 2^3 or 8 **3a.** Answers may vary. Sample: In $(2 \cdot 5)^2$, 10 is squared. In $2 \cdot 5^2$, 5 is squared. **b.** 50 **4.** 299 **5.** about 5.7 m

Checkpoint Quiz 2 **1.** −416 **2.** 4 **3.** −72 **4.** −27 **5.** 5 **6.** 12 **7.** 21 **8.** −12 **9.** −32 **10.** −20

Lesson 1-8 pp. 45–48

Check Skills You'll Need **1.** 99 **2.** 100 **3.** −21 **4.** 32

Check Understanding **1a.** Comm. Prop. of Mult. **b.** Ident. Prop. of Mult. **2a.** 48 **b.** −46 **3a.** 36,500 **b.** 2,420 **4a.** $6m + 18$ **b.** $-2t + 14$ **5a.** 800 **b.** 450 **6a.** The books will cost \$118. **b.** $20(6.1) = 20 \cdot 6 + 20 \cdot 0.1 = 120 + 2 = 122$

Chapter 2

Diagnosing Readines p. 60

1. −2 **2.** −2 **3.** 14 **4.** 120 **5.** −4 **6.** 1 **7.** −7 **8.** 6 **9.** −1 **10.** 1 **11.** 3 **12.** 16 **13.** 26 **14.** 24 **15.** $5c - 15$ **16.** $-2w - 16$ **17.** $-54 + 9t$ **18.** $-10 + 2a$ 19. $44 - 11b$ 20. $-x + 2$

Lesson 2-1 pp. 61–64

Check Skills You'll Need **1.** 7 **2.** 0 **3.** −11 **4.** −7 **5.** −6 **6.** 26

Check Understanding **1a.** 17 **b.** −3 **2.** $x + 8 = 52$; 44 **3a.** 22 **b.** −40 **c.** −13 **4.** −4

Lesson 2-2 pp. 69–70

Check Skills You'll Need **1.** −7 **2.** 6 **3.** 7 **4.** 14 **5.** $2.89 + m = 3.88$

Check Understanding **1a.** 4 b. −8.7 **2.** −32 **3a.** The video rental cost would increase by \$.75. **b.** $0.5 + 0.085c = 3.56$; 36 min

Lesson 2-3 pp. 73–76

Check Skills You'll Need **1.** $-8r - 24$ **2.** $-7s + 35$ **3.** $70 - 35t$ **4.** Comm. Prop. of Add. and Assoc. Prop. of Add.

Check Understanding **1a.** $11x$ **b.** $-15t$ **2a.** $2a$ **b.** $-8x$ **3a.** Let b = the cost of a board. Let n = the cost of a box of nails. Let h = the cost of a hammer. $26b + 3n + h$ **b.** $26b$ becomes $22b$. **4.** $5b + 4$ **5.** $9 - 6b$

Lesson 2-4 pp. 78–83

Check Skills You'll Need **1.** $16d - 6$ **2.** $22 - 26m$ **3.** $28 - 12r$ **4.** $9t + 47$ **5.** $8q + 5$ **6.** $60 - 12r$ **7.** First, distribute the negative to get $2x - 5x - 7$. Then combine like terms to get $-3x - 7$.

Check Understanding **1.** −11 **2.** $15(x + 12) = 1{,}440$; 84 students

3a.

$$\begin{aligned} 7 + 3h &= -1 - 5h \\ 7 + 3h - 3h &= -1 - 5h - 3h \\ 7 &= -1 - 8h \\ 7 + 1 &= -1 + 1 - 8h \\ \frac{8}{-8} &= \frac{-8h}{-8} \\ -1 &= h \end{aligned}$$

b. 2 **4a.** positive **b.** −9

Checkpoint Quiz 1 **1.** $-8m + p + 4$ **2.** $-2h + 20$ **3.** 11 **4.** −8 **5.** 3 **6.** 3 **7.** 15 **8.** −28 **9.** −3 **10.** −1

Lesson 2-5 pp. 85–86

Check Skills You'll Need **1.** $4 + b$ **2.** $9 - v$ **3.** $c - 7$ **4.** $8t$ **5.** $x + 17$ **6.** $-10 + y$

Check Understanding **1a.** Answers may vary. Sample: The *draw a diagram* strategy; a diagram helps you understand what the words mean. **b.** 20.5 in., 28.5 in.

Lesson 2-6 pp. 90–92

Check Skills You'll Need **1.** −18 **2.** −13 **3.** 24 **4.** 21

Check Understanding **1a.** −1 0 1 2 3 4 5 6

b. to the left **2a.** $w > 6$ **b.** $q \leq -7$ **c.** no **3.** $5 \leq u$ **4.** At most, 211 adults can attend.

Lesson 2-7 pp. 97–102

Check Skills You'll Need **1.** 11 **2.** −4 **3.** −101 **4.** 6.2 **5.** −8 **6.** −1.2 **7.** Write an equation in which the product of 12 and a number is equal to −1. Divide each side by 12 to get $-\frac{1}{12}$ as a solution.

Check Understanding 1a. $r \geq 3$ (−1 0 1 2 3 4 5 6) **b.** yes **2.** up to 16 players
3a. $b \leq -4$ (−6 −4 −2 0)
b. $s \geq -16$ (−16 −8 0 8)
c. $8 < t$ (0 4 8 12)
4a. $p \leq -17$ (−17 −9)
b. They do not include the values from −4 to 4.

Checkpoint Quiz 2 **1.** $a < 8$ **2.** $d \geq 16$ **3.** $m \geq -2$ **4.** $1 > w$ **5.** 90

Lesson 2-8 pp. 103–104

Check Skills You'll Need **1.** $-\frac{7}{2}$ **2.** 2 **3.** 9 **4.** 3 **5.** −8 **6.** 98 **7.** I would subtract 6 from each side of the equation to get $-14 = -2n$. Then, I would divide each side by −2. The solution is 7.

Check Understanding **1a.** $m > 3$ **b.** $x \geq -1$ **c.** $-1 > k$ **d.** The direction of the inequality is opposite and the 2 is negative. **2.** $5 + 1.75x \leq 25$; 11 or fewer rides

Chapter 3

Diagnosing Readiness p. 116

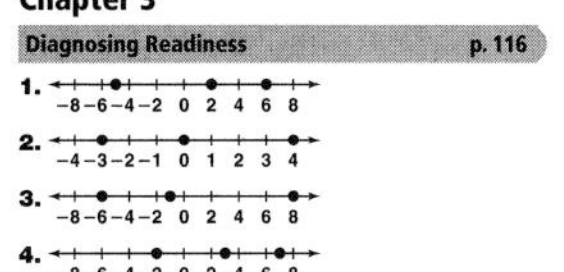

7. −9 **8.** 13 **9.** 46 **10.** −12 **11.** −23 **12.** 10 **13.** −5 **14.** −6 **15.** 6 **16.** −8 **17.** 4 **18.** −3 **19.** −28 **20.** 68 **21.** −4 **22.** 1 **23.** 8 **24.** −1 **25.** 4 **26.** −5 **27.** 102 **28.** 6 **29.** 76 **30.** −54

Lesson 3-1 pp. 117–118

Check Skills You'll Need

1. −5 −4 −3 −2 −1 0 1 2 3

Instant Check System™ Answers

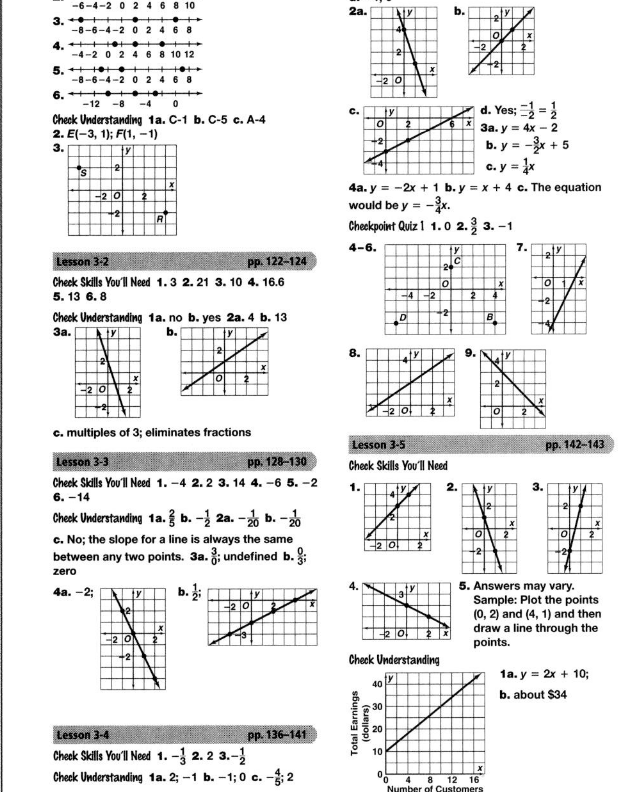

2. −6 −4 −2 0 2 4 6 8 10
3. −8 −6 −4 −2 0 2 4 6 8
4. −4 −2 0 2 4 6 8 10 12
5. −8 −6 −4 −2 0 2 4 6 8
6. −12 −8 −4 0

Check Understanding **1a.** C-1 **b.** C-5 **c.** A-4 **2.** $E(-3, 1)$; $F(1, -1)$ **3.**

Lesson 3-2 pp. 122–124

Check Skills You'll Need **1.** 3 **2.** 21 **3.** 10 **4.** 16.6 **5.** 13 **6.** 8

Check Understanding **1a.** no **b.** yes **2a.** 4 **b.** 13 **3a.** **b.**

c. multiples of 3; eliminates fractions

Lesson 3-3 pp. 128–130

Check Skills You'll Need **1.** −4 **2.** 2 **3.** 14 **4.** −6 **5.** −2 **6.** −14

Check Understanding **1a.** $\frac{2}{5}$ **b.** $-\frac{1}{2}$ **2a.** $-\frac{1}{20}$ **b.** $-\frac{1}{20}$ **c.** No; the slope for a line is always the same between any two points. **3a.** $\frac{3}{0}$; undefined **b.** $\frac{0}{3}$; zero

4a. −2; **b.** $\frac{1}{2}$;

Lesson 3-4 pp. 136–141

Check Skills You'll Need **1.** $-\frac{1}{3}$ **2.** 2 **3.** $-\frac{1}{2}$

Check Understanding **1a.** 2; −1 **b.** −1; 0 **c.** $-\frac{4}{5}$; 2 **d.** −1; 0

2a. **b.** **c.** **d.** Yes; $\frac{-1}{-2} = \frac{1}{2}$ **3a.** $y = 4x - 2$ **b.** $y = -\frac{3}{2}x + 5$ **c.** $y = \frac{1}{4}x$

4a. $y = -2x + 1$ **b.** $y = x + 4$ **c.** The equation would be $y = -\frac{3}{4}x$.

Checkpoint Quiz 1 **1.** 0 **2.** $\frac{3}{2}$ **3.** −1

4–6. **7.** **8.** **9.**

Lesson 3-5 pp. 142–143

Check Skills You'll Need

1. **2.** **3.** **4.** **5.** Answers may vary. Sample: Plot the points (0, 2) and (4, 1) and then draw a line through the points.

Check Understanding

1a. $y = 2x + 10$; **b.** about \$34

Total Earnings (dollars)
Number of Customers

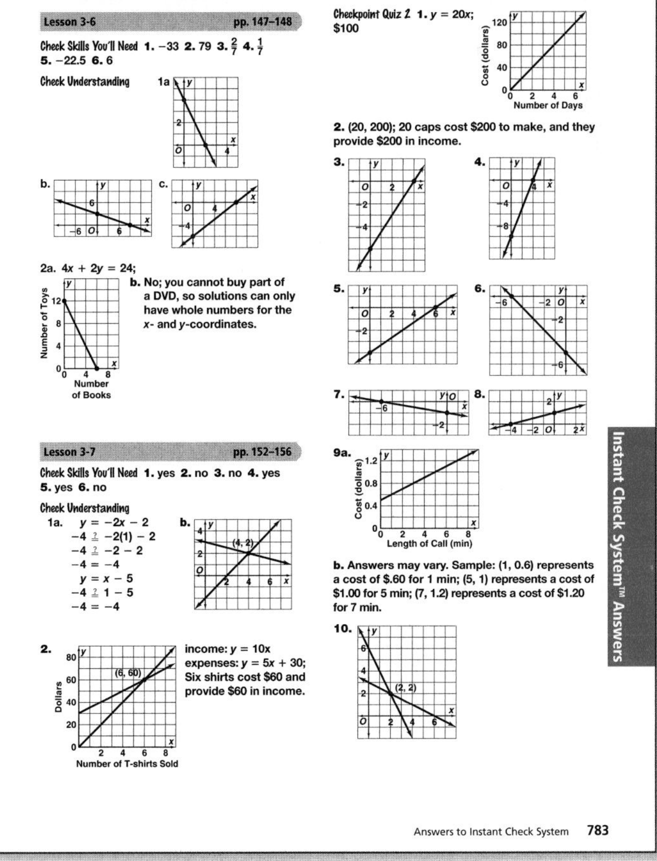

Lesson 3-6 pp. 147–148

Check Skills You'll Need **1.** −33 **2.** 79 **3.** $\frac{2}{7}$ **4.** $\frac{1}{7}$ **5.** −22.5 **6.** 6

Check Understanding 1a b. c.

2a. $4x + 2y = 24$;

Number of Toys
Number of Books

b. No; you cannot buy part of a DVD, so solutions can only have whole numbers for the x- and y-coordinates.

Lesson 3-7 pp. 152–156

Check Skills You'll Need **1.** yes **2.** no **3.** no **4.** yes **5.** yes **6.** no

Check Understanding

1a.

$$\begin{aligned} y &= -2x - 2 \\ -4 &\stackrel{?}{=} -2(1) - 2 \\ -4 &\stackrel{?}{=} -2 - 2 \\ -4 &= -4 \\ y &= x - 5 \\ -4 &\stackrel{?}{=} 1 - 5 \\ -4 &= -4 \end{aligned}$$

b. (4, 2)

2. income: $y = 10x$ expenses: $y = 5x + 30$; Six shirts cost \$60 and provide \$60 in income.

(6, 60)
Dollars
Number of T-shirts Sold

Checkpoint Quiz 2 **1.** $y = 20x$; \$100

Cost (dollars)
Number of Days

2. (20, 200); 20 caps cost \$200 to make, and they provide \$200 in income.

3. **4.** **5.** **6.** **7.** **8.**

9a.

Cost (dollars)
Length of Call (min)

b. Answers may vary. Sample: (1, 0.6) represents a cost of \$.60 for 1 min; (5, 1) represents a cost of \$1.00 for 5 min; (7, 1.2) represents a cost of \$1.20 for 7 min.

10. (2, 2)

Instant Check System™ Answers

Instant Check System™ Answers

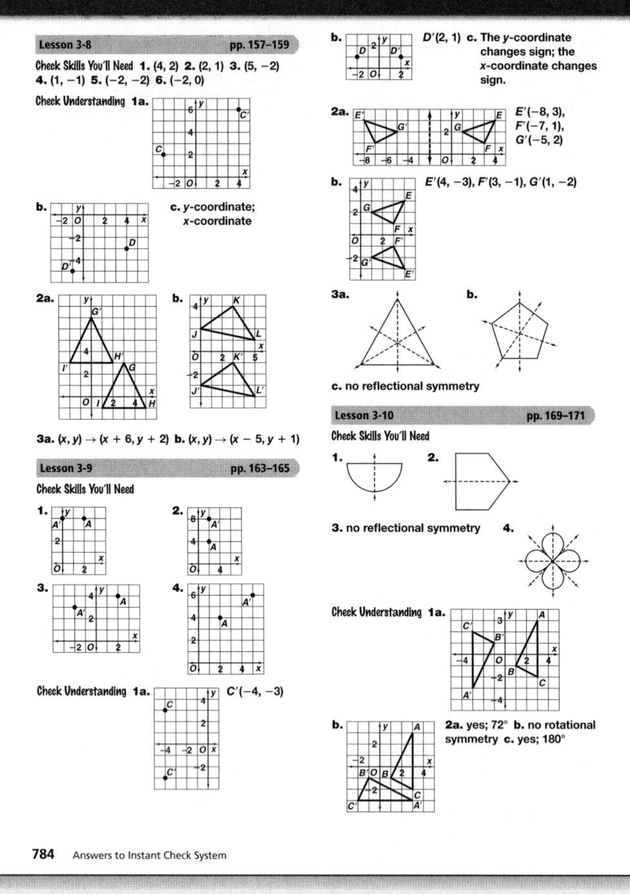

Lesson 3-8 pp. 157–159

Check Skills You'll Need **1.** (4, 2) **2.** (2, 1) **3.** (5, −2) **4.** (1, −1) **5.** (−2, −2) **6.** (−2, 0)

Check Understanding **1a.** [graph] **b.** [graph] **c.** y-coordinate; x-coordinate **2a.** [graph] **b.** [graph] **3a.** $(x, y) \rightarrow (x + 6, y + 2)$ **b.** $(x, y) \rightarrow (x - 5, y + 1)$

Lesson 3-9 pp. 163–165

Check Skills You'll Need **1.** [graph] **2.** [graph] **3.** [graph] **4.** [graph]

Check Understanding **1a.** $C'(-4, -3)$ **b.** $D'(2, 1)$ **c.** The y-coordinate changes sign; the x-coordinate changes sign. **2a.** $E'(-8, 3)$, $F'(-7, 1)$, $G'(-5, 2)$ **b.** $E'(4, -3)$, $F'(3, -1)$, $G'(1, -2)$ **3a.** [figure] **b.** [figure] **c.** no reflectional symmetry

Lesson 3-10 pp. 169–171

Check Skills You'll Need **1.** [figure] **2.** [figure] **3.** no reflectional symmetry **4.** [figure]

Check Understanding **1a.** [graph] **b.** [graph] **2a.** yes; 72° **b.** no rotational symmetry **c.** yes; 180°

Chapter 4

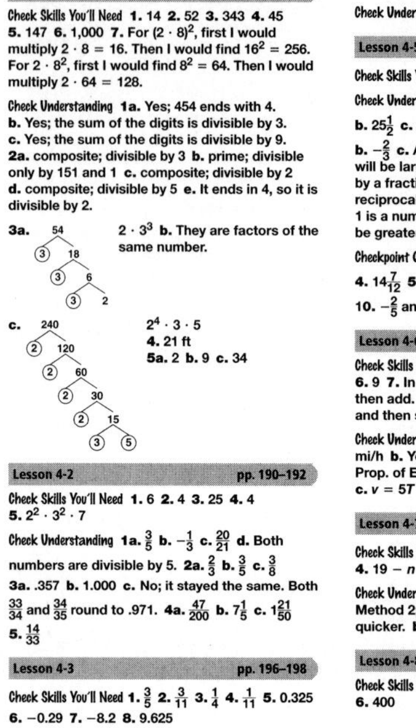

Diagnosing Readiness p.184

1. −14 **2.** −4 **3.** −48 **4.** 6 **5.** −6 **6.** 100 **7.** −200 **8.** −2 **9.** $2\frac{1}{2}$ **10.** $3\frac{1}{6}$ **11.** $6\frac{1}{8}$ **12.** $5\frac{1}{7}$ **13.** $2\frac{2}{5}$ **14.** $9\frac{2}{9}$ **15.** $5\frac{2}{3}$ **16.** $20\frac{2}{3}$ **17.** $\frac{11}{8}$ **18.** $\frac{13}{3}$ **19.** $\frac{17}{5}$ **20.** $\frac{13}{9}$ **21.** $\frac{11}{5}$ **22.** $\frac{29}{3}$ **23.** $-\frac{8}{7}$ **24.** $-\frac{13}{5}$ **25.** $\frac{7}{10}$ **26.** $-\frac{1}{5}$ **27.** $3\frac{1}{7}$ **28.** $9\frac{5}{9}$ **29.** $3\frac{1}{2}$ pizzas **30.** $2\frac{2}{3}$ miles

Lesson 4-1 pp. 185–187

Check Skills You'll Need **1.** 14 **2.** 52 **3.** 343 **4.** 45 **5.** 147 **6.** 1,000 **7.** For $(2 \cdot 8)^2$, first I would multiply $2 \cdot 8 = 16$. Then I would find $16^2 = 256$. For $2 \cdot 8^2$, first I would find $8^2 = 64$. Then I would multiply $2 \cdot 64 = 128$.

Check Understanding **1a.** Yes; 454 ends with 4. **b.** Yes; the sum of the digits is divisible by 3. **c.** Yes; the sum of the digits is divisible by 9. **2a.** composite; divisible by 3 **b.** prime; divisible only by 151 and 1 **c.** composite; divisible by 2 **d.** composite; divisible by 5 **e.** It ends in 4, so it is divisible by 2.

3a. [factor tree: 54, 3, 18, 3, 6, 3, 2] $2 \cdot 3^3$ **b.** They are factors of the same number.

c. [factor tree: 240, 2, 120, 2, 60, 2, 30, 2, 15, 3, 5] $2^4 \cdot 3 \cdot 5$ **4.** 21 ft **5a.** 2 **b.** 9 **c.** 34

Lesson 4-2 pp. 190–192

Check Skills You'll Need **1.** 6 **2.** 4 **3.** 25 **4.** 4 **5.** $2^2 \cdot 3^2 \cdot 7$

Check Understanding **1a.** $\frac{3}{5}$ **b.** $-\frac{1}{3}$ **c.** $\frac{20}{21}$ **d.** Both numbers are divisible by 5. **2a.** $\frac{2}{3}$ **b.** $\frac{3}{5}$ **c.** $\frac{3}{8}$ **3a.** .357 **b.** 1.000 **c.** No; it stayed the same. Both $\frac{33}{34}$ and $\frac{34}{35}$ round to .971. **4a.** $\frac{47}{200}$ **b.** $7\frac{1}{5}$ **c.** $1\frac{21}{50}$ **5.** $\frac{14}{33}$

Lesson 4-3 pp. 196–198

Check Skills You'll Need **1.** $\frac{3}{5}$ **2.** $\frac{3}{11}$ **3.** $\frac{1}{4}$ **4.** $\frac{1}{11}$ **5.** 0.325 **6.** −0.29 **7.** −8.2 **8.** 9.625

Check Understanding **1.** $\frac{7}{11}$ **2a.** $\frac{3}{18}, \frac{2}{18}; \frac{1}{6}$ **b.** $-\frac{4}{30}, -\frac{21}{30}; -\frac{2}{15}$ **c.** greater; $\frac{15}{28} > \frac{14}{28}$. **3a.** $\frac{3}{4}$ **b.** $\frac{14}{19}$ **c.** $\frac{22}{63}$ **d.** It is hard to find the LCD of 58 and 71. **4a.** $-\frac{7}{8}$, −0.625, $1\frac{1}{2}$, $\frac{8}{5}$, 1.61 **b.** $-\frac{1}{2}, -\frac{4}{9}, -\frac{5}{12}$, −0.4

Lesson 4-4 pp. 201–202

Check Skills You'll Need **1.** 5 **2.** 8 **3.** 3 **4.** 90 **5.** 14 **6.** 12 **7.** 100 + (−100) = 0

Check Understanding **1.** $\frac{7}{30}$ **2.** $-\frac{3}{20}$ **3.** $1\frac{1}{12}$ **4.** $2\frac{1}{2}$ in.

Lesson 4-5 pp. 205–207

Check Skills You'll Need **1.** $\frac{1}{3}$ **2.** 2 **3.** $\frac{1}{9}$ **4.** $\frac{6}{11}$ **5.** $\frac{1}{2}$ **6.** $\frac{3}{5}; \frac{3}{5}$

Check Understanding **1a.** $\frac{5}{8}$ **b.** $\frac{3}{10}$ **2.** $-2\frac{47}{50}$ **3a.** $5\frac{5}{6}$ **b.** $25\frac{1}{2}$ **c.** Answers may vary. Sample: 8 **4a.** 3 **b.** $-\frac{2}{3}$ **c.** Answers may vary. Sample: The answer will be larger than 10. **5a.** 5 lengths **b.** Dividing by a fraction is the same as multiplying by its reciprocal. The reciprocal of a number less than 1 is a number greater than 1, so the answer will be greater.

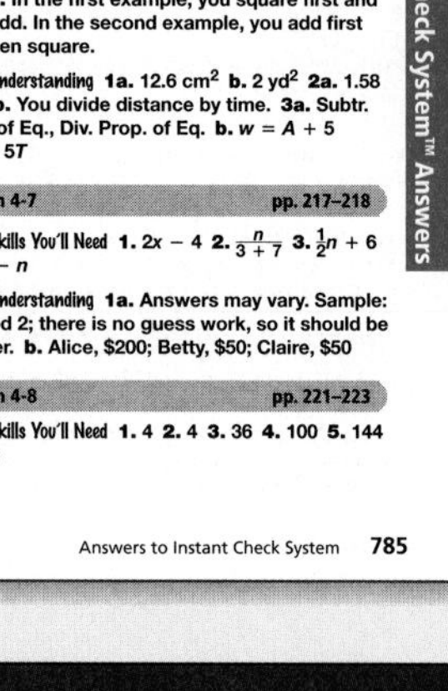

Checkpoint Quiz 1 **1.** $2^3 \cdot 3^2 \cdot 7$ **2.** $\frac{5}{11}$ **3.** $-4\frac{1}{20}$ **4.** $14\frac{7}{12}$ **5.** $\frac{7}{9}$ **6.** $4\frac{3}{5}$ **7.** $-\frac{5}{12}$ **8.** $\frac{8}{15}$ **9.** $1\frac{1}{8}$ c **10.** $-\frac{2}{5}$ and $-\frac{2}{5}$

Lesson 4-6 pp. 212–213

Check Skills You'll Need **1.** 5 **2.** −4 **3.** −4 **4.** 9 **5.** −9 **6.** 9 **7.** In the first example, you square first and then add. In the second example, you add first and then square.

Check Understanding **1a.** 12.6 cm² **b.** 2 yd² **2a.** 1.58 mi/h **b.** You divide distance by time. **3a.** Subtr. Prop. of Eq., Div. Prop. of Eq. **b.** $w = A + 5$ **c.** $v = 5T$

Lesson 4-7 pp. 217–218

Check Skills You'll Need **1.** $2x - 4$ **2.** $\frac{n}{3 + 7}$ **3.** $\frac{1}{2}n + 6$ **4.** $19 - n$

Check Understanding **1a.** Answers may vary. Sample: Method 2; there is no guess work, so it should be quicker. **b.** Alice, $200; Betty, $50; Claire, $50

Lesson 4-8 pp. 221–223

Check Skills You'll Need **1.** 4 **2.** 4 **3.** 36 **4.** 100 **5.** 144 **6.** 400

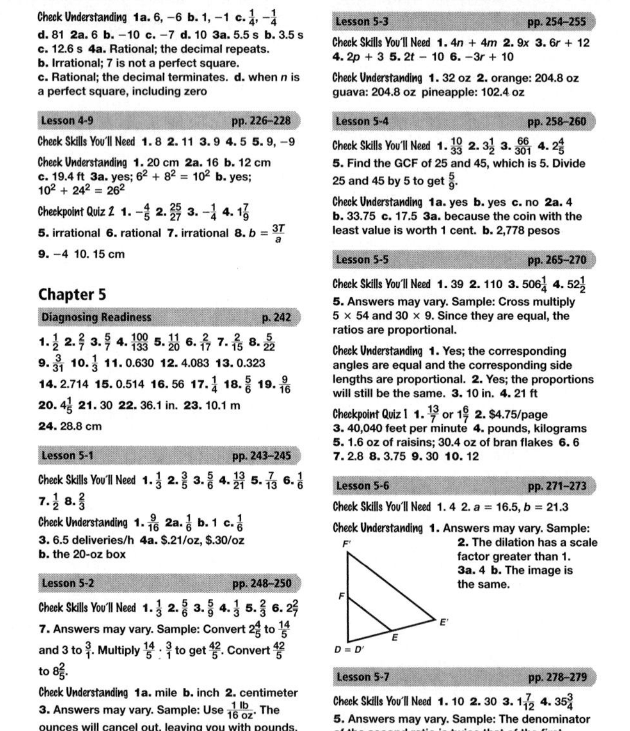

Check Understanding **1a.** 6, −6 **b.** 1, −1 **c.** $\frac{1}{4}, -\frac{1}{4}$ **d.** 81 **2a.** 6 **b.** −10 **c.** −7 **d.** 10 **3a.** 5.5 s **b.** 3.5 s **c.** 12.6 s **4a.** Rational; the decimal repeats. **b.** Irrational; 7 is not a perfect square. **c.** Rational; the decimal terminates. **d.** when n is a perfect square, including zero

Lesson 4-9 pp. 226–228

Check Skills You'll Need **1.** 8 **2.** 11 **3.** 9 **4.** 5 **5.** 9, −9

Check Understanding **1.** 20 cm **2a.** 16 **b.** 12 cm **c.** 19.4 ft **3a.** yes; $6^2 + 8^2 = 10^2$ **b.** yes; $10^2 + 24^2 = 26^2$

Checkpoint Quiz 2 **1.** $-\frac{4}{5}$ **2.** $\frac{25}{27}$ **3.** $-\frac{1}{4}$ **4.** $1\frac{7}{9}$ **5.** irrational **6.** rational **7.** irrational **8.** $b = \frac{3T}{a}$ **9.** −4 10. 15 cm

Chapter 5

Diagnosing Readiness p. 242

1. $\frac{1}{2}$ **2.** $\frac{2}{7}$ **3.** $\frac{5}{7}$ **4.** $\frac{100}{133}$ **5.** $\frac{11}{20}$ **6.** $\frac{2}{17}$ **7.** $\frac{2}{15}$ **8.** $\frac{5}{22}$ **9.** $\frac{3}{31}$ **10.** $\frac{1}{3}$ **11.** 0.630 **12.** 4.083 **13.** 0.323 **14.** 2.714 **15.** 0.514 **16.** 56 **17.** $\frac{1}{4}$ **18.** $\frac{5}{6}$ **19.** $\frac{9}{16}$ **20.** $4\frac{1}{5}$ **21.** 30 **22.** 36.1 in. **23.** 10.1 m **24.** 28.8 cm

Lesson 5-1 pp. 243–245

Check Skills You'll Need **1.** $\frac{1}{3}$ **2.** $\frac{3}{5}$ **3.** $\frac{5}{6}$ **4.** $\frac{13}{21}$ **5.** $\frac{7}{13}$ **6.** $\frac{1}{6}$ **7.** $\frac{1}{2}$ **8.** $\frac{2}{3}$

Check Understanding **1.** $\frac{9}{16}$ **2a.** $\frac{1}{6}$ **b.** 1 **c.** $\frac{1}{6}$ **3.** 6.5 deliveries/h **4a.** $.21/oz, $.30/oz **b.** the 20-oz box

Lesson 5-2 pp. 248–250

Check Skills You'll Need **1.** $\frac{1}{3}$ **2.** $\frac{5}{6}$ **3.** $\frac{5}{9}$ **4.** $\frac{1}{3}$ **5.** $\frac{2}{3}$ **6.** $2\frac{2}{7}$ **7.** Answers may vary. Sample: Convert $2\frac{4}{5}$ to $\frac{14}{5}$ and 3 to $\frac{3}{1}$. Multiply $\frac{14}{5} \cdot \frac{3}{1}$ to get $\frac{42}{5}$. Convert $\frac{42}{5}$ to $8\frac{2}{5}$.

Check Understanding **1a.** mile **b.** inch **2.** centimeter **3.** Answers may vary. Sample: Use $\frac{1 \text{ lb}}{16 \text{ oz}}$. The ounces will cancel out, leaving you with pounds. **4.** 13.2 ft/s **5a.** 7 **b.** 5

Lesson 5-3 pp. 254–255

Check Skills You'll Need **1.** $4n + 4m$ **2.** $9x$ **3.** $6r + 12$ **4.** $2p + 3$ **5.** $2t - 10$ **6.** $-3r + 10$

Check Understanding **1.** 32 oz **2.** orange: 204.8 oz guava: 204.8 oz pineapple: 102.4 oz

Lesson 5-4 pp. 258–260

Check Skills You'll Need **1.** $\frac{10}{33}$ **2.** $3\frac{1}{2}$ **3.** $\frac{66}{301}$ **4.** $2\frac{4}{5}$ **5.** Find the GCF of 25 and 45, which is 5. Divide 25 and 45 by 5 to get $\frac{5}{9}$.

Check Understanding **1a.** yes **b.** yes **c.** no **2a.** 4 **b.** 33.75 **c.** 17.5 **3a.** because the coin with the least value is worth 1 cent. **b.** 2,778 pesos

Lesson 5-5 pp. 265–270

Check Skills You'll Need **1.** 39 **2.** 110 **3.** $506\frac{1}{4}$ **4.** $52\frac{1}{2}$ **5.** Answers may vary. Sample: Cross multiply 5 × 54 and 30 × 9. Since they are equal, the ratios are proportional.

Check Understanding **1.** Yes; the corresponding angles are equal and the corresponding side lengths are proportional. **2.** Yes; the proportions will still be the same. **3.** 10 in. **4.** 21 ft

Checkpoint Quiz 1 **1.** $\frac{13}{7}$ or $1\frac{6}{7}$ **2.** $4.75/page **3.** 40,040 feet per minute **4.** pounds, kilograms **5.** 1.6 oz of raisins; 30.4 oz of bran flakes **6.** 6 **7.** 2.8 **8.** 3.75 **9.** 30 **10.** 12

Lesson 5-6 pp. 271–273

Check Skills You'll Need 1. 4 2. $a = 16.5, b = 21.3$

Check Understanding **1.** Answers may vary. Sample: [figure] **2.** The dilation has a scale factor greater than 1. **3a.** 4 **b.** The image is the same.

Lesson 5-7 pp. 278–279

Check Skills You'll Need **1.** 10 **2.** 30 **3.** $1\frac{7}{12}$ **4.** $35\frac{3}{4}$ **5.** Answers may vary. Sample: The denominator of the second ratio is twice that of the first denominator. So the numerator of the second ratio is twice the numerator of the first ratio.

Check Understanding **1a.** $2\frac{13}{16}$ in. **b.** Yes; when you use cross products, you get the same answer. **2a.** about 140 **b.** 150 mi

Lesson 5-8 pp. 282–283

Check Skills You'll Need **1.** 2 **2.** 3.6 **3.** 6 **4.** 76.5

Check Understanding **1.** 90 ft **2.** 460.7 m

Lesson 5-9 pp. 287–291

Check Skills You'll Need **1.** 14.4 **2.** 15.625 **3.** 4.4

Check Understanding **1a.** $\frac{80}{89}, \frac{39}{89}$ **b.** $\sin Z = \cos X$ because the side opposite $\angle Z$ is the side adjacent to $\angle X$. **2.** Find the cosine of 60° and multiply it by 14. **3a.** 14.6 **b.** 62.9 **c.** For each acute angle, the opposite side equals the adjacent side, so the sine will equal the cosine. **4.** 82.5 ft

Checkpoint Quiz 2 **1.** $X(1, 2)$, $Y(4, 0.5)$, $Z(1, 0.5)$ **2.** 10 in. **3.** 376 km **4.** 130 ft **5.** $\frac{5}{13}$, 0.3846

Chapter 6

Diagnosing Readiness p. 302

1. 20 **2.** $\frac{1}{13}$ **3.** 15.91 **4.** 237.5 **5.** 16 **6.** 1.75 **7.** 22 **8.** 4.5 **9.** 7.2 **10.** $\frac{1}{2}$ **11.** $\frac{5}{8}$ **12.** $\frac{1}{12}$ **13.** $\frac{9}{16}$ **14.** $\frac{4}{9}$ **15.** $\frac{2}{71}$ **16.** $\frac{5}{11}$ **17.** $\frac{3}{5}$ **18.** 30 **19.** $8\frac{1}{2}$ **20.** 100 **21.** 64 **22.** 180 **23.** 231 **24.** 36 **25.** 2 **26.** 32 **27.** 100 **28.** 19 **29.** 85.5

Lesson 6-1 pp. 303–305

Check Skills You'll Need **1.** $\frac{9}{10}$ **2.** $\frac{4}{5}$ **3.** $\frac{7}{20}$ **4.** $\frac{1}{4}$ **5.** $\frac{1}{25}$ **6.** $\frac{3}{20}$ **7.** Answers may vary. Sample: [figure]

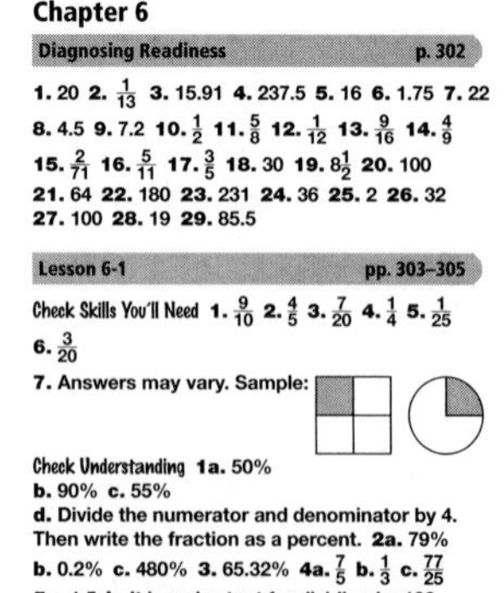

Check Understanding **1a.** 50% **b.** 90% **c.** 55% **d.** Divide the numerator and denominator by 4. Then write the fraction as a percent. **2a.** 79% **b.** 0.2% **c.** 480% **3.** 65.32% **4a.** $\frac{7}{5}$ **b.** $\frac{1}{3}$ **c.** $\frac{77}{25}$ **5a.** 1.5 **b.** It is a shortcut for dividing by 100.

Lesson 6-2 pp. 309–311

Check Skills You'll Need **1.** 1 **2.** 8 **3.** 54 **4.** 45 **5.** 27 **6.** 90 **7.** Answers may vary. Sample: [figure]

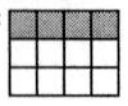

Check Understanding **1a.** about 20 **b.** Answers may vary. Sample: about 50 **2a.** about $6.00 **b.** about $3.00 **c.** about $10.80 **3a.** about 100 **b.** about 450 **c.** about 260 **4a.** About 156 albums; check students' work. **b.** about 8 students

Lesson 6-3 pp. 314–319

Check Skills You'll Need **1.** 20 **2.** $66\frac{2}{3}$ **3.** 100 **4.** 3 **5.** 25 **6.** 100 **7.** Answers may vary. Sample: Find the cross products, so $2{,}800 = 70m$. Then divide each side by 70, so $m = 40$.

Check Understanding **1a.** 70.3 **b.** Check students' work. **2a.** 199.75 **b.** 117.3 **c.** Answers may vary. Sample: 1.3 × 50 = 65; Since 65 is close to 59.8, the answer is reasonable. **3a.** 240 **b.** 35 **4a.** 275 students **b.** Check students' work. **5a.** 80% **b.** 20%

Checkpoint Quiz 1 **1.** 50% **2.** 9.09% **3.** 37.5% **4.** 250% **5.** 40% **6.** about 12 **7.** about 0.24 **8.** about 11 **9.** about 0.04 **10.** about 1,300,000 people

Lesson 6-4 pp. 320–321

Check Skills You'll Need **1.** 160 **2.** 40 **3.** 0.25 **4.** 1.25 **5.** 15 **6.** 0.03125 **7.** I divided both sides of the equation by 0.64.

Check Understanding **1a.** 4.76 **b.** 347.52 **2a.** $11.76 **b.** Check students' work. **3.** 90 **4.** 60%

Lesson 6-5 pp. 326–328

Check Skills You'll Need **1.** 112.5% **2.** 27.3% **3.** 26.7% **4.** 366.7% **5.** 18% **6.** 140%

Check Understanding **1.** 161.5% **2a.** 5.3% **b.** Answers may vary. Sample: $\frac{90}{250}$ = 36%; Since 36 is close to 34.7, the answer is reasonable. **3a.** 57.2% **b.** Answers may vary. Sample: $\frac{3{,}000}{3{,}300}$ = 90.9%; the answer of 89.4% is reasonable.

Lesson 6-6 pp. 331–334

Check Skills You'll Need **1.** 4 **2.** 1,100 **3.** 200 **4.** 14,000 **5.** 97.5 **6.** 3.78

Check Understanding **1a.** 90% **b.** Yes; answers may vary. Sample: An item may cost a store $3, but the store can mark it up 110% to $6.30. **2a.** $161.80 **b.** $195.16 **3a.** 10% **b.** 85% **c.** No; answers may vary. Sample: If a discount is greater than 100%, the sale price will be less than $0, which cannot happen. **4a.** $100.51 **b.** $22.19 **5a.** $116.47 **b.** 85%

Lesson 6-7 pp. 338–341

Check Skills You'll Need **1.** 17.1 **2.** 20.4 **3.** 300 **4.** 200 **5.** 25% **6.** 12.5%

Check Understanding **1.** between 118 and 147 beats per min

Checkpoint Quiz 2 **1.** 0.78 **2.** 5% **3.** 1,000% increase **4.** 1.6% decrease **5.** 80% decrease **6.** 270.7% increase **7.** $23.06 **8.** between 847 and 924 students

Lesson 6-8 pp. 342–344

Check Skills You'll Need **1.** 16 **2.** −343 **3.** 726 **4.** 1,296 **5.** 726 **6.** 800,000

Check Understanding **1.** $630 **2.** $369

3.

Year	Start of Year	Interest	End of Year
1	$415.00	$12.45	$427.45
2	$427.45	$12.8235	$440.27

4a. $875.57 **b.** $718.75

Lesson 6-9 pp. 349–352

Check Skills You'll Need **1.** 1 : 2 **2.** $\frac{2}{25}$ **3.** $\frac{1}{3}$ **4.** $\frac{5}{9}$ **5.** 1 : 4 **6.** 3 : 25

Check Understanding **1a.** $\frac{3}{8}$ **b.** $\frac{1}{4}$ **c.** 1 **2a.** Answers may vary. Sample: Since getting a hole in one occurs fewer than 1 out of 100 times, the probability will be less than 1%. b. 0.365% **3a.** 28% **b.** about 81 students **4a.** $\frac{5}{36}$ **b.** $\frac{1}{2}$ **c.** $\frac{1}{6}$ **5.** $\frac{3}{8}$; $\frac{1}{2}$

Chapter 7

Diagnosing Readiness p. 364

1. 3 tens **2.** 8 ten thousands **3.** 6 tenths **4.** 7 hundredths **5.** two tenths **6.** five hundredths **7.** one and thirty-four hundredths **8.** two and nine hundredths **9.** 4,500 **10.** 17,000 **11.** 0.061 **12.** 0.0012 **13.** 5.6 **14.** 0.912 **15.** 7^5 **16.** 5^2c^2 **17.** a^2b^3 **18.** x^3y^2 **19.** $(3x)^3$ **20.** cd^2e^2 **21.** 16 **22.** 16 **23.** −16 **24.** 32 **25.** 100 **26.** 1,000

Lesson 7-1 pp. 365–367

Check Skills You'll Need **1.** 20 **2.** 1,500 **3.** 451 **4.** 2,390,000 **5.** 18,030 **6.** 7,600 **7.** Move the decimal point 2 places to the right.

Check Understanding **1a.** 305,000 **b.** 50,000 **c.** 210 **d.** Answers may vary. Sample: When you move the decimal point 6 places to the right, it takes 2 moves to get to the right of 0.55. **2a.** 8.64×10^7 **b.** Answers may vary. Sample: The decimal point in each number needs to move 2 places to the left. **3a.** 5.6×10^{10}, 6.2×10^{10}, 9.2×10^{15}, 5.6×10^{21} **b.** The exponent of 10 is greater.

Lesson 7-2 pp. 370–374

Check Skills You'll Need **1.** 200 **2.** 9 **3.** −9 **4.** −1 **5.** 1 **6.** 27 **7.** -4^4 means $-1 \cdot 4^4$, and $(-4)^4$ means $(-4)(-4)(-4)(-4)$.

Check Understanding **1a.** 6^5 **b.** $(-4)^8$ **c.** m^{12} **d.** The bases are not the same. **2a.** 8×10^9 **b.** 6×10^{13} **c.** 9.6×10^{21} **3a.** 1.08×10^9 km **b.** 4.17×10^{23}

Checkpoint Quiz 1 **1.** 4.201×10^9 **2.** 4.8×10^6 **3.** 2.1×10^{10} **4.** 1.4×10^9 **5.** 3^{14} **6.** t^{12} **7.** h^{6w} **8.** $(-9)^5$ **9.** $5 \cdot 5^t = 5^1 \cdot 5^t$. Since the bases are the same, you add the exponents. **10.** 8.215×10^{33}

Lesson 7-3 pp. 376–379

Check Skills You'll Need **1.** 7^4 **2.** 4^3 **3.** 5^2 **4.** 1^5 **5.** 3^3 **6.** 8^4 **7.** An exponent tells how many times a number is used as a factor.

Check Understanding **1a.** 4^2 **b.** 10^3 **c.** a^1 **2a.** w^6 **b.** t^{10} **c.** 7^3 **d.** 123 **3a.** 1 **b.** 1 **c.** 2 **d.** Positive; any number to the power of zero is equal to one. **4a.** $\frac{1}{3}$ **b.** $\frac{1}{w^4}$ **c.** $-\frac{1}{8}$ **5a.** 0.00025 **b.** Greater; 81 millionths (0.000081) is greater than zero **6a.** 3.5×10^{-6} **b.** −4

Lesson 7-4 pp. 383–387

Check Skills You'll Need **1.** 2^6 **2.** 5^4 **3.** 10^4 **4.** y^6 **5.** $(-2)^{10}$ 6. $(-2)^{20}$

Check Understanding **1a.** 5^{-6} **b.** 12^6 **c.** 10^{18} **d.** $(y^4)^5$; $y^4 \cdot y^5 = y^9$ and $(y^4)^5 = y^{20}$, and $y^{20} > y^9$. **2a.** $100x^2$ **b.** $16u^{10}$ **c.** $8a^9b^3$ **3a.** 5.3×10^{10} m² **b.** 1.4×10^{-9} cm² **c.** less; $(10^{-4})^2 = 10^{-8}$; $10^{-8} < 10^{-4}$

Checkpoint Quiz 2 **1.** $\frac{1}{81x^4}$ **2.** 26^{40} **3.** $25b^6$ **4.** $\frac{1}{m}$ **5.** $\frac{1}{9y^2}$ **6.** a^{2b} **7.** 1.1304×10^{-4} m² **8.** 0.00000004 **9.** 0.00225 is less than 0.5. **10.** 5×10^{-2}; $0.05 > 0.0025$

Lesson 7-5 pp. 388–389

Check Skills You'll Need **1.** a^6 **2.** 10^7 **3.** 1.6^5 **4.** 10^1 **5.** w^{-4} **6.** d^{-7}

Check Understanding **1.** $3.\overline{3} \times 10^8$ hours **2.** 0.03 seconds

Lesson 7-6 pp. 392–393

Check Skills You'll Need **1.** 300 **2.** 205 **3.** 1,030 **4.** 46 **5.** 5,005 **6.** 6 **7.** 210

Check Understanding **1a.** 13 **b.** 7 **c.** 20 **2a.** 1001_2 **b.** 10001_2 **c.** 11100_2

Chapter 8

Diagnosing Readiness p. 406

1. 110° obtuse **2.** 35° acute **3.** 90° right **4.** 8 **5.** −69 **6.** −3 **7.** 12 **8.** −15 **9.** $1\frac{1}{7}$ **10.** 84 **11.** −35.7 **12.** 216 m² **13.** 28 in.² **14.** 169 ft²

Lesson 8-1 pp. 407–409

Check Skills You'll Need **1.** 20°; acute **2.** 145°; obtuse

Check Understanding **1a.** Vertical angles: $\angle DBJ$ and $\angle YBT$; adjacent angles may vary. Sample: $\angle DBJ$ and $\angle DBY$ **b.** 100°; vertical angles are congruent. **2a.** 133° **b.** 45° **c.** 94° **3a.** 54° **b.** 16° **c.** 27° **d.** No; obtuse angles do not have complements. **4.** 58°; 90°

Lesson 8-2 pp. 413–415

Check Skills You'll Need **1.** acute **2.** right **3.** obtuse

Check Understanding **1a.** alternate interior **b.** corresponding **c.** neither **2a.** 117° **b.** Since $m\angle 1 = 63°$ and $m\angle 4 + m\angle 1 = 180°$, then $m\angle 4 = 117°$. **3.** The right angles are ≅ corresponding angles, so $\ell \parallel m$.

Lesson 8-3 pp. 420–422

Check Skills You'll Need **1.** Not similar; corresponding sides are not in proportion. **2.** Similar; corresponding sides are in proportion and corresponding angles are ≅. **3.** Similar; corresponding angles are ≅ and corresponding sides are in proportion. **4.** Answers may vary. Sample: Two polygons are similar if they have the same shape and their corresponding sides are in proportion.

Check Understanding **1a.** $\angle T \cong \angle K$; $\angle R \cong \angle J$; $\angle S \cong \angle L$; $\overline{TR} \cong \overline{KJ}$; $\overline{RS} \cong \overline{JL}$; $\overline{ST} \cong \overline{LK}$; $\triangle TRS \cong \triangle KJL$ **b.** $\angle C \cong \angle M$; $\angle J \cong \angle Y$; $\angle L \cong \angle T$; $\overline{CJ} \cong \overline{MY}$; $\overline{JL} \cong \overline{YT}$; $\overline{LC} \cong \overline{TM}$ **2a.** 70 yd **b.** 40° **c.** 50° **d.** Answers may vary. Sample: Corresponding vertices are not listed in the same order. **3a.** $\triangle XYZ \cong \triangle RQP$ by SSS **b.** $\triangle KLM \cong \triangle JLM$ by SAS **c.** no; $\triangle ABC \ncong \triangle DEF$

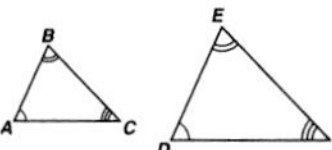

Lesson 8-4 pp. 426–429

Check Skills You'll Need **1.** 5^4 **2.** x^2y^3 **3.** 8^2m^2n **4.** 63 **5.** 71 **6.** −97

Check Understanding **1.** 35 paths **2a.** 25 triangles **b.** 100 triangles; n^2 triangles

Checkpoint Quiz 1 **1.** vertical **2.** alternate interior **3.** corresponding **4.** adjacent **5.** 100° **6.** 90° **7.** 0.9 m **8.** 1.6 m **9.** 23°; 113° **10.** 24 ways

Lesson 8-5 pp. 430–431

Check Skills You'll Need **1.** obtuse **2.** acute **3.** right **4.** straight

Check Understanding **1a.** isosceles, obtuse **b.** equilateral, acute **2a.** rectangle **b.** trapezoid **c.** It does not have four right angles.

Lesson 8-6 pp. 436–437

Check Skills You'll Need **1.** 53 **2.** 49 **3.** −9 **4.** −66 **5.** 34 **6.** 3

Check Understanding **1.** 900° **2a.** 151° **b.** hexagon **3a.** 108° **b.** 144° **c.** 140° **d.** square

Lesson 8-7 pp. 441–443

Check Skills You'll Need **1.** 80 cm² **2.** 5.4 m² **3.** 49 ft²

Check Understanding **1a.** 60 m² **b.** 30 ft² **2a.** 10.5 cm² **b.** The area is doubled. **3a.** 34 in.² **b.** 15 yd² **c.** No; addition is commutative.

Lesson 8-8 pp. 447–449

Check Skills You'll Need **1.** 91 ft² **2.** 9 in.² **3.** 32 cm² **4.** Perimeter is the distance around a figure. Area is the number of square units a figure encloses.

Check Understanding **1a.** 78.5 in. **b.** 15.7 cm **c.** 88.0 yd **d.** $d = 2r$, so $\pi d = 2\pi r$. **2a.** 50.3 in.² b. 201.1 km² **c.** 10.2 km² **d.** The area would be $\frac{1}{4}$ of the original. **3a.** 484.5 in.² **b.** 192.9 m²

Lesson 8-9 pp. 454–459

Check Skills You'll Need **1.** $\angle M \cong \angle A$; $\angle J \cong \angle U$; $\angle D \cong \angle R$; $\overline{MJ} \cong \overline{AU}$; $\overline{JD} \cong \overline{UR}$; $\overline{DM} \cong \overline{RA}$ **2.** $\angle P \cong \angle W$; $\angle K \cong \angle X$; $\angle O \cong \angle N$; $\angle C \cong \angle T$; $\overline{PK} \cong \overline{WX}$; $\overline{KO} \cong \overline{XN}$; $\overline{OC} \cong \overline{NT}$; $\overline{CP} \cong \overline{TW}$

Check Understanding **1.** T 25 mm R; S V

2a.

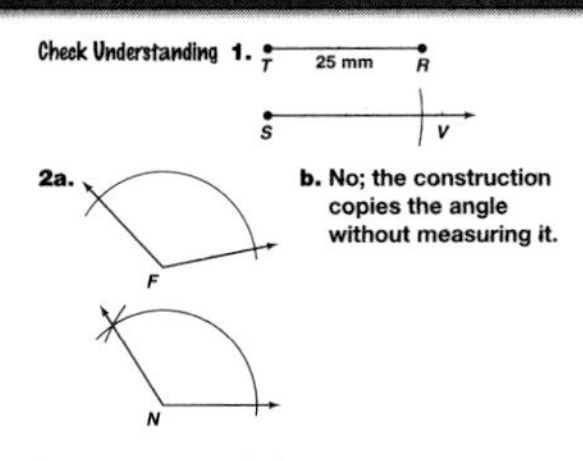

b. No; the construction copies the angle without measuring it.

3a. **b.** 3 cm

4a. **b.**

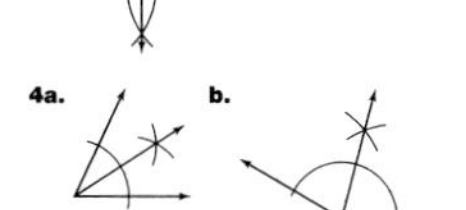

Checkpoint Quiz 2 **1.** parallelogram; 100.86 cm² **2.** obtuse isosceles triangle; 1.7 in.² **3.** trapezoid; 43.35 m² **4.** 133° **5–6.** Answers may vary. Samples are given. **5.** **6.** **7.** 7.2 in.; 4.2 in.² **8.** 113.7 ft; 1,029.2 ft² **9.** 40.8 cm; 132.7 cm²

10. Answers may vary. Sample:

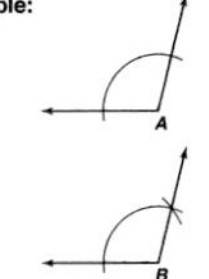

Chapter 9

Diagnosing Readiness p. 470

1. 20 in.² **2.** 96 cm² **3.** 7 ft² **4.** 13 m² **5.** 22 cm² **6.** 54 mm² **7.** 3 **8.** 7 **9.** 2.5 **10.** 12 **11.** 12.59 **12.** 192.6 **13.** 0.005 **14.** 0.01 **15.** 560 **16.** 1,000 **17.** 459 **18.** 64,000

Lesson 9-1 pp. 471–473

Check Skills You'll Need **1.** scalene triangle **2.** parallelogram **3.** trapezoid **4.** pentagon

Check Understanding **1a.** The two bases are triangles. The figure is a triangular prism. $\overline{JK}$ is a base edge. **b.** The only base is a triangle. The figure is a triangular pyramid. $\overline{JK}$ is a base edge. **c.** The two bases are pentagons. The figure is a pentagonal prism. $\overline{JK}$ is a lateral edge. **2a.** a trapezoidal prism and two rectangular prisms **b.** The top of the right-hand prism could be continued all the way to the left side. The result would be a triangular prism and two rectangular prisms. **3a–c.** Answers may vary. Samples are given. **a.** $\overline{DE}$ and $\overline{AC}$ are skew lines. $\overline{AC}$ and $\overline{DF}$ are parallel lines. $\overline{AB}$ and $\overline{BC}$ are intersecting lines. **b.** $\overline{VX}$ and $\overline{TU}$ are skew lines. $\overline{RT}$ and $\overline{SU}$ are parallel lines. $\overline{VW}$ and $\overline{WY}$ are intersecting lines. **c.** $\overline{LM}$ and $\overline{RS}$ are skew lines. $\overline{KN}$ and $\overline{PS}$ are parallel lines. $\overline{JO}$ and $\overline{OP}$ are intersecting lines.

Lesson 9-2 pp. 476–478

Check Skills You'll Need **1.**

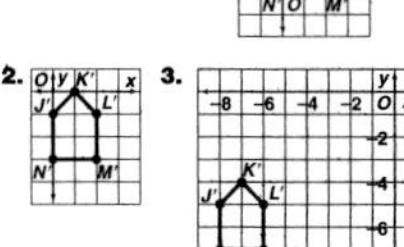

2. **3.**

4. $(x, y) \to (x + 3, y + 1)$
$(x, y) \to (x + 3, y - 2)$
$(x, y) \to (x - 5, y - 6)$

Check Understanding **1a.**

2	2
2	1
1	

Front; Right

b. 5

2a.

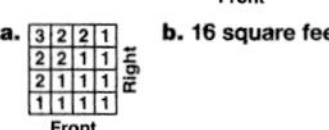

b. 16 square feet

3. Top view Front view Right view

Lesson 9-3 pp. 481–485

Check Skills You'll Need **1.** one circular base; cone **2.** two hexagonal bases; hexagonal prism **3.** two circular bases; cylinder

Check Understanding **1a.** six congruent squares **b.** Answers may vary. Sample: You create a rectangle when you split the lateral surface of a cylinder and spread it out flat. **2.** pentagonal pyramid

Checkpoint Quiz 1 **1.** triangular prism **2.** rectangles **3.** 2; 2 1 1 **4.** Top view Front view Right view **5.** Answers may vary. Sample: $\overline{AH}$, $\overline{DE}$

Lesson 9-4 pp. 488–491

Check Skills You'll Need **1.** 16.5 cm² **2.** 72 in.² **3.** 64 m²

Check Understanding **1a.** 936 cm² **b.** It becomes 1,332 cm². **2.** 392 in.² **3a.** 440 ft² **b.** It decreases by 42 ft² to 398 ft². **4.** about 679 in.² **5a.** about 14,137 in.² **b.** Circumference divided by π is the diameter. Half of that is the radius. Square the radius and multiply by π.

Lesson 9-5 pp. 494–496

Check Skills You'll Need **1.** 10 ft² **2.** 400 cm² **3.** 50 m²

Check Understanding

1.

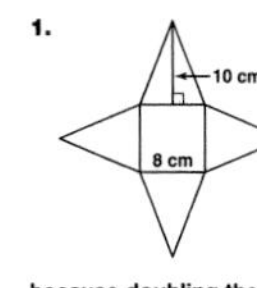

224 cm² **2a.** 6,552 m² **b.** Yes; the same formula will work, but you must use $\frac{1}{2}bh$ instead of b^2 to find B because the base of the pyramid is a triangle. **3.** 922,610 ft² **4a.** 113 yd² **b.** No, because doubling the slant height doubles the lateral area but does not change the base area.

Lesson 9-6 pp. 500–502

Check Skills You'll Need **1.** 96 cm² **2.** 105 ft² **3.** 207 m²

Check Understanding **1a.** 324 in.³ **b.** 52.5 ft³ **c.** They are the same, since the product of their base areas and their heights are the same. **2.** about 23,562 cm³

Lesson 9-7 pp. 506–508

Check Skills You'll Need **1.** 900 in.² **2.** 7,854 ft² **3.** 33 ft²

Check Understanding **1a.** 19,200 in.³ **b.** 48 m³ **2a.** 113 m³ **b.** The volume would be 50% of the original volume. $\frac{1}{3}B\left(\frac{1}{2}h\right) = \frac{1}{2}\left(\frac{1}{3}Bh\right)$ **3a.** about 2.5 in. **b.** no; $\frac{1}{3}\pi(r + 1)^2(h - 1) \neq \frac{1}{3}\pi r^2h$

Lesson 9-8 pp. 512–515

Check Skills You'll Need **1.** 16 cm³ **2.** 48 in.³ **3.** 236 cm³

Check Understanding **1.** 14 in. by 10 in. by 3 in.

Checkpoint Quiz 2 **1.** 1,232 cm²; 2,097 cm³ **2.** 1,759 in.²; 4,516 in.³ **3.** 332 mm²; 360 mm³ **4.** 60 mm **5.** 14 in. by 11 in. by 3 in.

Lesson 9-9 pp. 517–519

Check Skills You'll Need **1.** 1.75 **2.** 43.2 **3.** 9 **4.** 2 **5.** 8.125 **6.** 21.6

Check Understanding **1a.** 8.8 m **b.** Multiplying each side by six requires just two steps. Using cross products requires the extra steps of multiplying each side by 5 and then dividing each side by 5.

2. about 35 cm² **3a.** about 6 in.³ **b.** The creamer would be one third the height of the pitcher. Since the objects are similar, all their dimensions would be in the same proportion.

Chapter 10

Diagnosing Readiness p. 532

1. 38; 37; 36 and 45; 29 **2.** 23.9; 24; 22, 24, and 25; 12 **3–10.**

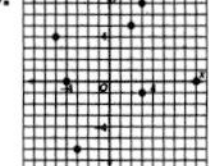

11. 18 **12.** 28

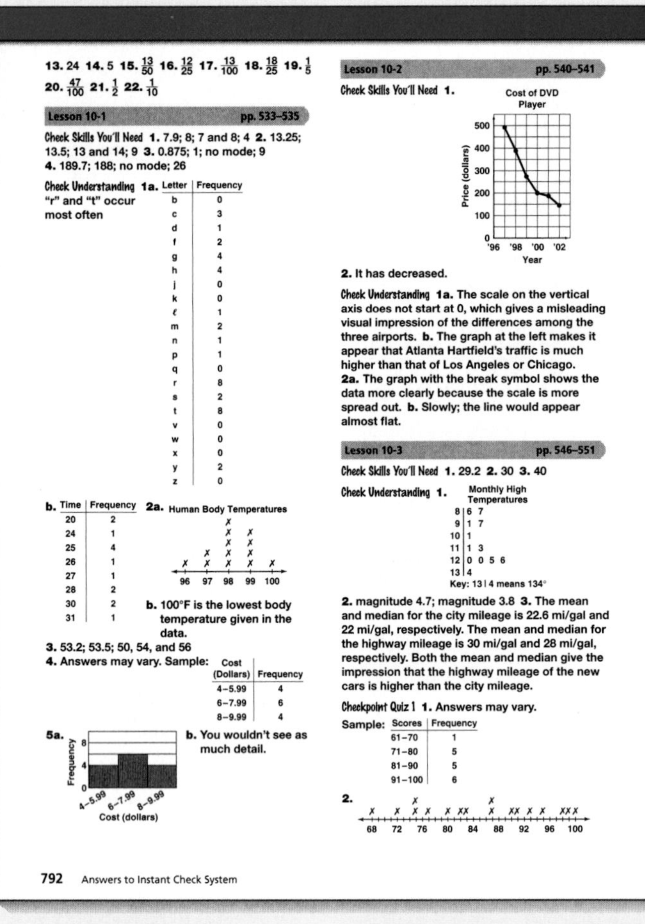

13. 24 **14.** 5 **15.** $\frac{13}{50}$ **16.** $\frac{12}{25}$ **17.** $\frac{13}{100}$ **18.** $\frac{18}{25}$ **19.** $\frac{1}{5}$ **20.** $\frac{47}{100}$ **21.** $\frac{1}{2}$ **22.** $\frac{1}{10}$

Lesson 10-1 pp. 533–535

Check Skills You'll Need **1.** 7.9; 8; 7 and 8; 4 **2.** 13.25; 13.5; 13 and 14; 9 **3.** 0.875; 1; no mode; 9 **4.** 189.7; 188; no mode; 26

Check Understanding **1a.** "r" and "t" occur most often

Letter	Frequency
b	0
c	3
d	1
f	2
g	4
h	4
j	0
k	0
ℓ	1
m	2
n	1
p	1
q	0
r	8
s	2
t	8
v	0
w	0
x	0
y	2
z	0

b.

Time	Frequency
20	2
24	1
25	4
26	1
27	1
28	2
30	2
31	1

2a. Human Body Temperatures
96 97 98 99 100

b. 100°F is the lowest body temperature given in the data.

3. 53.2; 53.5; 50, 54, and 56

4. Answers may vary. Sample:

Cost (Dollars)	Frequency
4–5.99	4
6–7.99	6
8–9.99	4

5a.
Frequency
Cost (dollars)
4–5.99 6–7.99 8–9.99

b. You wouldn't see as much detail.

Lesson 10-2 pp. 540–541

Check Skills You'll Need **1.**
Cost of DVD Player
Price (dollars)
Year
'96 '98 '00 '02

2. It has decreased.

Check Understanding **1a.** The scale on the vertical axis does not start at 0, which gives a misleading visual impression of the differences among the three airports. **b.** The graph at the left makes it appear that Atlanta Hartfield's traffic is much higher than that of Los Angeles or Chicago. **2a.** The graph with the break symbol shows the data more clearly because the scale is more spread out. **b.** Slowly; the line would appear almost flat.

Lesson 10-3 pp. 546–551

Check Skills You'll Need **1.** 29.2 **2.** 30 **3.** 40

Check Understanding **1.** Monthly High Temperatures

8	6 7
9	1 7
10	1
11	1 3
12	0 0 5 6
13	4

Key: 13 | 4 means 134°

2. magnitude 4.7; magnitude 3.8 **3.** The mean and median for the city mileage is 22.6 mi/gal and 22 mi/gal, respectively. The mean and median for the highway mileage is 30 mi/gal and 28 mi/gal, respectively. Both the mean and median give the impression that the highway mileage of the new cars is higher than the city mileage.

Checkpoint Quiz 1 **1.** Answers may vary. Sample:

Scores	Frequency
61–70	1
71–80	5
81–90	5
91–100	6

2.
68 72 76 80 84 88 92 96 100

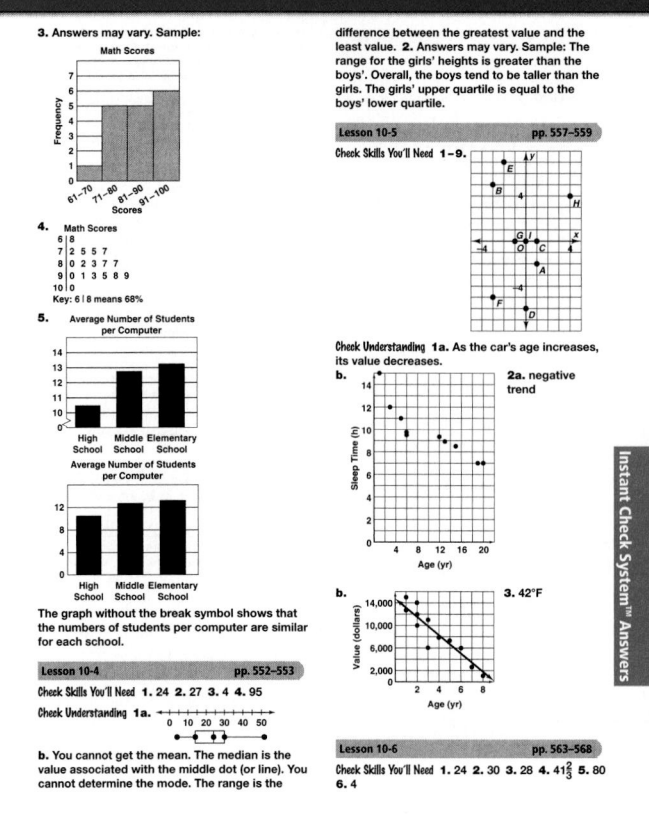

792 Answers to Instant Check System

3. Answers may vary. Sample:

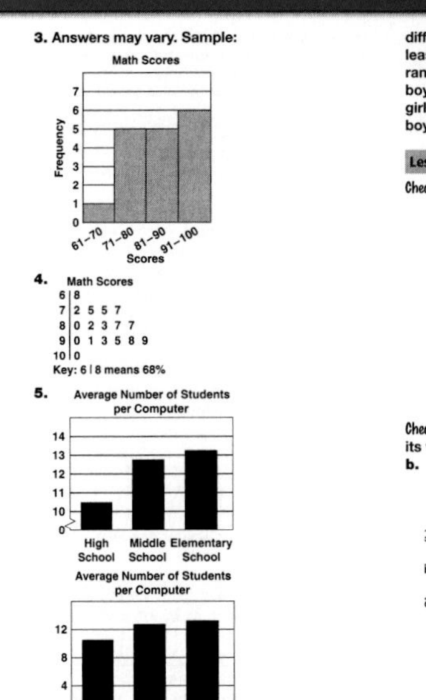

4. Math Scores

6	8
7	2 5 5 7
8	0 2 3 7 7
9	0 1 3 5 8 9
10	0

Key: 6 | 8 means 68%

5. Average Number of Students per Computer
High School Middle School Elementary School

Average Number of Students per Computer
High School Middle School Elementary School

The graph without the break symbol shows that the numbers of students per computer are similar for each school.

Lesson 10-4 pp. 552–553

Check Skills You'll Need **1.** 24 **2.** 27 **3.** 4 **4.** 95

Check Understanding **1a.**
0 10 20 30 40 50

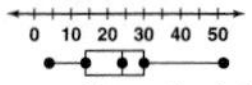

b. You cannot get the mean. The median is the value associated with the middle dot (or line). You cannot determine the mode. The range is the difference between the greatest value and the least value. **2.** Answers may vary. Sample: The range for the girls' heights is greater than the boys'. Overall, the boys tend to be taller than the girls. The girls' upper quartile is equal to the boys' lower quartile.

Lesson 10-5 pp. 557–559

Check Skills You'll Need **1–9.**

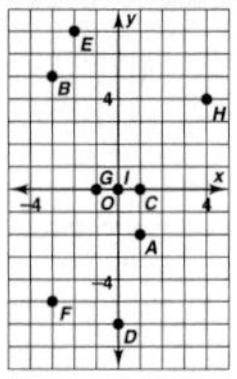

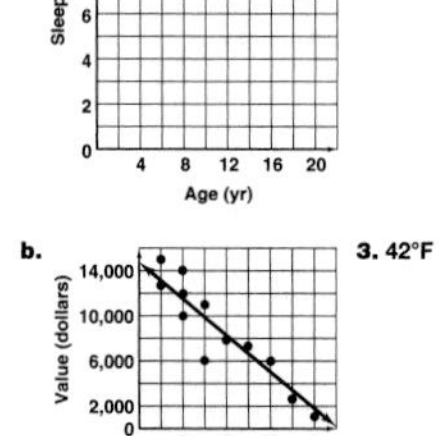

Check Understanding **1a.** As the car's age increases, its value decreases.

b.
Sleep Time (h)
Age (yr)

2a. negative trend

b.
Value (dollars)
Age (yr)

3. 42°F

Lesson 10-6 pp. 563–568

Check Skills You'll Need **1.** 24 **2.** 30 **3.** 28 **4.** $41\frac{2}{3}$ **5.** 80 **6.** 4

Answers to Instant Check System 793

Instant Check System™ Answers

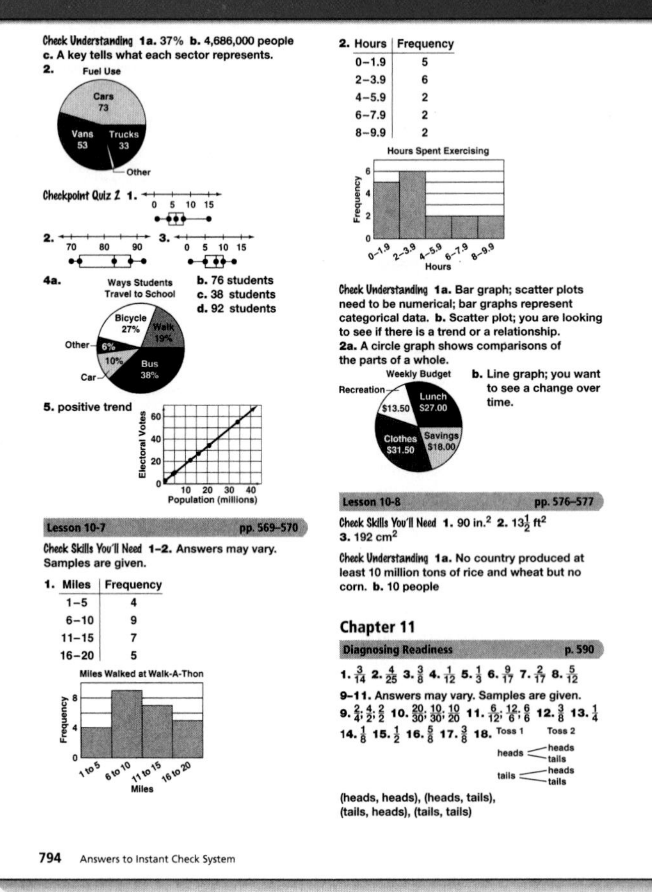

Check Understanding **1a.** 37% **b.** 4,686,000 people **c.** A key tells what each sector represents.

2. Fuel Use
Cars 73
Vans 53
Trucks 33
Other

Checkpoint Quiz 2 **1.**
0 5 10 15

2.
70 80 90

3.
0 5 10 15

4a. Ways Students Travel to School
Bicycle 27%
Walk 19%
Other 6%
10%
Car
Bus 38%

b. 76 students **c.** 38 students **d.** 92 students

5. positive trend
Electoral Votes
Population (millions)

Lesson 10-7 pp. 569–570

Check Skills You'll Need **1–2.** Answers may vary. Samples are given.

1.

Miles	Frequency
1–5	4
6–10	9
11–15	7
16–20	5

Miles Walked at Walk-A-Thon
Frequency
1 to 5 6 to 10 11 to 15 16 to 20
Miles

2.

Hours	Frequency
0–1.9	5
2–3.9	6
4–5.9	2
6–7.9	2
8–9.9	2

Hours Spent Exercising
Frequency
0–1.9 2–3.9 4–5.9 6–7.9 8–9.9
Hours

Check Understanding **1a.** Bar graph; scatter plots need to be numerical; bar graphs represent categorical data. **b.** Scatter plot; you are looking to see if there is a trend or a relationship. **2a.** A circle graph shows comparisons of the parts of a whole.

Weekly Budget
Recreation $13.50
Lunch $27.00
Clothes $31.50
Savings $18.00

b. Line graph; you want to see a change over time.

Lesson 10-8 pp. 576–577

Check Skills You'll Need **1.** 90 in.^{2} **2.** $13\frac{1}{2}$ ft^2 **3.** 192 cm^2

Check Understanding **1a.** No country produced at least 10 million tons of rice and wheat but no corn. **b.** 10 people

Chapter 11

Diagnosing Readiness p. 590

1. $\frac{3}{14}$ **2.** $\frac{4}{25}$ **3.** $\frac{3}{8}$ **4.** $\frac{1}{12}$ **5.** $\frac{1}{3}$ **6.** $\frac{9}{17}$ **7.** $\frac{2}{17}$ **8.** $\frac{5}{12}$
9–11. Answers may vary. Samples are given.
9. $\frac{2}{4}; \frac{4}{2}; \frac{2}{2}$ **10.** $\frac{20}{30}; \frac{10}{30}; \frac{10}{20}$ **11.** $\frac{6}{12}; \frac{12}{6}; \frac{6}{6}$ **12.** $\frac{3}{8}$ **13.** $\frac{1}{4}$ **14.** $\frac{1}{8}$ **15.** $\frac{1}{2}$ **16.** $\frac{5}{8}$ **17.** $\frac{3}{8}$ **18.**

Toss 1 Toss 2
heads — heads, tails
tails — heads, tails

(heads, heads), (heads, tails), (tails, heads), (tails, tails)

794 Answers to Instant Check System

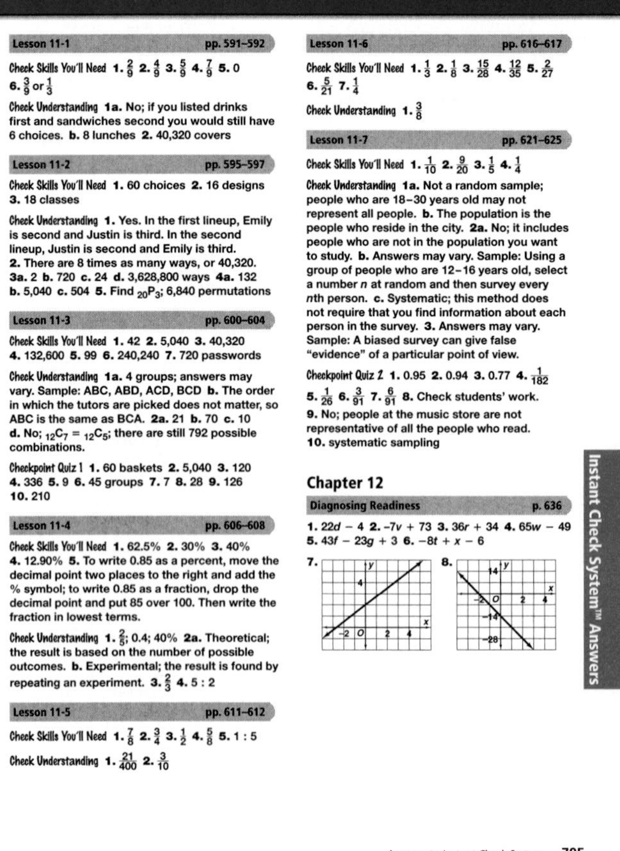

Lesson 11-1 pp. 591–592

Check Skills You'll Need **1.** $\frac{2}{9}$ **2.** $\frac{4}{9}$ **3.** $\frac{5}{9}$ **4.** $\frac{7}{9}$ **5.** 0 **6.** $\frac{3}{9}$ or $\frac{1}{3}$

Check Understanding **1a.** No; if you listed drinks first and sandwiches second you would still have 6 choices. **b.** 8 lunches **2.** 40,320 covers

Lesson 11-2 pp. 595–597

Check Skills You'll Need **1.** 60 choices **2.** 16 designs **3.** 18 classes

Check Understanding **1.** Yes. In the first lineup, Emily is second and Justin is third. In the second lineup, Justin is second and Emily is third. **2.** There are 8 times as many ways, or 40,320. **3a.** 2 **b.** 720 **c.** 24 **d.** 3,628,800 ways **4a.** 132 **b.** 5,040 **c.** 504 **5.** Find $_{20}P_3$; 6,840 permutations

Lesson 11-3 pp. 600–604

Check Skills You'll Need **1.** 42 **2.** 5,040 **3.** 40,320 **4.** 132,600 **5.** 99 **6.** 240,240 **7.** 720 passwords

Check Understanding **1a.** 4 groups; answers may vary. Sample: ABC, ABD, ACD, BCD **b.** The order in which the tutors are picked does not matter, so ABC is the same as BCA. **2a.** 21 **b.** 70 **c.** 10 **d.** No; $_{12}C_7 = {_{12}C_5}$; there are still 792 possible combinations.

Checkpoint Quiz 1 **1.** 60 baskets **2.** 5,040 **3.** 120 **4.** 336 **5.** 9 **6.** 45 groups **7.** 7 **8.** 28 **9.** 126 **10.** 210

Lesson 11-4 pp. 606–608

Check Skills You'll Need **1.** 62.5% **2.** 30% **3.** 40% **4.** 12.90% **5.** To write 0.85 as a percent, move the decimal point two places to the right and add the % symbol; to write 0.85 as a fraction, drop the decimal point and put 85 over 100. Then write the fraction in lowest terms.

Check Understanding **1.** $\frac{2}{5}$; 0.4; 40% **2a.** Theoretical; the result is based on the number of possible outcomes. **b.** Experimental; the result is found by repeating an experiment. **3.** $\frac{2}{3}$ **4.** 5 : 2

Lesson 11-5 pp. 611–612

Check Skills You'll Need **1.** $\frac{7}{8}$ **2.** $\frac{3}{4}$ **3.** $\frac{1}{2}$ **4.** $\frac{5}{8}$ **5.** 1 : 5

Check Understanding **1.** $\frac{21}{400}$ **2.** $\frac{3}{10}$

Lesson 11-6 pp. 616–617

Check Skills You'll Need **1.** $\frac{1}{3}$ **2.** $\frac{1}{8}$ **3.** $\frac{15}{28}$ **4.** $\frac{12}{35}$ **5.** $\frac{2}{27}$ **6.** $\frac{5}{21}$ **7.** $\frac{1}{4}$

Check Understanding **1.** $\frac{3}{8}$

Lesson 11-7 pp. 621–625

Check Skills You'll Need **1.** $\frac{1}{10}$ **2.** $\frac{9}{20}$ **3.** $\frac{1}{5}$ **4.** $\frac{1}{4}$

Check Understanding **1a.** Not a random sample; people who are 18–30 years old may not represent all people. **b.** The population is the people who reside in the city. **2a.** No; it includes people who are not in the population you want to study. **b.** Answers may vary. Sample: Using a group of people who are 12–16 years old, select a number *n* at random and then survey every *n*th person. **c.** Systematic; this method does not require that you find information about each person in the survey. **3.** Answers may vary. Sample: A biased survey can give false "evidence" of a particular point of view.

Checkpoint Quiz 2 **1.** 0.95 **2.** 0.94 **3.** 0.77 **4.** $\frac{1}{182}$ **5.** $\frac{1}{26}$ **6.** $\frac{3}{91}$ **7.** $\frac{6}{91}$ **8.** Check students' work. **9.** No; people at the music store are not representative of all the people who read. **10.** systematic sampling

Chapter 12

Diagnosing Readiness p. 636

1. $22d - 4$ **2.** $-7v + 73$ **3.** $36r + 34$ **4.** $65w - 49$ **5.** $43f - 23g + 3$ **6.** $-8t + x - 6$

7.
8.

Instant Check System™ Answers

Answers to Instant Check System 795

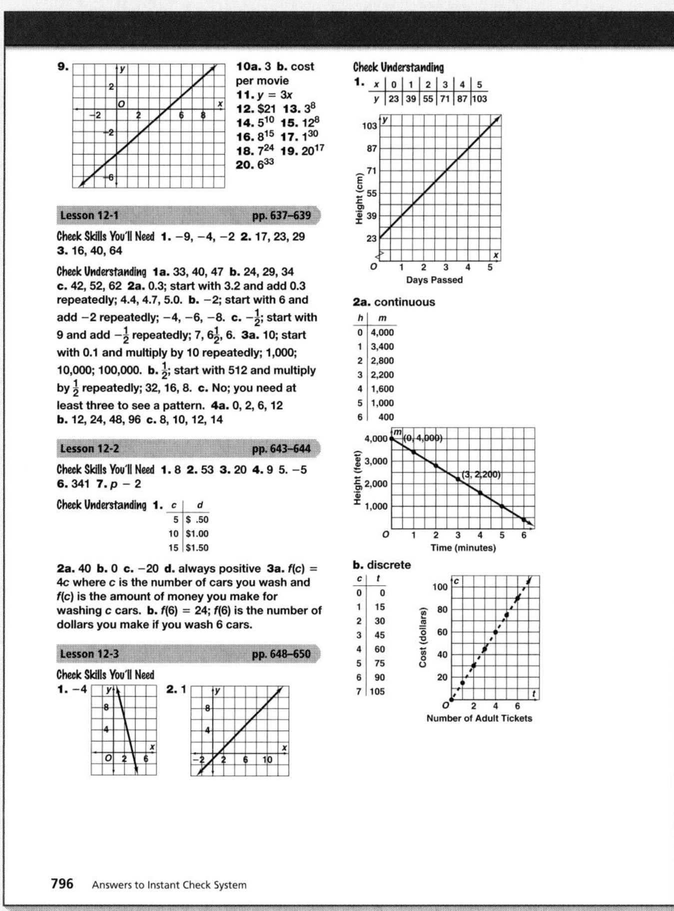

9\.

10a. 3 **b.** cost per movie **11.** $y = 3x$ **12.** \$21 **13.** 3^8 **14.** 5^{10} **15.** 12^8 **16.** 8^{15} **17.** 1^{30} **18.** 7^{24} **19.** 20^{17} **20.** 6^{33}

Lesson 12-1 pp. 637–639

Check Skills You'll Need **1.** −9, −4, −2 **2.** 17, 23, 29 **3.** 16, 40, 64

Check Understanding **1a.** 33, 40, 47 **b.** 24, 29, 34 **c.** 42, 52, 62 **2a.** 0.3; start with 3.2 and add 0.3 repeatedly; 4.4, 4.7, 5.0. **b.** −2; start with 6 and add −2 repeatedly; −4, −6, −8. **c.** $-\frac{1}{2}$; start with 9 and add $-\frac{1}{2}$ repeatedly; 7, $6\frac{1}{2}$, 6. **3a.** 10; start with 0.1 and multiply by 10 repeatedly; 1,000; 10,000; 100,000. **b.** $\frac{1}{2}$; start with 512 and multiply by $\frac{1}{2}$ repeatedly; 32, 16, 8. **c.** No; you need at least three to see a pattern. **4a.** 0, 2, 6, 12 **b.** 12, 24, 48, 96 **c.** 8, 10, 12, 14

Lesson 12-2 pp. 643–644

Check Skills You'll Need **1.** 8 **2.** 53 **3.** 20 **4.** 9 **5.** −5 **6.** 341 **7.** $p - 2$

Check Understanding **1.**

c	d
5	\$ .50
10	\$1.00
15	\$1.50

2a. 40 **b.** 0 **c.** −20 **d.** always positive **3a.** $f(c) = 4c$ where c is the number of cars you wash and $f(c)$ is the amount of money you make for washing c cars. **b.** $f(6) = 24$; $f(6)$ is the number of dollars you make if you wash 6 cars.

Lesson 12-3 pp. 648–650

Check Skills You'll Need

1. −4 **2.** 1

Check Understanding

1.

x	0	1	2	3	4	5
y	23	39	55	71	87	103

2a. continuous

h	m
0	4,000
1	3,400
2	2,800
3	2,200
4	1,600
5	1,000
6	400

b. discrete

c	t
0	0
1	15
2	30
3	45
4	60
5	75
6	90
7	105

796 Answers to Instant Check System

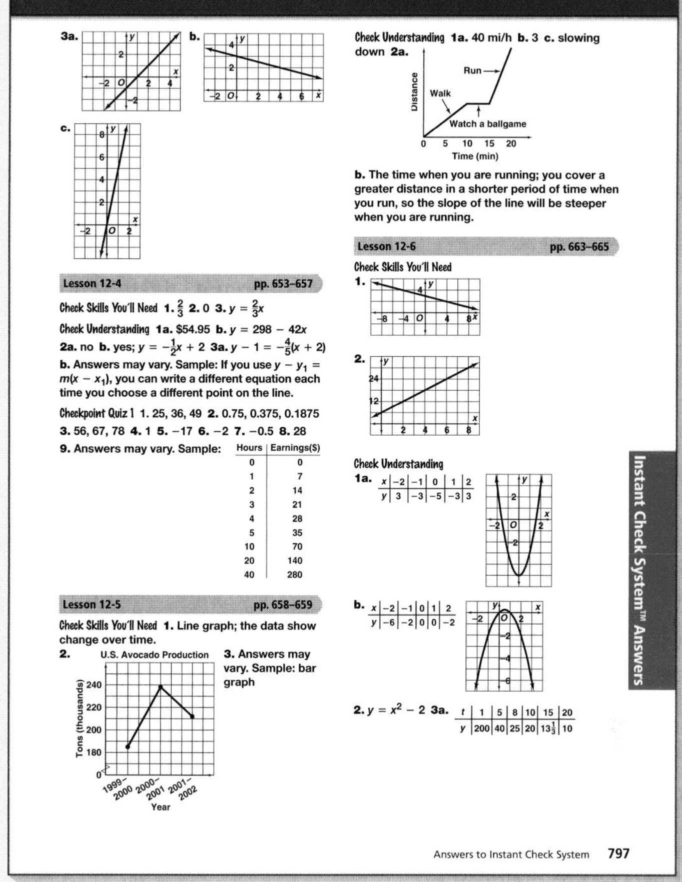

3a. **b.** **c.**

Lesson 12-4 pp. 653–657

Check Skills You'll Need **1.** $\frac{2}{3}$ **2.** 0 **3.** $y = \frac{2}{3}x$

Check Understanding **1a.** \$54.95 **b.** $y = 298 - 42x$ **2a.** no **b.** yes; $y = -\frac{1}{2}x + 2$ **3a.** $y - 1 = -\frac{4}{5}(x + 2)$ **b.** Answers may vary. Sample: If you use $y - y_1 = m(x - x_1)$, you can write a different equation each time you choose a different point on the line.

Checkpoint Quiz 1 **1.** 25, 36, 49 **2.** 0.75, 0.375, 0.1875 **3.** 56, 67, 78 **4.** 1 **5.** −17 **6.** −2 **7.** −0.5 **8.** 28 **9.** Answers may vary. Sample:

Hours	Earnings(\$)
0	0
1	7
2	14
3	21
4	28
5	35
10	70
20	140
40	280

Lesson 12-5 pp. 658–659

Check Skills You'll Need **1.** Line graph; the data show change over time.

2.

3. Answers may vary. Sample: bar graph

Check Understanding **1a.** 40 mi/h **b.** 3 **c.** slowing down **2a.**

b. The time when you are running; you cover a greater distance in a shorter period of time when you run, so the slope of the line will be steeper when you are running.

Lesson 12-6 pp. 663–665

Check Skills You'll Need

1. **2.**

Check Understanding

1a.

x	−2	−1	0	1	2
y	3	−3	−5	−3	3

b.

x	−2	−1	0	1	2
y	−6	−2	0	0	−2

2. $y = x^2 - 2$ **3a.**

t	1	5	8	10	15	20
y	200	40	25	20	$13\frac{1}{3}$	10

Answers to Instant Check System 797

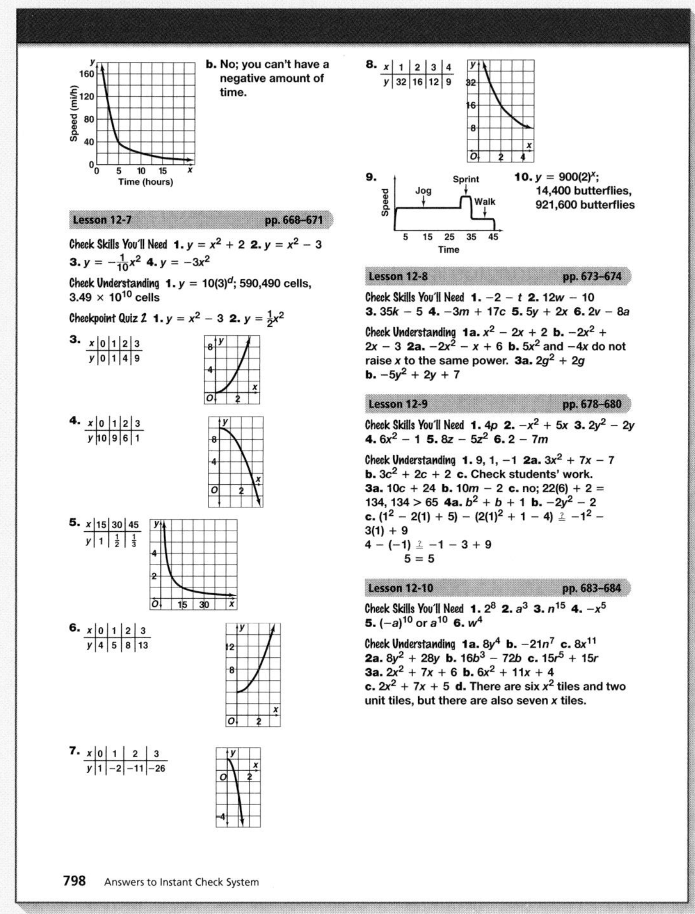

b. No; you can't have a negative amount of time.

Lesson 12-7 pp. 668–671

Check Skills You'll Need **1.** $y = x^2 + 2$ **2.** $y = x^2 - 3$ **3.** $y = -\frac{1}{10}x^2$ **4.** $y = -3x^2$

Check Understanding **1.** $y = 10(3)^d$; 590,490 cells, 3.49×10^{10} cells

Checkpoint Quiz 2 **1.** $y = x^2 - 3$ **2.** $y = \frac{1}{2}x^2$

3.

x	0	1	2	3
y	0	1	4	9

4.

x	0	1	2	3
y	10	9	6	1

5.

x	15	30	45
y	1	$\frac{1}{2}$	$\frac{1}{3}$

6.

x	0	1	2	3
y	4	5	8	13

7.

x	0	1	2	3
y	1	−2	−11	−26

8.

x	1	2	3	4
y	32	16	12	9

9.

10. $y = 900(2)^x$; 14,400 butterflies, 921,600 butterflies

Lesson 12-8 pp. 673–674

Check Skills You'll Need **1.** $-2 - t$ **2.** $12w - 10$ **3.** $35k - 5$ **4.** $-3m + 17c$ **5.** $5y + 2x$ **6.** $2v - 8a$

Check Understanding **1a.** $x^2 - 2x + 2$ **b.** $-2x^2 + 2x - 3$ **2a.** $-2x^2 - x + 6$ **b.** $5x^2$ and $-4x$ do not raise x to the same power. **3a.** $2g^2 + 2g$ **b.** $-5y^2 + 2y + 7$

Lesson 12-9 pp. 678–680

Check Skills You'll Need **1.** $4p$ **2.** $-x^2 + 5x$ **3.** $2y^2 - 2y$ **4.** $6x^2 - 1$ **5.** $8z - 5z^2$ **6.** $2 - 7m$

Check Understanding **1.** 9, 1, −1 **2a.** $3x^2 + 7x - 7$ **b.** $3c^2 + 2c + 2$ **c.** Check students' work. **3a.** $10c + 24$ **b.** $10m - 2$ **c.** no; $22(6) + 2 = 134$, $134 > 65$ **4a.** $b^2 + b + 1$ **b.** $-2y^2 - 2$ **c.** $(1^2 - 2(1) + 5) - (2(1)^2 + 1 - 4) \stackrel{?}{=} -1^2 - 3(1) + 9$

$4 - (-1) \stackrel{?}{=} -1 - 3 + 9$

$5 = 5$

Lesson 12-10 pp. 683–684

Check Skills You'll Need **1.** 2^8 **2.** a^3 **3.** n^{15} **4.** $-x^5$ **5.** $(-a)^{10}$ or a^{10} **6.** w^4

Check Understanding **1a.** $8y^4$ **b.** $-21n^7$ **c.** $8x^{11}$ **2a.** $8y^2 + 28y$ **b.** $16b^3 - 72b$ **c.** $15r^5 + 15r$ **3a.** $2x^2 + 7x + 6$ **b.** $6x^2 + 11x + 4$ **c.** $2x^2 + 7x + 5$ **d.** There are six x^2 tiles and two unit tiles, but there are also seven x tiles.

798 Answers to Instant Check System

Selected Answers

Chapter 1

Lesson 1-1 pp. 8–10

EXERCISES **1.** $27 + n$ **3.** $2x$ **11.** 1 **13.** 21 **19.** 49 **21.** 23 **27.** 3, 5, 8, 11,16 **29.** 7, 15, 23, 31, 39 **35.** The student did not multiply and divide from left to right. **37.** 14 **39.** 1 **43.** $37b + 65$ **45.** $37b + 205$ **47.** B **49.** A **51a.** $250b$ **b.** $1,250 **67.** 18.89 **69.** 8.101 **73.** < **75.** <

Lesson 1-2 pp. 14–15

EXERCISES **1.** $3.09 **3.** 130 votes **5.** 9 ways **7.** 78 squares **21.** 6 **23.** 12 **25.** 205.23 **27.** 4.24 **31.** 3.319

Lesson 1-3 pp. 18–21

EXERCISES **1.** [number line] **3.** [number line] **9.** 2 **11.** 8 **17.** 12 **19.** 91 **27.** −16, −13, −6, −4, 2, 7, 11 **29.** −31, −21, −17, 5, 22, 28 **33a.** The second golfer wins. **b.** by three **35.** 10 **37.** 9 **39.** > **41.** = **49.** −65 **51.** 200 **53.** 168 **55.** 71 **61.** E **63.** D **65.** Colorado **67.** Colorado **69.** 24.2 **81.** $25 + 34.95m$; $59.95, $94.90, $129.85, $164.80, $199.75, $234.70 **83.** $3\frac{1}{2}$ **85.** $1\frac{1}{6}$

Lesson 1-4 pp. 25–27

EXERCISES **1.** 1 **3.** −2 **9.** −9 **11.** 1 **21.** −5°F **23.** 6 **25.** −12 **31.** −70 **33.** 100 **37.** never **39.** sometimes **43.** No; you can add negative integers and come out with less than you started with. **45.** 5 **47.** 42 **51.** 26°C **65.** 19 **67.** 57 **69.** $7h$; $7, $14, $21, $28, $35

Lesson 1-5 pp. 31–32

EXERCISES **1.** −18 **3.** 8 **9.** −90 **11.** −14 **15.** −10 **17.** −8 **21.** −$52 **23.** −17 **25.** 1 **29.** 7 **31a.** −40,230 **b.** Answers may vary. Sample: 8 mi **33.** Negative; there are three negative factors. **35.** negative **37.** negative **53.** −6 **55.** 8 **57.** −10, −8, −5, −4, −3, −2, −1, 1, 2, 4

Lesson 1-6 pp. 36–38

EXERCISES **1.** 1; 1; 0; 3 **3.** $8.\overline{7}$; 9; 9; 3 **11.** 10; it raises the mean 1.05. **13.** 42; it lowers the mean 13.15. **17.** Median; there will be outliers. **19.** Mode; the data are non-numeric. **23a.** 97 **b.** 87 **25a.** The mean is positive because the sum is positive. **b.** The median is negative because there are more negative than positive numbers. **29.** 8 **31.** −2 **43.** 77 **45.** −15

Lesson 1-7 pp. 42–43

EXERCISES **1.** 4^5 **3.** 5^2x^3y **7.** 16 **9.** −64 **23.** 20 **25.** 16 **33.** 144 cm^2 **35.** 31 **37.** 405 **41.** 192 ft **43.** 2 **45.** 4, 2 **47.** −475 **49.** −32 **57.** 2 **59.** 2 **61.** 2.5 **63.** −7

Lesson 1-8 pp. 49–50

EXERCISES **1.** Ident. Prop. of Add. **3.** Assoc. Prop. of Add. **7.** 155 **9.** 488 **17.** $7b - 63$ **19.** $9v - 18$ **23.** 180 **25.** 670 **29.** $5.82 **31.** $14.75 **33.** false; $-42 \neq 66$ **35.** false; $20 + 5b \neq 20 + b$ **37.** −40 **39.** 23,200 **41.** $4.96 **43.** $8.40 **55.** mean = −1.8; median = −3; no mode; range = 12 **57.** −24 **59.** 60

Chapter Review pp. 52–53

1. simplify **2.** mode **3.** power **4.** absolute value **5.** measure of central tendency **6.** algebraic expression **7.** Distributive Property **8.** additive inverses OR opposites **9.** variable **10.** integers **11.** 6 **12.** −15.5 **13.** −5.6 **14.** 61 **15.** 54 **16.** 24 **17.** 5 m wide, 11 m long **18.** 6 **19.** 6 **20.** 105 **21.** < **22.** < **23.** > **24.** = **25.** −12 **26.** 5 **27.** −6 **28.** 17 **29.** 5 **30.** −3 **31.** 15.2; 15; 15; 14 **32.** 9.8; 9.85; 9.1 and 10.3; 1.7 **33.** −16,800; I multiplied −5 and 20 to get −100. Then I multiplied −100 by 168. **34.** 1,094; I added 125 and 575 to get 700. Then I added 700 and 394. **35.** 172; I used the Dist. Prop. and multiplied 4 by 18 (72) and 4 by 25 (100). Then I added 72 and 100.

Chapter 2

Lesson 2-1 pp. 65–66

EXERCISES **1.** −11 **3.** −35 **13.** $x + 450 = 512$; $62 **15.** 340 **17.** −27 **29.** $4x = 124$; 31 students **31.** no **33.** no **35.** Division by zero is undefined. **37.** −3, 3 **39.** −3, 1 **41.** If you subtract a larger number from a smaller number, you get a negative number. **43.** 7 **45.** 750 **55.** $-2w - 14$ **57.** $5a - 30$ **59.** −22 **61.** −7

Lesson 2-2 pp. 70–72

EXERCISES **1.** −1 **3.** 3 **7.** −36 **9.** 40

13. $0.39p + 1.19 = 3.92$; 7 pencils **15.** $1.99 + 6x = 7.33$; $.89 **17.** 12.6 **19.** −6 **23.** 81 grams **25.** Round 39.95 to 40 and 105.65 to 100. Solve $6p + 40 = 100$, to get $p = 10$. The solution 24.27 is not reasonable. **39.** 6 **41.** 20 **43.** −39

Lesson 2-3 pp. 76–77

EXERCISES **1.** $11b$ **3.** $31x$ **11.** $5x + 1$ **13.** $9n - 3r$ **17.** $5a - 17$ **19.** $2t + 63.5$ **29.** Answers may vary. Sample: $2m + m + 8$; $4m + 2 - m + 6$ **31.** Similar categories of CDs are grouped together, and terms with similar variables are grouped together. **33.** $3x - 2y$ **35.** $x + y + 9$ **51.** loss of 7 yd

Lesson 2-4 pp. 81–83

EXERCISES **1.** 5 **3.** 3 **11.** 2 **13.** 9 **21.** 5 **23.** 2 **29.** The student added x to the left-hand side, but subtracted x from the right-hand side.

$$3x + 4 - x = 7 + x$$
$$2x + 4 = 7 + x$$
$$2x - x + 4 = 7 + x - x$$
$$x + 4 = 7$$
$$x + 4 - 4 = 7 - 4$$
$$x = 3$$

31. $n + (n + 1) + (n + 2) = 48$; 15, 16, and 17 **33.** $460 + x = 11x$; 46 g **35.** $2x - 8 = 3x - 16$; 8 **37.** 2 **39.** −2 **61.** −75 **63.** −7 **67.** $n - 8$ **69.** $12y$

Lesson 2-5 pp. 86–88

EXERCISES **1.** 15 ft × 30 ft **3.** 11.5 mi and 20.5 mi **7.** $20 **9.** 85 cents **21.** $3m + 8$ **23.** $3y$ **27.** 168

Lesson 2-6 pp. 93–95

EXERCISES **1.** [number line] **3.** [number line] **9.** $t < -5$ **11.** $n \geq -2$ **15.** $x > 26$ **17.** $a > 14$ **27.** $x - 18 \geq 5$; $x \geq 23$ **29.** $x > -1$ **31.** $x \geq -2$ **35.** $g \leq 1$ **37.** $x < -21$ **43.** $p \leq 4$ **45.** $s \leq 20$ **47.** > **49.** $28,500 + \ell \leq 64,000$; $\ell \leq 35,500$ **51.** 6 **53.** 5 **69.** 10 handshakes **71.** −38 **73.** 15 **77.** 72.25, 75.5, no mode, 58

Lesson 2-7 pp. 100–102

EXERCISES **1.** $d > 12$ **3.** $y > 0$ **13.** 4 specials **15.** $r \geq -6$ **17.** $z \geq 96$

27. 0 **29.** −3 **31.** $5t \geq 19$; $t \geq 3.8$; 4 teachers **33.** $48x \geq 165$; $x \geq 3.44$; 4 buses **35.** $-5 < w$ **37.** $3,600 < w$

Lesson 2-8 pp. 104–106

EXERCISES **1.** $x < 6$ **3.** $w \leq -1$ **17.** 3 games or less **19.** $t \leq -3.6$ **21.** $1 \leq x$ **25.** $(87 + 92 + 85 + x) \div 4 \geq 90$; 96 or better **27.** $8x > 119.28 - 112.36$; 0.865 sec. **29.** 5 should have been subtracted from each side, not subtracted from the left and added to the right. **31.** Answers may vary. Sample: You need to buy 4 identical baskets and some ribbon. The ribbon costs $3 and you can only spend $39 in all. What is the most expensive basket you can buy? $b \leq 9$ **45.** $x \geq 17$ **47.** $x > 85$

Chapter Review pp. 108–109

1. like terms **2.** equation **3.** term **4.** solution **5.** inverse operations **6.** 30 **7.** 3 **8.** 7 **9.** 2 **10.** 12 **11.** $-\frac{11}{3}$ **12.** −15 **13.** −9 **14.** $-\frac{5}{6}$ **15.** 40 **16.** $11x - 12$ **17.** $8a + 1$ **18.** $\ell - 9$ **19.** −4 **20.** 5 **21.** $\frac{16}{5}$ or 3.2 **22.** −5 **23.** 9 bagels **24.** $22 **25.** $g > 19$ **26.** $u \leq 2$ **27.** $t \geq -11$ **28.** $c \leq 75$ **29.** $x \geq 150$ **30.** $x < -3$ **31.** $y \leq -2$ **32.** $a < 7$ **33.** $w \leq 128$ **34.** $c < -20$ **35.** $z > 12$ **36.** $j < 8$ **37.** $m \leq 1.9$ **38.** $-20 > e$

Chapter 3

Lesson 3-1 pp. 119–121

EXERCISES **1.** D-1 **3.** C-2 **5.** (−4, 3) **7.** (−3, 0) **19.** *C* **21.** *J* **25a.** (24, 8) **b.** (4, 8), (6, 8), (9, 8), (13, 8), (17, 8), (20, 8), (22, 8); same *y*-coordinate **27.** 93° W 45° N; 97° W 41° N **29.** Quadrant I **31.** Quadrant III **33.** Start at (−5, −3). Then move to (−4, −3), (−4, 1), (−3, 1), (−3, −2), (−2, −2), (−2, −3), (4, −3), (4, 3), (1, 3), (1, 1), (3, 1), and (3, 2) in that order.

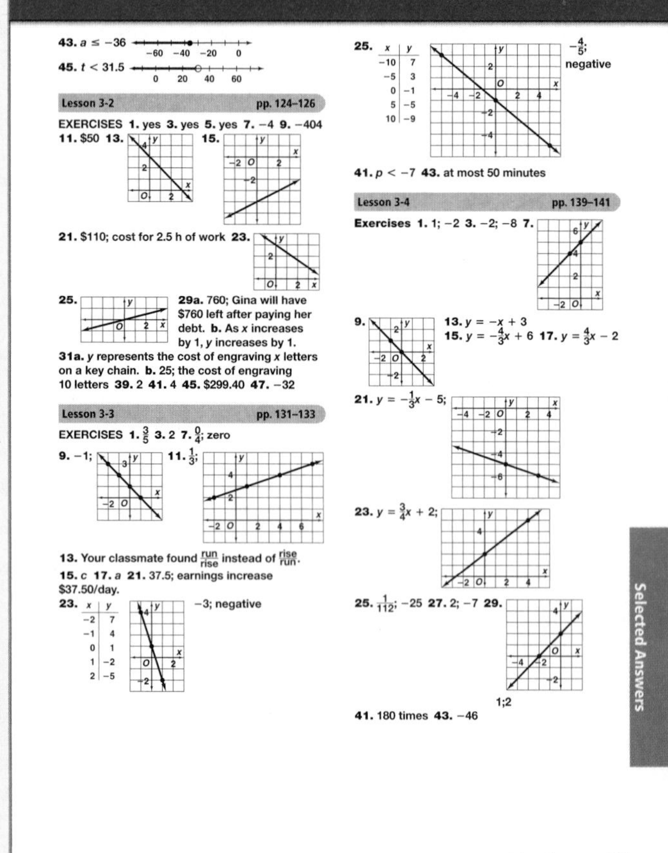

43. $a \leq -36$ **45.** $t < 31.5$

Lesson 3-2 pp. 124–126

EXERCISES **1.** yes **3.** yes **5.** yes **7.** −4 **9.** −404 **11.** $50 **13.** [graph] **15.** [graph] **21.** $110; cost for 2.5 h of work **23.** [graph] **25.** [graph] **29a.** 760; Gina will have $760 left after paying her debt. **b.** As x increases by 1, y increases by 1. **31a.** y represents the cost of engraving x letters on a key chain. **b.** 25; the cost of engraving 10 letters **39.** 2 **41.** 4 **45.** $299.40 **47.** −32

Lesson 3-3 pp. 131–133

EXERCISES **1.** $\frac{3}{5}$ **3.** 2 **7.** $\frac{0}{4}$; zero **9.** −1; **11.** $\frac{1}{3}$; **13.** Your classmate found $\frac{\text{run}}{\text{rise}}$ instead of $\frac{\text{rise}}{\text{run}}$. **15.** *c* **17.** *a* **21.** 37.5; earnings increase $37.50/day. **23.** −3; negative **25.** $-\frac{4}{5}$; negative **41.** $p < -7$ **43.** at most 50 minutes

Lesson 3-4 pp. 139–141

Exercises **1.** 1; −2 **3.** −2; −8 **7.** [graph] **9.** [graph] **13.** $y = -x + 3$ **15.** $y = -\frac{4}{3}x + 6$ **17.** $y = \frac{4}{3}x - 2$ **21.** $y = -\frac{1}{3}x - 5$; **23.** $y = \frac{3}{4}x + 2$; **25.** $\frac{1}{112}$; −25 **27.** 2; −7 **29.** 1;2 **41.** 180 times **43.** −46

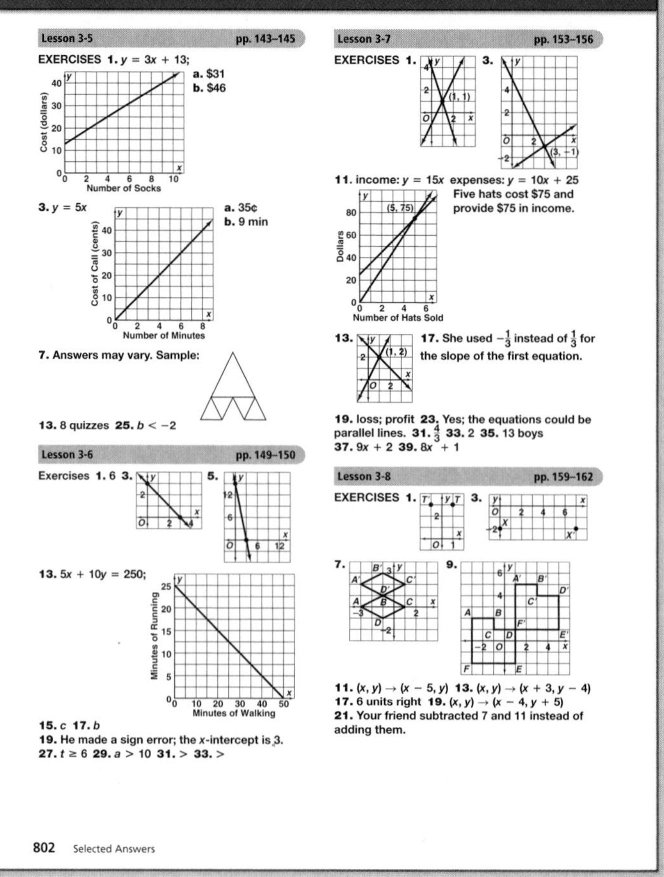

Lesson 3-5 pp. 143–145

EXERCISES **1.** $y = 3x + 13$; **a.** $31 **b.** $46 **3.** $y = 5x$ **a.** 35¢ **b.** 9 min **7.** Answers may vary. Sample: **13.** 8 quizzes **25.** $b < -2$

Lesson 3-6 pp. 149–150

Exercises **1.** 6 **3.** [graph] **5.** [graph] **13.** $5x + 10y = 250$; **15.** *c* **17.** *b* **19.** He made a sign error; the *x*-intercept is 3. **27.** $t \geq 6$ **29.** $a > 10$ **31.** > **33.** >

Lesson 3-7 pp. 153–156

EXERCISES **1.** [graph] **3.** [graph] **11.** income: $y = 15x$ expenses: $y = 10x + 25$ Five hats cost $75 and provide $75 in income. **13.** [graph] **17.** She used $-\frac{1}{3}$ instead of $\frac{1}{3}$ for the slope of the first equation. **19.** loss; profit **23.** Yes; the equations could be parallel lines. **31.** $\frac{4}{3}$ **33.** 2 **35.** 13 boys **37.** $9x + 2$ **39.** $8x + 1$

Lesson 3-8 pp. 159–162

EXERCISES **1.** [graph] **3.** [graph] **7.** [graph] **9.** [graph] **11.** $(x, y) \rightarrow (x - 5, y)$ **13.** $(x, y) \rightarrow (x + 3, y - 4)$ **17.** 6 units right **19.** $(x, y) \rightarrow (x - 4, y + 5)$ **21.** Your friend subtracted 7 and 11 instead of adding them.

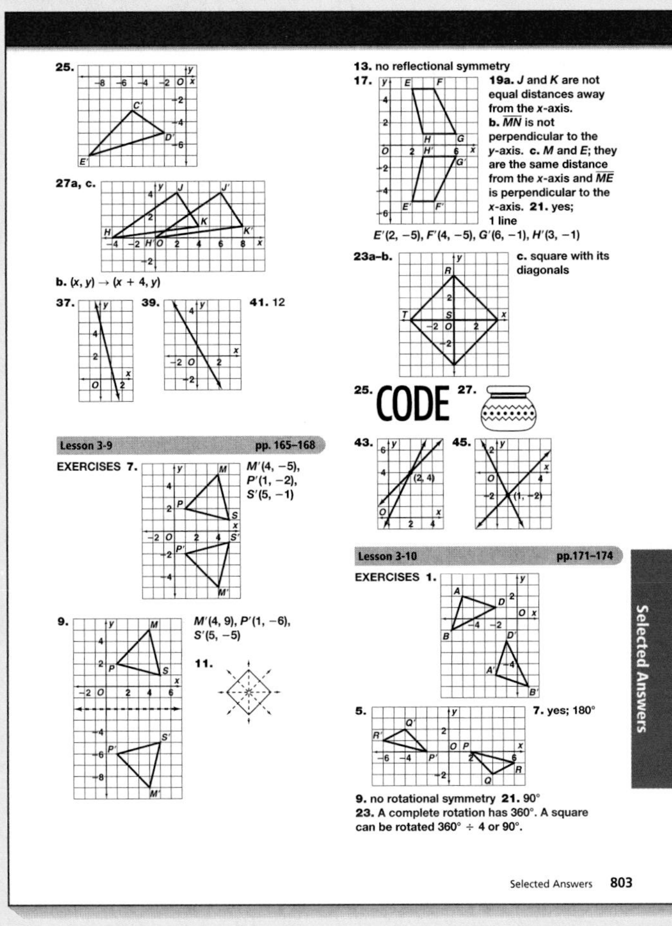

25. [graph]

27a, c. [graph]

b. $(x, y) \rightarrow (x + 4, y)$

37. [graph] **39.** [graph] **41.** 12

Lesson 3-9 pp. 165–168

EXERCISES **7.** $M'(4, -5)$, $P'(1, -2)$, $S'(5, -1)$

9. $M'(4, 9)$, $P'(1, -6)$, $S'(5, -5)$

11. [figure]

13. no reflectional symmetry

17. $E'(2, -5)$, $F'(4, -5)$, $G'(6, -1)$, $H'(3, -1)$ **19a.** *J* and *K* are not equal distances away from the *x*-axis. **b.** $\overline{MN}$ is not perpendicular to the *y*-axis. **c.** *M* and *E*; they are the same distance from the *x*-axis and $\overline{ME}$ is perpendicular to the *x*-axis. **21.** yes; 1 line

23a–b. [graph] **c.** square with its diagonals

25. CODE **27.** [figure]

43. [graph] **45.** [graph]

Lesson 3-10 pp.171–174

EXERCISES **1.** [graph]

5. [graph] **7.** yes; 180°

9. no rotational symmetry **21.** 90°
23. A complete rotation has 360°. A square can be rotated 360° ÷ 4 or 90°.

Selected Answers 803

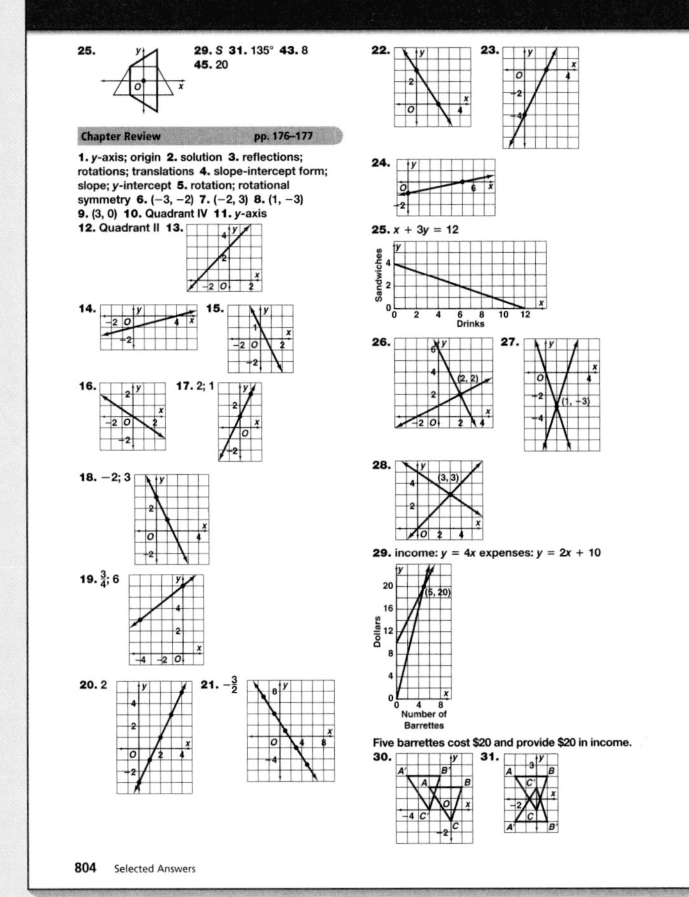

25. [graph] **29.** *S* **31.** 135° **43.** 8 **45.** 20

Chapter Review pp. 176–177

1. *y*-axis; origin **2.** solution **3.** reflections; rotations; translations **4.** slope-intercept form; slope; *y*-intercept **5.** rotation; rotational symmetry **6.** $(-3, -2)$ **7.** $(-2, 3)$ **8.** $(1, -3)$ **9.** $(3, 0)$ **10.** Quadrant IV **11.** *y*-axis **12.** Quadrant II **13.** [graph]

14. [graph] **15.** [graph]

16. [graph] **17.** 2; 1 [graph]

18. -2; 3 [graph]

19. $\frac{3}{4}$; 6 [graph]

20. 2 [graph] **21.** $-\frac{3}{2}$ [graph]

22. [graph] **23.** [graph]

24. [graph]

25. $x + 3y = 12$ [graph: Sandwiches vs. Drinks]

26. [graph] **27.** [graph]

28. [graph]

29. income: $y = 4x$ expenses: $y = 2x + 10$ [graph: Dollars vs. Number of Barrettes]

Five barrettes cost \$20 and provide \$20 in income.

30. [graph] **31.** [graph]

804 Selected Answers

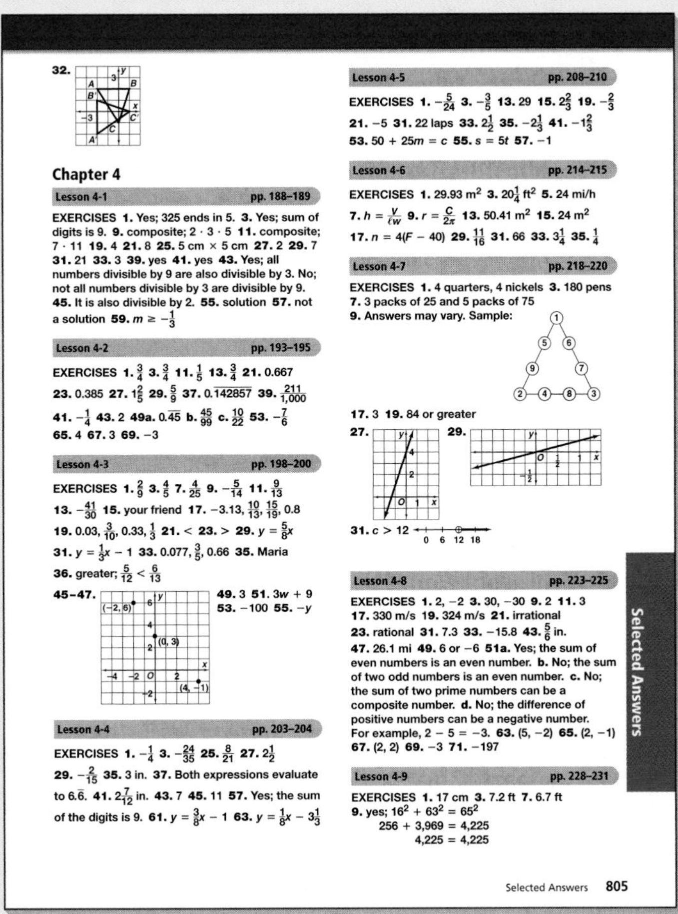

32. [graph]

Chapter 4

Lesson 4-1 pp. 188–189

EXERCISES **1.** Yes; 325 ends in 5. **3.** Yes; sum of digits is 9. **9.** composite; $2 \cdot 3 \cdot 5$ **11.** composite; $7 \cdot 11$ **19.** 4 **21.** 8 **25.** 5 cm × 5 cm **27.** 2 **29.** 7 **31.** 21 **33.** 3 **39.** yes **41.** yes **43.** Yes; all numbers divisible by 9 are also divisible by 3. No; not all numbers divisible by 3 are divisible by 9. **45.** It is also divisible by 2. **55.** solution **57.** not a solution **59.** $m \geq -\frac{1}{3}$

Lesson 4-2 pp. 193–195

EXERCISES **1.** $\frac{3}{4}$ **3.** $\frac{3}{4}$ **11.** $\frac{1}{5}$ **13.** $\frac{3}{4}$ **21.** 0.667 **23.** 0.385 **27.** $1\frac{2}{5}$ **29.** $\frac{5}{9}$ **37.** $0.\overline{142857}$ **39.** $\frac{211}{1,000}$ **41.** $-\frac{1}{4}$ **43.** 2 **49a.** $0.\overline{45}$ **b.** $\frac{45}{99}$ **c.** $\frac{10}{22}$ **53.** $-\frac{7}{6}$ **65.** 4 **67.** 3 **69.** -3

Lesson 4-3 pp. 198–200

EXERCISES **1.** $\frac{2}{9}$ **3.** $\frac{4}{5}$ **7.** $\frac{4}{25}$ **9.** $-\frac{5}{14}$ **11.** $\frac{9}{13}$ **13.** $-\frac{41}{30}$ **15.** your friend **17.** $-3.13, \frac{10}{13}, \frac{15}{19}, 0.8$ **19.** $0.03, \frac{3}{10}, 0.33, \frac{1}{3}$ **21.** < **23.** > **29.** $y = \frac{5}{8}x$ **31.** $y = \frac{1}{3}x - 1$ **33.** $0.077, \frac{3}{5}, 0.66$ **35.** Maria **36.** greater; $\frac{5}{12} < \frac{6}{13}$

45–47. [graph] **49.** 3 **51.** $3w + 9$ **53.** -100 **55.** $-y$

Lesson 4-4 pp. 203–204

EXERCISES **1.** $-\frac{1}{4}$ **3.** $-\frac{24}{35}$ **25.** $\frac{8}{21}$ **27.** $2\frac{1}{2}$ **29.** $-\frac{2}{15}$ **35.** 3 in. **37.** Both expressions evaluate to $6.\overline{6}$. **41.** $2\frac{7}{12}$ in. **43.** 7 **45.** 11 **57.** Yes; the sum of the digits is 9. **61.** $y = \frac{3}{8}x - 1$ **63.** $y = \frac{1}{8}x - 3\frac{1}{3}$

Lesson 4-5 pp. 208–210

EXERCISES **1.** $-\frac{5}{24}$ **3.** $-\frac{3}{5}$ **13.** 29 **15.** $2\frac{2}{3}$ **19.** $-\frac{2}{3}$ **21.** -5 **31.** 22 laps **33.** $2\frac{1}{2}$ **35.** $-2\frac{1}{3}$ **41.** $-1\frac{2}{3}$ **53.** $50 + 25m = c$ **55.** $s = 5t$ **57.** -1

Lesson 4-6 pp. 214–215

EXERCISES **1.** 29.93 m² **3.** $20\frac{1}{4}$ ft² **5.** 24 mi/h **7.** $h = \frac{V}{\ell w}$ **9.** $r = \frac{C}{2\pi}$ **13.** 50.41 m² **15.** 24 m² **17.** $n = 4(F - 40)$ **29.** $\frac{11}{16}$ **31.** 66 **33.** $3\frac{1}{4}$ **35.** $\frac{1}{4}$

Lesson 4-7 pp. 218–220

EXERCISES **1.** 4 quarters, 4 nickels **3.** 180 pens **7.** 3 packs of 25 and 5 packs of 75 **9.** Answers may vary. Sample: [diagram]

17. 3 **19.** 84 or greater

27. [graph] **29.** [graph]

31. $c > 12$ [number line]

Lesson 4-8 pp. 223–225

EXERCISES **1.** 2, -2 **3.** 30, -30 **9.** 2 **11.** 3 **17.** 330 m/s **19.** 324 m/s **21.** irrational **23.** rational **31.** 7.3 **33.** -15.8 **43.** $\frac{5}{6}$ in. **47.** 26.1 mi **49.** 6 or -6 **51a.** Yes; the sum of even numbers is an even number. **b.** No; the sum of two odd numbers is an even number. **c.** No; the sum of two prime numbers can be a composite number. **d.** No; the difference of positive numbers can be a negative number. For example, $2 - 5 = -3$. **63.** $(5, -2)$ **65.** $(2, -1)$ **67.** $(2, 2)$ **69.** -3 **71.** -197

Lesson 4-9 pp. 228–231

EXERCISES **1.** 17 cm **3.** 7.2 ft **7.** 6.7 ft
9. yes; $16^2 + 63^2 = 65^2$
$256 + 3,969 = 4,225$
$4,225 = 4,225$

Selected Answers 805

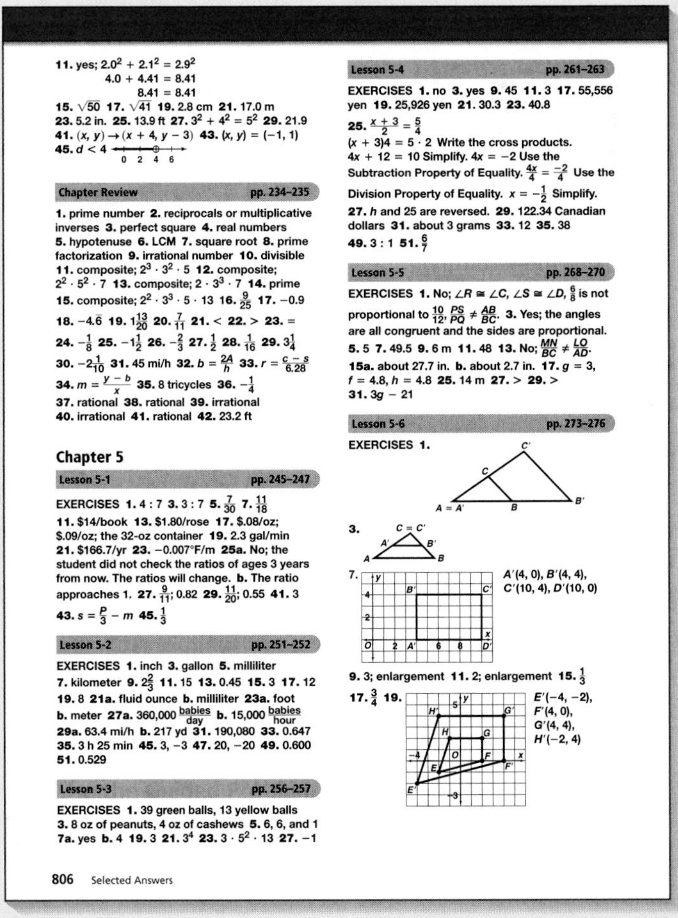

11. yes; $2.0^2 + 2.1^2 = 2.9^2$
$4.0 + 4.41 = 8.41$
$8.41 = 8.41$
15. $\sqrt{50}$ **17.** $\sqrt{41}$ **19.** 2.8 cm **21.** 17.0 m **23.** 5.2 in. **25.** 13.9 ft **27.** $3^2 + 4^2 = 5^2$ **29.** 21.9 **41.** $(x, y) \rightarrow (x + 4, y - 3)$ **43.** $(x, y) = (-1, 1)$ **45.** $d < 4$ [number line]

Chapter Review pp. 234–235

1. prime number **2.** reciprocals or multiplicative inverses **3.** perfect square **4.** real numbers **5.** hypotenuse **6.** LCM **7.** square root **8.** prime factorization **9.** irrational number **10.** divisible **11.** composite; $2^3 \cdot 3^2 \cdot 5$ **12.** composite; $2^2 \cdot 5^2 \cdot 7$ **13.** composite; $2 \cdot 3^3 \cdot 7$ **14.** prime **15.** composite; $2^2 \cdot 3^3 \cdot 5 \cdot 13$ **16.** $\frac{9}{25}$ **17.** -0.9 **18.** $-4.\overline{6}$ **19.** $1\frac{13}{20}$ **20.** $\frac{7}{11}$ **21.** < **22.** > **23.** = **24.** $-\frac{1}{8}$ **25.** $-1\frac{1}{2}$ **26.** $-\frac{2}{3}$ **27.** $\frac{1}{2}$ **28.** $\frac{1}{16}$ **29.** $3\frac{1}{4}$ **30.** $-2\frac{1}{10}$ **31.** 45 mi/h **32.** $b = \frac{2A}{h}$ **33.** $r = \frac{c - s}{6.28}$ **34.** $m = \frac{y - b}{x}$ **35.** 8 tricycles **36.** $-\frac{1}{4}$ **37.** rational **38.** rational **39.** irrational **40.** irrational **41.** rational **42.** 23.2 ft

Chapter 5

Lesson 5-1 pp. 245–247

EXERCISES **1.** 4 : 7 **3.** 3 : 7 **5.** $\frac{7}{30}$ **7.** $\frac{11}{18}$ **11.** \$14/book **13.** \$1.80/rose **17.** \$.08/oz; \$.09/oz; the 32-oz container **19.** 2.3 gal/min **21.** \$166.7/yr **23.** -0.007°F/m **25a.** No; the student did not check the ratios of ages 3 years from now. The ratios will change. **b.** The ratio approaches 1. **27.** $\frac{9}{11}$; 0.82 **29.** $\frac{11}{20}$; 0.55 **41.** 3 **43.** $s = \frac{P}{3} - m$ **45.** $\frac{1}{3}$

Lesson 5-2 pp. 251–252

EXERCISES **1.** inch **3.** gallon **5.** milliliter **7.** kilometer **9.** $2\frac{2}{3}$ **11.** 15 **13.** 0.45 **15.** 3 **17.** 12 **19.** 8 **21a.** fluid ounce **b.** milliliter **23a.** foot **b.** meter **27a.** 360,000 $\frac{\text{babies}}{\text{day}}$ **b.** 15,000 $\frac{\text{babies}}{\text{hour}}$ **29a.** 63.4 mi/h **b.** 217 yd **31.** 190,080 **33.** 0.647 **35.** 3 h 25 min **45.** 3, -3 **47.** 20, -20 **49.** 0.600 **51.** 0.529

Lesson 5-3 pp. 256–257

EXERCISES **1.** 39 green balls, 13 yellow balls **3.** 8 oz of peanuts, 4 oz of cashews **5.** 6, 6, and 1 **7a.** yes **b.** 4 **19.** 3 **21.** 3^4 **23.** $3 \cdot 5^2 \cdot 13$ **27.** -1

Lesson 5-4 pp. 261–263

EXERCISES **1.** no **3.** yes **9.** 45 **11.** 3 **17.** 55,556 yen **19.** 25,926 yen **21.** 30.3 **23.** 40.8
25. $\frac{x + 3}{2} = \frac{5}{4}$
$(x + 3)4 = 5 \cdot 2$ Write the cross products. $4x + 12 = 10$ Simplify. $4x = -2$ Use the Subtraction Property of Equality. $\frac{4x}{4} = \frac{-2}{4}$ Use the Division Property of Equality. $x = -\frac{1}{2}$ Simplify. **27.** *h* and 25 are reversed. **29.** 122.34 Canadian dollars **31.** about 3 grams **33.** 12 **35.** 38 **49.** 3 : 1 **51.** $\frac{6}{7}$

Lesson 5-5 pp. 268–270

EXERCISES **1.** No; $\angle R \cong \angle C$, $\angle S \cong \angle D$, $\frac{6}{8}$ is not proportional to $\frac{10}{12}$, $\frac{PS}{PQ} \neq \frac{AB}{BC}$. **3.** Yes; the angles are all congruent and the sides are proportional. **5.** 5 **7.** 49.5 **9.** 6 m **11.** 48 **13.** No; $\frac{MN}{BC} \neq \frac{LO}{AD}$. **15a.** about 27.7 in. **b.** about 2.7 in. **17.** $g = 3$, $f = 4.8$, $h = 4.8$ **25.** 14 m **27.** > **29.** > **31.** $3g - 21$

Lesson 5-6 pp. 273–276

EXERCISES **1.** [diagram]

3. [diagram]

7. [graph] $A'(4, 0)$, $B'(4, 4)$, $C'(10, 4)$, $D'(10, 0)$

9. 3; enlargement **11.** 2; enlargement **15.** $\frac{1}{3}$ **17.** $\frac{3}{4}$ **19.** [graph] $E'(-4, -2)$, $F'(4, 0)$, $G'(4, 4)$, $H'(-2, 4)$

806 Selected Answers

Selected Answers

21. 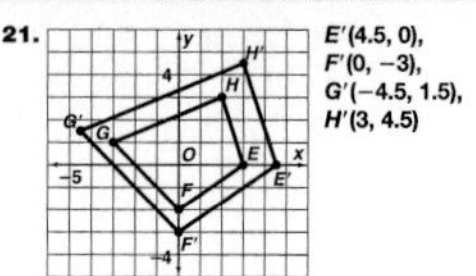
$E'(4.5, 0)$, $F'(0, -3)$, $G'(-4.5, 1.5)$, $H'(3, 4.5)$

23a. 4 **b.** $BC = 6$ cm, $A'C' = 40$ cm **c.** $\triangle ABC = 23$ cm, $\triangle A'B'C' = 92$ cm **d.** $\frac{1}{4}$ **33.** ≈ 4.3 **35.** no; $16^2 + 20^2 \neq 24^2$ **37.** yes, $9^2 + 12^2 = 15^2$ **39.** 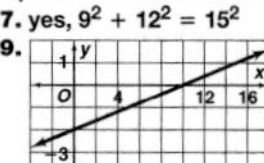

Lesson 5-7 pp. 279–281

EXERCISES **1.** 30 in. **3.** 12.5 in.; 2.5 in. **5.** 25 mi **7.** 53 m **9.** 21.5 in. **11.** 9.75 in. **13.** 300 mi **15.** 2.5 ft **17.** Yes; the narrow section of the bedroom is 5 ft wide by 7.5 ft long. **21.** about 6.9 in.; 3.75 in. **35.** 7 **37.** 16

Lesson 5-8 pp. 283–286

EXERCISES **1.** 8 m **3.** 360 m **5.** 1,269.7 m **7.** 27.1 ft **9.** 168 m **11.** 34 ft **13.** 112.5 ft **15.** 281.25 ft **25.** $A'(-\frac{9}{2}, -3)$, $B'(-\frac{9}{2}, 3)$, $C'(3, 3)$, $D'(6, -3)$

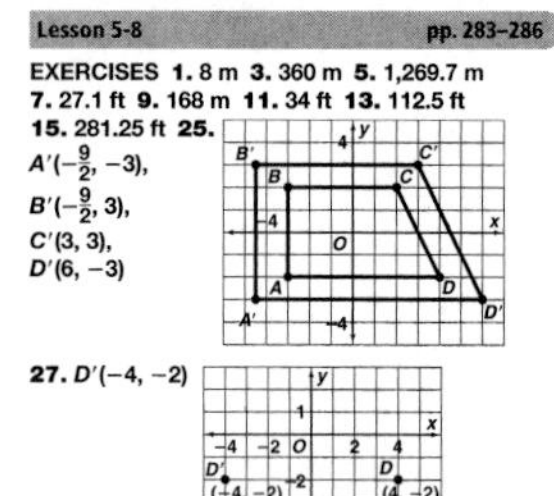

27. $D'(-4, -2)$ 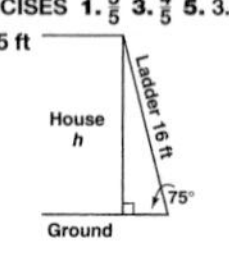

Lesson 5-9 pp. 289–291

EXERCISES **1.** $\frac{3}{5}$ **3.** $\frac{4}{5}$ **5.** 3.5 **7.** 59.3 **9.** 13.1 **11.** 15 ft

House h Ladder 16 ft 75° Ground

13a. $\sin 53° = \frac{x}{7.4}$ OR $\cos 37° = \frac{x}{7.4}$; 5.9 **b.** $\frac{x}{7.4}$ is cosine B, not sine B. **15.** 10, $\frac{3}{5}$, $\frac{4}{5}$ **25.** 56 ft

Chapter Review pp. 294–295

1. unit rate **2.** proportion **3.** scale factor **4.** sine **5.** reduction **6.** $\frac{1}{8}$ **7.** $3\frac{1}{3}$ **8.** $\frac{1}{3}$ **9.** \$28/h **10.** 59 mi/h **11.** 6.25 km/L **12.** 3,300 **13.** 256 **14.** $16\frac{2}{3}$ **15.** 380,160 **16.** 50 **17.** 18 **18.** liters **19.** feet **20.** 21 acres, 7 acres, 14 acres **21.** 16 **22.** 1 **23.** 12 **24.** 72 **25.** 10 cm **26.** 7.5 cm **27.** 4.5 cm **28.** 4; enlargement **29.** $2\frac{1}{4}$ in. by $1\frac{3}{8}$ in. **30.** 11 ft 9 in. tall **31.** 4.7 **32.** 13.8 **33.** 47.7

Chapter 6

Lesson 6-1 pp. 306–308

EXERCISES **1.** 40% **3.** 96% **7.** 36% **9.** 520% **13.** 62.5% **15.** 44.44% **19.** $\frac{2}{9}$ **21.** $\frac{2}{3}$ **23.** 6.3 **25.** 0.00007 **27.** $\frac{1}{3}$, $0.\overline{3}$, $33\frac{1}{3}$% **29.** $\frac{7}{10}$, 0.7, 70% **31.** 0.09%, 0.01, 1.01%, $\frac{1}{99}$ **33.** 1.5%, 150%, $\frac{9}{5}$, 150 **35.** 0.09% is equal to 0.0009, which is not the same as 0.09. **37.** 80% **39.** 432%

	Fraction	Decimal	Percent
40.	$\frac{7}{16}$	0.4375	43.75%
41.	$\frac{267}{50}$	5.34	534%
42.	$\frac{9}{1,000}$	0.009	0.9%
43.	$\frac{13}{20}$	0.65	65%

45. 0.5714; 57.14% **47.** 1.6667; 166.67% **50.** 5.24% **61.** $\sin A = \frac{3}{5}$; $\sin B = \frac{4}{5}$ **63.** 3 **65.** 12

Lesson 6-2 pp. 311–313

EXERCISES **1.** about 1 **3.** about 12 **9.** about \$1.80 **11.** about \$4.50 **15.** about 10 **17.** about 24 **25.** about 3 students **29.** about 605 **31.** about 60 **37.** > **39.** = **51.** \$31.44 **53.** 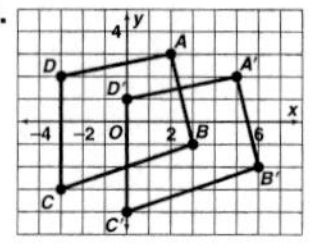

Selected Answers

Lesson 6-3 pp. 317–319

EXERCISES **1.** 57.6 **3.** 33 **13.** 7.5 **15.** 231.25 **19.** 180 people **21.** 64% **23.** 4% **27.** 154,567 votes **29a.** 8 **b.** 200 **c.** 50% **31.** 0.18% **33.** 49.80 **37.** about 120 million items **51.** about 45 **53.** 2 m : 5 m **55.** $\frac{7 \text{ oz}}{16 \text{ oz}}$

Lesson 6-4 pp. 323–325

EXERCISES **1.** 25.42 **3.** 11.4 **7.** \$2.40 **9.** \$4.32 **11.** 6.52 **13.** 11.1 **21.** \$3,540 **23.** \$943.05 **25.** \$930.47 **29.** about 37,403,000 households **31.** $p = 1.43 \cdot 65$ Write an equation. $= 92.95$ Multiply. **33.** $p = 0.00054 \cdot 43$ Write an equation. $p = 0.23274$ Multiply. **45.** Answers may vary. Sample: oz **47.** $\frac{15}{12}$ **49.** $\frac{1}{66}$

Lesson 6-5 pp. 328–330

EXERCISES **1.** 46.7% **3.** 1,300% **7.** 586.7% **9.** 85.2% **11.** 33.3% **13.** 26.4% **17.** 99.0% **19.** No; 20% of 100 is 20, so the result of a 20% increase from 100 is 120. Then 20% of 120 is 24, so the result of a 20% decrease from 120 is 96. **21.** 585.7% increase **23.** 75% decrease **27.** 187.6% **29.** An object can increase its weight by more than the original amount. An object cannot decrease its weight by more than the original amount because an object cannot have a negative weight. **41.** 2, enlargement **43.** $\frac{1}{2}$, reduction **45.** 24

Lesson 6-6 pp. 334–336

EXERCISES **1.** 50% **3.** 20% **5.** \$8.75 **7.** \$188.99 **11.** 62% **13.** \$22.60 **15.** \$111.41 **19.** \$16.25 **21.** \$50.89 **23.** \$6.62 **25.** 3 DVDs **27.** \$15.18 **29.** \$501.02 **31a.** \$28.40 **b.** Answers may vary. Sample: Divide the selling price by 1 plus the percent of markup written in decimal form. **33.** Yes; it is more than 40% off. **41.** 9 **43.** 25 **45.** $14\frac{11}{12}$ h

Lesson 6-7 pp. 339–341

EXERCISES **1.** between 39 and 44 mi **3.** between \$500 and \$875 **5.** 25 minutes **7.** 120 adult tickets **9.** 54 km **13.** 11 students **21.** 25% **23.** 50% **29.** 4 **31.** 9

Lesson 6-8 pp. 344–347

EXERCISES **1.** \$82.45 **3.** \$1,312.50 **5.** \$300.96 **7.** \$856 **9.** \$551.25 **11.** \$214.38 **13.** \$710.30 **15.** \$280.66 **17.** \$873.87 **19a.** \$4.50 **b.** \$304.50 **c.** 5 months **d.** Derek paid a total of $50 + 3 \cdot 100 + 9.32 = \$359.32$. So, Derek paid less by using his credit card to buy the television on sale. **21.** \$83.77 **23.** \$1,778.70 **27.** \$39.80 **29.** \$924.50 **39.** 62.4 **41.** 45.08 **45.** 102.6 ft^2 **47.** 114.49 m^2

Lesson 6-9 pp. 352–354

EXERCISES **1.** $\frac{1}{8}$ **3.** $\frac{1}{2}$ **7.** 0.025% **9a.** 83% **b.** 10% **c.** 78% **11.** $\frac{1}{2}$ **13.** $\frac{1}{8}$ **17.** $\frac{1}{4}$; 25% **19.** $\frac{364}{365}$; 99.7% **21a.** $\frac{1}{3}$ **b.** $\frac{1}{2}$ **c.** $\frac{1}{6}$ **23.** $\frac{1}{5}$ or 20% **25a.** $\frac{11}{20}$ **b.** 90 packages **33.** 533.3% increase **35.** 50.7% decrease **37.** 30 : 1 **39.** 32,400 to 127

Chapter Review pp. 356–357

1. markup **2.** principal **3.** outcome **4.** discount **5.** simple interest **6.** 87.5% **7.** 108.33% **8.** 31.25% **9.** 450% **10.** $\frac{9}{25}$ **11.** $\frac{1}{3}$ **12.** $1\frac{6}{25}$ **13.** $\frac{27}{100}$ **14–16.** Answers may vary. Samples are given. **14.** about 25 **15.** about \$5.25 **16.** about 63 **17.** 200 **18.** 40% **19.** 18 **20.** 150 **21.** 30.8% decrease **22.** 4,300% increase **23.** 0.6% increase **24.** 83.3% decrease **25.** \$64.75 **26.** \$199.99 **27.** between 68 and 80 questions **28.** \$3,636.70 **29.** \$574.75 **30.** Answers may vary. Sample: Compound interest pays more because it pays interest on the principal and the interest earned in previous interest periods. Simple interest only pays interest on the principal. **31.** $\frac{5}{9}$

Chapter 7

Lesson 7-1 pp. 367–369

EXERCISES **1.** 3,200 **3.** 239 **13.** 3×10^3 **15.** 3.42×10^4 **21.** 2.5×10^{10} **23.** 8.17×10^{21}, 8.29×10^{21}, 7.3×10^{25} **25.** 8×10^8 **27.** 3×10^{100} **31.** 1.3×10^8 **33.** 492 is not between 1 and 10 **35.** 5 **37.** 5.6194 **43.** 1×10^6 **53.** 20 **55.** 16 **57.** 0.04 **59.** 2.74 **61.** at most 6.6 inches wide

Lesson 7-2 pp. 372–374

EXERCISES **1.** 7^{10} **3.** $(-6)^4$ **13.** 8×10^9 **15.** 7.2×10^{11} **19.** about 4.55×10^{46} molecules **21.** < **23.** > **25.** 725, 6.3×10^3, 78×10^2 **27.** 1.244×10^{12}, 175.4×10^{10}, 24.45×10^{11} **29.** 4^{x+t} **31.** 1.5^{8+t} **51.** 14 **53.** 120 **55.** 45 **57.** about 23 **59.** \$5 per book **61.** \$.60 per lb **63.** \$.22/oz; \$.24/oz; the first brand

Lesson 7-3 pp. 379–381

EXERCISES **1.** $\frac{2 \cdot 2 \cdot 2 \cdot 2 \cdot 2 \cdot 2 \cdot 2}{2 \cdot 2 \cdot 2 \cdot 2 \cdot 2 \cdot 2} = 2^1$ **3.** $\frac{8 \cdot 8 \cdot 8 \cdot 8 \cdot 8}{8 \cdot 8} = 8^3$ **9.** x^4 **11.** 23^4 **15.** 1 **17.** 1 **23.** 0.0025 **25.** 0.0105 **27.** 0.000095 cm **29.** 5.81×10^{-3} **31.** 7.8×10^{-6} **33.** 12 **35.** 2 **41.** 1.09×10^2 times greater **43.** $\frac{1}{81}$ **45.** $-\frac{1}{2}$ **51.** 2.3×10^{-4} **53.** 1.23×10^{-4} **55.** False; $4^0 = 1$ and $4^{-1} = \frac{1}{4}$. **57.** True; $2^1 \cdot 2^{-1} = 2^{1+(-1)} = 2^0 = 1$. **59a.** 7.6×10^{-6} **b.** 7.6×10^{-3} **61.** 30 cm **73.** 29.3% **75.** 4.3125 **77.** about 23.2 ft

Lesson 7-4 pp. 385–387

EXERCISES **1.** 3^{21} **3.** h^4 **9.** $9x^2$ **11.** $16x^8$ **17.** 5.0×10^7 cm^2 **19.** < **21.** = **31.** 2^{12} **33.** 5^{12} **37.** Beth is correct; $x^2 \cdot x^2 = x^4$, and $x^2 + x^2 = 2x^2$. **39.** a^{bc} **41.** $5^{ax} \cdot 6^{bx}$ **53.** z^{14} **55.** $\frac{3}{5}$; 60% **57.** $\frac{1}{5}$ **59.** $\frac{7}{400}$

Lesson 7-5 pp. 389–391

EXERCISES **1.** 9.186×10^9 mi **3.** 1.02×10^9 people **5.** 1.91×10^8 atoms **7.** 6 routes **9.** \$12.49 **19.** 2^{12} **21.** r^{21} **27.** $\frac{1}{10}$ **29.** $\frac{2}{5}$

Lesson 7-6 pp. 394–395

EXERCISES **1.** 5 **3.** 8 **7.** 1111_2 **9.** 1100_2 **13.** 6 **15a.** 1111_2 **b.** 15 **17.** 11 **19.** 5 **35.** x^{18} **37.** $27y^3$ **41.** 1.234×10^7 **43.** 1.2×10^8 **45.** 69% decrease **47.** 2.4% decrease

Chapter Review pp. 398–399

1. binary **2.** scientific notation **3.** expanded form **4.** expanded form **5.** scientific notation **6.** 3.5×10^3 **7.** 8.01×10^5 **8.** 2.005×10^3 **9.** 8.104×10^6 **10.** 4,100 **11.** 103,000,000 **12.** 60,000 **13.** 5,005,000,000 **14.** 7×10^3, 5.4×10^5, 5.1×10^6 **15.** 9.1×10^9, 4×10^{12}, 9.9×10^{12} **16.** 8^{19} **17.** $(-3)^{13}$ **18.** 2.6^{24} **19.** 11^{11} **20.** 5^3 **21.** $(-8)^{10}$ **22.** 76^8 **23.** 1.8^1 **24.** 6×10^{18} **25.** 7×10^6 **26.** 3×10^{14} **27.** 1.47×10^{20} **28.** 1 **29.** $\frac{1}{5}$ **30.** 1 **31.** $-\frac{1}{8}$ **32.** 0.004 **33.** 0.0000019 **34.** 0.000601 **35.** 2×10^{-5} **36.** 1.05×10^{-3} **37.** 1.15×10^{-2} **38.** 5^8 **39.** 9^{20} **40.** 8^6 **41.** a^{-8} **42.** x^{-20} **43.** a^{40} **44.** 2^{-100} **45.** 333^{99} **46.** 3^0 **47.** w^0 **48.** $16x^2$ **49.** $8n^3$ **50.** 1.6×10^{19} **51.** 8×10^{12} **52.** a^4b^{20} **53.** $a^{14}b^{14}c^{14}$ **54.** $9a^{-8}$ **55.** $w^{10}x^{-10}$ **56.** $36a^2b^6$ **57.** 1 **58.** 2×10^5 cm **59.** 2.5×10^{14} blood cells **60.** 5 **61.** 4 **62.** 14 **63.** 13 **64.** 111_2 **65.** 1010_2 **66.** 11101_2 **67.** 11110_2

Chapter 8

Lesson 8-1 pp. 410–412

EXERCISES **1.** $\angle MRQ$ and $\angle NRP$; $\angle NRP$ and $\angle QRP$; 80° **3.** $\angle BDC$ and $\angle TDY$; $\angle CDV$ and $\angle VDY$; 40° **5.** 156° **7.** 141° **11.** 3° **13.** 69° **17.** $m\angle 1 = 46°$; $m\angle 2 = 90°$; $m\angle 3 = 44°$; $m\angle 4 = 136°$ **19.** adjacent **21.** 140° **23a–b.** Check students' work. **29.** 58°; 148° **31.** 4.1°; 94.1° **35a.** 50° **b.** 130° **46.** 8×10^7 **49.** 9.5×10^{12}

Lesson 8-2 pp. 415–418

EXERCISES **1.** alternate interior **3.** neither **9.** 58° **11.** 122° **15.** Corr. angles are ≅. **17.** Alt. int. angles are ≅. **21.** $m\angle 1 = 118°$; $m\angle 2 = 118°$; $m\angle 3 = 118°$; $m\angle 4 = 62°$ **23.** $m\angle 1 = 45°$; $m\angle 2 = 135°$; $m\angle 3 = 135°$; $m\angle 4 = 135°$ **25.** false **27.** true **29.** no parallel lines **31.** $a \parallel b$; $\angle 1$ is supplementary to a 110° angle, so its measure is 70°. Alternate interior angles are congruent. **33.** $\angle 1$ and $\angle 5$; $\angle 8$ and $\angle 4$; $\angle 7$ and $\angle 3$; $\angle 2$ and $\angle 6$ **43.** 724 **45.** 6,000,000 **49.** \$5.37; \$85.92 **51.** 31.98 **53.** 123.38

Lesson 8-3 pp. 423–425

EXERCISES **1.** $\angle Q \cong \angle J$; $\angle C \cong \angle E$; $\angle R \cong \angle V$; $\angle Z \cong \angle U$; $\overline{RC} \cong \overline{VE}$; $\overline{CQ} \cong \overline{EJ}$; $\overline{QZ} \cong \overline{JU}$; $\overline{ZR} \cong \overline{UV}$; $QCRZ \cong JEVU$ **3.** $\angle J \cong \angle W$; $\angle K \cong \angle T$; $\angle D \cong \angle B$; $\overline{JK} \cong \overline{WT}$; $\overline{KD} \cong \overline{TB}$; $\overline{DJ} \cong \overline{BW}$; $\triangle JKD \cong \triangle WTB$ **7.** 104° **9.** 0.9 cm **15.** SAS **17.** SAS **19.** congruent; SAS or SSS **25.** SAS or ASA; $x = 4$; $y° = 30°$; $z° = 60°$ **27.** ASA **29.** 0.13 km **39.** $\frac{1}{6}$ **41.** 1.8 **43.** 0.0049

Lesson 8-4 pp. 428–429

EXERCISES **1a.** 3 angles **b.** 28 angles **3.** 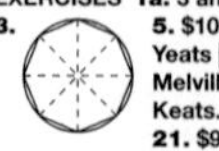 **5.** \$10 **9.** No; Keats ∥ Byron and Yeats ∥ Byron, so Keats ∥ Yeats. Melville ⊥ Yeats, so Melville ⊥ Keats. **17.** $2,401r^8s^{12}$ **19.** $x^8y^4z^{12}$ **21.** \$9.60 **23.** \$16.50

Lesson 8-5 pp. 432–433

EXERCISES **1.** scalene, obtuse **3.** isosceles, acute **7.** parallelogram; both pairs of opposite sides ∥ **17.** rectangle, square **19.** parallelogram, rhombus, rectangle, square **21.** If a rectangle is a square, then it has four congruent sides; true. **23.** all scalene triangles **25.** A square has four right angles like a rectangle and four congruent sides like a rhombus. **35.** $\frac{1}{a}$ **37.** 1 **39.** 63.6% increase **41.** 12.7% increase

Selected Answers

Lesson 8-6 pp. 438–439

EXERCISES **1.** 360° **3.** 1,440° **7.** 83° **9.** 100° **11.** 160° **13.** 156° **15.** heptagon **17.** octagon **19.** 135° **21.** 161° **23.** $a° = 105°$; $b° = 106°$ **33.** rectangle, square **35.** 132° **37.** 27° **39.** 6 **41.** 17

Lesson 8-7 pp. 444–446

EXERCISES **1.** 50 cm^2 **3.** 60 cm^2 **5.** 96 m^2 **7.** 84 m^2 **9.** 18 m^2 **11.** Answers may vary. Sample: Laser: 85 ft^2; 470: 95 ft^2; Soling: 140 ft^2; Finn: 100 ft^2 **13.** 231 in.^{2} **15a.** 189 ft^2 **b.** 5 cases **c.** \$195.80 **17.** 3.5 m **27.** 135° **29.** 165.6°

Lesson 8-8 pp. 450–452

EXERCISES **1.** 37.7 m **3.** 31.4 cm **7.** 201.1 cm^2 **9.** 706.9 m^2 **13.** 22.3 ft^2 **15.** 1,253.4 ft^2 **19.** 66 cm **21.** 22 m **23.** 66 cm^2; subtract the area of the smaller circle from the area of the larger circle. **25.** 3.56 cm; 7.11 cm **27.** 24.02 ft; 48.05 ft **29.** 315.8 ft^2 **31.** 228 ft^2 **33.** 2,946.7 ft^2 **43.** SAS **45.** The corresponding angles are congruent.

Lesson 8-9 pp. 457–459

EXERCISES **1.** 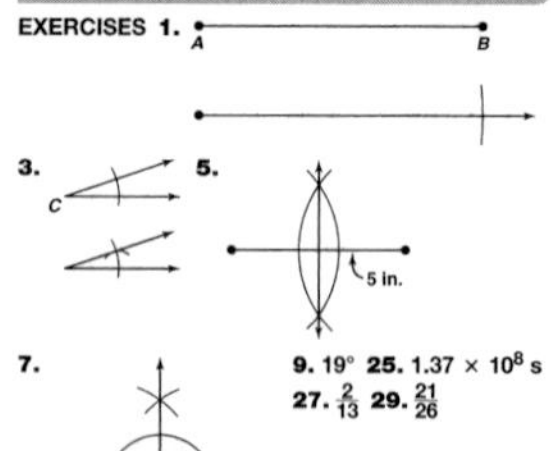

9. 19° **25.** 1.37×10^8 s **27.** $\frac{2}{13}$ **29.** $\frac{21}{26}$

Chapter Review pp. 462–463

1. transversal **2.** scalene **3.** supplementary **4.** rhombus **5.** regular **6.** 35°; 55° **7.** 48°; 132° **8.** 331 pages **9.** $\triangle CDE \cong \triangle HGF$; SAS **10.** $\triangle JLK \cong \triangle OMN$; SSS **11.** 120° **12.** 150° **13.** 160° **14.** 540 ft^2 **15.** 24 cm^2 **16.** 124.7 cm^2 **17.** A 3.5 cm B; R S **18.** P

Chapter 9

Lesson 9-1 pp. 473–475

EXERCISES **1.** The base is circular. The figure is a cone. $\overline{PQ}$ is a radius of the base. **3.** The two bases are circles. The figure is a cylinder. $\overline{PQ}$ is a radius. **5.** a cone and a cylinder **7.** 3 rectangular prisms, 2 cylinders, and a triangular prism **9.** Answers may vary. Sample: $\overline{DE}$ and $\overline{FH}$, $\overline{GD}$ and $\overline{EF}$, $\overline{EF}$ and $\overline{FH}$ **11.** rectangular pyramid **13.** cylinder **17.** Answers may vary. Sample: cylinder, cone, rectangular prism, triangular prism **19.** Kenji is right in that there are 2 parallel, congruent trapezoidal bases and the lateral faces are parallelograms. Ester is also right; a vertical cut could separate the figure into a rectangular prism and a triangular prism. **21.** skew **29.** 4.2048×10^7 times

Lesson 9-2 pp. 478–480

EXERCISES **1.** 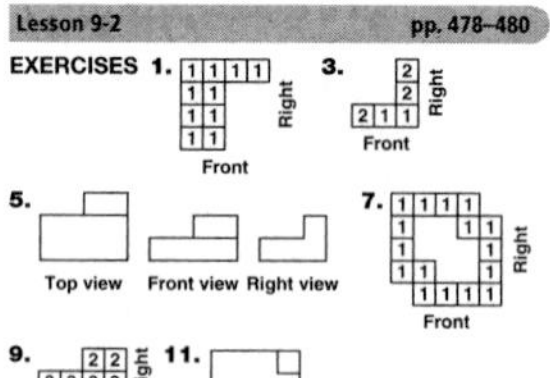

13a. Yes; the cross section is parallel to the bases. **b.** Yes; the cross section is perpendicular to the bases. **c.** No; the curved lateral surface makes a triangular cross section impossible. **25.** 11.9 in.^{2} **27.** 4 **29.** 2

Lesson 9-3 pp. 483–485

EXERCISES **1.** B **3.** A **5.** square pyramid **7.** cube **11.** 2 circles, 1 rectangle **19.** 5 **21.** Yes; one solid can have several different nets depending on which edges you cut along to unfold and flatten the solid. **23.** 1 trapezoid, 4 triangles **25.** 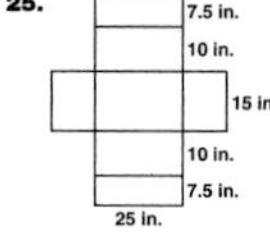

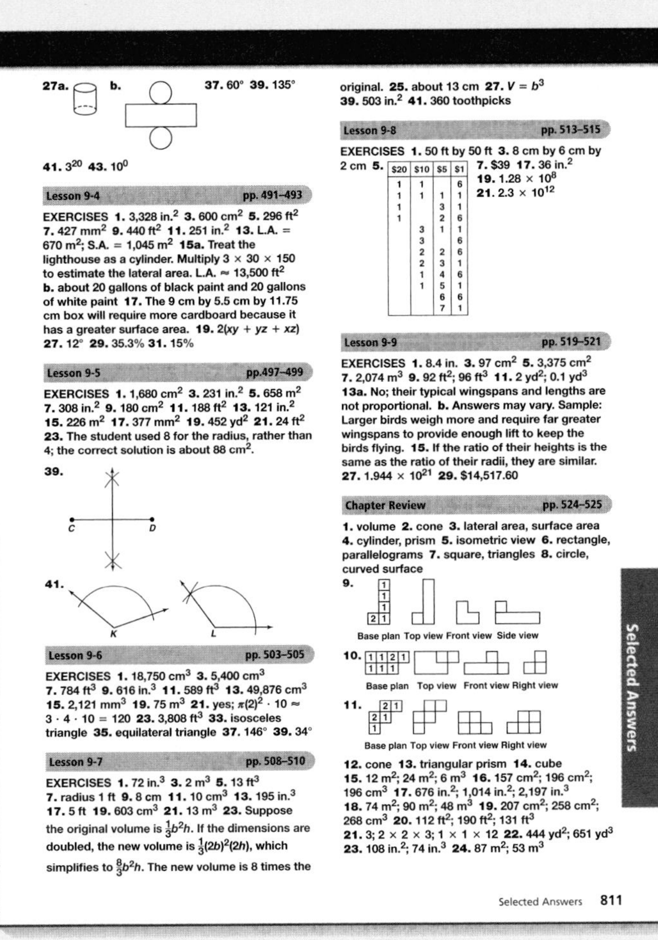

27a. b. **37.** 60° **39.** 135°

41. 3^{20} **43.** 10^0

Lesson 9-4 pp. 491–493

EXERCISES **1.** 3,328 in.^{2} **3.** 600 cm^2 **5.** 296 ft^2 **7.** 427 mm^2 **9.** 440 ft^2 **11.** 251 in.^{2} **13.** L.A. = 670 m^2; S.A. = 1,045 m^2 **15a.** Treat the lighthouse as a cylinder. Multiply 3 × 30 × 150 to estimate the lateral area. L.A. ≈ 13,500 ft^2 **b.** about 20 gallons of black paint and 20 gallons of white paint **17.** The 9 cm by 5.5 cm by 11.75 cm box will require more cardboard because it has a greater surface area. **19.** $2(xy + yz + xz)$ **27.** 12° **29.** 35.3% **31.** 15%

Lesson 9-5 pp.497–499

EXERCISES **1.** 1,680 cm^2 **3.** 231 in.^{2} **5.** 658 m^2 **7.** 308 in.^{2} **9.** 180 cm^2 **11.** 188 ft^2 **13.** 121 in.^{2} **15.** 226 m^2 **17.** 377 mm^2 **19.** 452 yd^2 **21.** 24 ft^2 **23.** The student used 8 for the radius, rather than 4; the correct solution is about 88 cm^2.

39.

41.

Lesson 9-6 pp. 503–505

EXERCISES **1.** 18,750 cm^3 **3.** 5,400 cm^3 **7.** 784 ft^3 **9.** 616 in.^{3} **11.** 589 ft^3 **13.** 49,876 cm^3 **15.** 2,121 mm^3 **19.** 75 m^3 **21.** yes; $\pi(2)^2 \cdot 10 \approx 3 \cdot 4 \cdot 10 = 120$ **23.** 3,808 ft^3 **33.** isosceles triangle **35.** equilateral triangle **37.** 146° **39.** 34°

Lesson 9-7 pp. 508–510

EXERCISES **1.** 72 in.^{3} **3.** 2 m^3 **5.** 13 ft^3 **7.** radius 1 ft **9.** 8 cm **11.** 10 cm^3 **13.** 195 in.^{3} **17.** 5 ft **19.** 603 cm^3 **21.** 13 m^3 **23.** Suppose the original volume is $\frac{1}{3}b^2h$. If the dimensions are doubled, the new volume is $\frac{1}{3}(2b)^2(2h)$, which simplifies to $\frac{8}{3}b^2h$. The new volume is 8 times the original. **25.** about 13 cm **27.** $V = b^3$ **39.** 503 in.^{2} **41.** 360 toothpicks

Lesson 9-8 pp. 513–515

EXERCISES **1.** 50 ft by 50 ft **3.** 8 cm by 6 cm by 2 cm **5.**

\$20	\$10	\$5	\$1
1	1		6
1	1	1	1
1		3	1
1		2	6
	3	1	1
	3		6
	2	2	6
	2	3	1
	1	4	6
	1	5	1
		6	6
		7	1

7. \$39 **17.** 36 in.^{2} **19.** 1.28×10^8 **21.** 2.3×10^{12}

Lesson 9-9 pp. 519–521

EXERCISES **1.** 8.4 in. **3.** 97 cm^2 **5.** 3,375 cm^2 **7.** 2,074 m^3 **9.** 92 ft^2; 96 ft^3 **11.** 2 yd^2; 0.1 yd^3 **13a.** No; their typical wingspans and lengths are not proportional. **b.** Answers may vary. Sample: Larger birds weigh more and require far greater wingspans to provide enough lift to keep the birds flying. **15.** If the ratio of their heights is the same as the ratio of their radii, they are similar. **27.** 1.944×10^{21} **29.** \$14,517.60

Chapter Review pp. 524–525

1. volume **2.** cone **3.** lateral area, surface area **4.** cylinder, prism **5.** isometric view **6.** rectangle, parallelograms **7.** square, triangles **8.** circle, curved surface

9.

10.

11.

12. cone **13.** triangular prism **14.** cube **15.** 12 m^2; 24 m^2; 6 m^3 **16.** 157 cm^2; 196 cm^2; 196 cm^3 **17.** 676 in.^{2}; 1,014 in.^{2}; 2,197 in.^{3} **18.** 74 m^2; 90 m^2; 48 m^3 **19.** 207 cm^2; 258 cm^2; 268 cm^3 **20.** 112 ft^2; 190 ft^2; 131 ft^3 **21.** 3; 2 × 2 × 3; 1 × 1 × 12 **22.** 444 yd^2; 651 yd^3 **23.** 108 in.^{2}; 74 in.^{3} **24.** 87 m^2; 53 m^3

Selected Answers

Selected Answers 811

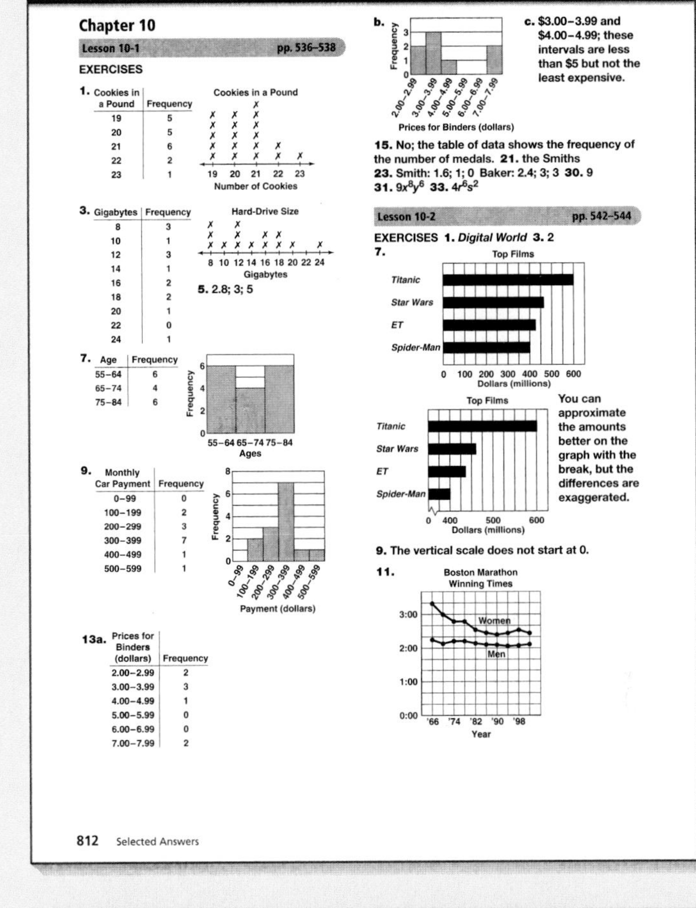

Chapter 10

Lesson 10-1 pp. 536–538

EXERCISES

1.

Cookies in a Pound	Frequency
19	5
20	5
21	6
22	2
23	1

3.

Gigabytes	Frequency
8	3
10	1
12	3
14	1
16	2
18	2
20	1
22	0
24	1

5. 2.8; 3; 5

7.

Age	Frequency
55–64	6
65–74	4
75–84	6

9.

Monthly Car Payment	Frequency
0–99	0
100–199	2
200–299	3
300–399	7
400–499	1
500–599	1

13a.

Prices for Binders (dollars)	Frequency
2.00–2.99	2
3.00–3.99	3
4.00–4.99	1
5.00–5.99	0
6.00–6.99	0
7.00–7.99	2

b.

c. \$3.00–3.99 and \$4.00–4.99; these intervals are less than \$5 but not the least expensive.

15. No; the table of data shows the frequency of the number of medals. **21.** the Smiths **23.** Smith: 1.6; 1; 0 Baker: 2.4; 3; 3 **30.** 9 **31.** $9x^8y^6$ **33.** $4r^6s^2$

Lesson 10-2 pp. 542–544

EXERCISES **1.** *Digital World* **3.** 2

7.

You can approximate the amounts better on the graph with the break, but the differences are exaggerated.

9. The vertical scale does not start at 0.

11.

812 Selected Answers

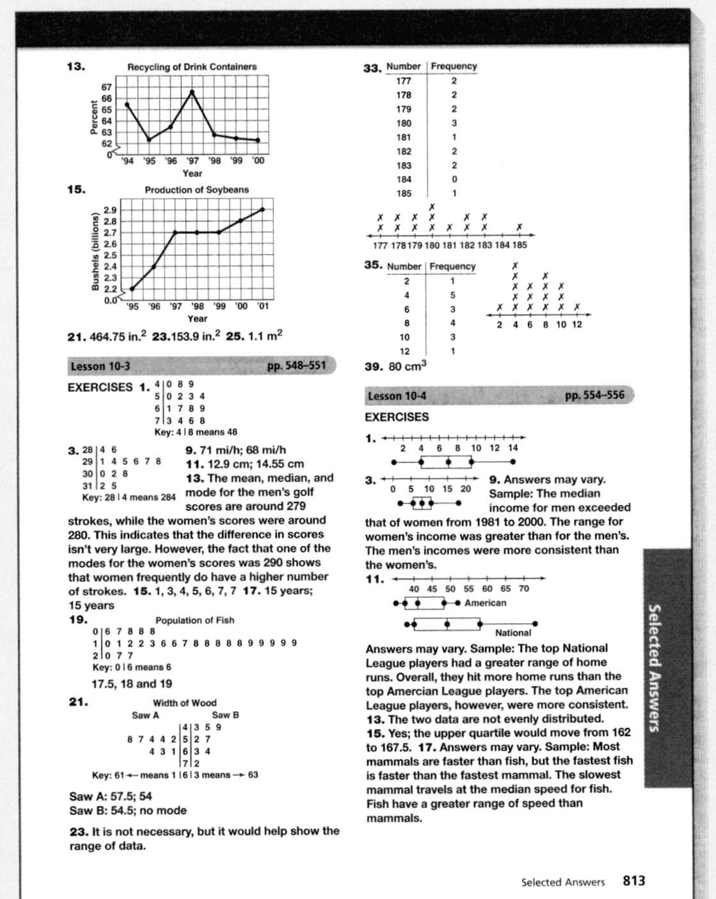

13.

15.

21. 464.75 in.^{2} **23.** 153.9 in.^{2} **25.** 1.1 m^2

Lesson 10-3 pp. 548–551

EXERCISES **1.**

4 | 0 8 9
5 | 0 2 3 4
6 | 1 7 8 9
7 | 3 4 6 8
Key: 4 | 8 means 48

3.

28 | 4 6
29 | 1 4 5 6 7 8
30 | 0 2 8
31 | 2 5
Key: 28 | 4 means 284

9. 71 mi/h; 68 mi/h **11.** 12.9 cm; 14.55 cm **13.** The mean, median, and mode for the men's golf scores are around 279 strokes, while the women's scores were around 280. This indicates that the difference in scores isn't very large. However, the fact that one of the modes for the women's scores was 290 shows that women frequently do have a higher number of strokes. **15.** 1, 3, 4, 5, 6, 7, 7 **17.** 15 years; 15 years

19. Population of Fish

0 | 6 7 8 8 8
1 | 0 1 2 2 3 6 6 7 8 8 8 8 8 9 9 9 9 9
2 | 0 7 7
Key: 0 | 6 means 6

17.5, 18 and 19

21. Width of Wood

Saw A | | Saw B
8 7 4 4 2 | 4 | 3 5 9
4 3 1 | 5 | 2 7
| 6 | 3 4
| 7 | 2
Key: 61 ← means 1 | 6 | 3 means → 63

Saw A: 57.5; 54
Saw B: 54.5; no mode

23. It is not necessary, but it would help show the range of data.

33.

Number	Frequency
177	2
178	2
179	2
180	3
181	1
182	2
183	2
184	0
185	1

35.

Number	Frequency
2	1
4	5
6	3
8	4
10	3
12	1

39. 80 cm^3

Lesson 10-4 pp. 554–556

EXERCISES

1. **3.** **9.** Answers may vary. Sample: The median income for men exceeded that of women from 1981 to 2000. The range for women's income was greater than for the men's. The men's incomes were more consistent than the women's.

11.

Answers may vary. Sample: The top National League players had a greater range of home runs. Overall, they hit more home runs than the top Amercian League players. The top American League players, however, were more consistent. **13.** The two data are not evenly distributed. **15.** Yes; the upper quartile would move from 162 to 167.5. **17.** Answers may vary. Sample: Most mammals are faster than fish, but the fastest fish is faster than the fastest mammal. The slowest mammal travels at the median speed for fish. Fish have a greater range of speed than mammals.

Selected Answers

Selected Answers 813

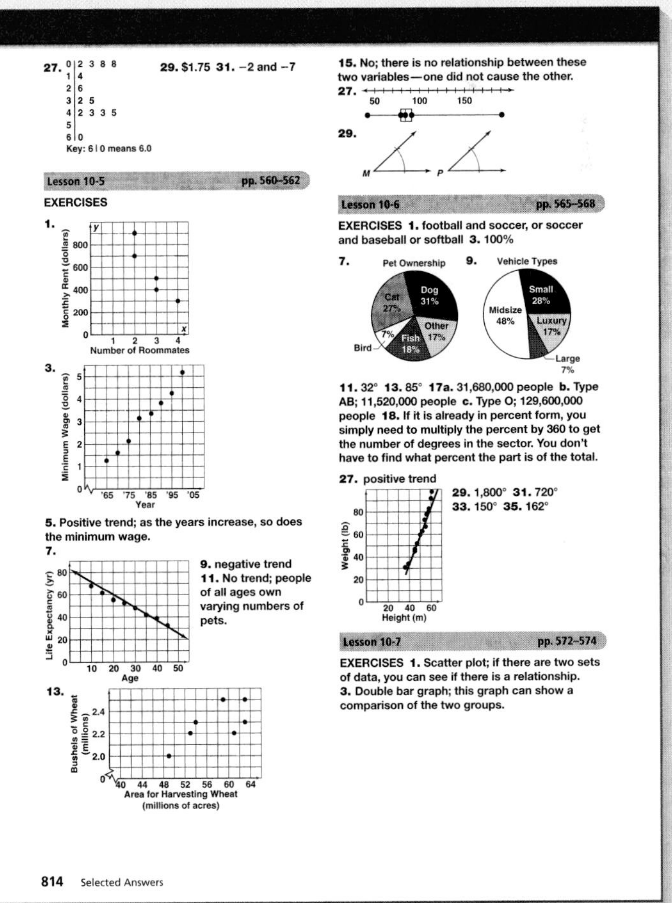

27.

0 | 2 3 8 8
1 | 4
2 | 6
3 | 2 5
4 | 2 3 3 5
5 |
6 | 0
Key: 6 | 0 means 6.0

29. \$1.75 **31.** −2 and −7

Lesson 10-5 pp. 560–562

EXERCISES

1.

3.

5. Positive trend; as the years increase, so does the minimum wage.

7.

9. negative trend **11.** No trend; people of all ages own varying numbers of pets.

13.

15. No; there is no relationship between these two variables—one did not cause the other.

27. **29.**

Lesson 10-6 pp. 565–568

EXERCISES **1.** football and soccer, or soccer and baseball or softball **3.** 100%

7. **9.**

11. 32° **13.** 85° **17a.** 31,680,000 people **b.** Type AB; 11,520,000 people **c.** Type O; 129,600,000 people **18.** If it is already in percent form, you simply need to multiply the percent by 360 to get the number of degrees in the sector. You don't have to find what percent the part is of the total.

27. positive trend

29. 1,800° **31.** 720° **33.** 150° **35.** 162°

Lesson 10-7 pp. 572–574

EXERCISES **1.** Scatter plot; if there are two sets of data, you can see if there is a relationship. **3.** Double bar graph; this graph can show a comparison of the two groups.

814 Selected Answers

Selected Answers

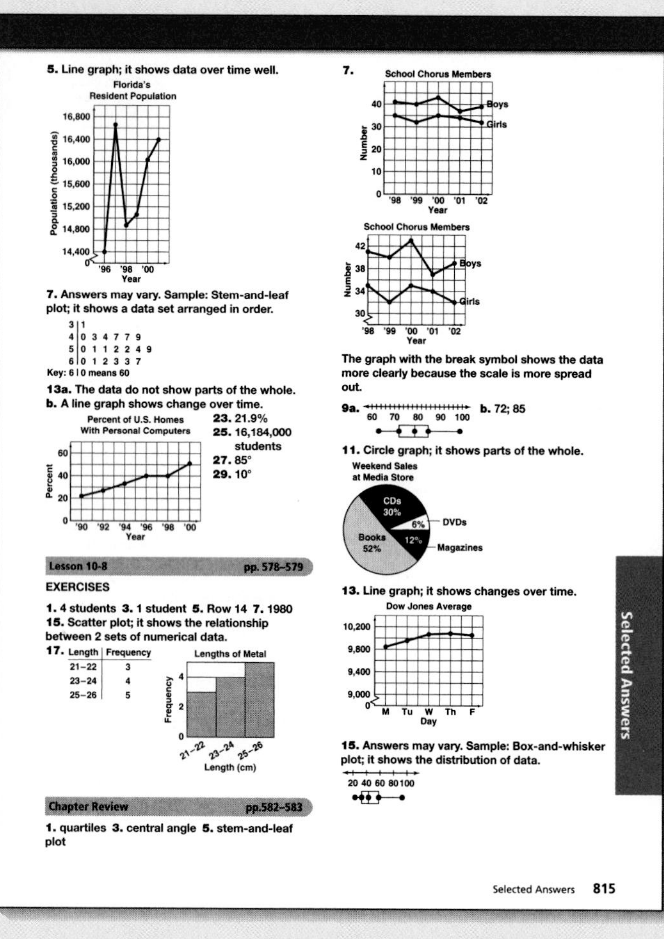

5. Line graph; it shows data over time well.

7. Answers may vary. Sample: Stem-and-leaf plot; it shows a data set arranged in order.

3 | 1
4 | 0 3 4 7 7 9
5 | 0 1 1 2 2 4 9
6 | 0 1 2 3 3 7
Key: 6 | 0 means 60

13a. The data do not show parts of the whole. b. A line graph shows change over time. 23. 21.9% 25. 16,184,000 students 27. 85° 29. 10°

Lesson 10-8 pp. 578–579

EXERCISES

1. 4 students 3. 1 student 5. Row 14 7. 1980 15. Scatter plot; it shows the relationship between 2 sets of numerical data.

17.

Length	Frequency
21–22	3
23–24	4
25–26	5

Chapter Review pp. 582–583

1. quartiles 3. central angle 5. stem-and-leaf plot

7. The graph with the break symbol shows the data more clearly because the scale is more spread out.

9a. b. 72; 85

11. Circle graph; it shows parts of the whole.

13. Line graph; it shows changes over time.

15. Answers may vary. Sample: Box-and-whisker plot; it shows the distribution of data.

Selected Answers 815

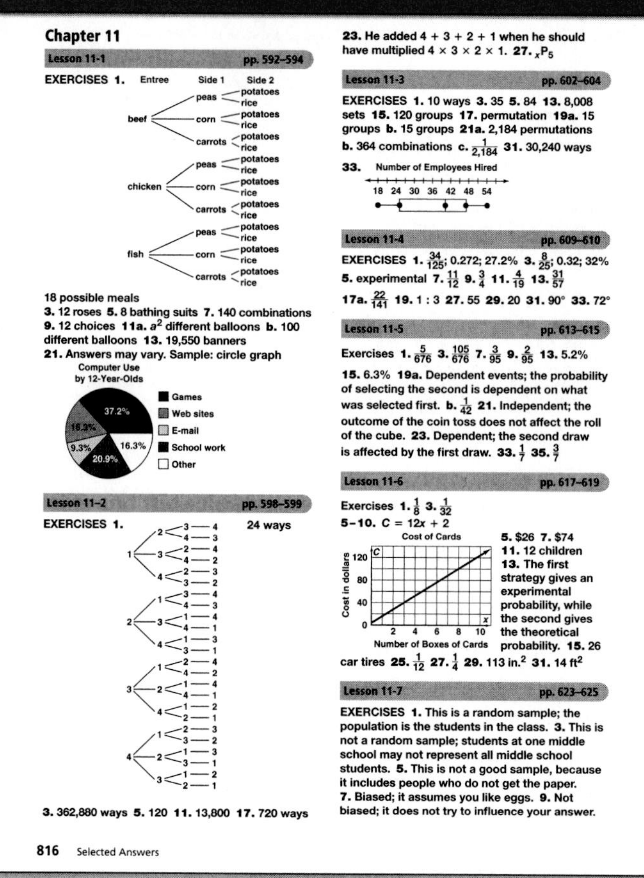

Chapter 11

Lesson 11-1 pp. 592–594

EXERCISES 1. 18 possible meals 3. 12 roses 5. 8 bathing suits 7. 140 combinations 9. 12 choices 11a. a^2 different balloons b. 100 different balloons 13. 19,550 banners 21. Answers may vary. Sample: circle graph

Lesson 11-2 pp. 598–599

EXERCISES 1. 24 ways 3. 362,880 ways 5. 120 11. 13,800 17. 720 ways 23. He added 4 + 3 + 2 + 1 when he should have multiplied 4 × 3 × 2 × 1. 27. $_xP_5$

Lesson 11-3 pp. 602–604

EXERCISES 1. 10 ways 3. 35 5. 84 13. 8,008 sets 15. 120 groups 17. permutation 19a. 15 groups b. 15 groups 21a. 2,184 permutations b. 364 combinations c. $\frac{1}{2,184}$ 31. 30,240 ways 33.

Lesson 11-4 pp. 609–610

EXERCISES 1. $\frac{34}{125}$; 0.272; 27.2% 3. $\frac{8}{25}$; 0.32; 32% 5. experimental 7. $\frac{11}{12}$ 9. $\frac{3}{4}$ 11. $\frac{4}{19}$ 13. $\frac{31}{57}$ 17a. $\frac{22}{141}$ 19. 1 : 3 27. 55 29. 20 31. 90° 33. 72°

Lesson 11-5 pp. 613–615

Exercises 1. $\frac{5}{676}$ 3. $\frac{105}{676}$ 7. $\frac{3}{95}$ 9. $\frac{2}{95}$ 13. 5.2% 15. 6.3% 19a. Dependent events; the probability of selecting the second is dependent on what was selected first. b. $\frac{1}{42}$ 21. Independent; the outcome of the coin toss does not affect the roll of the cube. 23. Dependent; the second draw is affected by the first draw. 33. $\frac{1}{7}$ 35. $\frac{3}{7}$

Lesson 11-6 pp. 617–619

Exercises 1. $\frac{1}{8}$ 3. $\frac{1}{32}$ 5–10. $C = 12x + 2$ 5. $26 7. $74 11. 12 children 13. The first strategy gives an experimental probability, while the second gives the theoretical probability. 15. 26 car tires 25. $\frac{1}{12}$ 27. $\frac{1}{4}$ 29. 113 in.[2] 31. 14 ft[2]

Lesson 11-7 pp. 623–625

EXERCISES 1. This is a random sample; the population is the students in the class. 3. This is not a random sample; students at one middle school may not represent all middle school students. 5. This is not a good sample, because it includes people who do not get the paper. 7. Biased; it assumes you like eggs. 9. Not biased; it does not try to influence your answer.

816 Selected Answers

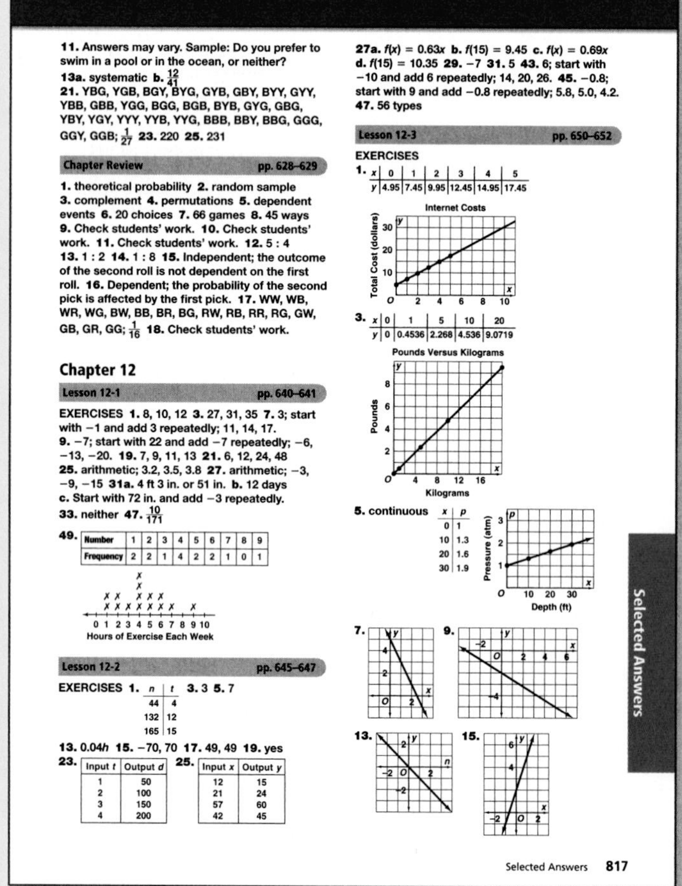

11. Answers may vary. Sample: Do you prefer to swim in a pool or in the ocean, or neither? 13a. systematic b. $\frac{12}{41}$ 21. YBG, YGB, BGY, BYG, GYB, GBY, BYY, GYY, YBB, GBB, YGG, BGG, BGB, BYB, GYG, GBG, YBY, YGY, YYY, YYB, YYG, BBB, BBY, BBG, GGG, GGY, GGB; $\frac{1}{27}$ 23. 220 25. 231

Chapter Review pp. 628–629

1. theoretical probability 2. random sample 3. complement 4. permutations 5. dependent events 6. 20 choices 7. 66 games 8. 45 ways 9. Check students' work. 10. Check students' work. 11. Check students' work. 12. 5 : 4 13. 1 : 2 14. 1 : 8 15. Independent; the outcome of the second roll is not dependent on the first roll. 16. Dependent; the probability of the second pick is affected by the first pick. 17. WW, WB, WR, WG, BW, BB, BR, BG, RW, RB, RR, RG, GW, GB, GR, GG; $\frac{1}{16}$ 18. Check students' work.

Chapter 12

Lesson 12-1 pp. 640–641

EXERCISES 1. 8, 10, 12 3. 27, 31, 35 7. 3; start with −1 and add 3 repeatedly; 11, 14, 17. 9. −7; start with 22 and add −7 repeatedly; −6, −13, −20. 19. 7, 9, 11, 13 21. 6, 12, 24, 48 25. arithmetic; 3.2, 3.5, 3.8 27. arithmetic; −3, −9, −15 31a. 4 ft 3 in. or 51 in. b. 12 days c. Start with 72 in. and add −3 repeatedly. 33. neither 47. $\frac{10}{171}$

49.

Number	1	2	3	4	5	6	7	8	9
Frequency	2	2	1	4	2	2	1	0	1

Hours of Exercise Each Week

Lesson 12-2 pp. 645–647

EXERCISES 1.

n	t
44	4
132	12
165	15

3. 3 5. 7 13. 0.04h 15. −70, 70 17. 49, 49 19. yes

23.

Input t	Output d
1	50
2	100
3	150
4	200

25.

Input x	Output y
12	15
21	24
57	60
42	45

27a. $f(x) = 0.63x$ b. $f(15) = 9.45$ c. $f(x) = 0.69x$ d. $f(15) = 10.35$ 29. −7 31. 5 43. 6; start with −10 and add 6 repeatedly; 14, 20, 26. 45. −0.8; start with 9 and add −0.8 repeatedly; 5.8, 5.0, 4.2. 47. 56 types

Lesson 12-3 pp. 650–652

EXERCISES

1.

x	0	1	2	3	4	5
y	4.95	7.45	9.95	12.45	14.95	17.45

3.

x	0	1	5	10	20
y	0	0.4536	2.268	4.536	9.0719

5. continuous

x	p
0	1
10	1.3
20	1.6
30	1.9

7. 9. 13. 15.

Selected Answers 817

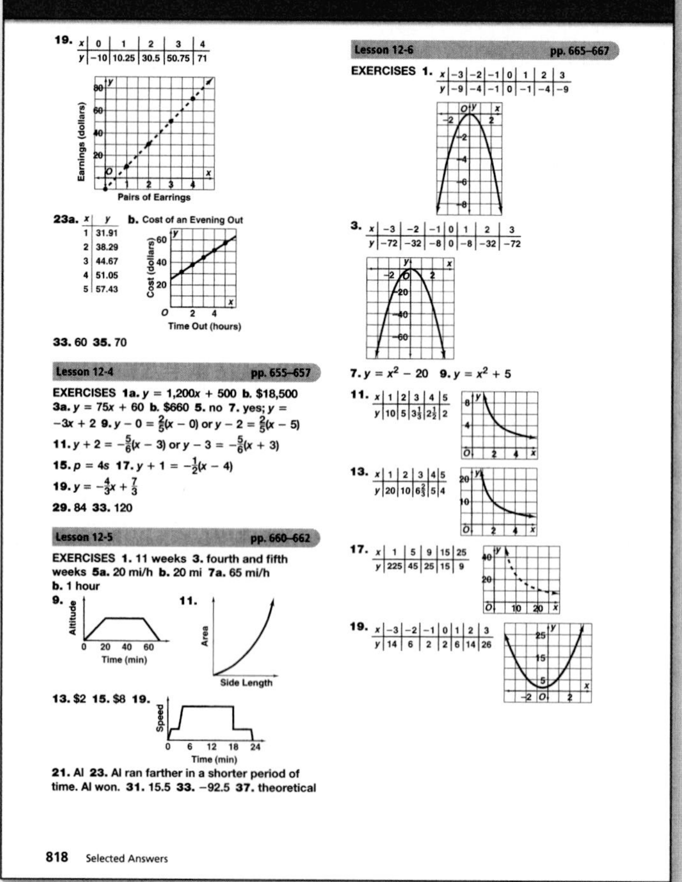

19.

x	0	1	2	3	4
y	−10	10.25	30.5	50.75	71

23a.

x	y
1	31.91
2	38.29
3	44.67
4	51.05
5	57.43

b. Cost of an Evening Out

33. 60 35. 70

Lesson 12-4 pp. 655–657

EXERCISES 1a. $y = 1{,}200x + 500$ b. $18,500 3a. $y = 75x + 60$ b. $660 5. no 7. yes; $y = -3x + 2$ 9. $y - 0 = \frac{2}{5}(x - 0)$ or $y - 2 = \frac{2}{5}(x - 5)$ 11. $y + 2 = -\frac{5}{6}(x - 3)$ or $y - 3 = -\frac{5}{6}(x + 3)$ 15. $p = 4s$ 17. $y + 1 = -\frac{1}{2}(x - 4)$ 19. $y = -\frac{4}{3}x + \frac{7}{3}$ 29. 84 33. 120

Lesson 12-5 pp. 660–662

EXERCISES 1. 11 weeks 3. fourth and fifth weeks 5a. 20 mi/h b. 20 mi 7a. 65 mi/h b. 1 hour 9. 11. 13. $2 15. $8 19. 21. Al 23. Al ran farther in a shorter period of time. Al won. 31. 15.5 33. −92.5 37. theoretical

Lesson 12-6 pp. 665–667

EXERCISES 1.

x	−3	−2	−1	0	1	2	3
y	−9	−4	−1	0	−1	−4	−9

3.

x	−3	−2	−1	0	1	2	3
y	−72	−32	−8	0	−8	−32	−72

7. $y = x^2 - 20$ 9. $y = x^2 + 5$

11.

x	1	2	3	4	5
y	10	5	$3\frac{1}{3}$	$2\frac{1}{2}$	2

13.

x	1	2	3	4	5
y	20	10	$6\frac{2}{3}$	5	4

17.

x	1	5	9	15	25
y	225	45	25	15	9

19.

x	−3	−2	−1	0	1	2	3
y	14	6	2	2	6	14	26

818 Selected Answers

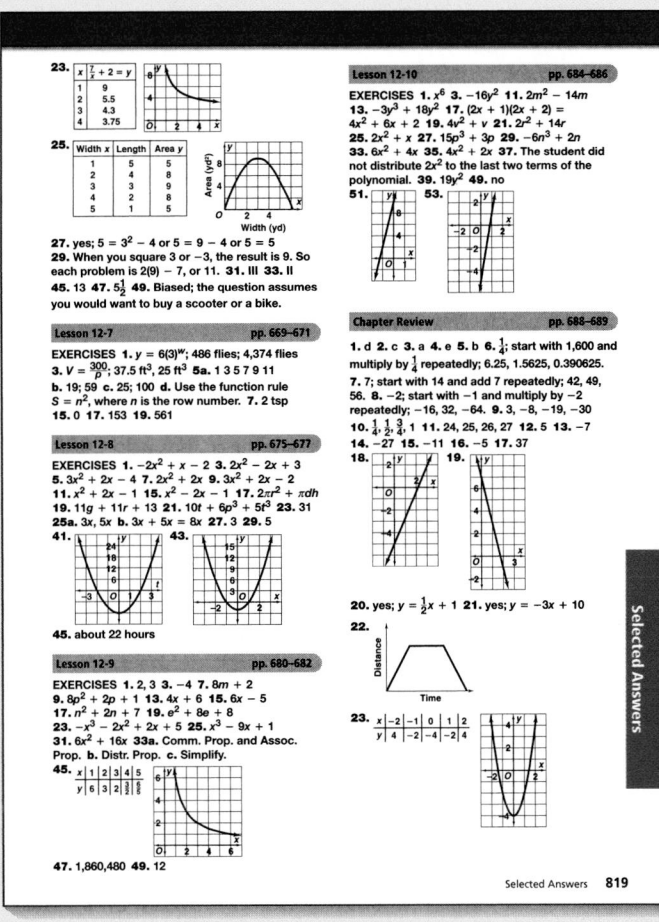

23.

x	$\frac{7}{x}+2=y$
1	9
2	5.5
3	4.3
4	3.75

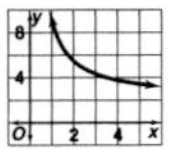

25.

Width x	Length	Area y
1	5	5
2	4	8
3	3	9
4	2	8
5	1	5

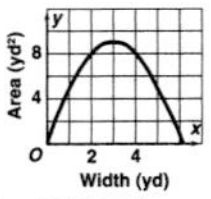

27. yes; $5 = 3^2 - 4$ or $5 = 9 - 4$ or $5 = 5$ **29.** When you square 3 or −3, the result is 9. So each problem is 2(9) − 7, or 11. **31.** III **33.** II **45.** 13 **47.** $5\frac{1}{2}$ **49.** Biased; the question assumes you would want to buy a scooter or a bike.

Lesson 12-7 pp. 669–671

EXERCISES **1.** $y = 6(3)^w$; 486 flies; 4,374 flies **3.** $V = \frac{300}{p}$; 37.5 ft³, 25 ft³ **5a.** 1 3 5 7 9 11 **b.** 19; 59 **c.** 25; 100 **d.** Use the function rule $S = n^2$, where n is the row number. **7.** 2 tsp **15.** 0 **17.** 153 **19.** 561

Lesson 12-8 pp. 675–677

EXERCISES **1.** $-2x^2 + x - 2$ **3.** $2x^2 - 2x + 3$ **5.** $3x^2 + 2x - 4$ **7.** $2x^2 + 2x$ **9.** $3x^2 + 2x - 2$ **11.** $x^2 + 2x - 1$ **15.** $x^2 - 2x - 1$ **17.** $2\pi r^2 + \pi dh$ **19.** $11g + 11r + 13$ **21.** $10t + 6p^3 + 5t^3$ **23.** 31 **25a.** $3x$, $5x$ **b.** $3x + 5x = 8x$ **27.** 3 **29.** 5

41. 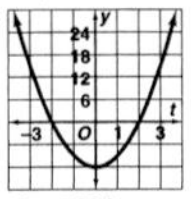 **43.** 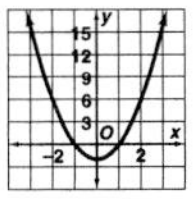

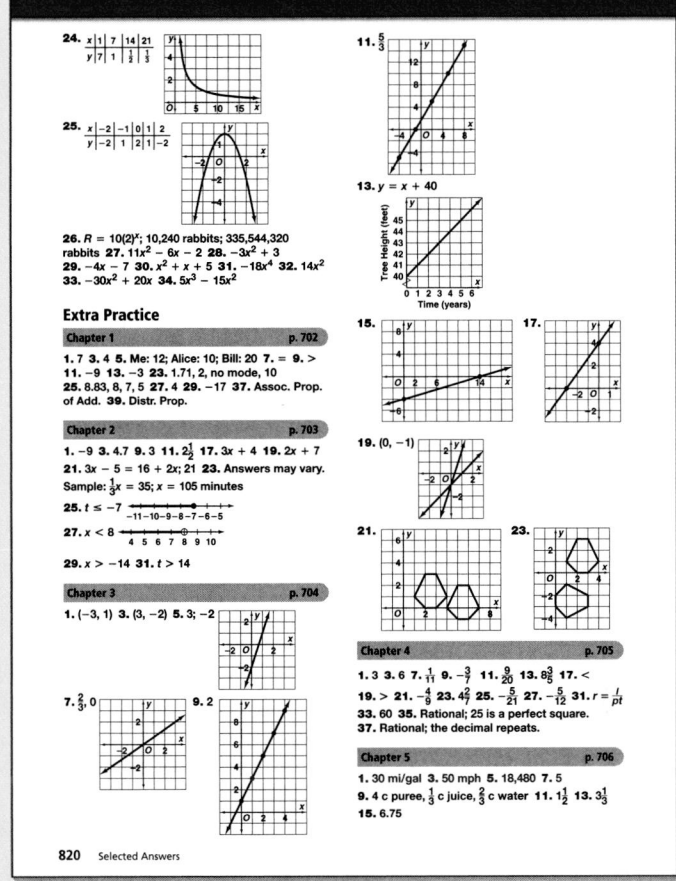

45. about 22 hours

Lesson 12-9 pp. 680–682

EXERCISES **1.** 2, 3 **3.** −4 **7.** $8m + 2$ **9.** $8p^2 + 2p + 1$ **13.** $4x + 6$ **15.** $6x - 5$ **17.** $n^2 + 2n + 7$ **19.** $e^2 + 8e + 8$ **23.** $-x^3 - 2x^2 + 2x + 5$ **25.** $x^3 - 9x + 1$ **31.** $6x^2 + 16x$ **33a.** Comm. Prop. and Assoc. Prop. **b.** Distr. Prop. **c.** Simplify.

45.

x	1	2	3	4	5
y	6	3	2	$\frac{3}{2}$	$\frac{6}{5}$

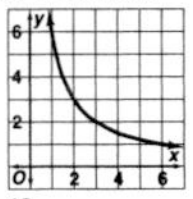

47. 1,860,480 **49.** 12

Lesson 12-10 pp. 684–686

EXERCISES **1.** x^6 **3.** $-16y^2$ **11.** $2m^2 - 14m$ **13.** $-3y^3 + 18y^2$ **17.** $(2x + 1)(2x + 2) = 4x^2 + 6x + 2$ **19.** $4v^2 + v$ **21.** $2r^2 + 14r$ **25.** $2x^2 + x$ **27.** $15p^3 + 3p$ **29.** $-6n^3 + 2n$ **33.** $6x^2 + 4x$ **35.** $4x^2 + 2x$ **37.** The student did not distribute $2x^2$ to the last two terms of the polynomial. **39.** $19y^2$ **49.** no

51. 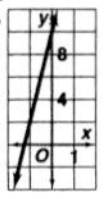 **53.** 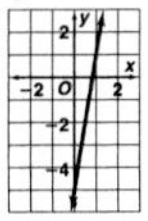

Chapter Review pp. 688–689

1. d **2.** c **3.** a **4.** e **5.** b **6.** $\frac{1}{4}$; start with 1,600 and multiply by $\frac{1}{4}$ repeatedly; 6.25, 1.5625, 0.390625. **7.** 7; start with 14 and add 7 repeatedly; 42, 49, 56. **8.** −2; start with −1 and multiply by −2 repeatedly; −16, 32, −64. **9.** 3, −8, −19, −30 **10.** $\frac{1}{4}, \frac{1}{2}, \frac{3}{4}, 1$ **11.** 24, 25, 26, 27 **12.** 5 **13.** −7 **14.** −27 **15.** −11 **16.** −5 **17.** 37

18. 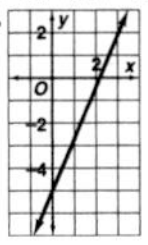 **19.** 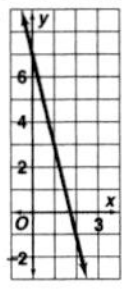

20. yes; $y = \frac{1}{2}x + 1$ **21.** yes; $y = -3x + 10$

22.

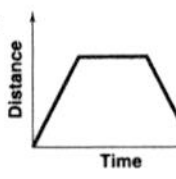

23.

x	−2	−1	0	1	2
y	4	−2	−4	−2	4

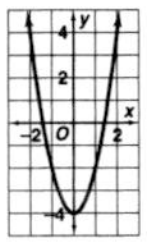

Selected Answers

24.

x	1	7	14	21
y	7	1	$\frac{1}{2}$	$\frac{1}{3}$

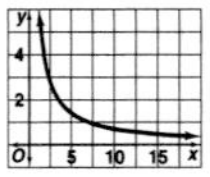

25.

x	−2	−1	0	1	2
y	−2	1	2	1	−2

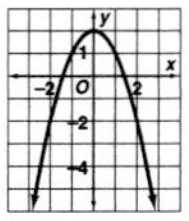

26. $R = 10(2)^x$; 10,240 rabbits; 335,544,320 rabbits **27.** $11x^2 - 6x - 2$ **28.** $-3x^2 + 3$ **29.** $-4x - 7$ **30.** $x^2 + x + 5$ **31.** $-18x^4$ **32.** $14x^2$ **33.** $-30x^2 + 20x$ **34.** $5x^3 - 15x^2$

Extra Practice

Chapter 1 p. 702

1. 7 **3.** 4 **5.** Me: 12; Alice: 10; Bill: 20 **7.** = **9.** > **11.** −9 **13.** −3 **23.** 1.71, 2, no mode, 10 **25.** 8.83, 8, 7, 5 **27.** 4 **29.** −17 **37.** Assoc. Prop. of Add. **39.** Distr. Prop.

Chapter 2 p. 703

1. −9 **3.** 4.7 **9.** 3 **11.** $2\frac{1}{2}$ **17.** $3x + 4$ **19.** $2x + 7$ **21.** $3x - 5 = 16 + 2x$; 21 **23.** Answers may vary. Sample: $\frac{1}{3}x = 35$; $x = 105$ minutes

25. $t \le -7$ 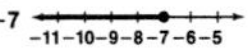

27. $x < 8$ 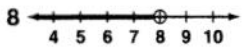

29. $x > -14$ **31.** $t > 14$

Chapter 3 p. 704

1. (−3, 1) **3.** (3, −2) **5.** 3; −2 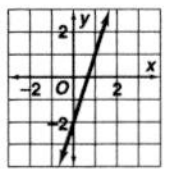

7. $\frac{2}{3}$, 0 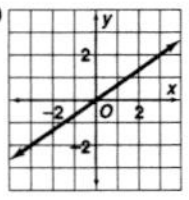 **9.** 2 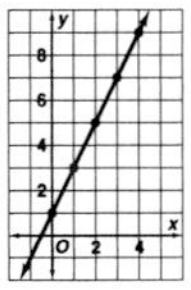

11. $\frac{5}{3}$ 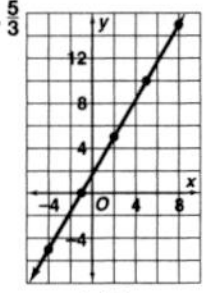

13. $y = x + 40$

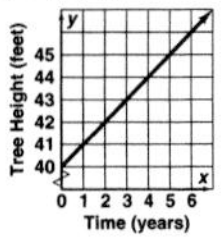

15. 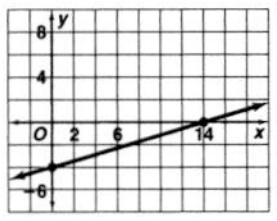 **17.** 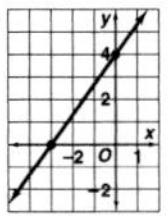

19. (0, −1) 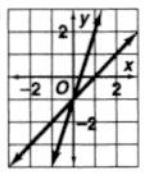

21. 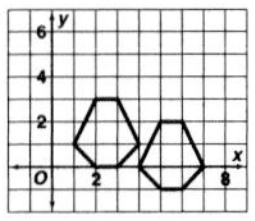 **23.** 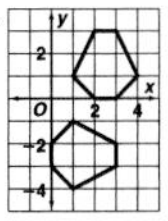

Chapter 4 p. 705

1. 3 **3.** 6 **7.** $\frac{1}{11}$ **9.** $-\frac{3}{7}$ **11.** $\frac{9}{20}$ **13.** $8\frac{3}{5}$ **17.** < **19.** > **21.** $-\frac{4}{9}$ **23.** $4\frac{2}{7}$ **25.** $-\frac{5}{21}$ **27.** $-\frac{5}{12}$ **31.** $r = \frac{I}{pt}$ **33.** 60 **35.** Rational; 25 is a perfect square. **37.** Rational; the decimal repeats.

Chapter 5 p. 706

1. 30 mi/gal **3.** 50 mph **5.** 18,480 **7.** 5 **9.** 4 c puree, $\frac{1}{3}$ c juice, $\frac{2}{3}$ c water **11.** $1\frac{1}{2}$ **13.** $3\frac{1}{3}$ **15.** 6.75

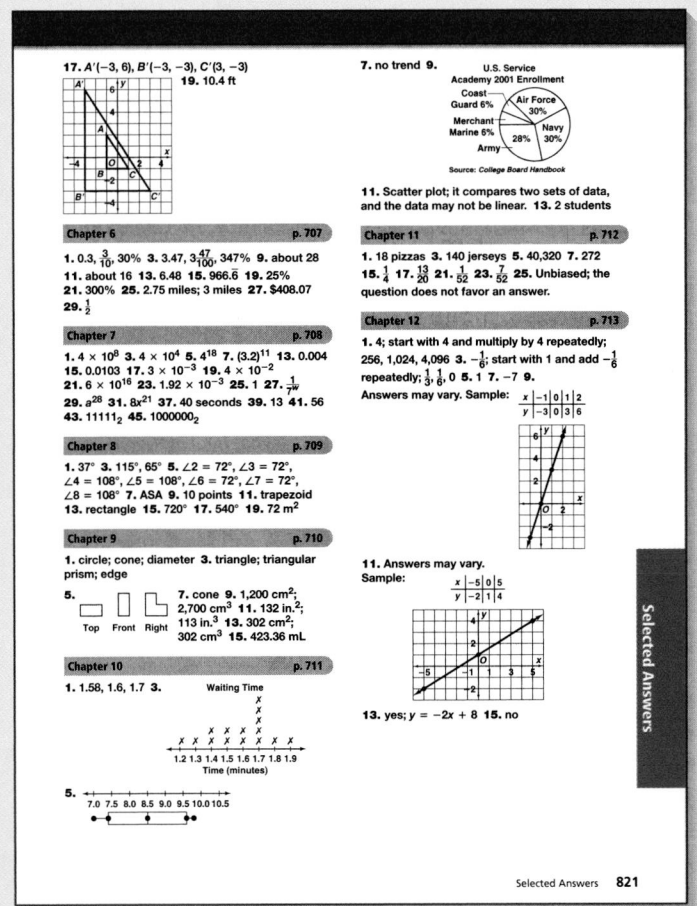

17. $A'(-3, 6)$, $B'(-3, -3)$, $C'(3, -3)$

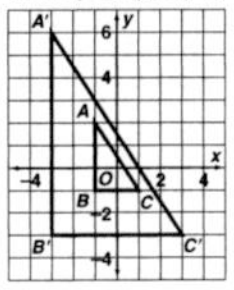

19. 10.4 ft

Chapter 6 p. 707

1. 0.3, $\frac{3}{10}$, 30% **3.** 3.47, $3\frac{47}{100}$, 347% **9.** about 28 **11.** about 16 **13.** 6.48 **15.** $966.\overline{6}$ **19.** 25% **21.** 300% **25.** 2.75 miles; 3 miles **27.** $408.07 **29.** $\frac{1}{2}$

Chapter 7 p. 708

1. 4×10^8 **3.** 4×10^4 **5.** 4^{18} **7.** $(3.2)^{11}$ **13.** 0.004 **15.** 0.0103 **17.** 3×10^{-3} **19.** 4×10^{-2} **21.** 6×10^{16} **23.** 1.92×10^{-3} **25.** 1 **27.** $\frac{1}{7^w}$ **29.** a^{28} **31.** $8x^{21}$ **37.** 40 seconds **39.** 13 **41.** 56 **43.** 11111_2 **45.** 1000000_2

Chapter 8 p. 709

1. 37° **3.** 115°, 65° **5.** ∠2 = 72°, ∠3 = 72°, ∠4 = 108°, ∠5 = 108°, ∠6 = 72°, ∠7 = 72°, ∠8 = 108° **7.** ASA **9.** 10 points **11.** trapezoid **13.** rectangle **15.** 720° **17.** 540° **19.** 72 m²

Chapter 9 p. 710

1. circle; cone; diameter **3.** triangle; triangular prism; edge

5. 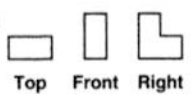

7. cone **9.** 1,200 cm²; 2,700 cm³ **11.** 132 in.²; 113 in.³ **13.** 302 cm²; 302 cm³ **15.** 423.36 mL

Chapter 10 p. 711

1. 1.58, 1.6, 1.7 **3.**

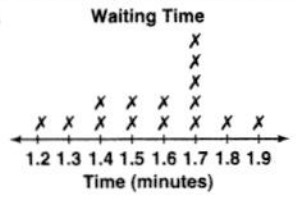

5. 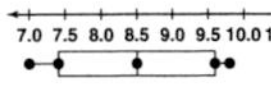

7. no trend **9.**

11. Scatter plot; it compares two sets of data, and the data may not be linear. **13.** 2 students

Chapter 11 p. 712

1. 18 pizzas **3.** 140 jerseys **5.** 40,320 **7.** 272 **15.** $\frac{1}{4}$ **17.** $\frac{13}{20}$ **21.** $\frac{1}{52}$ **23.** $\frac{7}{52}$ **25.** Unbiased; the question does not favor an answer.

Chapter 12 p. 713

1. 4; start with 4 and multiply by 4 repeatedly; 256, 1,024, 4,096 **3.** $-\frac{1}{6}$; start with 1 and add $-\frac{1}{6}$ repeatedly; $\frac{1}{3}, \frac{1}{6}, 0$ **5.** 1 **7.** −7 **9.** Answers may vary. Sample:

x	−1	0	1	2
y	−3	0	3	6

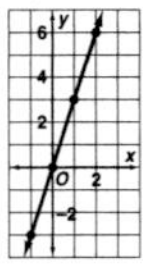

11. Answers may vary. Sample:

x	−5	0	5
y	−2	1	4

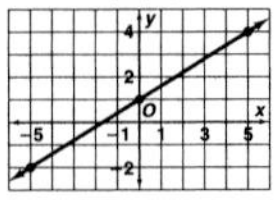

13. yes; $y = -2x + 8$ **15.** no

Selected Answers

17.

x	−4	−3	−2	−1	0	1	2	3	4
y	18	11	6	3	2	3	6	11	18

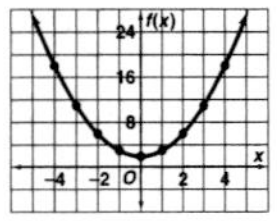

19.

x	−4	−3	−2	−1	0	1	2	3	4
y	48	27	12	3	0	3	12	27	48

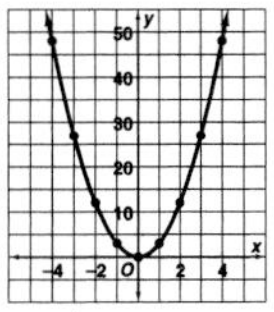

21. $y = 5 \cdot 2^t$; 80 paintings **23.** $x^2 - 6x + 1$ **25.** $-12x^6$

Skills Handbook

Decimals and Place Value p. 714

1. hundred-thousandths **3.** hundredths **7.** 0.0041 **9.** 0.000008 **13.** six hundredths **15.** eleven hundred-thousandths

Comparing and Ordering Decimals p. 715

1. < **3.** > **13.** 0.23, 0.231, 2.31, 3.21, 23.1 **15.** 0.002, 0.02, 0.22, 0.222, 2.22

Rounding p. 716

1. 105,000 **3.** 79,528,000 **7.** 3 **9.** 101 **11.** 82.0 **13.** 20.4 **17.** 96.40 **19.** 4.23 **21.** 7.06 **23.** 1,520

Adding and Subtracting Decimals p. 717

1. 3.67 **3.** 7.312 **13.** 34.023 **15.** 39.95 **17.** 67.92 **19.** 44.463 **37.** 28.81 **39.** 9.391

Multiplying Decimals p. 718

1. 5.328 **3.** 2.15 **11.** 2.07828 **13.** 0.48

Zeros in a Product p. 719

1. 0.027 **3.** 0.072 **11.** 0.00165 **13.** 0.0376

Dividing Decimals by Whole Numbers p. 720

1. 2.56 **3.** 0.776 **21.** 0.868 **23.** 2.551

Multiplying and Dividing by Powers of Ten p. 721

1. 560 **3.** 52 **5.** 2,367 **7.** 0.0009

Dividing Decimals by Decimals p. 722

1. 84 **3.** 452 **11.** 26 **13.** 31

Zeros in Decimal Division p. 723

1. 0.046 **3.** 0.075 **5.** 0.0095 **7.** 0.0025

Mixed Numbers and Improper Fractions p. 724

1. $1\frac{2}{5}$ **3.** $3\frac{1}{4}$ **27.** $\frac{8}{3}$ **29.** $\frac{16}{5}$

Adding and Subtracting Fractions With Like Denominators p. 725

1. $1\frac{2}{5}$ **3.** $\frac{4}{7}$ **5.** $1\frac{1}{5}$ **11.** 1 **13.** $4\frac{2}{5}$

Classifying and Measuring Angles p. 726

1. 110°; obtuse **3.** 60°; acute **5.** acute **7.** obtuse

Bar Graphs p. 727

1.

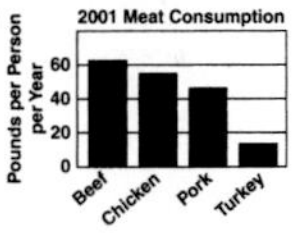

3.

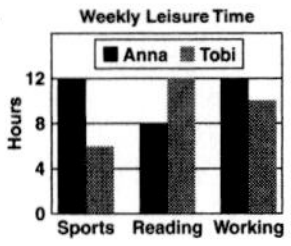

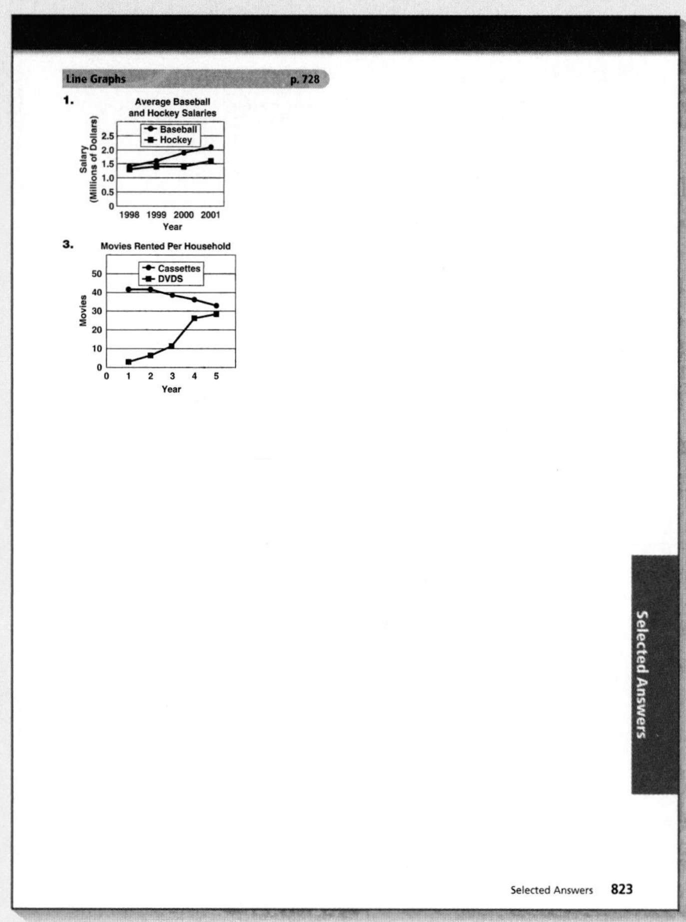
Line Graphs
p. 728
1.
Average Baseball and Hockey Salaries
Baseball
Hockey
Salary (Millions of Dollars)
2.5
2.0
1.5
1.0
0.5
0
1998
1999
2000
2001
Year
3.
Movies Rented Per Household
Cassettes
DVDS
Movies
50
40
30
20
10
0
0
1
2
3
4
5
Year
Selected Answers
Selected Answers 823

Additional Answers

CHAPTER 7

Lesson 7-3

page 379

6. $\frac{(-3)\cdot(-3)\cdot(-3)\cdot(-3)\cdot(-3)\cdot(-3)\cdot(-3)\cdot(-3)}{(-3)\cdot(-3)} = (-3)^6$

7. $\frac{(-4)\cdot(-4)\cdot(-4)\cdot(-4)\cdot(-4)\cdot(-4)\cdot(-4)\cdot(-4)\cdot(-4)\cdot(-4)}{(-4)\cdot(-4)\cdot(-4)\cdot(-4)\cdot(-4)\cdot(-4)} = (-4)^4$

Lesson 7-4

page 387

51. [4] Perimeter: $4 \times (7 \times 10^{-3}) = 0.028 = 2.8 \times 10^{-2}$ m; Area = $(7 \times 10^{-3})^2 = 49 \times 10^{-6} = 4.9 \times 10^{-5}\ \text{m}^2$

[3] Correct perimeter and area, but one answer not in correct scientific notation

[2] Correct perimeter and area, but neither answer in correct scientific notation OR either perimeter or area incorrect

[1] only area or perimeter is correct, and neither answer is in correct scientific notation, OR one answer correct with no work shown

Lesson 7-6

page 392 Investigation

1a. 3 medium, 2 small

b. 2 large, 4 medium, 4 small

c. 4 large, 2 medium, 5 small

d. 5 large, 3 medium, 2 small

2a. 1 super, 2 large, 2 medium

b. 2 super, 1 large, 5 medium, 2 small

c. 2 super, 4 large, 4 medium

d. 4 super, 3 large, 4 medium, 4 small

CHAPTER 8

Lesson 8-3

page 420 Check Skills You'll Need

2. Similar; corresponding sides are in proportion and corresponding angles are congruent.
3. Similar; corresponding angles are congruent and corresponding sides are in proportion.
4. Answers may vary. Sample: Two polygons are similar if they have the same shape and their corresponding sides are in proportion.

page 425

38. [2] No; explanations may vary. Sample:

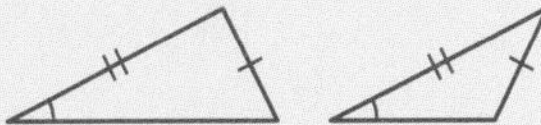

Triangles might not be congruent by SSA because the angle between the two given sides can vary, which makes the third side length vary.

[1] correct answer without figures drawn

Lesson 8-4

page 429

15. [2] $\frac{3\text{ qt}}{40\text{ min}} = 0.075\,\frac{\text{qt}}{\text{min}}$

$0.075 \cdot 4 = 0.3\,\frac{\text{qt}}{\text{min}}$ for 4 people

$\frac{15\text{ qt}}{x\text{ min}} = \frac{0.3\text{ qt}}{1\text{ min}}$

$0.3x = 15$

$x = 50$ min

[1] minor computational error OR correct answer without justification

Lesson 8-5

page 432

15. Answers may vary. Sample: right isosceles triangle: $\triangle DCJ$; right scalene triangle: $\triangle TCR$; obtuse scalene triangle: $\triangle TKR$; acute scalene triangle: $\triangle ADJ$; quadrilateral: *ABRD*; parallelogram: *DRSJ*; rectangle: *ABGJ*; square: *CDGJ*; trapezoid: *DRSG*

page 433

26.

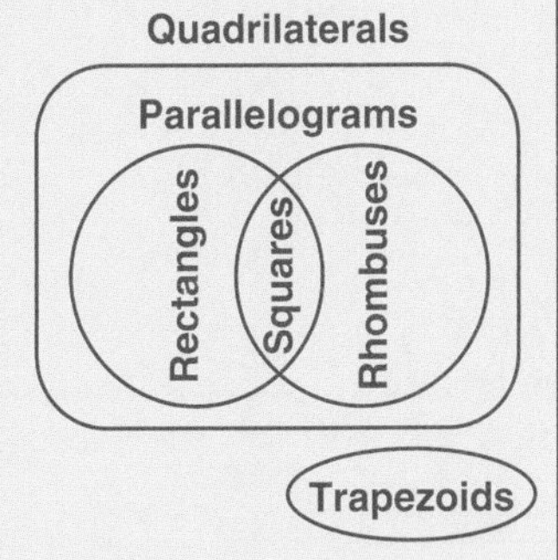

Additional Answers

page 434 Reading Math

1.

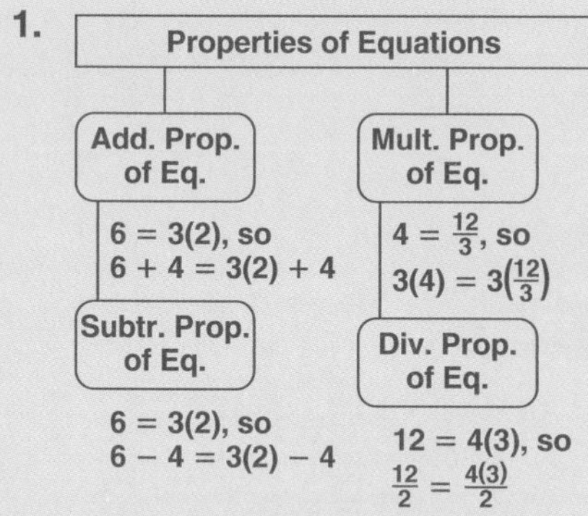

2.

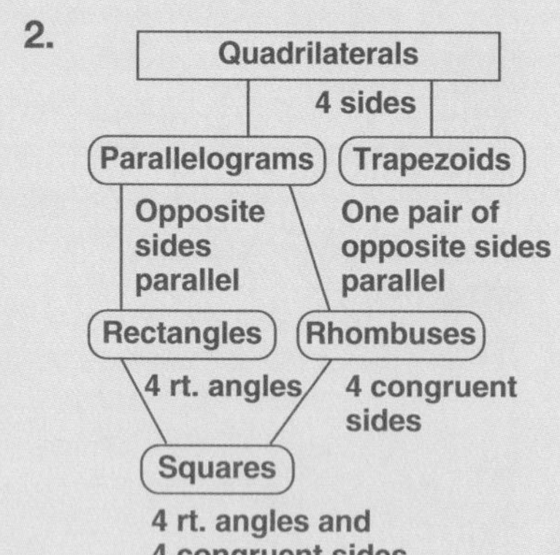

page 453 Writing in Math

4. $4\frac{1}{3} + 2\frac{5}{8} = 6\frac{23}{24}$
$4.\overline{3} + 2.625 = 6.958\overline{3}$
The sums are the same. One is a mixed number, while the other is a decimal.

page 455 Check Understanding

2a.

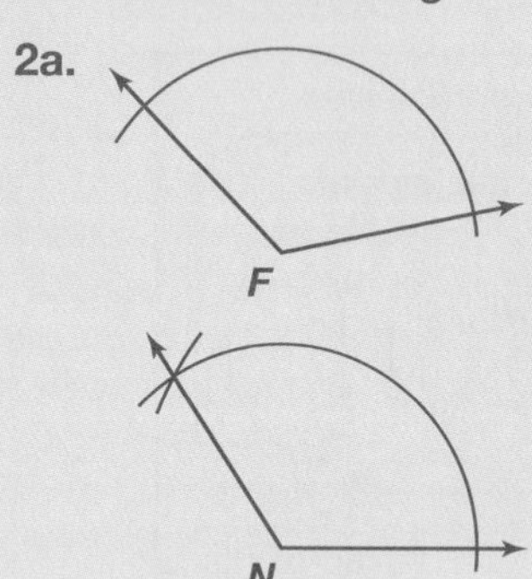

page 457

5.

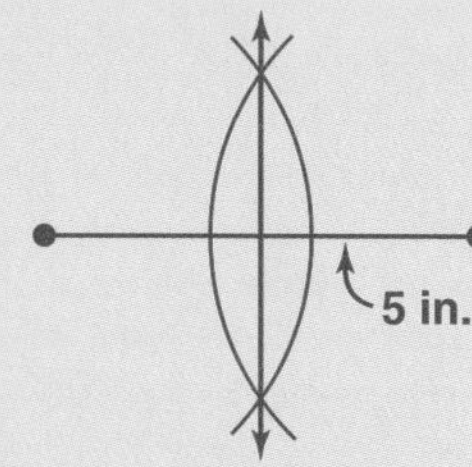

6.

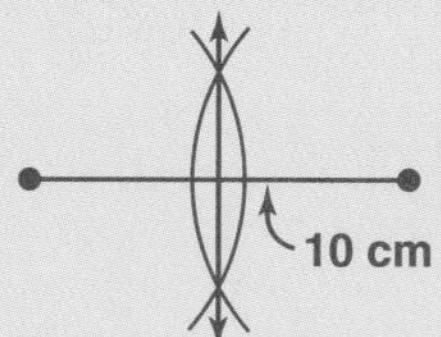

page 459

24. [4] To find x, write an equation based on the fact that $SM = MT$ because M is a midpoint.
$5x - 4 = 3x + 8$
$2x - 4 = 8$
$2x = 12$
$x = 6$
Then substitute 6 for x in $5x - 4$ to find SM.
$5(6) - 4 = 30 - 4 = 26$
ST is twice SM, so ST is 2(26) or 52
[3] one minor computational error
[2] length of $\overline{ST}$ missing OR two minor computational errors
[1] correct answers without explanation

page 459 Checkpoint Quiz 2

5.

6.

10. Answers may vary. Sample:

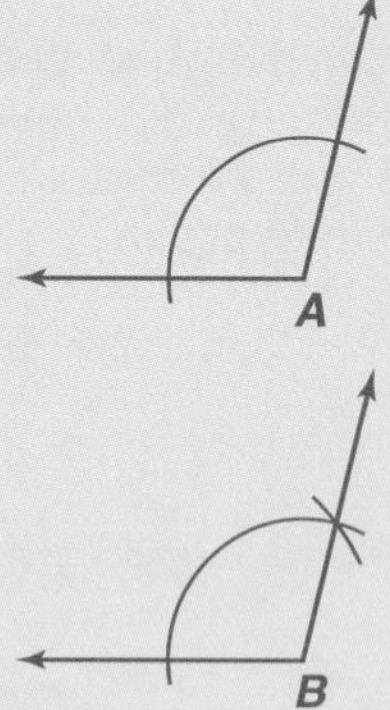

page 464 Chapter Test

7. In a rectangle and in a parallelogram, the opposite sides are congruent and parallel. A rectangle has four right angles. A parallelogram need not have right angles. All rectangles are parallelograms, but not all parallelograms are rectangles.

10.

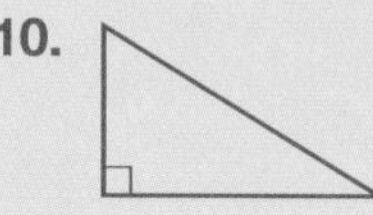

11.

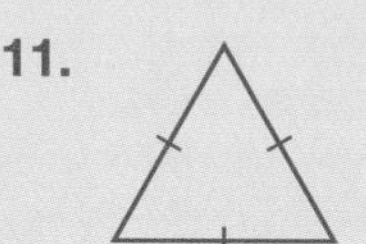

12.

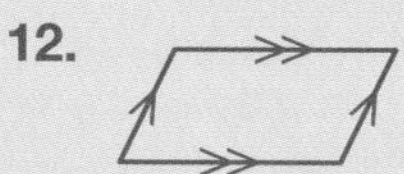

13.

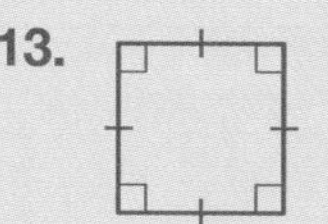

21.

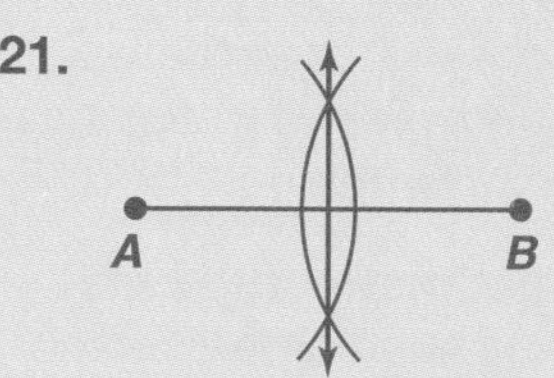

22.

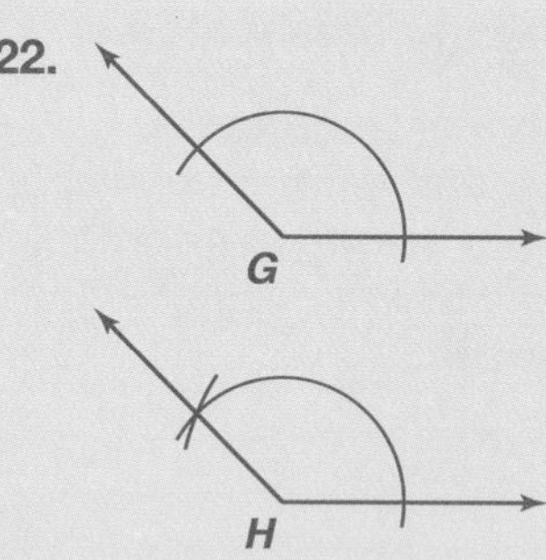

CHAPTER 9

Lesson 9-1

page 472 Check Understanding

2a. a trapezoidal prism and two rectangular prisms

b. The top of the right-hand prism could be continued all the way to the left side. The result would be a triangular prism and two rectangular prisms.

page 473

2. The figure has a square base. The figure is a square pyramid. $\overline{PQ}$ is a lateral edge.
3. The two bases are circles. The figure is a cylinder. $\overline{PQ}$ is a radius.
4. two trapezoidal prisms
5. a cone and a cylinder
6. two rectangular prisms

Lesson 9-2

page 476 Check Skills You'll Need

1. 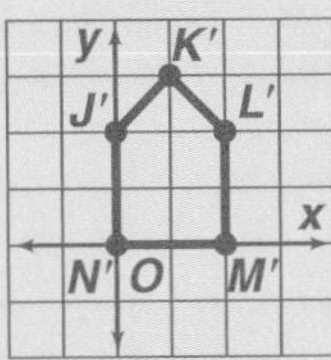

2. 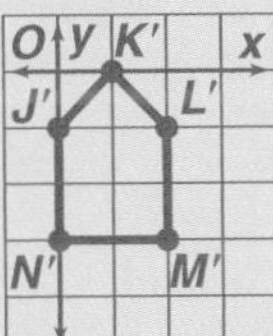

3. 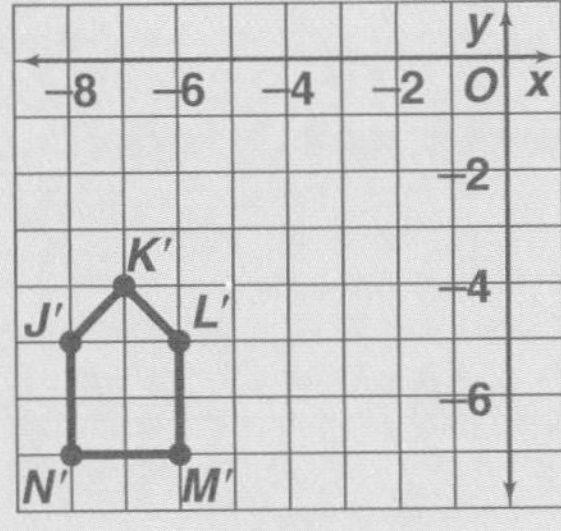

4. $(x, y) \rightarrow (x + 3, y + 1)$
$(x, y) \rightarrow (x + 3, y - 2)$
$(x, y) \rightarrow (x - 5, y - 6)$

page 479

5. 

Top view Front view Right view

6. 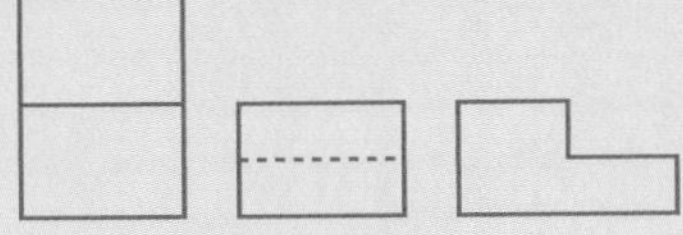

Top view Front view Right view

10. 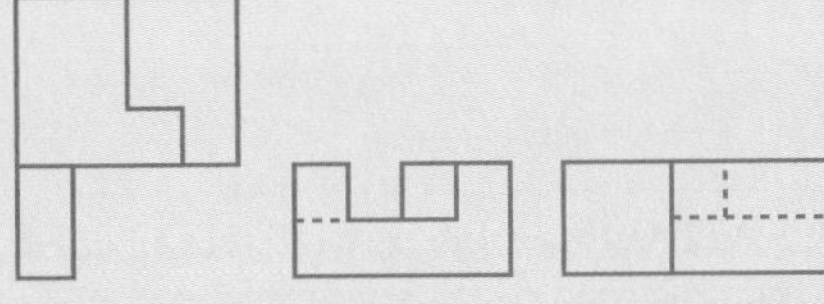

Top view Front view Right view

11. 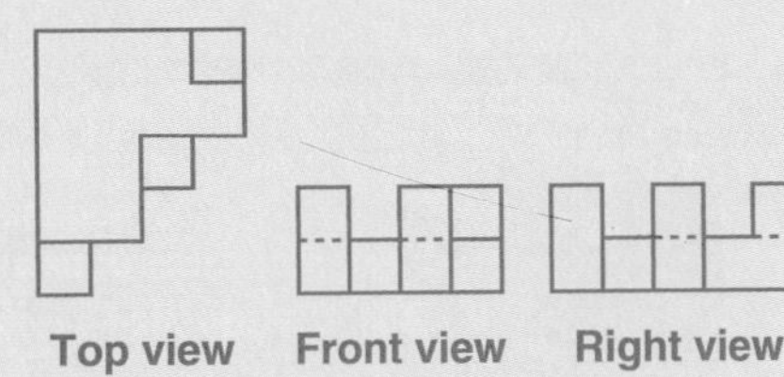

Top view Front view Right view

15. Answers may vary. Samples are given:
   a. building a set for the school play.
   b. designing a new school building.

page 480

16. 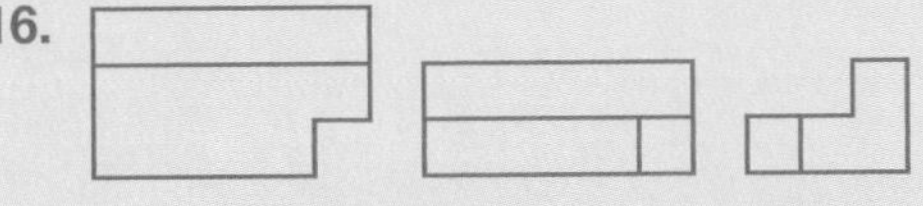

Top view Front view Right view

17. 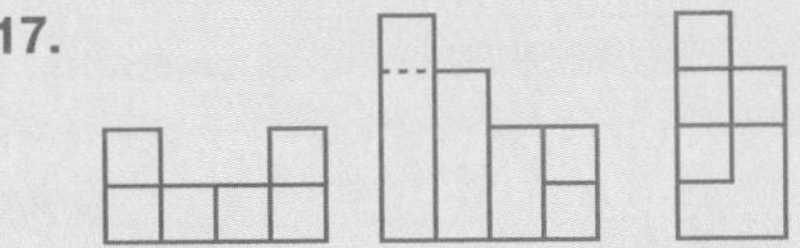

Top view Front view Right view

23. [4] 

Top view Front view Right view

[3] correct outlines of all three views, but with one interior segment omitted
[2] correct outlines of all three views, but with two interior segments omitted OR two views completely correct
[1] correct outlines of two views

Lesson 9-3

page 483

15. 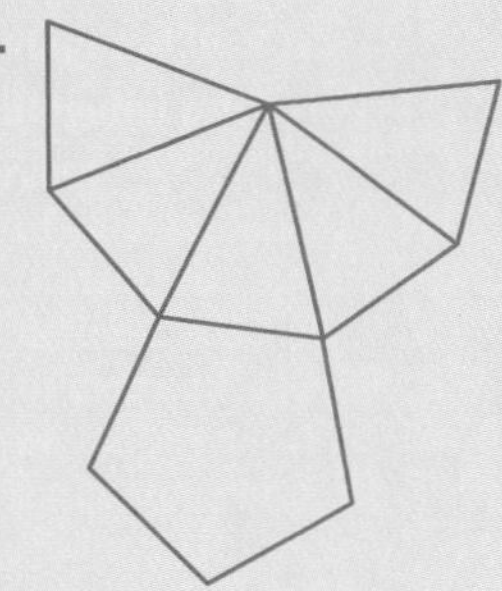

16. 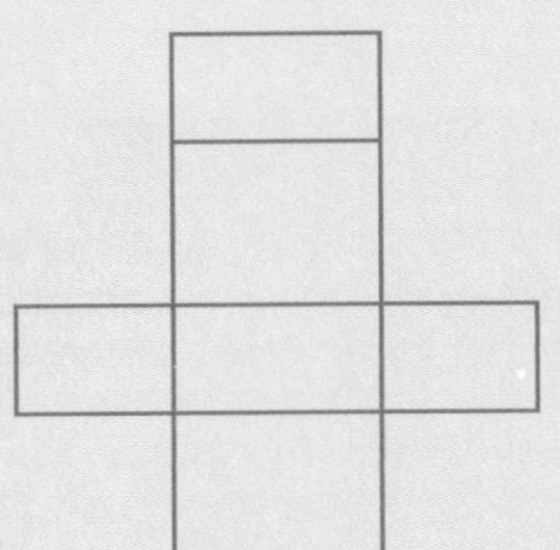

17. 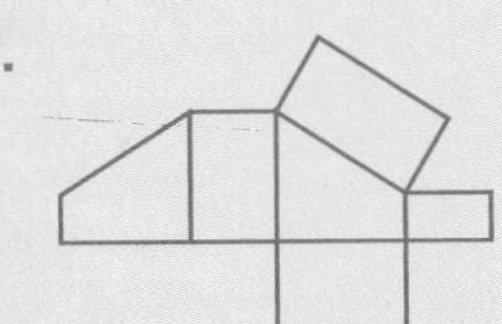

18. 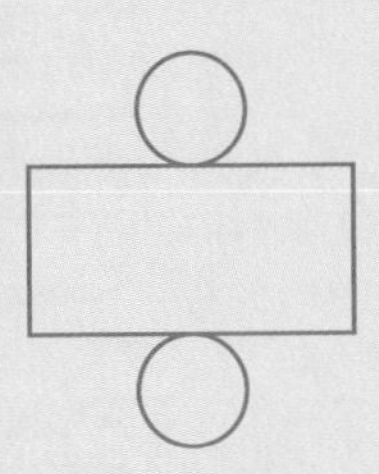

page 485 Checkpoint Quiz 1

4. 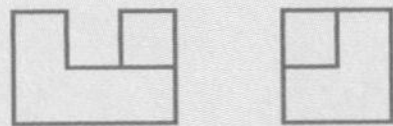

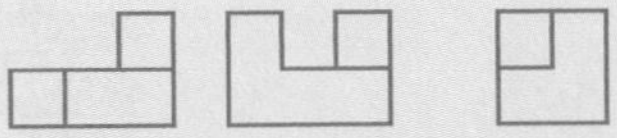

Top view Front view Right view

Lesson 9-4

page 492

18a.

Cube A		Cube B		Ratio	
Length of side	Surface area	Length of side	Surface area	Sides	Surface areas
1	6	2	24	$\frac{1}{2}$	$\frac{6}{24} = \frac{1}{4}$
2	24	5	150	$\frac{2}{5}$	$\frac{4}{25}$
3	54	6	216	$\frac{1}{2}$	$\frac{1}{4}$
3	54	8	384	$\frac{3}{8}$	$\frac{9}{64}$

Lesson 9-5

page 499

41. 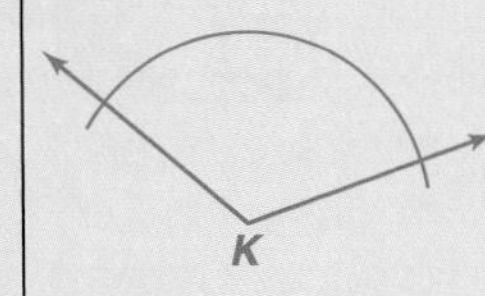

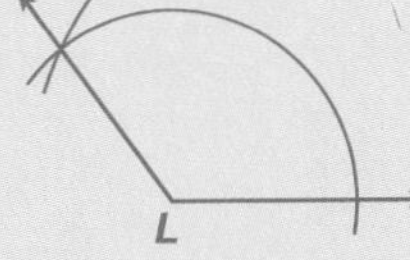

Additional Answers

Lesson 9-8

page 514

5.

$20	$10	$5	$1
1	1		6
1	1	1	1
1		3	1
1		2	6
	3	1	1
	3		6
	2	2	6
	2	3	1
	1	4	6
	1	5	1
		6	6
		7	1

Lesson 9-9

page 520

15. If the ratio of their heights is the same as the ratio of their radii, they are similar.

CHAPTER 10

Lesson 10-1

page 533 Check Skills You'll Need

1. 7.9; 8; 7 and 8; 4
2. 13.25; 13.5; 13 and 14; 9
3. 0.875; 1; no mode; 9
4. 189.7; 188; no mode; 26

pages 533–534 Check Understanding

1a.

Letter	Frequency
b	0
c	3
d	1
f	2
g	4
h	4
j	0
k	0
ℓ	1
m	2
n	1
p	1
q	0
r	8
s	2
t	8
v	0
w	0
x	0
y	2
z	0

"r" and "t" occur most often

b.

Time	Frequency
20	2
24	1
25	4
26	1
27	1
28	2
30	2
31	1

2a. Human Body Temperatures

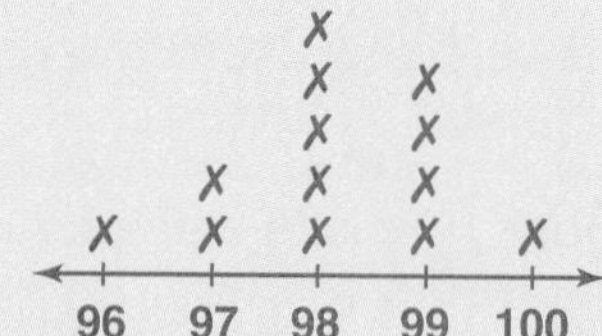

page 536

2.

Hours	Frequency
0	2
1	5
2	7
3	4
4	2

Hours Spent on Homework

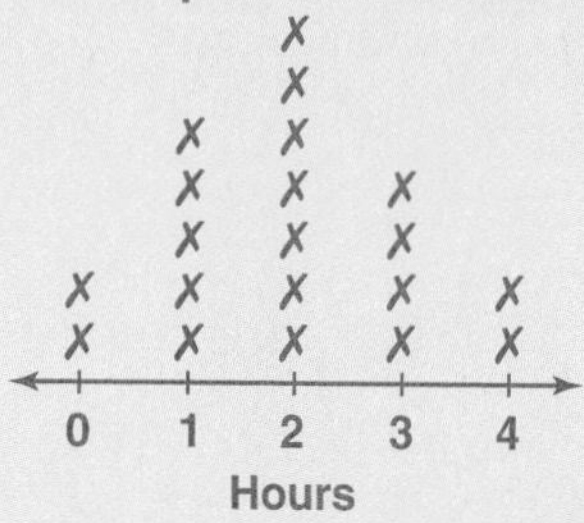

3.

Gigabytes	Frequency
8	3
10	1
12	3
14	1
16	2
18	2
20	1
22	0
24	1

Hard-Drive Size

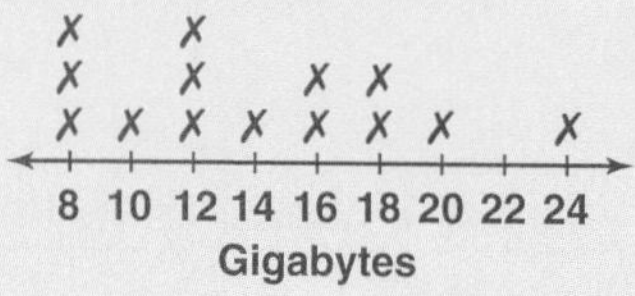

4.

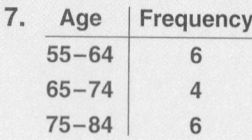

Temperature	Frequency
−4	1
−3	1
−2	3
−1	4
0	3
1	3
2	5
3	4
4	2
5	1
6	1

Low Temperatures in Feb (°F)

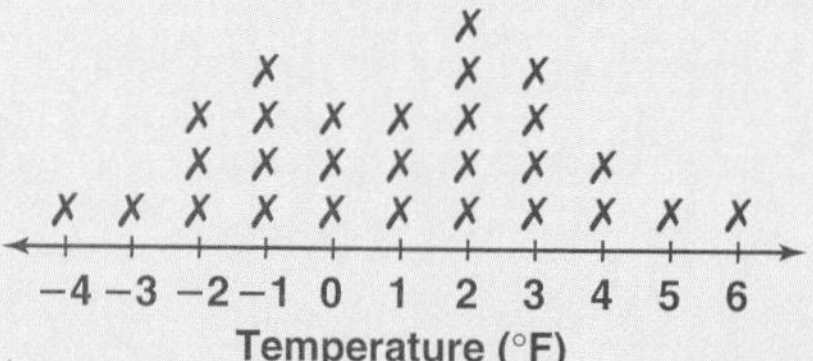

7–11. Answers may vary. Samples are givien:

7.

Age	Frequency
55–64	6
65–74	4
75–84	6

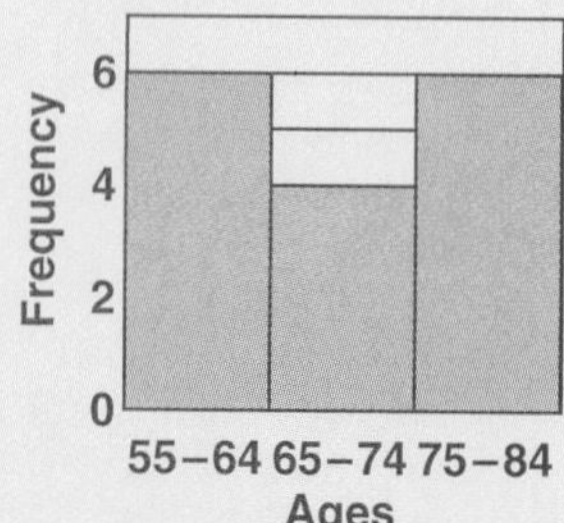

8.

TVs Sold	Frequency
0–4	1
5–9	10
10–14	6
15–19	2
20–24	1

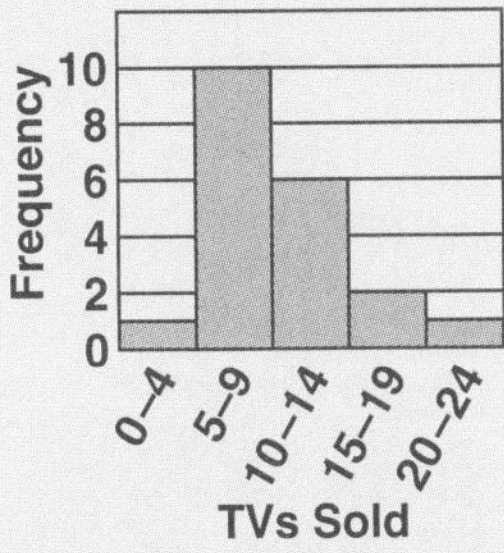

9.

Monthly Car Payment	Frequency
0–99	0
100–199	2
200–299	3
300–399	7
400–499	1
500–599	1

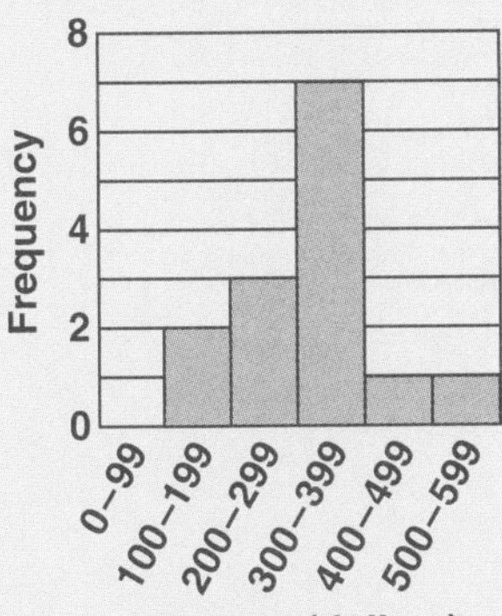

10.

Cars	Frequency
20–22	1
23–25	4
26–28	5
29–31	2

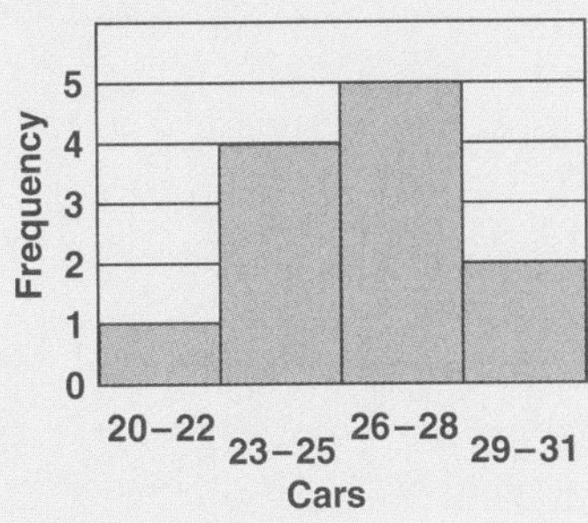

11.

Score	Frequency
(−5)–(−3)	1
(−2)–0	15
1–3	11
4–6	5

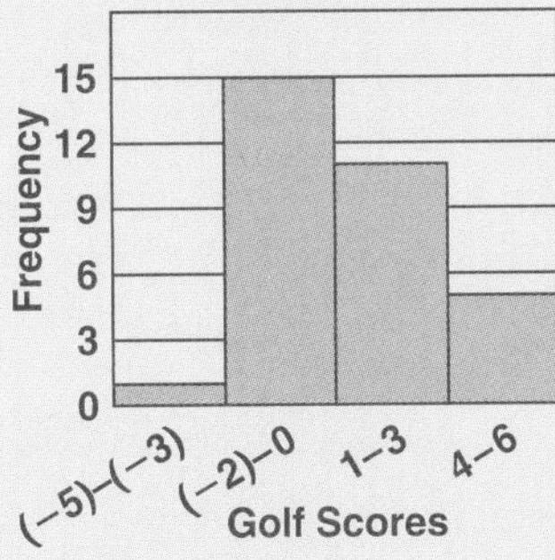

13a.

Prices for Binders (dollars)	Frequency
2.00–2.99	2
3.00–3.99	3
4.00–4.99	1
5.00–5.99	0
6.00–6.99	0
7.00–7.99	2

b.

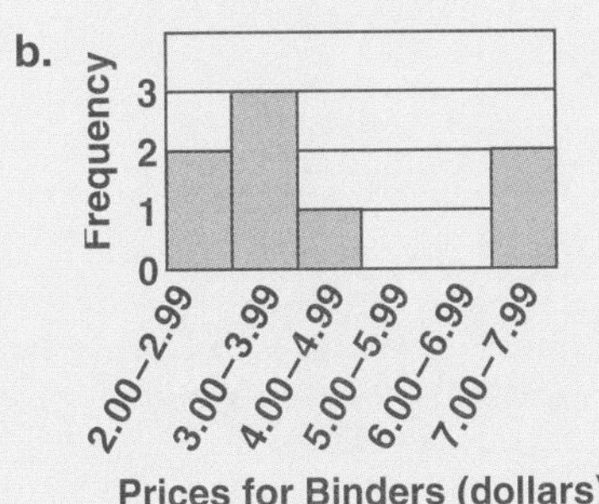

Lesson 10-2

page 540 Check Skills You'll Need

1.

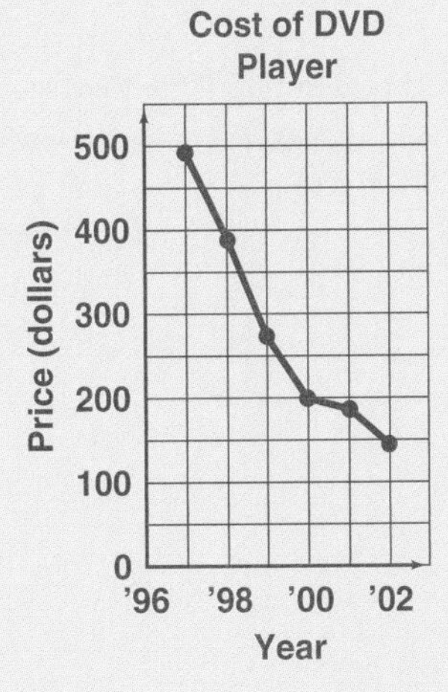

page 540 Check Understanding

1a. The scale on the vertical axis does not start at 0, which gives a misleading visual impression of the differences among the three airports.

b. The graph at the left makes it appear that Atlanta Hartfield's traffic is much higher than that of Los Angeles or Chicago.

page 541 Additional Examples

2. Sample:

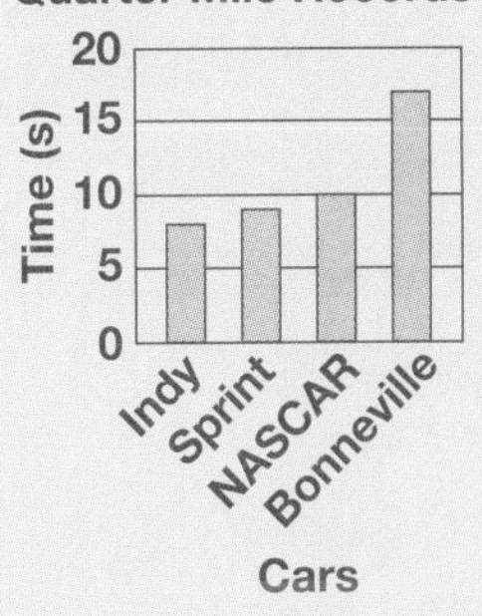

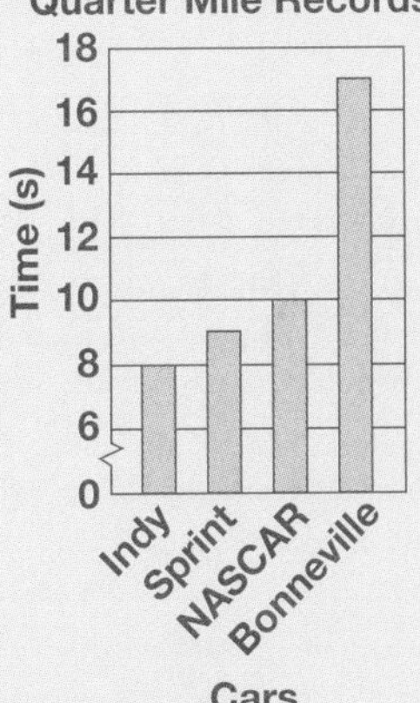

page 541 Investigation

1.

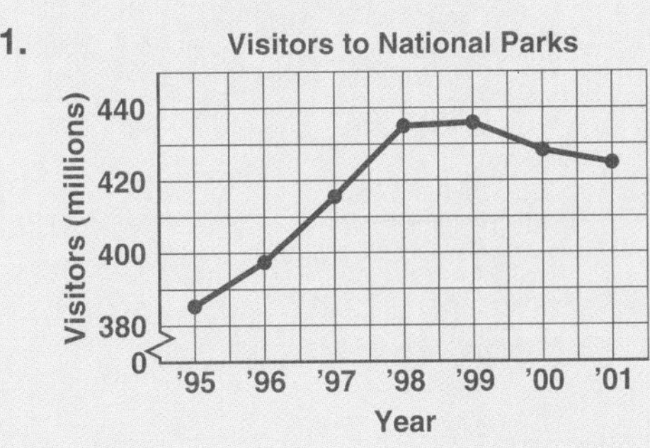

Additional Answers

2.

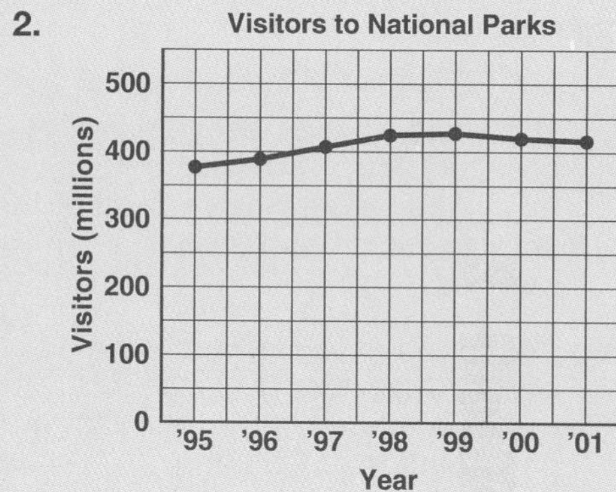

page 542

5.

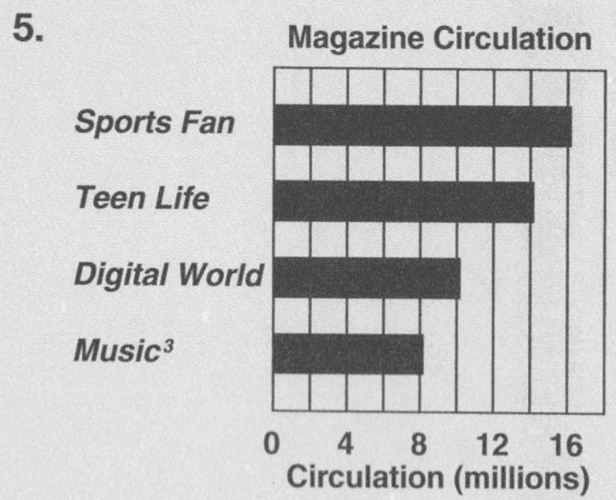

6.

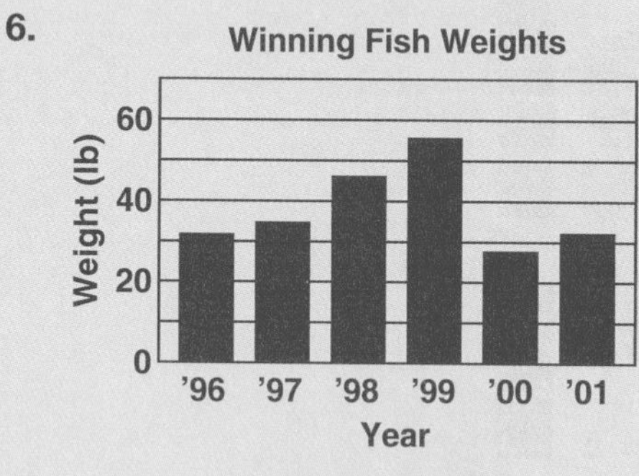

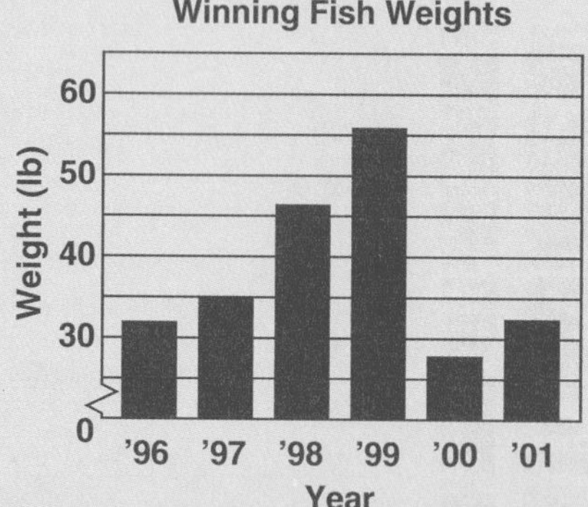

The graph with the break symbol allows you to read or approximate the weights better because the scale is more spread out.

7.

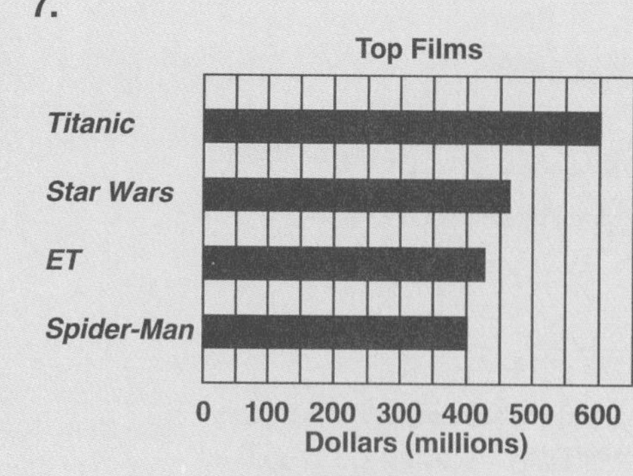

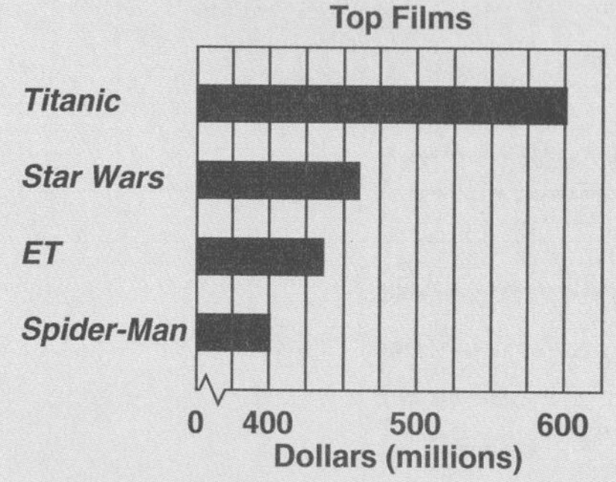

You can approximate the amounts better on the graph with the break, but the differences are exaggerated.

page 543

11.

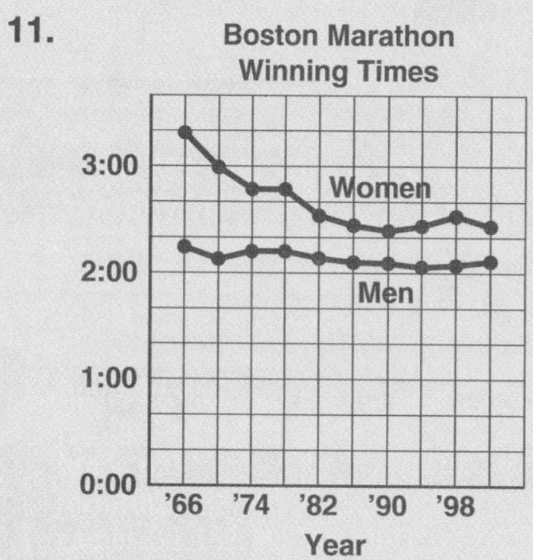

12.

15.

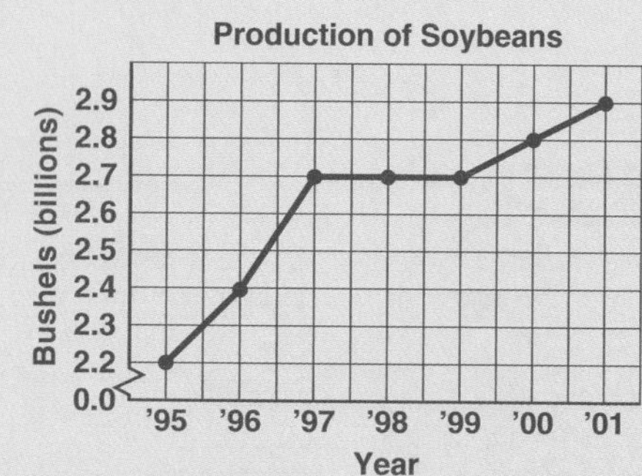

page 545 Extension

1.

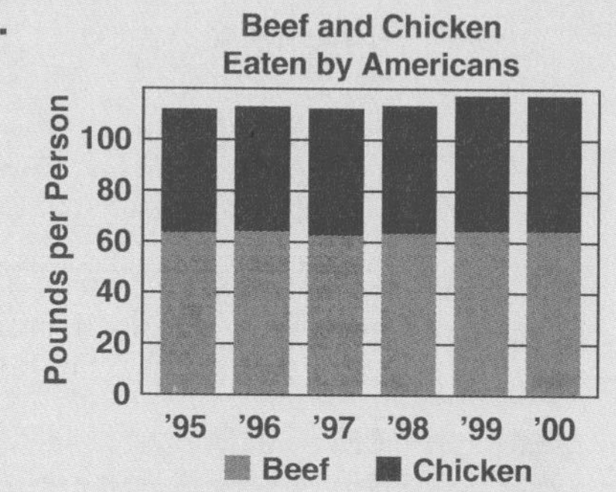

Beef and Chicken
Eaten by Americans

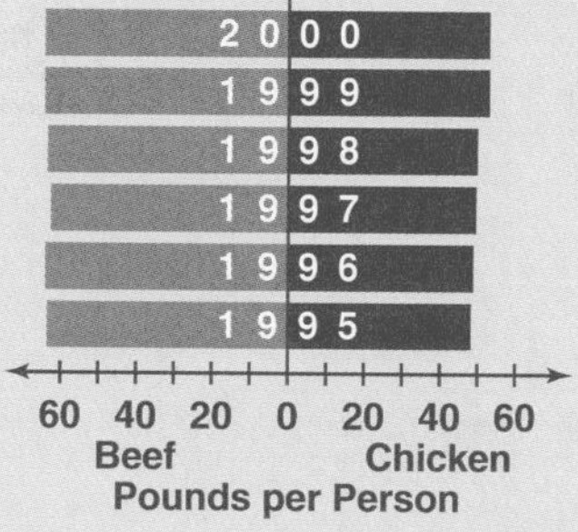

Lesson 10-3

page 546 Check Understanding

1. Monthly High Temperatures

8	6 7
9	1 7
10	1
11	1 3
12	0 0 5 6
13	4

Key: 13 | 4 means 134°

page 548

4.

3	2 7
4	1 3 5
5	0 0 2 8
6	3 7 9 9

Key: 3 | 2 means 3.2

5.

Stem	Leaves
85	0 3
86	4 9
87	2 5 5 9
88	1 3

Key: 88 | 1 means 88.1

6.

Stem	Leaves
0	2 6 8
1	2
2	0 2 6
3	2 5 6 8
4	3 3 5
5	
6	0

Key: 4 | 3 means 4.3

7.

Stem	Leaves
76	7
77	2 3 4 9
78	2 4 5 6 9
79	2 2

Key: 76 | 7 means 767

12. The mean and median for the men's blood pressure is 87 and 88.5, respectively. The mean and median for the women's blood pressure is 76.5 and 77, respectively. Both measures of central tendency indicate that the women's blood pressure in the survey was considerably less than the men's blood pressure.

page 549

22.

Daily Precipitation

First Two Weeks of May		Second Two Weeks of July
	0	0 0 0 2 7
	1	0
	2	8
	3	
5 5	4	0 8 8
5 5	5	0
7 5 3 3	6	1 3
	7	
8 7 1	8	1
4	9	
8 7	10	

Key: 0.45 ← means 5 | 4 | 0 means → 0.40

May: 0.66; 0.45, 0.55, and 0.63
July: 0.34; 0.00

page 551

32. [2]

Stem	Leaves
5	0
6	1 2 2 3 5 6 7
7	3 4 4 5 5 5 7 9 9 9
8	1 3 3

Key: 8 | 1 means 81

The median is 74 dinners.

[1] either correct plot OR correct median

33.

Number	Frequency
177	2
178	2
179	2
180	3
181	1
182	2
183	2
184	0
185	1

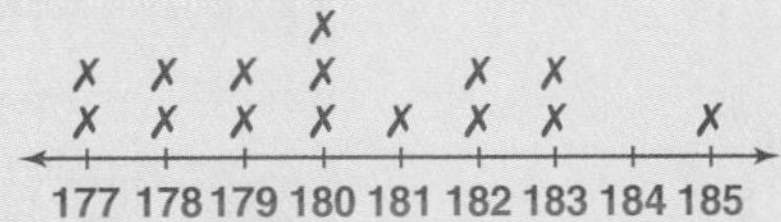

34.

Number	Frequency
10	2
20	1
30	4
40	4
50	3

35.

Number	Frequency
2	1
4	5
6	3
8	4
10	3
12	1

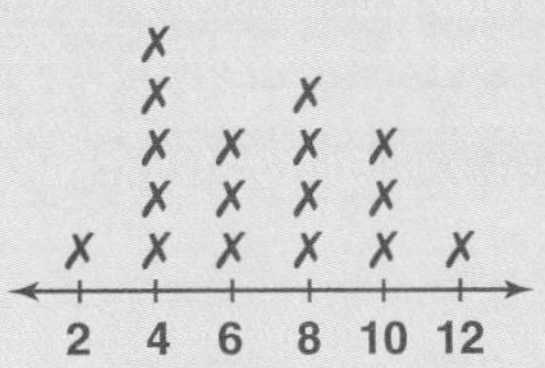

36.

Number	Frequency
12	3
13	1
14	4
15	5
16	2

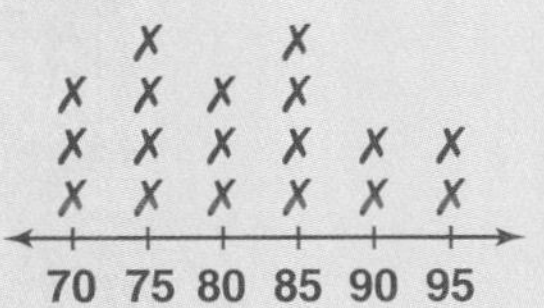

37.

Number	Frequency
70	3
75	4
80	3
85	4
90	2
95	2

page 551 Checkpoint Quiz 1

1. Answers may vary. Sample:

Scores	Frequency
61–70	1
71–80	5
81–90	5
91–100	6

2.

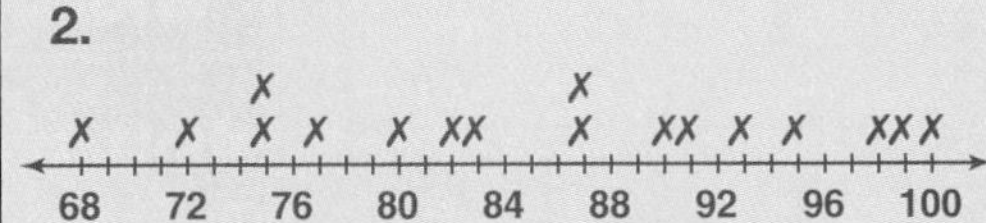

3. Answers may vary. Sample:

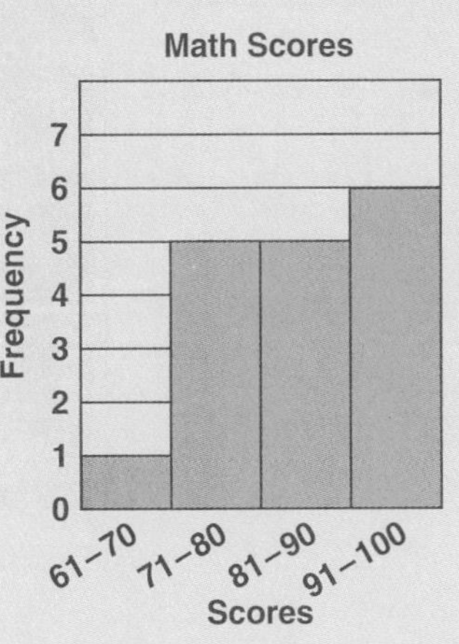

Additional Answers

4. Math Scores

6 | 8
7 | 2 5 5 7
8 | 0 2 3 7 7
9 | 0 1 3 5 8 9
10 | 0

Key: 6 | 8 means 68%

5.

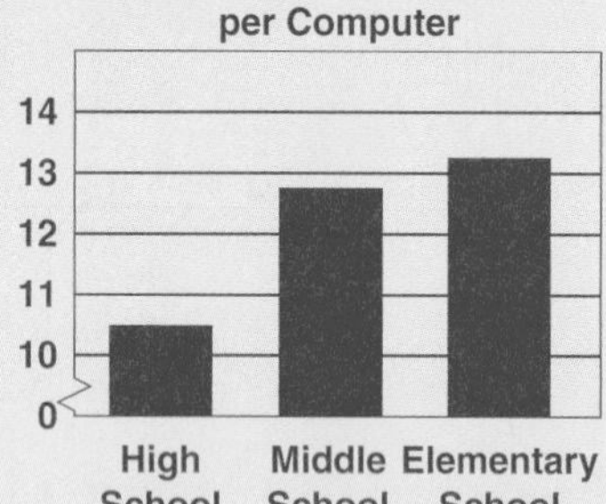

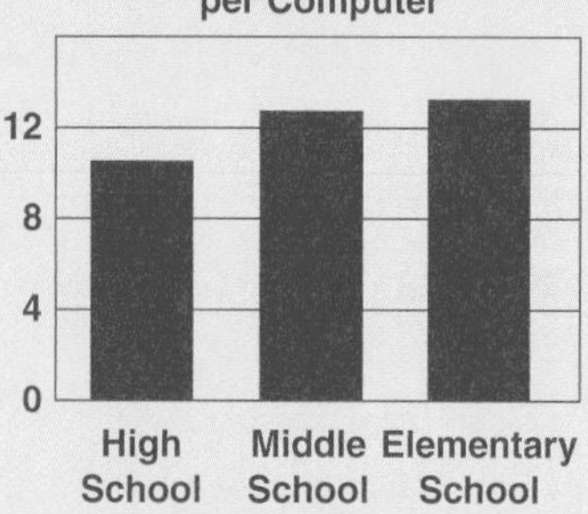

The graph without the break symbol shows that the numbers of students per computer are similar for each school.

Lesson 10-4

page 554

6.

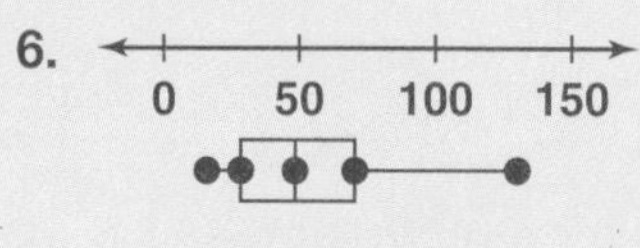

7.

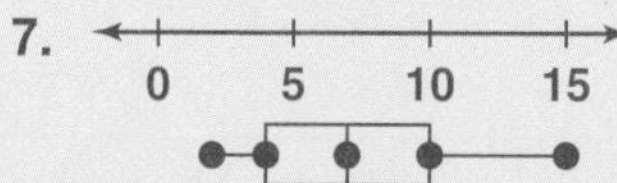

8. Answers may vary. Sample: Denver had a much greater range of percents of on-time arrivals than Atlanta. Overall, Atlanta had a greater percent of on-time arrivals per day in 2000 than Denver. Atlanta was also more consistent in the percent of on-time arrivals.

page 556

25. [4] least = 0.25,
lower quartile = 0.5,
median = 1.25,
upper quartile = 2,
and greatest = 6

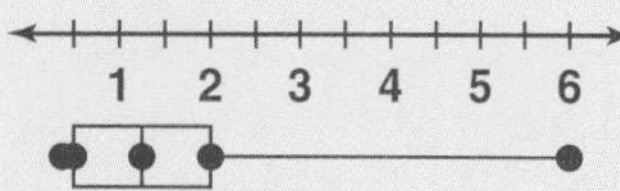

[3] one computational error
[2] correct values but graphed incorrectly OR incorrect values but graphed correctly
[1] correct graph without description

26.

11 | 8 9
12 | 0 3 3 4 5 5 6 6 7
13 | 0 1 2

Key: 13 | 0 means 130

27.

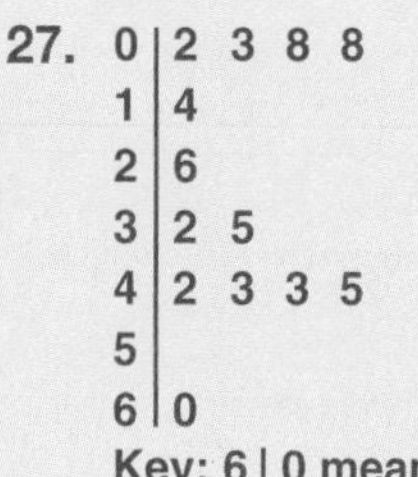

0 | 2 3 8 8
1 | 4
2 | 6
3 | 2 5
4 | 2 3 3 5
5 |
6 | 0

Key: 6 | 0 means 6.0

28. 2 | 1 1 2 3 3 3 4 5 5 5 6 6
Key: 2 | 1 means 21

Lesson 10-5

page 557 Check Skills You'll Need

1–9.

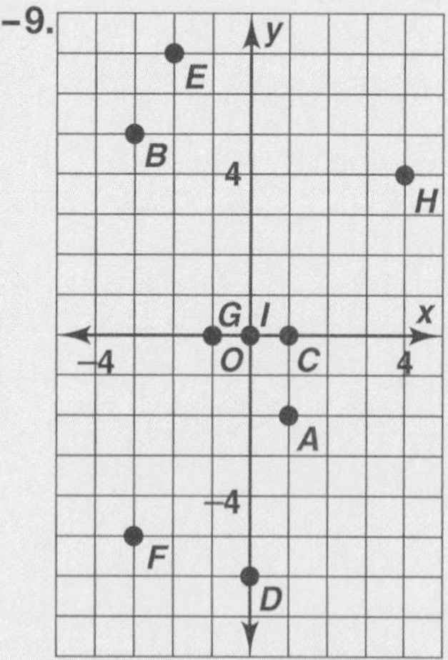

page 558 Check Understanding

1b.

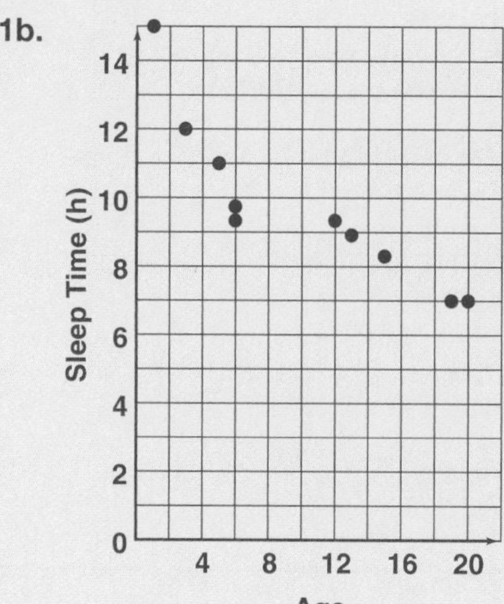

page 560

1.

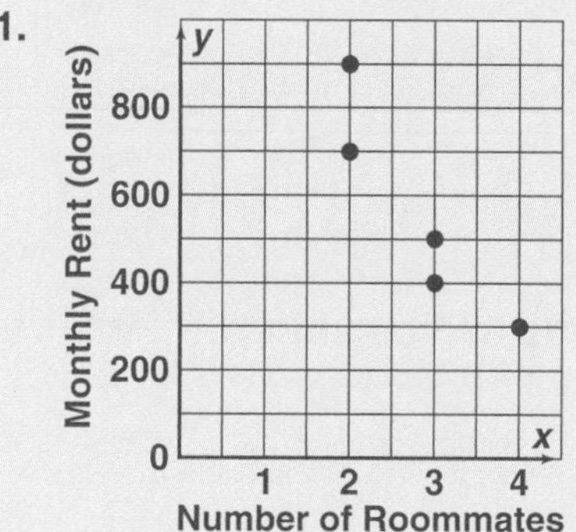

3.

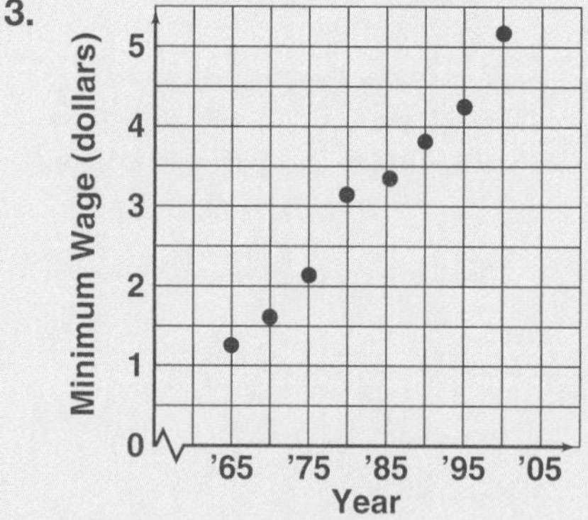

4.

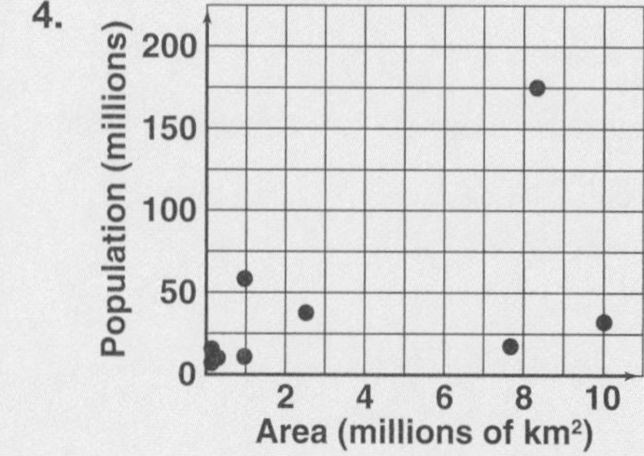

7.

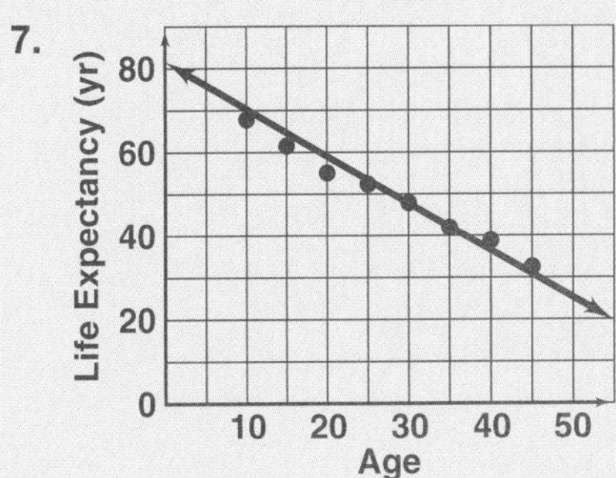

8.

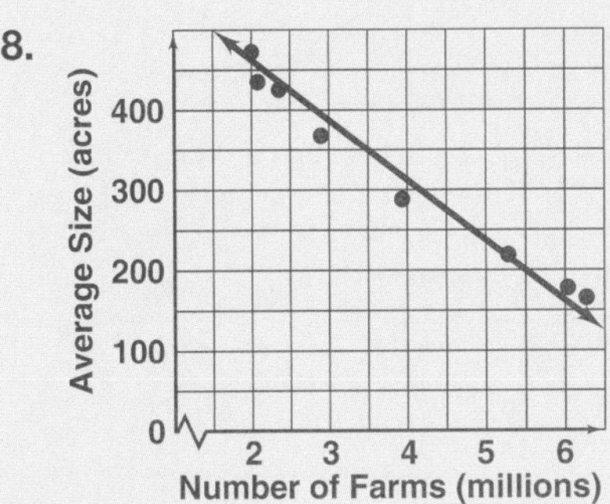

page 561

13.

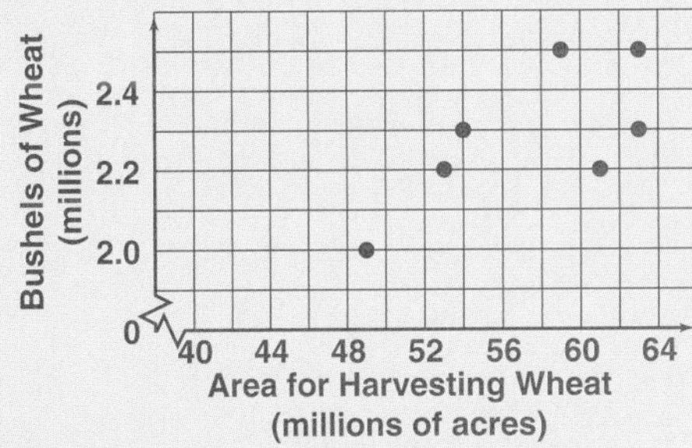

page 562

26.

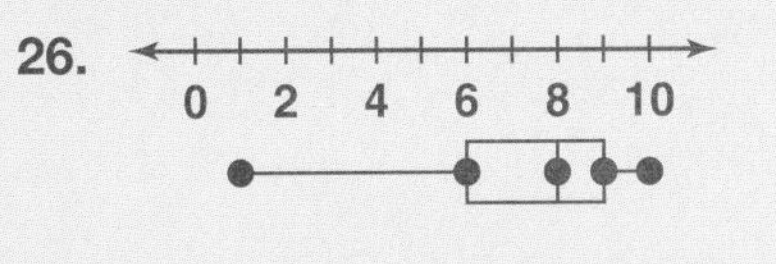

27.

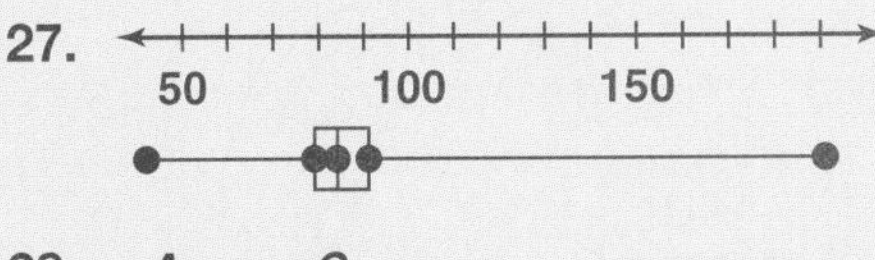

28.

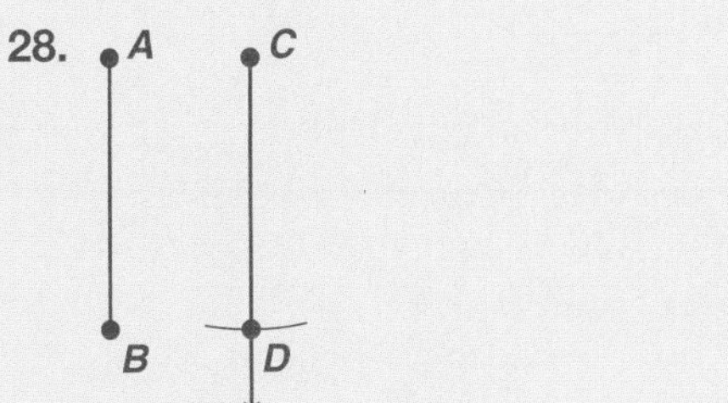

29.

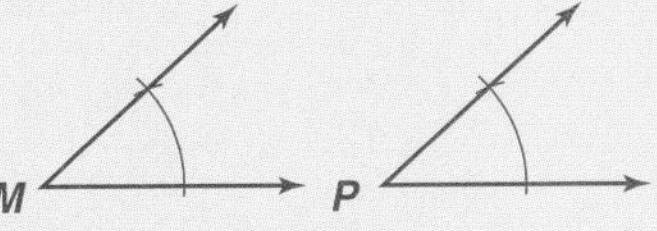

Lesson 10-6

page 564 Addtional Examples

2. Favorite Seasons

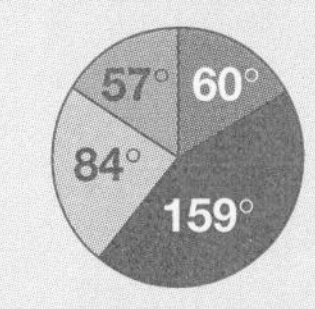

Spring Fall
Summer Winter

page 564 Check Understanding

2. Fuel Use

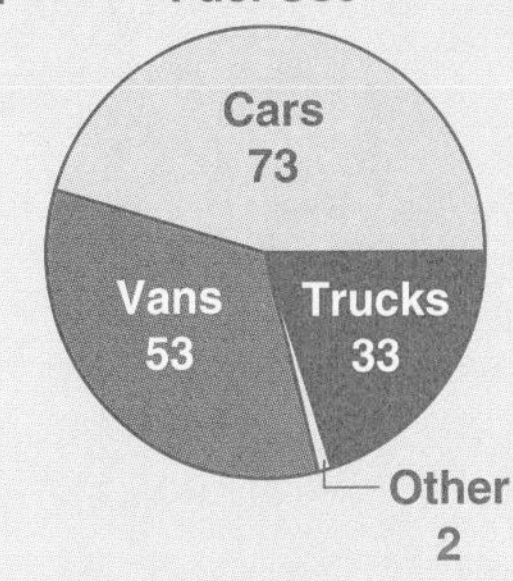

page 565

6. Sizes of Boxes Used

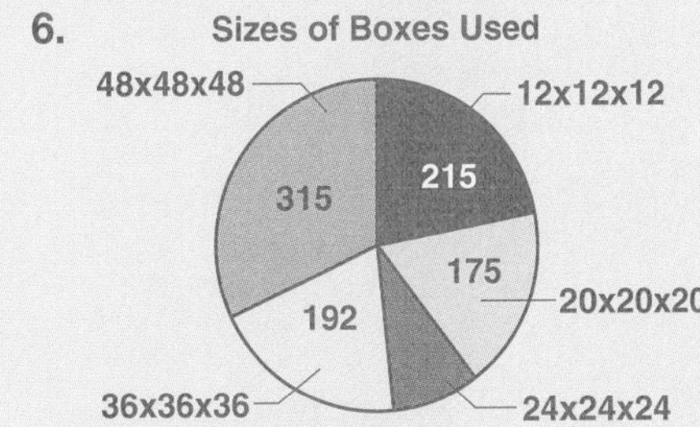

9. Vehicle Types

Small 28%

Midsize 48%

Luxury 17%

Large 7%

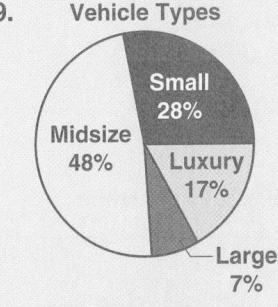

10. Miles of Running

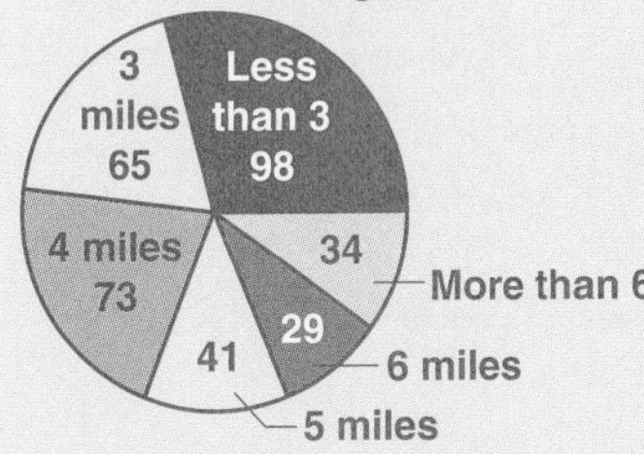

page 568

27. positive trend

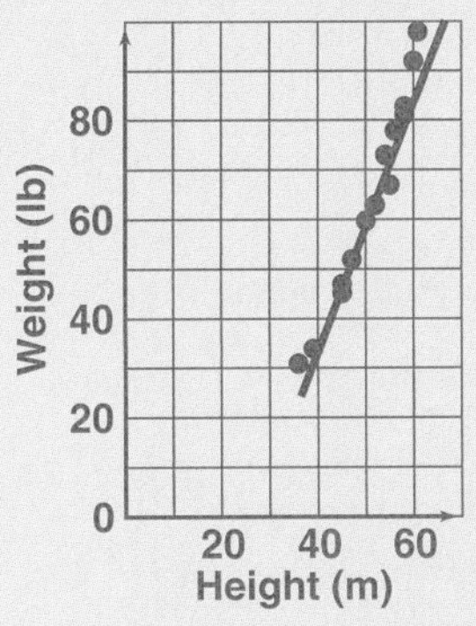

page 568 Checkpoint Quiz 2

1.

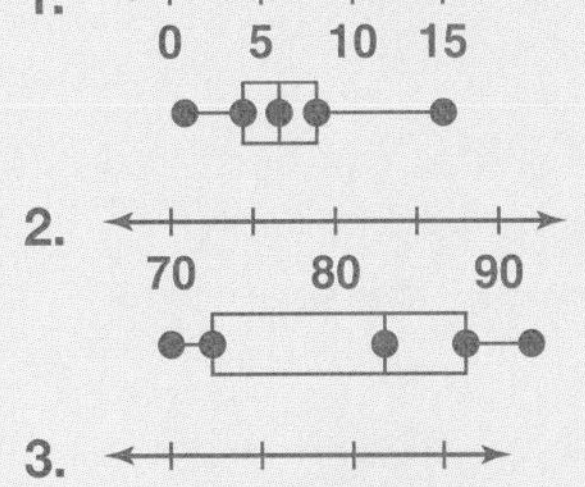

2.

3.

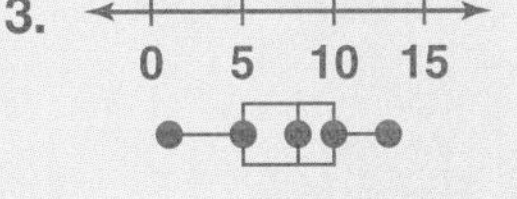

4a. Ways Students Travel to School

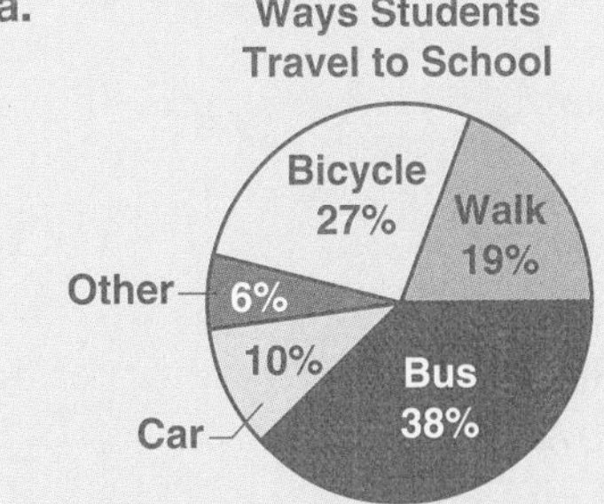

Lesson 10-7

page 569 Check Skills You'll Need

1–2. Answers may vary. Samples are given.

1.

Miles	Frequency
1–5	4
6–10	9
11–15	7
16–20	5

Miles Walked at Walk-A-Thon

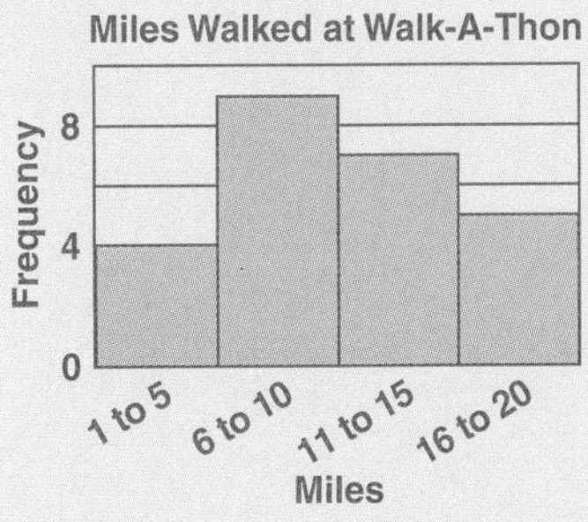

Additional Answers

2.

Hours	Frequency
0–1.9	5
2–3.9	6
4–5.9	2
6–7.9	2
8–9.9	2

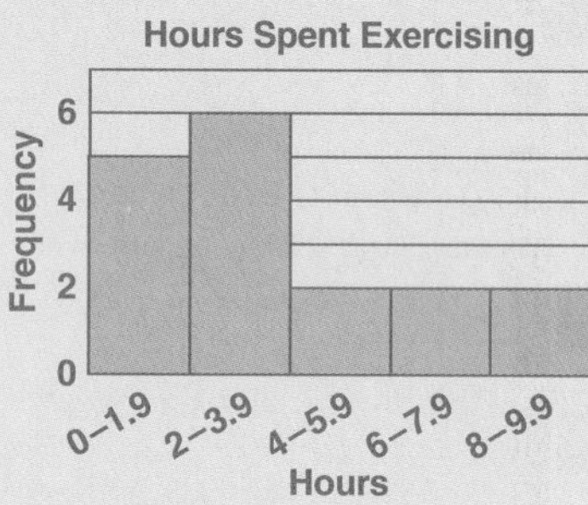

page 570 Check Understanding

2a. A circle graph shows comparisons of the parts of a whole.

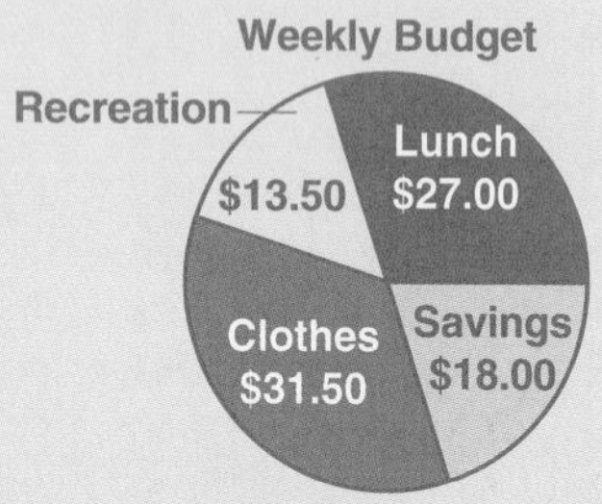

page 572

5. Line graph; it shows data over time well.

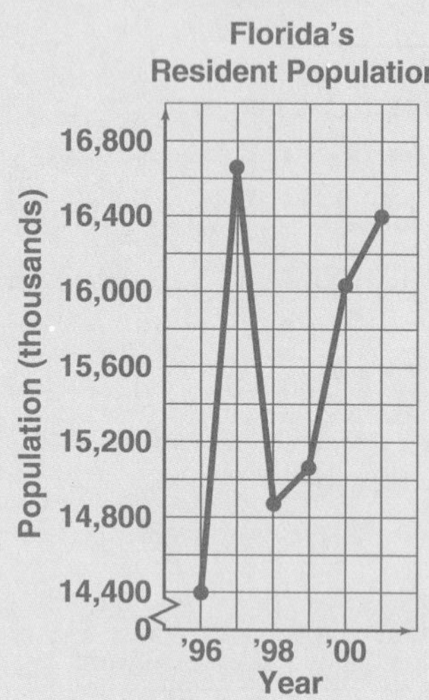

8. Bar graph; bar graphs show comparisons between categories.

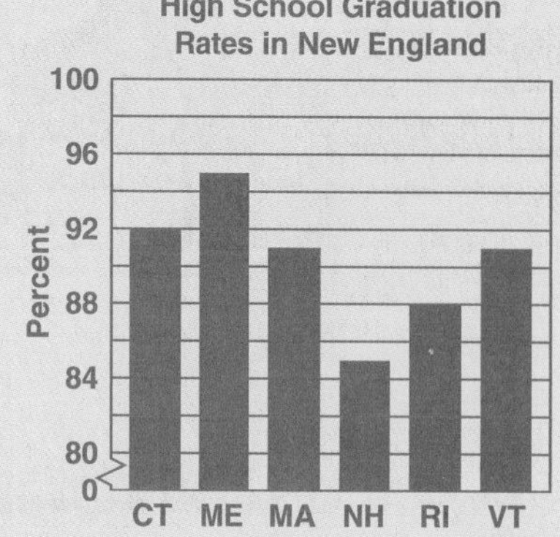

page 574

21. [4]

	%	angle measure
driving alone	78	281°
car pool	9	32°
mass transportation	5	18°
other	5	18°
work at home	3	11°

How Americans Get to Work

Driving Alone 78%
Work at Home 3%
Other 5%
Mass Transportation 5%
9%
Car Pool

[3] correct procedure with one computational error
[2] correct calculations but incorrect graph
[1] correct graph, without work shown

Lesson 10-8

page 577 Additional Examples

1.

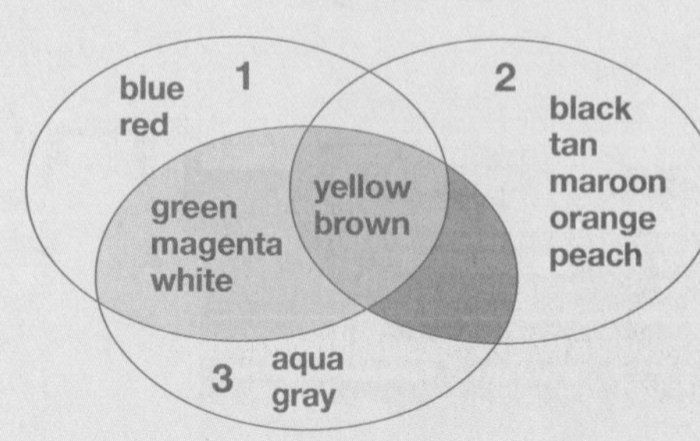

page 578

4.

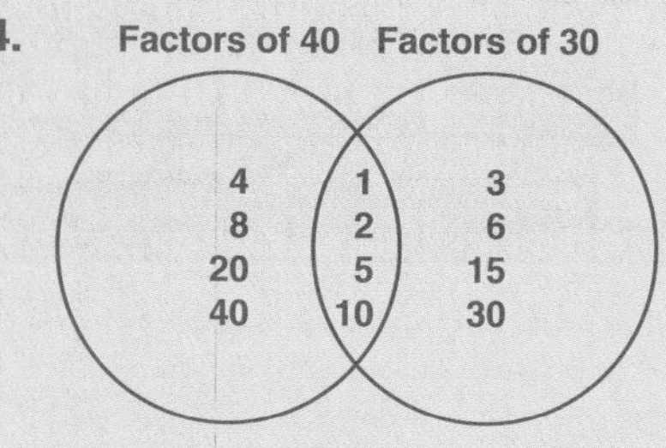

1, 2, 5, and 10; 10

page 579

17–18. Answers may vary. Samples are given.

17.

Length	Frequency
21–22	3
23–24	4
25–26	5

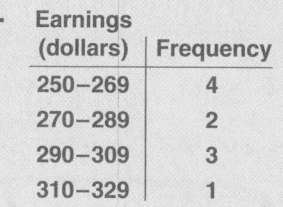

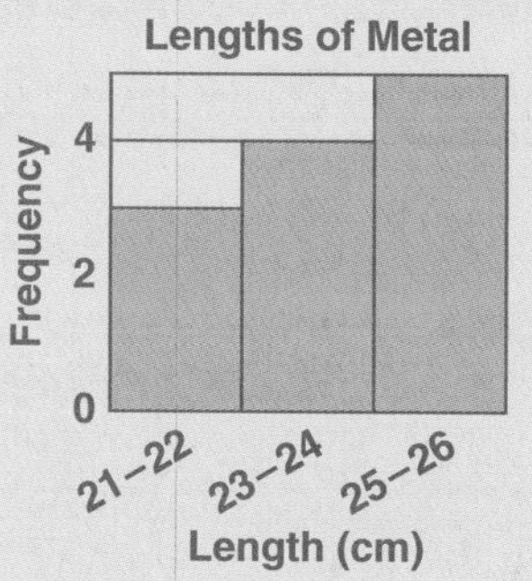

18.

Earnings (dollars)	Frequency
250–269	4
270–289	2
290–309	3
310–329	1

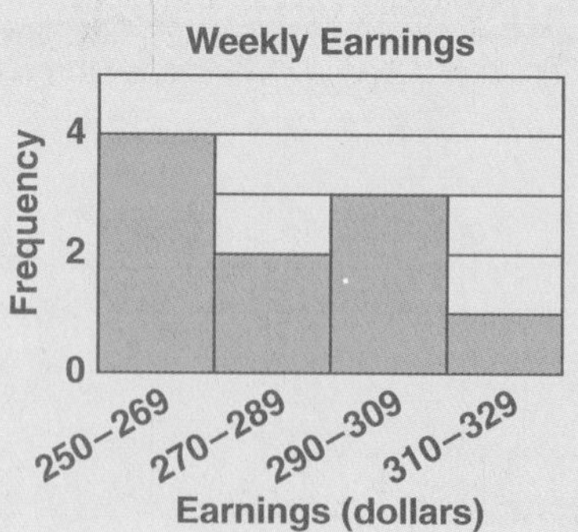

page 582–583 Chapter Review

7.

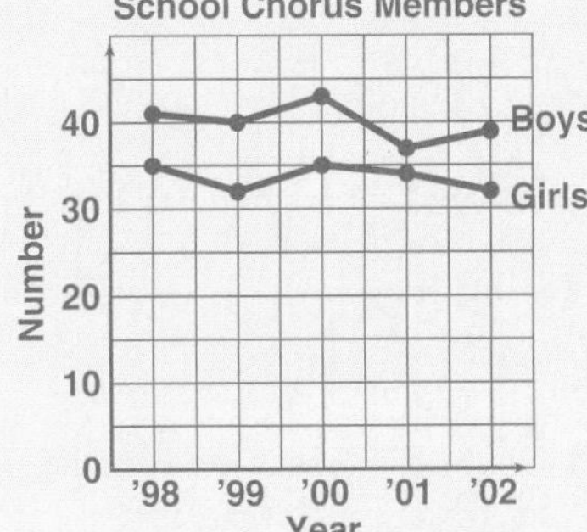

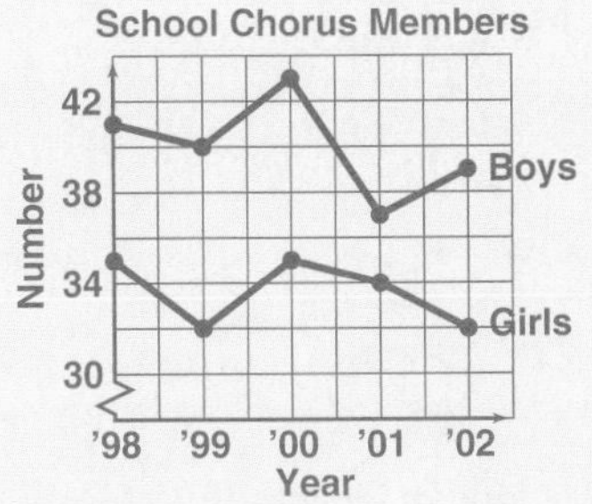

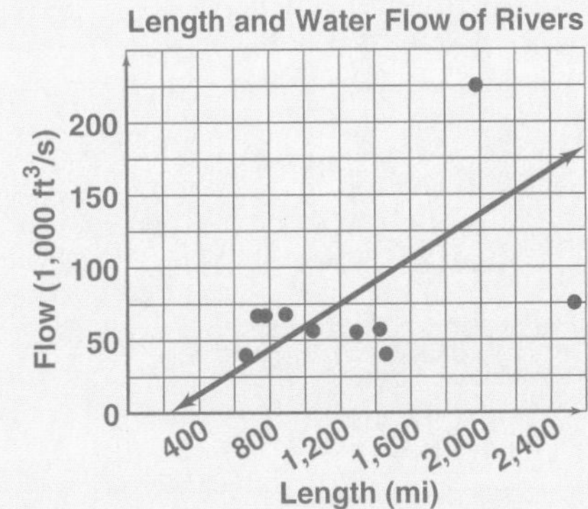

The graph with the break symbol shows the data more clearly because the scale is more spread out.

10.

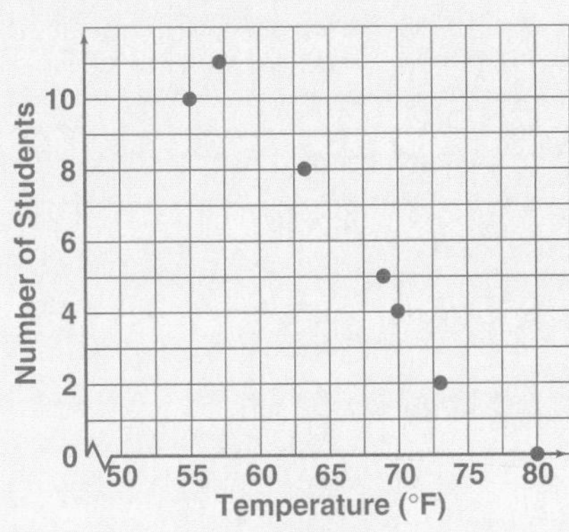

12. Answers may vary. Sample: Scatter plot; it shows the relationship between two sets of data.

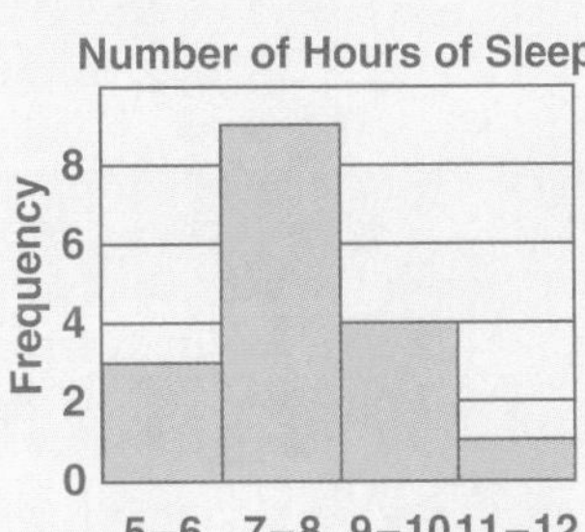

page 584 Chapter Test

1.

Movies	Frequency
0	3
1	4
2	6
3	3
4	2
5	1
6	0
7	1

4–5. Answers may vary. Samples are given.

4.

Hours	Frequency
5–6	3
7–8	9
9–10	4
11–12	1

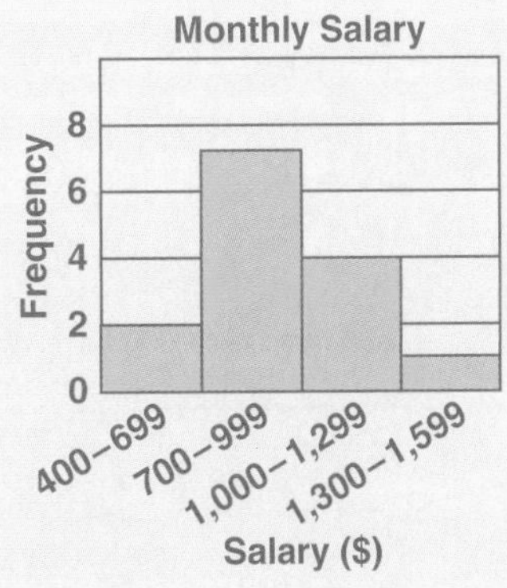

5.

Salary	Frequency
400–699	2
700–999	7
1,000–1,299	4
1,300–1,599	1

Monthly Salary

Frequency

0 2 4 6 8

400–699 700–999 1,000–1,299 1,300–1,599

Salary ($)

9.

81	0 0 3 3 8 8 9
82	1 5
83	3

Key: 83 | 3 means 83.3

11. Bar graph; it shows the relative size of categories.

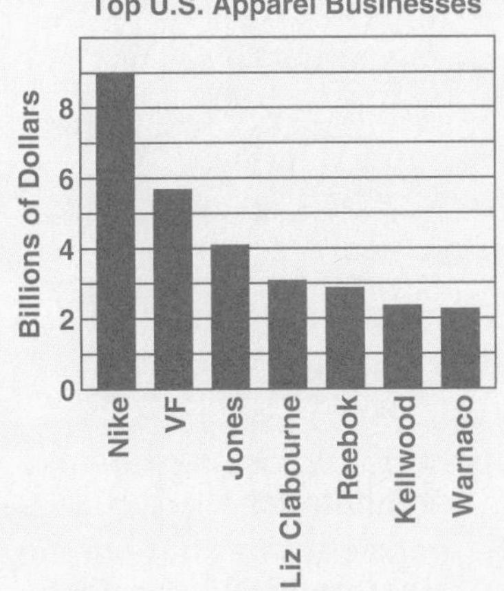

12. Line graph; it shows changes over time.

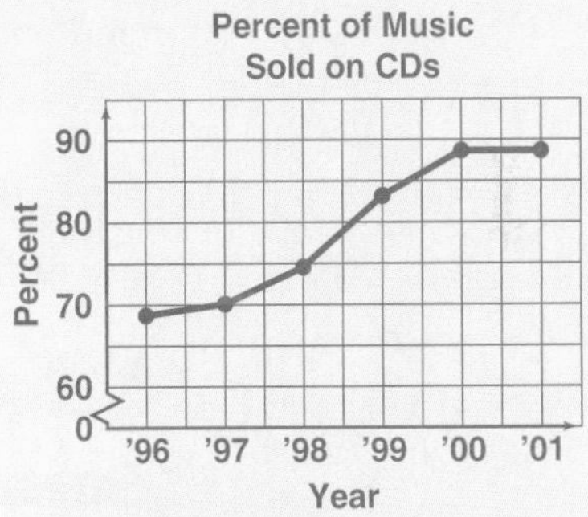

13. Bar graph; it shows usage by categories.

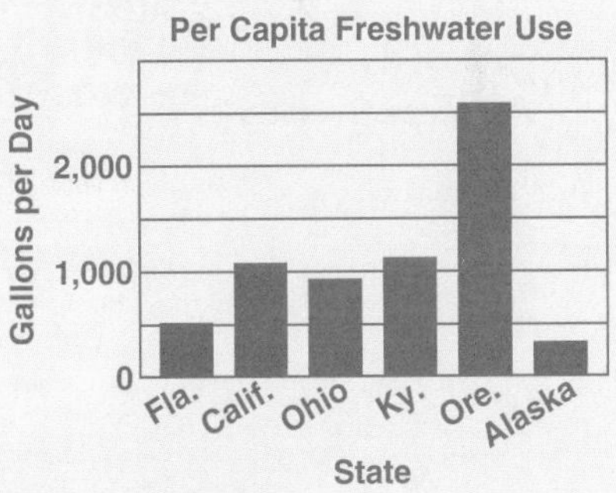

page 585 Test Prep

13. [2] \$7.99; \$50.00 − \$7.04 = \$42.96. She spent a total of \$42.96 on the shopping trip. \$42.96 − \$18.99 = \$23.97. She spent \$23.97 on the three books. $\frac{\$23.97}{3} = \$7.99$.

[1] correct procedure but with a computational error OR correct answer, without work shown

14. [4] 19 21 23 24 25 25 25 25 26 26 27 29 31 33 33 34 40
$n = 17$
median: 26
lower quartile: 24.5
$\frac{24 + 25}{2} = 24.5$
upper quartile: 32
$\frac{31 + 33}{2} = 32$

20 25 30 35 40

[3] correct procedures with one computational error
[2] correct values but graphed incorrectly OR incorrect values but graphed correctly
[1] correct box-and-whisker display, without work shown

CHAPTER 11

Lesson 11-1

page 592

1.

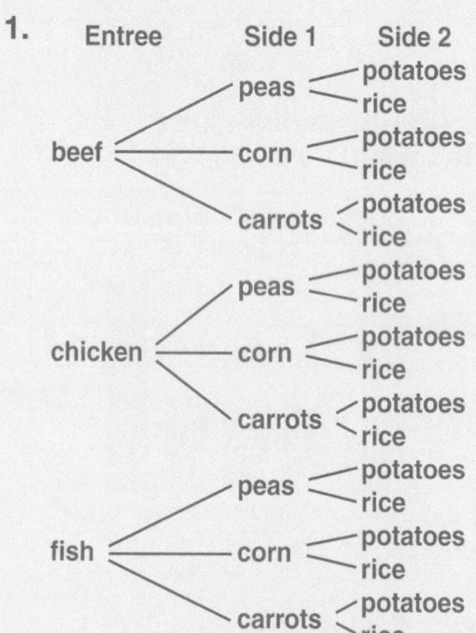

2.

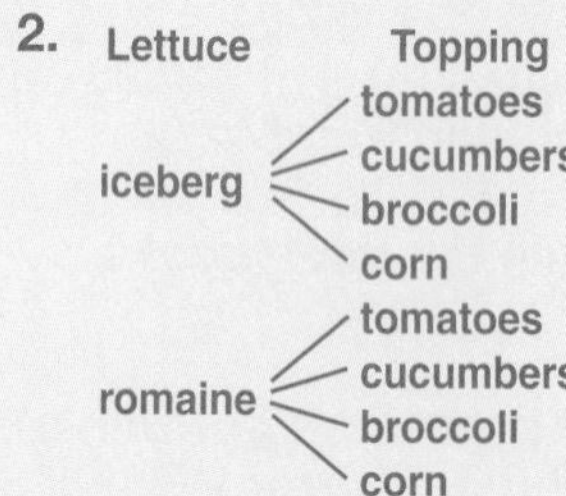

page 594

21–22. Answers may vary. Samples are given.

21. circle graph

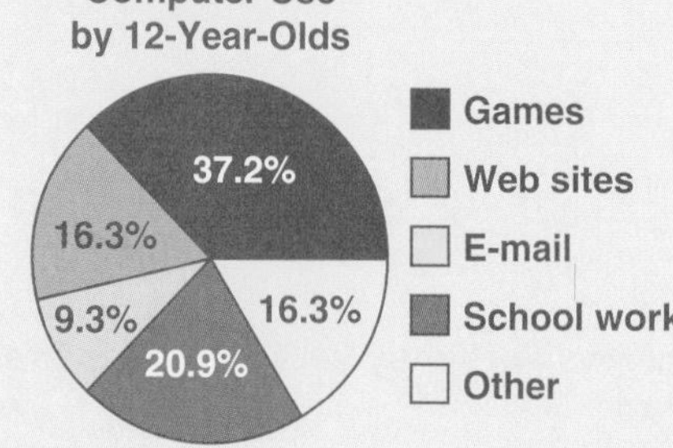

22. line graph

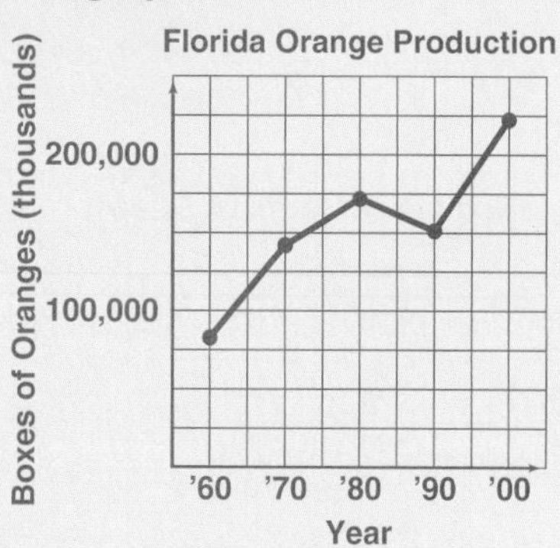

page 598

1.

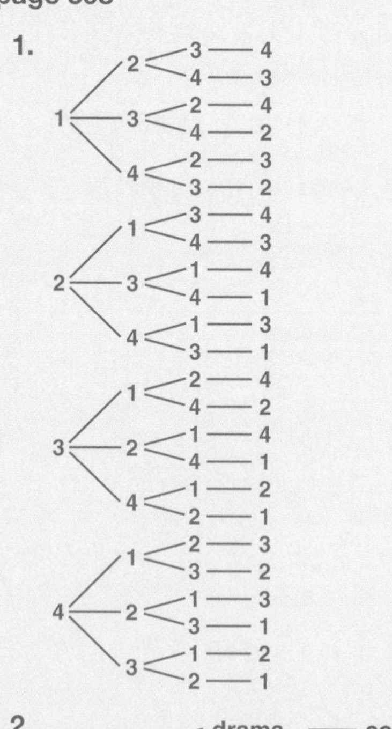

2.

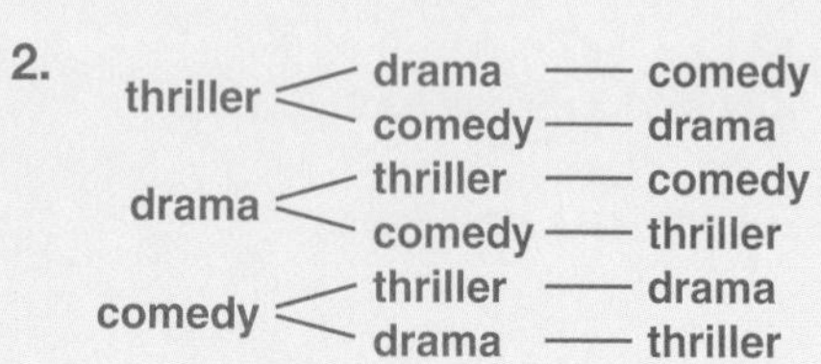

Lesson 11-2

page 599

39.

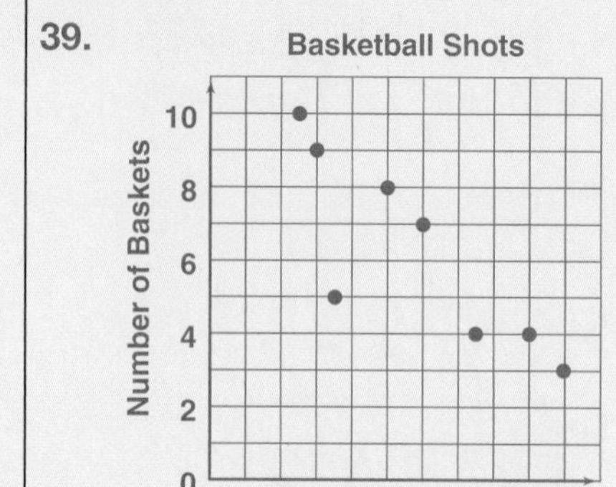

Lesson 11-3

page 604

32.

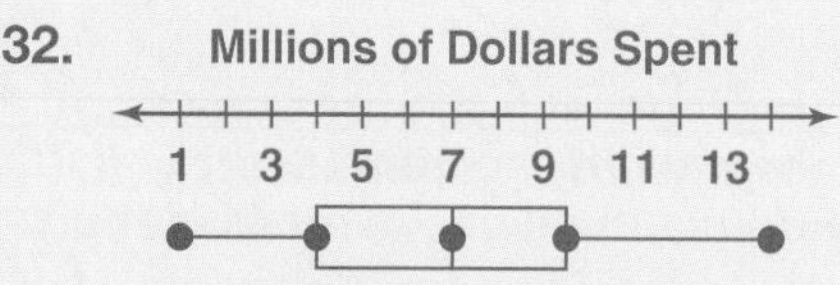

33.

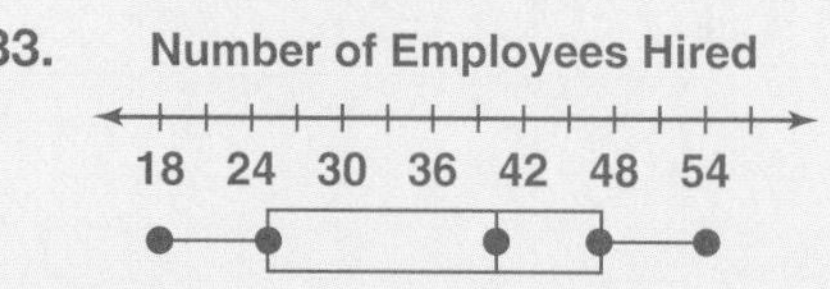

Lesson 11-6

page 618

16.

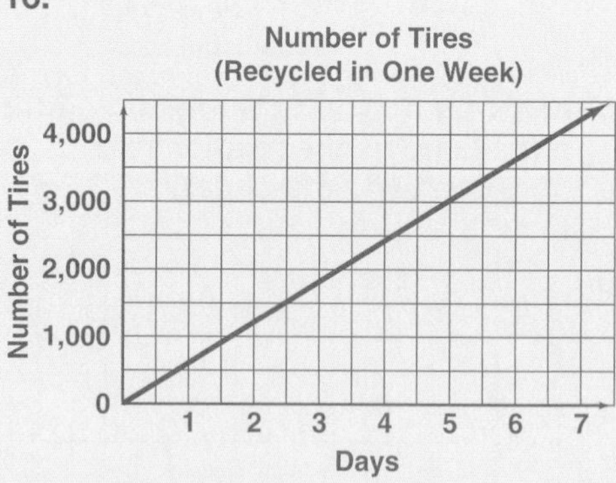

Lesson 11-7

page 621 Check Understanding

1a. Not a random sample; people who are 18–30 years old may not represent all people.

b. The population is the people who reside in the city.

page 625

20. [2] This is not a good sample. The people in the museum may not represent the students at a college. The population is the students at a college.
[1] incomplete answer OR wrong population given

21. YBG, YGB, BGY, BYG, GYB, GBY, BYY, GYY, YBB, GBB, YGG, BGG, BGB, BYB, GYG, GBG, YBY, YGY, YYY, YYB, YYG, BBB, BBY, BBG, GGG, GGY, GGB; $\frac{1}{27}$

CHAPTER 12

Lesson 12-1

page 640

14. 2; start with 100 and multiply by 2 repeatedly; 1,600, 3,200, 6,400.

15. $\frac{1}{2}$; start with 1 and multiply by $\frac{1}{2}$ repeatedly; $\frac{1}{16}, \frac{1}{32}, \frac{1}{64}$.

16. 2; start with 3 and multiply by 2 repeatedly; 48, 96, 192.

17. 3; start with 0.12 and multiply by 3 repeatedly; 3.24, 9.72, 29.16.

18. $\frac{1}{5}$; start with 125 and multiply by $\frac{1}{5}$ repeatedly; $\frac{1}{5}, \frac{1}{25}, \frac{1}{125}$.

28. geometric; 162, 486, 1,458

29. geometric; 0.125, 0.0625, 0.03125

30. neither; 1.0001, 1.00001, 1.000001

49.

Number	1	2	3	4	5	6	7	8	9
Frequency	2	2	1	4	2	2	1	0	1

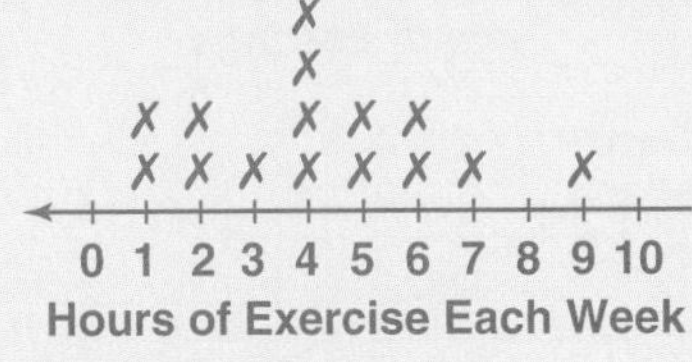

Lesson 12-3

page 648 Check Skills You'll Need

1. −4

2. 1

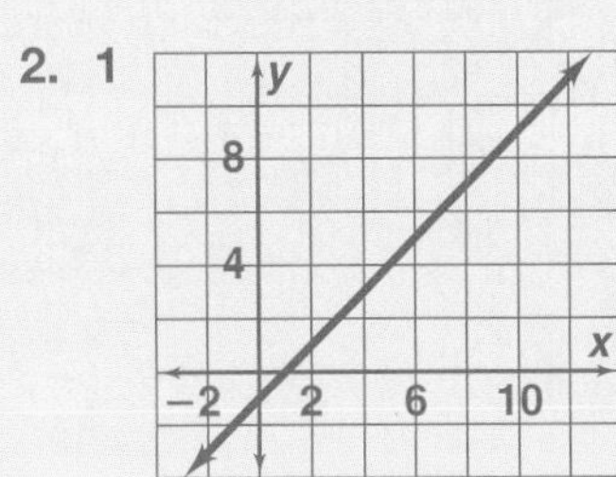

pages 648–649 Check Understanding

1.

x	0	1	2	3	4	5
y	23	39	55	71	87	103

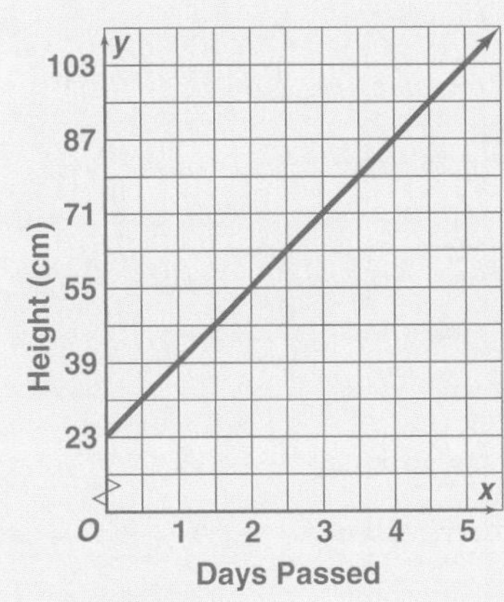

2a. continuous

m	h
0	4,000
1	3,400
2	2,800
3	2,200
4	1,600
5	1,000
6	400

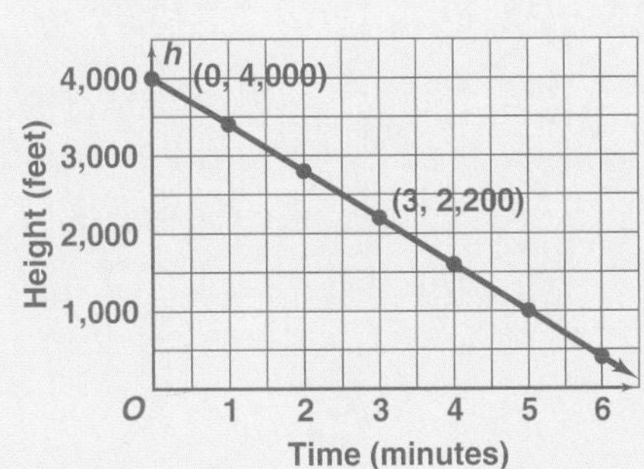

b. discrete

t	c
0	0
1	15
2	30
3	45
4	60
5	75
6	90
7	105

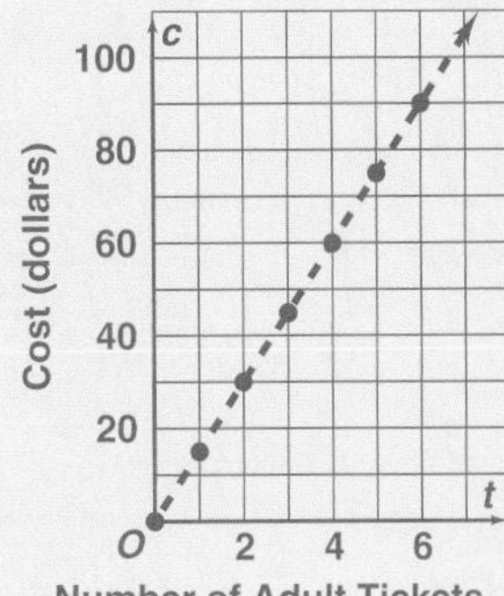

page 650

1.

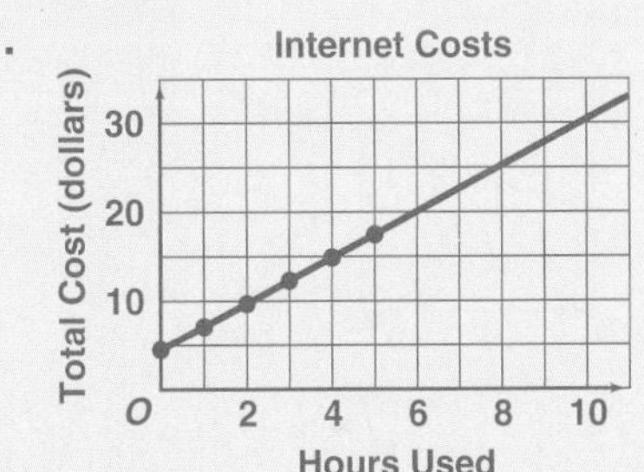

2.

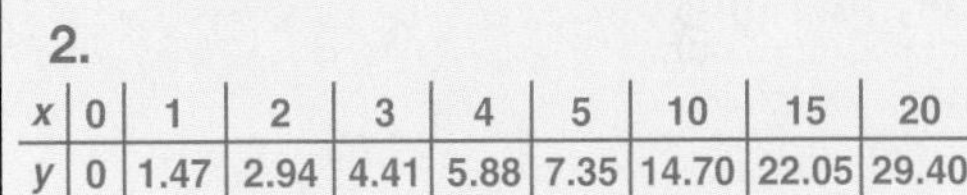

x	0	1	2	3	4	5	10	15	20
y	0	1.47	2.94	4.41	5.88	7.35	14.70	22.05	29.40

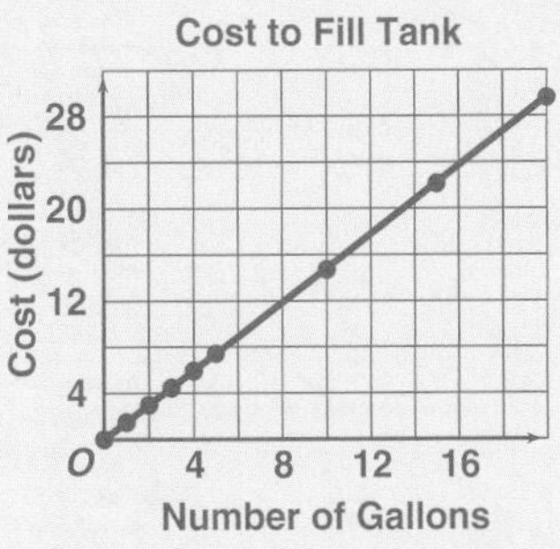

Additional Answers

3.

x	0	1	5	10	20
y	0	0.4536	2.268	4.536	9.0719

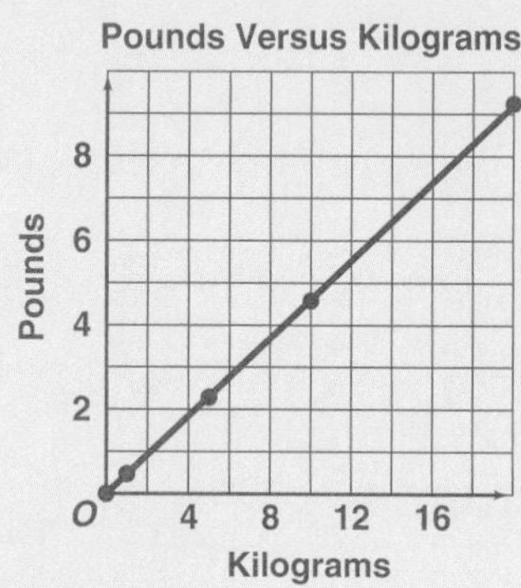

page 651

5. continuous

x	p
0	1
10	1.3
20	1.6
30	1.9

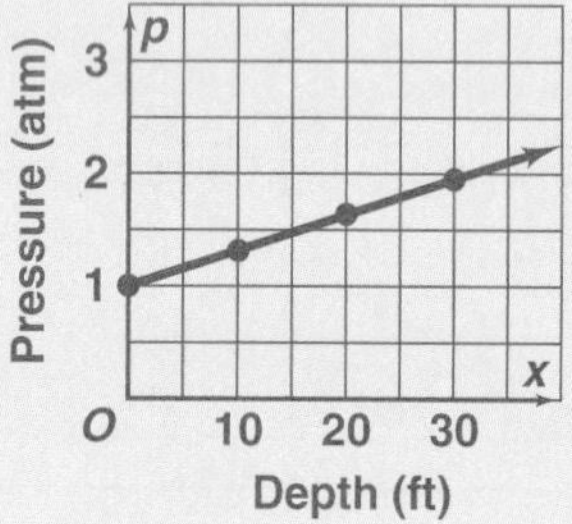

6. continuous

x	y
0	32
50	122
100	212

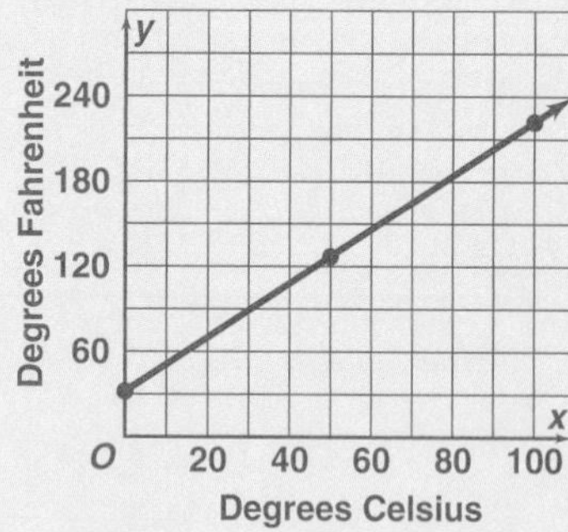

7.

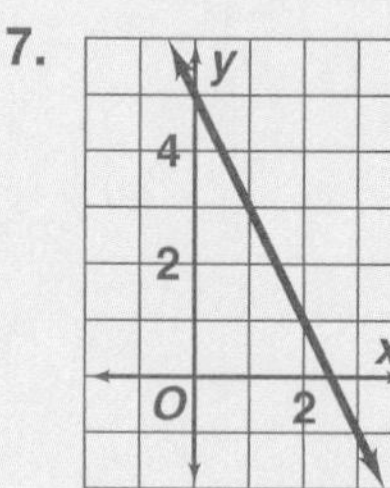

8.

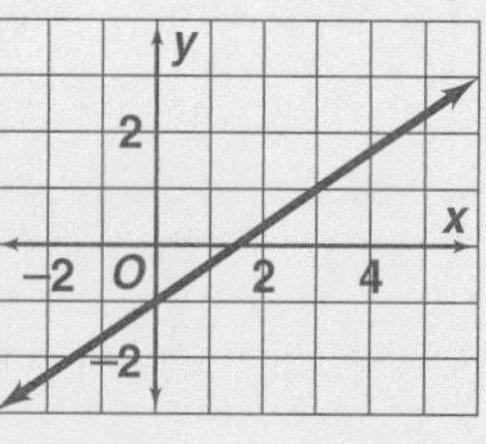

9.

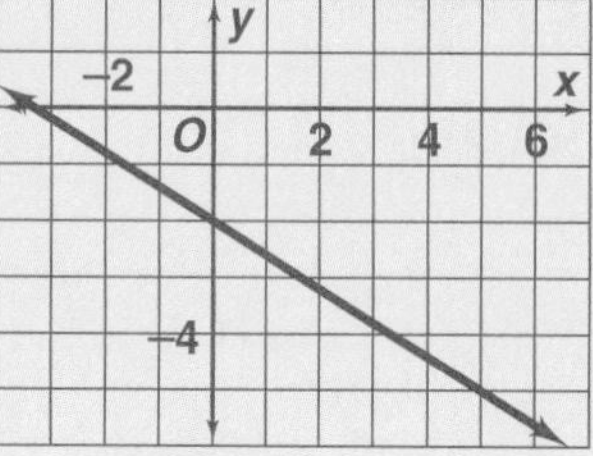

10.

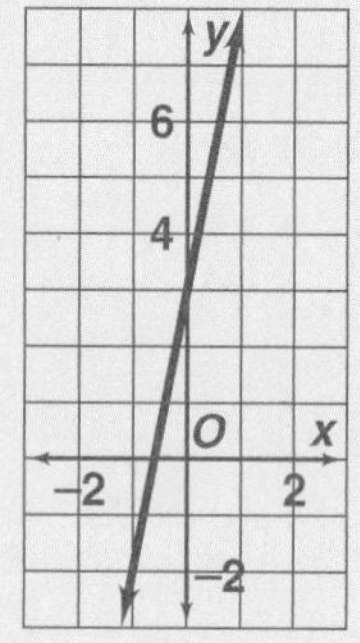

11.

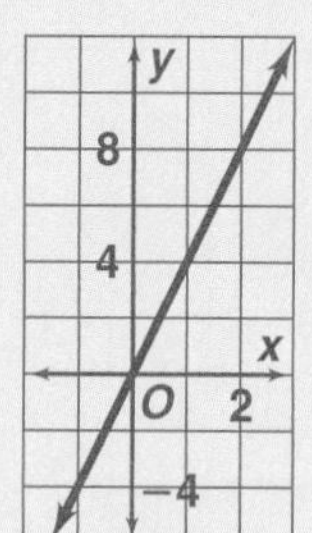

12.

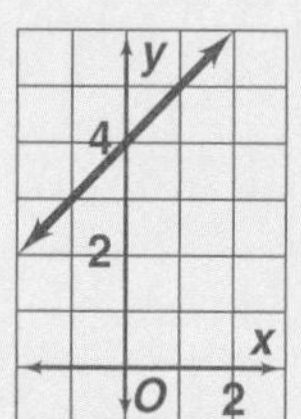

13.

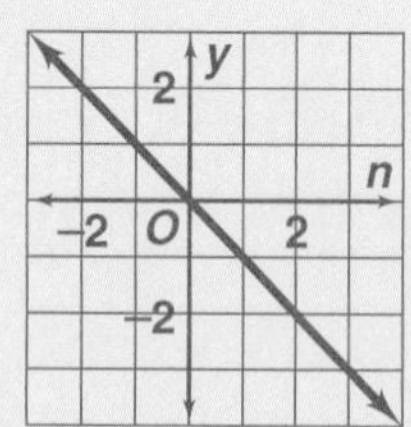

14.

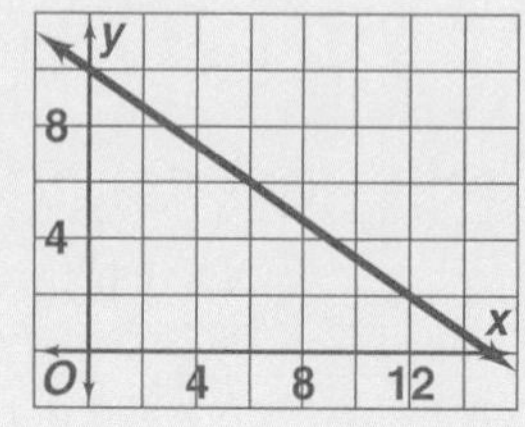

15.

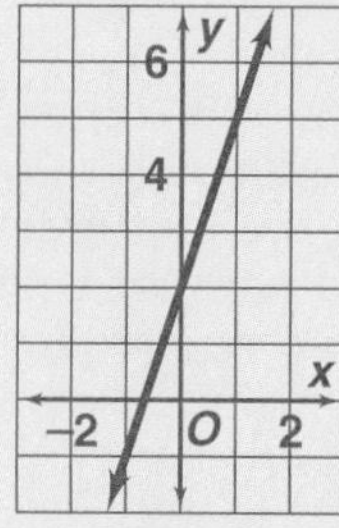

16.

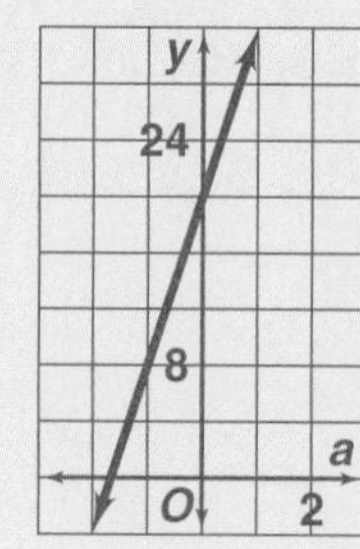

17.

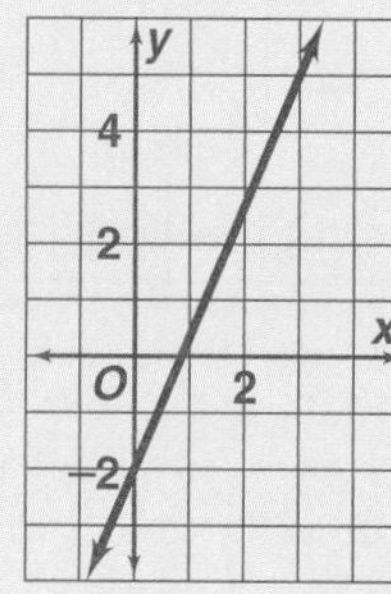

18.

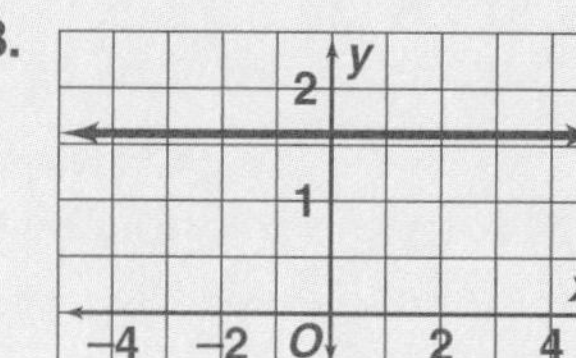

19.

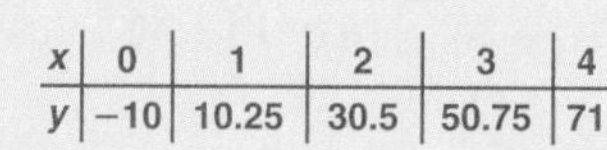

x	0	1	2	3	4
y	−10	10.25	30.5	50.75	71

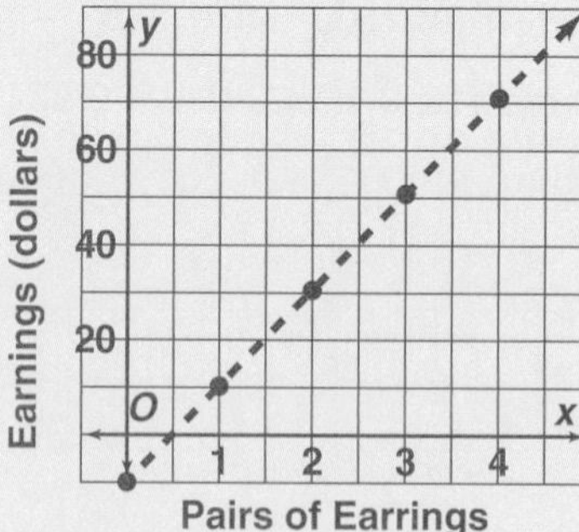

22a.

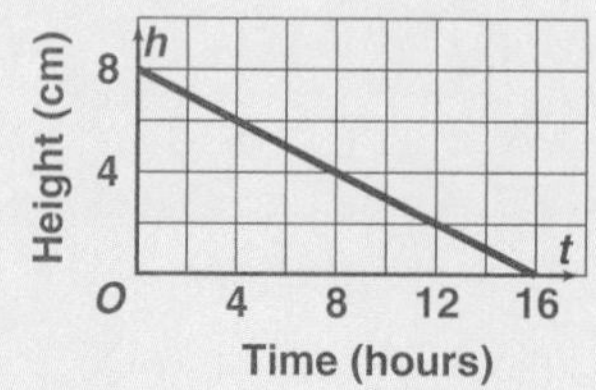

page 652

23b. Cost of an Evening Out

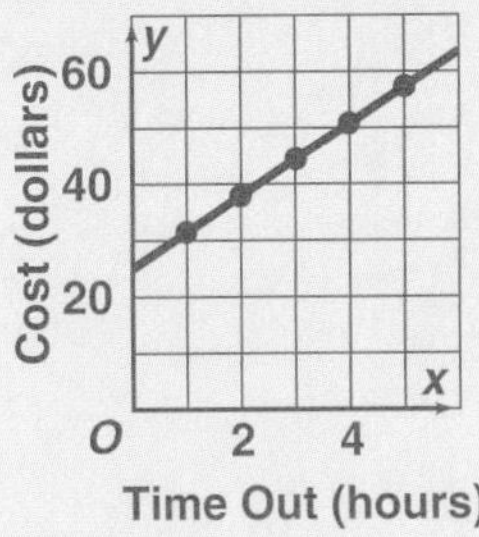

Cost (dollars) | Time Out (hours)

24.

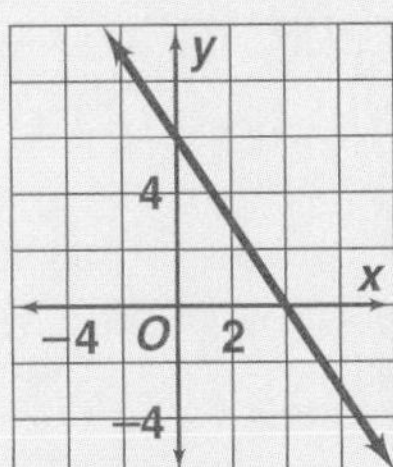

25.

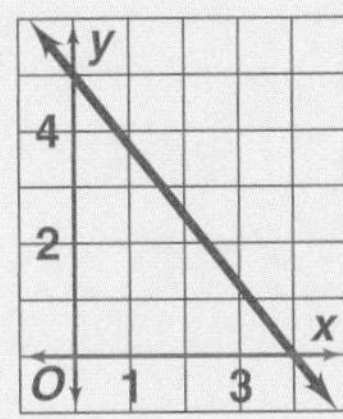

26.

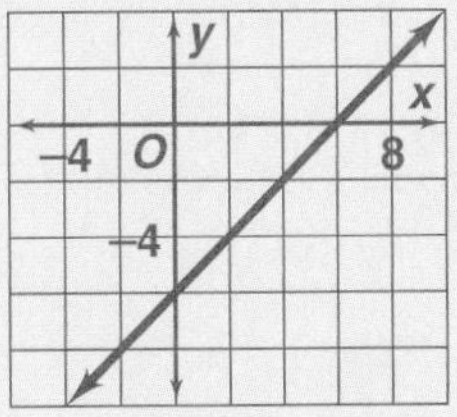

27b.

Crackers	Calories
0	0
4	70
8	140
12	210
16	280

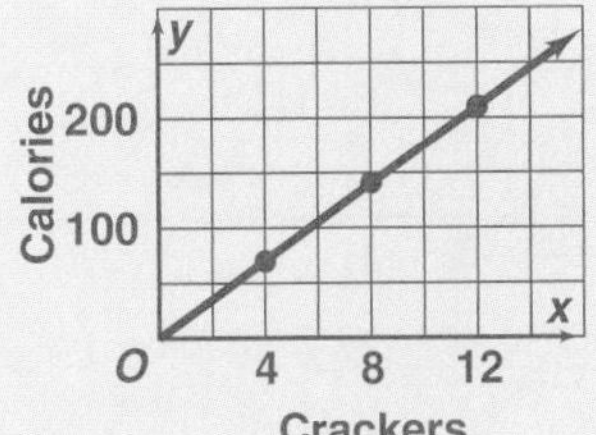

32. [2] $y = -x - \frac{2}{3}$

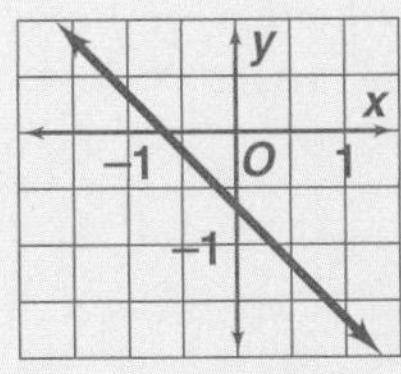

[1] correct form but incorrect graph OR incorrect form but correct graph based on equation

36.

0	6 8
1	5 6 9
2	0 3 4 4 7
3	5 6 8

Key: 3 | 5 means 35

Lesson 12-4

page 657

28. [4] a.

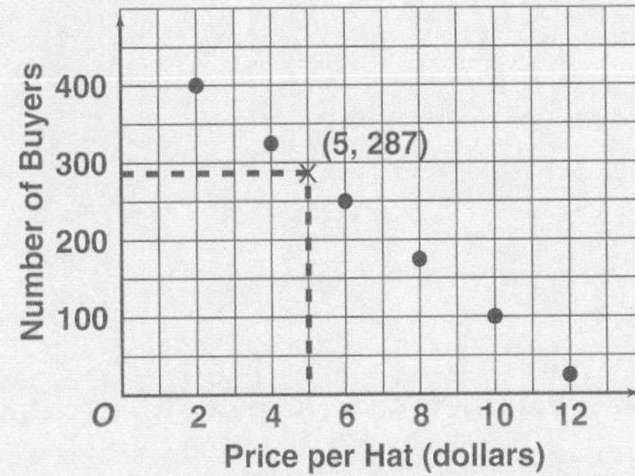

About 287 hats will sell if hats are priced at $5 each.

b. $H = -37.5p + 475$, where p is the price per hat and H represents the number of buyers at price p.

[3] one minor computational error

[2] correct graph but incorrect slope or y-intercept

[1] correct function without work shown

page 657 Checkpoint Quiz 1

9. Answers may vary. Sample:

Hours	Earnings (dollars)
0	0
1	7
2	14
3	21
4	28
5	35
10	70
20	140
40	280

Lesson 12-5

page 658 Check Skills You'll Need

2.

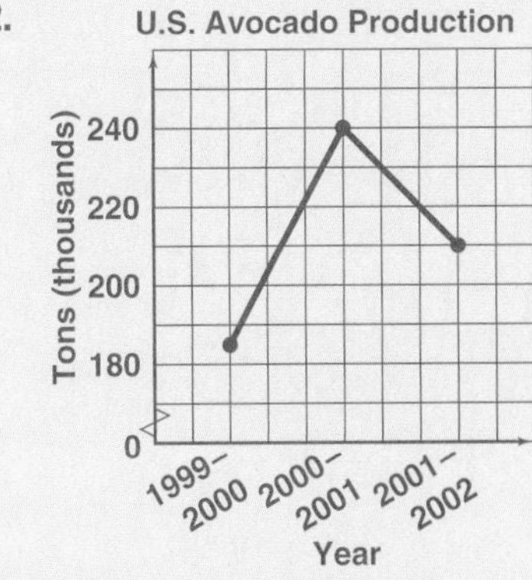

page 659 Check Understanding

2a.

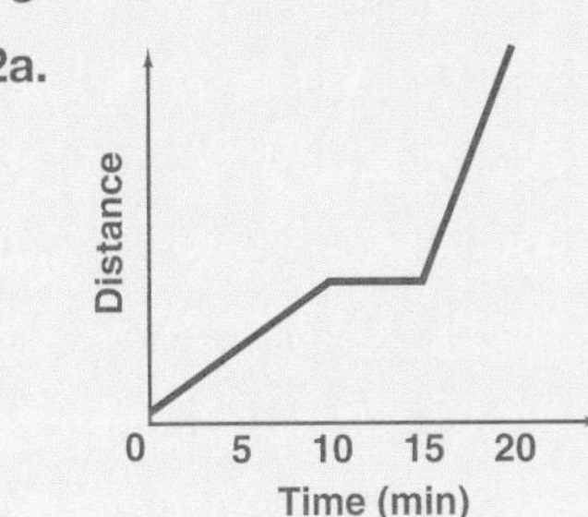

Lesson 12-6

page 663 Check Skills You'll Need

1.

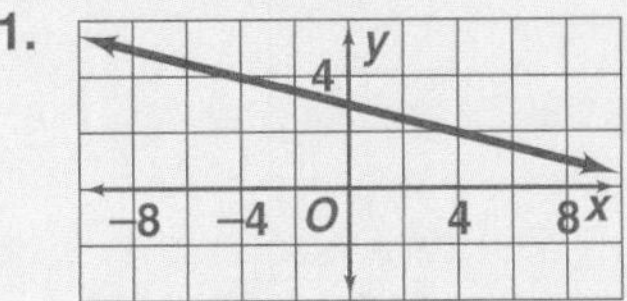

2.

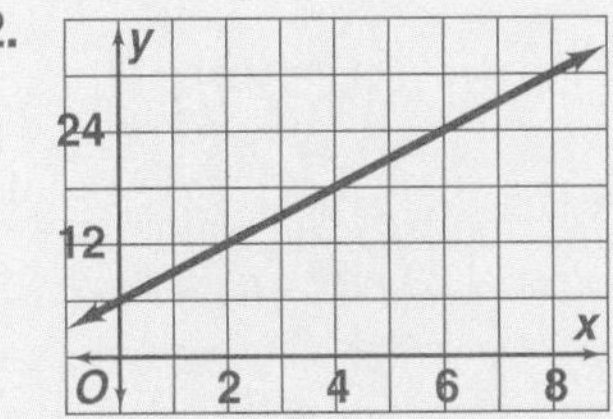

pages 663–665 Check Understanding

1a.

x	−2	−1	0	1	2
y	3	−3	−5	−3	3

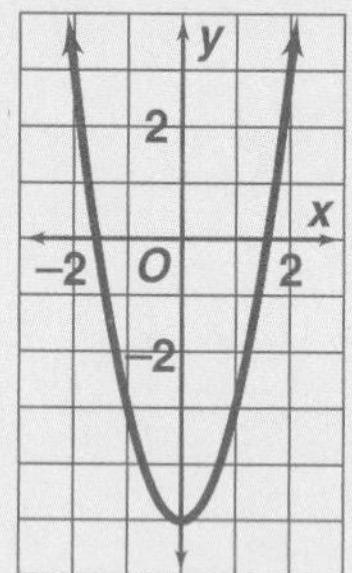

b.

x	−2	−1	0	1	2
y	−6	−2	0	0	−2

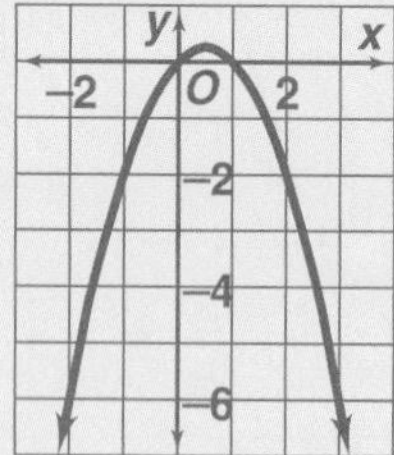

3a.

t	1	5	8	10	15	20
y	200	40	25	20	$13\frac{1}{3}$	10

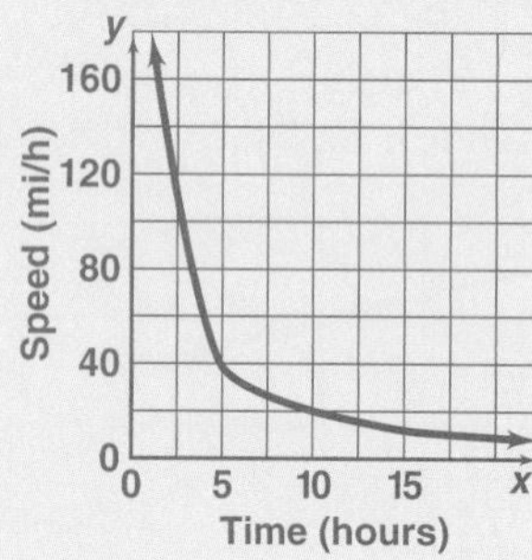

page 665

1.

x	−3	−2	−1	0	1	2	3
y	−9	−4	−1	0	−1	−4	−9

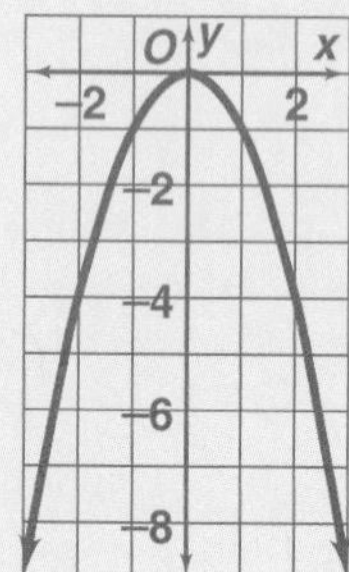

2.

x	−3	−2	−1	0	1	2	3
y	18	8	2	0	2	8	18

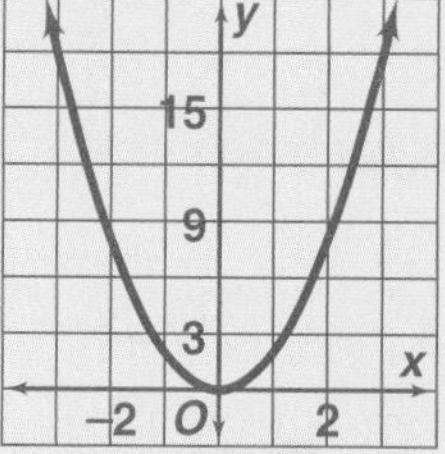

3.

x	−3	−2	−1	0	1	2	3
y	−72	−32	−8	0	−8	−32	−72

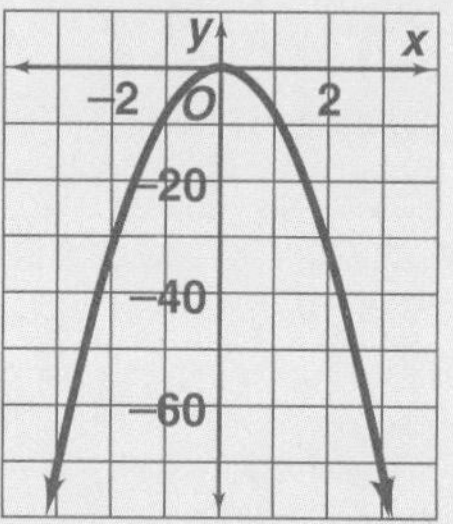

4.

x	−3	−2	−1	0	1	2	3
y	11	6	3	2	3	6	11

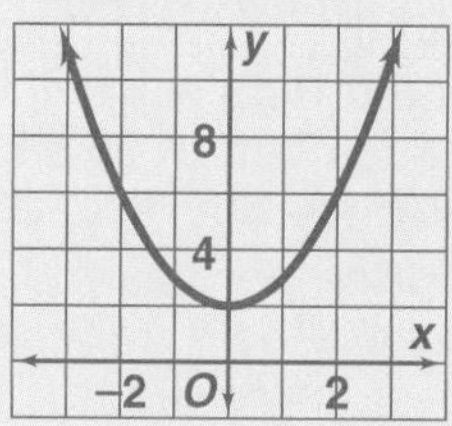

5.

x	−3	−2	−1	0	1	2	3
y	−36	−16	−4	0	−4	−16	−36

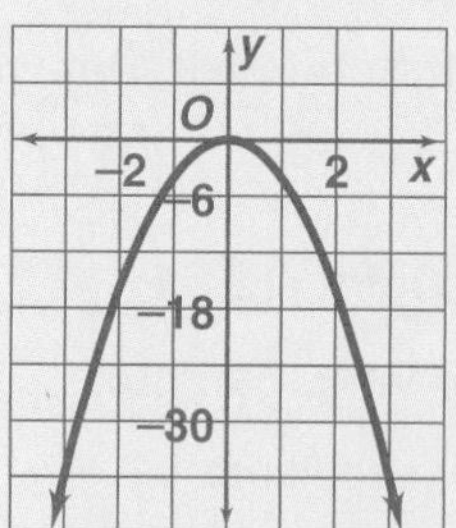

6.

x	−3	−2	−1	0	1	2	3
y	27	17	11	9	11	17	27

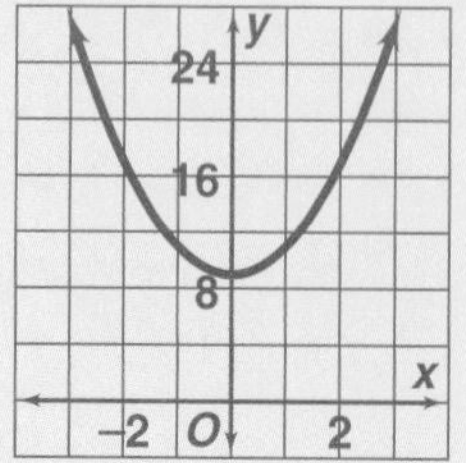

11.

x	1	2	3	4	5
y	100	50	$33\frac{1}{3}$	25	20

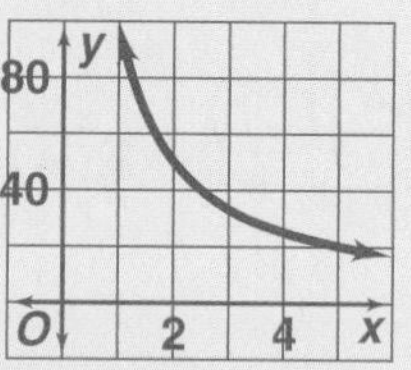

12.

x	1	2	3	4	5
y	8	4	$2\frac{2}{3}$	2	$1\frac{3}{5}$

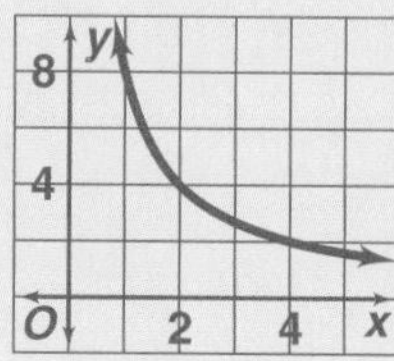

13.

x	1	2	3	4	5
y	20	10	$6\frac{2}{3}$	5	4

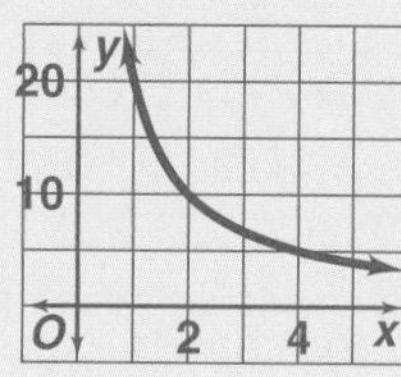

14.

x	1	2	3	4	5
y	16	8	$5\frac{1}{3}$	4	$3\frac{1}{5}$

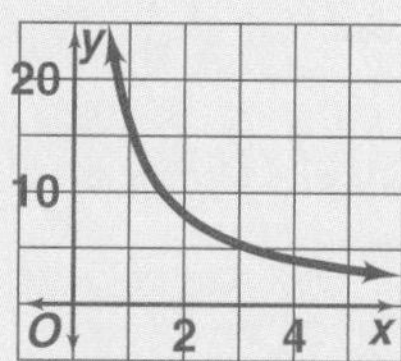

15.

x	1	2	3	4	5
y	10	5	$3\frac{1}{3}$	$2\frac{1}{2}$	2

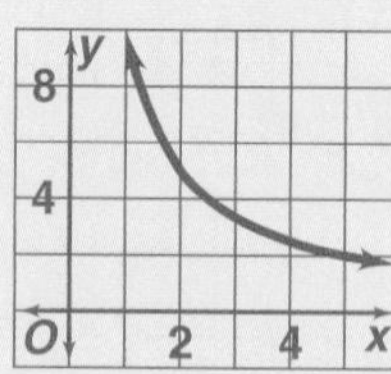

16.

x	1	2	3	4	5
y	18	9	6	$4\frac{1}{2}$	$3\frac{3}{5}$

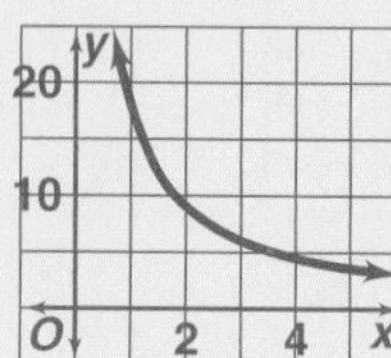

17.

x	1	5	9	15	25
y	225	45	25	15	9

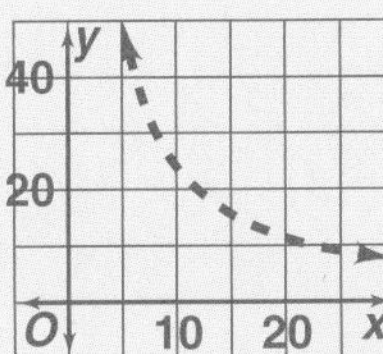

18.

x	−3	−2	−1	0	1	2	3
y	−24	−10	−2	0	−4	−14	−30

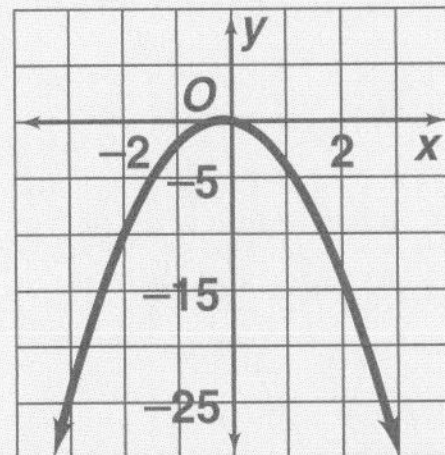

19.

x	−3	−2	−1	0	1	2	3
y	14	6	2	2	6	14	26

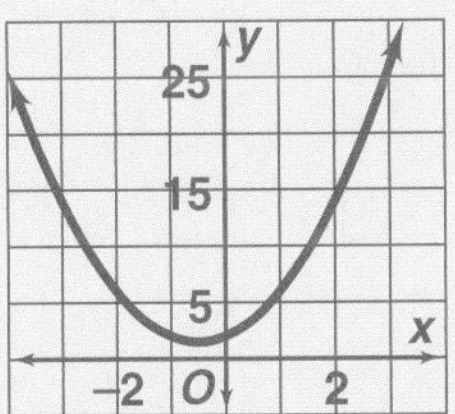

20.

x	−3	−2	−1	0	1	2	3
y	−12	−6	−2	0	0	−2	−6

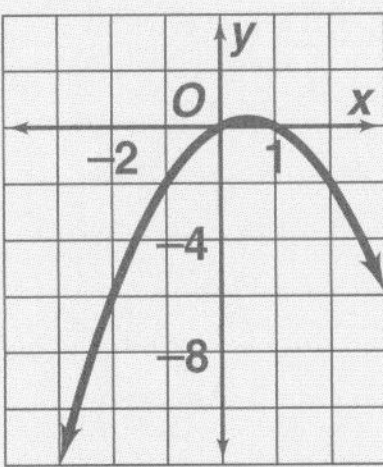

21a.

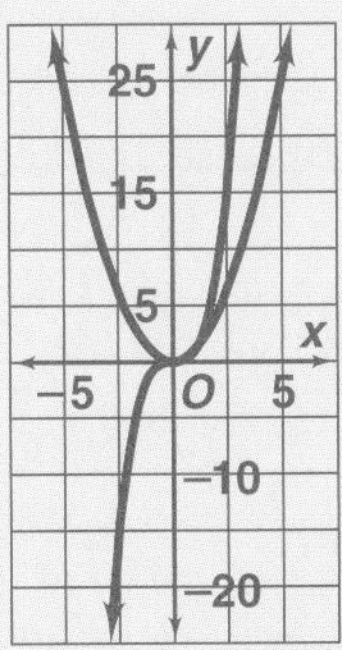

page 666

25.

Width x	Length	Area y
1	5	5
2	4	8
3	3	9
4	2	8
5	1	5

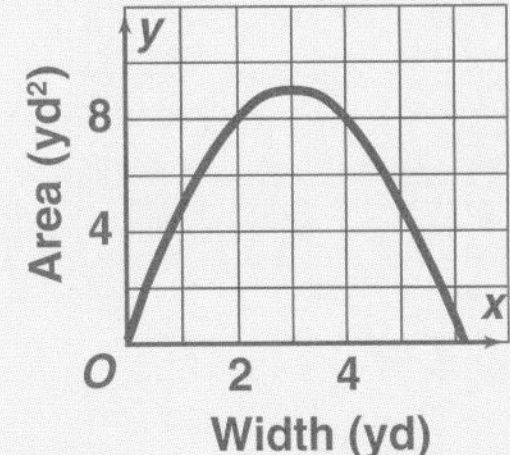

page 667

35.

x	−3	−2	−1	0	1	2	3
y	$\frac{1}{27}$	$\frac{1}{9}$	$\frac{1}{3}$	1	3	9	27

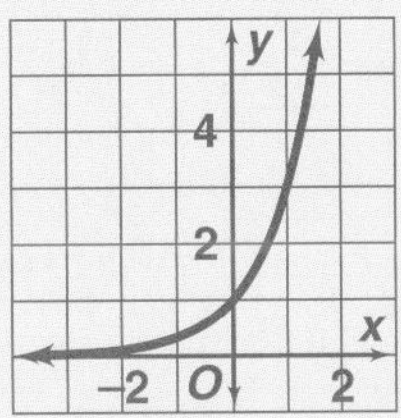

36.

x	−1	0	1	2	3	4	5
y	$\frac{1}{27}$	$\frac{1}{9}$	$\frac{1}{3}$	1	3	9	27

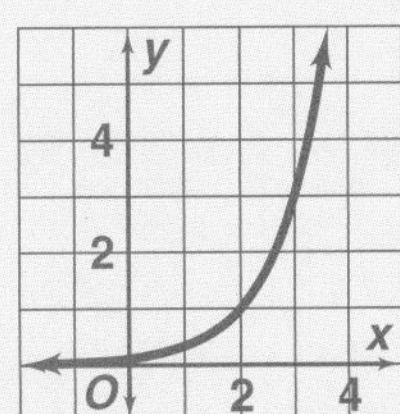

The graph is the same shape as the graph in Exercise 35, but it is shifted two units to the right.

37.

x	−4	−3	−2	−1	0	1
y	$\frac{1}{9}$	$\frac{1}{3}$	1	3	9	27

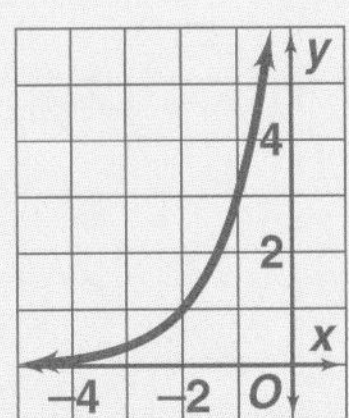

The graph is the same shape as the graphs in Exercises 35 and 36, but it is shifted two units to the left from Exercise 35.

38.

x	−3	−2	−1	0	1	2
y	$-\frac{1}{27}$	$-\frac{1}{9}$	$-\frac{1}{3}$	−1	−3	−9

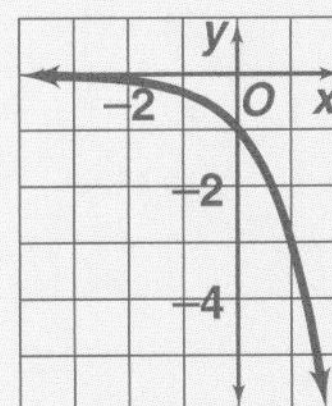

The graph is the same shape as the graph in Exercise 35, but it is reflected over the *x*-axis.

43. [2]

x	−2	−1	0	1	2	3
y	22	4	0	10	34	72

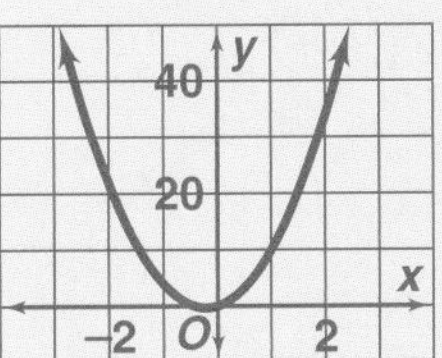

[1] one minor computation error

Lesson 12-7

page 671 Checkpoint Quiz 2

3.

x	−3	−2	−1	0	1	2	3
y	9	4	1	0	1	4	9

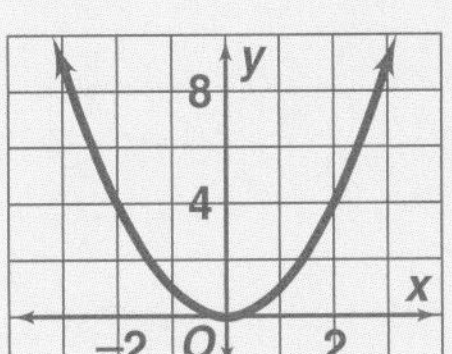

4.

x	−3	−2	−1	0	1	2	3
y	1	6	9	10	9	6	1

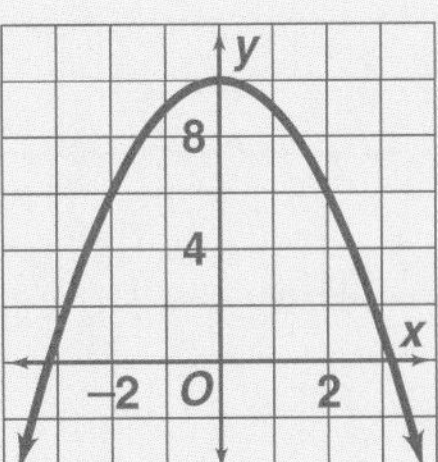

5.

x	15	30	45
y	1	$\frac{1}{2}$	$\frac{1}{3}$

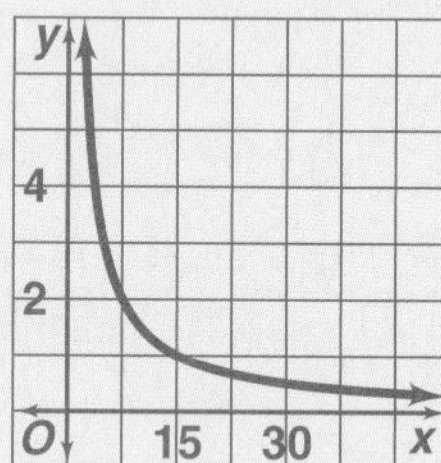

6.

x	−3	−2	−1	0	1	2	3
y	13	8	5	4	5	8	13

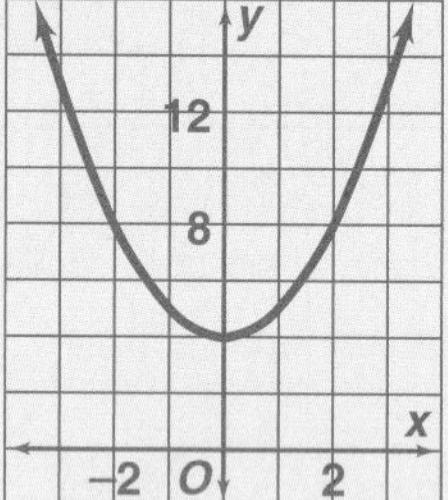

7.

x	−2	−1	0	1	2	3
y	−11	−2	1	−2	−11	−26

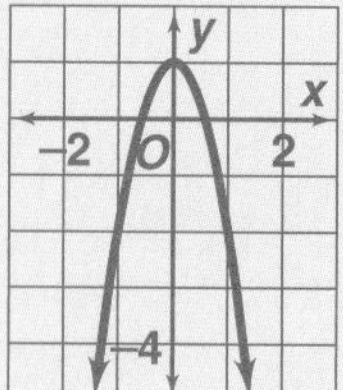

8.

x	1	2	3	4
y	36	18	12	9

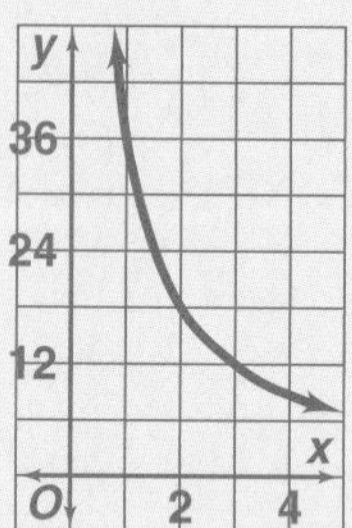

9.

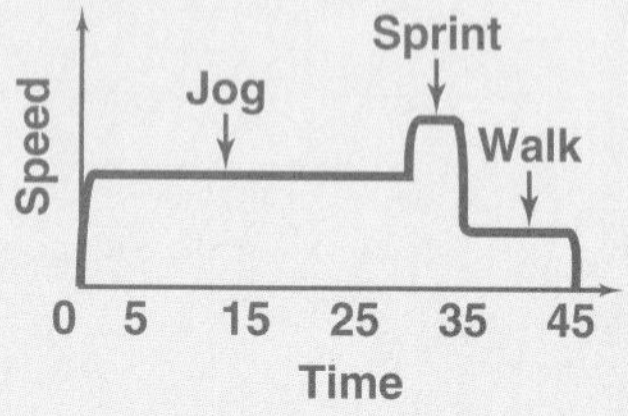

Sprint
Jog
Walk
Speed
0 5 15 25 35 45
Time

page 672 Reading Math

2. Table:

n	P
0	5
1	15
2	45
3	135
4	405
5	1,215

Graph:

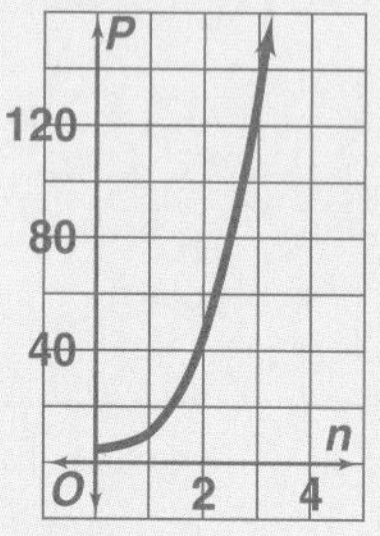

3. Function rule:
$y = 10 + 8x$
Graph:

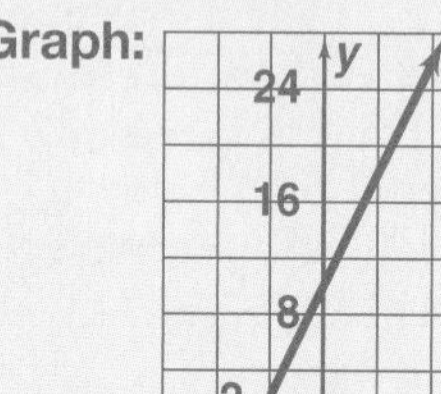

Lesson 12-8

page 677

43.

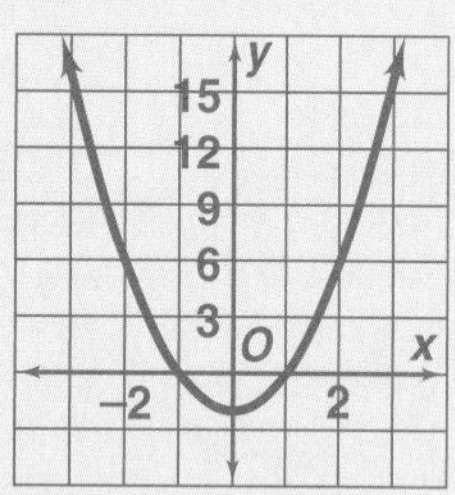

44.

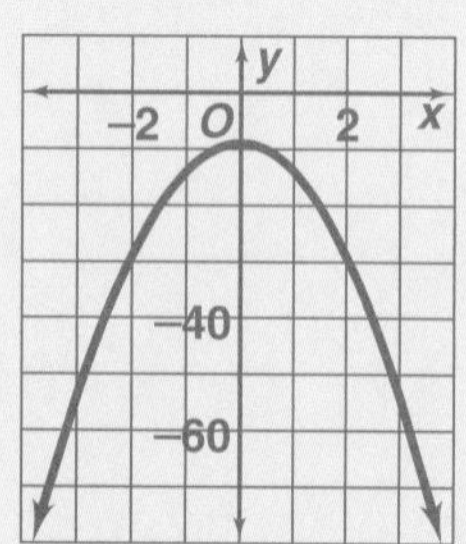

Lesson 12-9

page 682

44.

x	−2	−1	0	1	2
y	8	−4	−8	−4	8

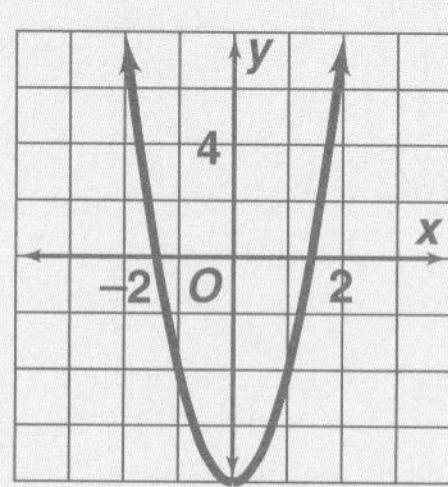

46.

x	1	2	3	4	5
y	1	$\frac{1}{2}$	$\frac{1}{3}$	$\frac{1}{4}$	$\frac{1}{5}$

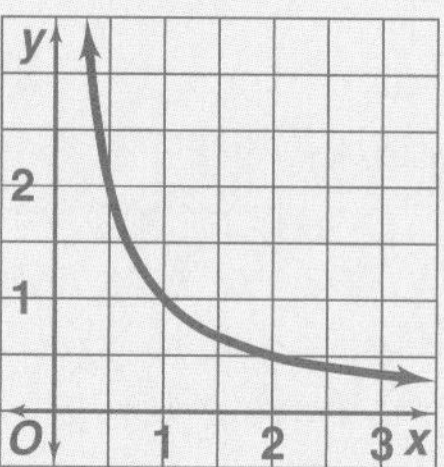

page 689 Chapter Review

19.

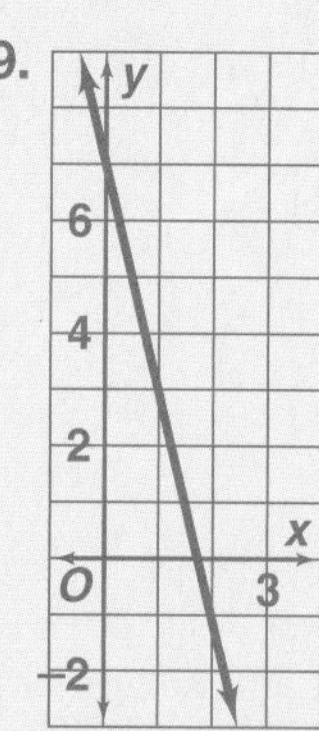

page 690 Chapter Test

6a.

t	0	1	2	5	10
p	5,000	5,400	5,800	7,000	9,000

b. 9,000 people

23. $-18x^2$

24. $3x^2 + 5x$

page 693 Test Prep

41. [2] 44.0 cm; 153.9 cm^2
[1] only one answer correct

42. [2] $30 + 4m = 60$
$4m = 30$
$m = 7.5$
She increased her daily workout by 7.5 minutes.

[1] appropriate procedure with one computational error OR correct answer without work shown

43. [4] a. $C = 3.99 + 3.99x$, where x is the number of minutes and C is the total cost.
b. $C = 3.99 + 3.99(10) = 43.89$
c.

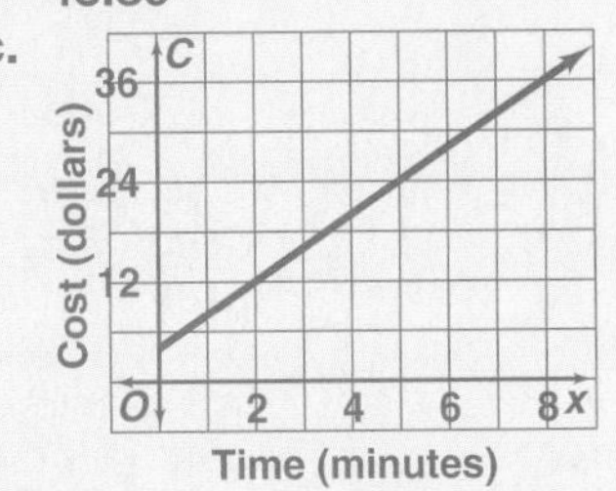

[3] appropriate methods with one error
[2] correct function evaluated correctly OR correct function graphed correctly but evaluated incorrectly
[1] correct solution without work shown

44. [4] a.

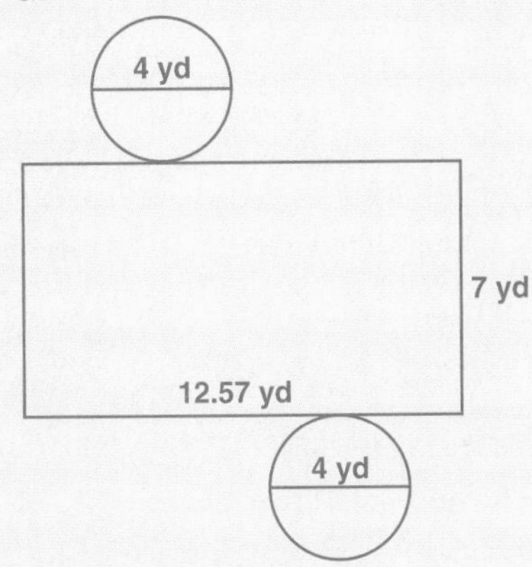

b. S. A. $= 2(\pi r^2) + 2\pi rh$
$2(\pi \cdot 2^2) + 2\pi(2)(7)$
$25.13 + 87.964$
113.097
The surface area is 113 yd^2.
[3] appropriate methods with one computational error
[2] correct net OR correct surface area
[1] correct solution without work shown

45. [4] a. $34 + 15w = 349$ where w is the amount of weeks he must save.
b. $34 + 15w = 349$
$15w = 315$
$w = 21$
He needs to save for 21 weeks.
[3] appropriate equation with one computational error
[2] correct equation solved incorrectly
[1] correct solution without work shown

46. [4] a. $2.5 \times 20 = 50$
The side will be 50 ft.
b. $0.5 \times 20 = 10$ ft
$A = S^2 = 10^2 = 100$
The area will be 100 ft^2.
[3] appropriate methods with one computational error
[2] correct lengths of sides but incorrect area
[1] correct solution without work shown

47. [4] a. markup $= 6 - 3.50 = 2.50$
$P \cdot 3.50 = 2.50$;
$P = 0.71428$;
The percent of markup is about 71.4%.
b. $15 \div 6 = 2.5$;
you can buy 2 bottles.
[3] correct procedure with one computational error
[2] correct percent of markup OR correct number of bottles
[1] correct answers without work shown

EXTRA PRACTICE

page T713

17.

x	−4	−3	−2	−1	0	1	2	3	4
y	18	11	6	3	2	3	6	11	18

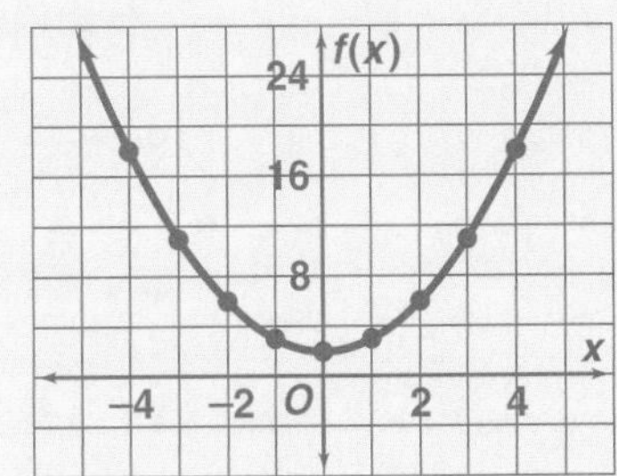

18.

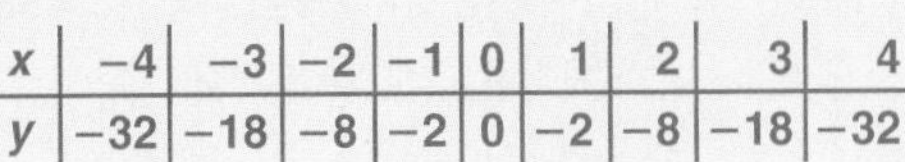

x	−4	−3	−2	−1	0	1	2	3	4
y	−32	−18	−8	−2	0	−2	−8	−18	−32

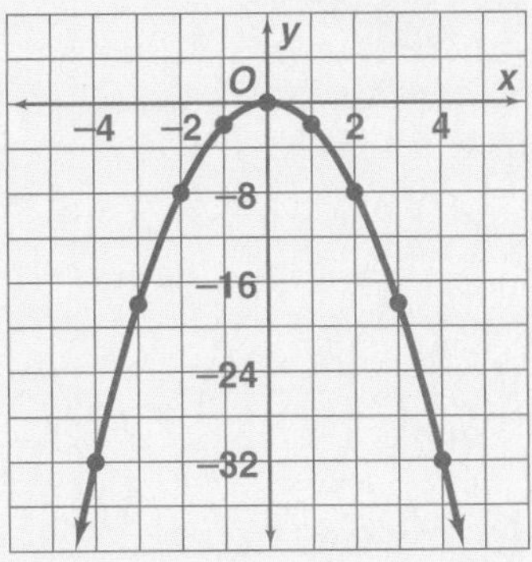

19.

x	−4	−3	−2	−1	0	1	2	3	4
y	48	27	12	3	0	3	12	27	48

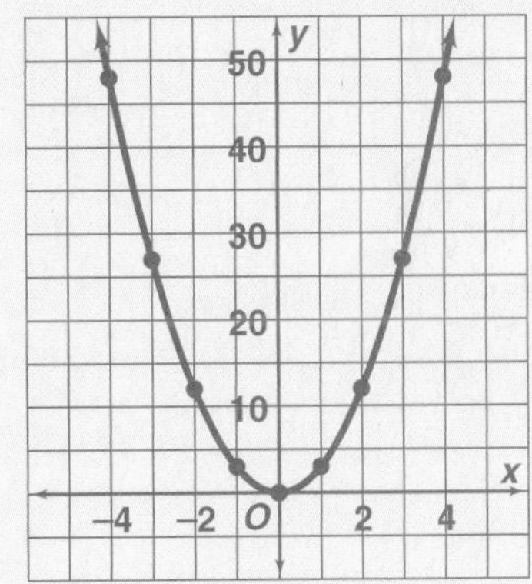

20.

x	−4	−3	−2	−1	0	1	2	3	4
y	−13	−6	−1	2	3	2	−1	−6	−13

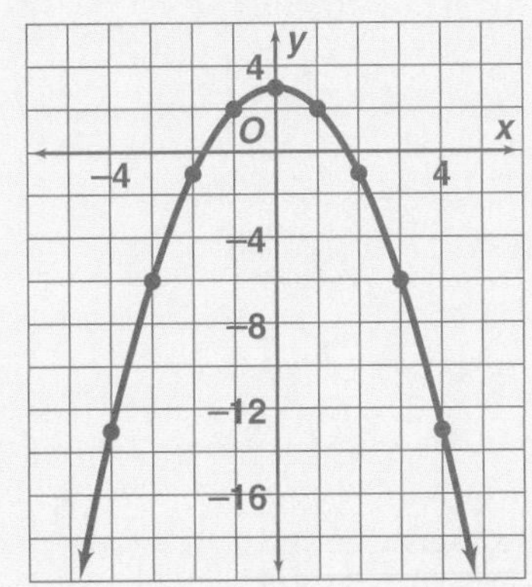

Index

B

C

D

E

F

J

K

L

M

N

O

P

Q

R

S

U

V

W

X

Y

Z

Acknowledgments

Staff Credits

The people who made up the *Prentice Hall Mathematics Courses 1, 2, and 3* team—representing design services, editorial, editorial services, market research, education technology, product services, project office, and publishing processes—are listed below. Bold type denotes the core team members.

Amy Acer, Leora Adler, Scott Andrews, Carolyn Artin, Barbara Bertell, Suzanne Biron, Stephanie Bradley, **Judith Buice,** Christine Cannon, Ronit Carter, Justin Collins, Bob Cornell, Patricia Crotty, Patrick Culleton, Carol Dance, Sheila DeFazio, Marian DeLollis, Jo DiGiustini, Delphine Dupee, Emily Ellen, **Janet Fauser,** Debby Faust, Suzanne Feliciello, Steve Fenton, Michael Ferrio, Jonathan Fisher, Barbara Hardt, Richard Heater, Kerri Hoar, Jayne Holman, Karen Holtzman, Kate House, Alan Hull, **Nancy Jones,** Judie Jozokos, Melissa Kent, Russ Lappa, Lisa LaVallee, Christine Lee, Carolyn Lock, Rebecca Loveys, Catherine Maglio, **Cheryl Mahan,** Barry Maloney, Chris Maniatis, **Tim McDonald**, Autumn Mellor, Eve Melnechuk, Terri Mitchell, Janet Morris, Sandra Morris, Kyai Mullei, **Cindy Noftle,** Marsha Novak, Greg Oles, Marie Opera, Jill Ort, Michael Oster, Christopher Ott, Steve Ouellette, Joan Paley, Dorothy Preston, Roberto Portocarrero, John Reece, Sandy Roedel-Baker, Rashid Ross, Irene Rubin, Alan Ruffin, Donna Russo, John Saxe, JoAnne Sgroi, Vicky Shen, Dennis Slattery, Lisa Smith-Ruvalcaba, **Nancy Smith,** Emily Soltanoff, Debby Sommer, David Spangler, Cynthia Speranza, Karen Swanson, Mark Tricca, Michael Vogel, Nate Walker, Lisa Walston, Roberta Warshaw, Matthew Wilson, Helen Young, **Carol Zacny**

Cover Design

Peter Brooks, Brainworx Studios

Cover Photos

t, Gary Randall/Taxi/Getty Images, Inc.;
b, Boden/Ledingham/Masterfile Corporation

Technical Illustration

Network Graphics

Photo Research

Sharon Donahue
Sue McDermott, Magellan Visual Research

Illustration

Brucie Rosch: 16, 20, 50, 61, 77, 87, 94, 104, 117, 145, 157, 197, 214, 245, 246, 280, 313, 331, 332, 335, 339, 354, 390, 444, 536
JB Woolsey: 229, 230, 244, 279, 281, 282, 283, 284, 285, 293, 324, 449, 474, 686
Joel Dubin: 144, 148, 221, 417, 418, 432, 474, 477, 478, 479, 482, 483, 490, 491, 497, 504, 514, 543, 593, 600, 608, 614, 615, 623, 679
John Edwards: 245
John Schreiner: 392, 541, 559
Kenneth Batelman: 18, 19, 37, 38, 65, 119, 207, 220, 350, 351, 475, 486, 487, 661
Roberta Warshaw: 62, 98, 153, 188, 346
Trevor Johnston: 162, 217, 243, 327, 329, 367, 392, 427, 445, 448, 451, 461, 484, 537, 538, 643
XNR Productions: 119, 120, 279, 280, 318, 330, 340, 411, 522, 662, 677

Photography

Front Matter: Page vii, Margot Granitas/The Image Works; **viii,** Steve Chenn/Corbis; **ix,** Poulides/Thatcher/Getty Images, Inc.; **x,** Rudi Von Briel/PhotoEdit; **xi,** Michael Newman/PhotoEdit; **xii,** Tom Stewart/Corbis; **xiii,** James A. Sugar/Corbis; **xiv,** *Stomp,* photo by Junichi Takanashi; **xv,** Phil Cantor/Superstock; **xvi,** D. Kraseman/Photo Researchers, Inc.; **xvii,** Keren Su/Getty Images, Inc.; **xviii,** Allsport/Getty Images, Inc.

Chapter 1: Pages 2, 3, Miles Ertman/Masterfile Corporation; **4,** Hurewitz Creative/Corbis; **5,** NASA; **7,** Lori Adamski Peek/Getty Images, Inc.; **9,** Ron Behrmann/International Stock; **11,** Ian Shaw/Getty Images, Inc.; **12,** Margot Granitas/The Image Works; **15,** David Young-Wolff/PhotoEdit; **18,** Wolfgang Kaehler/Corbis; **21,** Richard Haynes; **22,** Tom Hauck/Getty Images, Inc.; **24,** Dave G. Houser/Corbis; **26,** CALVIN AND HOBBES ©1990 WATTERSON. Reprinted with permission of UNIVERSAL PRESS SYNDICATE; **30 both,** Richard Haynes; **34,** Corbis; **36,** Tom and Pat Leeson; **41,** Esbin-Anderson/Photo Network/PictureQuest; **42,** Jeff Greenberg/PhotoEdit; **48,** The American Library Association; **57 tl,** Frank Greenaway/Dorling Kindersley; **57 tr,** Dorling Kindersley.

Chapter 2: Pages 58, 59, ©2000 Dreamworks, Pathe and Aardman; **60,** Don Smetzer/Getty Images, Inc.; **64 both,** Richard Haynes; **66,** David Stoecklein/Corbis Stock Market; **69,** Amy Smotherman/AP/Wide World Photos; **71,** Kathy McLaughlin/The Image Works; **72,** H. Morgan/Photo Researchers, Inc.; **75,** Spencer Grant/PhotoEdit; **79,** David Young-Wolff/PhotoEdit; **81,** composite Russell Illig/Getty Images, Inc.; **81,** composite Silver Burdett Ginn; **82,** David Young-Wolff/PhotoEdit; **82,** Russ Lappa; **85,** Jack Fields/Corbis; **87,** Courtesy of Kodak; **89,** Hot Ideas/Index Stock Imagery, Inc.; **92,** G. Ertl/AP/Wide World Photos; **93,** Eric Sanford/ImageState; **101,** Ellen Senisi/The Image Works; **104,** Mark Burnett/Stock Boston; **105,** Steve Chenn/Corbis; **106,** Rhoda Sidney/PhotoEdit; **112 t,** Courtesy MGM/RGA; **112 m,** With permission Universal Studios Media Licensing, Matte World Digital and Amblin Entertainment; **112 b,** With permission Universal Studios Media Licensing, Matte World Digital and Amblin Entertainment; **113 t,** Matte World Digital and the National Park Service; **113 m,** Matte World Digital and the National Park Service; **113 b,** Matte World Digital and the National Park Service.

Chapter 3: Page 116, Bob Daemmrich/Stock Boston; **120,** Tony Freeman/PhotoEdit; **121,** Poulides/Thatcher/Getty Images, Inc.; **125,** David Young-Wolff/PhotoEdit; **128,** Ryan McVay/Getty Images, Inc.; **133,** David Young-Wolff/PhotoEdit; **137,** Larry Lefever/Grant Heilman Photography, Inc.; **139 both,** Richard Haynes; **141,** Barbara Alper/Stock Boston; **142,** Kindra Clineff/The Picture Cube; **144,** ADAM @1995 HOME © by UNIVERSAL PRESS SYNDICATE. Reprinted with permission. All rights reserved.; **145,** AP Photo/The Flint Journal, Steve Jessmore; **149,** AFP/Corbis; **154,** Terry Vine/Getty Images, Inc.; **161,** Koji Sasahara/AP/Wide World Photos; **163 all,** Russ Lappa; **165,** Russ Lappa; **166 l,** Nuridsany et Perennou/Photo Researchers, Inc.; **166 m,** Russ Lappa; **166 r,** Russ Lappa; **171 l,** Runk/Schoenberger/Grant Heilman Photography, Inc.; **171 m,** George McCarthy/Corbis; **171 r,** Andrew J. Martinez/Photo Researchers, Inc.; **172 l,** Larry Grant/Getty Images, Inc.; **172 m,** Eric Neurath/Stock Boston; **172 r,** Steve Cole/Getty Images, Inc.; **173,** Russ Lappa; **180 l,** Jonathan Kannair/Index Stock Imagery; **180 t,** Alan Kearney/Getty Images, Inc.; **180 b,** Micheal Orton/Getty Images, Inc.; **181,** James Kay/Stock Connection/PictureQuest.

Chapter 4: Pages 182, 183, Gary Conner/PhotoEdit; **184,** Rudi Von Briel/PhotoEdit; **187,** A. Ramey/PhotoEdit; **191,** Allsport/Getty Images, Inc.; **193,** Amos Morgan/Getty Images, Inc.; **194,** 1993 King Features Syndicate,

Inc. World rights reserved.; **201,** Christi Carter/Grant Heilman Photography, Inc.; **202,** Tony Freeman/PhotoEdit; **205,** Rick Price/Corbis; **208 both,** Richard Haynes; **213,** Frank Flavin/AccentAlaska.com; **215,** Dennis Hallinan/FPG International/Getty Images, Inc.; **219,** Tom Uhlman/Visuals Unlimited; **222,** Spencer Grant/PhotoEdit; **224,** Pawel Libera/Corbis; **227 l,** NASA; **227 r,** Larry Mulvehill/The Image Works; **238 tr,** Getty Images, Inc.; **238 l,** Martin Bough/Fundamental Photographs; **238 b,** Dave King/Dorling Kindersley; **239,** Royalty Free/Corbis.

Chapter 5: Pages 240, 241, Michael Geissinger/The Image Works; **242,** Michael Newman/PhotoEdit; **243,** Bob Daemmrich/Stock Boston; **244,** David Oliver/Getty Images, Inc.; **247,** Robert Maass/Corbis; **250,** Kevin Fleming/Corbis; **251,** Comstock Images; **253,** Laura Dwight/ Corbis; **254,** Dennis MacDonald/PhotoEdit; **255,** Journal Courier/Steve W./The Image Works; **257,** Richard Megna/Fundamental Photographs; **260,** Stefano Bianchetti/Corbis; **261 both,** Richard Haynes; **262,** Robin Smith/Getty Images, Inc.; **267,** Dana Hursey/Masterfile; **269,** Benjamin Rondel/Corbis Stock Market; **275,** Francisco Cruz/SuperStock; **278,** Cameramann/The Image Works; **281,** Michael Newman/PhotoEdit; **283,** David Trood Pictures/Getty Images, Inc.; **286,** Bob Daemmrich/Stock Boston; **289,** George Hall/Corbis; **290,** Tom Carroll/Index Stock Imagery, Inc.; **298 tr,** Brian Hagiwara/Getty Images, Inc.; **298 l,** Paul Taylor/Getty Images; **298 bl,** San Francisco Chronicle; **299 tl,** Courtesy, Shuttle-Bike USA Inc.; **299 b,** NASA Dryden Flight Research Center.

Chapter 6: Pages 300, 301, Doug Dreyer/AP/Wide World Photos; **302,** H. Huntley Hersch; **304,** AFP/Corbis; **307,** Tom McCarthy/PhotoEdit; **311,** Ronnie Kamin/PhotoEdit; **312,** Amos Morgan/Getty; **316,** Tony Freeman/PhotoEdit; **321,** Spencer Grant/PhotoEdit; **322 both,** Richard Haynes; **328,** E.L. Miller/Stock Boston; **333,** Syracuse Newspapers/Dick Blume/The Image Works; **338,** Richard T. Nowitz/Photo Researchers; **344,** Bill Aron/PhotoEdit; **346,** FOXTROT ©2000 Bill Amend. Reprinted with permission of UNIVERSAL PRESS SYNDICATE. All rights reserved.; **349,** Russ Lappa; **350,** Reuters NewMedia Inc./Corbis; **352,** Tom Stewart/ Corbis; **360 tr,** Dennie Cody/Getty Images, Inc.; **360 b,** Ken Fisher/Getty Images, Inc.; **361,** Mark Wilson/Getty Images, Inc.

Chapter 7: Pages 362, 363, Roger Ressmeyer/Corbis; **364,** Tony Anderson/ Getty Images, Inc.; **366,** NSO/SEL/Roger Ressmeyer/Corbis; **368,** Bob Daemmrich; **372,** Albert Einstein(TM) Licensed by The Hebrew University of Jerusalem, Represented by The Roger Richman Agency, Inc. Photo courtesy of the Archives, California Institute of Technology.; **373,** Mug Shots/Corbis; **375,** Bonnie Kamin/Photo Edit; **378,** Strauss/Curtis/Corbis; **380,** Alan Carey/The Image Works; **381,** Eric Condliffe/Visuals Unlimited; **385 both,** Richard Haynes; **386,** James A. Sugar/Corbis; **388,** Roger Ressmeyer/ Corbis; **389,** Syracuse Newspapers/David Lassman/The Image Works; **390,** Kevin Fleming/Corbis; **393,** TRW/Science VU; **395,** Dennis O'Clair/ Getty Images Inc.; **396,** Richard Haynes; **397 l,** Photodisc/Getty Images, Inc.; **397 m,** Photodisc; **397 r,** Yann Arthus-Bertrand/Corbis; **402 t,** Dorling Kindersley/Paignton Zoo; **402 l,** Martin Bough/Fundamental Photographs; **402 ml,** Runk/Schoenberger/Photo Researchers, Inc.; **402 mr,** Amos Morgan/ Getty Images, Inc.

Chapter 8: Pages 404, 405, Pepe Diaz/Cover/The Image Works; **406,** Frank Siteman/Stock Boston; **408,** David Frazier; **411,** Joy Franklin; **412,** *Stomp,* photo by Junichi Takanashi; **413,** Mark Thayer; **415,** Russ Lappa; **416,** Richard Bryant/ARCAID; **420,** Deborah Davis/PhotoEdit; **424,** Photo Researchers, Inc.; **426,** David Young-Wolff/Getty Images, Inc.; **428,** Bob Daemmrich/Stock Boston; **430,** Irene Rubin; **432,** David Young Wolff/ PhotoEdit; **435,** Ryan McVay/Getty Images, Inc.; **437,** Sandy Felsenthal/Corbis; **438,** Dusty Willison/ International Stock; **440,** M.C. Escher's "Symmetry Drawing E25"©1997 Cordon Art-Baarn, Holland. All rights reserved; **442,** Joyce Photographics/Photo Researchers, Inc.; **444,** Richard Haynes; **444 tl,** Stephen Simpson/Getty Images, Inc.; **446,** By permission of Johnny Hart and Creators Syndicate, Inc.; **448,** Carol Lee/The Picture Cube; **449,** Andrew Laker/AP/Wide World Photos; **455,** Richard Wood/The Picture Cube; **466 b,** Dorling Kindersley; **466 tr,** Dorling Kindersley; **467 b,** Neil Rabinowitz/Corbis; **467 tl,** Ryan McVay/Getty Images, Inc.

Chapter 9: Pages 468, 469, Roland Seitre/Peter Arnold, Inc.; **470,** Bill Ross/Corbis; **473,** Fotopic; **474,** Ryan McVay/Getty Images, Inc.; **477 both,** Russ Lappa; **479,** Steve Vidler/Superstock; **482,** Terry Vine/Getty Images, Inc.; **484,** David Buffington/Getty Images, Inc.; **486,** Bill Truslow/ Getty Images, Inc.; **489,** James D. Wilson/Getty Images, Inc.; **492,** Rob Crandall/The Image Works; **493,** Rachel Epstein/Photoedit; **495 bl,** Dave G. Houser/Corbis; **495 br,** Geoffrey Clifford/Woodfin Camp & Associates; **498,** Craig Lovell/Corbis; **500,** Russ Lappa; **501,** David J. Sams/Stock Boston; **502 both,** Richard Haynes; **504,** Philip Bailey/Corbis; **508,** Adam Woolfitt/ Corbis; **509,** Joan Baron/Corbis/Stock Market; **511,** David Stoecklein/ Corbis; **512,** Phillippe Colombi/Getty Images, Inc.; **514,** Michael Pole/Corbis; **517,** Dorling Kindersley; **518 all,** Russ Lappa; **519,** Phil Cantor/Superstock; **520,** Nancy Sheehan/PhotoEdit; **522,** Linde Waidhofer/Getty Images, Inc.; **528 tr,** Tim Davis/Getty Images, Inc.; **528 b,** Dave King/Dorling Kindersley Picture Library; **528 l,** Simone End/Dorling Kindersley Picture Library; **529 tr,** Kenneth Lilly/Dorling Kindersley Picture Library; **529 br,** George Bernard/Photo Researchers, Inc.

Chapter 10: Pages 530, 531, Simon Jauncey/Getty Images, Inc.; **532,** Richard T. Nowitz/Corbis; **533,** UPI-Corbis/Bettmann; **534,** G.K. & Vikki Hart/Getty Images, Inc.; **540,** David Young-Wolff/PhotoEdit; **542,** Tony Freeman/ PhotoEdit; **543,** Reuters NewMedia Inc./Corbis; **547,** Roger Ressmeyer/ Corbis; **549,** F. Gohier/Photo Researchers, Inc.; **553,** David Young-Wolff/ Corbis; **555,** Duomo/Corbis; **557,** Ken O'Donoghue; **558,** Russ Lappa; **559,** Doug Wilson/Corbis; **561,** Jim Holland/Stock Boston; **563,** Jeff Greenberg/ Visuals Unlimited; **564,** Kennan Ward/Corbis; **566,** Stephen Frisch/Stock Boston; **567,** Amos Morgan/Getty Images, Inc; **570,** D. Kraseman/Photo Researchers, Inc.; **571 both,** Richard Haynes; **572,** Paul Barton/Corbis; **574,** David Sailors/Corbis; **576,** Simon Jauncy/Getty Images, Inc.; **577,** Corbis; **578,** Andersen Ross/Getty Images, Inc.; **586 t,** Richard Morrell/Corbis; **587 t,** Royalty Free/Corbis; **587 r,** Dorling Kindersley; **587 br,** Andy Crawford/Dorling Kindersley Picture Library.

Chapter 11: Pages 588, 589, Art Wolfe/Photo Researchers, Inc.; **590,** Charles Thatcher/Getty Images, Inc.; **593,** Flip Chalfant/Getty Images, Inc.; **595,** Joseph Sohm, Chromosohm Inc./Corbis; **596,** Syracuse Newspapers/Lisa Krantz/The Image Works; **597,** Mark Burnett/Stock Boston; **598,** Ellen Bradley/Brush Hill Boxers; **601,** Bill Howes;Frank Lane Picture Agency/Corbis; **602 both,** Richard Haynes; **603,** Steve Ruark/Syracuse Newspapers/The Image Works; **607,** Michael Rosenfeld/Getty Images, Inc.; **609,** Keren Su/Getty Images, Inc.; **611,** Russ Lappa; **612,** Annebicque Bernard/Corbis SYGMA; **613,** Skjoid Photographs; **617,** Gary Buss/Getty Images, Inc.; **618,** Ken McGagh; **621,** Richard T. Nowitz/Corbis; **623,** Bob Daemmrich/The Image Works; **624,** Spencer Grant/PhotoEdit; **627,** Syracuse Newspapers/David Lassman/ The Image Works; **636 tr,** Hank Morgan/Photo Researchers, Inc.; **636 l,** Flip Nicklin/Minden Pictures; **636 b,** Joseph Van Os/Getty Images, Inc.

Chapter 12: Pages 634, 635, Hillary Smith Garrison/AP/Wide World Photos; **636,** Jeff Hunter/Getty Images, Inc.; **639,** Allsport/Getty Images, Inc.; **640,** Kobal Collection; **645,** Tom Stewart/Corbis; **646,** Dorling Kindersley; **647,** Richard Haynes; **648,** John Elk III/Stock Boston; **651,** Debbie Tuch/ glitterlimes.com; **653,** International Stock/Image State; **655,** Gail Mooney/ Corbis; **658,** Image State/Alamy; **663,** Ken O'Donoghue; **664,** AFP/Corbis; **668 l,** M. Abbey/Visuals Unlimited, Inc.; **668 r,** Matthew Borkoski/Index Stock Imagery, Inc.; **670,** Philip Gould/Corbis; **675 both,** Richard Haynes; **676,** Tom Dietrich/Getty Images, Inc.; **681,** Tony Freeman/PhotoEdit; **682,** Kleinberg/Stock Boston; **694 t,** Digital Vision; **694 b,** Jon Riley/Getty Images, Inc.; **695,** C Squared Studios/Getty Images, Inc.

Teacher's Edition

Editorial and Production Services: The GTS Companies
Design Coordination: Susan Gerould/Perspectives